Hazardous Materials Management Desk Reference

Second Edition

Hazardous Materials Management Desk Reference

Second Edition

Doye B. Cox, PE, CHMM
Editor

Adriane P. Borgias, MSEM, CHMM
Editor

Academy of Certified Hazardous Materials Managers

Rockville, Maryland

Library of Congress Control Number: 2005931728
ISBN 0-9768576-0-X

 This book was printed on recycled, acid-free paper.

The Production Editor is Joe Wilferth, PhD, University of Tennesee at Chattanooga, TN

Designed and typeset by fusion environment&energy, LLC in Spokane, WA.

Cover design by Windsock Media in Harrison, TN

Printed and bound by Bang Printing in Brainerd, MN.

10 9 8 7 6 5 4 3 2 1

Academy of Certified Hazardous Materials Managers (ACHMM) books are available at special quantity discounts to use as premiums and sales promotions, to accompany the ACHMM National Overview Course (NOC), or for use in corporate training programs. For more information, please contact ACHMM at:

Academy of Certified Hazardous Materials Managers, Inc.
P.O. Box 1216
Rockville, MD   20849

Phone: (800) 437-0137 –or– (301) 916-3306
Fax: (301) 916-3308
Web: www.achmm.org
Email: academy@achmm.org

Table of Contents

Part II   **Safety Principles**

Chapter 12. Industrial Toxicology   183
Robert Roy, PhD, DABT
Robert Skoglund, PhD, DABT, CIH

Chapter 13. Process Safety Management of Highly Hazardous Chemicals   193
John S. Kirar, CSP, CEA, CHMM

Chapter 14. Bloodborne Pathogen Program   215
Frank Pfeifer, CSP, CHMM
Martha Boss, CIH, CSP

Part III   The Right to Know

Part IV   Land and Natural Resources

Chapter 19. CERCLA Liability and All Appropriate Inquiry   297
Lawrence J. (Sandy) Horan III, MBA, JD

Chapter 20. Human Health Risk Assessment   309
Frank Phillips CET, CIAQP, CHMM

Chapter 21. Property Assessments   325
Keith Liner, MCE, CHMM

Chapter 22. Brownfields   335
John E. Milner, JD
Charles A. Waggoner, PhD, CHMM

Part V   Management of Hazardous Materials and Hazardous Substances

Chapter 23. Department of Transportation Hazardous Materials
        Regulations   363
Dorothy Christman, CHMM
Michael Eyer, CHMM

Chapter 24. Underground Storage Tanks   381
Alan A. Eckmyre, CHMM

Chapter 25. Toxic Substances Control Act Basics   393
Valentino P. De Rocili, PhD, CHMM

Chapter 26. Federal Insecticide, Fungicide, and Rodenticide Act   405
Keith Trombley, CIH, CSP, CHMM

Chapter 27. Radiation Safety Principles   **415**
George D. Mosho, CHMM

Chapter 28. Lead   **425**
Chris Gunther, CHMM

Chapter 29. Asbestos   **433**
Margaret V. Naugle, EdD, JD, CHMM
Charles A. Waggoner, PhD, CHMM

Part VI   Homeland Security

Chapter 30. Chemical and Biological Weapons   **457**
Dwight H. Clark CET, CHMM

Chapter 35. A Step-by-Step Guide to Risk Management Planning   537
Dale M. Petroff, NRRPT

Chapter 36. Indoor Air Quality: A General Overview   559
Valentino P. DeRocili, PhD, CHMM

Part VIII   Water Quality

Chapter 37. Clean Water Act   573
Adriane P. Borgias, MSEM, CHMM

Chapter 42. Pollution Prevention   **689**
Patricia A. Kandziora, CHMM
K. Leigh Leonard, CHMM

Chapter 43. RCRA Corrective Action   **701**
Louis Martino, CHMM
David R. Green, MS

Chapter 44. Treatment Technologies in Hazardous Waste Management   **717**
Gazi A. George, PhD, CHMM

Chapter 45. Mixed Waste Management   **735**
Thomas Hillmer, CHMM

Part X   Chemical Perspectives

Contributors

This edition of the Hazardous Materials Mangement Desk Reference *is dedicated to the memory of Don Ott. Those of us who have known and worked with Don over these past many years cannot imagine a better example of a CHMM. Don served his profession as a happy warrior attacking every assignment in a "whole-hearted" and meticulous manner. He has been missed.*

The second edition of this text has been made possible by the support and vision of the contributors as well as the members of the Academy of Certified Hazardous Materials Managers. Specific contributors to this volume are noted below and at the end of each chapter. In our zeal to complete this publication, we may have inadvertantly neglected to mention one or two of the many people who have worked so hard to ensure that it represents the best that our profession can offer. If you are one of those people, please contact ACHMM so that your name can be included in subsequent printings.

Doye B. Cox, PE, CHMM, *Editor.* Mr. Cox has been certified since 1985 and has served the ACHMM in several capacities at the national level, including President. He is also Past President of the Tennessee Section of the American Society of Civil Engineers. He has almost 30 years experience in hazardous materials management and waste management. His specialties include remedial and environmental construction project management, decontamination, and demolition; and the chemistry of hazardous materials. Mr. Cox is a Senior Project Manager for Barge Waggoner Sumner and Cannon, Inc. in Chattanooga, Tennessee.

Adriane P. Borgias, MSEM, CHMM, *Editor.* Ms. Borgias has been certified since 1986 and is a Past President of ACHMM. She has worked for more than 25 years in the energy industry and with Tribal governments. She has a wide range of experience including collaborative decision making and environmental management systems. She is a contributor to *Women in Chemistry and Physics: A Biobibliographic Sourcebook*, and is highlighted in *Northwest Women in Science: Women Making a Difference.* Ms. Borgias is the owner of *fusion environment&energy, LLC* in Spokane, Washington.

Associate Editors

Charles M. Bessey, CHMM
Charley Kubler, CHMM
Donald W. Ott, CHMM
Cindy L. Savage, CHMM

Richard A. Senn, CHMM
Paul W. Studebaker, CHMM
Daniel L. Todd, QEP, CHMM
Richard F. Verch, CHMM
Allen R. Frederick, CHMM

Authors and Contributors

Charles M. Bessey, CHMM
Adriane P. Borgias, MSEM, CHMM
Martha Boss, CIH, CSP
Mark L. Bricker, PE, CHMM
Harry A. Bryson, CHMM
Brett A. Burdick, PG, CHMM
W. Scott Butterfield, MS, CHMM
Guy S. Camomilli, MPH, CSP CHSP, CHMM
Glenn R. "Chip" Carwell III, PE, CHMM
Dorothy Christman, CHMM
Dwight H. Clark, CET, CHMM
Doye B. Cox, PE, CHMM
Gregory C. DeCamp, MS, CHMM
Valentino P. De Rocili, PhD, CHMM
Alan A. Eckmyre, CHMM
John P. Englert, MS, JD
Michael Eyer, CHMM
Chris Gunther, CHMM
Gazi A. George, PhD, CHMM
David R. Green, MS
Richard E. Hagen, PhD, CHMM
Dawn Han, MS, CIH
Marilyn L. Hau, MS, RN-C, COHN-S, EMT-P,
    OHST, ASP, CHMM
Thomas Hillmer, CHMM
Laurence J. "Sandy" Horan III, MBA, JD
Michael A. Kay, ScD, CHMM
Patricia A. Kandziora, CHMM

John S. Kirar, CSP, CEA, CHMM
Harry S. Kemp, EMS-A, CHMM
K. Leigh Leonard, CHMM
Keith Liner, MCE, CHMM
Robert L. Lipscomb, CHMM
Louis Martino, CHMM
Michael R. Matthews, PE, PG, CHMM
A. Thomas Merski, MPH, MBA
Laureen A. McMurray Boyle, MS, CHMM
John E. Milner, JD
George D. Mosho, CHMM
Margaret V. Naugle, EdD, JD, CHMM
James L. Oliver
Dale M. Petroff, NRRPT
Frank Pfeifer, RS, CEP, CHMM
Franklin A. Phillips, CET, CIAQP, CHMM
Stephen D. Riner, CHMM
Robert Roy, PhD, DABT
Robert Skoglund, PhD, DABT, CIH
Daniel L. Todd, QEP, CHMM
David M. Trayer
Keith Trombley, CIH, CSP, CHMM
Tony Uliano, Jr., MS, CIH, CHMM
John A. Valicenti, PhD, CHMM
Charles A. Waggoner, PhD, CHMM
Eugene R. Wasson, JD
Steven G. Weems, MPH, CIH, CHMM
Phillip Wood, EMS-PA, CHMM
Michael H. Ziskin, CHCM, CHMM

Consultants

Neville Anderson, CHMM
Timothy J. Anderson, RS
Dan Anna, PhD
Richard B. Armstrong, Jr. EdD
Chuck D. Barlow, JD
Peter N. T. Barrett
Christopher G. Barricklow, CHMM
Jim Bartasis
Jeff Bates
Thomas R. Bernitt, CQM, CHMM
Brandan A. Borgias, PhD
R. Bruce Bowers, CGWP, CHMM
John F. Bojanek, MS, CHMM
Randy Boyington
Derrick K. Bradley
James M. Burckhalter, MPH, CHMM
John Butenhoff, PhD, CIH, DABT
Kevin Cannon, CHMM, CSP
Hillary Carpenter, PhD
Denny L. Carlson, PE, CHMM
Joseph C. Chandler, CHMM
Sybil Chandler, CHMM
Wing T.Chan, MSc, PhD, SM
Craig J. Chavet
Jerry Coalgate
Terry Coggins, PE, CHP, CSP
Patrick Coin, PhD
Kent Thomas Cubbage
Valentino P. De Rocili, PhD, CHMM
Mary Devany, CHMM
Daryl W. Dierwechter, CHMM
J. Peyton Doub, CEP
Karen Delahaut
Kevin Dressman
Jamie Farrow, AS
Lynn Fondren
Judy Foster, CIH, CSP
Allen R. Frederick, CHMM
James E. Gano, PhD
Andrew R. Grainger
Walter G. Green III, PhD
Julie B. Henderson, CHMM
George K. Hess
Trey Hess
Nicholas R. Hild, PhD
Matt Holub
Melvin E. Hook, PE, DEE
Kathy Huibregtse
Ronda Hirnyck
Kimberly Jacobs

Joe E. Jenkins, PG, CHMM
Craig Johnson
Charles Jones, CHMM
Michael A. Kay, ScD, CHMM
Patricia A. Kandziora, CHMM
Sean Kerpta, CIH
Todd Kimmell
David B. King, CIH
Cynthia L. Klein-Banai, CHMM
Lynn Koby, CHMM
Aaron A. Leritz, CHMM
Diana Lundelius, CHMM
Fred Malaby, CIH, CSP
Paul W. Martin, CHMM
Ann W. McIver, QEP
John E. Milner, JD
Emmett Moore, PhD
Amy S. Morgan
Hal W. Morris
Kelly Murray, CHMM
Paul M. Neeson, CHP
Mark Nelson
Eniola Olomiye, MPH, RS, COCH, CHMM
Russ Palmer
Raymond J. Patchak, CHMM
Frank A. Phillips, CET, CIAQP, CHMM
Frederick J. Plummer, CHMM
Howard Pope, CHMM
Matthew Redmann, CHMM
Bruce Reiter, RG, CHMM
Donna Rogers, CIH, CHMM
Vince Runde, CHMM
Cindy L. Savage, CHMM
Karen Schaefer, CHMM
William F. Scott II, CHMM, MS, PMP
Richard A. Senn, CHMM
James M. Shawver
Danielle Sheen, CIH, CSP
Ricky L. Shellenbarger
R. David Shiels, PG, CHMM
Ron Snyder
Laura L. Splichal, CHMM
Ram S. Suga, CHMM, CIH, CSP
Daniel L. Todd, QEP, CHMM
Venkateswara R. Veluri, PhD
Tilak R. Verma, PhD
Roger L. Wabeke, PE, CIH, CHMM
Charles A. Waggoner, PhD, CHMM
Jessica A. Warren, CHMM
Allen Williams
Frederick G. Wolf, PhD, CHMM
Robert A. Wynveen, PhD

Preface

<hr>

The Academy of Certified Hazardous Materials Managers (ACHMM), established in 1985, is a non-profit membership organization dedicated to fostering professional development through continuing education, peer group interaction, the exchange of ideas and information relating to hazardous materials management. With 66 Chapters and over 5,000 members, the Academy is represented in 37 states plus the District of Columbia. The ACHMM's headquarters are located in Rockville, Maryland, just outside of Washington, DC.

The purposes of ACHMM are to

- Educate and instruct ACHMM members in hazardous materials management, environmental health and safety

- Provide a means for hazardous materials managers to meet and communicate with each other

- Provide a meeting ground for members involved in different types of hazardous management work—academia, consulting, government, industry, and transportation

- Promote the CHMM certification as a standard of excellence in the hazardous materials management field

Eligibility in ACHMM is achieved through education, experience, and the successful completion of an examination administered by the Institute of Hazardous Materials Management. ACHMM would like to acknowledge the Institute of Hazardous Materials Management—the founding body for this organization and the administrator of the certification. It is the Institute's vision and leadership that has made ACHMM the premier organization for hazardous materials management professionals. For more information about becoming a Certified Hazardous Materials Manager, please visit the Institute's Homepage at <http://www.ihmm.org> or call the Institute at (301) 984-8969. For more information about ACHMM, please visit the ACHMM Homepage at <http://www.achmm.org> or call toll-free (800) 437-0137.

Introduction

The *Hazardous Materials Management Desk Reference* is designed to be a comprehensive overview of the field of hazardous materials management and related sciences. Its primary intent is to meet the management needs of environmental professionals who have responsibility for hazardous materials management. The topics included in this book are also of interest to professionals in the safety, engineering, industrial hygiene, and general environmental fields.

The authors and editors of the Second Edition of the *Hazardous Materials Management Desk Reference* have been selected because of their knowledge and practical expertise in their fields. Most of the authors are Certified Hazardous Materials Managers (CHMMs), having met the certification's rigorous experience, peer review, and technical requirements. Each chapter of the book has been peer-reviewed for technical content–in almost every case by three professionals representing the government, private and academic sectors.

Included in the desk reference are chapters on the science, laws and regulations, and management principles needed to properly manage hazardous materials. The chapters provide a general overview and guide to a comprehensive list of environmental and hazardous materials topics. The intent is to act as a reference or "jumping-off point" for more in-depth study. The comprehensive range of topics covered makes the book unique among currently available titles.

The topics covered by the desk reference are highly regulatory in focus and in constant change. Where appropriate, Internet references have been provided so that the reader can quickly link to reliable sources of current information. For those readers new to the field of hazardous materials management, a list of acronyms and a glossary are provided at the end of the book. Glossary items are noted in the text in ***bold italic***.

Chapters in the reference are grouped by general topics. Part I, Regulatory and Management Perspectives, gives the reader a "big picture" understanding of the profession. Included in this section are chapters that overview the development of environmental laws and regulations, liability and compliance, environmental management systems, auditing, risk analysis, project management and business.

In Part II, Safety Principles, the reader will find topics on the science and regulation of safety, including chapters on industrial toxicology, OSHA requirements, personal protective equipment, process safety managment, bloodborne pathogens, and industrial hygiene. Community and worker right-to-know requirements are found in Part III, The Right-to-Know. Part III overviews the fundamental requirements associated with release reporting, hazard communication, and Material Safety Data Sheets.

For information on land-related issues, the reader is urged to study Part IV, Land and Natural Resources. This part reviews the seminal National Environmental Policy Act, Superfund, environmental risk assessment, property assessments, and thoroughly researched state-by-state summaries of brownfields requirements.

In Part V, Management of Hazardous Materials and Substances, many of the topics that are of the highest interest to hazardous materials managers are covered. These include chapters on the transportation of hazardous materials, underground storage tanks, pesticides, the Toxic Substances Control Act, radiation safety, as well as overviews on the hazardous substances asbestos and lead.

This second edition contains a new section on homeland security, intended to respond to the evolving needs of the profession. Part VI, Homeland Security, provides information on a diverse set of topics such as chemical weapons, incident response, hazardous materials releases associated with natural disasters, and clandestine drug laboratories.

An overview of the Clean Air Act is provided in Part VII, Air Quality, as well as information about indoor air quality. Of particular interest is the step-by-step guide for preparation of a Risk Management Plan. Part VIII, Water Quality, overviews the Clean Water Act and the related Safe Drinking Water and Oil Pollution Acts. A chapter on ground water supplements these overviews and provides the reader with a fundamental understanding of the movement of pollutants in ground water systems.

After reviewing the chapter on the Resource Conservation and Recovery Act (RCRA) in Part IX Management of Wastes, the hazardous materials manager can learn more about the fundamentals of waste management from the complementary chapters on waste minimization/pollution prevention, treatment technologies, and RCRA corrective action. An additional chapter on mixed waste management highlights the requirements and challenges the disposal of mixed radioactive and hazardous waste pose to the hazardous materials manager.

Part X, Chemical Perspectives (last, but some say of highest importance to a hazardous materials manager), is a chapter that contains a basic chemistry foundation for hazardous management and is followed by an overview of the concepts of environmental sampling and analysis.

While the *Hazardous Materials Management Desk Reference* is comprehensive in scope, it is by no means complete. Complete coverage of these important topics would take far more than one volume to achieve and, given the rapidly changing regulatory environment, may not even be feasible. The reader, therefore, is urged to "take the leap"; to learn more by exploring the references provided in the bibliographies and Internet resource sections at the end of each chapter.

Doye B. Cox PE, CHMM
Adriane P. Borgias, MSEM, CHMM
Editors

Hazardous Materials
Management
Desk Reference

Part I

Regulatory and Management Perspectives

CHAPTER 1

Overview of Federal Laws and Regulations

Stephen D. Riner, CHMM

Introduction

In order to do the job effectively, every hazardous materials manager must have some knowledge of the scope of Federal laws that exist to protect the environment and human health and safety. Many professionals, however, are unaware of how to find and read these laws, or of the mechanisms for implementing and administering these laws. This section will provide a framework for understanding the legal foundation for the enactment and administration of environmental laws. We will focus on the Federal legislative and regulatory process, but most states also have similar processes.

The information discussed in this chapter applies to all forms of government regulation that the hazardous materials manager may be involved with: protection of the environment, worker health and safety, and hazardous materials transportation. Much of the discussion is specific to environmental laws because of the sheer number of separate laws, their numerous amendments and their complexity when compared to health and safety or transportation laws. Where the discussion is relevant to all types of these laws, we will use the term *EHS* as shorthand terminology for *environmental health and safety*.

Constitutional Framework for Enactment and Enforcement of Environmental Laws

The three branches of the Federal government—*executive*, *legislative*, and *judicial*—each have a role in enactment, enforcement and review of EHS laws. From the standpoint of EHS laws, this division of responsibilities can be summarized as follows.

Legislative Branch. The *legislative branch* (Congress) enacts laws that create regulatory agencies and gives them the authority to carry out their responsibilities, such as protecting the environment. These laws provide specific authority to regulatory agencies, and agencies cannot do anything that they have not been specifically given authority by Congress to do. Congress also enacts laws that govern how regulatory agencies perform their administrative functions such as rulemaking and enforcement.

Executive Branch. Regulatory agencies are located in the *executive branch*. The President heads the Executive Branch and names administrators of these agencies. The agencies may be independent like the United States Environmental Protection Agency (EPA), or cabinet departments like Labor and Transportation. These agencies

administer the laws for which Congress has given them responsibility, and develop regulations and program guidance. These agencies also administer the laws through enforcement actions, which often require involvement of the courts. Another agency within the executive branch, the Attorney General, may be involved in bringing action in the courts to enforce laws. Although Congress creates regulatory agencies and cabinet-level departments, the President and his subordinates have authority to organize the Executive Branch and executive departments and agencies, including agencies that assume responsibility for programs given by Congress to other agencies or departments. Neither the EPA nor the Occupational Safety and Health Administration (OSHA) were created by acts of Congress, but rather by Executive Reorganization Orders issued by the President (EPA) and Secretary of the Department of Labor (OSHA).

Judicial Branch. The *judicial branch* (the court system) is where EHS laws are interpreted and enforced. Regulated industries have recourse to the courts when governmental agencies take action to enforce the laws. In addition to trying civil and criminal cases for violations of the laws, courts review laws for constitutionality and review the actions of the regulatory agencies to make sure the actions conform to the law. Figure 1 below shows this flow of authority among the branches of government.

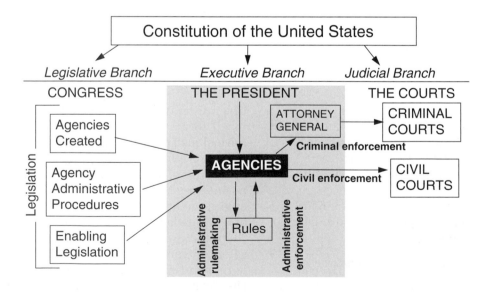

Figure 1. Flow of Authority to and from Regulatory Agencies

Legislation

The Federal government can take no action on any issue without a law that allows the government to act. We will not touch on the politically charged process of making laws, but will instead concentrate on building and understanding of laws.

The organization and structure of laws and the means of finding the most up-to-date version can be confusing. First, there are individual **acts** that are enacted by Congress, such as the Clean Air Act Amendments of 1990, the Superfund Amendments and Reauthorization Act of 1986, or the Toxic Substances Control Act of 1976. These names, or **short titles**, refer only to those portions of the law that are enacted by Congress at that time. These laws may be original acts that create an entirely new regulatory area, or (more often) acts that amend existing laws. In addition to the short title, each such act has a *Public Law* (PL) citation. For instance, the law commonly called the Clean Air Act Amendments of 1990 is PL 101–549, the 549th act passed by the 101st Congress.

Most major environmental laws have been revised many times. For example, the current Federal Water Pollution Control Act, as amended, has had a number of major and minor amendments, resulting in a law that now bears little resemblance to the original 1948 act. Laws that are amended must then be revised and republished to reflect all permanent amendments. This represents the **body of standing law**, or **statutes**.

Statutes are compiled in two ways. One way is to publish separately major laws, such as the Clean Air Act, as amended. (The use of the suffix *as amended* indicates that this is a compilation of the original Clean Air Act and all subsequent amendments, rather than just one amending act.) The second way is the **United States Code** (USC), a complete compilation of Federal statutes with all amendments up to the date of publication. The USC is organized into *Titles* that place statutes of similar subject matter in the same volume. The section numbers within a law differ somewhat between these two methods of compilation, so be careful when looking up a reference. For example, Section 102 of the Clean Air Act, as amended (CAA §102) is found in Title 42, Section 7402 of the USC (42 USC §7402). To determine the current legal requirements in a particular subject area, consult one of these compilations (after ensuring that all amendments to date have been included), rather than the individual acts of Congress.

Executive Branch Actions: Regulations, Permits, and Enforcement

Regulations. Laws enacted by Congress to establish regulatory programs can be very detailed, but they are usually general in their technical scope. The procedural matters covered by these laws (such as permit or enforcement programs) must be detailed more precisely than the law. So, agencies enact *regulations* that outline specific procedures for the administration and enforcement of EHS laws. The terms **rules** and **regulations** are synonymous, and both terms are used interchangeably in the law. For consistency, we will use the term *regulation* to refer to the final product (since it is compiled in the **Code of Federal Regulations**), but we will use **rulemaking** to refer to the process by which regulations are developed. Regulations cover such matters as the procedures for issuing permits, emission or effluent standards, and requirements for delegating authority from the Federal agencies to State EHS programs.

The statutory definition of a hazardous waste in the Resource Conservation and Recovery Act (RCRA) is a good example of the general language found in the law at 42 USC §6903(5):

> The term *hazardous waste* means a solid waste, or combination of solid wastes, which because of its quantity, concentration, or physical, chemical, or infectious characteristics, may
>
> (A) cause, or significantly contribute to, an increase in mortality or an increase in serious irreversible, or incapacitating reversible, illness; or
>
> (B) pose a substantial present or potential hazard to human health or the environment when improperly treated, stored, transported, or disposed of, or otherwise managed.

This statutory definition is inadequate to classify all of the potential industrial wastes without additional guidance. Congress did not intend the above definition to be the sole means of identifying hazardous wastes. RCRA also provides at 42 USC §6921(a):

[T]he Administrator shall, after notice and opportunity for public hearing, and after consultation with appropriate Federal and State agencies, develop and promulgate criteria for identifying the characteristics of hazardous waste, and for listing hazardous waste, which should be subject to the provisions of this subchapter, taking into account toxicity, persistence, and degradability in nature, potential for accumulation in tissue, and other related factors such as flammability, corrosiveness, and other hazardous characteristics. Such criteria shall be revised from time to time as may be appropriate.

The EPA has developed regulations that list specific industrial waste streams, and also describe the measurable physical characteristics for nonlisted wastes. These regulations allow any generator of waste to determine whether that waste is hazardous or not.

The following examples show the difference in scope between laws and regulations:

- The Clean Air Act directs EPA to develop ambient air quality standards, but for the most part does not dictate what pollutants should be included in these standards. The air quality standards are developed and issued as regulations. Amendments to environmental laws can be used by Congress to correct any shortcomings in the regulatory process. In the Clean Air Act Amendments of 1990, Congress specifically listed 189 hazardous air pollutants that it required to be regulated, 42 USC §7412(b). Congress took this step because of EPA's inability to enact standards for more than a few hazardous air pollutants.

- The Federal Water Pollution Control (Clean Water) Act requires facilities that discharge their wastewater into surface waters to obtain a National Pollutant Discharge Elimination System (NPDES) permit. EPA, through regulation, has set specific requirements for obtaining a permit. (40 CFR 122-124) The EPA regulations also specifically limit the effluents for various types of industrial wastewater discharges (40 CFR 401-471).

Although regulations are developed by nonelected government employees rather than by elected legislators, *regulations have the force of law.* Violation of a regulation is the same as violation of a statute, and in some instances can be prosecuted criminally.

Permits. Many environmental regulatory programs require permits for specific activities. Permits are not required for actions relating to occupational safety and health nor hazardous materials transportation. Although there are variances, there are registrations and licenses under these regulations that may be considered analogous to a permit. *Permits* are issued by Federal agencies or by State agencies that have been delegated authority under Federal law. The permits allow a permittee to conduct an activity that has an impact on the environment. For example, environmental permits are issued for the operation of hazardous waste treatment, storage or disposal facilities, the emission of air pollutants, or discharges of wastewater. A regulation describes the procedures for application, public notice, and agency decision that govern the permitting process. Any violation of terms of a permit is usually considered violation of the regulation(s) that govern the actions allowed by the permit.

Enforcement. Regulatory agencies not only develop and administer regulations and permits, they also *enforce* them. There are two kinds of enforcement: *administrative* and *judicial*. *Administrative enforcement* covers all enforcement actions taken by the agency, while *judicial enforcement* occurs once the agency takes a case to the courthouse for lawsuit or criminal prosecution. Administrative enforcement generally follows this process:

- An inspection or administrative review resulting in discovery of a violation.

- Official notice to the regulated party in a form such as a Notice of Violation or citation.

- The scope of the enforcement action is determined by the agency. This action can take one of the following paths:

  - For minor violations, the regulated party may be directed to correct the problems with no penalties assessed.

  - For more serious violations, the agency may assess an administrative penalty (if permitted by law). This is a unilateral agency action that the regulated party may appeal either to an administrative review board or to the courts.

  - As an alternative, the agency may try to negotiate an administrative document called a *consent order* (or some similar name). This order represents a settlement of the issues between the agency and the regulated party under which the agency agrees not to sue in exchange for payment of negotiated penalties and corrective actions to achieve compliance.

If the violation is so serious that criminal prosecution is appropriate, or if the agency and the regulated party are not able to negotiate a settlement, the agency may seek prosecution in criminal court or sue the regulated party in civil court. At this point, the process becomes a matter of judicial enforcement.

Most disputes between agencies and the regulated community do not end up in court. Major agencies usually have administrative review boards that arbitrate and rule on disputes such as administrative penalties and issuance or denial of permits. Disagreements that go through these processes usually never reach the Judicial Branch unless one party appeals the board's decision.

Most states have administrative processes similar to the Federal processes described above.

Involvement of the Courts

The Judicial Branch does not become involved in a case until regulatory agencies, regulated parties, or citizens bring it to them. The courts become involved in EHS matters in several ways:

- Lawsuits involving agencies that are unable to negotiate consent agreements are heard in civil court. Courts are typically asked by the regulatory agency to assess monetary penalties and compel the violator to take corrective action.

- If a statute provides for criminal prosecution of knowing and willful violations, a regulatory agency may take a company and/or individuals to criminal court. The criminal complaint may result in monetary penalties and may compel corrective action like a civil lawsuit. In order to convict in criminal court, the government must meet the *beyond a reasonable doubt* burden of proof, which is a higher level of proof than the *preponderance of evidence* (more likely than not) finding required in civil court.

- Regulated parties may sue a governmental agency if they believe that a regulation does not meet the requirements of the law. The underlying statute may also be challenged by a lawsuit that questions its constitutionality

or conformance with other laws. Lawsuits may also be filed by regulated parties for agency actions such as denial of a permit.

- Some environmental statutes provide for citizen lawsuits. These laws allow members of the public, who may not otherwise have legal standing to sue, to file lawsuits against regulated parties for failure to comply with the law.

Summary of the Roles of Each Branch of the Federal Government in Regulation

Congress. Congress enacts legislation to create regulatory agencies and give them the authority to regulate in particular subject areas.

Regulatory Agencies. Regulatory agencies develop regulations that describe in detail the requirements of these regulatory programs, and enforce these regulations by issuing permits and taking action against violations.

Courts. Courts determine whether or not a regulated entity is civilly or criminally liable for violating laws and regulations. The courts also rule on the constitutionality of laws and the conformance of agency actions to laws and regulations.

Development of Regulations

It is very important for the hazardous materials manager to understand how regulations are developed. Many of the technical details of Federal and State regulations are determined during the development process. There are numerous opportunities during the rulemaking process to comment on and have input into the final regulations. Anyone tracking the rulemaking process must be familiar with the *Federal Register*, which is published daily. All official notices regarding a proposed regulation are published in the *Federal Register*.

Laws from several sources govern rulemaking. First, there are Federal administrative procedure laws, originally enacted as the Administrative Procedures Act (but now recodified with other administrative statues at 5 USC §§500–596).

Second, the underlying statute that authorizes the agency to undertake the rulemaking may have specific procedural requirements for regulations enacted under that law (for example, Section 307(d) of the Clean Air Act, as amended, 42 USC §7607(d), which describes EPA's procedures for issuing regulations under this act). Finally, an agency may have administrative regulations that further lay out the details of rulemaking processes for that agency (*e.g.*, 49 CFR 106 and 29 CFR 1911, which respectively describe the rulemaking processes for the Department of Transportation, Research and Special Programs Administration and the Department of Labor, Occupational Safety and Health Administration). There are other laws also that specify requirements for rulemaking, especially concerning regulations that have a significant economic impact. These laws include the Small Business Regulatory Enforcement Fairness Act (SBREFA), the Unfunded Mandates Reform Act, and the Regulatory Flexibility Act.

A typical rulemaking process is described below. There may be variations in these steps depending on specific statutory requirements, the urgency of rulemaking, and statutory or judicial deadlines:

1) Congress enacts a law permitting or requiring an administrative agency to develop regulations. The law may require particular rulemaking within a given time, or an agency may determine that rulemaking is necessary in order to fulfill its statutory responsibilities. A court may determine that an agency is not fulfilling its statutory responsibilities, and direct the agency to develop regulations.

2) An agency may establish a rulemaking schedule to put interested parties on notice that a particular rulemaking process will reach the proposal stage soon. Some agencies periodically publish a list of regulations under development in the *Federal Register*.

3) The agency establishes a *docket*, or official administrative record, for a particular regulation. This is necessary to document that all administrative procedures, as well as any procedures specified in the enabling legislation, are followed. All comments that are submitted in response to a proposed regulation are kept with this docket. The official docket is a collection of documents in a regulatory agency office (usually in Washington, DC), and copies of docket materials are now being published on-line as well. Search the agency's web site for links to these dockets.

4) The agency internally develops the concept for how the regulation will work. Agencies may develop several alternatives that accomplish the same end, and may work with an advisory committee of interested parties on these ideas. An Advance Notice of Proposed Rulemaking (ANPR) may be published in the *Federal Register* in order to solicit comments on one or more regulatory concepts.

5) Once a regulation's concept is defined, the agency develops the proposed regulation and publishes it in the *Federal Register*. An important part of each proposal is the ***preamble***. The preamble describes the rationale for the regulation, how it complies with and/or fulfills the requirements of the underlying statutes. This section also summarizes the input received from interested parties to date and how this feedback has impacted development of the regulation. *The preamble contains the agency's interpretation of how the regulation will work*, and is a potential resource for any future questions of interpretation. The notice contains a deadline for comment.

6) If necessary, there may be a public hearing. Such proceedings can be quasi-judicial, with sworn witnesses, cross-examination and testimony kept by a court reporter. The hearing examiner issues findings on the issues of fact for the agency's consideration in the rulemaking process. An agency may choose to hold an informal hearing, intended strictly to gather information and discuss the agency's proposal.

7) After receiving comments, the agency may then withdraw the regulation for additional work or comment, make minor revisions to the regulation in response to comments, or publish the regulation in final form. If more than minor revisions are made, the agency must propose the regulation again and solicit further comment. The agency must also publish a preamble to the final regulation that discusses all comments received and the agency's response to these comments.

Amendments to existing regulations (including revocation) must go through the same process as a new regulation. Minor amendments may have short preambles, and technical amendments (corrections) may require little if any supporting data.

Once a final rule is published in the *Federal Register* (the entire rule or the parts proposed for revision are republished, including any changes that were made in response to comments), it is effective as of the date indicated in the notice. If the regulated community does not accept the final rule, there are options for legal review. In legal challenges to a regulation, litigants can argue that the agency did not follow administrative procedure requirements and/or specific requirements in either the enabling legislation or the agency's administrative rules. Litigants can also argue that the regulation is based on erroneous science or economic analysis. Litigants have a better case to challenge a regulation in court if they can show that their objections were raised during the rulemaking process and not properly considered by the agency, rather than raising their arguments for the first time in litigation. Any law that sets specific rulemaking requirements for the agency (*e.g.*, SBREFA) can be used to challenge a rulemaking process.

The rulemaking process can be relatively short (months) for noncontroversial proposals or may take years where there is significant controversy, lack of consistent data, or scientific uncertainty. Legal challenges to rules can delay these processes even longer. For example, a ten-year effort by the United States Department of Transportation (DOT) was required to extend DOT jurisdiction to most intrastate shipments of hazardous materials.

Congress can overturn or render regulations ineffective. Because the underlying statute gives an agency the authority to enact regulations, regulations become ineffective if Congress amends the underlying statute and changes the scope of the agency's authority. Also, under 1994 legislation, Congress can disapprove regulations by resolution within 60 days of enactment. The President can veto the resolution of disapproval but the veto is subject to override by a 2/3 vote of Congress.

Courts can overturn regulations if an agency fails to follow the rulemaking process. Examples of situations where agencies have failed to follow their administrative procedures include:

1) OSHA's permissible exposure levels (PELs) are limits on occupational exposure to toxic chemicals, listed at 29 CFR 1910.1000. The Occupational Safety and Health (OSH) Act of 1970 directed OSHA to adopt existing industry consensus standards for worker health and safety. OSHA adopted as its PELs existing consensus standards from two organizations that had developed chemical exposure limitations: the 1968 American Conference of Governmental Industrial Hygienists Threshold Limit Values (ACGIH TLVs), and American National Standards Institute (ANSI) standards. Because OSHA took action specifically directed by the enabling legislation, these PELs were not subject to legal challenge. By the mid-1980s it was clear that these standards were out of date. OSHA then sought to make a wholesale change to the standard by revising many of the standards in 29 CFR 1910.1000. These revisions were challenged on the grounds that OSHA is required by the OSH Act to provide detailed toxicity data for each compound for which it intended to revise the original standard; in this case, OSHA did not do so because of the sheer numbers of compounds involved. As a result, the revised standard was overturned, and the regulation reverted to the original pre-1970 criteria. OSHA's only recourse is to revise each compound's PEL individually, providing the necessary background (which is still subject to challenge in court), or to convince Congress to amend the OSH Act to allow OSHA to update the standards by adopting up-to-date ACGIH TLVs without having to provide the detailed supporting data.

2) EPA originally proposed hazardous waste regulations under the Resource Conservation and Recovery Act in 1978. The proposed regulation had the current *listed* and *characteristic* waste definitions, but some commenters were concerned that a listed waste could be rendered nonhazardous simply by mixing it with a nonhazardous waste. Because of this concern, EPA's final regulation, published in 1980, added the *mixture* and *derived-from* rules, whereby any waste mixed with or derived from a listed hazardous waste is also regulated as hazardous. In a subsequent challenge to this rule (Shell *vs.* EPA), which did not come to a decision for over 10 years, a United States District Court ruled that EPA went beyond what was permitted in its revisions to the proposed regulation without soliciting comments on the revised provisions. The addition of the mixture and derived-from rules was ruled to be so significantly different

from the original proposal that opportunity for comment was required.

The outcome of this second case was so significant that EPA immediately reissued the offending provisions as *interim final* regulations, and sought assistance from Congress. Congress passed legislation allowing the provisions to stay in place for a period of time until EPA could finish its effort to redefine hazardous waste (the *hazardous waste identification rule*, or HWIR).

Keeping up with Current Regulations

Given that regulations change over time, how does a person find the current requirements? The **Code of Federal Regulations** (CFR) is the body of standing regulation, and is accurate as of the annual publication date of each title. There are 48 titles of the CFR, identified by number, that contain regulations pertaining to a particular *subject matter*, not a specific agency. For example, although the vast majority of EPA regulations are in Title 40 (Protection of the Environment), there are also EPA regulations in Titles 5 (Administrative Personnel), 41 (Public Contracts and Property Management) and 48 (Public Acquisitions Regulations System). Title 40 also contains

regulations of the Council on Environmental Quality, the Chemical Safety and Hazard Investigation Board, and joint regulations of EPA with the Department of Justice and the Department of Defense. The Titles of most interest to hazardous materials managers are summarized in Table 1.

Each CFR title is published annually, and thus each volume contains only the amendments that were effective as of the publication date. Subsequent amendments and additions are not included until the next volume. Amendments published in the CFR that do not become effective until after the publication date have a note that indicates the date they will become effective; they also note any existing language that will cease to be effective at that time.

Even the most recently published CFR may not be up-to-date, so the regulated community needs to know how to locate the currently effective regulations, especially in subject areas where there are frequent changes. The tracking choices are:

1) Track the *Federal Register* daily or review its monthly index looking for proposed and final regulations.

2) Subscribe to the *List of CFR Sections Affected*, which is issued monthly by the Superintendent of Documents. This publication gives a cumulative listing of CFR sections that have been updated each year without having to

Table 1. CFR Titles Most Often Used by Hazardous Materials Managers

Department/Agency	Title	Parts
Nuclear Regulatory Commission	10: Energy	0-171
Department of Labor (Occupational Safety and Health Administration)	29: Labor	1900-1926
Department of Labor (Mine Safety and Health Administration)	30: Mineral Resources	1-104
Coast Guard	33: Navigation and Navigable Waters	125-338
Environmental Protection Agency	40: Protection of the Environment	1-799
Department of Transportation (Research and Special Projects Administration) *Includes hazardous materials transportation and pipeline safety*	49: Transportation	106-195

subscribe to or review each issue of the *Federal Register*. But, once you find that a section of interest has been modified, you then have to find the *Federal Register* issue that contains the changes.

3) The Information Age has drastically improved access to current regulations. You can subscribe to a CD-based or on-line service that updates Federal regulations as soon as amendments become effective. You need to be sure that these updates come out soon after the regulation's effective date; however, some services take several months to incorporate the changes into their databases. Also, be aware that *proposed* regulations are usually not included in the information these services provide, although they may be available through a separate subscription. These information services can cost hundreds to thousands of dollars per year.

4) The most significant development in providing ready access to up-to-date regulations to anyone with a personal computer is the Internet. The Government Printing Office operates a worldwide web site providing access to the current CFR. This site allows you to search for a particular subject or topic if you do not know the CFR citation. Current and recent past issues of the *Federal Register* are also accessible on-line. In addition, EPA and OSHA both have compilations of their regulations on their web sites, and many states have web sites providing access to their rules and statutes as well.

Those who need the text of current statutes can go to similar resources. The *United States Code* is also updated periodically, and some of the same commercial services that provide regulations also provide full text of statutes. There is at least one web site, operated by a law school which has a current compilation of the USC. Statutes change much less frequently than do regulations. Major statutory changes are generally publicized well enough that professionals in the field should be aware of their development and final adoption, and will know to look for the updated law.

Because of the rapid evolution of information technology, additional or more sophisticated sources of information may become available before this volume becomes obsolete. Hazardous

materials managers need to remain aware of developments in this area, and seek the most up-to-date sources of information.

Regulatory laws and their associated standards form the basis of the regulatory programs that hazardous materials managers work under each day. All hazardous materials managers should understand these laws and the process of developing regulations. For those who find reading and application of laws a bit overwhelming, national and local organizations offer training courses geared toward technical professionals who are not lawyers.

History of Federal Environmental Legislation

First Federal Regulatory Laws

Regulation of business by the Federal government began mostly in the late 20th century, and most Federal environmental and related laws have been enacted after 1970. But, there are much earlier examples of Federal laws that are forerunners of today's regulatory statutes:

- The first law that had direct environmental impact was the Rivers and Harbors Act of 1899. The motivation for the law was to protect navigable waterways from deposition of debris that would impede navigation, and it is doubtful that the law's authors saw pathogenic microorganisms as hazards to navigation. Around 1970, however, the law was resurrected to provide authority for an Army Corps of Engineers program to issue permits to wastewater dischargers.

- One of the earliest entities created by Congress as a regulatory agency was the Interstate Commerce Commission (ICC). The Transportation of Explosives Act of 1909 gave ICC authority to set manufacturing standards for shipping containers used to transport dangerous goods. The United States Department of Transportation (DOT) now has authority over many of the now-defunct ICC's regulatory areas, and some of the current manufacturing standards for compressed gas cylinders in DOT regulations date back to the ICC's original 1911 regulations.

- By the 1930s, Congress had enacted several laws directed at purveyors of snake oil patent medicines containing opium or other powerful drugs and carrying unsubstantiated claims of efficacy. While not significant from a strictly environmental standpoint, these laws represent a significant expansion of Federal agencies whose sole reason for existence is to regulate. The Federal Food Drug and Cosmetic Act of 1938 established the Food and Drug Administration.

Public Health–Directed Legislation

At this point we will digress briefly from this discussion of Federal laws, since many of the early efforts in protecting public health took place at the State level. In the early part of the 20th century, as major cities grew and provided both public water supplies and sewer systems, states began to enact legislation in response to the resulting public health concerns. Minnesota was a good example (and similar events no doubt occurred in other states): typhoid outbreaks resulted from the Minneapolis and St. Paul water intakes being downstream of the point where sewers discharged untreated sewage into the Mississippi River. To address the issue, the Board of Health (today's Minnesota Department of Health) was created in the 1920s, and by the 1930s had authority to regulate public water supplies. In 1947, the Water Pollution Control Commission was created within the Health Department to regulate discharges to surface waters; 20 years later, this commission became the separate Minnesota Pollution Control Agency. In many states, the environmental agency has evolved from the State health department, and in a few states is still part of the health department.

Signs of Environmental Deterioration

Except for the examples cited at the beginning of this chapter, there were no significant EHS laws enacted during the first half of the century. By the mid-1950s, early versions of the Clean Air Act and Clean Water Act were in place, but these laws imposed only planning and coordination requirements on the states. States with significant air quality problems (such as the dirty-air cities Pittsburgh and Los Angeles) enacted regulatory programs that had measurable impacts, but the environmental quality in other areas deteriorated with the economic and industrial boom after World War II. Specific environmental problems became apparent:

- Rachel Carson published her book *Silent Spring* in 1962. The book's impact was significant in increasing public awareness and concerns about environmental issues. While many disagree with her all-encompassing condemnation of pesticide use, evidence is strong that dichlorodiphenyltrichloroethane (DDT) residuals in certain bird species (*e.g.*, brown pelicans) resulted in thinning of eggshells, with a consequential decline in the bird populations. Following banning of DDT, bird populations rebounded.

- Gross water pollution from poorly controlled wastewater discharges in more heavily industrialized parts of the country became commonplace. Lake Erie was proclaimed to be dead (it was not, although it certainly was highly polluted), and chemical residuals floating on the Cuyahoga River in Cleveland, Ohio caught fire and burned for several days.

- Despite local efforts, air pollution was a continuing problem in major cities.

It was this evident deterioration, together with public awareness that increased by the late 1960s, that set the stage for the first significant Federal environmental legislation. Perhaps the first significant Federal act concerning the environment was the National Environmental Policy Act (NEPA) of 1969, which did not establish a regulatory program *per se*, but required analysis of the environmental impacts of significant Federal agency actions.

Creation of the Environmental Protection Agency; Medium-Specific Environmental Legislation

The first of the major regulatory laws was enacted in 1970, and that same year the United States Environmental Protection Agency (EPA) was created. Previously, diverse agencies such as the Corps of Engineers, Public Health Service, and Department of Health, Education and Welfare had responsibility for pieces of the environmental puzzle. Creation of the EPA put the responsibility in one place. Major laws were enacted during this era.

Clean Air Act, 1970. The intent of this act was to control gross air pollution problems by regulating the *dirty air* pollutants: ozone, nitrogen oxides, sulfur dioxide, and particulates. EPA was required to set ambient air quality standards that each state ultimately was to attain through pollution controls imposed on air pollutant sources under a State Implementation Plan (SIP).

protection of public health by control of water pollutants that affect public health, but also addresses secondary parameters that affect the aesthetic value of drinking water. All *public* water supplies are covered by this law, which in effect means that only private residential wells and wells serving businesses with small workforces are excluded from regulation.

Resource Conservation and Recovery Act, 1976. The Resource Conservation and Recovery Act (RCRA) extended protection to the last remaining

---

Bits and Pieces

An illustration of how fragmented the United States environmental regulatory efforts were in 1970, is the list of the various programs that were consolidated to create the Environmental Protection Agency:

- **Department of Interior:** Federal Water Quality Administration

- **Department of Health, Education, and Welfare:** National Air Pollution Control Administration; Food and Drug Administration pesticide research group; Bureau of Solid Waste Management; Bureau of Water Hygiene; Bureau of Radiological Health

- **Department of Agriculture:** Agricultural Research Service pesticide activities

- **Atomic Energy Commission and Federal Radiation Council:** Radiation criteria

---

Federal Water Pollution Control Act, 1972. This law (with subsequent amendments, now called Clean Water Act), established a nationwide wastewater discharge permitting program, the National Pollutant Discharge Elimination System (NPDES) permit program. States were also required to set surface water quality standards under this act. The pollutants that were the primary focus were those that degrade water quality by depleting oxygen: Biochemical Oxygen Demand (BOD_5), and suspended solids. The act set *fishable and swimmable* waters as its near-term goal, and dictated that discharges would ultimately meet *Best Available Technology* rather than merely enough treatment to meet water quality standards.

Safe Drinking Water Act, 1974. This law is directed at utilization of a resource rather than waste disposal or emission control. The primary focus is

environmental medium: the land. As the name implies, the law set forth an intent to promote conservation of resources through reduced reliance on landfilling. This law covers both solid waste and hazardous waste, although by far the most attention is paid to the hazardous waste aspect. It was not until the late 1980s that EPA issued rules setting minimum technical standards for solid waste landfills, and most technical standards relating to solid waste disposal are developed by individual states.

Recognition of the Role of Toxic Substances

The laws described above had one thing in common: they were directed at the gross contaminants that made the air and water visibly dirty. During this same period, however, analytical technology improved to the point where very small amounts of contaminants thought to have toxic effects in small concentrations could be detected. Environmental advocacy organizations sued EPA to require it to regulate toxic pollutants in addition to conventional pollutants. The initial major Clean Water Act and Clean Air Act reauthorizations (both 1977) were directed at increasing control of toxic substances.

Toxic Substances Control Act (1976). This unique law regulates toxic chemicals when they are manufactured and used, rather than only when they enter the environment. Under this law, manufacturers and importers must file a pre-manufacture notification when they propose to manufacture or import a chemical not previously included on EPA's inventory of chemical substances. Other provisions of this law addressed the manufacture, use, and disposal of poly-chlorinated biphenyls (PCBs), effectively phasing out the use of PCBs.

Multimedia and Incident-Driven Legislation

By the late 1970s, it was apparent that control of individual media (air, water) was not sufficient to protect the environment. There was growing recognition of the interrelationship of environmental media, especially because many traditional end-of-pipe pollution control measures merely transferred pollutants from one medium to another. Another aspect to legislation following the late 1970s was to respond to high-profile environmental incidents with laws designed to prevent recurrences or a means of quick response by government.

Comprehensive Environmental Response, Compensation and Liability Act of 1980. The Comprehensive Environmental Response, Compensation and Liability Act (CERCLA) is more commonly known by the unfortunate sobriquet *Superfund Act*. This law was enacted in large part in response to the contamination emanating from the Love Canal disposal site in Niagara Falls, New York, and the inability of State and Federal governments to provide quick relief to affected homeowners. CERCLA did not establish a regulatory program *per se*; rather, it established a

fund which could be used for responses to hazardous substance release sites, and established liability for these releases.

The Emergency Planning and Community Right-to-Know Act (1986)[1]. The Emergency Planning and Community Right-to-Know Act (EPCRA), was enacted in response to the chemical release disaster that occurred in Bhopal, India in 1984. Under this law, states and local governments were required to establish emergency planning and response organizations, and users of hazardous and toxic chemicals were required to report their usage and (for some chemicals) emissions to these newly established State and local agencies.

Oil Pollution Act (1990). The Oil Pollution Act of 1990 was a direct result of the accident involving the oil tanker *Exxon Valdez*. It imposed new stringent standards on transportation and storage of oil.

Pollution Prevention Act (1990). The Pollution Prevention Act of 1990 is a multimedia law not brought about by any headline event. This law is more a statement of policy than another regulatory program, and did not directly impose any responsibilities upon the regulated community. It did formally establish reduction of contaminants at the source—rather than end-of-pipe treatment—as the official environmental control policy of the United States, and directed EPA to develop its regulations in the future and incentives to bring this about.

Major Reauthorizations of Existing Environmental Statutes

We have previously discussed the reauthorizations of the Clean Water and Clean Air Acts in 1977 and how these laws were revised to focus more

---

[1] This law is often called *SARA Title III* because it was enacted as one title of the *Superfund Amendments and Reauthorization Act* (SARA). It is, however, a separate law, even though some of its subject matter overlaps with that of CERCLA.

attention on control of toxic substances. There are other significant reauthorizations of environmental laws that bear discussion.

The Hazardous and Solid Waste Amendments of 1984. The era of the early 1980s was the time when EPA was implementing the first RCRA regulations regulating the disposal of hazardous waste, which were published in 1980. However, this era was also part of the early Reagan years, and Reagan's first EPA administrator was openly hostile to environmental regulations. During this time the EPA budget was cut 23 percent, and many experienced staff left the agency. Opposition to these deregulatory efforts by the public and Congress resulted in a change in leadership at EPA. In response to the turmoil at EPA and perceived under-regulation of hazardous waste disposal, Congress took steps to achieve increased hazardous waste regulation by enacting the Hazardous and Solid Waste Amendments of 1984 (HSWA). This act reauthorized RCRA, severely limited land disposal of hazardous waste, and set stringent deadlines by which land disposal restrictions would become effective (*hammer provisions*) if EPA had not enacted rules. Its hammer provisions and level of detail were intended to minimize regulatory discretion on the part of EPA. Another significant aspect of this law was establishment of a program to regulate underground storage tanks holding petroleum products and hazardous substances.

Superfund Amendments and Reauthorization Act of 1986. Critics of the Superfund program expressed major concerns in the program's early years. One of these was that cleanups of the sites did not emphasize *permanent* solutions. Other concerns addressed included increasing participation of both states and the public in the remedy selection process, expanding health risk assessment capability in the Federal government, and providing a liability defense for *innocent landowners* who purchased property later found to be contaminated. This act was reauthorized as the Superfund Amendments and Reauthorization Act of 1986 (SARA) and also became a legislative vehicle for enactment of the Emergency Planning and Community Right-to-Know Act (EPCRA), discussed above.

Clean Air Act Amendments of 1990. This is the last major piece of environmental legislation that has passed Congress. The following are the major features of this law:

1) A nationwide permitting program was established for *major sources* of air pollution, administered by each state

2) Replacement of the former National Emission Standards for Hazardous Air Pollutants (NESHAPs) provisions, under which only seven hazardous air pollutants were regulated, with a requirement to regulate hazardous air pollutants on a source-specific basis. A list of 189 hazardous air pollutants was included in the legislation

3) Increased efforts by states to bring non-attainment areas, especially those for ozone, into compliance with ambient air standards

Safe Drinking Water Act Amendments of 1996. Because this law was enacted after the "Republican Revolution" of 1994, it may be a harbinger of future reauthorizations, and is therefore discussed below.

An Era of Retrenchment and Reconsideration

The 1994 elections produced a major shift in control of Congress. A number of the new conservative members of Congress were openly hostile toward the existing regulatory structure. Mainly due to strong public opposition, the new Congress' early attempts to make significant changes in environmental laws were mostly turned aside by a coalition of Democrats and moderate Republicans. A few laws that slightly weakened the ability of the Federal government and regulatory agencies to impose regulations were enacted, but stronger regulatory reforms that might have imposed strict cost-benefit analyses on regulations were defeated.

Reauthorization of several laws have been debated in the past and current Congresses, but the only significant piece of environmental legislation to pass since 1994 has been the Safe Drinking Water Act Amendments of 1996. The law did not gut the original act, but it did remove a requirement (liked by few, including EPA) that EPA regulate a large number of additional potential drinking water contaminants. Instead, EPA was directed to focus on those contaminants known to present significant hazards (including biological contaminants) and to enact regulations based on cost and feasibility as well as health impact.

Interrelationship of Federal Environmental Statutes

Despite the proliferation of laws, there has been an effort by Congress and regulatory agencies to minimize potential conflicts among the various statutes. These laws make frequent use of cross-referencing to draw in requirements from other laws. As an example, EPA worked closely with DOT in development of the hazardous waste regulations; EPA recognized DOT's jurisdiction over hazardous waste transportation, and DOT modified its regulations to include rules for identification of hazardous waste and to adopt the EPA hazardous waste manifest as the shipping paper for hazardous wastes. Still, there are areas of potential inconsistency, which are more of an inconvenience than an impediment to compliance:

- Emergency planning requirements do not always track. For instance, an OSHA hazard communication program is not laid out the same way as a RCRA hazardous waste training program, even though the RCRA part would seem to be a logical subset of the OSHA part. To help regulated entities avoid the need to have several separate plans covering the same subject matter, an Integrated Contingency Plan concept has been developed outside the regulatory arena.

- Definitions may be inconsistent or duplicative between laws. Hazardous Substance has different meanings under OSHA (in its Hazardous Waste Operations and Emergency Response Standard) and under CERCLA and the Clean Water Act.

A Look into the Future

One constant in the 30-plus years since serious environmental regulations have been in place has

---

Other Laws Establishing Significant Regulatory Programs

There have been several other significant laws enacted over the years, affecting the environment, safety, or public health. These laws do not fit neatly into the discussion of the progression of environmental legislation, but are important from the standpoint of environment, health, and safety professionals.

- **Federal Insecticide, Fungicide and Rodenticide Act (FIFRA), 1947.** Initially, the law was administered by the Department of Agriculture, and set labeling requirements for pesticides. Jurisdiction was transferred to EPA, and in 1972, a major amendment to this law established a program to control the manufacture, distribution and use of pesticides. EPA was given authority to register all pesticides, and to suspend, cancel, or restrict pesticides that could pose environmental hazards.

- **Occupational Safety and Health Act (OSH Act), 1970.** This law directed the Department of Labor to establish standards for physical, chemical, and biological hazards in the workplace. The Occupational Safety and Health Administration (OSHA) was set up within the Department of Labor to administer this program.

- **Hazardous Materials Transportation Act (HMTA), 1975.** The Department of Transportation regulates shipments of hazardous materials by highway, rail, vessel, and air. Previously, this regulation principally covered interstate shipments, and many intrastate shipments were unregulated (depending on the state). DOT has recently extended its authority to most intrastate hazardous materials shipments as well.

been a perpetual state of evolution of attitudes toward the environment and how to protect it. At the beginning of this era, it was believed that only strong command-and-control regulation would work (and, given the litigious and hostile attitude of many in the regulated community at that time, this may well have been true). Since then, there has been movement toward the use of performance-based standards and environmental management systems to accomplish these ends. Development of the ISO 14000 series of internationally recognized environmental management standards has laid the groundwork for responsible companies to develop voluntary internal programs that document their commitment to environmental protection.

The political climate at the beginning of the 21st century provides an interesting contrast to the mid-1990s. Even with a conservative Congress and President, there are no serious moves afoot to undermine the current regulatory structure. Some regulations enacted since 2001 are more stringent than the older regulations they replaced, such as the arsenic drinking water standard and Spill Prevention, Control, and Countermeasure (SPCC) plan requirements. There are some initiatives to modify existing regulations taking into consideration specific industry concerns, but these modifications do not represent major changes in the overall regulatory scheme. While there is controversy over such moves as regulatory changes in New Source Review or legislative proposals such as the Clear Skies Initiative to reduce power plant emissions, it is evident that they do not represent wholesale rollbacks of existing regulations. And, despite disagreement over the benefits or costs of these proposals, in the long run air emissions from major source facilities will continue to decrease. In addition, building on the success of the Clean Air Act Acid Rain Program, there are likely to be changes in regulation that will expand the use of the marketplace to limit pollution through selling of pollution credits.

Climate change is one area where serious disagreement exists within Congress for taking any serious actions to reduce greenhouse gas emissions. Until overwhelming and incontrovertible scientific evidence of a human-caused effect is presented and cost-effective countermeasures are proposed, it is unlikely that any initiatives such as those prescribed by the Kyoto Protocols will be enacted into law. Still, forward-thinking businesses are taking voluntary emission reduction actions in anticipation of being able to claim early reduction credits (and tout their environmental credentials) when mandatory greenhouse gas reductions finally do become law.

Environmental regulation continues to have strong support from the American public, and politicians who propose doing away with strong environmental protection do so at their own peril. Barring an unprecedented change in public attitude, environmental regulation as we know it will not change significantly any time soon.

Stephen D. Riner is a Senior Environmental Scientist with Aquila, Inc. in Pueblo, Colorado, providing regulatory compliance assistance and employee training for Aquila's electric generation facilities in Colorado and Kansas. Mr. Riner has broad experience in environmental and safety management and auditing, including the areas of air quality, hazardous waste management, and hazardous materials transportation. He has a BS in Chemistry from Loyola University of Los Angeles and a MS in Chemistry from New Mexico State University. Mr. Riner has over 25 years of hazardous materials management experience, working in government, consulting, manufacturing, and utilities.

CHAPTER 2

Overview of the Law in an Environmental Context

Eugene R. Wasson, JD

This chapter provides a brief overview of the legal system that creates and implements what we know as *environmental law*. The discussion divides environmental law into two categories: ***common law*** and ***statutory law***. However, this division is strictly for ease of discussion. In real situations, it is imperative that the implications of both common law and statutory law be considered together.

Common Law

Common law originated in England and was adopted in the American colonies. It consists of various rules of law that have evolved over centuries from judicial decisions that relied on usages and customs of the people. It is often called *case law*, which is an easy way to distinguish it from statutory law that is enacted by legislative bodies. Common law is a work in progress, which is always evolving, case by case, to meet the needs of a changing society and new technology. New causes of action and rules are created as necessary to address new wrongs for which there is no existing common law or statutory cause of action. For example, new causes of action have evolved in the past few decades for interference with business relations and for infliction of emotional distress.

Common law and statutory law directly affect each other and neither should be considered alone. For example, the common law tends to fill voids in the statutory law by providing remedies for wrongs that the statutory law does not address. It is simply impossible for a legislature to address every factual scenario that may arise. On the flip side, a legislative body may determine that a cause of action or rule of the common law is not consistent with current public policy and enact a statutory law that the court must then follow instead of the common law.

The common law causes of action applicable to environmental law are known as **torts**.[1] One definition of a tort is a legal wrong committed upon the person or property of another, independent of contract. Often the most costly environmental liability is not a government penalty for violation of a regulation, but is tort liability to an individual for harm to his person or property. Typically, actions filed by private individuals will allege numerous theories of liability, usually including negligence, strict liability, nuisance, and trespass, or some combination of these. The damages sought in a typical case may include diminution in property value, medical monitoring expenses, medical costs, lost earnings, reduced life expectancy, emotional distress, pain and suffering, and punitive damages. Such actions are often filed against companies when their activities adversely affect others. For example, the release of a harmful substance into the environment or onto the lands of another is likely to prompt surrounding landowners to file civil lawsuits. Lawsuits may be filed and potentially be successful even if the release of the harmful substance was not a violation of any regulatory requirement or permit condition. Private actions may be directed against excessive noise, light, odors, particulate fallout, vibrations, and physical invasion of another's property, just to name a few. In some cases, liability may be imposed even though the facility operator did everything humanly possible to operate his facility in a safe manner and was not aware of and did not intend any harm to the other party.

Although there are numerous tort causes of action, such as assault, defamation and invasion of privacy, the ones most likely to be applicable in an environmental matter are trespass, nuisance, negligence, and strict liability.[2]

Trespass

The tort of **trespass** is a physical invasion of another's rights, whether in his person, personal property, or land. We are concerned here with trespass to land. Trespass to land involves either (1) intentionally entering or causing something to enter onto the lands of another, with or without resultant harm or (2) recklessly, negligently, or as the result of an abnormally dangerous activity, entering or causing something to enter onto the lands of another with resultant harm. The second category, negligent entry onto the land of another, is the most likely source of liability in an environmental context. The entry onto the plaintiff's property may be either by a person or by some tangible matter, such as ash from a smokestack. Intangibles such as light, sound, vibrations, and odor do not provide grounds for a trespass claim, although such invasions may be actionable based on private nuisance as discussed below.

---

[1] Common law also provides **contract-based remedies**. We do not address contract-based actions here, but it is important to note that contracts may have an important impact on a given environmental situation. For example, a lease agreement for a facility usually requires that the tenant comply with all applicable laws. Thus, failure to comply with environmental laws may be a basis for the landlord to require the tenant to clean up any releases of hazardous substances on the property. Similarly, a contract may require that a purchaser of a chemical product will ensure its lawful usage and disposal. A contract also might affect the factors such as control and knowledge that an environmental agency might consider in determining who has responsibility for complying with a particular environmental regulation.

[2] The common law of the various states is not identical, because each state has its own court system. Although all of the states started out with the common law adopted from England, except Louisiana which was a French territory and therefore has the Napoleonic Code as the foundation of its law, the courts of each state have developed their own common law case by case over the years so that each state now has its own legal peculiarities. For that reason, it is critical to consult an attorney familiar with the law of the state applicable to your situation.

For example, if a plant emits arsenic from its stack that is deposited on neighboring lands, the adjoining landowners may have a trespass action against the plant operator. The landowners might obtain judgments for damages such as diminution in the value of their land, harm to their cattle, personal injuries from exposure to the arsenic, *etc.*

As another example, the plant might have had an underground storage tank from which gasoline leaked into the groundwater and migrated onto a neighbor's land. The plant may have taken every precaution required by law and may not have even known that its tank was leaking, but it would still be liable for damage to the neighboring land. However, if the plant violated the law or knowingly allowed the tank to continue to leak, then the neighbor might have a case for punitive damages.

Nuisance

The tort of nuisance has traditionally been divided into public nuisance and private nuisance, although the line is often hard to draw in a particular case. ***Public nuisance*** is a use of one's property to intentionally cause or permit a condition to exist that injures or endangers the public health, welfare or safety. It is distinguishable from a private nuisance because it (1) affects all the residents of a particular area similarly, *e.g.*, a public stream becomes polluted and (2) does not require an interference with the right to use and enjoy one's land. Traditionally, a public nuisance was a crime subject to a fine, *e.g.*, operating a brothel. However, it may also provide grounds for a private cause of action if the plaintiff suffers a harm different than the public in general. For instance, if a lake is polluted so that commercial fishermen cannot practice their livelihood, then the fishermen may have a private cause of action for public nuisance because they have suffered a special damage over and above the harm to the general public, *i.e.*, the right to clean waters.

In contrast, a ***private nuisance*** requires an intentional act by the defendant which substantially and unreasonably interferes with the plaintiff's use and enjoyment of his land. The intent required is not that the defendant intend the resulting harm, but only that the defendant intend to commit the act when he knew or should have known that harm to others would result from his action. The interference must be of such a continuing and substantial nature that a reason-

able person would expect compensation for exposure to such a condition. As a general rule, the interference constituting a private nuisance will be by an intangible means such as noise, light, vibrations, odor, gaseous emissions, or even fear or repulsion if reasonable. The interference is not actionable if the plaintiff is overly sensitive; rather, the standard is whether an ordinary person would be substantially affected under ordinary conditions.

A slaughterhouse is a prime example of a use of one's land that may constitute a private nuisance. The operation may be actionable if it emits odors that interfere with the adjoining landowners' use and enjoyment of their property. To be actionable, the defendant slaughterhouse must have been aware or should have been aware that the odors were interfering with the adjoining landowners' use of their property. The interference must have been such that a reasonable person could not have enjoyed the use of the property while such an interference was occurring. Finally, the plaintiff must have some legal interest in the land affected. If successful, the plaintiff might receive an injunction against the interference, damages for the diminution in the value of his property, or both.

A minority of courts have held that the plaintiff's *coming to a nuisance* provides the defendant a defense. Traditionally, this defense was applied where the defendant had an existing operation and the plaintiff subsequently bought land in the area affected by the defendant's operation. Obviously the thought was that the plaintiff should not have moved into the area if he did not like the effects of the defendant's operation. However, the majority of courts no longer recognizes this defense. One possible basis for the majority position is that the defense allows the defendant to diminish the value of the surrounding land without paying for it.

For harms for which money damages are not sufficient or are not readily determinable, a court may grant the plaintiff injunctive relief.[3] Injunctive relief is often sought to abate, or stop, a nuisance; however, it may also be available as relief

---

[3] For example, injunctive relief may be appropriate where health or safety are threatened, because monetary damages cannot restore the plaintiff's health. However, flooding of the plaintiff's crop may be more suited to monetary damages than injunctive relief if there is a reasonable method for estimating the value

against other torts such as trespass. An *injunction* is a court order directing the defendant to take some action or to refrain from an action. If the plaintiff needs immediate relief, he may seek a temporary restraining order. This is a form of injunctive relief that may be issued by the court without notice or with only short notice to the defendant upon the plaintiff demonstrating to the court (1) that he would suffer immediate and irreparable harm without the order and (2) that he has attempted to give the defendant notice of the hearing. A temporary restraining order, as evident by its name, lasts only a few days. For longer relief pending a full trial, the plaintiff must seek a preliminary injunction. To obtain a preliminary injunction, the plaintiff must show:

1) A substantial likelihood that he will prevail on the merits at trial.

2) A substantial threat that he will suffer irreparable injury if the injunction is not granted.

3) That the threatened injury to him outweighs the threatened harm the injunction may do to the defendant, and

4) That granting the preliminary injunction will not disserve the public interest. If the plaintiff obtains a preliminary injunction, then the defendant will be restrained until the matter reaches a full trial, at which the issue will be whether the plaintiff is entitled to have the defendant permanently enjoined.

Negligence

Negligence is another common environmental tort. The elements of a *negligence* claim include:

1) A duty owed by the defendant to the plaintiff

2) A breach of that duty by the defendant

3) The plaintiff was damaged by the breach, and

4) The breach was the proximate cause of damage

---

of the crop. Generally, the courts will not provide injunctive relief if monetary damages will make the plaintiff whole, *i.e.,* compensate the plaintiff for his injury.

The duty alleged in most environmental cases is the duty of the defendant to conduct his activities so that he does not harm other persons. The question of whether or not this duty has been breached is judged on an after-the-fact, objective standard; in other words, the jury exercises its hindsight to decide what a reasonable person would have done under similar circumstances. The issue of causation addresses whether or not the defendant's action or inaction did in fact cause the plaintiff's harm and whether that harm was a reasonably foreseeable result. The damages may include property damage or personal injuries, but must be supported by some evidence from the plaintiff.

In determining whether a defendant was *negligent,* which generally means that the defendant owed a duty and breached that duty—the first two factors in establishing a cause of action for negligence—it is not necessarily a defense that the defendant obeyed all applicable laws or followed the practice accepted in the particular industry. Compliance with law and industry standards is a minimum standard, and the jury may determine that more was required of the defendant under the particular facts. On the other hand, non-compliance with a law or an industry standard is very likely to establish that the defendant acted negligently. If the plaintiff can establish the remaining two elements, causation and damages, then the jury should return a judgment for the plaintiff.

In order for the violation of a law to establish the defendant's negligence, the plaintiff must show that the statute, regulation, or ordinance was enacted to (1) protect the class of individuals to which the plaintiff belongs and (2) prevent the kind of harm that occurred. If the plaintiff can prove the violation and that he was in the class of persons to be protected by the statute and the harm was the type intended to be prevented by the statute, then he still must prove causation and damages. The defendant's statutory violation is said to have been negligent *per se*, or, in itself.

As an example of a negligence action, a suit might arise from a company mishandling a hazardous waste so that it is accidentally released onto the ground or down a drain. If the waste migrates onto neighboring properties, the neighbors might be exposed to it through drinking water from shallow ground water wells, eating vegetables from their gardens, inhaling dust from roads, *etc.*

Lawsuits might result if, for example, a governmental health agency or the members of the neighborhood noticed a higher incidence of cancer or mental disorders in the area and zeroed in on the waste and traced it back to the defendant company. The resulting lawsuits would be based on the company's duty to conduct its operations so as not to harm others, the breach of that duty by carelessly handling a harmful waste, causation based on medical reports and the tracing of the waste back to the company, as well as damages based on medical evidence. Possible weak links in the plaintiff's case might be a lack of scientific evidence that the particular waste causes the types of harm reported by the plaintiffs, a lack of proof that the waste came from the defendant's plant, or the unforeseeability of harm due to an unlikely exposure pathway. However, a jury drawn from the community and blessed with 20/20 hindsight would likely return a judgment for the plaintiffs.

The plaintiff in the above example might establish duty and breach of duty through use of the doctrine of negligence *per se*, which was discussed above. For instance, if the company failed to report the release and the plaintiff's harm was within the scope of harms intended to be prevented by an applicable reporting statute, the plaintiff would not have to present evidence of the defendant's duty of care. Instead of debating with the jury whether a reasonable person would have notified everyone within 100 feet or 2 miles of the plant, the plaintiff need only show that the company violated its statutory duty to report the release.

In the above example, if the company had committed gross negligence which was likely to shock the conscience of the jury, such as throwing the waste into a nearby stream which it knew was used by other persons for drinking water or fishing, then punitive damages would likely be imposed. *Punitive damages* are damages imposed in addition to actual damages that compensate the plaintiff for his injury. The purpose of punitive damages is, as the name implies, to punish the defendant. Punitive damages may exceed the defendant's actual damages and may far exceed any civil or criminal penalty imposed by an enforcement agency. The United States Supreme Court has recently indicated that punitive damages normally should not exceed ten times the actual damages in a case. Thus, a plaintiff who drank contaminated water might suffer only $1,000.00 in medical and other actual damages, but receive $10,000.00 in punitive damages. The case law in this area continues to evolve and the award of punitive damages remains case-specific.

Strict Liability

Strict liability for abnormally dangerous activities may cause a defendant to be liable for harm to the person, land, or personal property of another resulting from that activity, although the defendant has exercised the utmost care to prevent the harm. Generally, courts consider the following factors to determine whether a particular activity is abnormally dangerous:

1) The high risk of harm occurring from the activity

2) The likelihood that the resulting harm will be great

3) The ability to eliminate the risk by exercising ordinary care

4) The extent to which the activity is not common to the community

5) The appropriateness of the activity to the place where it was carried on, and

6) The activity's value to the community

The prime example of an ultrahazardous activity is the storing of dynamite in the middle of a city. Storage of dynamite in a populated area poses a significant threat to the population regardless of the care used in its handling. Therefore, any harm caused by an explosion of the dynamite would subject the owner to liability, regardless of how careful he was in storing the dynamite. Other examples of activities that have been subject to strict liability are gas wells, gasoline storage tanks, and pipelines operated in populated areas.

Torts in General

The above discussion of torts is not exhaustive, but is intended to place environmental managers on notice that there are considerations other than just what the Environmental Protection Agency (EPA) may require. There are numerous other existing tort causes of action, and new tort theories are limited only by the imagination of the plaintiff's attorney. Finally, as noted above, common law varies from state to state, as do the statutes that may alter the common law, so it is imperative to consult with an attorney familiar with the law of the particular state.

The Courts

Because common law is made by the courts, it is important to understand the structure of the courts. If there are conflicts in the cases that you find on an issue, you must know what weight to give those cases. Generally, decisions by the courts in the state where a case is pending carry more weight in that matter than the decisions of out-of-state courts, and Federal courts in your district or circuit control over cases from other Federal jurisdictions. Whether State or Federal, higher courts have control over lower courts. As between State and Federal cases, Federal courts defer to State courts on matters of State law. On matters of Federal law, such as constitutional issues, the United States Supreme Court is the ultimate authority.

The State court systems usually consist of a hierarchical set of courts. At the bottom are trial courts at the city, county, or multicounty level. In most states, appeals from the trial courts are to one or more levels of intermediate appellate courts, and then to a court of final jurisdiction, usually called the supreme court. In states with lighter caseloads there may not be an intermediate appellate court, and appeals are instead taken directly to the supreme court.

The State courts are separate from the Federal courts. In contrast to the State courts, which have general jurisdiction, the Federal courts have limited jurisdiction. Basically, the Federal courts have jurisdiction over cases involving Federal questions or parties of diverse state citizenship. Federal question jurisdiction includes cases arising under Federal statutes, such as the Comprehensive Environmental Response, Compensation, and Liability Act (CERCLA), the Resource Conservation and Recovery Act (RCRA), *etc*. Thus, Federal enforcement actions will be in Federal court. **Diversity jurisdiction** is intended to protect a defendant who is a citizen of one state from being subjected to a lawsuit in the plaintiff's State court where the plaintiff might be shown favoritism. For instance, if the defendant injured the plaintiff while driving through the plaintiff's state, the plaintiff could file suit in his state's courts

but the defendant could *remove* the case to the Federal district court due to the party's diverse citizenship. In addition to diversity of citizenship, diversity jurisdiction requires that the amount in controversy be at least $75,000. If the Federal courts have jurisdiction in a case, they may also hear other claims over which they might not otherwise have had jurisdiction. For example, if a private plaintiff asserts both a CERCLA cost recovery claim and a negligence claim arising from the same facts, the Federal court will have Federal question jurisdiction over the CERCLA claim and may then hear the negligence claim as a supplemental matter.

The Federal court system is hierarchical like the state courts. In each state, there are one or more federal district courts that are the trial courts of the Federal system. Decisions of the district courts may be appealed to the Federal circuit court of which they are a part. There are twelve Federal circuit courts that are each comprised of several states. The circuit court for the District of Columbia is especially important in environmental law, because several of the environmental statutes give it jurisdiction over matters such as challenges to regulations. Of course, the final court of appeal is the Supreme Court.

Statutes

Sources and Limits of Statutory Law

Although common law plays an important role in *environmental law*, people generally think of statutes like the Clean Air Act and the Resource Conservation and Recovery Act when they hear the term *environmental law*. These are Federal statutes enacted by the United States Congress.[4] These statutes are addressed in detail in other

---

[4] In addition to the obvious environmental statutes such as RCRA, several provisions of the Federal criminal code may also be invoked in an environmental case. These statutes pertain to false statements to the Federal government, mail fraud, and conspiracy. Other laws may also be applicable even though the matter is primarily environmental.

chapters. Here, however, we will address only the enactment and implementation of such statutes.

Congress is the source of Federal statutes. Congress is limited to enacting legislation that falls within one of its enumerated powers under the United States Constitution.[5] For example, Congress often relies upon the ***Commerce Clause of the Constitution*** which authorizes it to regulate interstate and foreign commerce. The applicability of the Commerce Clause to some environmental statutes is readily apparent, such as the regulation of certain products under the Toxic Substances Control Act. However, the constitutional basis for other statutes is less apparent, such as the regulation of the quality of waters that do not cross State boundaries. Nonetheless the Supreme Court, which hears lawsuits challenging the validity of Federal legislation, has shown great deference in determining whether Congress has remained within its constitutional limitations.

---

[5] Unlike Congress, the states have broad authority to protect the health and safety of their citizens. However, when Congress enacts legislation it may preempt any state or local laws on the same subject. Preemption may occur when Congress specifically declares that it is preempting state and local law or if Congress has established a regulatory scheme that completely occupies or covers the particular field. Similarly, a state cannot enact laws that impermissibly burdens *interstate commerce* by discriminating against interstate commerce in favor of state businesses or that deny *equal protection* between different regulated entities without a reasonable basis for the distinction.

[6] When Congress passes a bill and it is subsequently approved by the President, either through signing it or simply not vetoing it, the bill becomes a statute. Each statute is then codified in the *United States Code*, which is the official cumulative set of all statutes organized by subject matter titles. For example, many environmental statutes are codified in Title 42–Health and Environment. The complete text of the new statute may not be included in the Code in a single undivided block. Instead, the Congress will designate in the statute how the various sections of the statute will affect the existing Code—a paragraph may be added here or there, or a word may be changed, or a whole new subchapter may be added. For example, the Resource Conservation and Recovery Act is a statute that was passed in 1976 and which was codified as amendments to Sections 6901 to 6992k of Chapter 82, entitled "Solid Waste Disposal," of Title 42 of the Code. That is why you may hear someone refer to Section 7002 of RCRA but the provision is codified at 42 USC §6972.

Federal statutes are codified in the ***United States Code***.[6] That is the starting point for the Federal system of environmental law. Generally, Congress will specify in a statute a vague requirement, *e.g.*, that there shall be no discharge of any pollutant into the waters of the United States except pursuant to a permit that incorporates effluent limits. Congress will then delegate responsibility for implementing the statutory provision to a particular agency and will authorize the agency to take certain steps, such as implementing regulations to flesh out the statutory requirement and to enforce the statute and implementing regulations. However, Congress is prohibited by the constitutional doctrine of separation of powers from delegating unfettered and undefined power to an agency, and the agency is prohibited from exceeding the limits of its statutory delegation of authority. Thus, Congress cannot simply delegate to EPA the authority to establish whatever environmental regulations it deems necessary. Likewise, EPA could not establish regulations applicable to solid waste if the enabling statute only authorized regulation of hazardous waste.

The statutory delegation of authority is critical, because an agency has only the authority delegated to it by statute.[7] This limitation, however, is not as limiting as it may seem at first. An agency has discretion to work within the framework established by the enabling statute to construct the detailed program that Congress did not have the time or the expertise to supply.

If Congress acts beyond its constitutional limits or an administrative agency exceeds its statutory authorization, a party that is adversely affected has *standing* to bring a lawsuit in Federal court to challenge the law or regulation. As a practical matter, the Supreme Court has seldom held that Congress exceeded its constitutional limits. More frequently, courts have found that an administrative agency has exceeded its statutory authorization.

In reviewing challenges to agencies' actions, courts have typically divided the cases into three categories: interpretation of the statute, factual basis for the agency's action, and agency procedure.

---

[7] Agencies also may receive authority in an area by ***executive order*** of the President. The President delegates authority that he may have as a direct result of his office or as a result of a Congressional delegation of authority to him.

When the case involves interpretation of the authorizing statute, courts generally will follow the agency's interpretation of the statute it is charged with enforcing if that interpretation is reasonable but the court is not bound by that interpretation. Instead, the court will focus primarily on the language of the statute. If the statute is not clear, then the court will consider other evidence of Congress's intent such as the legislative history of the statute. The court will also consider the purpose and public policy underlying the statute. If a party challenges the factual basis for an agency's action, such as the denial of a permit, then the court will usually apply an *arbitrary and capricious* standard which requires only that the agency had some evidence to support its action. In some cases, the court will apply the slightly more stringent standard of *substantial evidence*. Finally, if a party challenges an agency's action on the grounds that it did not follow procedural re-quirements, such as notice of the proposed action or the right to a hearing before the agency, the court will review the matter to determine if the agency complied with the procedural requirements of the particular statute, the Administrative Procedures Act,[8] the Constitution, and the agency's rules. In short, agency actions are generally upheld by the courts in the absence of a clear exceedance of statutory authority, complete lack of factual support, or a major failure to follow procedural requirements.

Enforcement

Each of the Federal environmental statutes provides for enforcement of its requirements through administrative orders, civil penalties and relief, as well as criminal sanctions. Generally, the statute will provide a maximum monetary penalty, which typically is applied cumulatively on a per-day-of-violation basis. While civil penalties are imposed on a strict liability basis, the criminal penalties may require either a knowing violation or even a negligent violation, depending on the statute. Although the statutes

---

[8] For establishing new regulations, the federal Administrative Procedures Act generally requires publication in the *Federal Register*, an opportunity for the public to comment, a public hearing in some circumstances, response by the agency to the public's comments and final publication.

set forth the maximum penalties, various EPA and Department of Justice (DOJ) policies provide further guidance on the penalties which may actually be imposed in a given situation. It is important for an environmental manager to (1) be aware of the civil and criminal penalties authorized under the Federal environmental statutes, (2) be familiar with how the statutory penalties may be influenced under EPA and DOJ enforcement policies, and (3) take steps to prevent violations and mitigate any possible penalties.

Statutory Penalty Amounts and Standards for Imposition. Although a full discussion of the penalty amounts and the standards for imposing penalties under each of the Federal environmental statutes is beyond the scope of this chapter, the standards of the RCRA and the CWA for *knowing* violations, which are discussed immediately below, are indicative of the standards under most of the statutes.

Resource Conservation and Recovery Act
Knowing violations of the requirements applicable to generation, transportation, treatment, storage and disposal of hazardous waste under the Resource Conservation and Recovery Acy (RCRA) are felony offenses subject to two to five years in prison and fines of up to $50,000 per day of violation. These include, but are not limited to, recordkeeping and manifesting violations.

A *knowing* violation of RCRA does not necessarily coincide with our common, everyday under-standing of that term. For instance, in *United States (US) v. Hoflin*, 880 F.2d 1033, 1038–1040 (9th Cir. 1989), the defendant was convicted of disposing of hazardous waste without a permit even though he neither knew the material was a RCRA hazardous waste nor that the party actually doing the disposal lacked a RCRA permit. The court found *knowing* disposal of a hazardous waste where, even though the defendant did not know the paint was a RCRA hazardous waste, he did know the paint was not "an innocuous substance like water." *Accord, US v. Sellers*, 926 F.2d 410, 417 (5th Cir. 1991) (affirming conviction for unlawful disposal of RCRA hazardous waste where defendant knew paint solvent was "potentially dangerous to human beings and the environment", and would therefore be subject to some form of government regulation); *US v. Baytank (Houston), Inc.*, 934 F.2d 599, 613 (5th Cir. 1991) (*knowingly* means no more than that the defendant knows factually what he is doing—storing, what is being stored, and that what is being stored factually has the potential for harm to others or the environment—and it is not required that he know that there is a regulation which says what he is storing is hazardous waste under RCRA).

Knowing endangerment under RCRA is a more serious offense than a *knowing* violation of a RCRA requirement. Consequently, RCRA imposes harsher penalties for *knowing endangerment.* Specifically, 42 USC §6928(e) states:

> Any person who knowingly transports, treats, stores, disposes of, or exports any hazardous waste identified or listed [under Subtitle C of RCRA] or used oil not identified or listed as a hazardous waste . . . who knows at that time that he thereby places another person in eminent danger of death or serious bodily injury, shall, upon conviction, be subject to a fine of not more than $250,000.00 or imprisonment for not more than 15 years [felony], or both. A defendant that is an organization shall, upon conviction of violating this subsection, be subject to a fine of not more than $1,000,000.00.

For purposes of *knowing endangerment*, a defendant *knows* of the endangerment he creates if he is aware or believes that his conduct is substantially certain to cause danger of death or serious bodily injury. Circumstantial evidence may be used, including evidence that the defendant took affirmative steps to shield himself from relevant information. For example, if a manager tells his employee to "get rid of it but don't tell me how," it may be sufficient to establish *knowing endangerment* that the manager knows the hazardous waste could harm anyone exposed to it and that the employee is likely to dispose of the waste in an unsafe manner.

Clean Water Act. Of particular interest under the Clean Water Act (CWA) is the fact that criminal penalties may be imposed not only for *knowing* violations, but also for *negligent* violations. For *negligent* violations of the Clean Water Act or permits issued thereunder, the violator may be convicted of a misdemeanor with imprisonment of up to one year and/or a fine of between $2,500.00 and $25,000.00 per day of violation. For example, criminal misdemeanor charges based on negligence were prosecuted in the *Exxon Valdez* incident. The captain of the *Exxon Valdez* was

convicted, but the conviction was overturned on procedural grounds.

The CWA also provides for penalties and imprisonment for *knowing* violations of the Act's provisions. Specifically, the Act states:

> Any person who commits a *knowing* violation may be convicted of a felony and shall be punished by a fine of not less than $5,000.00 nor more than $50,000.00 per day of violation, or by imprisonment for not more than 3 years, or by both.

In 1992, for instance, Chevron pleaded guilty to knowingly exceeding oil and gas discharge limits in its National Pollutant Discharge Elimination System (NPDES) permit at an offshore drilling platform and paid a criminal fine of $6.5 million. *US v. Chevron USA*, No. CV–88–7836 (D.C. Cal. May 18, 1992). Other charges included diluting samples, concealing test results, by-passing the wastewater treatment system, and dumping sandblast waste into the ocean.

To Whom Does the Penalty Apply? Environmental statutes may provide for monetary penalties and imprisonment for various categories of violations, but who has to pay the fine or go to jail? That may depend on the particular requirement that is violated. For example, the Clean Water Act requires that *any person in charge* of a facility shall report a discharge of oil or a hazardous substance as soon as he knows of such discharge. Under that provision, an employee in charge of the operation that causes the release and the corporation for which he works may both be responsible. Other requirements under the various environmental laws are applicable to the *owner* and/or *operator*. Under such an *owner or operator* standard, both an employee and his employer could be liable as operators. Still other statutory and regulatory requirements are applicable to *any person*. In that case, an employee and/or his employer might be responsible.

Generally, if a person is directly involved in a violation, then he is potentially subject to an enforcement action. For example, if the janitor dumps his mop bucket of trichloroethylene into the ditch behind the plant, then the janitor is personally responsible for his violation because of his direct involvement. Likewise, if a manager told the janitor to dispose of the waste in that manner, then the manager is also directly liable for the violation. The manager could also be liable if he knew the janitor had the waste and chose to remain ignorant of the janitor's method of disposal.

In addition to direct liability for violations, persons in positions of authority within a corporation may be held liable for indirect responsibility for violations. In its purest form, the ***Responsible Corporate Officer Doctrine*** allows the criminal conviction of a corporate officer based purely on the fact that he was in a position of responsibility and authority within the corporation which would have allowed him to prevent the violation. Under this theory, the corporate officer could be convicted even though he knew absolutely nothing about the violation; all that is necessary is that he had the authority to prevent the violation. The doctrine is not limited to corporate officers as the name implies, but may impose liability on any person with the authority to prevent a violation.

The Responsible Corporate Officer Doctrine was developed in two cases under the Federal Food, Drug and Cosmetic Act of 1938, *US v. Dotterweich*, 320 U.S. 277 (1943) and *US v. Park*, 421 US G58 (1975). In *Dotterweich,* the court set forth its rationale for the doctrine as follows:

> The prosecution to which Dotterweich was subjected is based on a now familiar type of legislation whereby penalties serve as effective means of regulation. Such legislation dispenses with the conventional requirement for criminal conduct—awareness of some wrongdoing. In the interest of the larger good it puts the burden of acting at hazard upon a person otherwise innocent but standing in responsible relation to a public danger.

Because both the Food and Drug Act and the environmental acts are intended to protect the public welfare, the Department of Justice has attempted in the past to apply the Responsible Corporate Officer Doctrine to environmental prosecutions. More recently, DOJ has taken the position that it will not prosecute based solely on the responsible corporate officer doctrine, but will require *some actual knowledge* of the violative acts. Despite DOJ's position, the Clean Water Act and the Clean Air Act expressly state that the *responsible corporate officers* may be persons liable under those Acts. However, because those acts did not define *responsible corporate officer*, it has been

left to the courts to determine the application of this term in environmental prosecutions. Some courts have held that an officer cannot be convicted of a *knowing* violation based solely on knowledge imputed to him as a result of his position, but have allowed his position, authority, and responsibility to serve as circumstantial evidence that he possessed knowledge of the violation.

Nonindividual entities, such as corporations, may also be liable for violations. Referring back to the example of the janitor, the company that employs him may also be liable for his violation. Generally, under the ***Doctrine of* Respondeat Superior**, employers are responsible for the acts of their employees in the course of their employment. Therefore, because it was generally within the scope of the janitor's job to generate his mop waste and to dispose of that waste, his employer may also be liable. On the other hand, if the janitor was using some of his free time on the night shift to change the oil in his personal car and then dumped that oil into the ditch behind the plant, the employer would not be responsible because changing the oil in his personal car was not part of his job.

Administrative Civil Penalty Policies. Although the Federal environmental statutes set the maximum civil and criminal penalties for their violation, the penalties actually imposed are usually below those statutory maximums. The penalties are set in accordance with EPA penalty policies, the Department of Justice enforcement policy, and the United States Sentencing Guidelines (USSG).

On February 16, 1984, EPA issued two documents; one entitled "Policy on Civil Penalties" and the other entitled "A Framework for Statute-Specific Approaches to Penalty Assessments." These two documents jointly set forth EPA's general scheme for calculating civil penalties and authorized program-specific penalty policies. Over the years, penalty policies have been developed in programs such as the Toxic Substances Control Act (TSCA), RCRA, CWA, the Clean Air Act (CAA), the Emergency Planning and Community Right-to-Know Act (EPCRA), and CERCLA. In fact, some of these programs have multiple policies which are tailored to specific areas within the overall program; for instance, the TSCA program has a penalty policy specifically for polychlorinated biphenyls (PCBs). Because all of the penalty policies generally follow EPA's 1984 penalty framework, the RCRA penalty policy is discussed briefly below as an example.

The RCRA civil penalty policy calculates penalties by

1) Determining a gravity-based penalty for a particular violation from a penalty assessment matrix

2) Adding a *multiday* component, as appropriate, to account for a violation's duration

3) Adjusting the sum of the gravity-based and multiday components, up or down, for case specific circumstances, and

4) Adding to this amount the economic benefit gained through noncompliance

The sum of the gravity-based component plus the multiday component may be adjusted upward or downward based on good or bad faith, degree of willfulness and/or negligence, and other unique factors, including the risk and cost of litigation. The penalty may be adjusted upward for history of noncompliance and downward for an inability to pay the penalty or for projects to be undertaken by the violator. After the penalty has been adjusted, an amount will be added for the economic benefit the violator gained from noncompliance. The resulting amount is the figure EPA would take in a settlement of the complaint. If the complaint were to go to trial, no downward adjustments of the penalty amount would be taken into consideration.

Enforcement Agencies

Environmental Protection Agency. The EPA is the agency charged with enforcing most of the Federal environmental statutes. However, many of the Federal environmental statutes authorize states to establish permitting and enforcement programs to operate *in lieu of*, or to be *delegated*, the Federal program within their borders. Generally, to obtain **delegation** of a Federal program, a state must enact laws and establish regulations that are at least as stringent as their Federal counterparts. Upon receiving delegation of a program, the state is the primary enforcement authority for that program. However, the EPA retains the right to intervene if it believes the state has not been diligent in its enforcement of the Federal requirements. There is currently an issue as to whether the EPA has the right to take additional enforcement actions against a violator that has resolved its violation with a delegated state, or whether EPA is limited to revoking the state's delegation as to future enforcement.

Department of Justice. When the EPA decides to proceed beyond civil penalties and pursue criminal penalties, it notifies the United States Attorney's office for the jurisdiction in which the violation occurred or the Environment and Natural Resources Division (ENRD) of the Department of Justice (DOJ) in Washington.

On July 1, 1991, DOJ issued its policy encouraging self-auditing, self-policing, and **voluntary disclosure** of environmental violations by the regulated community. The stated purpose of the DOJ document is "to describe the factors that the Department of Justice considers in deciding whether to bring a criminal prosecution for a violation of an environmental statute, so that such prosecutions do not create a disincentive to or undermine the goal of encouraging critical self-auditing, self-policing, and voluntary disclosure." DOJ set forth several nonexclusive factors which should be considered in determining whether and how to prosecute. These factors include voluntary disclosure, cooperation with investigators, preventative measures and compliance programs, the pervasiveness of noncompliance, internal disciplinary action, and subsequent compliance efforts.

A voluntary disclosure must be voluntary in the sense that it is not already required by law, regulation, or permit. The voluntary disclosure must also be timely and complete, such that the violator comes forward promptly as soon as possible after discovering the noncompliance and provides sufficient information to aid the government's investigation with information not already obtained by the government through another source.

The violator's full and prompt cooperation is another factor to be considered, including the violator's willingness to make all relevant information, including all internal and external investigations and the names of all potential witnesses, available to the government.

The existence and scope of any regularized, intensive, and comprehensive environmental compliance program maintained by the violator is also considered. The compliance program must have included sufficient measures to identify and prevent future noncompliance, and the program must have been adopted in good faith in a timely manner. The compliance program should also contain an effective internal disciplinary action program to make employees aware that unlawful conduct will not be condoned.

The DOJ memorandum includes an example of the application of the factors to a *good* defendant. The company conducted regular, comprehensive environmental compliance audits. It also had a compliance program, which included clear policies, employee training, and a hotline for suspected violations. When an audit uncovered employees disposing of hazardous waste by dumping in an unpermitted location, the company disclosed all pertinent information to the appropriate government agency after confirming the violations. The company undertook compliance planning with that agency and carried out satisfactory remediation measures. The company also undertook to correct any false information previously submitted to the government in relation to the violations, and the company disciplined the employees actually involved in the violations, including any supervisor who was lax in preventing or detecting the activity. Finally, the company reviewed its compliance program to determine how the violations slipped by and corrected the weaknesses found by that review. The company also disclosed the names of the responsible employees and cooperated in providing documentation necessary to investigate those employees. As a result of its actions, the DOJ memorandum states that the company would stand a good chance of being favorably considered for prosecutorial leniency, to the extent of not being criminally prosecuted at all.

State and Local Enforcement Agencies. All of the states have environmental programs that parallel all or a part of the Federal programs. They have their own statutes, regulations, penalty policies, and enforcement agencies. As noted above, many of the State programs operate in lieu of the Federal programs where the Federal agency determines that the State program is at least as stringent as the Federal program. The *at least as stringent as* language means that states may have additional requirements over and above those imposed by the Federal agency. This is especially common in environmentally active states such as California and New Jersey.

In addition, states and local governments may have laws that cover entirely different topics, such as ground water pollution, disclosure laws applicable to real property transfers, criminal litter laws, *etc.*

By and large, the discussion of the Federal system in this chapter is also applicable to State laws and enforcement. However, each state has its own quirks. Therefore, it is absolutely necessary to consult someone familiar with a particular state's laws and regulations if an issue arises in that state.

Citizen Suit Enforcement. Several of the Federal environmental statutes provide for enforcement by citizens acting as private attorneys general. (See, *e.g.,* RCRA §7002, 42 USC §6972, and CWA §505, 33 USC §1365.) These provisions allow any person who has an interest that is or may be adversely affected to file an enforcement action in Federal district court to compel compliance through court order or imposition of penalties and/or to seek injunctive relief against imminent endangerments to human health or the environment. Prior to filing suit, a citizen plaintiff must notify the violator, the EPA, and any applicable State enforcement agency to allow them to correct the violation. Also, a citizen cannot file suit if an appropriate enforcement agency is already taking action. Citizens' suits are becoming more prevalent, due in large part to the possibility of obtaining their attorneys' fees and expert witnesses' fees if they substantially prevail in the case.

United States Sentencing Guidelines. If the EPA and the DOJ obtain a conviction of a violator, the judge must decide what sentence to impose. In the past, Federal district court judges had tremendous discretion in sentencing criminals convicted of Federal crimes. Furthermore, once sentenced, the actual length of time the violator spent in jail depended on parole guidelines. In 1984, Congress decided to standardize sentences for Federal criminals and pursuant to the Sentencing Reform Act of 1984 established the United States Sentencing Commission. The Commission has developed the *United States Sentencing Guidelines* with the objectives of increasing the uniformity of sentencing, removing the uncertainty of sentences caused by the parole system, and ensuring proportionality in sentencing criminal conduct of differing degrees of severity.

Persons acting either individually or as agents of a corporation may be held personally liable both civilly and criminally for their personal actions. The *Guidelines* provide a step-by-step process for determining a sentencing range for convicted individuals. Basically, the *Guidelines* operate on a point system by assigning an initial point value to the violation, and then adjusting that point value up or down based on several factors. The resulting point value and a number corresponding to the defendant's criminal history are used jointly to determine the range of sentences from a sentencing table.

For example, if a manager directs one of his employees to dispose of paint by pouring it out on the plant property, both the manager and the employee who did the actual dumping would be guilty of mishandling a hazardous waste under RCRA. The base offense level is adjusted based on five factors, including:

1) The nature of the victim of the crime

2) The defendant's role in the offense

3) Whether there was an attempted or actual obstruction of the administration of justice

4) Whether the defendant was convicted on multiple counts, and

5) Whether the defendant accepted responsibility for the crime

In considering the defendant's role in the offense, the base offense level may be increased if the defendant was an organizer, leader, manager, or supervisor in any criminal activity. If the defendant obstructs justice by committing perjury or producing a false or altered document or record during an official investigation or judicial proceeding, the base offense level may be increased. The base offense level may be decreased if the defendant clearly demonstrates acceptance of responsibility for his offense or if the defendant has timely notified the authorities of his intention to enter a plea of guilty prior to the government preparing for trial.

There are separate sentencing guidelines for crimes in general, not just environmental crimes, by organizations such as corporations. In 1993, draft organizational sentencing guidelines specific to environmental crimes were proposed, but they have not been adopted. Nonetheless, a few comments on the draft are worthwhile. Because an organization cannot be placed in jail, the draft provides for monetary penalties. Instead of operating on a points system as with individual violators, the draft organizational guidelines provide for a percentage of the maximum statutory fine. The base fine under the organizational guidelines is the greater of (1) the economic gain plus costs directly attributable to the offense or (2) a percentage of the maximum statutory fine that could be imposed for the offenses.

Economic gain is defined as (1) the economic benefits that an offender realized by avoiding or delaying capital costs necessary to comply with the environmental statute, based upon the estimated costs of capital to the offender; (2) the continuing expenses (*e.g.*, labor, energy, leases, operation, and maintenance) the offender avoided or delayed by noncompliance; and other profits directly attributable to the offense. Costs include: (1) actual environmental harm including degradation of a natural resource and (2) harms incurred in remediation or other costs borne by others.

According to the draft guidelines, the base offense level could be increased if one or more members of the substantial authority personnel of the organization participated in, condoned, solicited, or concealed criminal conduct, or recklessly tolerated conditions or circumstances that created or perpetuated a significant risk that criminal behavior of the same general type or kind would occur or continue. If a corporate manager lacking the authority or responsibility to be classified as a member of the organization's substantial authority personnel, but having supervisory responsibility to detect, prevent, or abate the violation, engaged in the criminal conduct, the base fine may be increased by a different percentage. The draft guidelines define **substantial authority personnel** to include high-level personnel, individuals who exercise substantial supervisory authority (*e.g.*, a plant manager, a sales manager), and any other individuals who, although not a part of an organization's management, nevertheless exercise substantial discretion when acting within the scope of their authority (*e.g.*, an individual with authority in an organization to negotiate or set price levels or an individual authorized to negotiate or to approve significant contracts).

Conclusion

Environmental law is broader than the Federal environmental statutes and EPA's regulations. There may be existing court decisions that interpret or limit the pertinent statutes and regulations, or there may be grounds to challenge the validity of the statute or regulation or its enforcement in a particular case. Likewise, agencies such as EPA have policies that affect the enforcement of the statutes and regulations. In addition, private tort actions and State environmental laws may play a role in a particular situation. Thus, it is important to be familiar with the *big picture* of environmental law.

Eugene R. Wasson is a member of the law firm of Brunini, Grantham, Grower and Hewes, PLLC, in Jackson, Mississippi. Mr. Wasson is a member of the firm's Environmental Group and devotes the majority of his practice to environmental administrative and litigation matters. After receiving a bachelor of science degree in biological engineering with honors from Mississippi State University, he graduated with honors from the University of Mississippi School of Law. Mr. Wasson currently is active in the American Bar Association and the Mississippi Bar Association.

CHAPTER 3

Federal Facility Compliance Act of 1992

Harry A. Bryson, CHMM

Federal Facility Compliance Act of 1992

Background/History

Regulatory Impact

FFCAct Description by Section

Title I. Federal Facility Compliance Act of 1992 • Title II. Metropolitan Washington Waste Management Study Act

Impacts of Key Sections of the FFCAct

§102 (Application of Certain Provisions to Federal Facilities) • §104 (Facility Environmental Assesments) • § 105 (Mixed Waste Inventory Reports and Plan) • §107 (Munitions) • §109 (Small Town Environmental Planning)

Bibliography

Laws • Hazardous Waste Management • Military Munitions • Mixed Waste

---

The Federal Facility Compliance Act (FFCAct) of 1992 (PL 102–386, October 6, 1992) amended the Solid Waste Disposal Act (SWDA) of 1965, as amended, with respect to a number of issues which affected primarily (but not only) Federal facilities and installations. The SWDA is alternatively referred to as the Resource Conservation and Recovery Act (RCRA), as amended, because RCRA was essentially a complete rewrite of the SWDA when it was enacted in 1976. RCRA will be used in this discussion instead of SWDA for clarity, since RCRA has become the most commonly used term in the regulatory arena. The acronym FFCAct will be used to avoid confusion with the acronym FFCA, which is generally used for Federal Facility Compliance Agreement by the United States (US) Department of Energy, the Federal agency most affected by the FFCAct.

The Federal Facility Compliance Act of 1992 consists of two titles:

- Title I–Federal Facility Compliance Act of 1992

- Title II–Metropolitan Washington Waste Management Study Act

Title I addressed a range of topics, and consisted of ten sections: §§101–110. By section, the topics are:

- §101: Short Title of Title I
- §102: Application of Certain Provisions to Federal Facilities
- §103: Definition of Person
- §104: Facility Environmental Assessments
- §105: Mixed Waste Inventory Reports and Plan
- §106: Public Vessels
- §107: Munitions
- §108: Federally Owned Treatment Works
- §109: Small Town Environmental Planning
- §110: Chief Financial Officer Report

Title II was very narrowly focused on the federally owned Interstate Highway 95 (I-95) sanitary landfill near Lorton, Virginia. It consisted of Sections 201–204, as described below:

- §201: Short Title of Title II
- §202: Findings
- §203: Environmental Impact Statement
- §204: Definitions

Background/History

The primary purposes of Title I of the FFCAct were to broaden the existing waiver of Federal sovereign immunity from Federal and State RCRA enforcement actions and to force resolution of two hazardous waste issues. The waiving of sovereign immunity made it possible for regulatory agencies to carry out enforcement actions as they did for non-Federal entities. The two waste issues were treatment and disposal of radioactive mixed waste (MW) at Federal (primarily US Department of Energy) facilities and installations, and the determination of when military munitions became solid wastes subject to RCRA regulations. The MW issue itself affects nonfederal entities, and the munitions issue also affected nonmilitary munitions, since both wastes from Federal, other governmental, and nongovernmental activities are ultimately under the same regulatory programs.

The other issues addressed by Title I of the FFCAct were clarifications regarding RCRA administrative requirements, RCRA Subtitle C storage requirements for public vessels, allowable

discharges into Federally owned wastewater treatment plants, and Federal review and evaluation of small town environmental compliance problems. Federal employee liability under RCRA was also clarified.

Title II of the Act addressed the singular issue of the I-95 Sanitary Landfill in Lorton, Virginia, near Washington, DC.

Regulatory Impact

The FFCAct for the most part has had little direct effect on the overall technical aspects of Federal regulations. Rather, by amending RCRA, it

1) Broadened and clarified the waiver of sovereign immunity

2) Clarified a number of Federal, State, and local jurisdictional issues

3) Mandated greater US Environmental Protection Agency (EPA) oversight of Federal facilities, and enacted certain provisions which somewhat simplified EPA's execution of its Federal facility oversight mandate

4) Mandated a major effort by the US Department of Energy (DOE) to address radioactive mixed waste treatment, storage, and disposal, to include development of current status reports, Site Treatment Plans (STPs), and annual progress reports

5) Put other Federal agencies *on notice* regarding mixed waste management violations

6) Required EPA, in concert with the US Department of Defense (DoD), to specify when munitions (and more specifically, military munitions) were to be determined to be solid wastes, so that subsequent hazardous waste determinations could be made and management requirements identified

7) Clarified certain RCRA issues regarding hazardous waste storage on *public vessels*

8) Clarified certain issues regarding discharges to Federally Owned Treatment Works

The radioactive mixed waste and munitions issues did require certain actions. The MW issue, which has been an ongoing challenge since the RCRA regulations first went into effect in 1980, continues to be addressed within the RCRA and Atomic Energy Act (AEA) framework. The phase in of the RCRA Land Disposal Restrictions (LDRs, 40 Code of Federal Regulations [CFR] 268) has required cooperation between the EPA, US Nuclear Regulatory Commission (NRC), and DOE in addressing the MW issue. The FFCAct has forced an intensive effort by DOE to develop MW treatment technology so that stored MW could be treated to meet RCRA LDRs.

The munitions issue has generated additional and specific EPA rulemaking under RCRA. This rulemaking, known as the Military Munitions Rule (MMR), was promulgated as RCRA Subtitle C regulations on February 12, 1997 (62 Federal Register [FR] 6622). The MMR included provisions not required by the FFCAct, but which were determined to be desirable in the course of rulemaking and within the authority of existing legislative authority. These additional actions are explained in the preamble to the final rule.

In addition, EPA's MMR has had a significant effect on the development of DoD's *Range Rule*, proposed 32 CFR 178. While the Range Rule does not cite authority under the FFCAct, the MMR, which was mandated by the FFCAct, was a key determinant on formulation of regulations for the operation, transfer, and disposal of former and current military bombing and artillery ranges.

FFCAct Description by Section

A brief description of each section of the FFCAct follows in numerical order. An expanded discussion of the significance (*i.e.*, technical, programmatic, and regulatory impact) of Sections 102, 103, 104, 105, 107, and 109 then follows.

Title I. Federal Facility Compliance Act of 1992

§101: Short Title. This section simply stated the short title of the Act, "Federal Facility Compliance Act of 1992."

§102: Application of Certain Provisions to Federal Facilities. This section amended RCRA Section 6001, and addressed several issues of Federal sovereign immunity; Federal, State, and local jurisdiction; Federal employee personal liability protection; and Federal government entity immunity from criminal sanction. Specifically, this section

1) Amended the Solid Waste Disposal Act (RCRA) to waive the sovereign immunity of the United States for purposes of enforcing Federal, State, interstate, and local requirements with respect to solid and hazardous waste management

2) Provided that such substantive and procedural requirements include all administrative orders and civil and administrative fines

3) For acts within the scope of their duties, absolved Federal government agents, employees and officers from personal liability under Federal, State, interstate or local solid and/or hazardous waste laws

4) Made Federal employees subject to criminal sanctions under such laws

5) Forbade Federal entities from being subject to criminal sanctions under such laws

6) Provided EPA authority for commencement of enforcement authority against a Federal government department, agency, or instrumentality

7) Required fines collected by the states from the Federal government for violations of hazardous and solid waste management requirements to be used only for projects to improve or protect the environment or to defray the costs of environmental protection or enforcement

8) Provided a 3-year lead time for waiver of sovereign immunity with respect to radioactive mixed waste storage time violations at DOE facilities (subject to certain conditions)

9) Provided that the above would be effective upon the date of enactment of the Act, with specified exceptions and delayed effective dates for the waiver of sovereign immunity for violations involving the storage of certain mixed waste

§103: Definition of Person. Section 103 amended RCRA Section 1004(15) to add departments, agencies, and instrumentalities of the US to the definition of *person* with respect to regulated entities.

§104: Facility Environmental Assessments. This section amended RCRA Section 3007(c) to require Federal agencies that own or operate hazardous waste facilities to reimburse EPA for costs of inspections. It also directed the EPA to conduct comprehensive ground water monitoring evaluations at such facilities unless an evaluation was conducted during the 12-month period preceding this Act's enactment date (October 6, 1992). In addition, states with authorized hazardous waste programs under RCRA were authorized to conduct inspections of Federal facilities for the purpose of enforcement.

§105: Mixed Waste Inventory Reports and Plan. Section 105 amended RCRA Section 1004 and added a new RCRA Section 3021. The amendment to RCRA Section 1004 required the Comptroller General to report, 18 months after enactment of the Act, on DOE's progress in complying with the new RCRA Section 3021(b), to include:

1) DOE's progress in submitting Site Treatment Plans (STPs) to the states and EPA, and the status of the State and EPA review

2) DOE's progress on entering into Compliance Orders

3) An evaluation of the completeness and adequacy of each plan

4) Identification of any recurring problems in the plans

5) A description of MW treatment technologies and capacities developed by DOE since FFCAct enactment, and a list, by facility, of the wastes expected to be treated

6) DOE's progress in characterizing MW streams at each site

7) Identification and analysis of additional DOE actions to

    a) Complete submission of all plans

    b) Obtain Compliance Orders

    c) Develop MW treatment technologies and capacities

8) Defined *mixed waste* as waste that is a mixture of hazardous wastes as defined under RCRA, and source, special nuclear, or by-product (*i.e.*, radioactive) material subject to the Atomic Energy Act (AEA) of 1954.

The new Section 3021 required the Secretary of the Department of Energy to submit to EPA and the states two reports: (1) a report containing a national inventory, on a state-by-state basis, of all mixed wastes at DOE facilities, regardless of time of generation and (2) a report containing a national inventory of mixed waste treatments, capacities, and technologies at each site. The reports were to be made to the EPA Administrator and the governor of each state in which the DOE generates or stores mixed wastes.

This section also required DOE to prepare a plan for each DOE facility for developing treatment capacities and technologies to treat all the facility's mixed waste, regardless of when generated, to the standards promulgated pursuant to RCRA Section 3004(m), *i.e.*, EPA's Land Disposal Restrictions (LDRs). This plan has been termed the facility's Site Treatment Plan (STP). Exempted from such requirements were facilities which produced or stored no mixed waste, and any facility subject to a permit establishing a schedule for treatment of such wastes or any existing agreement or administrative or judicial order governing the treatment of such wastes to which the state is a party.

STPs were to be approved by: (1) State regulatory officials, in the case of facilities located in states with authority to prohibit land disposal of mixed waste, and to regulate hazardous components of such waste and (2) the EPA Administrator, in the case of states without such authority. A state is authorized to waive the requirement for STP submission if the state enters into an agreement with the Secretary that addresses compliance with respect to mixed waste and issues an order requiring compliance.

It should be noted that this section of the FFCAct applies only to US Department of Energy (DOE) facilities. However, the specific requirements for radioactive mixed waste management under RCRA and the AEA apply to all generators, transporters, storage, treatment, and disposal facilities.

§106: Public Vessels. This section added a new RCRA Section 3022 to address hazardous waste management on public vessels. This amendment stated that a public vessel was not subject to the storage, manifest, inspection, or recordkeeping requirements until the waste is transferred to a shore facility. Exceptions to this provision are: (1) if waste is stored on the vessel for more than 90 days after the vessel is placed in reserve or is otherwise no longer in service or (2) if the waste is transferred to another vessel within the territorial waters of the US and is stored on that vessel for more than 90 days after the date of transfer. As defined in the US Coast Guard's 33 CFR 151.1006, *Definitions, public vessel* means a vessel that:

1) Is owned, or demise chartered, and operated by the United States government or a government of a foreign country; and

2) Is not engaged in commercial service

Vessel means every description of watercraft or other artificial contrivance used, or capable of being used, as a means of transportation on water.

§107: Munitions. This section amended RCRA Section 3004 by adding a new Subsection 3004(y), which required EPA to develop regulations identifying when conventional and chemical military munitions became hazardous waste under RCRA, and providing for the safe transportation and storage of such wastes. EPA was to consult with DoD and the States in rule development. The regulations were to be proposed within 6 months of FFCAct enactment, and finalized within 24 months of enactment.

§108: Federally Owned Treatment Works. This section added a new RCRA Section 3023 to establish a prohibition against the introduction of a hazardous waste into *federally owned treatment works* (FOTWs) which operate under a permit issued under Section 402 of the Federal Water Pollution Control Act (Clean Water Act). This type of permit is normally issued under the National Pollutant Discharge Elimination System (NPDES). This provision applies to treatment works belonging to a Federal department, agency, or instrumentality and which is used primarily to treat domestic sewage. The provisions of Section 108 essentially further defined acceptable materials which can be discharged to the FOTW, and specifically prohibits discharge of hazardous waste to a FOTW. This section also defines an FOTW.

§109: Small Town Environmental Planning. This section did not amend RCRA. Essentially, this section of the Act was intended to address problems faced by small towns (defined as those with populations less than 2500) in complying with Federal environmental regulations. This section required EPA to establish the Small Town Environmental Planning Program and a Small Town Environmental Planning Task Force. The program required EPA to publish and update annually a list of requirements under Federal environmental and public health statutes. A significant aspect of this program was a mandate for EPA to evaluate and report to the Congress on the feasibility of establishing a multimedia (*e.g.*, air, water, land) permitting program for small towns.

§110: Chief Financial Officer Report. This section did not amend RCRA. It addressed Federal agencies that generate mixed waste streams. It required the Chief Financial Officer of each *affected agency* to submit an annual report to Congress detailing mixed waste compliance activities and associated fines and penalties imposed for violations involving mixed wastes. While DOE seems to be the Federal agency most affected, Section 102 of the FFCAct references separately DOE and other "department, agencies, and instrumentalities of the executive branch of the Federal government" for violations of mixed waste storage regulations under RCRA Section 3004(j).

Title II. Metropolitan Washington Waste Management Study Act

Title II dealt with the I-95 Sanitary Landfill in Lorton, Virginia, and is not of general interest or significance. No Federal regulations were affected. A brief description of the four sections follows. No further discussion is provided.

§201: Short Title of Title II. This section designated the short title, the "Metropolitan Washington Waste Management Study Act."

§202: Findings. This section was a statement by Congress that the landfill was on Federal land and as such was the responsibility of the Federal government.

§203: Environmental Impact Statement. Section 203 required an Environmental Impact Statement (EIS) before expansion of the landfill. It prohibited the expansion of the landfill on lands owned by the US Government unless (1) an Environmental Impact Statement regarding such expansion has been completed and approved by the EPA Administrator and (2) the costs incurred in completing such statement are paid from the landfill's enterprise fund or in accordance with another payment formula based on jurisdictional usage of the landfill. It allowed the landfill to be expanded for purposes of the ash monofill if it was used solely for the disposal of incinerator ash from the parties of the July, 1981 Memorandum of Understanding. It also allowed the use of the monofill for solid waste disposal for a maximum of 30 days whenever a resource recovery facility or an incinerator operated by or for such parties is unavailable because of an emergency shutdown. The landfill was prohibited from receiving or disposing of municipal or industrial waste other than incinerator ash, unless the environmental impact statement and cost-sharing requirements were met.

§204: Definitions. This section contains definitions of *expansion* (of the landfill), land ownership, and a previously existing Memorandum of Understanding (MOU).

Impacts of Key Sections of the FFCAct

The following is an assessment of the technical and regulatory impacts of key sections of the FFCAct: Sections 102, 104, 105, 107, and 109.

§102 (Application of Certain Provisions to Federal Facilities)

The impact of this amendment to RCRA was to rather dramatically alter the status of all Federal facilities with respect to RCRA compliance by mandating EPA oversight and by waiving Federal sovereign immunity to prosecution. It also provided a 3-year delay in the waiver with respect to MW storage time violations under RCRA Section 3004(j).

§104 (Facility Environmental Assessments)

This section focused sudden attention of Federal facilities with respect to RCRA. It specifically required a ground water quality investigation at each Federal facility within 12 months of FFCAct enactment, unless an investigation had been performed within the previous 12-month period. The Act also required Federal facilities to reimburse EPA for inspection costs.

In the several years following enactment, activity at EPA Regional Offices was redirected to perform inspections of (primarily) DoD and DOE facilities, since such facilities typically were both large in areal extent, used large quantities of hazardous materials, and were substantial hazardous waste generators.

§105 (Mixed Waste Inventory Reports and Plan)

Section 105 has had a substantial and far-reaching effect on DOE mixed waste management activities. The Mixed Waste Inventory Reports and the Site Treatment Plans required a substantial effort to prepare and review by the affected parties, as discussed below. The MW treatment technology development is an ongoing activity which, in itself, constitutes a very large research and development program.

DOE possesses approximately 98% of the mixed waste in the United States. Of this, approximately 50% is stored at the Hanford site in Washington State. Approximately 72% of this mixed waste is High Level Waste (HLW), 20% low level waste (LLW), and 8% mixed transuranic (MTRU) waste. DOE's Waste Isolation Pilot Plant (WIPP) in New Mexico was designed to accept transuranic (TRU) and MTRU waste only. EPA published its certification of WIPP in the *Federal Register* on May 18, 1998 (63 FR 27354). Because the WIPP was certified as a *no migration* facility, RCRA LDRs do not apply. **No migration** means that waste constituents will not migrate from the facility; *i.e.*, there is no migration pathway.

Mixed Waste Inventory Reports. The waste inventory report was required to contain a detailed state-by-state inventory of mixed waste, regardless of the time of generation. The inventory had the following specific requirements:

1) A detailed description of each mixed waste

2) The amount of each type of mixed waste, differentiated by MW subject to and MW not subject to RCRA LDRs

3) An estimate of each MW type expected to be generated during the following five years

4) DOE waste minimization activities implemented

5) EPA hazardous waste code for each MW

6) An inventory of all noncharacterized MW

7) Basis of each hazardous waste code determination

8) Description of each waste source

9) LDR treatment technology specified for each MW

10) A statement regarding the affect of radionuclide content on the treatment technologies

Waste Treatment Capacities and Technologies Report. This report was required to include the following:

1) Estimate of treatment capacity for each inventoried waste based on existing treatment technology

2) A description of each treatment unit identified for the above

3) A description of existing treatment units not included, and the reasons they were not included

4) A description of proposed treatment units

5) Information needed to address treatment of waste for which no treatment technology existed

DOE Site Treatment Plans. The FFCAct amended RCRA Section 3021(b) to require DOE to prepare Site Treatment Plans for developing treatment capacities and technologies for mixed waste at each site where DOE stores or generates mixed waste. As used here, *mixed waste* is specifically a mixture of radioactive and RCRA hazardous wastes.

Specifically, as defined in the FFCAct, MW is "waste that contains both hazardous waste and source, special nuclear, or by-product material subject to the Atomic Energy Act of 1954."

In 1995, DOE submitted 40 proposed STPs for sites in 20 states. In fiscal year 1997, the number of STPs required had dropped to 38; of these, 37 had been approved by the end of the fiscal year. The remaining STP has been approved in principle at the last site, Argonne National Laboratory–East in Illinois. However, the State of Illinois placed a low priority of activity on this site, and is taking no further action to issue a Compliance Order, according to DOE.

The STPs were required to contain:

1) For MWs for which treatment technologies existed, a schedule for submitting all applicable permit applications, entering into contracts, initiating construction, *etc.*, and processing backlogged and currently generated MW

2) For MW with no existing treatment technology, a schedule for identifying and developing such technologies

3) An estimate of waste volumes that would exist based on various radionuclide separation technologies

An annual progress report for the STPs was also required from the DOE Secretary for three consecutive years after the Act passage (*i.e.*, October 1993, October 1994, and October 1995); these were submitted.

STPs were developed to enable DOE to meet RCRA LDR requirements. STPs address the treatment aspects of mixed waste management, including how, where, and when mixed waste is treated to meet LDRs.

After consultation with EPA and State regulators, DOE published its plan to submit the STPs in three stages (58 FR 17875, April 6, 1993). In Stage 1, conceptual STPs were submitted in October 1993, which described a wide range of possible treatment technologies for each mixed waste at each site. From these, Draft Site Treatment Plans (Stage 2) were submitted for review (59 FR 44979, August 31, 1994). DOE planned to submit the revised Proposed Plans (Stage 3) in February, 1995 (60 FR 10840, February 28, 1995), but issue was delayed until April 5, 1995 (60 FR 17346). A total of 37 proposed plans were prepared to address 40 sites in 20 states.

Radioactive Mixed Waste Regulatory History.
Radioactive mixed wastes are problematic in that they can only be stored, treated, or disposed at facilities which are permitted for both hazardous and radioactive wastes. There are few such facilities. The preferred approach for managing existing wastes is to treat the wastes so that they are either hazardous, or radioactive. Pollution Prevention (P2) initiatives are developed and employed to avoid generation of radioactive mixed wastes. Common P2 approaches include material substitution to reduce use of hazardous materials and/or reduce generation of hazardous wastes, and process modifications to reduce or eliminate wastes. Waste minimization techniques are employed to manage the wastes that are generated after P2 efforts have been employed.

MWs are wastes which are hazardous wastes under RCRA and radioactive wastes under the Atomic Energy Act (AEA). MWs are generated in particular by research facilities, medical facilities, laboratories, nuclear power plants, and nuclear weapons program activities.

There are three categories of MW: (1) high-level waste (HLW), (2) mixed transuranic waste (MTRU), and (3) low-level mixed waste (LLMW).

The regulatory history of MW begins with the passage of RCRA in 1976, with the systematic *cradle-to-grave* regulatory program for hazardous waste, as such wastes were defined at that time. Prior to that time, MWs were managed as radioactive wastes with varying degrees of success by various generators. However, RCRA specifically excluded source, special nuclear, and by-product material as defined in the Atomic Energy Act (AEA) of 1954. This effectively prevented these types of radioactive materials from being defined as solid waste under RCRA. Since hazardous wastes are a subset of solid wastes under RCRA, these wastes were not regulated under RCRA. They were, however, regulated by both the Nuclear Regulatory Commission (NRC) for commercial activities and DOE (Federal nuclear weapons related activities) under the AEA.

In 1981, NRC recognized the need for joint regulation of mixed waste under the AEA and RCRA while in the process of promulgating land disposal regulations for low-level radioactive waste (10 CFR 61). At the same time, DOE maintained that RCRA did not apply to DOE activities. This issue was resolved in Federal court in 1984 with the decision that RCRA did indeed apply to DOE activities.

Also in 1984, the Hazardous and Solid Waste Amendments (HSWA) to RCRA were enacted, which set the stage for more stringent land disposal regulations (*e.g.*, LDRs and treatment standards).

In 1986, the EPA published notice that it intended to exercise regulatory authority over the hazardous constituents of mixed waste. In 1986, EPA also promulgated the Land Disposal Restrictions for what were called the *California List* wastes.

In 1987, NRC and EPA published joint draft guidance on the definition and identification of LLMW. Also in 1987, the NRC and EPA published joint siting guidelines for disposal of LLMW and a conceptual design approach for commercial LLMW disposal facilities, and joint guidance on mixed waste storage (60 FR 40204, August 7, 1987).

From 1988 to 1992, consolidation of efforts continued among the three Federal agencies in regulation of MW. EPA had also banned land disposal of MW under its RCRA authority, if such MW exceeded LDRs.

In 1992, the FFCAct was enacted. Among other things, the definition of mixed waste was established for RCRA, and EPA was mandated to regulate mixed waste activities. At the same time, DOE was given the task of spearheading MW treatment technology.

From 1994 to the present, progress has been made in both the treatment of existing (stored) MW and in the reduction or elimination of generation of MW (pollution prevention). The EPA and NRC published joint guidance on the storage of LLMW.

In 1997, the EPA and NRC published joint guidance on testing requirements for MW (62 FR 62079, November 20, 1997).

In 1998, EPA certified DOE's WIPP (as codified in 40 CFR 194) for disposal of Transuranic Waste (TRU) and MTRU wastes. EPA also renewed its enforcement policy on MW storage violations under RCRA §3004(j), as progress continued to be made on treatment technologies.

EPA activity on a mixed waste disposal rule is progressing concurrently with EPA's Hazardous Waste Identification Rule (HWIR). MW is being addressed as a special hazardous waste identification issue in order to focus on the radioactive aspect of MW, with which relatively few hazardous generators have to deal. The proposed rule was issued for comment on February 19, 1999 (64 FR 63464–63501), and the final rule was promulgated as a new Subpart N to 40 CFR 266 on May 16, 2001 (66 FR 27218–27265). The rule went into effect on November 13, 2001.

Note: Radioactive mixed wastes also exist which contain toxic substances (*e.g.*, polychlorinated biphenyls–PCBs) regulated under the Toxic Substances Control Act (TSCA) of 1976. Such waste is also subject to both AEA and TSCA regulations, and potentially RCRA LDRs. In cases where all three regulations apply, the most stringent requirements of each will normally apply.

Related DOE Initiatives. Concurrent with actions to achieve compliance with RCRA Subtitle C requirements, DOE has initiated two related actions: a Waste Management Programmatic Environmental Impact Statement (PEIS), and the Baseline Environmental Management Report (BEMR). The PEIS was begun to address MW treatment and disposal under the National Environmental Policy Act (NEPA) issues. The BEMR is a congressional budgetary requirement and addresses DOE (including FFCAct) budgetary issues.

Related EPA Initiatives. EPA has been working closely with NRC on the commercial MW disposal issue since the 1970s and with DOE since the early 1980's. The LDR requirement mandated by HSWA has added additional restrictions for land disposal of hazardous waste, and so mixed waste. Currently, EPA is pursuing a MW management rule (concurrently with the HWIR) which should simplify hazardous waste disposal requirements.

§107 (Munitions)

The primary regulatory action implemented pursuant to this section has been EPA's promulgation under RCRA Subtitle C at 40 CFR 260–266 and 270 of what became known as the Military

Table 1. RCRA Regulatory Changes Pursuant to Promulgation of the MMR

Reference	RCRA Regulatory Change
40 CFR 260	Addition to 40 CFR 260.10 of definitions related to explosives
40 CFR 261	Addition of 40 CFR 261.2(a) (2) (iv): "A military munition identified as a solid waste in 40 CFR 26.202."
40 CFR 262	Exemption under 40 CFR 262.10 and 262.20 for emergency response to an explosives emergency
40 CFR 263	Exemption under 40 CFR 263.10 to transportation requirements for response to explosives emergencies
40 CFR 264	Exemptions under 40 CFR 264.1 and 264.70 for explosives emergency response
	New Subpart EE—Hazardous Waste Munitions and Explosives Storage as 40 CFR 264.1200-264.1202 (alternatives to general storage requirements)
40 CFR 265	Exemptions under 40 CFR 265.1 and 265.70 for explosives emergency response
	New Subpart EE—Hazardous Waste Munitions and Explosives Storage as 40 CFR 265.1200-265.1202 (alternatives to general storage requirements)
40 CFR 266	New Subpart M—Military Munitions as 40 CFR 266.200-266.206, which provide for identification of munitions as solid waste and, if hazardous under 40 CFR 261, applicable management standards as alternatives to 40 CFR 264 and 265 requirements
40 CFR 270	Conditional exemption for explosives emergency response under new 40 CFR 270.1(c)(3)(i)(D) and 270.1(c)(3)(iii)
	Permit modification for addition munitions waste acceptance under 40 CFR 270.42(h)

Munitions Rule (MMR). This rule addresses both conventional and chemical military munitions, as required by the FFCAct. In addition, both military and nonmilitary conventional munitions are addressed by the MMR under other RCRA authority with respect to emergency response requirements.

Table 1 is a synopsis of RCRA regulatory changes pursuant to promulgation of the MMR.

EPA's Military Munitions Rule. The primary regulatory action implemented pursuant to this section has been EPA's promulgation under RCRA Subtitle C at 40 CFR 260–266 and 270 of what became known as the Military Munitions Rule. This rule is a subset of the rulemaking activity which is called the Hazardous Waste Identification Rule (HWIR). The MMR addresses both conventional and chemical military munitions, as required by the FFCAct. In addition, both military and nonmilitary munitions are addressed by the MMR under other RCRA authority with respect to emergency response requirements. Nuclear weapons and components were not subject to this action; they are regulated by DOE and DoD under (primarily) AEA authority.

As stated in the preamble to the Final Rule (62 FR 6622), the final rule established a process for identification of munitions as solid waste, and then further classification as either hazardous or nonhazardous solid waste. The rule also provides for safe transport and storage of hazardous waste munitions, and makes provisions for conditional exemptions from RCRA regulation for emergency response. The MMR allows for storage under either RCRA regulations or in accordance with the Department of Defense Explosives Safety Board (DDESB) requirements as specified in DoD 6055.9–STD–DoD Ammunition and Explosives Safety Standards.

Three categories of munitions (conventional and/or chemical) are addressed by EPA's MMR:

1) Unused munitions

2) Munitions being used for their intended purpose

3) Used or fired munitions

Military munitions are now solid wastes when *being used for their intended purpose.* Conditional exemptions exist for RCRA manifesting and marking requirements for shipments from one DoD Treatment, Storage, and/or Disposal Facility (TSDF) to another, and for RCRA Subtitle C storage requirements for storage under Department of Defense Environmental Safety Board regulations.

The MMR also clarified that chemical munitions are not subject to RCRA Section 3004(j) storage prohibitions codified at 40 CFR 268.50. Such munitions are subject more specifically to a series of other management and disposal requirements specifically mandated by Congress beginning in 1985. A chemical munitions destruction program is in progress at all DoD storage sites. However, other RCRA Subtitle C requirements apply unless specifically superseded.

In promulgating the MMR, EPA included nonmilitary munitions in most of the regulatory changes. Only 40 CFR 266, Subpart M is exclusively applicable to military munitions. It should also be noted that 40 CFR 266, Subpart M provides management standards tailored to DDESB standards, while 40 CFR 264/265, Subpart EE standards are applicable to military and nonmilitary parties. The Subpart EE standards are also tailored alternative standards; other standards in 40 CFR 264 and 265 may be applied as appropriate, as specified in facility permits.

DoD's Range Rule. One reason the proposal and promulgation of EPA's MMR was delayed was to allow for close coordination between EPA and DoD, the entity which was primarily affected. The MMR has had a significant effect on the development of the Range Rule, since the MMR determined munitions waste management. DoD's long record of safe management of military munitions provided much useful input into EPA's rulemaking process. In fact, DoD's Explosives Safety Board (DDESB) had long-established standards in place, which served as both technical input and an alternative for EPA's rules, as discussed above. Terminology, definitions, and intent are consistent between the MMR and the Range Rule.

The Range Rule was proposed as 32 CFR 178, "Closed, Transferred, and Transferring Ranges Containing Military Munitions," on September 26, 1997 (62 FR 50796) under authority of the Defense Environmental Restoration Program, the DDESB, the Comprehensive Environmental Response and Compensation Act of 1980 (CERCLA) Section 104, as amended, and Executive Order 12580. The

Range Rule was designed to be compatible with the response actions taken under CERCLA. It contains a five-part process which is not inconsistent with CERCLA, and is tailored to the special risks posed by military munitions and military ranges. DoD has five categories of ranges: Active, Inactive, Closed, Transferred, and Transferring. The Range Rule does not apply to Active and Inactive ranges.

While the Range Rule does not have authority under the FFCAct, the EPA's MMR, which was mandated by the FFCAct, was a key determinant on formulation of regulations for the operation, transfer, and disposal of former and current military bombing and artillery ranges.

DoD's proposed 32 CFR 178 is in the process of being revised to address other agency and state concerns, while other DoD initiatives, interim and long-term, are being offered. The new initiatives are being addressed in the context of the overall issue of *encroachment*–the term used to describe the ongoing and growing conflicts of military range operation and the with other uses on range lands–(*e.g.,* environmental management), use of surrounding lands, airspace, and radio frequency allocations.

On March 20, 2002, DoD issued an Advanced Notice of Proposed Rulemaking for a new 32 CFR 179 (see 67 FR 12937), for development of a Munitions Response Site Prioritization Protocol for ranking DoD munitions response sites. This proposed rule would address some of the concerns expressed about the proposed 32 CFR 178.

In a closely related matter, DoD is also pursuing legislative relief for ranges regarding several key environmental statues. The overall legislative relief initiative is called the Readiness and Range Preservation Initiative (RRPI). These efforts have been largely pursued through the annual fiscal year (FY) National Defense Authorization Acts beginning with the FY 2002 Act and continuing to the present.

Concurrently, DoD is developing and issuing interim DoD policy as DoD Directives and Instructions. DoD Directive 3200.15, "Sustainment of Ranges and Operating Areas (OPAREAS)," was issued on January 10, 2003. The development of an implementing DoD Instruction is in progess.

§109 (Small Town Environmental Planning)

The Small Town Task Force (STTF) was created by EPA in 1992 as mandated by Congress. The purpose of the task force was to advise EPA on how to work better with small communities in order to improve compliance with environmental regulations. The STTF was presented with a challenging scope of work by Congress. The legislation identified five specific responsibilities. These were to

1) Identify regulations developed pursuant to Federal environmental laws, which pose significant compliance problems for small towns

2) Identify means to improve the working relationship between the Environmental Protection Agency and small towns

3) Review proposed regulations for the protection of the environmental and public health, and suggest revisions that could improve the ability of small towns to comply with such regulations

4) Identify means to promote regionalization of environmental treatment systems and infrastructure serving small towns, to improve the economic condition of such systems and infrastructure

5) Provide such other assistance to the Administrator as the Administrator deems appropriate.

The Task Force consisted of 14 members from towns with populations under 2,500. The STTF met six times between enactment of the legislation in October, 1992 and June, 1996. The STTF issued its draft report in August, 1994 and the final report in June, 1996. The report contained 39 recommendations, which include continued small town advisory work with EPA, establishment of a small town ombudsman, increased technical support, regulatory changes, increased flexibility, small town involvement in regulation development, increasing financial resources for small towns, inter-agency coordination of environmental programs, requirements and processes and recommendations requiring Congressional action.

The Small Community Advisory Committee (SCAC) of the Local Government Advisory Committee (LGAC) took over the role of the STTF following submission of the STTF's Final Report in 1996. The LGAC operates under the Office of Congressional and Intergovernmental Relations (OCIR), which serves as EPA's principal liaison with the State and local government officials and the organizations which represent them. This office consolidates Section 109 requirements and those of other legislative statutes and Executive Orders with respect to Federal-State-local government interaction and cooperative efforts.

The Environmental Council of the States (ECOS), which was founded in December, 1993, has teamed up with US EPA's Office of State and Local Relations in a cooperative agreement aimed at improving how small towns and communities deal with environmental matters.

The ECOS/EPA Small Towns Project follows up on the work completed by the STTF. The primary goal of the project is to work towards the implementation of a few key recommendations presented by the STTF. In 1998, the major activities of the ECOS/EPA partnership were the National Environmental Performance Partnership System (NEPPS), under which a state and EPA negotiate a Performance Partnership Agreement (PPA) which lays out what each partner will do in the coming year. The PPA is a key element in the continuing process of devolving enforcement authority from the Federal to the State governments.

In essence, the original EPA Headquarters–STTF relationship has been merged into the overall and evolving relationship which involves EPA Headquarters, EPA Regions, states, local governments, and small communities. As the trend toward greater State responsibility for both Federal and State environmental protection and management programs continues, the unique problems faced by small communities are increasingly addressed at the State and local (city, county) level.

Currently, EPA efforts to address small community concerns seem to be consolidated under EPA's Office of Cooperative Environmental Management.

Bibliography

Laws

"Comprehensive Environmental Response, Compensation and Liability Act of 1980, as amended." PL 96–510, 94 *Statutes* 2767. *US Code*. Title 42, Sec. 9601–9675.

"Federal Facility Compliance Act of 1992." PL 102–386, 106 *Statutes* 1505. October 6, 1992.

"National Defense Authorization Act, FY 2002." PL 107–107, 115 *Statutes* 1012. December 28, 2001.

"National Defense Authorization Act, FY 2003." PL 107–314, 116 Statutes 2458. December 2, 2002.

"National Defense Authorization Act, FY 2004." PL 108–136, 117 *Statutes* 1392. November 24, 2003.

"Resource Conservation and Recovery Act of 1976, as amended." PL 94–580. 90 *Statutes* 2795. *US Code*. Title 42, Sec. 6901–6992k.

Hazardous Waste Management

"EPA Administered Permit Programs: The Hazardous Waste Permit Program." *Code of Federal Regulations*. Title 40, Pt. 270.

"Hazardous Waste Management System. General." *Code of Federal Regulations*. Title 40, Pt. 260.

"Identification and Listing of Hazardous Wastes." *Code of Federal Regulations*. Title 40, Pt. 261.

"Interim Status Standards for Owners and Operators of Hazardous Waste Treatment, Storage and Disposal Facilities." *Code of Federal Regulations*. Title 40, Pt. 265.

"Procedures for Decisionmaking." *Code of Federal Regulations*. Title 40, Pt. 124.

"Standards Applicable to Generators of Hazardous Waste." *Code of Federal Regulations*. Title 40, Pt. 262.

"Standards Applicable to Transporters of Hazardous Waste." *Code of Federal Regulations*. Title 40, Pt. 263.

"Standards for Owners and Operators of Hazardous Waste Treatment, Storage, and Disposal Facilities." *Code of Federal Regulations*. Title 40, Pt. 264.

"Standards for the Management of Specific Hazardous Wastes and Specific Types of Hazardous Waste Management Facilities." *Code of Federal Regulations*. Title 40, Pt. 266.

Military Munitions

"Closed, Transferred, and Transferring Ranges Containing Military Munitions; Proposed Rule. (32 CFR 178.)" *Federal Register* 62 (26 September 1997): 50796–50843.

"Military Munitions Rule: Hazardous Waste Identification and Management; Explosives Emergencies, Manifest Exemption for Transport of Hazardous Waste on Right-of-Ways on Contiguous Properties, Final Rule. (40 CFR Parts 260, 261, 262, 263, 264, 265, 266, and 270.)" *Federal Register* 62 (12 February 1997): 6622–6657.

"Sustainment of Ranges and Operating Areas (OPAREAs)." Directive 3200.15. US Department of Defense. January 10, 2003.

Mixed Waste

"Approach to Reinventing Regulations on Storing Mixed Low-Level Radioactive Waste. Advanced Notice of Proposed Rulemaking." *Federal Register* 64 (1 March 1999): 10064–10073.

"Development of a Munitions Response Site Prioritization Protocol. Advanced Notice of Proposed Rulemaking." *Federal Register* 67 (3 March 2002): 12937–12936.

"Extension of the Policy on Enforcement of RCRA Section 3004(j) Storage Prohibitions at Facilities Generating Mixed Radioactive/Hazardous Waste." *Federal Register* 61 (26 April 1996): 18588–18592.

"Extension of the Policy on Enforcement of RCRA Section 3004(j) Storage Prohibition at Facilities Generating Mixed Radioactive/Hazardous Waste." *Federal Register* 63 (9 April 1998): 17414.

"Extension of the Policy on Enforcement of RCRA Section 3004(j) Storage Prohibitions at Facilities Generating Mixed Radioactive/Hazardous Waste." *Federal Register* 63 (6 November 1998): 59989–59992.

"Joint Nuclear Regulatory Commission/Environmental Protection Agency Guidance on the Storage of Mixed Radioactive and Hazardous Waste." *Federal Register* 60 (7 August 1995): 40204–40211.

"Joint Nuclear Regulatory Commission/Environmental Protection Agency Guidance on Testing Requirements for Mixed Radioactive and Hazardous Waste." *Federal Register* 62 (20 November 1997): 62079–62094.

"Office of Environmental Management Proposed Site Treatment Plan. Notice of Availability." *Federal Register* 60 (5 April 1995): 17346–17349.

"Storage, Treatment, Transportation, and Disposal of Mixed Waste. Proposed Rules." *Federal Register* 64 (19 November 1999): 63464–63501.

"Storage, Treatment, Transportation, and Disposal of Mixed Waste. Final Rule." *Federal Register* 66 (16 May 2001): 27218–27266.

Harry A. Bryson is a CHMM at the Master's level and a Senior Environmental Scientist with Earth Technologies, Inc. He is currently employed by Titan Systems in Huntsville, Alabama as part of the Continuity of Operations (Coop) plan supporting the Army Aviation and Missile Command at Redstone Arsenal. He has 22 years experience in environmental regulatory compliance, and 26 years experience in military flight operations and emergency planning. He has Master's degrees in Environmental Engineering (University of Tennessee, Knoxville; 1984), and Biology (Butler University, Indianapolis; 1979) and Bachelor of Science degrees in Engineering Physics (University of Tennessee, Knoxville; 1981) and Life Sciences (USAF Academy, Colorado; 1971).

CHAPTER 4

Introduction to Environmental Management

Philip Wood, EMS-PA, CHMM
Harry S. Kemp, EMS-A, CHMM

When the first edition of this book was published in 1999, the use of environmental management systems (EMS) was a relatively new, but rapidly expanding phenomenon. Considerable experience in EMS design and implementation has been gained since the first edition of this book was published. The authors' primary goal in preparing this chapter is to take advantage of the many new developments in the EMS field, the insights and experiences of many organizations that have implemented EMS, and to introduce the concept of sustainability.

Environmental Management: What Is It?

Environmental management is the organizing and controlling of affairs related to an organization's impact on the natural world, our surroundings, people, animals, and plants. Environmental management requires strong administrative skills and an understanding of environmental regulations, the fate and transport of chemicals, as well as the interaction of people and processes. Environmental management also requires other business skill attributes such as an understanding of the costs and benefits of handling environmental issues. To understand environmental management, one must understand its unifying principles and the way the elements of environmental management contribute to the overall objective—achievement of environmental goals and improvement in environmental performance.

The effective handling of environmental issues is one of the most complex challenges facing business and environmental managers today. This is due in part to the large number of issues, conflicting business interests, and the large number of diverse stakeholders influencing the management process. Environmental managers are increasingly facing the challenges of reducing costs and satisfying increasing regulatory and public pressure to reduce both direct and indirect environmental impacts from their operations. Successful achievement of these competing goals suggests that new approaches to environmental management, ones that use more effective strategy, maybe required.

Some business managers are becoming more aware that environmental issues can significantly affect the profitability of their organizations. However, the overall level of top management recognition and knowledge of the importance of proactive environmental management is relatively low. It is important that environmental issues are handled simultaneously with other business management functions, since any benefits gained in one area could be lost altogether by shortcomings in another. Environmental managers should promote the benefits of environmental improvement by insisting that environmental issues be managed differently than any other business issues.

Key Definitions

Environmental
1) **of the natural world:** relating to the natural world, especially to its conservation
2) **of your surroundings:** relating to, or caused by, a person's or animal's surroundings

Environment
1) ENVIRONMENT **natural world:** the natural world, within which people, animals, and plants live.
2) ENVIRONMENT ECOLOGY **surrounding influences:** all the external factors influencing the life of organisms, such as light or food supply
3) SOCIAL SCIENCES **social and physical conditions:** the conditions that surround people and affect the way they live
Encarta® World English Dictionary [North American Edition]

management
1) **administration of business:** the organizing and controlling of the affairs of a business or a particular sector of a business
2) **managers as a group:** managers and employers considered collectively, especially the directors and executives of a business or organization
3) **handling of something successfully:** the act of handling or controlling something successfully
4) **skill in handling or using something:** the skillful handling or use of something such as resources
Encarta® World English Dictionary [North American Edition]

Environmental management system
part of an **organization's** management system used to develop and implement its **environmental policy** and manage its **environmental aspects.**
Note 1. A management system is a set of interrelated elements used to establish policy and objectives and to achieve those objectives.
Note 2. A management system includes organizational structure, planning activities, responsibilities, practices, **procedures** processes and resources.
The International Organization for Standardization's Environmental Management Systems (EMS)–Specification With Guidance For Use–ISO 14001:2004 (ISO 14001).

The Environmental Management Toolkit

The environmental management toolkit contains some new and some familiar names. Environmental management guidelines are generally composed of a series of interlinking and supporting components:

- A set of *principles* to help understand environmental management;

- A series of *tools* that can be used to achieve environmental objectives;

- A series of *management programs* traditionally used to solve environmental issues; and

- A *management framework* to integrate environmental issues into the core business processes and decisionmaking

Let's look briefly at some of the supporting guidance currently available to the environmental manager in his or her quest for improved performance. Some tools have been specifically developed as environmental management guidelines (ISO 14001, for example), some have been adopted from other management practices (for example, environmental cost accounting) and some tools are being combined into one guidance document to provide a more sustainable management framework (for example, the SIGMA Project—Sustainability–Integrated Guidelines for Management).

Although not comprehensive, and some would say open to discussion, Table 1 illustrates the large number of tools and guides available for environmental managers to use. When confronted by an environmental issue, there is a tendency to select a single tool or management program in order to resolve the issue or improve the process. Often this approach is a temporary fix that fails to generate the benefits envisioned at the start of the process and it is frequently repeated over time if and when the issues reoccur. Also, strategic planning is essential for linking the principles, programs and the management frameworks listed in Table 1. The tools environmental managers need and use to do their work effectively in today's business environment requires a well thought-out strategic plan linked to a conceptual management framework in order for the tool to be successful and effective. In other words, a framework or system approach for environmental management creates a more robust solution and prevents the recurrence of many environmental issues, especially when combined with a strategic plan.

Most of the conceptual management frameworks listed in Table 1 have been designed to help organizations address their environmental issues, irrespective of their size, location, and business. The frameworks generally provide guidance on how to take the principles and turn them into action items. Likewise, the tools and programs/guidelines are not prescriptive or detailed and do not attempt to be site- or organization-specific. Each organization needs to address its own issues differently and can use one of the conceptual management frameworks to formulate and implement its own environmental action and improvement plan. In addition, the management frameworks do not directly include expected levels of performance but rely on the organizations themselves to set performance objectives and targets that are consistent with their principles; report their performance; and take appropriate corrective and preventive action in order to achieve continual improvement. The management framework is then used to embed environmental thinking and action into the organization's business processes and decisionmaking.

The conventional model for a management framework that follows a logical progression of activities aimed at improving the performance of the organization is the "Plan, Do, Check, Act" or PDCA approach. Originally developed and used by Walter Shewart in 1924 as the Plan-Do-Study-Act cycle and popularized by Deming, the successful well-tried and tested approach has not changed over time even as its application changes. During each PDCA cycle, decisions are made based upon facts and not unfounded opinion. The most advantageous point about this approach is that it is a cycle and can be repeated as many times as is required until the desired result is achieved.

As clearly illustrated by regulatory management systems over the last 10 years, simply striving to meet, or meeting, the regulatory compliance requirement and staying within "the permit-to-pollute" threshold, has done little for the overall improvement in environmental quality and integration of environmental issues into business decisionmaking. The ideal goal is to use a management framework that combines voluntary, regulatory, and business elements to improve

Actions or Principles	Specific Tools	Typical Management Programs	Conceptual Management Frameworks	Overall Goal
Code of Environmental Management Principles	Material substitution	Pollution Prevention	EMS	S
The SIGMA Principles	Product substitution	Waste minimization	Industrial ecology	U
UN Global Compact	Product reformulation	Source reduction	Design for the environment	S
The Global Sullivan Principles	Process change	Cleaner production	Sigma Guidelines	T
OECD Guidelines for Multinational Enterprises	Equipment change	Total Quality Environmental Management	Malcolm Baldrige Quality Model	A
Caux Roundtable Principles for Business	ISO 14000 family of standards	Material selection	The Balanced Scorecard	I
Amnesty International's Human Rights Guidance for Companies	ISO 9001:2000	Inventory management		N
The Principles for Global Corporate Responsibility	ISO 19011	Process management		A
Bellagio Principles	Waste stream analysis	Regulatory compliance		B
CERES Principles	Life cycle analysis	Media program management, e.g., hazardous waste		I
Prevention of pollution	Life cycle costing	Environmental Supply Chain Management		L
	Activity based costing			I
	Material accounting			T
	Energy accounting			Y
	BS8880			
	AA1000 Assurance Standard			
	SA 8000			
	Global Reporting Initiative			
	IISD dashboard			
	Compass index of sustainability			
	The Natural Step			
	Greenhouse Gas Reporting Protocol			

Table 1. The Environmental Management Tool Kit

environmental performance. The common starting point for this more integrated approach is the environmental management system (EMS).

What Is an EMS?

An EMS is a framework that allows an organization to address its operational or process effects on the environment in a consistent manner and to improve continually how its business practices interact with the environment. The EMS is a continual PDCA cycle of planning, implementing, reviewing, and improving the processes and actions that an organization undertakes to meet its environmental objectives by focusing management's attention and resources on its own priorities. The use of a conceptual management framework provides the appropriate flexible, non-prescriptive and systematic approach towards managing environmental issues and delivering superior environmental and business results. The most commonly recognized guidance for implementing an EMS is The International Organization for Standardization's "Environmental Management Systems (EMS) – Specification With Guidance For Use" (ISO 14001:2004, issued November 15, 2004), which promotes an EMS that has five components:

- Environmental Policy
- Planning
- Implementation and Operation
- Checking and Corrective Action
- Management Review

Potential Costs of Implementing an Environmental Management System

Internal
- Staff (manager) time
- Other employee time

(Note: Internal labor costs represent the bulk of the EMS resources expended by most organizations)

External
- Potential consulting assistance
- Training or personnel

What Is the Cost of Implementing an EMS?

Recently, EPA completed a 5-year study of 83 facilities (large manufacturers, utilities, small businesses, military bases, and a waste water treatment plant) in 17 states. The study, documented in the University of North Carolina National Database on EMS, shows that the average cost to implement an EMS is approximately $40,000 per facility.

For most organizations, the leadership, involvement, and visibility of top management in the project is the most significant resource requirement. Beyond that, the amount of time and money needed to implement an EMS will vary with size and the organizations business activities. In-house labor costs typically constitute the most significant portion of implementation costs. Although many

---

The Five Components of an Environmental Management System

Environmental Policy	Environmental Policy written and signed by the organization's top managers
Planning	Detailed data collected (usually by the appropriate environmental staff)
Implementation and Operation	Environmental plan implemented throughout the entire organization
Checking and Corrective Action	The system is evaluated and checked
Management Review	Review and feedback by top management

organizations use a consultant to facilitate implementation, the organization's personnel, not just the environmental staff, should do the bulk of the implementation work.

Why Develop an EMS?

An organization may choose to implement an EMS for many reasons, such as enhancing business performance through the following

- Developing an environmental management structure that is effective and responsive to the organization's needs

- Making operational improvements

- Changing the operational culture

- Improving public image

- Improving relationship with regulators

- Enhancing the ability to meet regulatory requirements

- Providing for greater employee environmental awareness and commitment to environmental performance

The implementation of an EMS can improve an organization's environmental performance. But because no two organizations are alike, each organization will experience significantly different benefits from the EMS. It is also important to consider the more generally accepted drivers for implementing an EMS:

- Business requirements—For example, US automobile manufacturers require ISO 14001 certification from their suppliers

- Regulatory requirements—Executive Order (EO) 13148 "Greening the Government through Leadership in Environmental Management," released in April 2000 requires that all Federal agencies implement an EMS at each appropriate facility by 2005

- Other business drivers such as the key desire most companies have to maximize their profitability

Would organizations implement an EMS if it were not for these regulatory or business drivers? Many would say probably not, especially since the main business drivers have not yet received the recognition they deserve. However, experience has shown that depending on the market sector, companies with a strong integrated approach to

---

Benefits of Implementing an Environmental Management System

- Improved environmental performance

- Enhanced compliance

- Fewer fines and notices of violation

- Less pollution through prevention

- More efficient use of resources

- Reduced or mitigated risks to people, the business, and the environment

- Increased safety

- Reduced liability

- Increased efficiency and reduced costs

- Reduced accidents

- Reduced business delays

- Improved internal communication

- Improved employee awareness of environmental issues and responsibilities

- Enhanced image with public and regulators

- Improved relations with regulators and other stakeholders

- Enhanced stakeholder trust

- Enhanced environmental stewardship and sustainable development

- Greater integration of environmental activites and operational procedures achieving greater consistency of performance

environmental management consistently out-perform those that do not. For example, Innovest's EcoValue'21® funds and the FTSE Index of Corporate Environmental Engagement both gauge the extent to which a company systematically addresses environmental issues. A growing number of major companies can attest to the value of an EMS and report many benefits.

The Environmental Protection Agency (EPA) has developed several initiatives to encourage the use of an EMS, as part of its effort to assist organizations in improving environmental performance (including compliance) and making greater use of pollution prevention approaches. These initiatives include the "National Environmental Performance Track" (NEPT), the "EMS Initiative for Local Governments," and the "Design for the Environment" EMS Guide. Information on these initiatives can be found at <http://www.epa.gov/ems>. EPA is also currently working on proposals that would allow those NEPT members that have an EMS in place to:

- Use innovative air permitting options

- Eliminate or reduce the frequency of routine reporting

- Increase the length of time that hazardous waste may be stored onsite

- Improve permitting, reporting and record keeping

- Encourage *beyond-compliance*

EPA and state governments are partners in implementing the NEPT program and many states have developed performance-based incentive programs.

Challenges to EMS Implementation

Although there is limited information available from organizations on the specific benefits associated with implementing an EMS, experience indicates that EMS benefits may:

- Take time to appear

- Be difficult to quantify monetarily because they are likely a result of efficiencies across the entire organization due to changes in work and management practices

- Be difficult to quantify because costs cannot be assigned to benefits such as having a better reputation, being a better neighbor, and attaining greater stakeholder trust

Most organizations have dealt with environmental issues reactively, in response to laws and regulations, and in a manner that has separated environmental issues from the business and processes that created them. More proactive business organizations are now moving from a management culture that views compliance as a foregone conclusion, towards focusing management attention on the business by identifying and eliminating the environmental impacts of the business regardless of legal or regulatory drivers.

States with Environmental Performance-Based Incentive Programs

Colorado	Massachussetts	Texas
Florida	Michigan	Utah
Idaho	New Mexico	
	North Carolina	Vermont
Illinois	Oregon	Virginia
Louisiana	South Carolina	West Virginia
Maine	Tennessee	Wisconsin

This change has arisen from a growing recognition that both environmental and business performance improves when environmental issues are managed proactively and as an integral part of the business activities that generate them.

What Is Sustainable Development?

Surprisingly, the term ***sustainable development***, the current buzzword among environmentalists and some leading companies, has been in existence since the 1974 book, *The Limits to Growth*. The word *sustainable* comes from the Latin *sustenare* (*to hold up*), and means *able to continue indefinitely*. The idea of sustainability, defined by the Brundtland Commission in 1987 as, "Development that meets the needs of the present without compromising the ability of future generations to meet their own needs," is probably best summarized by the SIGMA Guidelines as, "Capacity for continuance into long term future."

While a definitive definition of sustainability has not been agreed upon, it is generally agreed that the term involves the economic, environmental, and social aspects of development—often referred to in business as the *triple bottom line*. Probably the best way to identify and work toward a sustainable organization is to identify the core principles that govern the organization's business actions. The Sigma Principles promote active management of five assets:

- Natural capital (the environment)

- Human capital (people)

- Social capital (social relationships and structures)

- Manufactured capital (fixed assets)

- Financial capital (profit and loss, sales, shares, cash *etc.*).

The SIGMA Guidelines then assist organizations in developing a management framework in order tackle sustainability. The guidelines provide

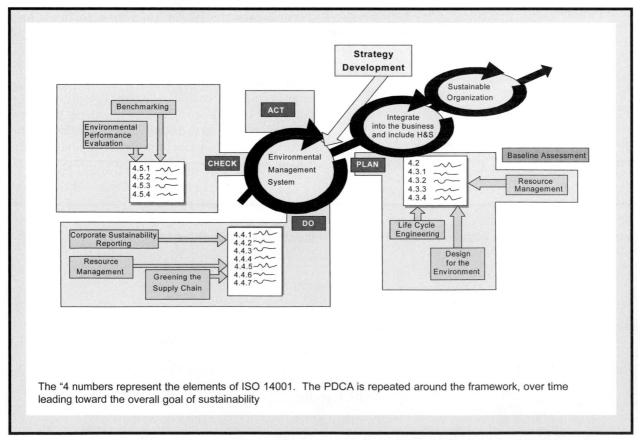

The "4 numbers represent the elements of ISO 14001. The PDCA is repeated around the framework, over time leading toward the overall goal of sustainability

Figure 1. Using the Environmental Toolkit to Progress Toward Sustainability

practical guidance and tools to help move them towards a more sustainable way of doing business.

Because of the uncertainty surrounding the term sustainable development, *i.e,* what it is, how it can be achieved, and what the future holds, the assessment of progress toward sustainable development should be based more upon factual determinations such as

- Is an organizing framework in place (an EMS, for example)?

- Does the organization have a vision and goals?

- Are indicators and detailed assessment criteria used?

- Are all the latter points linked to provide a clear signal of progress and performance?

The list of tools and programs in Table 1 and definitions of environmental, management and sustainability discussed earlier, can be used in an integrated manner. By applying the correct tools in a PDCA cycle supported by a management framework the "desired result" of an integrated management system leading to the overall goal of sustainability could be achieved. Figure 1 illustrates this thought process.

The term *desired result* usually implies that the organization has a vision of the end result and potentially a strategic plan to get there. However, in general it would be fair to conclude that most organizations are still struggling in the functional EMS approach phase, "let's implement the 17 elements of ISO 14001," as opposed to the strategic focus of, "let's integrate environmental programs with our business processes to bring about both environmental performance improvement and business success."

So What Should Environmental Managers Really Do?

Given that the implementation of systematic environmental management is a virtual mandate for achieving sustainable operations, the primary goal for environmental managers should be to implement a strategic EMS that fully incorporates

the PDCA cycle as well as the environmental management toolkit and moves the organization toward sustainable development. Other appropriate action items that would fully support this goal include:

1) Assisting top management in developing a corporate environmental strategy so that environmental issues are integrated into business decisions

2) Aligning environmental programs with the organization's values, vision, and strategic direction; focusing on the specific environmental issues that can reduce costs and liabilities and/or enhance business revenues to bring about both environmental performance improvement and business success

3) Using "Design for the Environment" protocols when designing and developing new products

4) Developing an environmental performance evaluation system that builds upon the existing business budgeting system

5) Developing a corporate knowledge management system that can be used organization-wide for collecting business essential data for internal and external reporting purposes

6) Developing a responsible and transparent relationship with the organization's stakeholders and clearly communicate the organization's stewardship of the environment and how the business affects others

7) Reporting corporate economic, social, and environmental performance

8) Implementing an EMS and participating in the NEPT program and other State performance-based incentive programs. These will continue to evolve, recognizing and encouraging top environmental performers to go beyond compliance and attain higher levels of environmental performance in exchange for better and more innovative regulatory controls

Although ISO 14001 has achieved international recognition as an EMS guide and organizations have attained benefits from using it, environmental managers should not forget about all the other useful management tools in the market place. The traditional view of environmental management is changing from one of *it's the cost of doing business* to one where environmental improvements are seen as *let's improve environmental efficiency so that business costs can be reduced and processes improved.* Environmental and health and safety management is not about compliance anymore—it is about *business performance.* Truly effective business performance must be founded upon safe and healthy workplaces that consider their environmental impacts and simultaneously support their business goals. The overall goal should be to integrate environmental thinking into business strategy and business process improvement, with a sustainable future in mind.

Bibliography

Meadows, Donella H., Dennis L. Meadows, Jorgen Randers, and William H. Behrens III. *The Limits to Growth*. New York, NY: Universe Books, 1972.

Internet Resources

<http://globalsullivanprinciples.org/index.htm> (Global Sullivan Principles of Social Responsibility)

<http://indicators.hciflorida.org/index.cfm> (Healthy Community Initiative of Greater Orlando. Legacy 2002 Indicators Report)

<http://www.accountability.org.uk> (Institute of Social and Ethical Accountability, AA1000 Assurance Standard)

<http://www.amnesty.org.uk/business/pubs/hrgc.shtml> (Amnesty International. Human Rights Guidance for Companies)

<http://www.bsi-global.com/> (British Standards Institute)

<http://www.bsi-global.com/Environmental/Management/bs8555.xalter> (British Standards Institute. BS 8555:2003 Environmental Management Systems)

<http://www.cepaa.org/SA8000/SA8000.htm> (Social Accountability International. SA 8000 Overview)

<http://www.ceres.org/our_work/principles.htm> (CERES Network for Change. Our Work: The CERES Principles)

<http://www.eli.org/isopilots.htm> (Environmental Law Institute and University of North Carolina. National Database on Environmental Management Systems)

<http://www.epa.gov/ems/> (Environmental Protection Agency. Environmental Management Systems)

<http://www.epa.gov/performancetrack/> (Environmental Protection Agency, National Environmental Performance Track)

<http://www.iccr.org/issues/corpgov/resources.php> (Interfaith Center on Corporate Responsibility. The Principles for Global Corporate Responsibility)

<http://www.iisd.org/measure/> (International Institute for Sustainable Development. Measurement and Assessment Homepage)

<http://www.innovestgroup.com> (Innovest Strategic Value Advisors. Homepage)

<http://www.iso.org/iso/en/ISOOnline.frontpage> (International Organization for Standardization, Homepage)

<http://www.iso.org/iso/en/iso9000-14000/index.html> (International Organization for Standardization. ISO 9000 and ISO 14000, In Brief)

<http://www.iso14000-iso14001-environmental-management.com/iso-19011.htmISO> (BSI Business Information. BS EN ISO 19011 Guidelines for Quality and Environmental Management Systems Auditing)

<http://www.itcilo.it/actrav/actrav-english/telearn/global/ilo/code/caux.htm> (International Labor Office. Caux Roundtable: Principles for Business)

<http://www.naturalstep.org> (The Natural Step Homepage)

<http://www.oecd.org/dataoecd/56/36/1922428.pdf> (Organisation for Economic Cooperation and Development. OECD Guidelines for Multinational Enterprises)

<http://www.osha-bs8800-ohsas-18001-health-and-safety.com/BSI> (BSI Business Information. Health and Safety—OHSAS 18001, OSHA and BS8800)

<http://www.projectsigma.com/> (The Sigma Project. Homepage)

<http://www.quality.nist.gov/> (National Institute of Standards and Technology. Baldrige National Quality Program)

<http://www.sustainability.com/> (SustainAbility OnLine. Homepage)

<http://www.unglobalcompact.org> (United Nations Global Compact. Homepage)

Phil Wood has more than 20 years of progressive responsibility in environmental, health and safety management services, emphasizing a systematic approach to managing environmental, health and safety affairs such as regulatory compliance, permitting, environmental management systems, merger and acquisition services, and international business development. Mr. Wood has provided technical assistance on environmental management systems to EPA Headquarters, National Environmental Performance Track Program. He is the primary author and instructor for the Navy's EMS implementation, EMS Coaching, and EMS auditing training courses. He has supported strategic environmental management system development leading to sustainable installation status at many key Department of Defense installations; for example, Fort Hood, Texas and NAS JRB Willow Grove, Pennsylvania. In that role he developed 25-year sustainability plans, EMS metrics, and annual Global Reporting Initiative reports. Mr. Wood has had numerous speaking engagements, presenting papers on environmental performance evaluation, developing EMS metrics, EMS and sustainability, and EMS implementation through strategic planning. He has a published article on environmental management systems in The Military Engineer magazine.

Harry S. Kemp has more than 28 years of management experience with environmental organizations. Armed with an education in business management, he gained his first systems experience establishing and managing hazardous waste treatment, storage, and disposal facilities for the late 1970s into the early 1990s. As a facility manager, he utilized environmental management system principles to operate the facility within permitted parameters, continually improving the system performance while serving customers and maintaining the sustainability of the facility. Since 1995, Mr. Kemp has been integrally involved in numerous environmental management system development and implemetnation projects in both the private and public sectors. Mr. Kemp is certified as an EMS Auditor by the Registrar Accreditation Board and conducts third party ISO 14001 registration audits under contract to several accredited registrars. His skill in business management and systems implementation are complemented by his many years of experience in the environmental, health, and safety fields. Mr. Kemp is also a past national Treasurer of ACHMM and a Fellow of the Institute of Hazardous Materials Managers.

CHAPTER 5

Auditing

Robert L. Lipscomb, CHMM
Harry S. Kemp, EMS-A, CHMM

Introduction

It is said that, "auditing is auditing, is auditing"—
the difference between regulatory compliance
auditing and management system auditing just
being the difference between the topics. The steps
of the process to prepare, execute and report are
essentially the same. It is, however, a little more
complicated than that. Compliance auditing
assesses adherence to prescriptive performance
requirements whereas management system
auditing assesses conformance to requirements
(internal and external) as well as the effectiveness
of the system. An audit, of any kind, is fundamentally a comparison of *audit evidence* to *audit
criteria*. It is used to develop *audit findings*, which
then lead to an audit conclusion on the conformance or compliance with the audit criteria.
More simply said, an audit is the comparison of
actual conditions to expected conditions followed
by a determination about whether or not the actual
conditions are in conformance with the expected
conditions. The audit evidence consists of the
objective information that is collected through
interviews, visual reconnaissance, and documentation review. The audit criteria are the
requirements, regulations and/or internal expectations by top management of how conditions
should be. These criteria are what distinguish one
type of audit from the other.

In compliance auditing the criteria are the applicable regulations, found in the Code of Federal Regulations (CFR) (40 CFR, 29 CFR, 49 CFR, *etc.*). The criteria for a management system audit are derived from the standard upon which the system was built (such as the International Organization for Standardization [ISO] ISO 14001:1996 and ISO 9001:2002, or the British Standards Institute's OHSAS 18001:1999) plus the internal description of how the system elements are to be implemented (the upper-level system-management procedures). In addition, the management system auditor identifies improvement in the system and improvements in performance of the organization due to the system. In either type of audit, the objective evidence is compared to the audit criteria, and findings are developed. Findings are either *compliance/conformance*, or *noncompliance/nonconformance* with the audit criteria. An audit will always produce findings, even if what is being audited is in full conformance with the criteria. The auditor then uses the findings to determine whether the *auditee* does (or does not) *conform* or *comply* with the audit criteria.

This chapter outlines the general *process* for auditing and then discusses *strategies* for conducting successful environmental compliance and management system audits. A *strategy* is a way of understanding and approaching the audit process in terms of the desired outcome and is a more effective approach than simply walking through a manufacturing plant with a clipboard and checklist in one hand and a printout of the current regulations or standard in the other. The strategy is based on first understanding why the management of the organization, or the client, wants the audit to be performed. With that information, the auditor can determine what questions need to be answered or what problem areas need to be investigated so that the client receives the information needed to make informed decisions about any necessary follow-up actions.

It must also be understood that the very word *audit* conjures up many negative connotations. (If you have any doubt about this, imagine yourself in an Internal Revenue Service audit.) Sometimes employees at the facility may view the auditors and the audit process as a threat to their career or livelihood. Therefore, auditors need to remain professional, objective, courteous, and diplomatic at all times. It is important to establish good communications with the client in order to minimize misperceptions and alleviate undue anxiety.

Because certain processes, and the materials that are used in those processes, may be confidential (trade secrets), the auditor must establish the appropriate lines of communication for collecting proprietary information. This includes keeping a record of the names of the primary contacts from which information has been collected. Also, it is important to verify the level of confidentiality that the company management requires for the information, including the list of names, phone numbers, and addresses of the sources. One way to document that appropriate lines of communication have been established is to provide copies of the list (if appropriate) to company management. The auditor should also maintain a log documenting all formal contacts that are made during the audit process (*e.g.*, telephone calls, meetings, emails, correspondences, *etc.*)

The Auditing Process

Some auditors use a cookie-cutter approach to auditing, employing a set of step-by-step procedures and marking boxes on checklists. They go through the processes believing that they have completed an audit simply because they filled in all of the forms, compiled the information into a report, and presented it to management or their client. The question is, did they understand enough about the criteria and the auditing process to be able to conduct a thorough investigation? Have they added value to an organization's operations by conducting the audit? A cookie-cutter approach lacks a fundamental understanding of the audit's overall purpose and an auditor's role in carrying it out.

A successful and value-added audit is the result of a pragmatic process that begins by under-standing the audit purpose and objective(s) as well as what regulations apply to the specific facility. A clear understanding of the processes that are conducted at the facility being audited is key. Understanding the process steps in the proper sequence will often allow the auditor to identify or verify regulatory requirements as well as understand the adequacy of the management system.

It must be understood that the process is *iterative* as well. That is, information that the auditor comes across later in the discovery process may require revisiting earlier steps, either to integrate the newly discovered information based on an understanding of the audit's purpose, to conduct additional research into applicable regulations, or to follow an audit trail. The underlying principle is that auditing is a continuous process of discovery.

Guidance for environmental auditing was originally provided in EPA's "Environmental Auditing Policy Statement" of July 9, 1986 and has been built upon by the management system auditing guidance provided in ISO 19011:2002. The steps identified below are generally accepted for the organization and execution of an audit:

- Initiate the audit (appoint the lead auditor, define the audit objectives and scope, select the audit team, and establish initial contact with the auditee)

- Conduct a document review

- Prepare for the on-site audit activities (prepare the audit plan, assign work to the audit team, and prepare work documents)

- Conduct on-site audit activities (conduct the opening meeting, communicate during the audit, identify roles and responsibilities of guides and observers, collect and verify information, generate audit findings, prepare audit conclusions, and conduct the closing meeting)

- Prepare, approve and distribute the audit report

- Complete the audit

- Conduct an audit follow-up

Initiating the Audit

Appointing the Lead Auditor and Selecting the Audit Team

Whether the audit is an internal audit conducted by employees of the organization, a second party audit by a corporate office or a hired consultant, or a third-party audit by a customer or regulating agency, it is important that the lead auditor have the knowledge and the skill needed to complete the audit successfully. In addition to appropriate education and training, the lead auditor must have experience with leading an audit team and with the industry or the organization being audited. Having this experience will support achieving a successful audit; but once the objective and scope of the audit are identified, the lead auditor must also have the skill to form an audit team that possesses the appropriate skills and experience needed to complete an effective audit.

Objectives and Scope of the Audit

When one embarks on a journey, the chances of reaching the destination are greater if one understands the destination. Establish the *purpose* of the audit before proceeding with any other steps. Knowing ahead of time what the audit is trying to achieve and communicating this understanding to everyone involved may seem to run counter to the intuitive concept of objectivity, but there is a difference in determining in advance the *objective(s)* of an audit and determining the *findings* of an audit. The objectives of the audit must be clearly understood between the client and the lead auditor. This should then be placed into context by documenting the *scope* of the audit. An understanding of the extent and the boundaries of the audit, including the audit criteria, will support achieving the objective by identifying its limitations. This understanding between the client and the lead auditor will support the appropriate selection of audit team members as well as ensure a successful audit. This will also support the completion of a useful audit report.

Part of this initial process should be to identify the audience for the audit report. In order to avoid miscommunication, find out the report's primary audience. When the actual readers of the report are known (management, technical personnel, potential buyer, *etc.*) the report can support an understanding of the central purpose of the audit. For instance, attorneys and investors who are participating in a property transfer will read an audit report with a different goal in mind than a plant manager who is assessing the facility's environmental management system. If the primary audience is an investor, the purpose of the report will usually be to identify major liabilities, whereas a plant manager may be interested in ensuring that the compliance inspection logs have been properly completed.

Potential Readers of the Audit Report

- Employees directly responsible for the facility's environmental management
- Facility managers outside the environmental management group
- Other facility employees
- Other managers in the company, *but* outside the facility
- Lending institutions and potential buyers and their staff of environmental specialists, accountants, and attorneys
- Government regulators
- Business competitors
- News media
- General public

Once it is determined *who will read the report*, then *what the reader wants to know* must be defined. Usually the questions will be, "Is the facility in compliance with environmental regulations," or "Is the management system in conformance with the standard?" However, environmental audits can also lead to questions about broader issues such as those listed below.

Liability and Risk. What are the existing environmental liabilities associated with the facility? What probable future liabilities will the facility incur? What real environmental risks are being created by the facility?

Business Systems. Does the facility conform to the environmental management systems standard prepared by the International Organization for Standardization (ISO 14001)? Is the facility as good as its benchmark, and has the correct benchmark been chosen?

Internal Communications and Training. Are breakdowns in communication occurring? Is employee training adequate?

Internal Accountability, Supervision, and Staffing. Is the environmental management team properly staffed and supervised? How is accountability for facility compliance defined?

Resource. Are there proper staff and financial resources available for adequate follow-up on environmental compliance issues?

Agreement between the client and the lead auditor must be reached on what questions the report will and will not answer so that a successful audit may be conducted. Even if the report is not intended to immediately answer some of these larger questions, or address specific needs, the audit can be tailored so that these questions or needs can be addressed more easily in the future. For instance, with a compliance audit the report may not directly assess ISO 14001 conformance, but the audit may be conducted and documented so that the information gathered can be used in a future management systems audit.

Initial Contact with the Auditee

Once the purpose, scope and objectives of the audit are clearly documented and understood by the lead auditor and the client, these must be communicated to the auditee. The auditee may or may not be part of the client's organization. This initial contact will set the stage for the tone and success of the entire audit, so it must be thought out before contact is made. A common joke is that the first two lies of an audit are, "Hi, we are here to help you," and "We are glad to see you." The lead auditor must handle him or herself in a manner that creates a positive atmosphere. Little good comes from an audit conducted in an environment of suspicion and distrust.

In addition to discussing the objective(s) and scope of the audit, the lead auditor should also begin to address the needs of the audit team (private room, desks and chairs, telephone, photocopier and printer access, *etc.*), and should also initiate a document request. If it is possible to do so, a review of documentation prior to the site visit will facilitate development of the audit plan as well as save time once the audit team is on-site.

Document Review

During the site visit there will be a finite amount of time to achieve the objectives of the audit plan; there is never enough time. This makes it important to be knowledgeable about the organization, their operations and, in the case of a compliance audit, the facility's regulatory status before arriving on-site so no time is lost. Get a thorough description of the facility from facility personnel in order to prepare.

Knowledge of environmental regulations is crucial to conducting any type of environmental audit. During a management system audit the focus is on the system and its policies and procedures so a decision can be made whether or not the requirements of the standard and intent of management have been implemented. An identified compliance deficiency can be important evidence of a system problem. In a compliance audit, it is more important to know the details of the regulations because an identified compliance deficiency is the finding. For a compliance audit, it is important to conduct a preliminary review of State and local regulations in order to determine the scope of regulations that may apply to the facility. Many states regulate local environmental issues that are not addressed at the Federal level. Even when regulations duplicate one another, the State and local regulations may vary significantly in detail.

In a compliance audit, an on-site review of documents may not be avoidable since there will probably be too many records to inspect prior to the site visit in order to verify that operations are in compliance with regulatory requirements. Usually, only part of the information requested will be provided prior to the visit. However, the more information that is obtained and digested before the visit, the more effective and efficient the audit team can be during the visit. For this reason, it is important to stress to the facility contacts that a pre-visit document review will provide a time-savings benefit and will minimize the disruption of operations that usually occurs during a audit.

To determine which regulations apply, consider the industry or facility type and have an understanding of the actual industrial processes carried out by the auditee. Information is readily available in industry sector publications prepared by the Environmental Protection Agency (EPA) and other

Document Request

Compliance and Management System Auditing

- Organization chart identifying the names and titles of key personnel
- Identification of departments and operating groups with a description of the operations conducted
- General site-specific information describing number of employees, square feet of building space, location
- Site plot plan showing buildings and set-up of processes inside the buildings
- Environmental policy
- Comprehensive list of buildings
- Process descriptions and flow charts for those with the greatest environmental risk.
- Lists of raw materials, products, by-products, and waste streams
- Listing of environmental permits
- Listing of environmental plans and best management practices
- Training matrix showing environmental training required for job positions
- Most recent internal and/or external environmental audit reports

Management System Auditing

- Vision/mission statements and strategic plan
- Environmental manual with ISO 14001 policies and management level procedures that address the core elements of the EMS
- Current EMS standard operating procedures (SOP) or work instructions for environmental requirements
- Sustainability program and list of long term sustainability objectives
- Listing of environmental aspects and impacts
- Environmental performance metrics and identification of the environmental performance data that is currently collected
- Listing of set environmental objectives and targets and the environmental management programs developed to achieve environmental objectives

government sources. The regulations are usually available in electronic formats that facilitate computerized searches. The EPA and most State and local agencies offer their regulations via the Internet. These are typically searchable by regulatory citation and by keyword. Should a specific interpretation be needed the regulatory agency should be contacted for guidance.

Although telephone calls and Internet searches can accomplish some of the information collection, a great deal of information may be obtained through a personal visit. Depending on the objective of the audit, third-party companies may also be able to provide relevant regulatory information at a reasonable cost. Regardless of the sources used, it is important to confirm that the audit team has the authority to make these information requests as part of the audit. This authority, and any subsequent communication with any regulatory agency, should be documented to avoid misunderstanding.

Make the most of publicly available information if the company has authorized its use. Do not be surprised, though, if agency records are not as complete and current as anticipated or if they are not as useful as they could be. For instance, much of what is in agency files will be copies of reports submitted by the facility that is being audited. If the agency experiences a high turnover of employees, its current personnel may have gaps in their knowledge of the facility. A small to medium-sized facility may not have much interaction with the regulatory agencies. A lack of notices of violations does not necessarily confirm absolute compliance. Conversely, a facility with a past history of violations and fines may now be a model environmental citizen. For these reasons, it is important to evaluate agency records and put them into their proper context. Remember, for all their limitations, the existing agency records do define the facility's official compliance status history.

All of these tools and information sources are useful but they are no substitute for personal knowledge of the regulations and experience in applying regulatory requirements. In order to conduct an effective compliance audit, the team as a whole must be well versed in the regulations that apply to a particular process and operation. With the knowledge gained from the documents provided by the auditee, the next step is to determine which regulations apply to this facility.

Regulatory compliance is not as important for a management system audit, which will become evident when reviewing the legal documentation and other requirements that the auditee has identified. The completeness of the list can be verified during the on-site work. Information can be collected from facility personnel through a written questionnaire or a simple form listing what is needed to develop the audit plan. If a questionnaire is used, it should be designed to provide the lead auditor with an outline of the facility's environmental management system. This is the most crucial aspect of a management system audit because it verifies that top management's intent is being implemented through established policy and procedures. By understanding the procedures and requirements prior to the site visit, the audit team can concentrate on the collection of objective evidence rather than document review.

Preparing for On-Site Audit Activities

Once the lead auditor has communicated the objectives and the scope of the audit to the auditee and received all of the requested documentation, this information must be shared with the audit team. The next step is to develop an audit plan. Team involvement is required in order to ensure that a complete and workable plan is developed. The plan must be structured to identify the audit days, the tasks to be performed, and the schedule for each team member. Some tasks and interviews may be conducted as a team, but most will be assigned to individual team members based on their experience and skills.

The audit plan should indicate what departments, operations and individuals the audit team wishes to visit and interview. This will help the auditee schedule operations in a way that avoids disruption to both the audit team and to the facility operations. Safety issues may also be identified so that they may be addressed in an effective manner. For example, it is best to know that steel-toed boots and eye protection are needed for entry into the plant before arriving for the site visit.

The draft audit plan must be reviewed by the client and communicated to the auditee as soon as it is developed. Negative attitudes towards the site visit can be reduced when the auditee is involved in the development of the audit plan. This can also provide a communication opportunity that will help to avoid barriers toward achieving the audit objective(s). The auditee knows the facilty operations better that the audit team and can help to structure a smooth site visit. It is important to remember that the audit plan is just that, a plan. Plans change and the lead auditor must be prepared to modify the plan during the site visit based on changing circumstances. Of course, the lead auditor must also control the audit to ensure changing circumstances do not prevent achievement of the audit objectives.

Once agreement has been reached on the audit plan, the audit team can then decide on what working documents are needed for the site visit. The manner in which notes are taken and findings are documented is important for the completion of a useful audit report. Issues relating to creation of the report must be resolved by the team before the site visit.

Conducting On-Site Audit Activities

The site visit is only one part of the audit process; but it is the most important part. Typically, the site visit is a one-time opportunity. By the time the audit team arrives at the facility the team should be well acquainted with the (1) nature of the facility, (2) operations that are conducted there, (3) organizational structure and its requirements (regulatory and/or management system depending on the scope), (4) regulatory history, and (5) applicable environmental regulations. Good preparation prior to the site visit will minimize disruption to the facility operations and the work schedules of the auditee.

An auditor must always remember that the site visit is just that—a *visit*—and the audit team are *visitors*. Information may be requested, but the auditor has no right to demand it. An auditor walks a fine line between being diligent in obtaining all relevant information and overstepping authority in obtaining it. If an auditor believes that he or she is not receiving enough cooperation to conduct a worthwhile audit, then the lead auditor should be notified. The lead auditor is responsible for discussing the situation with the client and working it out with the auditee. Never let the issues become personal ("You are not giving me what I want"). Rather, try to emphasize mutual goals with statements such as "An acceptable audit that will benefit your organization cannot be performed without the requested information, and here are the reasons why."

Opening Meeting

At the beginning of the audit, encourage the auditee to schedule an opening meeting between the audit team and company management as well as other key personnel. Initiating the site visit by briefing management can create a positive tone to the audit that will support achievement of the audit objectives. During the opening meeting, go over the purpose, scope, and objectives of the audit in order to alleviate any misunderstanding and anxiety. Then describe the audit process and review the audit plan so that everyone has a clear understanding of the audit plan and the needs of the audit team. For a compliance audit, clearly explain that during the site visit the audit team will be collecting information to use in assessing compliance so that conclusions may be developed subsequent to the visit. For a management systems audit, inform the company that the findings and conclusion will be presented during the closing meeting, if this is agreeable to the client.

The opening meeting can make or break a site visit; so be honest and answer all questions. Be positive in all descriptions and discussions and remember that you are there to help. Take this opportunity to establish how the team will conduct itself during the site visit. Be certain that any applicable safety issues are identified and satisfactorily addressed. Confirm that guides have been arranged for each audit team member, and that everyone's roles and responsibilities are understood. Find out what flexibility the team has in making unescorted walks through the facility, taking photographs, and copying documents. Confirm that the time for the closing meeting is workable. For a management system audit, particularly when it is a third-party audit, it is important to describe the difference between a management system and compliance audits. Establish who the lead auditor will contact should any compliance issues be identified.

Communication During the Audit

Historically, compliance auditing has been an exercise in *gotcha* where the auditor was trying to find something wrong. Current management systems auditing is quite different from compliance auditing. The auditor is part of the continual improvement process and should be trying to find what the organization is doing right. Regardless of the type of audit, constant communication between the auditor and the auditee is important so that the auditee understands what the auditor is seeing and thinking. The advantage of this is that the auditee is learning from the auditor but, more importantly, good communication provides the auditee with a chance to provide objective evidence that the auditor may not have been aware of. This helps prevent spurious findings of nonconformance or noncompliance.

In some cases, the auditor is restricted from consulting with the auditee, this is particularly true for compliance audits or for management system audits that are for the purpose of registration to a standard. The lead auditor must provide the audit team with a clear understanding of any restrictions to communication with the client. In any case, the auditor must always remember to maintain objectivity, to avoid drawing premature conclusions based on preliminary information. It is good practice for the audit plan to include a 30-minute daily briefing so that issues may be pointed out, and questions may be answered. This is also an opportunity to point out any barriers or difficulties that the audit team is having in achieving the audit objectives so that corrective action may be taken.

Collecting and Verifying Information

During a compliance audit, a portion of the site visit may be dedicated to evaluating whether or not the physical facilities are in compliance with the regulations and permit requirements. Although a facility walk-through can answer some of these questions it may require taking field measurements and inspecting as-built engineering drawings to determine that: all the necessary pieces of equipment, tools, and supplies are present; all of the pieces are built and stationed in conformance with the design regulations; and the tools, equipment, and supplies meet the regulatory performance standards.

It may be beneficial to assign one auditor to spend a specific amount of time just reviewing documents and records. It is customary to spend considerable time on document and record review during the site visit portion of a compliance audit because the focus of the audit is determining whether or not the auditee is operating in compliance with laws, regulations (Federal, State, local), operating permits, and environmental media plans. Important evidence may be collected that can help support the development of findings by the other auditors who are investigating operations while trying to determine if the facility recordkeeping is meeting the regulatory and permit requirements.

General knowledge of the facility is important but knowledge of the facility's chemical processes is particularly significant during a compliance audit. During the site visit there is no time for *nice to know* information; there is a requirement for *need to know* information. It is important to identify and understand all of the ways that chemicals are used and managed in the facility—from receiving, to processing, to shipping—in order to verify that permits and permit applications are correct, reports are being completed accurately, and controls are adequate. Delineation of the individual chemical processes, including pollution control systems, can be done by documenting these processes with simplified process flow diagrams (PFDs), in consultation with production and maintenance employees. Using the PFDs, and other information provided by these same personnel, material flows can be calculated, including pollutant emissions and discharges, and the chemical storage capacities. These calculated values can be used to verify regulatory status as well as the accuracy and completeness of records.

Records kept by purchasing will usually fill in any needed areas of information. Material Safety Data Sheets (MSDSs) can often provide the component make-up of chemicals in the chemical compounds used in production in order to make usage calculations for specific chemicals.

Typically, the material balance is the most difficult part of the audit—and the most important. The audit team must use professional judgment when determining the appropriate levels of detail and accuracy necessary for the material balance in order to be reasonably confident in assessing which regulatory requirements are applicable to the facility. There will often be unfamiliar chemical compounds and the auditor may be unable to determine whether the compound is regulated without referring to some other source. It is important to bring a list of regulated compounds on the site visit and, if possible, have it available on a CD-ROM for use with a laptop computer.

Each auditor on a compliance audit should already have knowledge of relevant environmental regulations and their requirements. The auditors who are focusing on auditing operations must be in close communication with the auditor(s) responsible for document and records review so they are completely knowledgeable of the requirements. Since no one can know everything about the regulations it is useful to bring copies of the relevant sections of the regulations that apply to the facilities operations, or bring a laptop with a regulatory update CD-ROM or modem so regulatory research can be conducted on-line.

Verification of the compliance audit information comes from the facility records as well as personnel interviews. Verification in this case may come from asking the individual to show where the information is documented in the records or procedures. The auditor should be quiet and let the interviewee talk. This is essentially the same process that should be followed to verify that the auditee has addressed the evidence that is collected during a management systems audit.

The document review prior to the management system site visit should have allowed the auditor to determine whether or not the requirements of the standard have been met. The upper level management system procedures should address all of the requirements. Most evidence collected on-site during a management system audit will be acquired from personnel interviews. The answers to leading questions of key personnel provide evidence that the intent of top management, as documented in the environmental policy and the upper level management system procedures, has been implemented. The evidence collected must then be verified. For a management system audit, which investigates how something is done, there is an expectation that the explanation will match the controlled management system procedures.

If the auditor is inquiring about ISO 14000 environmental aspect assessment, operational controls, training, or environmental performance, there is an expectation that there will be records that can be used to verify that the operation is in conformance with management system requirements or in compliance with regulatory requirements. The auditor should ask for records in order to verify what is claimed by the facility personnel. Unlike a compliance audit, an extensive amount of time should not be spent reviewing facility records. Only those records that are necessary to verify the statements made during the interviews must be reviewed in order to ensure that the evidence truly is objective.

Compliance Records to Review

- Environmental permits and permit applications

- Environmental logs and inspection sheets

- Correspondence to and from regulatory agencies

- Regulatory report filings (Form R, Sara Tier Two, Annual Hazardous Waste, *etc.*)

- Facility material balances

- Emission inventories

- Material Safety Data Sheets

- Hazardous waste manifests, and other shipping papers for industrial waste and recyclable materials

---

Generating Audit Findings

Audit findings are developed through a comparison of the objective *evidence* that was collected by the audit team and the audit *criteria*. For a regulatory compliance audit, the audit criteria are the applicable regulations and permits. In regulatory compliance auditing, there is the potential for many findings because each identified noncompliance with an applicable regulation is a finding.

For a management systems audit, the audit criteria are developed from the applicable management system standard (ISO 14001:2004, ISO 9001:2000, OHSAS 18001:1999, *etc.*) plus the intent of top management, as documented in management system procedures. In management system auditing, an identified noncompliance with an applicable regulation is simply objective evidence. To develop a finding in support of conformance with or nonconformance with the management system, the auditor must determine where in the management system the opportunity for the nonconformance occurs. There may actually be multiple nonconformances of differing issues that are used as evidence to develop one management system finding. They will usually not be looked upon as multiple findings.

Because the management system auditor is part of the continual improvement process the audit should also result in the identification of opportunities for improvement. Typically, these are presented as statements about issues where there is not quite a nonconformance but where, in the judgment of the auditor, and without corrective action, the issue may become a nonconformance in the future.

Preparing Audit Conclusions

The audit plan should allow ample time for the audit team to meet and exchange information. At least one formal auditors' meeting should occur each day during the audit, but there should be numerous informal meetings between auditors. The evidence that is collected during the pursuit of one audit trail often produces evidence that may be used in pursuit of another. This frequent sharing of information will facilitate the development of audit findings and the audit conclusions.

Because the conclusions drawn from a regulatory compliance audit are dependant on complex and detailed regulations it might not be possible to develop audit findings to their full extent, much less render appropriate conclusions. In order to ensure that the audit findings are accurate it might take more research. If this is the case, it should be fully explained during the closing meeting. In any case the audit conclusions should be consistent with the purpose of the audit, the scope of the audit, and the objectives of the audit.

During a management system audit, the audit team usually develops its conclusion before the closing meeting. The conclusion of an environmental management system audit will be that the management system *is* or *is not* in conformance with the requirements of the applicable standard and that the intent of top management, and *does* or *does not* support continual improvement. There will be a distinction between minor nonconformances, which are isolated incidents, and major nonconformances, which are systemic issues.

The Closing Meeting

There should be no surprises by the time the audit team gets to the closing meeting. The lead auditor point of contact and top management should already know if the audit has revealed anything of significance. This will be true if there has been close communication between the audit team and the organization's contacts, as well as daily briefing meetings. The lead auditor's goal during the audit is to ensure that all parties are in general agreement by the time of the closing meeting.

The client and the lead auditor should agree upon the format of the closing meeting before the audit team is assembled. The closing meeting should be short and to the point. It is important to thank top management for the cooperation of the facility personnel and for their hospitality. If there were other organizations like a union, or contractors that provided support to achieving the audit objectives, then they should be thanked as well. Restating the purpose, scope and objectives of the audit will be helpful to the audience's understanding of the preliminary report. Then review the audit evidence and the status of the audit findings. Finally, identify any gaps in the collected data and present a written list of what the organization is expected to provide after the site visit. If the auditor is taking any original documents or copies of documents, then include those items on the list as well. *Avoid rendering preliminary conclusions* until all relevant information has been provided and reviewed.

The audit team should understand the requirements and the boundaries of the closing meeting, but in any case they must use care and professional judgment when articulating findings and issues. It is important that the audit team have command over the objective evidence needed to support all claims during the closing meeting.

In a compliance audit the client might compel the auditor to identify broad, red-flag issues during the closing meeting. But more time might be needed by the auditor to adequately address these issues in a full report. If the report is not provided during the closing meeting, then provide a clear schedule for completion of the report. Establish appropriate deadlines for the receipt of additional information from the auditee, the provision of a draft report, the receipt of comments on the draft report, and then the creation of the final report. During a management system audit, it is generally appropriate to present the audit report to the auditee.

The Audit Report

The audit report must be written to meet the needs of the client, while keeping in mind the various parties that will potentially have access to the report. Each potential reader will have a different purpose for reading the report and might use the information for their specific purposes. Although the audience for the audit report should have been identified early in the process, take the time to confirm this with the client before writing the report.

Preparation

The lead auditor is responsible for the preparation of the audit report. Typically, the report writing tasks are assigned to individual auditors, each individual section then being combined by the lead auditor to compile the report. Each auditor must have a clear vision of the purpose, scope and objectives of the audit, and of the report's audience. This is the only way to ensure that the readers receive the needed information in a way that is understood.

With both types of auditing, the audit team must keep in mind the sensitive nature of the audit. Audit results might have significant health, financial, legal, or political implications for some readers. Although the report must be understandable and answer the basic questions that the audit was intended to address, the fact that individuals might be held responsible for any shortcomings found in the audit must be taken into account. Be careful to avoid inflammatory

---

Report Considerations

- The audience
- Number of copies
- To whom the cover letter is addressed
- For whom the report is written
- Color copies of photographs or originals
- Executive summary, conclusions, recommendations
- Appendicies included
- Draft executive summary faxed to receipients prior to final report
- Detailed regulatory applicability analysis even for nonapplicable regulations
- Double sided copies
- Line spacing
- Font size/type

---

language (*e.g.*, "The audit revealed numerous areas where management has been negligent. . .") or to present the results of the audit in ways that might overstate or understate potential liability.

The level of detail for the audit should be established between the lead auditor and the client in the early stages of the audit process. This is very important with compliance auditing and the following questions should be answered: Will most readers be familiar with the production processes or will they need explanations? How much supporting detail should be appended to the report and how much should be included in the body? Because there will be more than one audience, the report must provide the needed level of detail for each reader. A well-constructed executive summary of one to three pages might be the best bridge between the bottom-line conclusions one reader wants and the exhaustive details another reader may need.

Although it might be difficult to avoid technical language with a regulatory compliance audit, some consideration should be given to the technical background of the audience. Environmental attorneys and environmental specialists will be familiar with the environmental technical language, while potential buyers or investors may not understand the nuances of specific word choices such as hazardous waste *storage* and *accumulation*. An audit report that cannot be understood is of little value. Differences in the technical background of the report audience, in both regulatory compliance and management system auditing, makes it more of a challenge to communicate the audit findings accurately and in terms each reader can understand.

Management system reports are typically short and to the point; providing details only when describing nonconformances and improvement opportunities. The reports are written to support continual improvement of the system by pointing out in a positive way the problems with the management system. The supporting evidence should be carefully documented for possible review by the client, if desired, but is typically not included in the report.

Approval

If possible and appropriate, submit a draft to all the stakeholders for review and comment, including the auditee (even if the auditee is not the client). This step can be invaluable in the preparation of a complete, accurate, and precise report. One benefit of a draft is that it gives the auditee a final chance to point out any mistaken impressions the audit team may have developed. There is nothing wrong with allowing the auditee to provide additional evidence at the last minute as long as it can be verified. A large amount of information can be consolidated into a concise description of the situation by responding to comments that are received as part of the draft review process. A good draft report can also help to begin the corrective action process by providing a context for the discussion of many issues unknown to the auditee and other stakeholders.

The lead auditor must be careful not to let the process of review and comment on a draft report change the accuracy and integrity of the final version. The review process should only result in a more accurate and understandable report.

Distributing the Audit Report

The auditor must confirm the client's distribution list for both the draft and final reports. If the report is being prepared under *attorney-client privilege*, this should be indicated in the header or footer on each page. The attorney should supervise the structure of the document and any exact wording required by any particular State legislated protection in order to ensure that legal privileges will be maintained.

Regardless of how limited the direct distribution by the client may be, the actual readership of the report may be much greater. The audit report is the property of the client so it is important to remember that the client's confidentiality must be maintained.

Completing the Audit and Audit Follow-Up

The audit is complete when the approved audit report has been distributed. Before this distribution happens the lead auditor must ensure that audit files are complete and properly stored. This may be one of the most important parts of the audit process. Information from prior management system audits is important because typically this information is used during periodic surveillance audits of the organization's management system. Historical information provides a frame of reference for evaluating continual improvement, which is an essential part of system auditing. If the report identifies any nonconformances, the auditee typically gains approval of corrective and preventive action from the auditor. The agreed upon corrective actions will be evaluated and verified by the auditor as being effective during the next surveillance audit. Even documented opportunities for improvement are evaluated at the subsequent surveillance audit in order to evaluate how the auditee responded to the suggestions and to assess the continual improvement process.

Compliance auditing might follow a similar process. The important issue with regulatory compliance auditing is that the issue of corrective action may have legal consequences. On May 11, 2000 the EPA amended its "Incentives for Self-

Policing: Discovery, Disclosure, Correction and Prevention of Violations," originally issued in 1996 and commonly referred to as the *Audit Policy*. There are major incentives in the policy for regulated entities to voluntarily discover, promptly disclose, and expeditiously correct noncompliances. In addition to the penalty waivers and reductions granted under EPA's enforcement response and incentive policies, EPA grants waivers and

---

Incentives for Self-Policing

- No *gravity-based penalties* for disclosing entities that meet all nine penalty mitigation conditions of the Policy, including *systematic discovery*.

- Reduction of gravity-based penalties by 75% for entities that meet all the Policy conditions except systematic discovery.

- No recommendation for criminal prosecution for entities that disclose violation of criminal law and meet all applicable conditions under the policy.

- No routine requests for audit reports from entities who disclose under the Audit Policy.

---

reductions under the Compliance Incentive Program (CIP). Under the CIP, specific segments of the regulated community (*e.g.*, telecommunications industry, industrial organic chemicals) are invited to disclose and correct violations in exchange for reduced or waived penalties. At the same time, the CIP increases the enforcement risk for those entities not taking advantage of the program. Typically, the issuance of disclosures is preceded by a meeting with the EPA in order to establish the level of detail as well as acceptable corrective action schedules. Additional information about the Audit Policy can be found at <http://www.epa.gov/compliance/incentives>.

The Audit Policy has additional incentives for self-policing. The "Small Business Compliance Policy" and the "Small Community Policy" were promulgated to further clarify the Audit Policy as it applies to these two segments of the regulated community. Companies with multiple facilities that conduct corporate-wide audits can enter into agreements

with EPA that provides flexibility in reporting and corrective action schedule requirements.

Market-based incentives for compliance are also created through the Securities and Exchange Commission (SEC). The SEC requirement that publicly traded corporations disclose environmental legal proceedings increases public access to information and helps maintain a level playing field for environmentally responsible corporate citizens. Additional information can be found in EPA's "Notice of SEC Registrants' Duty to Disclose Environmental Legal Proceedings" and guidance to enforcement staff on distribution of the notice.

Passage of "The Public Company Accounting Reform and Investor Protection Act of 2002" (better known as Sarbanes-Oxley Act) was passed in response to a series of scandals regarding misleading or even fraudulent financial statements from publicly traded corporations. Under Sarbanes-Oxley, corporate officers who willfully

---

Penalty Mitigation Conditions

- Systematic discovery of the violation through an environmental audit or a compliance management system

- Voluntary discovery, sampling or auditing

- Prompt disclosure in writing within 21 days

- Independent discovery and disclosure

- Correction and remediation within 60 days

- Prevent recurrence of the violation

- Repeat violations are ineligible

- Violations that result in serious actual harm, those that may have presented an imminent and substantial endangerment, and those that violate the specific terms of an administrative or judicial order or consent agreement are ineligible

- Cooperation is required

---

make false financial statements may receive a fine of up to $5 million, or a prison sentence of up to 20 years, or both. Sarbanes-Oxley extends to the *systems* and *subsystem* used to generate financial statements. Environmental audits, especially those that generate valuations of environmental liabilities, meet the definition of *subsystems* under Sarbanes-Oxley. The "Standard Guide for Estimating Monetary Costs and Liabilities for Environmental Matters" (ASTM E2137–01), published by the American Society for Testing and Materials can be used for calculating valuation.

Individual State audit policies are evolving concurrently and are layered atop the EPA policies. A discussion of the legal issues surrounding the possible uses of the audit report is beyond the scope of this chapter. It is enough to say that ultimately an audit report may be used as evidence in a civil or criminal action. The plaintiff in such legal actions may be the client, a lender, a new owner, the state, the Federal government, a neighbor to the facility, or an environmental activist group. Therefore, it is important to work closely with the client and the client's attorney to determine how to appropriately manage the file. It must also be made clear to the auditee by the client that if they are privy to the findings and conclusions of the audit, and do not pursue corrective action, this can be interpreted by the court as *willful* violation, potentially subjecting the management of the organization to criminal prosecution.

Summary

An audit is a structured process for the collection of information, analysis of that information in comparison to the audit criteria, and the development and reporting of conclusions. It should not be confused with a site visit and review, which is informal and brief by nature. An effective audit is the result of a skilled auditor thoroughly preparing for and implementing each stage of the process as described in this paper. To conduct a successful regulatory compliance audit, or a management system audit, the audit team must know and understand the requirements (the regulations for compliance auditing; the standard for management system auditing), the facility, and the report audience.

The goal of compliance auditing is just that: pointing out where the organization is not in compliance with a regulation. The goal of management system auditing is improvement. Consideration of the organization's regulatory compliance status is an important part of a management system audit, but noncompliance with a regulation is used only as evidence to determine where the system has failed. Even though certain types of audits such as those for real estate or business purchase transactions may simply need a professional judgment (*in compliance* or *out of compliance*), the true value of an audit comes from presenting the positives and then making it clear where the organization needs to focus its attention in order to improve. Improvement will come from the identification of nonconformances with requirements and the organization's own internal management procedures. Management systems auditing can benefit compliance auditing, making environmental auditing a value-added process. This is because it is assumed that if the management system is improving, then the compliance position of the organization will also be improving.

Bibliography

"Environmental Audit Policy Statement." *Federal Register* 51 (9 July 1986): 25004.

"Incentives for Self-Policing: Discovery, Disclosure, Correction and Prevention of Violations." *Federal Register* 60 FR (22 December 1995): 66705–66712.

"Incentives for Self-Policing: Discovery, Disclosure, Correction and Prevention of Violations." Revised Final Policy. *Federal Register* 65 (11 April 2000): 19617–19627.

International Organization for Standardization. *Guidelines for Quality and/or Environmental Management Systems Auditing.* ISO 19001:2002. Geneva, Switzerland: ISO, 2002.

"Small Business Compliance Policy." *Federal Register* 65 (11 April 2000): 19629–19634.

Robert L. Lipscomb *is the Brownfield Program Manager with Barge, Waggoner, Sumner and Cannon, Inc., in Nashville, Tennessee. Mr. Lipscomb has over 20 years of experience in the hazardous materials management field. His areas of expertise include Brownfield management, compliance auditing, due diligence investigation, environmental accounting, management of commercial and industrial hazardous materials, and investigation and cleanup of contaminated property.*

Harry S. Kemp *currently works for Tetra Tech EM Inc. as an EMS Specialist and Senior Project Manager. His skills in business management and systems implementation are complemented by his 26 years of experience in the environmental and health and safety fields. Mr. Kemp gained his first systems experience utilizing EMS principles to operate hazardous waste treatment, storage and disposal facilities (TSDF) within permitted parameters and the requirements of top management. This included auditing regulatory compliance as well as conformance to the EMS internal requirements. Since 1995, Mr. Kemp has been integrally involved in numerous EMS implementation projects for the private and public sectors; most notable is his work for the U.S. Navy on EMS implementation at the seven major installations in the Mediterranean and England. Additionally he is a certified ISO 14001 auditor and conducts third-party registration audits under contract to several accredited registrars.*

CHAPTER 6

Environmental Health and Safety Risk Analysis

Tony Uliano, Jr., MS, CIH, CHMM

Environmental Health and Safety Risk Analysis

Historical Risk Assessment

Risk analysis, as defined by the Society for Risk Analysis, is the detailed examination including risk assessment, risk evaluation, and risk management alternatives performed to understand the nature of unwanted, negative consequences to human life, health, property, or the environment; an analytical process of quantification of the probabilities and expected consequences for identified risks.

Risk analysis techniques have a wide variety of applications. Included among these are evaluations of Superfund sites, contaminated ecological systems, and property transfers involving potentially contaminated sites, currently called **brownfields.**

Risk analysis also helps to predict the risk for accidents at industrial facilities, to assess the hazards of newly introduced chemicals or pharmaceutical products, and even to evaluate such diverse risks as following certain dietary patterns, transportation safety, and smoking.

This chapter addresses the risks posed by hazardous substances to workers, the public and the environment. The most applicable assessments are in the area of occupational and environmental exposures.

Risk assessment, as it is understood today, is a relatively new field (20 years), though its origin dates back to unrefined estimations of toxicological hazards that were performed centuries ago. The immediate precursor of modern risk assessment originated in the United States Food and Drug Administration's *Margins of Safety* for food additives. The science of risk assessment evolved from qualitative opinion to more precise quantitative techniques of measurement and estimation of risk. This evolution paralleled the technological advancements that enabled us to detect toxins at much lower limits, and to gain a better understanding of the risks of exposure to hazards at levels much lower than were previously considered acceptable.

A number of epidemiological studies were performed in the 1950s and 1960s that revealed significantly high risks of cancer in workers who were exposed to substances such as asbestos, benzene, benzidine, 2-napthylamine, and radon gas derived from uranium mines.

In 1980, the Supreme Court ruled that regulatory decisions should contain quantitative risk analysis. This analysis is usually reserved for occupational carcinogens, as evidenced by the Occupational Safety and Health Administration's (OSHA's) more recent (since 1980s) "expanded health standards for formaldehyde, ethylene oxide, and others."

Two fundamental approaches to risk assessment are derived from toxicological/epidemiological methodologies and more recent integrated environmental assessment protocols.

Environmental assessments originated from the Environmental Protection Agency's (EPA) Comprehensive Environmental Response, Compensation, and Liability Act (CERCLA/Superfund) rules relating to releases of hazardous substances into the environment. Initial assessments were performed on petrochemical release sites, such as leaking underground storage tanks and oil spills.

EPA developed a hazard ranking system to determine whether a site contaminated with any hazardous substance would gain National Priority Listing (NPL Site) and be eligible for cleanup funds.

Such assessments are employed in almost any situation where a potential hazard to the environment or public may exist. Violations of any of the environmental regulations might be applicable, such as the illegal dumping or storage of hazardous chemicals under the Resource Conservation and Recovery Act (RCRA). These regulations are intended to facilitate the cleanup of uncontrolled waste sites and to prohibit the indiscriminate dumping of untreated chemicals into landfills in order to protect the environment and the public. The Agency for Toxic Substances and Disease Registry was charged under CERCLA to perform health assessments of National Priorities List (NPL) Superfund sites.

Basic Elements of Risk Assessments

In 1983, the National Research Council developed a four-part risk assessment strategy that included:

- Hazard identification

- Dose-response assessment (also known as hazard assessment)

- Exposure assessment

- Risk characterization or risk analysis

Some form of this strategy is used today in most environmental risk analyses. Risk analysis is fraught with numerous uncertainties. It is as much an art as it is science, and the uncertainties make risk analysis problematic. If we are to protect the public and the environment, our risk analysis methodologies must be scientifically defensible and offer a level of protection that takes into account the degree of uncertainty in each situation.

Hazard Identification

Hazard identification is the first step in risk assessment. The goal is to determine the hazardous chemical's relative toxicity, concentration, extent of contamination, and toxicological endpoint(s) of concern.

Many studies have been published on the toxicity of chemical substances. The data that are most useful for analyzing public health risks are those that most closely approximate the risks posed to humans. Unfortunately, the human epidemiological studies that provide this information are limited and have inherent weaknesses. Improved confidence is achieved when the following guidelines are met:

- *Biological plausibility*—The investigated agent is known to cause the health effect.

- *Consistency*—Two or more studies yield comparable findings of excess risk, preferably using different test models.

- *Concordance*—The same end point (*e.g.*, type of tumor) arises in more than one species, strain, or sex, and concordance in the type of pathological change is found in both animals and humans.

Some of the techniques used to determine the toxicity of the numerous chemical compounds in use today are listed below.

Epidemiological Studies. Epidemiological studies are studies of the distribution and determinants of diseases and injuries in the human population. There are three basic types of epidemiological studies: cohort, case control, and cross-sectional or prevalence studies.

A cohort, or incidence study, examines the incidence of disorders that accrue following an exposure, and generally is prospective in nature. Exposed and unexposed groups or cohorts are being compared.

A case control study starts with the presence of a disease and then attempts to trace it back to a suspected exposure (retrospective in nature). It compares the cases with disease to controls without disease.

A cross-sectional study simply measures the prevalence of disease in a group of individuals. It offers no information about causation, but may offer insights into a potential exposure. Cross-sectional studies can point out human data that involves accidental exposures resulting in disease. Many occupational disease-agent correlations were discovered in this way.

There are some drawbacks to epidemiological studies, however. The most notable problems include:

- Selecting an acceptable control group, one that is as similar to the study group as possible, with the exception of the exposure or disease being evaluated

- Numerous confounding factors, such as other exposures; gender, racial, and health differences; fluctuations in dose among subjects, and inconsistent sampling data

- Difficulty in obtaining information from a large population in the study, difficulty in obtaining old records, and extensive time to follow up disease occurrence in prospective studies

In Vivo **Bioassays.** *In vivo* bioassays are studies performed on live animals, usually rodents, though other animal classes have been utilized. These assays study the effects (*e.g.*, tumor formation, or other pathological changes) of high dose and exposure to chemical or other agents on the test animals. The doses must be sufficiently high to observe effects in a reasonable amount of time for the limited animal populations studied. Responses at the lower end of the dose-response curve must be interpolated, since these animals are dosed at the maximum tolerated dose (MTD). *In vivo* assays are among the most common research methods, and provide most of the current information on human toxicity potential. These studies provide data such as lethal dose (LD_{50}), lethal concentration (LC_{50}), and other exposure values that may be extrapolated to provide human exposure levels. However, extrapolation to human toxicity continues to be problematic and controversial.

In Vitro **Methods.** *In vitro* methods refer to laboratory scale studies performed in test tubes. These tests are performed on tissue or cells in order to observe changes in the structure or growth of cells.

One widely used test (the Ames test) looks for mutagenicity, or alterations, in the deoxyribonucleic acid (DNA) in Salmonella bacteria. This is a test that is used to screen chemicals that might pose a mutagenic risk. Studies on the teratogenic effect of various agents are performed on animal embryos. *In vitro* testing is yet another level removed from direct human studies, and extrapolation has intrinsic uncertainties, such as the discrepancies between cellular and human metabolic interactions. Other *in vitro* approaches are listed below.

Experimental animal-human comparisons examine existing human data and compare exposure levels and effects to studies performed on animals. This experimental methodology attempts to establish correlations between the effects observed in animals and those observed in humans.

Molecular and experimental embryology studies are performed in order to detect abnormal changes at the molecular and embryonic levels. Studies are currently being performed on endocrine disrupters, classes of chemical pollutants that adversely affect reproduction.

Biological effects of complex chemical or other mixtures examine the synergistic, additive, and antagonistic effects of exposure to a number of chemicals. This includes the correlation between chemical and physical agents, (*i.e.*, noise, temperature, humidity, vibration and stress), and between chemical and environmental interactions, (circadian rhythms, seasonal changes), *etc.*

Structure/activity relationships have long been studied in the field of toxicology, and involve the assessment of the toxicity of a chemical based upon its molecular structure. Physio-chemical properties such as molecular and atomic structure, molecular weight, and chemical class can be a predictor of toxicity. Adding chemical groups or altering the placement of some groups is known to either increase or decrease toxicity. The chemical structure provides hints about its ability to be introduced via critical human metabolic pathways.

Finally, the risk assessments for carcinogens and noncarcinogens follow from different assumptions. For noncarcinogens, there are threshold levels below which adverse effects are not likely to occur. Juxtaposed to this is the fact that little is known as to the threshold levels of the carcinogens that are capable of inducing tumors. The more conservative estimate states that there is no "safe" level of exposure for a carcinogen. The International Agency for Research on Cancer (IARC) publishes assessments on the carcinogenicity of over 600 chemicals. IARC has catalogued these agents by virtue of their likelihood to promote cancer in animals and/or humans. In the 1986 "Guidelines for Carcinogen Risk Assessment," a similar rating system was employed. The following table shows the rating numbers and interpretations.

Table 1. Weight-of-Evidence Classification for Carcinogens

Human Evidence	Animal Evidence				
	Sufficient	Limited	Inadequate	No Data	No Evidence
Sufficient	A	A	A	A	A
Limited	B1	B1	B1	B1	B1
Inadequate	B2	C	D	D	D
No Data	B2	C	D	D	E
No Evidence	B2	C	D	D	E

(51 FR 33992)

This chart is not the only scheme for the classification of carcinogens. Industrial Hygienists may be more familiar with the American Conference of Governmental Industrial Hygienists' classification:

A-1 Confirmed human carcinogen

A-2 Suspected human carcinogen

A-3 Confirmed animal carcinogen

A-4 Suspect animal carcinogen, no sufficient evidence for human carcinogenicity

A-5 Not a human carcinogen

Hazard Assessment

A *hazard or toxicity assessment* is also referred to as a *dose-response assessment* because it seeks to determine whether dose-response information is available for the chemical of interest. While the hazard identification provides a basis for establishing evidence of an agent's effects, a hazard assessment relies on toxicological and epidemiological data to ascertain specific threshold exposure levels. It examines and attempts to quantify the severity of a potential hazard. This assessment requires information to establish risks for both carcinogens and noncarcinogenic agents.

Max tolerated dose

The documentation of risk differs between carcinogens and noncarcinogens, due to the different mechanisms that are understood to operate in carcinogenesis. In both cases, the availability of dose-response data is crucial.

For chemical carcinogens, slope factors define the potency of various agents, since we presume that no threshold dose has been established for carcinogens, and most animal studies rely on doses at the MTD levels. The linear portion of the low dose section of the dose-response curve is interpolated using a 95% confidence interval. This is referred to as the *slope factor*. Slope factors for various carcinogens are listed in EPA's Integrated Risk Information System (IRIS) database.

Varying models have been employed which impart a range of slope factors dependent upon the interpretation of the carcinogenesis process, from a conservative model (one molecule of exposure or less) to EPA's multistage and other models. (Carcinogenesis involves promotion, time factors, *etc*.)

Dose-response curves exist for many noncarcinogenic substances. These curves are estimated on the basis of human and animal studies, mostly from the latter. Dose-response may also be observed empirically through clinical evaluations of individuals who were accidentally exposed to known concentrations of chemicals.

Dose-response curves are only as valid as the organism or population studied. A dose-response curve for one chemical may vary amongst a population of a single species. This is due to individual variations in responses and con-

founding factors; for example, the response of individuals to low levels of chemical agents, such as sensitizers, or individuals' varying susceptibilities to other non-allergic response provoking chemicals, such as diesel exhaust or tobacco smoke. Little information is available for very low doses because any response is subclinical; or else the chemical may have no effect due to a lack of absorption or impedance by metabolic or other processes.

The intent of the dose-response curve is to establish *safe* or acceptable dose levels. These dose levels vary, depending on the hazardous chemical and its dose (concentration), the route of entry, duration of exposure, and other time factors.

There are a number of terms describing dose levels. The *no observed adverse effect level* (NOAEL) represents the highest dose at which no adverse effects have been detected.

Due to many uncertainties in the study methods, this dose level should contain built-in safety factors. Safety factors may range from 10–2000, depending upon the available information.

The safe dose level may be interpolated to calculate a *lifetime acceptable daily intake* (ADI), taking into account safety and other modifying factors. Interestingly, ADI levels initially were employed for food additives.

Another term, *reference dose* (RfD), takes the NOAEL and attaches uncertainty and modifying factors, given the differences in animal and human responses and the varying sensitivities of humans. If human data were available, adjustment factors might not be necessary:

$$RfD = NOAEL/(UF)(MF) \qquad (1)$$

Where:

RfD	=	the reference dose in mg agent/kg body weight-day
NOAEL	=	the no observed adverse effect level in mg agent/kg body weight-day
UF	=	the uncertainty factor
MF	=	the modifying factor

The dose is expressed in milligrams of agent/ kilogram of body weight per day. RfDs vary according to the route of entry. An exposure dose, or *chronic daily intake* (CDI), may be calculated as follows:

$$CDI = \frac{(C_m)(I_m)(EF)(ED)}{(BW)(AT)} \qquad (2)$$

Where:

C_m = concentration of agent in affected media (*e.g.*, mg/l)

I_m = intake of affected media (*e.g.*, l/day)

EF = exposure frequency (days/yr)

ED = exposure duration (yr)

BW = body weight (average adult is 70 kg)

AT = average exposure time (days)

The human acceptable dose would equal the exposure dose divided by the product of the safety factors.

A ***virtually safe dose*** (VSD) is that dose in which the risk is very low (10^{-6} or one excess tumor, *etc.*, per one million persons). This is the value accepted as the *safe dose* for humans by regulatory policy.

Exposure Assessment

Once overlooked as a component of risk assessment, exposure assessment is now a critical element of an integrated risk evaluation. The exposure assessment examines all avenues of exposure and may utilize mathematical models and projections based upon different scenarios. Some exposures may be confined to the occupational setting and thus can be monitored fairly easily. In the case of environmental risk assessments, exposure may spread through various media and pathways, such as air, soil, water, or food, though the actual exposure will be through inhalation, ingestion, dermal contact, and/or absorption or injection (however rare). The important point is that the agent must be available to the receptor, and the actual intake or dose should be quantifiable or estimated using all available data.

Exposure assessments look at environmental transport mechanisms, such as ground water-surface water movement, geologic and soil conditions, sources of chemical leakage and leachate, fugitive dust emissions, off-gassing, and the presence of contamination in the daily intake of food and water products. These mechanisms affect the route of exposure being analyzed. The assessments may also include a detailed analysis of the human or ecological species lifestyle or life cycles.

Analyzing the average ingestion of toxins includes surveying consumptive products, rates, soil consumption (usually for children), body weight, age and sex. Inhalation studies can verify the number of hours at a site where inhalation exposure occurs (duration) as well as age, activity, and sex-adjusted ventilation rates.

The Lawrence Berkeley National Laboratory (LBNL) is conducting research to improve the scientific basis of risk assessment. As an example, they are conducting integrated research of total human exposure to environmental pollutants in the indoor environment where individuals spend, on an average, ninety percent of their daily lives. LBNL researchers are focusing on transport and transformation (photochemical and combustion) of pollutants, complex chemical mixtures and population distributions relative to various pollutant exposures. Additionally the staff at LBNL is looking at Physiologically-Based Pharmacokinetic (PBPK) Models to ascertain the distributions of persistent environmental toxins and their metabolites within the body.

Risk Characterization (Risk Analysis)

Risk analysis, the composite of the hazard assessment and exposure assessment, plus an uncertainty analysis forms the core of risk assessment. ***Risk analysis*** is a quantitative appraisal of the levels of exposure that may pose risks because they exceed the ambient levels found in an unexposed population. In the case of noncarcinogens, a ***hazard quotient*** is used. The hazard quotient (HQ) may be expressed as:

$$HQ = \frac{CDI}{MAD} \quad or \quad \frac{CDI}{RfD} \qquad (3)$$

Where:

CDI   =   chronic daily intake in mg/kg-day

MAD   =   maximum allowable daily intake in mg/kg-day

RfD   =   reference dose in mg/kg-day

Both the numerator and the denominator are expressed in mg/kg-day; therefore the HQ is dimensionless.

For carcinogens, risk is measured by extrapolating from a low dose to the level in which the risk (excess mortality, tumor growth, *etc.*) does not exceed 10^{-6}. In a formula, it is expressed as:

Risk = CDI x SF   (4)

Where:

CDI   =   chronic daily intake in mg/kg-day

SF   =   a slope factor in $(\text{mg/kg-day})^{-1}$

One of the numerous models of carcinogenesis is the classical linear model, which assumes no threshold for carcinogenesis. This mechanistic approach includes the one-hit model, in which a critical cell *hit* by a carcinogen will induce a tumor, and the multi-hit model, which assumes that several *hits* (which occur randomly and are time-dependent) are required to induce a tumor.

Other models include the more widely accepted linear multi-stage model (which assumes that cancer involves both initiation and promotion processes), the Armitage-Doll Multi-stage model, the Moolgavker version of the Knudsen model, the dose distribution model, and the probability model (which is also called the probit, logit, or Weibull model). The choice of model should be based upon sound risk management practices, although it may be influenced by economic or political factors.

Environmental Risk Assessments

The normal risk analysis occurs at complex sites where contamination may spread outside the boundaries of a single location. Environmental contamination may pose a hazard to both public health and ecological systems. One of the objectives of an environmental assessment is to provide a technically defensible strategy for decision making in a variety of remediation scenarios. This remediation is referred to as ***risk-based corrective action*** (RBCA).

The assessments have been structured by a number of regulatory and technical agencies and associations (see the American Society for Testing and Materials [ASTM], "Standard Guide for RBCA Applied at Petroleum Sites," and EPA's "Guidelines for Carcinogenic Risk Assessments"). They all have tiered levels of investigational steps from basic site assessment to the more specific and quantitative assessments outlined previously. The methods often utilize standard sampling techniques, identification of the chemicals of interest (COIs), determination of receptor (animal and human) populations, critical habitat evaluation, exposure and transport pathways, risk estimates, and mathematical and computer modeling. Some methods employ a decision point system based upon all the variables, and most have built-in default assumptions for use when precise data is not available. These defaults might be assumptions for average daily intake (via inhalation, ingestion, or absorption) of contaminants found in water, soil, dust, gases, or vapors for a specific group of individuals.

Decisions about cleanup may be made after only one tier level of sampling; however, the assessed risk may be too conservative. Proceeding to the next tier provides more data for evaluating the true risk. In fact, it is often necessary to complete all of the tier levels of evaluation. The additional data may validate initial assumptions about the level of risk. An example flowchart of the environmental risk assesment process is found in Figure 1.

Integrated Risk Assessments

Integrated risk assessments are employed in order to formulate policies and manage   resources in the risk assessment process. This is a multi-disciplinary process encompassing a broad spectrum of considerations ranging from scientific, social, economic, health and environmental data models. Recent research in this area is exemplified by the work of the Oak Ridge National Laboratory (ORNL). Among their extensive work the following projects are being undertaken:

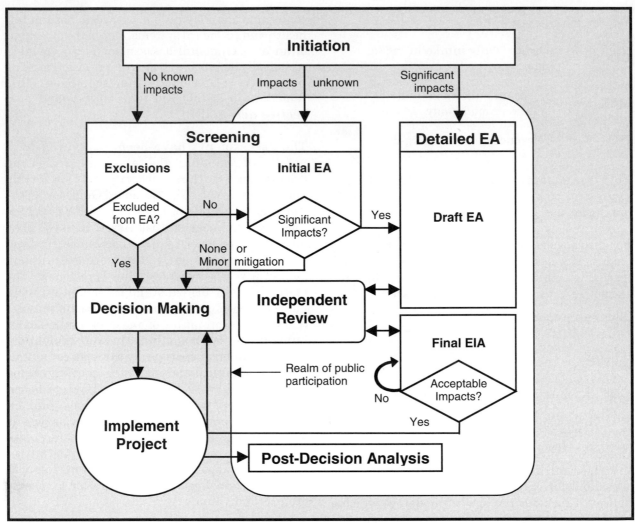

Source: L.L. Sigal, *Sourcebook for the Environmental Assessment Process.* EPA 300-B-93-007. USEPA, 1993.

Figure 1. Environmental Risk Assessment Flowchart

- A regional scale model for atmospheric and food web transport of iodine–131 integrated with Monte Carlo simulations to estimate of risk for higher radiological doses to human infants

- A risk analysis for the determination of the health and ecological risk posed by the global transport mercury, polychlorinated biphenyls (PCBs), dichlorodiphenyltrichloroethane (DDT), cesium–137 and pesticides, as well as radioactive fallout from Chernobyl.

- Evaluation of alternate concentration limits for successful cleanup of contaminated groundwater under the Resource Conservation and Recovery Act (RCRA)

- The Protective Action Dose Reduction Estimator (PADRE) model used to predict exposure to accidental releases of chemical weapons

agents over time allowing the user to predict exposure values under varying conditions and thereby providing a means to effectively manage risk

- Charting of biological indicators to evaluate the effects of environmental stressors, such as contaminants on aquatic ecosystem health. This may be used to evaluate the effectiveness of remedial actions on these ecosystems as well as to monitor industry compliance

- A scoring system to screen out chemicals of concern from the thousands of unregulated, but potentially carcinogenic compounds. This method called RASH (Rapid Screening of Hazard) is a model based on toxicity-induced compensatory cell proliferation as a surrogate for carcinogenic promotion. This method has been shown more accurate than other bio-assays

Risk Management and Communication

Risk management decisions may be as simple as *no action*, or the decision tree may require further investigation at the next tier level. The more complex the site, and the greater the difficulty in assigning risk, the more sophisticated the risk analysis. Often, *Monte Carlo* analyses are employed.

Monte Carlo analyses are valuable for evaluating the risk analyses for site conditions that involve many complex variables and a significant degree of uncertainty. This differs from the deterministic risk assessments that use numerical estimates of each variable in calculations. In a Monte Carlo analysis, the probability curves for various uncertainty parameters are inserted into the calculations of risk.

Probability Bounds Analysis is a more recent addition to the repertoire of variability analysis and adds to the tool by providing the bounds, or an envelope for a distribution analysis.

RBCA-type risk assessments attempt to minimize heroic efforts at cleanup and to manage sites according to the risks they represent.

Risk management decisions take into account assumptions about future site use, whether or not the area is a critical habitat for animal species, and many other factors. These factors are weighed in order to establish the minimum level of remediation that is required to satisfy both public and environmental health concerns while reducing the cost of cleanup.

Rather than relying on market forces to provide controls, hierarchal, top down regulatory rules, or sectarian, emotional bases for decision making; the United States National Academy of Sciences suggests that the appropriate response to managing risk is the use of *inference guidelines* which involve comprehensive, but flexible recommendations that adapt to emerging technology.

Risk communication may be the most difficult step in this process. Risk communication requires both an understanding of the risks from the public's perspective and the ability to communicate difficult concepts in terms the general public can understand. The risk of not taking the concerns of the potentially exposed public seriously may be far greater than the risk of inaction.

Summary

There are many limitations to risk assessment, such as the various interpretations of acceptable models for carcinogenesis, and levels of uncertainty. Uncertainty can be demonstrated in the animal-to-human extrapolations of risk, the lack of data on multiagent exposure, and collective exposures that do not translate easily to individual risks. Thus, the definition of an *acceptable risk* is still controversial, and there will always be conflict between the forces of economics and the assurance of public and environmental health and safety for the most sensitive ecological species or individuals.

Risk analysis must continue to use sound science in order to understand the integral mechanisms of human toxicology, how toxic chemicals impact ecosystem health, and how both areas are interconnected.

Bibliography

Agency for Toxic Substance Disease Registry, Division of Toxicology. *Health Assessment Guidelines.* Atlanta, GA: ATSDR, 1992.

AIHA Roundtable. *The Changing Face of Risk Assessment: Revolution or Evolution?* Washington, DC: AIHCE, 1996.

American Society for Testing and Materials, "Standard Guide for Risk Based Corrective Action (RBCA) Applied at Petroleum Sites." ASTM Standard E–1739–95. West Conshohocken, PA: ASTM, 2002.

Doull, John. *Principles of Risk Assessment: Overview of the Risk Assessment Process.* Conference on Chemical Risk Assessment: Science, Policy and Practice. Cincinnati, OH: ACGIH, 1992.

Gochfeld, Michael. "Environmental Risk Assessment." In *Public Health and Preventive Medicine*. East Norwalk, CT: Appleton-Century-Crofts, 1992.

Gold, Lois, Neela Manley, and Bruce Ames. *Quantitative and Qualitative Extrapolation of Carcinogens Between Species*. Conference on Chemical Risk in the DOD: Science, Policy and Practice. Cincinnati, OH: ACGIH, 1992.

"Guidelines for Carcinogen Risk Assessment." *Federal Register* 51 (24 September 1986): 33992.

Hattis, Dale and John Froines. *Uncertainties in Risk Assessment*. Conference on Chemical Risk Assessment in the DOD: Science, Policy and Practice. Cincinnati, OH: ACGIH, 1992.

Herrick, Robert. *Exposure Assessment in Risk Assessment*. Conference on Chemical Risk Assessment in the DOD: Science, Policy and Practice. Cincinnati, OH: ACGIH, 1992.

Johnson, Barry. *Principles of Chemical Risk Assessment*. Conference on Chemical Risk Assessment in the DOD: Science, Policy and Practice. Cincinnati, OH: ACGIH, 1992.

Kodell, Ralph. *Risk Assessment for Non-Carcinogenic Chemical Effects*. Conference on Chemical Risk Assessment in the DOD: Science, Policy and Practice. Cincinnati, OH: ACGIH, 1992.

Krisnan, Kanaan, Rory Conolly, and Melvin Andersen. *Biologically Based Models in Risk Assessment*. Conference on Chemical Risk Assessment in the DOD: Science, Policy and Practice. Cincinnati, OH: ACGIH, 1992.

Lu, Frank. "Toxicolological Evaluation: Assessment of Safety/Risk." In *Basic Toxicology*. Washington, DC: Taylor and Francis, 1996.

Murdock, Duncan, Daniel Krewski, and John Wargo. *Cancer Risk Assessment with Intermittent Exposure*. Conference on Chemical Risk Assessment in the DOD: Science, Policy and Practice. Cincinnati, OH: ACGIH, 1992.

Nelson, B. K. "Exposure Interactions in Occupational/Environmental Toxicology." *Appl. Occup. and Envir. Hyg.*, 12(5): 356-361, 1997.

Nelson, Deborah Imel. "Risk Assessment in the Workplace." In *The Occupational Environment– Its Evaluation and Control*. Fairfax, VA: AIHA, 1997.

Nicholson, William. "Quantitative Risk Assessment for Carcinogens." In *Environmental and Occupational Medicine*. William Rom, Ed. Boston, MA: Little and Brown, 1992.

Oak Ridge National Laboratory. *Integrated Assessment Briefs*. ORNL/M4227. Oak Ridge, TN: USDOE, 1995.

Oregon Department of Environmental Quality. *Guidance for Ecological Risk Assessments*. Portland, OR: DEQ, 1997.

Putzrath, Resha. *Use of Risk Assessment in Evaluating Remediation of PCBs*. Conference on Chemical Risk Assessment in the DOD: Science, Policy and Practice. Cincinnati, OH: ACGIH, 1992.

Staynor, Leslie. *Methodological Studies for Quantitative Risk Assessments*. Conference on Chemical Risk Assessment in the DOD: Science, Policy and Practice. Cincinnati, OH: ACGIH, 1992.

Tucker, Troy W. and Scott Ferson. *Probability Bounds Anaylsis in Environmental Risk Assessments*. Setauket, NY: Applied Biomathematics, 2003.

Werner, Michael. *Site Risk Assessment: A Primer*. West Chester, PA: Roy F. Weston, Inc., 1996.

Yost, Lisa. *Risk Assessment Strategies*. Responsible Environmental Management Conference. Portland, OR, 1997.

Tony Uliano, Jr. is currently the Manager of Environmental Health and Safety at Oregon Health & Science University in Portland, Oregon. He has been involved in hazardous materials management from both occupational and environmental perspectives for over 27 years. His diverse experiences were gained during his career as an Industrial Hygienist. Mr. Uliano was an OSHA compliance officer for 10 years and worked at Department of Veterans Affairs medical/research facilities for over 12 years. His major areas of specialty include hazardous waste management, emergency response, indoor environmental air quality, and field investigations; as well as environmental health and safety compliance. In addition to his day job, he performs consulting work and teaches a variety of hazardous materials and environmental science–related courses at several colleges and universities in the Portland area. He is a member of numerous professional societies and is listed in the Marquis Who's Who in Science and Industry. Acknowledgements go to his wife Andrea for her continuous encouragement and support, and to his daughters Megan and Caitlin for being such an inspiration in his life. Thanks also goes to his fellow running friends who continue to encourage him to pursue his enjoyment of the trails and of good health and cheer.

CHAPTER 7

Project Management

Laureen McMurray Boyle, MS, CHMM

From Training to Shutdowns

Every environmental, health and safety (EHS) professional uses some aspect of project management on a regular basis. Examples of EHS projects that require some level of project management include:

- Training employees or clients
- Equipment installation or removal
- Pollution prevention and waste minimization
- Cleaning operations
- Investigation and remediation
- Emergency response plan development

The success of these EHS projects is determined by increases in productivity, cost, time spent in implementation and maintenance, and improved compliance performance. For a project to meet these expectations, one must plan carefully. Therefore, the key to success is an effective project plan.

Project Plan

A *project plan* is the tactical approach to the endeavor, which helps a manager to both define and meet goals. This tactical approach has several elements designed to achieve success with any project. These elements are:

- Setting the goals

- Identifying the specifications to be considered

- Establishing the objectives or milestones

- Creating the project structure

- Setting the schedule

- Selecting the resources

- Instituting the methods of control and communication

- Determining the appropriate metrics to measure success

These elements are interdependent and equally important for accomplishing the project's desired outcome. This chapter describes each project management element and its value.

Goals

The most important step in project management is often overlooked—setting goals. Goals are assumed to be intuitively obvious, but project stakeholders may have the same or divergent goals. Therefore, to ensure stakeholders understand and agree upon the goals of a project, the setting of goals should be the first step in the project management process.

For example, corporate managers may decide that each of their facilities needs to implement a waste minimization program. But what is the goal of that waste minimization program? Is the goal simply to minimize the volume of solid waste hauled off-site from the facility? Is the goal to minimize the volume of all waste streams generated by the facility, its customers and vendors? Or is the goal to minimize both the volume and toxicity of the wastes generated by the plant? These are very different goals and will require varying degrees of effort to achieve.

Specifically, a *project goal* should describe the desired outcome of the project and when that outcome should be achieved.

Specifications

After the project goal is set, the project manager must also determine what other specifications may be applicable. These specifications will drive the approach taken to reach the desired goal. For example, a facility charged with establishing a waste minimization program may be subject to regulatory and permit compliance conditions that dictate many operational factors. For example, the facility may already have permit limits on the process rates or heat input. Therefore, increasing temperatures to improve operational efficiency and decrease waste generation rates may not be feasible due to these permit limits. In addition, regulatory requirements that prescribe how wastes may be handled once they are generated may affect how the desired goal is achieved.

A wide range of specifications may apply to any given project. These specifications may measure a product against an industry benchmark or against similar products. Some of the more common specifications are:

- *Quality*. One definition of *quality* is providing clients with a superior product in an efficient manner. Is this product superior to the competition's product?

- *Reliability*. What is the potential for product failures?

- *Product life*. How long will the product last in the marketplace?

- *Functionality*. How easy is the product to use? Does it meet all of the needs?

- *Ease of manufacture*. Are the resources readily available to make this product?

- *Flexibility*. Can this product be modified to fit other markets? Can this product be modified to meet a variety of uses within this market?

- *Regulatory compliance*. What regulatory requirements are applicable to the manufacture of this product?

- *Materials use*. What materials are used? Are there restrictions for manufacture or purchase of those materials?

- *Publicity*. How will this affect the surrounding community or our corporate image?

Not all of these questions will necessarily be asked for a single project. However, it is best to ask these questions and consider these specifications before the approach or objectives are established.

Objectives or Milestones

In considering the specifications, the project manager also has to determine how to attain the project goals. One way to reach the goal is to break the project into logical segments, similar to climbing steps, moving down from one project level to another. This is called a **top-down approach**. With the **bottom-up approach**, all of the tasks that need to be completed are defined. Similar tasks are then grouped together. In some instances, a manager may combine both of these approaches by defining major segments as well as some key tasks that must be completed as part of the project.

In the example of the waste minimization project, either a top-down or bottom-up approach could be used. The top-down approach would be comprised of the following steps:

- Identify all of the processes in the facility and the wastes created from each

- Evaluate methods to minimize these wastes

- Prioritize the waste minimization methods

- Implement the waste minimization methods

- Track the progress of each waste minimization method

- Assess the effectiveness of each waste minimization method

A bottom-up approach would include programs required by local, State and Federal regulations. Examples of such programs include phasing out certain chlorinated solvents for degreasing operations or utilizing silver recovery units for photo processing units.

Each project segment or grouping of similar project tasks becomes an **objective** or **milestone**. Objectives and milestones are used to measure the progress of the project.

Structure

The purpose of structuring a project is to cut the project into pieces that can be managed in a reasonable and efficient manner. Objectives or milestones are broken down into smaller segments or tasks that are related to each other in some way due to resource requirements or their required sequencing within the project. Depending upon the size or complexity of the project, these tasks may be further divided into subtasks.

The outline of these milestone divisions is called the **work breakdown structure** (WBS). The top level of the outline or WBS is the project goal or *Level 1*. The milestones or objectives are *Level 2* in the WBS. Tasks and subtasks are *Level 3* and *Level 4*, respectively. A project manager may use as many levels as necessary to manage the project.

After the project outline is established, each task and subtask within the project should be thoroughly defined to flesh out the project. The definition includes

- Task description

- End product(s) or deliverables

- Completion criteria

- Assumptions

- Required start and finish dates

- Estimated completion time

- Relationship to other tasks

- Necessary resources

A task analysis work sheet may be used to record all of this information for each task. These work sheets should then be assembled into a project notebook. A **Gantt chart** is a tool often used to depict the chronology of interrelated tasks within the project. The chart may also show resources, duration, and costs.

Individual tasks and subtasks are related based upon the order in which they must be completed and the resources required for completion. As may be expected, both the schedule and resources must be balanced against each other. For example, the schedule may depend upon the resources available to complete the project, just as the resources available may change depending upon the required schedule.

For the waste minimization example, the facility could break the first task of process waste identification down further into production areas. Then, wastes from each production area would be evaluated based upon media (air, water, or waste) or regulatory status (hazardous or nonhazardous).

Schedule

The schedule for a project is dependent upon many things including the available resources. Two of the primary scheduling factors are the required start and finish dates for each task within the project. A task may have items, or **predecessors**, that must be completed before the task can be started. Likewise, a task may be critical to another task, or **successor**. There are five typical relationships that can occur between successor and predecessor tasks and their respective start and finish dates:

- *Finish-to-start*. The predecessor task must be finished before the successor tasks can be started.

- *Lead/overlap*. The predecessor task must be started before the successor task can be started. These tasks may overlap each other.

- *Lag/gap*. A set period of time must separate the predecessor task and the successor task. This set period or lag may be dependent upon other participants, such as regulatory agencies, corporate personnel or others needed for the task.

- *Start-to-start*. Two or more tasks begin concurrently.

- *Finish-to-finish*. Two or more tasks end at the same time.

Once the relationship between tasks has been determined, the potential paths for completing the project become evident. The longest possible path between the start and completion of the project is the **critical path**. A project manager must recognize the critical path and plan accordingly in order to ensure that the project can be completed in the allotted time.

In the waste minimization example, the facility processes and their respective wastes must be identified before the facility can evaluate waste minimization methods. Therefore, the identification step is the predecessor to the evaluation step. Further, the identification step and evaluation step have a finish-to-start relationship.

Resources

Resources are the items needed to complete a project. For any given project, a variety of resources may be required including: people, funding, tools, facilities, travel, and materials. In keeping with the old adage *the devil is in the details*, the detailed resources needed for a project should be carefully considered in order to assure the project's success.

People

The people involved with and affected by the project are its most important resource. A strong project manager will ensure that the resource needs are properly identified and allotted. The project manager is also key to maintaining effective communications with those affected by the project. The project manager is responsible for clearly understanding the project goals. In many cases, the project manager leads the planning effort by working with those affected by the project to design the objectives and milestones. He or she must balance the available resources and the desired schedule as described below.

Rarely can the project manager attain the objectives alone; therefore, a project team must be assembled. Members of this team should be selected based upon their skills and availability. A skills matrix is often completed to list the specific skills needed for each of the tasks. Then, the skills of potential team members are listed. These two lists are compared to determine a best fit for the team. The comparison and subsequent assignment of project team members to tasks is called **resource loading**. Making certain that each task can be adequately performed in the time required by assigning personnel is called **resource leveling**. Once the team is assembled, a kick-off meeting should be held to discuss the responsibilities of each team member, the effort required to complete tasks, task deliverables, tools available, and communication methods.

Funding

The funding needed to accomplish this project is very important. When planning the project a budget should be established. The budget should include material, labor, travel, and overhead costs. Because most accurate data for cost estimates is at the lowest WBS or task level, it is recommended that cost estimates be made at this level. Cost estimates, like task schedules may be based upon historical information or industry standards. There are several computer-based programs that will assist a project manager to both estimate and track project costs.

The project manager should attempt to identify potential project difficulties and where possible, plan for them in order to successfully control costs. Accurate estimates of both resources and required effort as well as contingency planning can help the project manager prepare for unforeseen project delays or difficulties. These considerations may include resource availability of less than the standard forty hours per week, equipment malfunctions, material supply or selection issues.

This identification and planning effort should continue throughout the project at set intervals through project reviews. Reviews should compare budgeted costs of each task with the actual cost to date and the percentage of the task completed. The project plan should be modified as needed to meet the objectives with the budget allotted.

In designing the project, it is important to itemize the project assumptions. Such assumptions may be related to availability of equipment, documents to be supplied, baseline information, skill levels of personnel, training requirements and other matters. The itemization of assumptions is particularly valuable when managing contracts within the scope of the project. Requests by either party in the contract that are outside of the project's defined scope or assumptions may be result in contract change orders and potentially affect project costs.

Materials

Material requirements range from raw materials to finished products and may be in the form of chemicals, documents, or other goods. It is helpful to *begin with the end in mind* when considering project materials. Defining the desired project output is essential to establish the necessary project inputs. Once the necessary input and desire output are defined, intermediate materials and by-products can be ascertained.

For materials such as chemicals or other commercial goods, material specifications should be obtained or created. Material costs, certificates of analysis, shipping considerations, vendor qualifications and other requirements should be included in the task definitions. In addition, disposal costs, marketing strategies and client requirements should also be involved in the task analyses.

Service industries and program development projects often have fewer tangible materials to consider within the project. However, reports, software programs, and manuals may be referred to as materials or project deliverables. The format for these materials should be scoped to ensure they are developed properly.

Tools

Project tools include software programs, computer hardware, process and monitoring equipment, and procedures used within the project. The tools may be needed for project management, production of materials, or process monitoring. Size; availability; cost of rental, purchase or operation; technical capabilities and requirements; efficiency and other technical specifications about the required project tools should be categorized as assumptions within the resource list.

In order to avoid unbudgeted overhead costs, a project manager must consider the training and skill level requirements for the personnel using the tools.

Facilities

Facility requirements include space for the project team and the utilities. Other facility issues may include accessibility for personnel, vehicles, and equipment. Rental, lease or purchase costs for the facility should be included in the budget. In addition, the availability of the facility may affect the schedule and should be included as a project assumption.

Travel

Travel costs may be a significant aspect of the project budget. Transportation, per diem and lodging costs should be considered for both local as well as corporate or regional/national personnel and contractors. Travel may also affect the schedule of a task based upon flight schedules, drive times, or traffic congestion. These issues may become crucial factors in the evaluation of various project elements.

Control and Communication

Control and communication are two complimentary project management components. Good project communication often leads to tight project control.

Routine Communication

A project manager must maintain several levels of communication within a project. This communication may take the form of memos, reports, or meetings. Some forms of communication can be casual, whereas other forms should be formal. A multilevel communication plan should be developed to set proper expectations for the project.

First, the project manager should ensure that the stakeholders are in agreement with project goals and objectives. The stakeholders should be given periodic project status reports which may include status of milestones, a budgetary report, successes and challenges. These reports may be presented during a meeting or formal presentation, in a written report or simply by memo. Once the project is complete, a final project presentation or report may be required and project follow-up reports may be requested.

Second, the project manager should communicate effectively with the project team. Typically, a project manager will hold a kick-off meeting to set expectations, discuss responsibilities and layout the overall project. During the kick-off meeting,

the project manager informs the team of any communication requirements such as

- Milestone meetings
- Status reports
- Budget reports
- Task analyses or worksheets
- Deliverables
- Communication format (written or oral)
- Due dates
- File locations and formats
- Confidentiality agreements
- Attorney client privilege statements

It is often useful for the project manager to provide templates for written communications and maintain the templates as well as actual project documentation in a project notebook. This notebook may be paper or electronic depending upon the project manager's style.

The project manager may also need to discuss project performance with individual team members as yet a third level of communication. In this capacity, the project manager needs to be able to develop a rapport, which fosters motivation, understanding, and respect. Performance issues such as cost overruns, delays in task completion, or quality of work are best dealt with on an individual basis—as promptly and objectively as possible.

Finally, the project manager needs to nurture a team dynamic. Team members should discuss project aspects with each other in order to develop innovative and/or effective methods of accomplishing the project goals and objectives, write presentations and reports, and provide quality controls. If a dysfunction arises within the team, the project manager has the responsibility of assisting the team to work through it.

Control and Changes

During milestone meetings or within status reports, it is essential that team members convey, for each of their assigned tasks, the percentage complete, budget expended, successes and challenges. These items will enable the project manager to evaluate the overall project status and develop or implement contingency plans as needed.

Contingency plans may have to be approved by the stakeholders particularly if they require a change in the objective or budget. Therefore, change orders should be carefully documented to justify resource allocations or budget overages. Examples of contingency plans are to add or reassign resources to compensate for projects that are behind schedule; find alternate facilities to adjust for changes in schedule; or identifying alternate vendors to address quality issues.

Metrics

A project should contain metrics related to how the project is meeting its goals. Two of the most typical metrics for a project are measurement against the budget and schedule. Both of these are generated through the frequent status reports and milestone meetings set within a project.

Another important metric is the measurement against project objectives that generally takes place after the project has been completed. For example, in the waste minimization project, the facility could measure the volume of waste generated on an annual basis and compare it to previous years. Or the facility could measure the amount of waste generated *versus* the amount of product generated. Other possible metrics include waste disposal costs or the cost of disposal *versus* cost of production. All of these statistics indicate how well the project has met its objectives.

Bibliography

Belanger T. C. *How to Plan Any Project: A Guide for Teams (and Individuals)*, 2nd ed. Philadelphia, PA: Project Management Institute, 1995.

Briner W, C. Hastings C, and M. Geddes. *Project Leadership.* 2nd ed. Brookfield, VT: Gower Publishing Company, 1996.

Knudsen J, and I. Bitz. Project Management: How to Plan and Manage Successful Projects. New York, NY: AMACOM, 1991.

Lientz B. P and K. P. Rea. *Project Management for the 21st Century*, 2nd ed. San Diego, CA: Academic Press, 1998.

Laureen McMurray Boyle earned a B.S. in Chemical Engineering from Case Western Reserve University in 1991 and a M.S. in Natural Resources, with an emphasis on environmental education, from Ohio State University in 1997. She has worked as an environmental engineer and Regulatory Manager in the chemical industry since 1993. During that time, Ms. Boyle implemented and maintained regulatory compliance programs for the environmental, health, safety, and transportation areas. Currently, she is working as a Senior Project Manager for ENSR. In this capacity, she works on redevelopment of brownfield sites, environmental management systems, compliance auditing, emergency response planning, training, and other regulatory tasks.

CHAPTER 8

Business Practices for Environmental Professionals

Doye B. Cox, PE, CHMM
Daniel L. Todd, QEP, CHMM
Glenn R. Carwell III, PE, CHMM

Introduction

Scope and Intent

The intent of this chapter is to provide an overview of the basic business principles and practices that may be important to the environmental professional. No single chapter can adequately begin to address the volume of knowledge that is *business practices*. Indeed, the study of business extends from the *technical* school through the baccalaureate, to the doctor of philosophy and beyond. Literally thousands of articles, treatises, and texts are written each year. However, the practicing scientific or engineering professionals probably had no business training as a part of their formal education and may or may not have any *on-the-job* training in business. This chapter is intended to provide a basis for understanding the terminology, principles, and practices of business.

Technical professionals often find themselves promoted into positions where the ability to develop a Business Plan, market for clients, understand financial statements, and manage people within the constraints of applicable laws are necessary and important parts of their job.

Other technical professionals may aspire to start and own their own businesses. Still others have a need to understand the economic drivers behind the businesses of their suppliers, subcontractors, and/or professional service providers in order to better evaluate the value of the service, equipment, or material supplied. This chapter is designed to assist the technical professional in each of these areas.

Types of Businesses

Environmental (and perhaps all) businesses can be separated into two broad categories, services and products. The *services* category is commonly divided into *professional* services; contract or construction services; as well as operation and maintenance (O&M) services. The *products* category generally refers to businesses that provide equipment or materials and supplies.

Services

Professional Service Providers include traditional architectural and engineering (A&E) firms, environmental consulting firms, geotechnical firms, and *specialty*—or *niche*—environmental firms, whose market may be very specialized (for example, stream morphology, threatened and endangered species of limited taxonomy, or engineering/process knowledge in a very limited technical area). Businesses providing professional services vary in size from a single person operation working out of a home office to major corporations with tens of thousands of employees. They are characterized by the fact that, in general, they sell the collective knowledge of their employees in the form of engineering design, professional advice, technical reports, or other professional assistance. In years past, these services were provided primarily on an hourly fee basis. More and more, clients are demanding lump sum or not-to-exceed fee contracts. Barriers to entry, at least on a small scale, are virtually nonexistent. In many states, the only requirement is a business license, while other states require specific environmental certifications (PE, PG, CHMM, *etc.*). The intrinsic value of a professional service company lies in its personnel, existing clients and contracts, as well as good will (or professional reputation). The business may or may not have any significant tangible assets. Office space, telephone, clerical, office equipment, and nonbillable time are all significant contributors to overhead and often drive billing rates three or four times actual raw salary rates.

Environmental Contractors include remediation firms, emergency response contractors, well drillers, environmental system construction contractors (wastewater treatment facilities, landfills, air pollution control systems, *etc.*) and specialty contractors (soil treatment contractors, artificial wetland or stream restoration contractors, *etc.*). Single-person firms in the environmental contracting business are much rarer than in the professional services business; however, many firms operate with a relatively small permanent staff consisting of management, estimators, project managers and sometimes superintendents. Other staff, including foremen, heavy equipment operators, laborers, and technicians are frequently retained on a job-by-job basis. Most contracting projects are procured on a lump-sum or unit-price basis or some combination thereof. Time-and-materials contracts have become increasingly rare. Barriers to entry range from modest to substantial. Most states require a contractor's license and all that such a license entails. Most contracting operations involve the use of heavy equipment or some specialty equipment. While much equipment may be rented, and almost all contractors rent some equipment, owning equipment can provide a significant competitive advantage to rental. The relatively large asset pool and employee base result in higher overhead costs in the form of employee benefits and insurance coverages. Environmental contractors frequently have millions of dollars in equipment assets. In environmental contracting, variable markups are applied across manpower, equipment, material, supplies, subcontractors, and other items that contribute significantly to job costs. As a result, depending on the contractor, size of job, and market sector, combined markups on cost for overhead and profit often range from ten to twenty-five percent of job cost.

O&M Services companies include waste collection, treatment and disposal firms; transportation companies; and industrial cleaning services. Waste disposal and treatment firms frequently have millions or even tens of millions of dollars invested prior to opening for business. Although transportation companies may start as one-person operations, they require a significant investment of tens of thousands of dollars per employee in upfront equipment costs. Industrial cleaning services may start with a relatively modest investment in steam cleaners and pressure washers or may invest hundreds of thousands of dollars in fleets of vacuum trucks. In this diverse group of service providers, the barriers to entry can vary greatly—from almost insurmountable to relatively modest. Because of diversity within this category of service, generalizations regarding markup and overhead costs are not applicable.

Products

Providers of products can generally be classified into two groups: providers of equipment and providers of materials and supplies. Products provided by *equipment suppliers* range from relatively small and inexpensive handheld instruments, like a pH meter, to large pieces of process equipment, like a thermal oxidizer. Smaller common pieces of equipment are essentially commodities that are purchased based primarily on price with features and quality of construction as secondary issues. Larger pieces of process equipment are often built to order. In these cases, payment often is made in various stages of production so that payment is complete prior to shipment. Lead times for such equipment are commonly eight weeks or more. Barriers to entry can be significant. Production facilities, work force, raw material and preconstructed components must be in place for large equipment, while small equipment must be in production and ready for off-the-shelf shipment when initially offered for sale.

Materials and supplies include such diverse items as personal protective equipment, spill control materials like boom and sorbant materials, sediment and erosion control products, wastewater treatment chemicals, and specialty microbe mixtures for soil or wastewater treatment. As with small equipment, these products are frequently commodity items that are ordered and shipped or even picked up from distributors as off-the-shelf items. Similar barriers to entry exist in that these items must generally be in stock and ready for sale at the time of their initial offering.

How to Get Started in Business

Developing a Business Plan

A *Business Plan* is a document that consolidates the various aspects of the business unit—whether a single-employee sole proprietorship or a multinational corporation employing thousands. It assesses the current status of the business and competitive environment, and offers projections into the future. It is vital; it presents the business' goals, evaluates the potential market, plans for market penetration, and discusses various operational and financial strategies. It provides the preparer, owners, and management a process to gauge "where the business is now, and where it is going." Also, the Business Plan gives investors some insight into the business and its expectations.

This section is intended to provide an overview of topics to be considered in the preparation of a Business Plan for a new venture, and also to provide insight to the first-time reader of an existing Business Plan. For the entrepreneur looking to hang out a shingle, it might not be feasible to address every topic mentioned. At a minimum, however, an abbreviated Business Plan should consist of a brief business description and goals, as well as forecasts for revenue, profit/loss, capital spending, and cash flow for a three-year to five-year horizon.

Description of the Business. At the beginning of the Business Plan, it is important to define the Business and to consider its vision. This can be accomplished in a straightforward manner by presenting the firm's Mission Statement, followed by a brief discussion of the kinds of products or services that will be offered.

For the small business, it is essential to discuss briefly the relevant education and experience of key staff in order to demonstrate that necessary expertise is on-hand. It is important to relate this background to the products or services provided. For the large company or corporate division, this is not as crucial a topic.

For any business to operate, it needs customers (clients). Successful businesses align their services (or products) to solve customers' problems or otherwise meet their needs. To do this, the customers' needs and wants must be recognized, and the business must develop and offer solutions to these needs and wants. The identification of needs and solutions is a significant topic in the Business Plan.

Even though it does not need to be a lengthy discussion, the Business Plan should identify the legal form of the business. For existing entities, obviously, this has already been established. However, for the entrepreneur looking to start a new venture, it is imperative to evaluate and decide how the business will be legally structured. The environmental professional has several options:

- **Partnership.** In a *partnership*, two or more partners share ownership of a single business. The law does not distinguish between the business and its owners. All partnerships should be based on a binding legal agreement that establishes how decisions will be made, how profits will be shared, how disputes will be resolved, how future partners will be admitted to the partnership, how partners can be bought out, and how the partnership can be dissolved, if and when needed.

  — *General Partnership.* Investors share in the risk and the rewards.

  — *Limited Partnership.* The general partner (usually the entrepreneur working full-time) bears the risk and has day-to-day control; other investors have limited exposure.

  — *Joint Venture.* Much like a general partnership except the relationship is for a limited time period or for a specific project.

- **Corporation.** In a *corporation*, all investors have limited exposure.

  — *Limited Liability Company (LLC).* An LLC provides the tax efficiencies and operational flexibility of a partnership and the limited liability features of a corporation. LLCs are distinguished from regular corporations in that they can not have more than two of the four characteristics that define corporations: limited liability to the extent of assets; continuity of life; centralization of management; and free transferability of ownership interests.

  — *Subchapter S Corporation.* A Subchapter S Corporation allows the owners (shareholders) to treat the earnings and profits as distributions, and appear as such on their personal tax return. The shareholder, if working for the company, and if there is a profit, must receive wages, and it must meet standards of *reasonable compensation*. Reasonable compensation means that the wages are within the range of salary expected within the industry for the person's qualifications.

- **Sole proprietorship.** In a *sole proprietorship,* one person has 100% ownership, 100% control, and 100% risk.

The Market and the Plan. The Business Plan needs to provide an assessment of the total market in which the business unit operates. The *market* is not only defined as the products or services offered, but also the geographical area and clients or customers that the business intends to serve. As a part of evaluating the market, several key issues/questions arise:

- Is it important to identify the category of potential customers: government, small companies, or large companies?

- Are the products (or services) most needed by a select few industries? Or a wide variety?

- An accurate assessment of the size of the market (*i.e.*, within the defined geography) is imperative. In other words, how much money is being spent overall for these products/services in the area and who is spending it?

The next step is to define the competition: who is providing these products/services now? If at all possible, an estimation of competitor's fees, markups, or sales prices should be performed and addressed in the Business Plan.

Armed with this information, the next step is to prepare a Marketing Plan, as a stand-alone chapter within the Business Plan. The *Marketing Plan* describes the market and how the company plans to acquire new customers (and, if relevant, keep the existing ones). A significant element of developing the strategy is to consider various potential communication avenues. Both indirect and direct methods may be effective.

Indirect marketing does not involve direct advertising, yet it increases visibility and credibility. Generally, indirect marketing does not cost much money, but does demand time. Examples of indirect marketing methods are: developing and nurturing a professional network, lecturing to professional or community groups, organizing and leading seminars, joining and participating in trade associations, authoring and presenting papers. Another indirect marketing method—one that cannot be fully planned—is the referral from satisfied customers; thus, high-quality work products are, in and of themselves, oftentimes the most valuable marketing tools.

Some sort of self-promotion is almost always necessary for a successful marketing strategy (*direct marketing*). Direct marketing techniques include written materials; such as magazine ads, business cards, brochures, newsletters, and statement of qualifications. Other approaches include maintaining a dynamic website, exhibiting at a trade show, making cold calls, and utilizing a direct mail campaign.

In the process of developing the marketing strategy, the concept of *teaming* with another business deserves consideration. In such an arrangement, the two companies refer customers to each other, usually for one of two reasons: to provide for customer needs during times of overbooking, or in situations where one company provides a product (or service) that the other does not. Teaming relationships can prove very valuable; however, they should not be pursued lightly. Each teaming partner must have full confidence in each other's competence and ethics. Such arrangements are not necessarily appropriate for all businesses.

A valuable Marketing Plan does not necessarily have to address each and every item listed above; furthermore, there may be additional effective marketing methods specific to a particular business. This brief discussion is to assist the thought processes. The overriding question that the Marketing Plan is to consider is, "Why will a customer hire our business (buy from us)?"

The Money and the Plan. For a business to be self-sustaining, the revenue must cover all of the costs; to make a profit, there must be more income than outgo. The financial component of the business plan is arguably the most important—indeed, it will likely be the section that investors read initially, and perhaps the most thoroughly.

For the person just starting an enterprise, a preliminary step is the preparation of a break-even analysis. This analysis will not take the place of a complete business plan, rather it is a screening tool, providing a *go/no go* indication. The process consists of estimating sales revenue, fixed costs, gross profit (per dollar of revenue), and finally, the break-even sales revenue (the amount needed each week [or month] to pay for both direct costs and fixed costs—it does not include any profit).

The next step is to develop the *Financial Plan*, as a chapter within the Business Plan. It needs to include the following elements:

Pro forma. This is a refinement of the break-even analysis. Business profits result from the simple arithmetic of subtracting the direct costs and the fixed costs from the sales revenues, utilizing the same given time period for each number. In developing the *pro forma*, each number should be closely examined to ensure it reflects the best knowledge (assumptions) available, and is presented on a month-by-month basis, projecting for two years. Large existing entities may have three-year or five-year forecasts. To assure an effective process, budget line items should be used in this step. See Table 1 for an example of an abbreviated list of a *Chart of Accounts*—a listing of budget line items. The use of such a listing provides continuity, avoids oversight, and provides a mechanism to track trends in revenues and expenditures. For a new venture, an Accountant should be able to provide an initial Chart of Accounts.

Capital Spending Plan. The *Capital Spending Plan* includes all of the items that must be purchased before any revenue is received. This consists of equipment, inventory, and fixtures. For a start-up company, this also includes licenses, insurance, initial deposits, advertising, office supplies, *etc.* These costs fall into two categories: *capital* (assets with useful life of more than one year) and *expense*. Additionally, for a start-up company, it is appropriate to include initial working capital, *i.e.*, the cash needed to operate until the company consistently shows a profit.

Cash Flow Forecast. Cash is vital to all businesses and it can be the Achilles' heel of the small start-up company. The *Cash Flow Forecast* begins with the monthly profit (or loss) figures calculated

ASSETS:			
	1000	Cash in Bank	Current assets
	1001	Accounts Receivable	Current assets
	1002	Work-In-Process (WIP)	Current assets
	1003	Inventory	Current assets
	1100	Vehicles	Non-current assets
	1101	Accumulated Depreciation–Vehicles	Non-current assets
	1102	Field Equipment	Non-current assets
	1103	Accumulated Depreciation–Field Equipment	Non-current assets
LIABILITIES:			
	2000	Accounts Payable	Current liability
	2001	Withholding Taxes Payable	Current liability
	2002	Accrued Payroll–Net	Current liability
INCOME:			
	4000	Revenue	Income
	4015	Work-In-Process (WIP)	Income
COST OF GOODS SOLD (DIRECT COST):			
	5000	Salaries	Cost
	5001	Shipping and Freight	Cost
	5002	Contract Services	Cost
	5003	Field Equipment Expense	Cost
	5004	Travel	Cost
	5005	Field Supplies Expense	Cost
	5006	Equipment Rental	Cost
	5007	Chemical Analysis	Cost
EXPENSE (OVERHEAD):			
	6000	Administrative Salaries	Expense
	6001	Advertising/Marketing	Expense
	6002	Mileage, *etc.*	Expense
	6003	Auto Expenses	Expense
	6004	Bank Charges	Expense
	6005	Contributions	Expense
	6006	Depreciation Expense	Expense
	6007	Insurance–Business	Expense
	6008	Interest Expense	Expense
	6009	Legal and Accounting	Expense
	6010	Rent Expense	Expense
	6011	Taxes	Expense
	6012	Professional Development	Expense
	6013	Books	Expense
	6014	Utilities	Expense

Table 1. Example Chart of Accounts

in the *pro forma*. Adjustments are made for time differences in the expected collecting (accounts receivable) and spending (accounts payable) of money. Impacts of credit sales and collections, credit purchases and payments, tax withholding, depreciation, debt payments, and asset purchases (from the Capital Spending Plan) are also considered.

Financial Plan. The Financial Plan should include a strategy for raising the necessary funds to meet the shortfall identified in the Cash Flow Forecast. Possible sources of money are bank loans and equity ownership (stock). For the start-up business additional possibilities include personal savings; close friends/relatives; as well as borrowing against equity in property, partners, and venture capitalists.

Risk Analysis. All businesses face risks. Investors and lenders are quite aware of the concept of risk, and a complete Business Plan needs to address the topic. What are the possible forces that could negatively impact the business? This section should include an assessment of the competition, business cycles and trends, slow times, and cash flow forecasts. Businesses that are providing a new product or service have some inherent risk in developing a new market.

Day-to-day Tactics. In the process of creating (or refining) the Business Plan, it is crucial to consider the logistics of how the business will *get the product out the door*. What materials, supplies, or components will be needed? Who will supply them? Is there a lead-time for these materials? What sort of credit arrangements will be necessary to procure these materials, supplies, and components?

Another very important deliberation of the processes of production is staffing. How many employees will need to be involved? What types of qualifications or special training are required? If staff requires specialized qualifications or training, what plans have been made for staff retention or replacement? Are there staffing requirements for part-time or full-time employees? Perhaps contract staff?

Bricks and mortar also deserve attention. The Business Plan should address where the business will be (or already is) located. Is this a business that needs Client access and meeting space? Is it important to be near a certain customer or resource? How much space and what type of space is needed? What are the costs of rent, utilities, Internet access, *etc.*? For the small business, can it operate out of the owner's home? In the case of working out of the home, some consideration should be given to securing a separate telephone line and fax line. An answering service might also be appropriate.

Staff professional development (*continuing education*) deserves attention in the planning process. In the daily stress of marketing, producing, paying the bills, and handling customer crises, it is easy to overlook the need to stay current with the improvements in technology and equipment, the changes in the rules, and advances in relevant research. There are several avenues available to increase knowledge and competence. Attendance at conferences, seminars, and courses provide educational opportunities. Active participation in professional associations can lead to exposure to leaders in the field. For certain staff, it can be appropriate and important for them to prepare and present relevant papers in a lecture-type setting. As mentioned above, these avenues support the Marketing Plan.

Advisors/External Resources

There is no person that knows every detailed aspect of a business. Therefore, it is essential to recognize where the needs are and to determine the appropriate sources of assistance. An informal referral network is often very helpful. For the start-up company, or the small business, it is important to ensure that the service provider works with similar types of businesses. For those in existing businesses, these resources may not be necessary, but it is reassuring to know they exist.

An accountant will understand and make recommendations regarding the tax implications of a variety of decisions (*e.g.*, legal form of the business, buy *vs.* lease) as well as advice on establishing appropriate record keeping and financial controls. The fee basis should be discussed and negotiated upfront.

An attorney will provide assistance in the determination of the legal form of the business, and in drawing up the required documentation and filings. An attorney can also provide invaluable help in interpreting suppliers' and customers' contracts and leases, and in the development of the company's own standard contractual terms and conditions. Again, the fee basis should be discussed and negotiated upfront.

A banker will provide guidance in setting up business accounts, providing loans, opening credit card accounts, and providing a limited amount of (free) financial counsel. In certain instances, a banker may provide computerized accounting services, investment services, and pension and profit-sharing plans. It is best to comparison shop for the best overall banking package.

An insurance agent that specializes in the relevant business can provide advice regarding insurance needs and recommendations on obtaining the best package. In addition, insurance professionals are often excellent resources for limiting risks by reviewing contract terms and conditions and by providing training to a firm's professional staff.

In addition to working with advisors face-to-face, there are a myriad of other resources to provide guidance. There are countless links on the Internet (some are listed at the end of this chapter) and there are many, many books in libraries and bookstores. For the person developing a Business Plan for a brand new venture, it will be valuable to invest time in studying some of these resources. However, do not become overwhelmed by the amount of information and advice on hand. Using this Chapter as an overview, along with a couple of key books (ones to keep), and a trusted advisor or two (also ones to keep), one can work through the process, and write the plan.

Sales and Marketing

How To Market

As stated in the How to Get Started section, the marketing plan is an essential tool for all business. No matter how valuable the product and service, unless it is accepted and purchased by the target customer base, the business will fail. It is the job of management to set marketing goals, to identify the target market, to establish pricing, and to assure that resources are available to balance production with marketing goals.

Sales and marketing programs vary radically for the differing environmental business sectors. Professional service organizations rely significantly on engineering, scientific, and technical staff for sales. While there is often a regional sales manager, virtually every employee may be expected to play a role in sales and promotions are often awarded to those accomplished in sales and marketing as opposed to those with only technical accomplishments. Professional service firms market to all levels of government, business, and industry. Environmental contractors often rely more on sales staff but not completely. Contractors acquire many jobs from publications such as the Commerce Business Daily, from government web sites, from plan rooms where plans and specifications for prospective jobs are available for inspection, and significantly by marketing to professional service providers who prepare plans and specifications for their client's construction projects. O&M providers use traditional sales and marketing techniques to a targeted market audience. Product providers often rely on traditional sales and marketing techniques with emphasis on *environmentally oriented* magazines, as well as, to professional service providers that specify materials and select products for use on their clients' projects.

Marketing Program Evaluation

As previously discussed, a key component of the Business Plan is the Marketing Plan. The Marketing Plan must have goals and target dates associated with those goals. Goals must be realistic in the context of the market niche and the financial, management, and staff resources of the company. Many companies in the environmental business sector fail due to ill conceived and improperly planned growth. Monitoring sales and marketing results is required to assure growth.

Measurement of marketing success can be particularly difficult. The obvious tendency would be to measure the growth of gross revenue. However, failure to achieve revenue goals may be due to other failures besides marketing. Management must ask

- Are the right contacts being made?

- Are enough contacts being made?

- Are the contacts resulting in opportunities?

- Do opportunities result in additional business?

If opportunities do not result in business:

- Do the contacts provide sufficient business intelligence?
  - Is the price too high?
  - Does the product meet needs?
  - Is the approach wrong?

- Do the client/customer and sales/marketing staff communicate effectively?

- Are they professionally/socially compatible?

Management must continuously evaluate these factors and their relationship to the marketing plan. Changes in approach, targets, goals, and personnel may be necessary.

Marketing Secrets

Marketing *secrets* presented here are not secrets to veterans of the *business wars* but bear repeating as a reminder to some and a starting point to others. Many are obvious but often overlooked.

- No sales and marketing approach will work unless a quality product/service is provided at a fair price to satisfy a real need. All three elements are required for long-term success.

- The best salespersons and marketers for *Service Providers* are the front-line staff in direct contact with the customer. They are the ambassadors of quality and service. A customer will always be more impressed by the good job a heavy equipment operator or laborer is doing than by the elegance of the corporate logo, the proposal letter, or the invoice design. Conversely, it is almost impossible to overcome the stigma of poor performance or a sloppy job.

- The most important sales tool for *Product Providers* is the product. Does it work? Does it last? Is it a good value, regardless of price?

- Get in/stay in. Serve the client or customer in a manner that is designed to continuously convince him or her that the company/product is the best choice. Be available to the client/ customer without becoming a pest. Good sales staff will be able to identify the correct level of contact. Don't become complacent—your competitors will not.

Administrative Framework

Accounting and Project Tracking

Accounting is a vital task in any sustainable firm, because it ensures the financial health of the enterprise by organizing financial information in ways that help management make decisions regarding expenditures. Accounting is often perceived as confusing by technical professionals without formal business training. However, the basic concepts are not difficult to understand. There are two accounting methods common in the environmental industry that are defined below:

Accrual Basis. The *Accrual Method of Accounting* assigns revenues to the periods in which they are earned and matches expenses with the revenues. The objective is to recognize the effects of revenues and expenses when they are earned or incurred, not when the cash is received or paid. Enterprise performance is generally better indicated by the accrual process, which is also the basis for Generally Accepted Accounting Principles (GAAP). GAAP is more credible for external reporting to shareholders, the IRS, *etc.*

Cash Basis. Revenues are recognized when cash is received and expenses are reported when cash is paid. Although it is common for small businesses to use this system for internal reports, it is important to note that *cash basis* methods are not consistent with GAAP. There is also more risk of unethical reporting and manipulation using this method.

Cooking the Books (Know What It Is So You Don't). Although it can be done unintentionally, or can seem like an innocent ploy to *tide-us-over* to next month, this is a *very* destructive business practice that is sure, over the long term, to ruin the business or worse, land somebody in jail. Cooking the books, or more correctly, misrepresenting the financial status of the business, most often involves the overaccrual of revenue, overestimation of assets, or the underaccrual of costs. This typically occurs when revenues are recognized in one period and expenses are recorded in a future period in an effort to overinflate the performance of the earlier period. Year-end periods are the most susceptible to this practice, since management bonuses are often contingent on year-end performance.

The authors are personally aware of several remedial services companies that have accrued revenue as a percentage of project costs. This relationship is often tenuous, at best, and assumes the actual field costs are equivalent to the costs used in estimating the project. Revenue in these cases should always be accrued by an accurate estimate of the percent complete of the contract value. Inflated revenue can be re-accrued almost indefinitely, especially if the auditors do an incomplete job on the financial statement. Opening projects without authorization from clients to inflate sales figures or backlog, or to hide overages from other projects is another disreputable practice. Overestimation of assets can involve inflating inventory or inflating appraisals of property or equipment. Common costs subject to underaccrual include subcontracted costs, material and equipment costs, or waste disposal or treatment costs. Eventually, these deceptions must always end either due to arriving invoices or project overruns that must be reported.

Billing. Billing should be conducted in accordance with the firm's contractually agreed upon rates, fee, or sales price and should be done regularly, at least monthly. The outstanding invoice amount is tracked as Accounts Receivable until it is paid.

Many firms have a *paid when paid* policy, which means they will pay their subcontractor's invoices once the client has paid their invoice. It is important to keep track of the amount of time it takes to get paid by clients. If an invoice hasn't been paid within a reasonable time from their average, there usually is a reason why. Generally, most clients pay invoices within 90 days. Accounts Receivables that age beyond 180 days usually will be difficult to collect, and beyond one year, probably should be written off. The financial impact of Accounts Receivable should not be underestimated. Reducing the average age of Accounts Receivable by 10 days can result in savings of hundreds of thousands of dollars for larger businesses.

Project Tracking and Administration. Labor effort, subcontractors, and material charges applied to a specific project must be properly assigned and tracked to ensure that the firm can recover their expenses and the client is fairly charged. In addition, comparison of expenses *versus* percent complete or production level allow for timely modifications to operations so the project schedule and budget can be achieved. Employee time sheets are very important for tracking labor charges and should be compiled and entered into the accounting system weekly. Materials and supplies are generally tracked through a purchase order system. Subcontractors are tracked by demanding routine and timely progress and expenditure reports.

Business Statistics

A variety of benchmarks exist for service industries. These are important, because they provide targets that are necessary for a sustainable operation. Because of this, it is important to also understand the interdependent relationships between the variables and the ranges of acceptable performance.

Raw labor is defined as the hourly wage for an employee, less benefit costs. The *raw labor multiplier,* or sometimes just *multiplier*, is the number applied to an employee's base salary in order to determine a billable rate. An acceptable range for the multiplier may be 2.5 to 3.5, depending on the firm's utilization performance and overhead cost. However, the firm would likely lose money if the multiplier falls to less than 2.0,

and business might be lost if the multiplier exceeds 4.0. As an example, an employee making $52,000/year makes $25.00/hr. The billable rate for this employee at a raw labor multiplier of 3.0 would be $75.00/hr. The 3.0 multiplier covers all mandated benefits (FICA, unemployment insurance, workers comp, *etc.*), all nonmandated benefits (holidays, health insurance, vacation, pension, *etc.*), non-salary overhead (building rent, furniture, phone, computer, liability insurance, *etc.*), management and sales (the boss, secretaries, accounting, legal, sales and marketing, other nonbillable employees) and, finally, profit. For professional service providers, the raw labor multiplier is usually benchmarked at 3.0.

Because of the interdependence of these two variables, another benchmark, *labor yield*, is also tracked. Labor yield is the product of the firm's utilization and net multiplier. *Utilization* is the percentage of hours billed to a client or profit-generating project in relation to total hours available. So, a firm operating at 67% utilization with a net multiplier of 2.5 will have a labor yield of 1.675, which would be the same for another firm operating at 56% utilization with a 3.0 net multiplier, such a company would indeed be operating *lean and mean*. *Margin yield* or *margin* is the percentage of gross profit in relation to net sales. Margin should not be confused with *mark-up*, which is the percentage that is applied to cost of sales in order to produce a selling price.

Figure 1 illustrates other common benchmarks for service industries. These benchmarks are also useful for budgeting purposes and required growth.

In addition to these benchmarks, environmental contractors often track equipment utilization hours as a percentage of available hours, equipment maintenance records, and crew production rates, as well as manpower utilization.

Understanding Financial Statements

Accounting exists for the purpose of providing useful information to people who make financial business decisions. Most organizations provide accounting information in the form of financial statements that describe the financial performance in a condensed format.

Three major financial statements are ordinarily required for external reports: an income

Benchmark	Definition	Benchmark Value
Margin Yield	Net Income/Net Sales x 100	20%
Labor/Net Revenue	Salaries/Net Income x 100	52%
Nonsalaried Overheads/Net Revenue		30%
Utilization	Hours billed/total available hours	65%
Labor Yield	Utilization x net multiplier	1.9
Backlog	Value of contracts/labor run rate	6+ months
Sales Pressure	Amount sold (Fees under contract)/ Amount burned (Fees spent)	1.15

Figure 1. Common Benchmarks for Service Industries

statement, a balance sheet, and a statement of cash flows.

- *Income Statements* show whether the business earned a profit (net income is positive). By describing the change in owner's equity, the income statement links the company's balance sheets from the beginning to the end of the reporting period.

- The *Balance Sheet's* purpose is to provide information that helps management understand a company's financial status by listing the types and dollar amounts of assets, liabilities, and equity of the business. The balance sheet reports the balances of the assets, liabilities, and equity on a given date. Creditors will often use a balance sheet to help them decide whether to loan money to a

Key Definitions in Financial Statements

Net Income: The amount of profit earned. A company earns a net income if its revenues exceed its expenses.

Net Loss: A company earns a net loss if its expenses exceed its revenues.

Revenue: Revenues are inflows of assets received in exchange for goods and services provided.

Expenses: Outflows or the using up of assets as a result of the major operations of a business.

Assets: Economic resources owned by the business. Examples include: cash, amounts owed to the business by its customers for goods or services sold to them (Accounts Receivable), merchandise held in inventory, supplies, equipment, buildings, and land.

Liabilities: Debts to others including amounts owed for goods and services bought on credit (Accounts Payable), salaries and wages owed to employees, taxes payable, notes payable, and interest payable.

Owner's Equity: Difference between the company's assets and its liabilities

business, by comparing the amounts of existing liabilities and assets.

- The purpose of the **Statement of Cash Flows** is to highlight the major activities that directly and indirectly impact cash flows and the overall cash balance. The statement of cash flows answers questions that are not discernable from the income statement and balance sheet, such as, is the firm generating sufficient positive cash flows from its operations to remain viable? Will the firm be able to repay debts? Will it pay a dividend? To what extent will the company have to borrow money in order to make needed investments?

Sources of cash include net income, decreases in assets, increases in liabilities, and increases in stockholders' capital accounts. Uses of cash include increases in assets, decreases in liabilities, decreases in stockholders' capital accounts and dividends. For external reporting purposes, the statement of cash flows must be organized in terms of operating, investing, and financing activities. Changes in noncurrent assets are generally included in financing activities. Operating activities include net income and changes in current assets and current liabilities. Net cash provided by operating activities provides a measure of how successful the company is in generating cash on a continuing basis.

Insurance

There are several types of insurance coverage to be evaluated. The purpose of business insurance is to transfer the risk (or at least, most of the risk) of loss to the insurance company in exchange for premium paid. In today's litigious society, it is very rare to find a business that does not have some form of insurance. In some cases, the building landlord will require insurance. In other cases, a customer may require insurance, especially in the case of doing work on his premises. Most states require specific types of insurance (for example, workers compensation insurance, general liability, commercial auto, and professional liability). In any case, insurance coverage should not be left to chance. After working though the financial forecasts, including the capital spending, it is important to evaluate the risks. Only then, does it make sense to assess insurance policies.

Professional liability insurance (sometimes referred to as errors and omissions or **E&O**) is the

equivalent of malpractice insurance. This type of insurance protects the firm and its owners, operators, directors, employees (present, past and temporary) from injury—either physical or financial—as a result of an error or omission by the professional (*i.e.*, anyone who would be held to a higher standard, due to training, education, or special knowledge). This coverage is only for the services provided by the insured firm. As with all liability coverage, this protection provides defense and any award for damages as a result of a negligent act on the part of the insured.

General liability insurance provides coverage in the event that someone is injured or has property damaged while on the insured's premises, the customer's premises, or while using the company's products or services. Some general liability policies have a pollution exclusion, which states that there will be no coverage for a pollution event, nor related testing, monitoring, consulting, *etc.* All environmentally-related firms need to assess any exposure related to dealing with pollutants, and if warranted, obtain pollution contractors' liability insurance. Some insurance companies offer a combination policy to cover professional, general, and pollution contractors' liability. Additionally, most landlords require a certain amount of this type of general liability insurance as protection from liability claims.

Almost all states require **Workers' Compensation insurance**. It is necessary to procure this type insurance in each state where the work is performed (as opposed to the state of the company's office or the workers' location). It is best to consult with the insurance agent concerning specific requirements for each state.

Property insurance generally covers the loss of real and personal property, as well as loss of income, due to earthquakes, flood, tornadoes, fire, hail, lightning, smoke, wind, *etc.* Property insurance can be written on a replacement cost basis, or a depreciated value basis. All property forms include co-insurance, and it is necessary to understand the difference between what might be owed on the equipment, what it is worth, and what its book value is. Also, it is important for the insured to understand the level of coverage (replacement cost today, or replacement cost today minus applicable depreciation). Another form of property insurance covers testing equipment, tools, *etc.*, that move from job-to-job.

If the company owns any vehicles, then **auto-mobile insurance** is mandatory. Most states have minimum coverage requirements. Automobile insurance includes liability (bodily injury and property damage), medical payments, uninsured (and underinsured) motorist, collision, and comprehensive coverages.

In the situation where the business has equipment being transported, then **inland marine coverage** is appropriate. This provides coverage for property that is actually in transit, is at a fixed location awaiting transport, or is a movable type of goods that is often at different locations.

Recently, several larger companies—customers or potential customers—are requiring an excess liability policy, providing **umbrella** coverage over and above the coverages previously described. The customer may agree to pay for the additional insurance as a part of the total scope of services.

Often, a small company that depends heavily upon the skills and experience of a single, crucial individual will carry key person insurance. In the event that this person is not able to work, this type insurance will pay a fixed amount to the business.

In the event a fire, flood, tornado, or other disaster forces a stoppage in business activity, business interruption insurance will provide some funds to replace the loss of sales.

Other insurance may be appropriate for any particular business. It is very important to secure the assistance of a qualified insurance agent. The agent should provide advice on the types and amounts of coverage that are appropriate. The agent then can explore the insurance market to offer the best coverage for the best price. Many insurance companies offer training and written materials providing lessons in minimizing risk. Some will offer discounts when such instruction is successfully completed.

There are two standard forms of liability insurance—*claims-made* and *occurrence* policies. The difference centers upon the event that causes coverage to be invoked, and is known as the **coverage trigger.** It is important to consult with the trusted insurance agent to obtain a more complete understanding of the nuances of each type of coverage.

An **occurrence policy** requires the insurance company to pay claims arising out of an occurrence causing bodily injury or property damage during the policy period regardless of when the claim is reported. The occurrence policy's coverage trigger is tied to the date of the event or accident that generates the claim. The policy in force on the date of the event causing the loss must respond. This may even be years after the policy has expired. Commercial general liability insurance is typically written on an occurrence basis.

A **claims-made** policy differs from the occurrence policy form in that it protects the insured against claims that are reported while the policy is in force, or during the extended reporting period. A claims-made policy may reach back in time to provide coverage for services provided years before the policy period. Several conditions must be met before prior acts are covered. The most common professional liability and pollution liability insurance policies are written on a claims-made basis. To preserve the rights under a claims-made policy, it is advisable to make note of any potential liability as an incident or *early warning* and to report the incident to the insurance agent as soon as possible.

Contracts

It is absolutely essential that professional service and contracting businesses always perform work under a written contractual agreement. All terms agreed upon in the customer-provider contracting process need to be confirmed in writing. This mutual-decision process provides the mechanism for both parties to

- Assure that the project/purchase is approved by the appropriate person within each organization

- Confirm all important items, arrangements, and understandings addressed in the contracting process

- Have a reference document, listing previous decisions and understandings, at a later time when neither party has a perfect memory of the agreement

- Provide important liability protection and risk reduction

Several types of documents are utilized to hire services or purchase goods. Three common ones are: the Letter of Intent, the Purchase Order, and the Contract. All of these formats include a definition of the service to be performed (scope of work) or product to be purchased, specified timeframe for delivery, and details of invoicing and fee payment schedules.

The **Letter of Intent** is the simplest and least formal kind of contract. It is legal and binding; however, it tends to diminish nervousness in certain customers. A Letter of Intent is a standard business letter produced in duplicate with a space for the signatures of the contracting parties. The terms of the agreement are clearly defined within the body of the letter, but in a less formal language than a general contract.

The **Purchase Order** is generated by the customer, and is typically in a pre-printed format. In addition to the items listed above, it includes the purchaser's terms and conditions. Upon acceptance by the contractor, it is a legal and binding document.

Contracts are formal, detailed, elaborate, legal and binding documents in which relevant conditions of the agreement are spelled out. In some relationships, the seller offers the contract; in others, the purchaser will supply the contract. There are three basic sections of the contract:

1) the definitions of the specific services to be performed or products to be supplied

2) the general terms and conditions and

3) the authorizing signatures

It is crucial to have a thorough understanding of what is contained in any contract, paying special attention to limitations of liability and indemnification—especially a contract presented by the customer.

A contractor-supplied contract should be in the format specifically adapted to the needs of the business. It needs to be developed in conjunction with the attorney. The following items are suggested for inclusion in the general terms and conditions:

- Customer Responsibilities, such as designation of project contact and clarification of site access

- Provider's Responsibilities, such as defining the acceptable standard of performance, and confidentiality requirements

- State governing law

- Indemnification (risk assignment)

- *Force majeure*, which removes liability for causes or circumstances beyond the control of the contractor

- Dispute resolution

- Termination

- Severability and survival

- Limitation of liability

- Payment

- Disclaimers

- Definitions of the terms used in the other sections of the Terms and Conditions

Contracting with the government offers special rewards and special challenges. This paragraph will deal with Federal government contracting. Many of the generalizations and concepts hold true for State and local government contracting but jurisdictions vary greatly. The Federal government is easily the largest contracting entity in the United States. The largest of the Federal government contracting entities is the Department of Defense. Three characteristics make contracting with the Federal government unique as compared to contracting with the private sector.

- The Federal government has designed their contracting mechanisms to curb misappropriation of funds and provide for uniform policies and practices. The regulations establishing the rules for government contracting are the Federal Acquisition Regulations (FAR) issued by the General Services Administration. The FAR are codified at 48 CFR 1.

- The FAR contract terms have been the subject of uncounted adjudications and, as such, have received distinct and binding meanings and interpretations. An attorney with government contracting experience can be invaluable.

- Disputes with the Federal government follow a much different path and are subject to much different rules than private sector contract disputes.

The FAR and technical assistance in government contracting can be obtained at <http://www.arnet.gov/far/>.

Employment Law and Human Resources

Fair Labor Standards Act

The Fair Labor Standards Act (FLSA) serves as a landmark piece of legislation. It establishes a standard 40-hour work-week. It requires payment of overtime at a rate of one and a half times the standard rate of pay. It establishes a minimum wage, except for certain workers including farm labor, workers where tips and/or commissions form part of the wage, and certain teen workers. It outlaws child labor, generally prohibiting, with certain specific exemptions, employment of individuals less than 16 years of age.

A key definition is that of an ***employment relationship***. This definition distinguishes between an independent contractor and an employee, who is subject to the FLSA. In the application of the FLSA, an employee, as distinguished from an independent contractor, is one who, "as a matter of economic reality, follows the usual path of an employee and is dependent on the business which he or she serves." Many businesses fall prey to the temptation to misclassify employees as a matter of economic convenience and suffer the consequences later.

A key distinction between employees is *exempt vs. non-exempt*. Section 13(a)(l) of the FLSA exempts executive, administrative, professional, and outside sales employees from the minimum wage and overtime requirements of the FLSA, provided they meet certain tests regarding job duties and responsibilities and are compensated *on a salary basis* at not less than stated amounts. In general, specific tests apply and no more than twenty percent of an employee's tasks may fall outside the guidelines.

Occupational Safety and Health Act

The Occupational Safety and Health Act (OSH Act) requires that employers provide "safe and healthful working conditions for working men and women." Significant detail regarding this legislation and resulting regulations may be found in the chapters entitled "Safety Overview" and "OSHA and the Hazardous Materials Manager," of this text and, as such, will not be covered here. It is incumbent upon all employers, especially those involved in the environmental business sector to be familiar with the requirements of the OSH Act. A key concept is the *General Duty Clause*. Specific requirements for general industry are found in 29 CFR 1910 and for the construction industry in 29 CFR 1926.

Title VII of the Civil Rights Act of 1964

Title VII of the Civil Rights Act of 1964 made it unlawful for an employer to "fail or refuse to hire or to discharge any individual, or otherwise to discriminate against any individual with respect to his compensation, terms, conditions or privileges or employment, because of such individual's race, color, religion, sex, or national origin." The final bill also allowed sex to be a consideration when sex is a bona fide occupational qualification for the job. Title VII of the act created the Equal Employment Opportunity Commission (EEOC) to implement the law. Title VII prohibits not only intentional discrimination, but also practices that have the effect of discriminating against individuals because of their race, color, national origin, religion, or sex.

A key concept is prohibition against ***sexual harassment*** which includes practices ranging from direct requests for sexual favors to workplace conditions that create a hostile environment for persons of either gender, including same sex harassment. (The *hostile environment* standard also applies to harassment on the basis of race, color, national origin, religion, age, and disability.) In addition, *pregnancy based discrimination* is prohibited. Pregnancy, childbirth, and related medical conditions must be treated in the same way as other temporary illnesses or conditions.

Other Federal Laws and Requirements

The Americans with Disabilities Act. The Americans with Disabilities Act (ADA) was designed to provide civil rights protections to individuals with disabilities similar to those provided to individuals on the basis of race, color, sex, national origin, age, and religion. It guarantees equal opportunity for individuals with disabilities in public accommodations, employment, transportation, State and local government services, and telecommunications. The ADA prohibits discrimination in all employment practices, including job application procedures, hiring, firing, advancement, compensation, training, and other terms, conditions, and privileges of employment. It applies to recruitment, advertising, tenure, layoff, leave, fringe benefits, and all other employment-related activities. Since July 26, 1994, the Title I employment provisions apply to private employers, State and local governments, employment agencies, and labor unions with 15 or more employees. Key definitions of the Act are *qualified disability* and *reasonable accommodation*. An employer must make a reasonable accommodation to allow an employee with a disability to perform a job function for which they would otherwise be qualified. Although very uncommon in the environmental business arena, businesses that offer public accommodation must provide accessibility and utility of their premises and environs.

The Rehabilitation Act. The Rehabilitation Act (1973) prohibits employers holding Federal government contracts and subcontracts totaling more than $2,500 in value from discriminating against handicapped people. If the employer holds Federal government contracts and subcontracts worth more than $50,000, then it has to develop and implement a written affirmative action program for handicapped people.

The Family and Medical Leave Act. The Family and Medical Leave Act (1993) requires employers with 15 or more employees to grant qualified employees unpaid leave for serious illness, birth, adoption or a variety of health-related issues that the employee or his or her immediate family members, may experience. Employers must keep the employee's job open until he or she returns.

The Immigration Reform and Control Act. The Immigration Reform and Control Act (1986, 1990, and 1996) requires all employers to determine whether their employees are legally able to work in the United States.

The Older Workers Benefit Protection Act. The Older Workers Benefit Protection Act (1990) prohibits employers with 20 or more employees from discriminating against employees aged 40 or more in early retirement and other benefit plans.

The Pregnancy Discrimination Act. The Pregnancy Discrimination Act (1978) requires employers with 15 or more employees to class pregnancy as a medical condition. The effect of this is to ensure that pregnant employees receive the same benefits and medical leave as do employees who are not pregnant.

The Age Discrimination in Employment Act. The Age Discrimination in Employment Act (1967) prohibits all employers with 20 or more employees from discriminating against employees aged 40 or more. It eliminates company policies that mandate retirement at age 70 (with the exception of certain executives who may be required to retire at age 65).

The Equal Pay Act. The Equal Pay Act (1963) requires employers with two or more employees that produce goods for interstate commerce to pay men and women equally for the same job.

Tax Law. Tax Law whether local, State or Federal, is well beyond the scope of this chapter. Acquiring the services of an accountant with knowledge of all applicable tax codes is perhaps the best investment a small business person can make in the start-up of a new business. Midsized and larger businesses usually have in-house accounting and legal counsel, backed up by independent professional services.

Management Topics

Personnel Management

In service organizations, people are the main asset and effective management is essential to maximizing the return to the company. One pitfall technical professionals must avoid is approaching management issues in the same fashion as they approach technical issues. People are very complex and do not all respond the same way to stimuli encountered in the workplace. Construction and product suppliers face different problems in dealing with skilled and unskilled labor. Many markets are unionized and union labor must be used in whole or in part. It is important to note that a firm generally is prohibited from interfering with labor union membership or employees organizing into unions.

In addition, construction businesses must deal with personnel and policy issues associated with the extensive travel that is often required.

Typical responsibilities of personnel management include

- Recruiting and hiring
- Classifying job titles
- Preparing salary scales
- Counseling and dealing with disciplinary issues
- Developing safety standards
- Providing benefit programs (insurance, 401k, *etc.*)
- Conducting performance reviews
- Identifying strengths for professional development
- Matching skill sets with project needs for proper staffing
- Providing training

Motivation

Some employees may perform satisfactorily as long as their firm offers competitive compensation, benefits, and working conditions. However, many employees want responsibility, the opportunity to develop, and recognition of accomplishment in addition to financial compensation.

Employees' feelings about their jobs are greatly influenced by workplace atmosphere. The office or worksite should be a pleasant place to work. Little things can make a big difference. Employee get-togethers sponsored by the company are an effective way to motivate professional staff and construction crews alike.

Performance-based compensation will encourage employees to perform in ways that result in the attainment of the firm's goals, while also meeting employees' personal objectives. Company goals usually include growth, profitability, quality service, efficiency, effectiveness, as well as image and reputation. To attract desirable employees, base pay and earnings potential should be competitive within the industry (equal to or better than the main competitors for employees). The pay plan must be objective and fair to all employees. Rewards should be commensurate with contributions.

Most studies have shown that salary alone is not a motivator. In fact, salary raises and promotions are most effective as motivators when they are announced (not the amount of the raise, but the fact itself). Employees respond to positive motivation and the ability to communicate with management where management listens and cares.

Discipline

Disciplinary actions are usually viewed as one of the most unpleasant realities management must face. However, effective leadership includes adequately addressing problems with employees. If problems aren't addressed, the morale of other good performing employees will be lost, as well as their loyalty and respect for the firm's leadership. Discipline must be implemented quickly and fairly and should not be delayed until the annual performance review. Discipline must be presented as an issue separate from personal feelings. A prevalent management theory of discipline administration follows these simple steps:

- Open the encounter with something positive, if possible (Sue, you have been doing well with project "A", lately.)
- State that there is a problem and be direct and precise in its description
- State what the disciplinary measures will be
- Provide a mechanism or plan for correction
- State what the consequences will be for future violations
- Remember, this is business, not personal. Discipline friends the same as those not personally liked

Myers-Briggs

Myers-Briggs is a personality test that measures four typological factors, Introversion/Extroversion, Thinking/Feeling, Intuition/Sensing, and Judging/Perceiving. This test is useful when assembling teams to work together. Also, the test can help avoid the classic problem of trying to fit a "square peg in a round hole." The first criterion defines a person's source and direction of energy expression. The second criterion defines the method of information perception a person gravitates toward. The third criterion defines the method of information processing, logic or emotion. The fourth criterion defines how the person implements the information that they have processed. The combination of the four criteria determines the personality type, which is named with the letters corresponding to the strongest element of each criterion. For example, ISTJ, stands for Introvert, Sensing, Thinking, Judging, and a generalized profile description for this personality type includes perfectionists and system builders. The process offers guidance as to which types of personalities will work well together and which ones will not.

Change

One thing that is constant in business is change, and with change usually comes resistance. Most employees are in an emotionally stable state during times of little change. However once a change occurs, employees undergo an emotional transformation that has several distinct phases that will take a certain time period to traverse. These phases include: Can't Function, Denial, Anger, Negotiation, Depression, Testing, and finally, Emotional Stability. This process is a normal human reaction that also takes place during the grieving process. It is important to understand that this process will occur and will take different people different time periods to go through. For example, if after a change is announced, one employee is angry and another depressed, a manager can infer that the depressed one is likely closer to acceptance. Many managers erroneously assume that change acceptance will occur just because they are the authority mandating it.

Organizational Theory

Organizational theory is a broad topic that encompasses the growth patterns of companies and character traits inherent in organizations at various stages in their development. Most young companies are small, most large companies have been around awhile, and most small old companies share characteristics that span both. Small companies can react faster and are less bureaucratic. Conversely, large companies make decisions slower and have more red tape. As companies grow, they will experience changes that are part of the process. More rules and procedures will be developed, some of which will formalize processes that have previously been unwritten. Having a better understanding of the structure, power, politics, and culture elements of organizations, will give not only a better understanding of what to expect in a growing company, but also, a better understanding of what to expect when dealing with various external organizations.

Strategic Planning

There are a variety of techniques that have been utilized for strategic planning purposes throughout the years. However, modern views have shifted from long-term planning to short-term planning, because most long-term plans have fallen by the wayside as firms act and react to more rapidly changing competitive landscapes. The following discussion focuses on a technique that is useful for strategic planning by evaluating a firm's internal strengths and weaknesses as well as its external opportunities and threats.

SWOT Analysis

SWOT is an acronym for Strengths, Weaknesses, Opportunities, and Threats. Strengths and Weaknesses are internal and Opportunities and Threats are external. An individual, a group, or an entire firm can perform the SWOT analysis. It is a useful tool for strategic planning, since it matches resources and capabilities to the competitive environment.

An example SWOT analysis for a firm is provided on the following page.

A general strategic plan can be formulated using the results of this analysis. From the example below, the firm may decide that its weaknesses will shift its focus to teaming opportunities that will capitalize on its strengths and help shield it from external threats. Alternatively, strategic decisions might include figuring out how to recruit and train new personnel to make up for some of the retiring work force and upgrading technology, which would keep the strength of the brand name and utilize the strong financial resources.

Ethics

Corporate Policy

It is necessary and proper for a business to develop and communicate to management and each employee a code of ethics. The code of ethics must be incorporated as an enforceable corporate policy. This code of ethics must include acceptable business practices as well as personal and professional conduct at the workplace. The emphasis here is *at the workplace.* Management must define acceptable conduct in specific terms. Acceptable conduct must, of course, comply with all applicable laws and regulations. Company policy should advocate and require personal responsibility for all management and non-management accountability in acceptance and implementation of the code of ethics. Key components of the code of ethics include

- Conduct with clients/customers
- Conduct with fellow employees
- Dealing with suppliers
- Conflicts of interest
- Gifts and entertainment
- Insider trading
- Intellectual property
- Protection of confidential information

- Proper use of company assets, *e.g.*, computers, vehicles, tools, and premises
- Compliance with laws and regulations
- Corporate responsibilities for implementation
- Employee responsibilities for implementation

Personal Professional Ethics

In addition to corporate policy, and the corporate code of ethics, it is incumbent on every environmental professional to adhere to a personal code of ethics and conduct. These codes define who we are and how we view ourselves and wish to be perceived by others. They are defined by our upbringing and contacts with peers whom we respect. It is not the business of this chapter to define this code for each individual but rather to remind the reader that the cornerstone of character is constructed on our views of fair and ethical treatment.

Codes of Ethics for Professional Organizations

Many professional organizations, including the *Academy of Certified Hazardous Materials Managers* have adopted codes of ethics for their members. Membership in the organization usually requires at least an implicit, if not literal, acceptance of these codes. In some cases, as in

---

Elements of a SWOT Analysis

Strengths

- Technical knowledge and skills
- Strong financial resources
- Brand name

Weaknesses

- High costs
- Retiring work force
- Outdated technology

Opportunities

- New regulations create client needs
- New technologies
- Teaming with complementary firms

Threats

- New regulations diminish client needs
- Increased competition
- Competition for new hires increases

most State boards of engineering registration, adherence to the canons of ethics is mandatory. Ethical violations can be punished by fines or even revocation of registration. The *Institute of Certified Hazardous Materials Managers* can and does revoke certifications where violations of the code of ethics or unethical or criminal behavior have occurred.

Bibliography

Allen, K. A., and P. Economy. *The Complete MBA for Dummies.* Foster City, CA: IDG Books Worldwide, 2000.

Chiappetta B, Larson K. D. *Fundamental Accounting Principles.* Chicago: Irwin, 1996.

Drake, S. M. *Freelancing for Dummies.* New York: Hungry Minds, Inc., 2001.

Garrison R. H., and E. W. Noreen. *Managerial Accounting.* Boston: Irwin McGraw-Hill, 2000.

McKeever, M. *How to Write a Business Plan*, 4th ed. Berkeley, CA: Nolo Press, 1997.

Mintzberg H. and J. B. Quinn. *The Strategy Process.* New Jersey: Prentice Hall, 1998.

Internet Resources

<http://amanet.org> (American Management Association. Homepage)

<http://www.bplans.com/> (Bplans: The Business Planning Experts. Homepage)

<http://www.business.com/> (Business.com, Smart Business Results. Homepage)

<http://www.business.gov> (The U. S. Government Official Business Link. Homepage)

<http://cbd.cos.com/> (U. S. Government Printing Office. FedBizOpps)

<http://www.construction.com/Network/Overview.asp> (McGraw-Hill Companies. McGraw-Hill Construction Network)

<http://www.dol.gov> (U. S. Department of Labor. Homepage)

<http://www.dol.gov/elaws/esa/flsa/screen5.asp> (U.S. Department of Labor . E-Laws–Fair Labor Standards Act Advisor)

<http://enr.construction.com/> (McGraw-Hill Companies. enr.com Engineering News Record)

<http://www.environmental-expert.com/> (Environmental Expert.com, Environmental Business Information. Homepage)

<http://www.firstgov.gov/Business/Business_Gateway.shtml> (The U. S. Government's Official Web Portal. Homepage)

<http://www.hoovers.com/free/> (Hoover's Online. Homepage)

<http://www.irs.gov/business/small/> (U.S. Internal Revenue Service, Department of the Treasury. Homepage)

<http://www.onlinewbc.gov/docs/starting/> (U.S. Small Business Administration, Online Women's Business Center. Starting Your Own Business)

<http://www.sba.gov> (U. S. Small Business Administration. Homepage)

<http://www.score.org/> (SCORE: Counselors to America's Small Business. Homepage)

<http://www.shrm.org> (Society for Human Resource Management. SHRM Online)

Doye B. Cox is a Senior Engineer/Project Manager for Barge Waggoner Sumner and Cannon, Inc. He has had major hazardous materials management responsibilities for over 29 years. Mr. Cox has extensive experience in the design and hands-on remediation of hazardous waste/materials sites. He has specific knowledge in the areas of hazardous materials chemistry, soil and water treatment techniques, and RCRA and OSHA regulations. Mr. Cox serves as the BWSC "expert" in preparation of demolition plans and specifications. In 1988, Mr Cox was elected to the Board of Directors of the Academy and served on the Board, and as an officer through 1993-1994 when he served as President of the Academy. He also served on the Board as Past President in 1994-1995. In 1986, along with Tom Carson, Mr. Cox edited a Certified Hazardous Materials Managers Study Guide for the Tennessee Valley Authority. By 1988 a CHMM Study Guide edited by Carson and Cox was published by the Institute of Hazardous Materials Management. Mr. Cox helped develop several TVA/State Regulatory Agency Sponsored CHMM training courses in Tennessee, Kentucky, Alabama, and Mississippi. The Handbook of Hazardous Materials Management continued to be edited by Mr. Cox through the 5th edition in 1995, and was used as the primary text for CHMM review courses until 1999. In 1999 the Hazardous Materials Desk Reference *was published with Mr. Cox serving as Editor-in-Chief. Mr. Cox continues to teach in review courses periodically.*

Daniel L. Todd is the Vice President and General Manager of Air Quality Services, LLC of Evansville, Indiana. He has been involved with advancing the field of air quality management since 1974, serving as a regulator, as a researcher, as the principal air specialist for an electric utility, and is currently managing a multi-faceted air related service provider. Mr. Todd has directed projects pertaining to ambient air monitoring, continuous emissions/opacity monitoring, source emissions testing, consulting, permitting, and regulatory development. He holds a BS (Environmental Science) from the University of Evansville and a MS in Environmental Science from Indiana University. Mr. Todd has been a Qualified Environmental Professional since 1995 and a Certified Hazardous Materials Manager since 1998. He is active in both the Indiana and national Air & Waste Management Association, serving on several committees. He also is involved with numerous industry organizations, and has provided air-related presentations at regional and national meetings.

Glenn R. "Chip" Carwell III, is a Senior Project Engineer with Golder Associates and has more than twelve years of experience assisting both industries and municipalities throughout the eastern United States on a wide variety of environmental engineering projects. He is licensed as a professional engineer in the state of Virginia and a Certified Hazardous Materials Manager (Master Level). His primary practice areas are Environmental Engineering and Industrial Compliance programs. Mr. Carwell has a BS in Civil Engineering from Old Dominion University and an MBA from Tennessee State University. His work experience includes storm water evaluation and modeling, storm water pollution prevention plans, SPCC and Facility Response Plans, NPDES and storm water permitting, hazardous waste contingency plans and manifest preparation, industrial wastewater treatment operation and maintenance, multi-media regulatory compliance audits, landfill closure design, and groundwater contamination fate and transport evaluation. Mr. Carwell is a member of the American Society of Civil Engineers (ASCE), and the Academy of Certified Hazardous Materials Managers.

Part II

Safety Principles

CHAPTER 9

Safety Overview

Guy S. Camomilli, MPH, CSP, CHSP, CHMM

Introduction

An in-depth discussion about safely managing hazardous materials would take more than a single book, let alone a single chapter. Therefore, this chapter will attempt to deal broadly with the principles of safety and health associated with managing hazardous materials and substances. First, it is necessary to define the categories and subcategories of hazardous materials.

Hazardous materials can be characterized as having one or more of the following three hazardous properties: chemical, physical, and/or biological. For example, carbon monoxide is a chemical toxicant, but is also a physical hazard when it is stored under high pressure.

Chemical Hazards

Chemical hazards are generally divided into toxic, reactive, corrosive, and flammable subcategories.

Toxic chemicals may produce reactions that are either acute or chronic, depending on the exposure concentrations. ***Acutely toxic*** materials are usually irritants that produce an immediate effect. Acute reactions are characterized by rapid onset and short duration of symptoms. Damage to the body from acute reactions may be reversible or irreversible.

A *chronic toxin* is one that exhibits no symptoms or only mild symptoms at the time of exposure, but may build up after a series of exposures. A period of latency may follow, but chronic toxins will typically produce unhealthy systemic effects some time later. Chronic reactions may be triggered by a build-up of the material (*e.g.,* lead) in body tissues, or by the immune system becoming sensitized to specific toxins, such as organic solvents.

Toxic chemicals are subdivided into irritants, sensitizers, tumorogens, mutagens, and teratogens. *Sensitizers* are substances that change the body's proteins. Once these proteins are altered, the body fails to recognize them as its own and reacts by stimulating the immune system to produce antibodies. The antibodies are not immediately produced but are built up after a period of exposure. Then, when next exposed to the same substance, the body tries to fight off what it perceives as an infection. An allergic reaction occurs as the antibodies try to destroy the altered proteins. This reaction can cause many harmful symptoms, including the inability to breathe.

Tumorogens produce tumors. These tumors may be *benign* (noncancerous) or *malignant* (cancerous). Tumorogens alter the genetic code in body tissues and cause the abnormal growth of body tissues. This abnormal growth is a tumor and is usually seen as a swelling or enlargement. Those tumorogens that cause malignant growth are called *carcinogens*.

Mutagens are substances that alter the genetic code in the gametes (sperm and/or eggs) of the body. The altered genetic code changes the appearance or function of the affected part of the body. This change is passed along to following generations as a permanent alteration of the genetic structure.

Teratogens produce genetic changes or tumors in developing fetuses. Like mutagens, the altered genetic code produces some change in the appearance or function of the body. However, unlike mutagens, teratogens do not affect the genetic code of the gametes and so are not passed on to following generations.

Reactive chemicals produce a violent reaction when exposed to or mixed with another substance, sometimes even water. The usual textbook example of a reactive chemical is pure sodium metal which is reactive in water.

Corrosive chemicals are materials that disintegrate body tissues. They particularly affect the water and fatty tissues of the body, and are capable of causing rapid and deep destruction of tissue. Examples of corrosives are lye and sulfuric acid.

Flammable substances are defined differently by the standards of various Federal agencies and industry organizations. Additionally, different agencies define substances that will ignite and burn differently. For example, the Department of Transportation defines

- *Combustible liquid* as any liquid having a flashpoint at or above 100°F and below 200°F

- *Flammable liquid* as any liquid having a flash point below 100°F

- *Pyrophoric liquid* as any liquid that may ignite spontaneously when exposed to air that is 55°C (130°F) or below

- *Flammable gas* as any compressed gas meeting the requirements for lower flammability limit, flammability limit range, flame projection, or flame propagation criteria

- *Flammable solids* as any solid material, other than an explosive which is liable to cause fires through friction, absorption of moisture, spontaneous chemical changes, retained heat from manufacturing or processing, or which can be ignited readily and when ignited burns so vigorously and persistently as to create a serious transportation hazard

However, OSHA defines

- *Flammable liquid* as any liquid having a flashpoint below 100°F (37.8°C), except any mixture having components with flashpoints of 100°F (37.8°C) or higher, the total volume of which make up 99 percent or more of the total volume of the mixture

- *Combustible liquid* as any liquid having a flashpoint at or above 100°F

EPA says that a waste exhibits the *characteristic of ignitability* if a representative sample of the waste has any of the following properties:

- It is a liquid (other than an aqueous solution containing less than 24 percent alcohol by volume)

- Has a flash point less than 60°C (140°F), as determined by a Pensky-Martens Closed Cup Tester, using the test method specified in ASTM Standard D–93–79 or D–93–80, or a Setaflash Closed Cup Tester, using the test method specified in ASTM Standard D–3278–78, or as determined by an equivalent test method approved by the Administrator under procedures set forth in 40 CFR 260.20 and 260.21

Which standard (and which definition) applies to a specific situation will depend on which agency has jurisdiction (*i.e.,* Occupational Safety and Health Administration [OSHA], Environmental Protection Agency [EPA], Department of Transportation [DOT], *etc.*). When in doubt, the best approach is to use the most conservative parameters.

Physical Hazards

Materials that are in the category of physical hazards fall into the following groups: ionizing and nonionizing radiation, thermal, and pneumatic high-pressure hazards. Radiation safety hazards will not be discussed in this chapter but are covered in the chapter on radiation safety principles in this book.

Thermal hazards can be subdivided into substances that are cold or hot. These divisions are *not* related to heat or cold stress from exposure to the environment. Temperature tolerance limits vary with the part of the body that is exposed and the duration of exposure. The guideline temperatures given below are for exposure of the bare hand. The duration of these exposures is the human reflex time. The temperature tolerances become more critical when the duration of exposure is longer. The following temperatures are only guidelines.

Cold substances are considered hazardous to the touch if they are 32°F (0°C) or colder. This is because moist skin will stick to the surface of frozen material. Extremely cold substances are known as *cryogenics* and are defined as substances which are −148°F (−100°C) or colder.

Hot substances are considered thermally hazardous if they are 120°F (49°C) or hotter to the touch.

Pneumatic and hydraulic high-pressure hazards come from pressurized gases and liquids. In addition to the chemical hazards associated with some gases, compressed gases contain considerable potential energy and can be serious physical hazards. Even gases stored at very low pressures can present a danger, and small volumes can be hazardous at high pressures. Vessels or systems that are overpressurized may leak, or they may suddenly and catastrophically fail, releasing a violent shock wave of energy.

Any fluid being propelled out of an opening produces thrust in the opposite direction. If a valve or fitting has broken off, the container may become a missile or pressure lines may whip violently. Pressure vessels have been known to fly through cement block walls and chain link fences.

Injury can also result from the injection of gases or fluids into the body. Injection injuries can come from undetected, pin-hole sized, high-pressure leaks. Highly pressurized streams of fluid can also cause injuries. High pressure streams of fluid often penetrate several layers of tissue. Once this liquid is inside the body, it may be very difficult to remove. To minimize pneumatic and hydraulic high-pressure hazards, regulators for compressed *shop* air should be set at 30 pounds per square inch or less. Piping and tubing should be used wherever possible; flexible pressurized lines should be tied securely to immovable structures, or otherwise secured, to prevent the lines from whipping if they become detached.

The ensuing OSHA standards discussed in this chapter apply either specifically, or generally to the safe use, handling, and/or control of hazardous materials. Every Certified Hazardous Materials Manager (CHMM) should study each standard in greater detail before assessing materials and/or their hazards for practical applications.

Hazardous Noise. Although *noise* is not a substance, it bears discussion here because it is a pervasive problem in many industries that utilize hazardous materials and/or hazardous materials processes. Exposure to high levels of noise may cause hearing loss and other harmful health effects. The extent of damage depends primarily on the intensity of the noise and the duration of the exposure. Noise-induced hearing loss can be temporary or permanent. Temporary hearing loss results from short-term exposures to noise, with normal hearing returning after period of rest.

Generally, prolonged exposure to high noise levels over a period of time gradually causes permanent damage.

OSHA's hearing conservation requirements necessitate that employers monitor noise exposure levels in a way that accurately identifies which employees are exposed to noise at or above 85 decibels (dB) averaged over 8 working hours, or an 8-hour time-weighted average (TWA). Employers must monitor all employees whose noise exposure is equivalent to or greater than a noise exposure received in 8 hours where the noise level is constantly 85 dB. The exposure measurement must include all continuous, intermittent, and impulsive noise within an 80 dB to 130 dB range and must be taken during a typical work situation. Employers must establish and maintain an audiometric testing program that provides baseline audiograms, annual audiograms, training, and follow-up procedures if employees are found to have noise induced, sensorineural hearing loss. Employers must make audiometric testing available at no cost to all employees who are exposed to an action level of 85 dB or above, measured as an 8-hour TWA. The National Institute for Occupational Safety and Health (NIOSH) has considerable information on hazardous noise and is recommended reading. NIOSH can be contacted at NIOSH at 1-800-35-NIOSH or visit the NIOSH web site at http://www.cdc.gov/niosh for more information.

Occupational Safety and Health Act of 1970

The Occupational Safety and Health Act (OSH) Act of 1970 (PL 91–596), was passed by the 91st Congress on December 29, 1970. It has been amended since then. The intent of the OSH Act is

> [t]o assure safe and healthful working conditions for working men and women; by authorizing enforcement of the standards developed under the Act; by assisting and encouraging the States in their efforts to assure safe and healthful working conditions; by providing for research, information, education, and training in the field of occupational safety and health; and for other purposes.

The 91st Congress intended to reduce the number of occupational safety and health hazards. The law sought to motivate employers and employees to be responsible for achieving and maintaining safe and healthful working conditions.

Congress also adopted the idea of *national consensus standards* as a way to establish nationally recognized standards of safety and health. They then created the ***general duty clause*** in Section 5(a)1 of the OSH Act. The general duty clause declared that each employer has a duty to furnish to his employees a workplace free from recognized hazards that are likely to cause serious physical harm or death. The implication of the clause is that employers must use common sense in providing a safe and healthful workplace.

Several conditions must be met before OSHA can invoke the general duty clause: (1) there must be a hazard which caused or is likely to cause serious physical harm or death; (2) the employer must have recognized the hazard and failed to remedy the hazardous condition; and (3) there must have been a feasible way to correct the hazard. If all of the above conditions are met, OSHA can invoke the general duty clause.

OSHA's objectives are to attain the highest degree of health and safety protection for the employee that is reasonably obtainable. For this reason, many standards are expressed in terms of *objective criteria* and of *the performance desired*.

The prudent employer utilizes ***best practices***. Best practices means the employer provides the best possible engineering and administrative means (over and above the specific requirements of law) to control hazards in the workplace. In other words, the employer does what is necessary to best protect the employee. This concept is difficult to market to many employers because ***prevention*** (nonoccurrence) is neither quantifiable nor easily proven. The employer who looks only at the costs for short-term best practices may not recognize them as a way to prevent greater long-term expenses. The employer who truly holds at heart the safety and well-being of the employees will reap the additional long-term benefits of employee dedication, productivity, efficiency and safety.

In addition to the Federal OSHA standards, many states have their own OSHA-approved occupational safety and health regulations. The provisions of State regulations must be *at least* as stringent as the OSHA requirements. The hazardous materials manager must evaluate all requirements and invoke the most judicious standards and/or best practices for his area of responsibility.

General Industry Standards: 29 CFR 1910—Occupational Safety and Health Standards

Subpart B—Adoption and Extension of Established Federal Standards

29 CFR 1910.19: Special Provisions for Air Contaminants. This standard makes all of 29 Code of Federal Regulations (CFR) 1910 applicable to various specialized industries: construction, shipyard employment, longshoring, and work in marine terminals.

Subpart C—General Safety and Health Provisions

29 CFR 1910.20: Access to Employee Exposure and Medical Records. The provisions of this standard give employees the right of access to their exposure and medical records. Employees must be provided access to their records within 15 working days of a written request. The records are to be provided at no cost to the employee.

Subpart G—Occupational Health and Environmental Control

20 CFR 1910.94: Ventilation. The ventilation standard encompasses the application of many requirements for employee protection from airborne materials, and deals with topics such as abrasive blasting, grinding, polishing, buffing, spray finishing, and open surface tanks. The standard requires that certain breathable dusts and chemical vapors be kept below the levels specified in the 29 CFR 1910.1000 series of standards. Exposure to abrasives and surface coatings of materials must be kept to a minimum. The standard allows Personal Protective Equipment (PPE) such as safety glasses, exhaust

ventilation, respiratory protection, Mine Safety and Health Administration (MSHA) approved respirators and cartridges, gloves, *etc.*, to be used in order to minimize the employees' exposure to hazardous materials.

However, ventilation must be provided in accordance with the provisions of 29 CFR 1910.107(d) of the Standard for Spray Finishing Using Flammable or Combustible Materials, and fresh air, free of contamination must be supplied to a spray booth or room in quantities equal to the volume of air exhausted through the spray booth.

Keep in mind that the best way to minimize exposure is to substitute nonhazardous materials for hazardous ones wherever possible or use engineering controls, such as local exhaust ventilation to remove hazardous airborne gases, vapors, mists, dusts, *etc.* Substitution of less hazardous materials or use of engineering controls should always preferable over the use of PPE.

Subpart H—Hazardous Materials

Hazardous materials can be a threat not only to employees, but also to the community. OSHA does not require that businesses report their inventories of hazardous substances to the community or local fire department but it does require that employers have MSDSs for all hazardous substances.

The Emergency Planning and Community Right to Know Act (EPCRA) Section 311 picks up where OSHA leaves off and requires facilities that have MSDSs for chemicals held above certain quantities, to submit copies of their Material Safety Data Sheets (MSDSs) or a list of MSDS chemicals to their State Emergency Response Commissions (SERC), Local Emergency Planning Committees (LEPC), and local fire departments.

Even if it were not required to do so, it makes sense to coordinate with the local fire department so that they will be aware of any hazardous substances in your facility. Doing so will better prepare them for any emergencies that may arise at your facility.

29 CFR 1910.101: Compressed Gases (General Requirements). Compressed gases offer unique material hazards. In addition to the obvious physical hazards, compressed gases may also possess the hazardous properties of some liquids or solids. They may be toxic, flammable, corrosive, reactive, *etc*. OSHA recognizes that the Compressed Gas Association (CGA) and Department of Transportation (DOT) provide an industry consensus on the ways that compressed gas hazards can be effectively controlled. OSHA refers to and incorporates this industry consensus into the 29 CFR 1910.101 standard.

Under this standard, employers are required to ensure that any compressed gas containers under their control are in a safe condition. *Safe conditions* are listed in the DOT Hazardous Materials Regulations (49 CFR 171–179) and the CGA Pamphlets C–6–2001, "Standards for Visual Inspection of Compressed Gas Cylinders" and C–8–1997, "Standards for Requalification of DOT–34T, CTC–34T, and TC–34HTM Seamless Steel Cylinders." Handling, storage, and use of all compressed gases in cylinders, portable tanks, rail tankcars, or motor vehicle cargo tanks, must be accomplished according to CGA's Pamphlet P–1–2000, "Safe Handling of Compressed Gases in Containers." The safety relief equipment for compressed gas containers must have pressure relief devices installed on them and must be maintained as is outlined in CGA's Pamphlets S–1.1–2002, "Pressure Relief Device Standards Part 1–Cylinders for Compressed Gases" and S–1.2–1995, "Pressure Relief Device Standards, Part 2–Cargo and Portable Tanks or Compressed Gases."

The following standards are referred to here because they apply to the specific hazardous gases named in their headings. Each standard outlines the safe handling, transportation, and storage of its named substance. The OSH Act requires compliance to the standards that are incorporated by reference, such as those from the CGA, American Society of Mechanical Engineers (ASME), or DOT:

- 29 CFR 1910.102 Acetylene
- 29 CFR 1910.103 Hydrogen
- 29 CFR 1910.104 Oxygen
- 29 CFR 1910.105 Nitrous oxide

29 CFR 1910.107: Spray Finishing Using Flammable and Combustible Liquids. Spray finishing uses a liquid or powdered material to provide a coating on an article. The 29 CFR 1910.107 standard regulates many aspects of spray finish-

ing, such as (1) the construction of spray booths, (2) the use of electrical equipment, and (3) other potential sources of ignition in the spray finishing process. This standard also covers:

- Ventilation requirements for spray finishing
- Storage and handling of flammable and combustible liquids
- Locations in which spraying is permitted
- Cleaning of tools and equipment
- Disposal of coating residues
- Control of contaminated employee clothing
- Use of cleaning solvents
- Combining hazardous materials
- Requirements for fire protection during spray finishing work

29 CFR 1910.108: Dip Tanks Containing Flammable or Combustible Liquids. Any tank or other container which contains a flammable or combustible liquid and in which articles or materials are immersed for any process, is considered by this standard to be a *dip tank*. The 29 CFR 1910.108 standard covers:

- Dip tank ventilation
- Dip tank construction
- Storage and handling of dip tank liquids
- Potential sources for ignition of dip tank vapors (including electrical sources)
- Operation and maintenance of dip tanks and their surrounding facilities
- Requirements for extinguishing fires
- Requirements for special dip tank processes

Dip tanks containing flammable or combustible liquids produce vapors. Vapors can be dangerous, and so dip tank areas must be limited to the smallest practical space. Tanks and drain boards must be constructed of noncombustible materials, be properly supported, and be equipped with bottom drains and automatic fire extinguishing hardware. Only the proper National Electrical Code (NEC) Class, Division, and Group rated electrical services are allowed to be installed in the vapor areas of dip tanks. These fixtures are rated by the National Fire Protection Association's

(NFPA) NEC to prevent any inadvertent ignition of the vapors by an electrical spark. Only the minimum amounts of combustible materials are allowed to be stored at the work site, and the storage of combustible debris is prohibited.

The 29 CFR 1910.108 standard requires periodic inspections. Warning signs must be posted, and there must be easy access to fire extinguishers. The extinguishers must be suitable for use on burning flammable and combustible liquids.

29 CFR 1910.109: Explosives and Blasting Agents.
The 29 CFR 1910.109 standard outlines the proper storage, handling, and transportation of explosives, including requirements for ammonium nitrate, and small arms ammunition. The proper packaging, marking, transportation, use, loading, and initiation of explosive charges and small arms ammunition, and construction of storage magazines, are also covered.

29 CFR 1910.110: Storage and Handling of Liquefied Petroleum Gases.
This standard regulates many aspects of the commercial use and handling of liquid petroleum (LP) gases. The requirements for LP gas systems, equipment, and facilities are discussed, as well as the specific requirements for valves, accessories, piping, gauges, hoses, and safety devices. The standard covers how to transfer LP gases into and out of certain vehicles and how to properly mark LP gas containers. There are also safety requirements concerning the location of LP gas tanks and cylinder systems.

Many liquid petroleum gases are odorless in their natural states. Therefore, the 29 CFR 1910.110 standard requires that all LP gases be *odorized* so that leaks may be quickly detected. The standard also addresses the requirements for LP gas systems on commercial vehicles and at LP gas service stations.

29 CFR 1910.111: Storage and Handling of Anhydrous Ammonia.
The 29 CFR 1910.111 standard imposes specific requirements on the design, construction, marking, location, testing, requalification, installation, and operation of anhydrous ammonia systems. Provisions are included in the standard for:

- Refrigerated ammonia storage systems
- Any associated pumps and compressors

- Safety relief devices
- Gauges, fittings, and valves
- Hoses, piping and tubing

This standard also has components which outline the requirements for respiratory protection, quick-drench facilities, and how to safely transfer ammonia liquid.

[handwritten margin note: No – Does not apply if no chilling required in storage — see p 194 (correct on 194)]

29 CFR 1910.119: Process Safety Management of Highly Hazardous Chemicals.
This standard applies to nonretail processes that use chemicals at or above the threshold quantities listed in Appendix A of the standard. Also covered is any process that uses 10,000 pounds or more of a flammable liquid or gas stored below its natural boiling point (without using chilling or refrigeration), except for those substances used as fuels.

The 29 CFR 1910.119 standard requires employees to participate in the employer's development of Process Hazard Analyses (PHAs). PHAs are conducted to identify and define the hazards posed by the processes that use hazardous chemicals. PHAs must go into enough detail to adequately deal with the complexity of the system. PHAs are required to use specific methods in order to

- Identify and evaluate hazards
- Pinpoint previous incidents that have catastrophic potential
- Select engineering and administrative safeguards against hazards
- Outline detection methods for sensing hazardous materials releases
- Describe the possible effects on employees if the workplace safeguards fail

The standard requires PHAs to be updated at least every five years. Operating procedures must conform to current practices. At least once a year, the employer is required to certify that its operating procedures are both current and accurate. Operating procedures are required to

- Reflect the entire range of routine operations
- Outline emergency operations
- Discuss the consequences of deviation from written procedures

- List the precautions that will prevent personnel exposure

- Warn of special or unique hazards

Written procedures must also establish the protocol for making changes to processes, equipment, and materials used. The operating procedures must also include an emergency action plan and procedures for handling small releases of chemicals.

Both initial and refresher training is required by the standard. *Initial training* is required before an employee begins participating in operations that use highly hazardous chemicals, and *refresher training* is required a minimum of every three years. The employer must document all training. (Test results are considered evidence of training and understanding.) Similar requirements apply to any contractors and maintenance personnel of the employer who work on or around the process equipment.

Each process-related incident that resulted, or could have resulted, in a catastrophic release must be investigated within 48 hours of occurrence. Employers should keep a record of these operational mishaps as they occur. The record can be analyzed for trends that reveal weak spots in the PHAs and operating procedures. Operating procedures can then be improved in response to these mishaps and close calls. Compliance audits are required by the standard in order to ensure that procedures are adequately safe.

The 29 CFR 1910.119 standard includes appendices containing examples of safe processes, voluntary guidelines, and recommendations to help guide the employer and/or hazardous materials manager toward compliance.

29 CFR 1910.120: Hazardous Waste Operations and Emergency Response.
This standard covers hazardous substances spill, cleanup, and emergency response operations. Emergency responses are not limited to hazardous waste operations. Once any toxic chemical is spilled, it becomes a hazardous waste by definition and is covered under the provisions of this standard. Training and other provisions of the standard are required to protect workers and are necessary whenever exposure to toxicants is possible. Exposure potential is particularly high during emergencies.

Sites that generate small quantities of hazardous materials are conditionally exempt to certain provisions of the 29 CFR 1910.120 standard.

OSHA believes that "[t]he treatment and disposal of hazardous wastes under [the Resource Conservation and Recovery Act (RCRA) and the Comprehensive Environmental Response, Compensation, and Liability Act (CERCLA)] creates a significant risk to the safety and health of employees who work in treatment and disposal operations." The most significant risks to employees come from exposure to hazardous wastes by means of absorption through the skin and inhalation. See 40 CFR 260—265 and 305 for more information.

The standard emphasizes the necessity of limiting an employee's exposure to any health hazards on the worksite. The requirements include:

- A safety and health program which incorporates the employer's organizational structure

- A comprehensive plan to develop procedures, and identify and control hazards

- Standard operating procedures for safety and health

- A safety and health plan that integrates the general program with procedures for specific sites

- A safety and health training program

- A medical surveillance program

Hazardous waste sites are evaluated in order to identify specific hazards and determine the appropriate procedures for controlling these risks to safety. The preliminary evaluation determines the potential hazards and recommends the appropriate protection employees must have before entering the site. The evaluators must be especially careful to identify any hazards that may be Immediately Dangerous to Life or Health (IDLH), such as confined spaces or hazardous atmospheres. They must pay attention to *biological indicators*, such as dead animals or vegetation. Based on the preliminary evaluation, Personal Protective Equipment (PPE) is selected, and the appropriate site-control procedures are implemented.

Site evaluation and characterization is a continuous process, and the assessments are used to develop and *maintain* a valid safety and health plan. *All* site personnel should be constantly alert to changing site conditions and respond to any new information on the hazards around them.

Employees at hazardous waste operations face serious health and safety risks. Frequent training is needed to reinforce the safe work practices necessary to avoid exposure to these hazards. The employer must provide training that is consistent with the worker's job function and responsibilities. The training must be provided frequently enough to strengthen the initial training and to update employees on any new policies or procedures.

All employees who may be exposed to hazardous substances, including supervisors and managers, must be trained to the level their job requires *before* they are permitted to engage in, supervise, or manage hazardous waste operations. All employees whose routine activities may potentially expose them to hazardous substances are required to have a minimum of 40 hours of off-site classroom instruction, and three days of actual field experience. Once again, this includes supervisors and managers who are potentially exposed. The field experience portion of the training must be accomplished under the direct guidance of a trained and experienced supervisor. Employees who are on-site, but are not potentially exposed over the Permissible Exposure Limit (PEL), are required to have a minimum of 24 hours of off-site instruction and one day of field experience. All affected employees must complete eight hours of refresher training annually.

Instructors and supervisors who train employees for hazardous waste operations must have either completed a training program for the subjects they teach, or earned academic credentials and have experience teaching those subjects. Trainers must demonstrate that they are competent to instruct and that they possess sufficient knowledge of the subject matter.

Some site conditions require a medical surveillance program. The program must include free medical examinations and consultations. The employer is required to keep records of these examinations and consultations, and to provide the results to the employees.

The employer needs to know the hazards faced by employees in order to develop and implement effective control measures. A written safety and health program forces the systematic identification of hazards in the workplace, makes employees aware of these hazards, and identifies the proper response employees should have to them. The more accurate and detailed the information available about a site, the more protective measures can be tailored to the actual hazards that the employees may encounter.

Employers use engineering controls, work practices, and/or personal protective equipment to protect their employees. These controls and/or equipment must keep employee exposures below the permissible exposure limits. Specific methods for hazardous materials exposure determination and limits are provided in 29 CFR 1910, Subparts G and Z, and in the American Conference of Governmental Industrial Hygienist's *Documentation of the Threshold Limit Values and Biological Exposure Indices* (ACGIH's TLVs). At the time of this writing, the latest edition was published in 2003, but three supplemental updates had already been issued. Employers who use the ACGIH's TLVs must be certain to use the most up-to-date values.

In situations where an employee may be exposed to hazardous concentrations of chemicals, the conditions of the site must be monitored. Before entering into potentially hazardous atmospheres, the employee or supervisor must check for the presence of any conditions that may be Immediately Dangerous to Life or Health (IDLH), including flammable and oxygen-deficient atmospheres. If IDLH conditions exist, employees must not enter the area. The employee or supervisor must continue periodic monitoring of site conditions when the possibility of an IDLH condition exists. If exposure levels may possibly have risen over the PEL or over the previously documented level of the location being monitored, then the employee or supervisor must continue periodic monitoring while the employee is exposed. The root cause of the IDHL condition must be rectified prior to employee entry.

DOT, OSHA, EPA, and State regulations describe the correct way to handle drums and other containers during cleanup operations. The people in charge of cleanup operations should pay particular attention to container inspection, labeling, and handling; fire safety; and protection of the environment.

Every employer must develop a decontamination procedure in order to minimize the employees' contact with hazardous substances. All employees who enter contaminated areas are required to decontaminate or dispose of their clothing and equipment *before* leaving the contaminated area. A commercial laundry or other cleaning establishment familiar with the potentially harmful effects of the contaminated clothing should launder the clothing. The employers may also need to provide showers and change rooms.

Any employer who assigns employees to the danger area when an emergency occurs must develop an emergency response plan. The plan must address:

- Pre-emergency planning

- Evacuation routes and procedures

- Emergency recognition and prevention

- Personnel assignments

- Lines of authority

- Communication

- Decontamination procedures

- First aid and emergency medical treatment

- Safe distances

- Places of safe refuge

- Security

- Critique of the response and follow-up

The plan must contain the topography, layout, and weather conditions at the site, and the procedures for reporting incidents to the Federal, State, and local authorities. The plan must be compatible with the Federal, State, and local plans, and must be reviewed and rehearsed regularly.

Employers who provide temporary storage or disposal services under the Resource Conservation and Recovery Act must comply with special requirements in the standard. There are also special provisions for professionals who respond to emergencies involving hazardous materials.

Appendices A, B, and C of the standard provide tests and guidelines which may be used to assess compliance, and Appendix E provides training and curriculum guidelines for assistance in developing training for specific sites.

Subpart J—General Environmental Controls

29 CFR 1910.146: Permit-Required Confined Spaces. The Permit-Required Confined Spaces standard was formulated to protect employees in general industry from exposure to the hazards which may be found in *confined spaces*. This standard is a re-creation of the previous confined space standard. The main difference is that confined spaces have been separated into two categories: *non-permit confined spaces* and *permit-required confined spaces*. Non-permit confined spaces must have all of the following characteristics:

- Be large enough for an employee to enter and

- Have a limited or restricted means of entry or exit and

- Not have been designed for continuous occupancy

A permit-required confined space need only have one or more of the following qualities:

- Contains or has the potential to contain a hazardous atmosphere or

- Contains a material that has the potential to engulf an entrant or

- Has inwardly converging walls or a floor which slopes downward and tapers to a smaller cross section so that an entrant could be trapped or asphyxiated inside or

- Contains any other recognized serious safety or health hazard

Periodic reevaluation of the workplace for any changes, additions, or eradications of confined spaces is required. All assessments of confined spaces must be documented, and include information on the location(s) evaluated, the date of the evaluation, and the name and signature of the person performing the evaluation.

The employer has several duties under the 29 CFR 1910.146 standard. First, the workplace must be evaluated to determine if any areas meet the criteria of confined spaces. If any spaces are found that meet the criteria, danger signs or other effective means must be used to warn personnel not to enter the space. If an employer decides that its employees will *not* enter the confined space, the employer must take positive measures to ensure that no employee will be able to enter. If the employer decides that it is necessary for employees to enter the space, then the employer must develop and implement a written program that satisfies the requirements of the standard.

Many elements go into a program covering permit-required confined spaces, beyond controlling entry and identifying and evaluating the hazards. For example, the employer is required to

- Furnish all equipment necessary for the employee to enter safely

- Monitor the permit-required confined space when anyone is inside

- Provide at least one attendant throughout the duration of the entry

- Assign specific responsibilities to each person who has an active role in the entry

- Develop and implement emergency rescue procedures

- Develop and implement a detailed system for granting confined space entry permits

- Coordinate entries with other employers at the site

- Review entry operations and permit requirements when conditions change

Permits are required to display the following:

- Responsible supervisor's signature

- Date and authorized duration of the permit

- Permit space to be entered

- Reason for entry

- Names of the authorized entrants

- Names of attendants

- Name of the entry supervisor

- Any hazards of the space being entered

- Measures used to isolate or eliminate the hazards in the confined space

- Acceptable entry conditions

- Test results

- Available rescue and emergency services

- Communication procedures

- Required equipment

- Hot-work permits and any other pertinent information

Because the conditions in confined spaces can change, employers are required to reevaluate confined spaces if changes occur, in order to determine if the space must be reclassified.

When an employer makes arrangements for the employees of another employer to enter a confined space, the host employer is responsible for informing the contractor about the presence of the confined space(s) under its control. Additionally, the host employer must notify the subcontractor that a permit system for entry into confined spaces is in effect and that entries must be coordinated prior to their execution. The standard requires that personnel be debriefed after their entry work has been completed. Other information that must be made known is the hazards associated with the confined spaces, and the precautions and/or procedures implemented by the host.

As with most hazardous operations, training is crucial to guaranteeing that the risks are reduced to acceptable levels. Training must ensure that employees have mastered the procedures for entering a permit-required confined space. The training and evidence of mastery must be sufficient to do the job, and must be documented.

The requirements for entrants, attendants, supervisors, and rescue personnel are outlined in the 29 CFR 1910.146 standard, and Appendices A through E provide information and guidelines to assist in compliance.

29 CFR 1910.147:   The Control of Hazardous Energy (Lockout/Tagout). The lockout/tagout standard is covered here because it complements other measures that control exposure to materials that contain chemical and/or physical energy. This standard fits hand in glove with the process safety standard 29 CFR 1910.119 for general industry during servicing and/or maintenance of machines and equipment. It requires employers to set up a program and procedures to lock out and tag out devices in order to prevent employees from being exposed to uncontrolled energy.

OSHA classifies employees by their relationship to the potentially hazardous energy sources. *Affected employees* are those who operate or use the machinery, processes, or systems that are being maintained or serviced; *authorized employees* are those who actually perform the service or maintenance. Although OSHA does not name another category, it mentions the group of *all other employees*, who may have limited or indirect contact with the machinery, processes, or systems that are locked or tagged out.

The program requires the employer to control hazardous energy, train employees, and provide periodic inspections to ensure that starting the machine, activating the process or system, or releasing energy cannot injure an employee. At least once a year, the program must be inspected in order to certify the employer's compliance with the standard.

A *tagout system* is a system that only uses a tag, without a lock. A *tagout* system may be used in place of a *lockout and tagout* system *only* when the system cannot be locked out, and when it can be *proven* that the tagout is as effective in preventing injury as the lockout/tagout system.

As always, proper training is vital to effectively protecting employees. The degree and type of training required depends on the employee's role: affected, authorized, or other. The employer must train employees on the

- Purpose and function of the energy control program

- Recognition of hazardous energy sources

- Type and magnitude of the energy present in the workplace

- Means required for energy isolation and control

- Purpose and use of the control procedure

- Prohibition relative to starting or energizing machinery, or activating the process or system which is locked and/or tagged out

The employer must also verify that the employees possess the knowledge and skills necessary to follow the lockout/tagout procedures.

Other requirements of the standard outline how and by whom lockout/tagout operations may be performed. Lockout and/or tagout will only be performed by authorized employees. Prior to beginning the lockout/tagout of the machinery, process, or system, the authorized employee must notify all affected employees of the coming outage. Next, the machine must be shut off using the approved methods. All energy-isolating devices must be installed and all potential energy must be relieved or otherwise rendered safe. Then the authorized employee must verify that the machine, process, or system cannot transmit any hazardous energy. After the maintenance or repairs are completed and before energy is restored, the authorized employee must inspect the area to make sure that the machine, process, or system can be restored to operational status. Also, the authorized employee must make certain that all other employees are a safe distance from the machine, process, system, and/or energy source when it is made operational. The employee who placed the lock or tag will then remove the device(s). After the devices are removed, the authorized employee must notify all the affected employees that the machinery, process, or system is no longer locked or tagged out.

If a subcontractor's employees use this equipment, then they must advise the host employees of their lockout/tagout procedures and *vice versa*.

Where work continues across shifts, arrangements must be made between the authorized employees of interfacing shifts in order to assure continuity of information about operations performed and any new potential hazards. It is a good idea to have a *tie-in log* for this purpose.

Subpart Z—Toxic and Hazardous Substances

OSHA recognized that many employee deaths, diseases, and injuries were associated with exposure to hazardous substances. The objectives of the 29 CFR 1910.1000 series of standards were to: identify selected chemicals used in industry and determine their safe exposure limits (Personal Exposure Limits [PELs]).

Under some standards, monitoring of biological specimens and periodic medical examinations are required for exposed employees. Periodic analyses of blood and/or urine or specialized testing, such as pulmonary function testing, may be required. Medical monitoring may be required for employees who are required to use air-purifying respirators on the job, or work with asbestos, heavy metals, or other substances.

29 CFR 1910.1000: Air Contaminants. With air contaminants, as with all other toxicants, *the dose makes the poison.* Concentrations of air contaminants that are gases are generally expressed in parts per million (ppm). Concentrations of contaminants that exist in air as particles, such as dusts, are generally expressed in milligrams per cubic meter mg/m^3, or μg/m^3. Some mineral dusts, such as asbestos, talc, diatomaceous earth, soapstone, and graphite, are expressed as million particles per cubic foot of air (mppcf).

The 29 CFR 1910.1000 standard requires the employer to use *engineering controls* (where feasible) to protect employees from exposure to hazardous chemicals. *Administrative controls* and PPE are allowed only when engineering controls are not feasible. It also defines the limits to which an employee may be exposed to any chemical listed in the standard's tables. The exposure limits for the listed chemicals are defined in a number of ways.

There are two types of PEL. The eight-hour time weighted average (TWA) and the short term exposure limit (STEL). Employees must never be exposed beyond either of them.

The eight-hour *time-weighted average* of a chemical exposure is defined as the summation of the product $C \times T$, divided by the total duration of exposure; where C is the measured concentration during any period of time T (in hours), where the concentration remains constant. The eight-hour TWA refers to the time weighted exposure in an eight-hour period. The *equivalent exposure for an eight-hour work shift,* E, *can be calculated as follows* and must not exceed the limit for an eight-hour constant exposure at the PEL (assuming an eight-hour workday and a 40-hour workweek):

$$(E = C(a)T(a) + C(b)T(b) + ...C(n)T(n)) \text{ divided by } 8$$

The E value must not be greater than the value given in the Tables Z–1, Z–2, or Z–3 as applicable. Other formulas for calculating TWAs are provided in the standard.

The *short-term exposure limit* is a 15-minute TWA exposure that must not be exceeded at any time during a workday. The 15-minute periods are limited to four times per day with at least one hour between exposures.

The *action level* is one half the level of the eight-hour TWA. Employee exposure monitoring is needed when levels reach the action level.

The *ceiling* is the highest concentration of air contaminants to which any employee may be exposed. Employees may never be exposed to levels above the ceiling value.

Since the Air Contaminants Standard became effective in 1971, OSHA has lowered the PELs for several of the substances listed in the table of the standard. However, OSHA has been unsuccessful in lowering the levels of other substances, mainly due to resistance from industry. The American Conference of Governmental Industrial Hygienists (ACGIH) publishes its, *Documentation of the Threshold Limit Values and Biological Exposure Indices.* This publication provides a more conservative assessment criteria that are generally accepted by Certified Industrial Hygienists (CIH) around the world. This is because it endeavors to adjust recommended levels of exposure based upon current studies and other information regarding toxicity of substances, rather than legislation. The vigilant Hazardous Materials Manager should always strive for the more conservative approach to exposure of personnel to hazardous substances and, when in doubt, seek the advice of a CIH where a potential human exposure to toxic substances exists.

The remaining one thousand series standards, 1910.1001 through 1910.1052 provide special requirements, controls, and other information on specific hazardous substances. Where a specific standard exists for a hazardous substance, it must be followed in lieu of the general 1910.1000 standard requirements.

29 CFR 1910.1030: Bloodborne Pathogens. The scope of this standard is not based on a few specified industries. It is based upon the reasonable possibility that an employee may be exposed to bloodborne pathogens. The risk of exposure to bloodborne pathogens is not exclusive to the healthcare industry. The employee is at risk of exposure anytime he or she can come into contact with another person's blood, blood products, or body fluids. OSHA believes that there is a reason for national concern for the occupational safety and health of employees exposed to bloodborne pathogens.

The 29 CFR 1910.1030 standard covers *all* bloodborne pathogens, not just Hepatitis B Virus (HBV) and Human Immunodeficiency Virus (HIV).

The severity of acute reactions associated with chemicals is generally related to the dose that the individual receives. Said another way, there is a *dose-response relationship* with chemicals, the greater the dose, the more severe the reaction. This is not always true, such as in the case of carcinogens or in the case of sensitizers, where even a little exposure to a chemical by a sensitized person can cause severe allergic reaction. However, it is true for the acute reactions seen by most chemicals.

Although the risk of contracting a disease depends on a minimum number of viable organisms being ingested or injected, for all practical purposes the effects of exposure to bloodborne pathogens are not dose related. Each time an employee is exposed to a pathogen, infection either occurs or does not occur depending on the ability of the individual's immune system to fight off the disease.

OSHA realized that assessing the risk of exposure to bloodborne diseases is different from quantifying the risks that come from exposure to toxic chemicals. OSHA concluded that the best way to reduce the risk of the transmission of bloodborne diseases is to reduce exposure.

Exposure to blood or other potentially infectious materials place workers at risk. OSHA notes: "[a]ll employees who are exposed to blood and other potentially infectious materials may be at risk of infection." The agency requires employers to conduct an exposure determination in order to identify any occupational exposure to bloodborne pathogens (traditional and nontraditional). OSHA's intent is to identify and protect all employees who are reasonably at risk of skin, eye, mucous membrane, or parenteral contact with blood or other potentially infectious materials during the performance of their job duties.

Every employer needs to know who among its employees is potentially exposed to bloodborne pathogens so that the proper training, engineering, work practice controls, personal protective equipment, and the other provisions required by the standard, can be provided to the employee.

To learn who is potentially exposed, the employer should examine the tasks and procedures carried out by employees, and ascertain any exposure that can reasonably be anticipated to occur. For example, it would be reasonable to anticipate that someone who provides first aid at a construction site will eventually be exposed to blood in the course of his or her work duties. The employer must identify those tasks and procedures where occupational exposure may occur, and identify the workers whose duties include those tasks and procedures. The Exposure Control Plan is a key provision of the standard. It requires employers to identify the individuals who will receive training, personal protective equipment, vaccination, and other protection required by standard.

OSHA names 24 industry sectors where the exposure to bloodborne pathogens is significant, but the 29 CFR 1910.1030 standard encompasses *all* workplaces in which employees might be exposed to blood or other potentially infectious materials during the performance of their duties. Although most of the 24 named sectors are directly related to patient care, 11 are not. They are:

- Personnel services
- Funeral homes and crematories
- Research laboratories
- Linen services
- Medical and dental equipment repair
- Law enforcement
- Fire and rescue
- Correctional institutions
- Schools
- Lifesaving
- Regulated waste removal

OSHA's plan for reducing an employee's exposure to bloodborne pathogens is based on *universal precautions* of infection control. The carriers of any disease are not usually identifiable, and contaminated materials and articles are not always properly identified. As a result, the exposed worker could be unaware of a grave hazard. Universal precautions require employees to assume that all human blood and body fluids contain potentially infectious bloodborne pathogens, and to handle those articles and substances as if they were pathogenic.

The 29 CFR 1910.1030 standard is a *performance standard*. It requires the employer to implement *effectively* a program that protects employees from bloodborne pathogens. The employer must develop measures to abate this hazard, that best suit the work place and protect the worker from contact with blood, body fluids, and other potentially infectious materials.

Employers must develop an exposure control program that identifies the tasks and/or positions at risk from bloodborne pathogens, and then document the implementation of the measures that will reduce the potential risk. They must then develop procedures to evaluate the circumstances surrounding exposure incidents. Careful documentation of the circumstances leading to an exposure can help managers more efficiently identify future problems. The standard also requires employers to offer the HBV vaccine and to provide evaluation and treatment to employees following an exposure.

In 1999 Congress passed the Healthcare Worker Needlestick Prevention Act and in 2001 OSHA concluded a final ruling that made the provisions of the Act requirements part of the Bloodborne Pathogens standard. OSHA requires healthcare industry employers to have needleless systems and sharps with engineered sharps protections. It also requires them to develop a written exposure control plan to select and implement needleless systems, and to keep logs of all needlesticks and sharps injuries. The law now requires that all needlesticks and sharps injuries be reported on the employers' OSHA 300 logs.

Work practices and the design features of equipment can also lessen exposure to bloodborne pathogens. If necessary, an employer should alter the way a task is performed or change the way equipment is designed in order to prevent occupational exposure.

Many employees are exposed to bloodborne disease because of broken skin, or through their mucous membranes. Personal protective equipment (PPE) is a direct line of defense for all workers who come into contact with blood or other potentially infectious materials. Very small breaks in the skin and airborne particles (*e.g.*, from a cough or sneeze) often cannot be seen. Since PPE isolates such portals of entry from potentially infectious materials, it is an effective means of preventing infections when properly used.

Training is an integral part of reducing risks. Communicating hazards to employees and providing training and information is critical to the implementation of the 29 CFR 1910.1030 standard.Training that accurately informs the employee about risks is an indispensable link in hazard abatement. PPE and proper work practices will not protect personnel unless the workers are instructed in their effective use.

Safe work practices are essential to preventing exposure to biohazards. These controls will reduce risk by requiring employers to make sure that employees are performing their tasks in the safest manner possible, consistent with universal precautions. Examples of work practice controls would be prohibiting the recapping of syringe needles, forbidding mouth-pipetting, and requiring hands to be washed after removing personal protective equipment.

Engineering controls reduce the risk of employee exposure in the workplace by either removing the hazard or isolating the worker from exposure. Work practices and engineering controls work in tandem. It is often necessary to employ work practice controls to assure that engineering controls operate effectively. For example, a sharps disposal container provides no protection if an employee persists in recapping needles by hand or disposing of them in the wastebasket.

When this is coupled with safe engineering controls, work practices, operating procedures, PPE, and education are used together, the employee will have the best protection possible against occupational bloodborne diseases.

Hazardous materials managers who provide professional guidance for the control of human blood, blood products, or body fluids, (such as professions in the traditional health-related industries) should supplement the material in this chapter with readings from James Tweedy's *Healthcare Hazard Control and Safety Management.*

29 CFR 1910.1200: Hazard Communication. The objective of the 29 CFR 1910.1200 standard is to require employers to notify employees about hazardous chemicals, including how to recognize and protect themselves from the hazards. The 1910.1200 standard is the kingpin of the hazardous materials regulations. This standard states that employees have the ***right-to-know*** about the hazards present in their workplace, and outlines the specific methods of how employees will be informed of those hazards.

Besides the specific items of compliance in the standard, should your workplace be inspected, compliance officers will be assessing the adequacy of the program. A list of the items which compliance officers may ask to see is included in Appendix E of the standard.

Any chemicals which fit the standard's definition of a carcinogen, corrosive, highly toxic, irritant, sensitizer, toxic, hepatotoxin, nephrotoxin, neurotoxin, agent acting on the blood or hematopoietic system, agent damaging the lung, reproductive toxin, cutaneous hazard, or eye hazard are regulated by the 29 CFR 1910.1200 standard. These definitions can be found in Appendix A of the standard.

Employers must implement a hazard communication program, which includes container labeling, employee training, Material Safety Data Sheets (MSDSs), and other forms of information and warning.

Employers must also develop a written hazard communication program which contains a list of the hazardous chemicals known to be present in the workplace. Each substance must have an MSDS that is easily accessible by the employees. The substances on the list must match the product names and numbers on the MSDSs. The written program must also outline the methods used to inform employees of the hazards of nonroutine tasks.

If more than one employer shares a workplace, each employer is required to provide the others with information about on-site access to MSDSs, the precautionary measures to be taken in order to protect employees during normal operating conditions and in foreseeable emergencies, and of the labeling system used in the workplace.

The manufacturer, importer, or distributor of a chemical is responsible for ensuring that the containers of hazardous chemicals leaving the workplace are labeled, tagged, or marked with hazard warnings and the identity of the hazardous chemical(s), and the manufacturer's name and address. The chemical manufacturer must also supply the employer with an MSDS the first time the employer purchases the product.

The employer's responsibilities include ensuring that each container of hazardous chemicals remain labeled, tagged, or marked with the hazardous chemical identity, appropriate hazard warnings, and the specific information regarding the physical and health hazards of the hazardous chemical.

Material Safety Data Sheets may be in any language (in support of the language spoken by the employees) but must also be in English. All MSDSs must contain:

- The identity used on the label

- The chemical and common names

- The physical and chemical characteristics, and hazards of the chemical

- The health hazards and medical symptoms of the chemical

- The chemical's primary route of exposure

- The OSHA PEL, ACGIH TLV

- Whether the chemical is listed in the National Toxicology Program (NTP) Annual Report on Carcinogens or has been found to be a potential carcinogen by the International Agency for Research on Cancer (IARC)

- Any precautions for safe handling procedures, cleanup of spills, and leaks

- Appropriate engineering controls, work practices, and personal protective equipment

- Emergency and first aid procedures

- The date of preparation of the MSDS or the date of the last change

- The name, address and telephone number of the chemical manufacturer, importer, employer or other responsible party preparing or distributing the Material Safety Data Sheet. The objective of the last bulleted item is to provide an expert who can give additional information on the hazardous chemicals and appropriate emergency procedures if necessary

Appendix E, although nonmandatory, provides an excellent primer for compliance with the 29 CFR 1910.1200 standard, and a concise, no-nonsense explanation of the intent of the regulation.

29 CFR 1910.1201: Retention of DOT Markings, Placards and Labels. The 29 CFR 1910.1201 standard simply states that employers must preserve the shipping labels of the shipping packages of hazardous materials, and that the labels must be visible. For the purposes of the standard, the term *hazardous material* has the same definition as the one contained in 49 CFR 171–180.

29 CFR 1910.1450: Occupational Exposure to Hazardous Chemicals in Laboratories. OSHA designed the Hazard Communications Standard (HCS) such that, except for minimal requirements of identification amd labeling, it does not apply to research laboratories. In the 1910.1450 standard, OSHA provided requirements specifically for research-type laboratories:

Laboratory means a facility where the *laboratory use of hazardous chemicals* occurs. It is a workplace where relatively small quantities of hazardous chemicals are used on a nonproduction basis. *Laboratory scale* means work with substances in which the containers used for reactions, transfers, and other handling of substances are designed to be easily and safely manipulated by one person. *Laboratory scale* excludes those workplaces whose function is to produce commercial quantities of materials. *Laboratory use of hazardous chemicals* means handling or use of such chemicals in which all of the following conditions are met:

i)   Chemical manipulations are carried out on a *laboratory scale*

ii)   Multiple chemical procedures or chemicals are used

iii) The procedures involved are not part of a production process, nor in any way simulate a production process and

iv)   *Protective laboratory practices and equipment* are available and in common use to minimize the potential for employee exposure to hazardous chemicals

Laboratories that do not fall under the 29 CFR 1910.1450 standard must comply with the requirements of the HCS.

Employers whose laboratories must comply with the 29 CFR 1910.1450 standard must measure the employees' exposure to any regulated substance that requires monitoring. If the exposure level is over the action level or the PEL, the employer must comply with the requirements for monitoring of exposure prescribed for that substance, or introduce engineering or adminitrative measures that will assure minimal exposure.

Employers who come under the 29 CFR 1910.1450 standard must develop and implement a written Chemical Hygiene Plan (CHP). The plan must ensure that employees are protected from the health hazards associated with hazardous chemicals, and that employee exposures to hazardous chemical substances do not exceed the permissible exposure limits. (The Permissible Exposure Limits may be found in 29 CFR 1910, Subpart Z.) The plan must also be readily available to employees, and must include the specific measures that the employer will take to protect its laboratory employees. The employer must review and evaluate the effectiveness of the Chemical Hygiene Plan annually and update it as necessary. Employers must also appoint a Chemical Hygiene Officer (CHO). The CHO must be an employee who is qualified by training or experience to provide technical guidance in the development and implementation of the CHP.

The 29 CFR 1910.1450 standard's training requirements include instruction on how the presence or release of hazardous chemicals may be detected, the physical and health hazards of the chemicals in the workplace, the actions employees can take to protect themselves from hazards, and the details of the CHP.

All employees who work with hazardous chemicals have the right to receive medical attention, examinations, and/or consultations by a licensed physician if the employee develops the symptoms of hazardous chemical exposure as a result of employment. If exposure monitoring indicates that the employee may have been exposed above the action level or PEL, or if there is a spill or other event which may have exposed the employee, these same medical services must be provided. All records must be kept, transferred, and made available in accordance with 29 CFR 1910.1020, "Access to employee Exposure and Medical Records."

The employer must also make sure that the labels on incoming materials are preserved, that MSDSs are maintained on all hazardous chemicals, and that the MSDSs are easily accessible.

Appendix A of 29 CFR 1910.1450, "The National Research Council Recommendations Concerning Chemical Hygiene in Laboratories," is non-mandatory. However the recommendations provide an excellent reference for the development of a CHP. The references in the Appendix were extracted from *Prudent Practices for Handling Hazardous Chemicals in Laboratories* (referred to as *Prudent Practices*), published in 1981 by the National Research Council, and are listed in such a way that the recommendations correspond to specific sections of the standard.

A Final Note on Exposure to Hazardous Substances. People react differently to different substances and chemicals because of their genetic differences, prior exposures, medical histories, and other factors. The PELs, TLVs, and MSDSs are only guidance on how much the *average person* may be exposed to a substance without acute or chronic illness or injury. In reality, many people react to much lower concentrations of substances, than are listed the literature. Hazardous materials managers should use caution when endeavoring to determine safe exposure levels and seek the advice of a Certified Industrial Hygienist (CIH) if in doubt.

Construction Industry Standards: 29 CFR 1926—Safety and Health Regulations for Construction

Subpart C—General Safety and Health Provisions

29 CFR 1926.21: Safety Training and Education. The 29 CFR 1926.21 standard points out that "[e]mployees required to handle or use poisons,

caustics, and other harmful substances shall be instructed regarding the safe handling and use, and be made aware of the potential hazards, personal hygiene, and personal protective measures required." Later in the standard it states, "Employees required to handle or use flammable liquids, gases, or toxic materials shall be instructed in the safe handling and use of these materials."

29 CFR 1926.55: Gases, Vapors, Fumes, Dusts, and Mists. The 29 CFR 1926.55 standard prohibits employees to be exposed to any material or substance at a concentration above those specified in the ACGIH *Documentation of the Threshold Limit Values*. Here too, the first measure of hazard control is engineering. Only when engineering controls are not feasible, may employers use other protective measures. In any case, full compliance with the regulation and protection of the employee must be achieved. This section also contains references to the specific substance rules in the General Industry Standard. For example, "Whenever any employee is exposed to formaldehyde, the requirements of 29 CFR 1910.1048 of this title shall apply."

29 CFR 1926.57: Ventilation. The terms and applications of the 29 CFR 1926.57 rule are different from the 29 CFR 1910.94 General Industry Standard. However, the principles of the two standards are the same.

29 CFR 126.59: Hazard Communication and 29 CFR 1926.61—Retention of DOT markings, placards and labels. OSHA chose to apply the General Industry 29 CFR 1910.1200 standard to the construction industry. Both the 29 CFR 1926.59 and the 29 CFR 1926.61 standards state: "Note: The requirements applicable to construction work under this section are identical to those set forth at 29 CFR 1910.1200 of this chapter."

29 CFR 1926.64: Process Safety Management of Highly Hazardous Chemicals. With few exceptions, the General Industry and Construction Industry rules for process safety, hazardous waste operations, PPE, and respiratory protection are alike in principle.

Voluntary Protection Program

The Voluntary Protection Program (VPP) is an OSHA initiative to involve themselves with management and labor to promote effective worksite-based safety and health. Organizational inclusion into the program is official recognition by OSHA that the employer and employees have attained a workplace that is outstanding, with respect to safety and health.

VPP sets criteria for safety and health programs that are performance based. Sites apply for approval and are assessed by OSHA and/or experts from other organizations that have previously been VPP approved by OSHA.

Sites can qualify at three levels: Star, Merit, or Star Demonstration, with Star being the highest level of recognition. Sites that qualify perform annual evaluations and submit them to OSHA. They also undergo periodic evaluations by OSHA.

What are the benefits to employers and employees? The average VPP worksite is 52% below the average industry rates in incidents. Employers and employees enjoy fewer injuries. This is an obvious and direct benefit to employees, but this reduction reduces workers' compensation premiums and increases profits by decreasing direct and indirect losses to production, which is a benefit to employers.

TED 8.3 – *Voluntary Protection Programs (VPP): Policies and Procedures Manual* is available at the OSHA web site and explains the details of the program's requirements.

Bibliography

American Conference of Governmental Industrial Hygienists. *Documentation of the Threshold Limit Values.* Cincinnati, OH: ACGIH, 2003.

Brauer, R. L. *Safety and Health for Engineers.* Hoboken, NJ: John Wiley and Sons, 1993.

Klaassen, C. D. *Casarett and Doul's Toxicology, The Basic Science of Poisons.* 6th ed. New York NY: McGraw-Hill, Health Profession Division, 1996.

National Research Council. *Prudent Practices for Handling Hazardous Chemicals in Laboratories.* Washington, DC: National Academy Press, 1981.

Moeller, D. W. *Environmental Health.* Cambridge, MA: Harvard University Press, 1997.

Parker, James F. and Vita R. West, Eds. *Bioastronautics Data Book.* 2nd ed. NASA SP–3006. Washington DC: National Aeronautics and Space Administration, Scientific and Technical Information Office, 1973.

Plog, B. A., *Fundamentals of Industrial Hygiene.* 4th ed. Itasca, IL: National Safety Council, 1996.

Tweedy, J. T. *Healthcare Hazard Control and Safety Management.* Delray Beach, FL: GR/St. Lucie Press, 1997.

Internet Resources

<http://www.cdc.gov/niosh> (National Institute for Occupational Safety and Health. Homepage.)

<http://www.osha-slc.gov/> (Occupational Safety and Health Administration. Homepage.)

Guy S. Camomilli is employed as the Manager of Safety, Quality, and Environmental Compliance with Dynamac International, Inc. He works at the Kennedy Space Center on the Life Sciences Support Contract. Mr. Camomilli is a Certified Safety Professional, a Certified Hazardous Materials Manager, and a Certified Health Care Professional. He has 16 years experience in hazardous materials management, predominantly in safety and environmental compliance management of life sciences research, biomedical procedures, and space life sciences.

CHAPTER 10

OSHA and the Hazardous Material Manager

Steven G. Weems, MPH, CIH, CHMM

Today, over 95 million employees are guaranteed a safe and healthful workplace by Federal law. Prior to 1970, industry saw enormous losses in manpower due to death, dismemberment, and illness. More time was lost to job-related accidents than to strikes. To remedy this situation, Congress passed the Occupational Safety and Health Act of 1970 (OSH Act) and created the Occupational Safety and Health Administration (OSHA).

What Is OSHA?

The OSH Act

The Occupational Safety and Health Administration came into existence as a result of the OSH Act of 1970 (PL 91–596; 29 December 1970). The purpose of the law was "to assure safe and healthful working conditions for working men and women; by authorizing enforcement of the standards developed under the Act; by assisting and encouraging the States in their efforts to assure safe and healthful working conditions; by providing for research, information, education, and training in the field of occupational safety and health; and for other purposes."

Duties. The OSH Act spells out in Section 5(a) the duties of the employer:

- The employer shall furnish to each of his employees employment and a place of employment which are free from recognized hazards that are causing or are likely to cause death or serious physical harm to his employees[this is the 5(a)(1) General Duty clause]

- [The employer] shall comply with occupational safety and health standards promulgated under this Act

The employee's duties are spelled out in Section 5(b): "Each employee shall comply with occupational safety and health standards and all rules, regulations, and orders issued pursuant to this Act which are applicable to his own actions and conduct."

Research. OSHA adopted by reference industry's consensus standards in 1970. The research arm under the OSH Act is NIOSH (National Institute for Occupational Safety and Health). NIOSH is not under control of OSHA, or even the Department of Labor; NIOSH is under the United States (US) Department of Health, Education, and Welfare (now the Department of Health and Human Services). This separation was intended to keep the law enforcer, OSHA, from also establishing worker exposure limits. NIOSH has no compliance authority like OSHA, but does have right of access into a work site to establish industry's exposure data.

NIOSH conducts research on various safety and health problems, provides technical assistance to OSHA, and recommends standards for OSHA to adopt. While conducting its research, NIOSH may conduct workplace investigations, gather testimony from employers and employees, and require employers to measure and report the exposure of employees to potentially hazardous materials. NIOSH also may require employers to provide medical examinations and tests in order to determine the incidence of occupational illness among employees. When such examinations and tests are required by NIOSH for research purposes, they may be paid for by NIOSH rather than the employer.

Informational Resources. OSHA maintains a large library of pamphlets and books on a large variety of safety and health topics. The standards are public domain materials and can be freely copied, unless the book or article has been copyrighted. Most of these publications are available from OSHA or can be downloaded from the Internet (refer to the "Help" section in this chapter).

Training and Education. As stated in the OSH Act, OSHA will provide training and education. The OSHA Training Institute (OTI) at Des Plaines, Illinois, provides a formal classroom for use by the OSHA Compliance Safety and Health Officer (CSHO), State consultation members, and (on certain subjects) the general public. Periodically, the institute will export some of their classes. These courses cover areas such as electrical hazards, machine guarding, ventilation, noise, respiratory protection, and laboratory safety. The OTI facility also has a laboratory, library, and audiovisual support. The instructors are former field compliance officers. OSHA also allows various industries to conduct some courses for a small fee.

OSHA currently has 73 Area Offices that are also fully functioning service centers. These offices offer a wide variety of informational services such as speakers, publications, audiovisual aids on workplace hazards, and technical advice. The laboratories contain various demonstrations and equipment, such as power presses, woodworking and welding shops, a complete industrial ventilation unit, and a sound demonstration laboratory.

Inspections!

The OSH Act gave OSHA the responsibility to conduct inspections of the workplace. As stated in the preamble, OSHA is "to assure safe and healthful working conditions for men and women; by authorizing enforcement of standards developed under the Act . . ." The type of workplace you work in determines how or whether OSHA has jurisdiction. Federal officers monitor an employer's compliance issues unless the specific state has an approved plan to conduct its own resident inspections.

These are called *State Plan* states. About half of the states have their own approved plans. For approval of the State Plan, OSHA requires that the State's standards must be at least as strict as the Federal OSHA. The requirements for a State Plan state are found in 29 CFR 1902.

Federal

Under the Act, the heads of Federal agencies are responsible for providing safe and healthful working conditions for their employees. An Executive Order requires agencies to comply with standards consistent with the OSHA standards for private sector employers. OSHA conducts Federal workplace inspections in response to employees' complaint reports, and as part of a special program that identifies Federal workplaces with higher-than-average rates of injury and illness.

OSHA's Federal sector authority is different from that in the private sector in several ways. The most significant difference is that OSHA cannot propose monetary penalties against another Federal agency for failure to comply with OSHA standards. Instead, compliance issues that cannot be resolved at the local level are raised to higher organizational levels until they are resolved. Another significant difference is that OSHA does not have the authority to protect the Federal employee that becomes a "whistle-blower." However, the Whistle-Blower Protection Act of 1989 affords present and former federal employees (other than US Postal Service employees and certain intelligence agencies) an opportunity to file their reports of reprisal with the Office of Special Counsel, US Merit Systems Protection Board.

State and Local Government

Federal OSHA has no jurisdiction over state and local government employees. However, if compliance is done as part of a *State Plan* state's program, then the state's compliance officers cover these employees.

Private Sector

Any private sector employer can be inspected under certain situations. There are several reasons for inspections. These are (in order of priority) imminent danger, catastrophes and fatal accidents, employee complaints, programmed high hazard inspections, other programmed inspections, and follow-up inspections.

Imminent Danger. An *imminent danger* is any condition where there is the reasonable certainty that an immediate danger exists that may cause death or serious physical harm before the danger can be eliminated through normal enforcement procedures.

Catastrophic and Fatal Accidents. *Catastrophic injuries* occur when three or more employees are hospitalized as the result of a single incident. The employer must report catastrophic injuries and any fatalities to OSHA within 8 hours of the occurrence. OSHA will investigate for possible violations of standards and to prevent the recurrence of similar accidents. There are strong penalties for failure to report these accidents to OSHA.

Employee Complaints. All employees have the right to request an OSHA inspection if they feel they are in imminent danger, threatened by physical harm, or that OSHA standards are not being met. OSHA keeps the complaints in strictest confidence and the employer cannot take actions against any employee for making such a complaint, even if he finds out the identity of the employee. OSHA will notify the complainant of the results, if requested. Complaints can be formal or informal. Formal complaints are a signed statement containing the allegations, and a compliance officer will visit the site of alleged offense. Informal complaints are transferred to a form letter and mailed or faxed to the employer. The employer is asked to investigate the allegations and inform OSHA whether or not they are legitimate. If the complaint is legitimate, the employer must explain how and when corrections were made. Compliance officers rarely visit on an informal complaint, unless no reply or a false reply is returned.

That Knock on the Door

Contrary to popular belief, OSHA's job is not to harass businesses or to drive them to bankruptcy. It does not matter how compliant or well run your company is, the "dreaded knock on the door" happens. Preparedness is the best defense. It is illegal for anyone but OSHA to reveal the news of an upcoming visit. OSHA can reveal upcoming visits if it notifies both the employer and the employees.

All inspections have the following in common: (1) inspector's research, (2) inspector's credentials, (3) the opening conference, (4) the inspection tour, and (5) the closing conference.

Inspector's Research. This is the preparation stage. Each case is normally assigned to either a safety or a health compliance officer, but sometimes to both specialities. The OSHA Compliance Safety and Health Officer (CSHO) assigned to the case becomes familiar with the company's history of past inspections and complaints (if any), the nature of the business, and the particular standards involved. After researching, the CSHO obtains any necessary sampling media, selects and calibrates the appropriate equipment, and travels to the site.

Inspector's Credentials. The inspection begins when the CSHO arrives at the site and displays official credentials. The CSHO will ask to meet an appropriate employer representative (the representative should insist upon seeing the inspector's credentials, because there have been impostors in the past). The inspector's credentials can be verified by calling the nearest OSHA office.

The Opening Conference. In the opening conference, the CSHO explains why the company has been selected (*i.e.*, imminent danger, catastrophes or fatalities, programmed high hazard, or follow-up). The CSHO will also determine whether the company falls under an exemption program or is covered by an ongoing OSHA consultation (refer to the "Consultation" section of this chapter). The CSHO will give the owner/operator copies of the applicable standards and the complaint (if any). The complaint will not contain the identity of the complainant if the complainant wishes to remain anonymous.

The Inspection Tour. The CSHO, accompanied by an employer representative, will tour the site. In an organized labor plant, the unions are allowed to designate representatives to accompany the CSHO in the inspection if they so desire. If the inspection was prompted by a complaint, then only the affected areas are visited. The CSHO may also conduct confidential interviews with employees. The CSHO will also review recordkeeping and injury and illness (OSHA Form 300) logs. If

sampling is required, the CSHO may return to acquire full-shift noise or air contaminant samples. If the CSHO sees additional hazards that are not contained in the original scope of the visit, these areas may also be included in the inspection. Sometimes the CHSO suspects hazards that are of the other speciality. Thus, a safety CHSO may do a health referral or the other way around.

The Closing Conference. During the closing conference the CSHO will discuss the results of the inspection and give the employer an opportunity to ask questions about the findings. If any "on-the-spot" corrections have been made, it is in the employer's best interest to point them out during the closing conference. The compliance officer will explain appeal procedures, informal conferences, and how to contest any citations. Next, the CSHO's supervisor will review the complete inspection file. The results of any sampling that has been carried out will not be known until later, and the supervisor will review these results as well.

Citations

The prospect of citations as a result of the inspection can be compared to a scene in the movie, *Jaws*. One character describes a shark attack saying, "Sometimes, the shark, he goes away, sometimes the shark, he doesn't go away." OSHA has several classes of violations. In order of seriousness, they are: *de minimus*, regulatory, other than serious, serious, willful, repeat, and failure to correct prior violations. These violations are found in 29 CFR 1903.

De Minimus. *De minimus* violations are small infractions and don't carry a monetary penalty.

Regulatory. Like *de minimus*, these are small recordkeeping infractions. They normally don't carry a monetary penalty, but if one is imposed, its maximum is $1,000. An example is failure to post the OSHA Form 300.

Other Than Serious. These infractions would probably not result in death or physical harm. Fines are not required but may be imposed of up to $7,000 per incident.

Serious. Serious violations could cause death or serious physical injury. The employer knew or should have known that these hazards existed. Fines of up to $7,000 per violation must be imposed.

Willful. These are violations that the employer intentionally and knowingly commits. Fines for willful violations range from $5,000 to $70,000 per violation. In addition, if the violation resulted in the death of an employee, the fine could be as much as $250,000 per individual and $500,000 for the corporation. There may also be jail time of up to six months.

Repeat. Repeat offenses are similar violations that are noted on a follow-up visit. Fines may reach $70,000 per violation. An infraction is a repeat violation only after the original citation has become final and is not contested.

Failure to Correct Prior Violation. Failure to correct these violations may result in fines of up to $7,000 per day past the prescribed abatement date.

Additional Violations. Additional violations may include: falsifying records or; assaulting, intimidating, or interfering with compliance officers in the performance of their duties. Fines range from $10,000 plus six months jail, $7,000, and $5,000 plus three years jail, respectively.

The Standards

All the OSHA standards are found in 29 CFR (the US Department of Labor) 1900 series. With two exceptions, parts 1900–1909 are OSHA and OSHA Consultation procedures.

The standard that affects most employers is the General Industry Standard.

General Industry

The General Industry Standards are found in 29 CFR 1910. There are two additional parts: 29 CFR 1903 (OSHA poster), and 29 CFR 1904 (OSHA Form 300). The major areas cited are:

- Subpart D, Walking–Working Surfaces (29 CFR 1910.21–30)

- Subpart E, Exit Routes, Emergency Action Plans, and Fire Prevention Plans (29 CFR 1910.33–39)

- Subpart F, Powered Platforms, Manlifts, and Vehicle-Mounted Work Platforms (29 CFR 1910.66–68)

- Subpart G, Occupational Health and Environmental Control (29 CFR 1910.94–98)

- Subpart H, Hazardous Materials (29 CFR 1910.101–126)

- Subpart I, Personal Protective Equipment (29 CFR 1910.132–39)

- Subpart J, General Environmental Controls (29 CFR 1910.141–147)

- Subpart K, Medical and First Aid (29 CFR 1910.151–152)

- Subpart L, Fire Protection (29 CFR 1910.155–165)

- Subpart M, Compressed Gas and Compressed Air Equipment (29 CFR 1910.166-169)

- Subpart N, Materials Handling and Storage (29 CFR 1910.176–184)

- Subpart O, Machinery and Machine Guarding (29 CFR 1910.211–219)

- Subpart P, Hand and Portable Powered Tools and Other Hand-Held Equipment (29 CFR 1910.241–244)

- Subpart Q, Welding, Cutting, and Brazing (29 CFR 1910.251–255)

- Subpart R, Special Industries (29 CFR 1910.261–272).

- Subpart S, Electrical (29 CFR 1910.301–399)

- Subpart T, Commercial Diving Operations (29 CFR 1910.401–441)

- Subpart Z, Toxic and Hazardous Substances (29 CFR 1910.1000–1500)

Of the standards listed, the most frequently cited are:

- Hazard Communication (29 CFR 1910.1200)

- Lead (29 CFR 1910.1025)

- Respiratory Protection (29 CFR 1910.134)

- Noise (29 CFR 1910.95)

- Machine Guarding (anything in Subpart O)

- Lockout/Tagout (29 CFR 1910.147)
- Air Contaminants (29 CFR 1910.1000)
- Confined Space (29 CFR 1910.146)

Construction

The construction standards basically mirror the General Industry standards, but have a different numbering system. For example, Hazard Communication is 29 CFR 1926.59 and the lead standard is 29 CFR 1926.62. Another difference is in the lead standard itself. Respirators and personal protective equipment (PPE) are required unless the employer has monitoring data showing that the employee's exposure does not exceed the permissible exposure limits.

Maritime

The maritime standards are divided into four major areas: Shipyards (29 CFR 1915), Marine Terminals (29 CFR 1917), Longshoring (29 CFR 1918), and Gear Certification (29 CFR 1919). The standards are specific to their own area and the maritime safety specialist must become familiar with them all.

Others

There are a whole host of other parts in the 1900 series of standards. Three of the more important parts are 29 CFR 1924, Workshops and Rehab Facilities; 29 CFR 1925, Federal Service Contracts; and 29 CFR 1928, Agriculture.

The General Duty Clause

The general duty clause of the Act states that each employer "shall furnish . . . a place of employment which is free from recognized hazards that are causing or are likely to cause death or serious physical harm to his employees." This is the catchall clause that applies to all employers.

OSHA does not have a standard for everything. It uses the recommendations of industry, research, and professional associations. For example, OSHA uses the American Conference of Governmental Industrial Hygienists' (ACGIH) Threshold Limit Values (TLV) if it does not have an established exposure limit.

Consultation

Every state and territory has an OSHA consultation program, sometimes referred to as the 7(c)(1) program. The consultation program is conducted under the guidelines in the OSH Act and 29 CFR 1908.

Consultants are trained by OSHA and often sit in on the compliance classes. Many of these consultants are former compliance officers, hold advanced degrees, and many have Certified Safety Professionals (CSP) and Certified Industrial Hygienists (CIH) certifications. This consultation service is available to the smaller employers (250 employees or less at one site, 500 total at all sites). The service is free, but there is a catch: the employer must agree to correct all serious hazards by an agreed-upon abatement date. Failure to abate the hazard will result in the case being turned over to OSHA. This drastic measure rarely occurs, and then only after all means of getting the employer to abate the identified hazards have been exhausted. In situations beyond the company's control, the abatement date can be extended if the employer requests it.

The consultation services may be run from the state's Department of Labor, or at a State university. In large states there may be several consultation offices. You can contact your state's consultation project by contacting the OSHA area office in your state, or by calling the OSHA number on the poster that is displayed in the work area.

The consultation can be wall-to-wall or specific in nature (*i.e.*, noise only). The information will be kept in confidence between the company and the consultation project. Ordinarily, the project office does not discuss consultations with OSHA. The only time OSHA will find out about a consultation visit is if

- The company tells OSHA
- OSHA sees the report posted in a common area

- The consultation file is subpoenaed for a court case
- The file is turned over to OSHA for failure to abate

In addition to verifying whether the company is or is not in compliance, the consultant will explain the various standards and offer suggestions on how to fix identified problems. Sometimes the consultant will have model programs that the employer may use. Many of the projects have references to products that have been used with good results. The consultant cannot recommend a specific manufacturer or brand name, but may have a variety from which the employer may choose.

Help and Information

Help

Confused? Many are, and they get help by calling their local OSHA office. OSHA personnel are helpful and ready to explain a standard or to send some of their literature. You don't have to give your name, company, or location, and OSHA does not trace the phone call so it can visit the plant the next day. You can also contact your state's consultation service.

The Safety and Health Information Superhighway

Good news! OSHA is on the Internet. Dial up

<http://www.osha.gov>

You can find the latest standards, complete with the preambles. You can download these standards and print them. Also available are the Field Inspection Reference Manual (FIRM), Industrial Hygiene Tech Manual, Most Frequently Asked Questions (FAQs), and interpretations. For sampling questions, OSHA's Salt Lake City Laboratory can also be accessed at

<http://www.osha.slc.gov>

OSHA makes the above items available on CD-ROM. Many commercial companies make versions of these standards in CD-ROM and binder formats.

Some offer updates quarterly by replacement CDs or paper inserts to the binders. The updates are also available through the government printing office, the publisher, or many of the safety products distributors.

The *Federal Register* can be consulted if you want the latest news from the Federal government. Unfortunately, each volume contains everything that came out of any branch of the Federal government on that day. That's a lot of daily reading!

Summary

OSHA is not a mindless bureaucracy. It can assist you in staying current with the ever-changing field of safety and health. Use it like another map in your quest for safety. By learning about OSHA, its mission, and how it operates, you will become a better safety manager.

Bibliography

91st Congress. *Occupational Safety and Health Act.* PL 91–569, S2193, 29 December 1970; as amended by PL 10–552, Section 3101, 5 November 1990; as amended by PL 105–198, 16 July 1998.

Mintz, Benjamin W. "Occupational Safety and Health: The Federal Regulatory Program—A History." In *Fundamentals of Industrial Hygiene.* 3rd ed. Barbara A. Plog, MPH, CIH, CSP, Ed. Itasca, IL: National Safety Council, 1988.

Occupational Safety and Health Administration. *OSHA Handbook for Small Businesses.* Pamphlet Number 2209. Washington, DC: OSHA, 1990.

Occupational Safety and Health Administration. *All About OSHA.* Pamphlet Number 2056. Washington, DC: OSHA, 1995.

Robbins, Chain M. "Governmental Regulations." In: *Fundamentals of Industrial Hygiene.* 3rd ed. Barbara A. Plog, MPH, CIH, CSP, Ed. Itasca, IL: National Safety Council, 1988.

Steven G. Weems *is currently the Industrial Hygiene Supervisor for the Department of Environmental and Industrial Programs at Safe State. Mr. Weems joined Safe State, Alabama's OSHA consultation program, in July 1989 as an Industrial Hygienist. Prior to joining Safe State Mr. Weems was the Safety Administrator of Southern Research Institute in Birmingham, Alabama. He is a veteran of over 28 years in the active and reserve components of the US Army and holds the rank of Colonel. Mr. Weems earned board certification in the comprehensive practice of Industrial Hygiene in July 1994. He also became a Certified Hazardous Materials Manager in December 1993. Mr. Weems has extensive experience in evaluating workplace hazards and prescribing controls in a variety of industries and services. He serves as an instructor for numerous training courses. He has a Master's degree in Public Health from the University of Alabama at Birmingham (1992) and a Bachelor of Science degree in Chemistry from Auburn University (1976).*

CHAPTER 11

Personal Protective Equipment

Michael H. Ziskin, CHCM, CHMM
Dawn Han, MS, CIH

Introduction

Personal protective equipment (PPE) includes all clothing and other protective devices designed to be worn to protect workers from workplace hazards. PPE is generally needed for physical or health hazards that cannot be eliminated through engineering or administrative control techniques. The effective use of PPE is dependent upon the commitment of the organization's management, the effectiveness of the risk assessment process, the objective selection of equipment, the training and demonstrated competency of the wearer, as well as the budget to maintain, care for, repair, replace, and properly dispose of the equipment. This chapter will review related regulatory requirements, hazard assessment, types of different equipment, PPE selection processes, various PPE-related factors, management approaches, new trends, and resources.

Personal protective equipment is anything that a worker can wear, carry, or use to protect himself or herself against some of the hazards that may be encountered while doing work. In reality, the workplace can require complex choices about PPE use. This chapter covers a broad range of PPE, including primary PPE items such as:

- Full and partial body protective garments
- Protective gloves and other handwear
- Protective footwear
- Protective headwear
- Protective face and eyewear
- Respirators
- Hearing protectors or hearing protection devices

Other types of clothing and equipment, often considered as PPE, are described in this chapter but not discussed in detail. These items include fall protection and cooling devices. See Figure 1 for examples of personal protective equipment.

This chapter also covers selection and use of PPE with information relevant to different environments, as it emphasizes the following types of protection:

- Physical
- Environmental
- Chemical
- Biological
- Thermal
- Electrical
- Radiation

Because of the broad range of PPE types and applications, this chapter will focus on those areas in which there is less information available to industry for selection of the *appropriate* PPE.

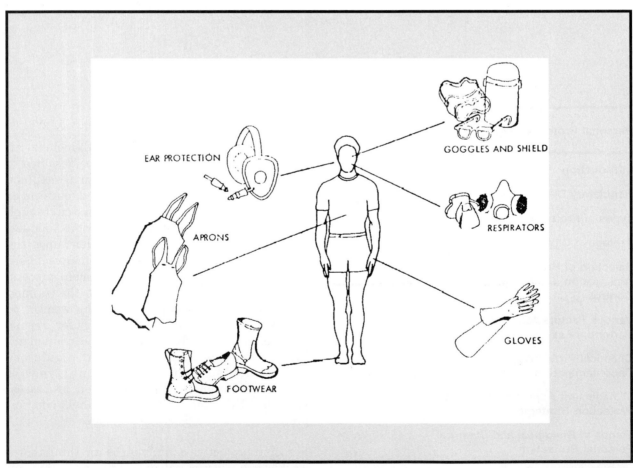

Source: US Air Force

Figure 1. Personal Protective Equipment

PPE and Its Role in Providing Worker Protection

Personal protective equipment includes items of clothing and equipment which are used by themselves or in combination with other protective clothing and equipment to isolate the individual wearer from a particular hazard or a number of hazards. PPE is also used to protect the environment from the individual, such as in the case of cleanroom apparel and medical devices for infection control.

PPE is considered the *last line of defense* against particular hazards when it is not possible to prevent worker exposure by using engineering or administrative controls. *Engineering controls* should be first used to eliminate a hazard from the workplace by modifying the work environment or process to prevent any contact between workers and the hazard. An example of an engineering control is the replacement of a manual task involving potential hazard exposure with an automated process. In the absence of engineering controls, *administrative controls* should be used to prevent worker contact with the hazard. For example, establish a procedure which dictates that workers be out of an area when the hazards are present or to limit the time of exposure to those hazards. Finally, when neither engineering nor administrative controls are possible, PPE should be used.

While PPE is designed for protection of personnel against various hazards, *PPE cannot provide protection to the wearer against all hazards under all conditions.* Workers should not rely on PPE exclusively for protection against hazards, but should use PPE in conjunction with mechanical guards, engineering controls, and sound manufacturing practices in the workplace setting. The use of PPE in itself may create additional hazards or stress for the wearer: heat stress, or reduced mobility, dexterity, and tactility, and/or impaired vision or hearing.

Regulatory Overview—OSHA 29 CFR 1910

In the United States, the majority of PPE-related regulations are promulgated by the Occupational Safety and Health Administration (OSHA). The Administration provides regulations that address selection and use of PPE in Title 29, *Code of Federal Regulations* (CFR) Subpart I, Parts 1910.132 through 1910.140 for General Industry. The standard was first adopted in 1971 and was revised in 1994. *States with their own OSHA plans must meet or exceed these requirements.* Other specific PPE standards are found in various OSHA standards (for example, the Maritime Industry Regulations 29 CFR 1915, 1917, and 1918 and 1926.28 for the Construction Industry). This chapter focuses primarily on General Industry Standards although many of the other PPE standards referenced above cover the same topics, but also have other unique PPE requirements.

The PPE standards included in Subpart I are shown in Table 1.

Table 1. Overview of OSHA PPE Standards

29 CFR Section	Topic
1910.132	Provides general requirements for PPE
1910.133	Pertains to eye and face protection
1910.134	Pertains to respiratory protection
1910.135	Pertains to head protection
1910.136	Pertains to foot protection
1910.137	Pertains to electrical protective equipment
1910.138	Pertains to hand protection
1910.139	Pertains to respiratory protection for *Mycobacterium tuberculosis*
1910.140	Provides a list of standards organizations relative to PPE

OSHA released a revision to the Respiratory Protection Standard in January 1998, replacing the standard with the same name and number that was released in 1971. The original standard was renamed 29 CFR 1910.139 and pertains to respiratory protection for tuberculosis only.

The OSHA standards require that workers use eye, face, respiratory, head, foot, hand and electrical protective equipment where there are hazards that cannot be sufficiently controlled by other means. This would include the use of engineering controls (for example, ventilation) or changing or modifying the way in which specific tasks are performed (such as avoiding heavy lifting). It also requires that the equipment for use by workers must be reliable, clean, and in good working condition. In most cases, employers are required to provide workers with PPE.

The employer is required by OSHA to: perform a hazard assessment at each workplace in order to determine whether PPE is needed; document the assessment in a written certification; select the appropriate PPE if needed; and train employees about PPE usage, proper care, maintenance, useful life, and disposal.

OSHA requires the employer to ensure that the PPE used to protect the worker meets minimum

Table 2. Other OSHA PPE-Related Standards

29 CFR Section	Topic	29 CFR Section	Topic
1910.66	Working with chemicals on elevated work surface	1910.1012	Ethyleneimine
		1910.1013	beta-Propiolactone
1910.94	Work around open-surfaced tanks	1910.1014	2-Acetylaminofluorene
1910.95	Occupational noise and hearing protectors	1910.1015	4-Dimethylaminoazobenzene
		1910.1016	N-Nitrosodimethylamine
1910.119	Process safety management of highly hazardous chemicals	1910.1017	Vinyl chloride
		1910.1018	Inorganic arsenic
1910.120	Hazardous waste operations and emergency response (HAZWOPER)	1910.1025	Lead
		1910.1027	Cadmium
1910.146	Permit-required confined spaces	1910.1028	Benzene
1910.156	Fire brigades	1910.1029	Coke oven emissions
1910.183	Helicopters	1910.1030	Bloodborne pathogens
1910.242	Hand and portable powered tools and equipment, general	1910.1043	Cotton dust
		1910.1044	1,2-Dibromo-3-chloropropane (BCP)
1910.252	Welding, general requirements	1910.1045	Acrylonitrile
1910.331	Electrical work	1910.1047	Ethylene oxide
1926.102	Subpart E: Lasers	1910.1048	Formaldehyde
1910.250	Subpart Q: Welding, cutting and brazing	1910.1050	4-4' Methylenedianiline
1910.262	Acid and caustics in textile production	1910.1200	Hazard Communication
1910.1001	Asbestos	1910.1450	Occupational exposure to hazardous chemicals in laboratories
1910.1003	13 Carcinogens (4-Nitrobiphenyl, *etc.*)		
1910.1004	alpha-Naphthlamine	1915 Subpart I	PPE for shipyard employment
1910.1006	Methylchloromethyl ether	1917 Subpart E	PPE for marine terminals
1910.1007	3,3'-Dichlorobenzidine	1918 Subpart J	PPE for longshoring
1910.1008	Bis-Chloromethyl ether	1926 Subpart E	PPE for the construction industry
1910.1009	beta-Naphthylamine	1926.60	Methylenedianiline
1910.1010	Benzidine	1926.62	Lead
1910.1011	4-Aminodiphenyl		

performance requirements as specified. For example, OSHA specifies that employers shall provide National Institute for Occupational Safety and Health (NIOSH) certified respiratory protection as specified in the OSHA respiratory protection standard. OSHA also requires eye, face, hearing, and foot protection to meet specific American National Standards Institute (ANSI) standards.

OSHA also recommends that the employer follow several nonmandatory standards. For example, OSHA's Hazardous Waste Operations and Emergency Response (HAZWOPER) standard recommends that chemical protection needed for response to hazardous materials emergencies meet the National Fire Protection Association's (NFPA) 1991 or 1992 standards. The NFPA standards and other related standards/guidelines will be discussed later in this chapter.

Other OSHA Standards

In addition to the general personal protective equipment and respiratory protection regulations from OSHA, there are other standards that relate to PPE applications when exposed to specified hazards. For example, the standard for laser protection specifies *suitable* safety goggles that will offer adequate protection for the specific wavelength of the laser and optical density for the energy involved, while the welding standard provides shade requirements for optical protection during welding operations. Table 2 contains a partial list of OSHA standards that relate to PPE.

Other Related Standards and Guidelines

There are other PPE-related standards and guidelines available from nationally recognized organizations, in addition to the OSHA regulatory requirements. These organizations are shown in Table 3.

Standards and guidelines from these organizations may be incorporated by reference into the regulations. For example, OSHA specifically references the American National Standards Institute

Table 3. Other Organizations with PPE-Related Standards and Guidelines

Organization or Agency	Acronym
American National Standards Institute	ANSI
American Industrial Hygiene Association	AIHA
American Conference of Governmental Industrial Hygienists	ACGIH
American Petroleum Institute	API
American Society for Testing and Materials	ASTM
Food and Drug Administration	FDA
International Organization for Standardization	ISO
International Standards Equipment Association	ISEA
National Fire Protection Association	NFPA
National Institute for Occupational Safety and Health	NIOSH
Safety Equipment Institute	SEI
US Coast Guard	USCG
US Department of Defense	DoD
US Department of Energy	DOE
US Department of Homeland Security	DHS
US Department of Justice	DOJ
US Environmental Protection Agency	EPA
US Food and Drug Administration	FDA

(ANSI) for eye and face protection and other personal protective equipment. OSHA also references the NFPA chemical protective clothing standards (NFPA 1991 and NFPA 1992) in 29 CFR 1910.120 Hazardous Waste Operations and Emergency Response Standard nonmandatory appendices. Other widely utilized NFPA PPE standards may not be directly referenced by OSHA, including those for thermal protection, flash fire protection and protection from chemical, biological and radiological terrorism agents.

General Employer Selection Responsibilities under OSHA 29 CFR 1910.132

Under the OSHA regulations, the employer is responsible for conducting a hazard assessment of the workplace to determine if hazards requiring PPE are present or are likely to be present. If hazards are present, the employer must

- Select and have the affected employees use the types of PPE that will protect them from the hazards identified in the hazard assessment

- Communicate selection decisions to each affected employee

- Select PPE that properly fits each affected employee

The employer must verify that the required workplace hazard assessment has been performed through a written certification that identifies

- The workplace evaluated

- The person certifying that the evaluation has been performed

- The date(s) of the hazard assessment

- Signed documentation of certification of the hazard assessment

For selection of PPE for protection against respiratory and electrical hazards, the employer should refer to OSHA's Respiratory Protection Standard at 29 CFR 1910.134 and the Electrical Protection Standard at 29 CFR 1910.137.

General Employer Training Responsibilities under OSHA 29 CFR 1910.132

The employer must train the employee who is required to use PPE so that he or she knows

- When PPE is necessary

- What PPE is necessary

- How to don, doff, adjust, and wear PPE properly

- The limitations of PPE

- The proper care, maintenance, useful life, and disposal of PPE

The employer must have each affected employee demonstrate an understanding of the required training and the ability to use PPE properly before being allowed to perform work requiring the use of PPE. If the employer has reason to believe that any affected employee who has already been trained does not have the required understanding, then the employer must retrain each such employee. The employer must conduct retraining under circumstances that include, but are not limited to, situations in which

- Changes in the workplace render previous training obsolete

- Changes in the types of PPE to be used render previous training obsolete

- Inadequacies in an affected employee's knowledge or use of assigned PPE indicate that the employee has not retained the requisite understanding or skill

The employer must verify that each affected employee has received and understood the required training through a written certification that

- Lists the name of each employee trained

- Indicates the date(s) of training

- Identifies the subject of the certification

For additional training requirements against respiratory and electrical hazards, the employer should refer to 29 CFR 1910.134 for respiratory protection and 29 CFR 1910.137 for electrical protection.

Overview of Requirements in OSHA 29 CFR 1910.133—1910.138

OSHA 29 CFR 1910.133 through 1910.138 cover PPE in varying levels of detail but do not specifically address all hazards or types of PPE. For example, no specific requirements are provided for overall skin or body protection. Some of the specific requirements are summarized below.

Eye and Face Protection. 29 CFR 1910.133 on eye and face protection requires

- The use of eye and face protection for specific hazards, including:

  - flying particles

  - molten metal

  - liquid chemicals

  - acids or caustic liquids

  - chemical gases or vapors

  - potentially injurious light radiation

- Side protection for flying object hazards, provision for prescription lenses, PPE marking, and use of filter lenses for protection against injurious light radiation

- Compliance of protective eye and face devices with ANSI standard Z87.1–1989, "American National Standard Practice for Occupational and Educational Eye and Face Protection." (Devices purchased before July 4, 1994 must meet ANSI Z87.1–1968.) ANSI has also recently issued a revision to this standard— ANSI Z–87.1–2003. This revised standard has not yet been referenced in the OSH Act.

Respiratory Protection. 29 CFR 1910.134 on respiratory protection requires

- The use of engineering controls where feasible and the use of respirators when necessary to protect employee health against occupational diseases caused by contaminated air

- The establishment of a respiratory protective program

- That an individual be named as the administrator for the respiratory protection program

- The selection of respirators based on an evaluation of respiratory hazards and relevant workplace and user factors that affect respirator performance and reliability. This evaluation must include an assessment of the air contaminants and employee exposure levels to those air contaminants

- Medical exams for employees who must wear respirators

- Fit testing of employees who must wear respirators

- That employers implement procedures for use of respirators that provide

  - proper facepiece seal protection

  - continuing respirator effectiveness

  - protection in Immediately Dangerous to Life or Health (IDLH) atmospheres

  - protection during interior structural fire fighting

- Specific maintenance and care of respirators, including:

  - inspection for defects

  - cleaning and disinfection

  - repair

  - storage

- Meeting minimum air quality standards

- Identification of respirator filters, cartridges, and canisters

- That employers provide effective training to employees who must use respirators

- Evaluation of the workplace to ensure that provisions of the respirator program are being carried out

- Recordkeeping of medical examinations and fit testing

Head Protection. 29 CFR 1910.135 on head protection requires

- The use of protective helmets in areas where potential exists for head injury from falling objects

- The use of protective helmets designed to reduce electric shock when employees are near exposed electrical conductors that could contact the head

- That protective helmets comply with ANSI standard Z89.1–1986, "American National Standard for Personnel Protection–Protective Headwear for Industrial Workers–Requirements." (Protective helmets purchased before July 5, 1994 must meet ANSI Z89.1–1969. A new edition of this standard exists as ANSI Z89.1–1997)

Foot Protection. 29 CFR 1910.136 on foot protection requires

- The use of protective footwear in areas where the potential for foot injury exists from:
  - falling or rolling objects
  - objects piercing the sole
  - exposure to electrical hazards
- That protective footwear comply with ANSI standard Z41–1991, "American National Standard for Personal Protection–Protective Footwear." (Protective footwear purchased before July 5, 1994 must meet ANSI Z41.1–1967). ANSI has also recently issued a revision to this standard—ANSI Z–41–1999. This revised standard has not yet been referenced in the OSH Act.

Electrical Protective Equipment. 29 CFR 1910.137 regulates electrical protective equipment by:

- Addressing insulating electrical protective equipment made from rubber. Including:
  - blankets
  - mattings
  - covers
  - line hose
  - gloves
  - sleeves
- Setting specific design requirements for electrical protective equipment that include
  - manufacture and marking
  - electrical requirements
  - workmanship and finish
- Setting requirements for in-service care and use for electrical protective equipment

Hand Protection. 29 CFR 1910.138 on hand protection requires

- Employers to select *appropriate* hand protection when employees' hands are exposed to hazards from
  - skin absorption of harmful substances
  - severe cuts or lacerations
  - severe abrasions
  - punctures
  - chemical burns
  - thermal burns
  - harmful temperature extremes
- Employers to base selection of hand protection on
  - performance of hand protection relative to task(s) to be performed
  - conditions present
  - duration of use
  - identified hazards and potential hazards

Limitations and Shortcomings of Regulations

Regulations specifying the selection and use of PPE are often general in scope, limited to specific applications, or do not provide specific guidance. In only a few areas regulations specify particular types of PPE in terms of design, performance properties, and service life. The majority of OSHA and other governmental regulations simply specify the use of general types of PPE (*e.g.*, they only require the employee to use *protective clothing*) without indicating a particular configuration and required performance.

The principal exceptions to generic requirements exist when there are national standards such as:

- Protective footwear (ANSI Z41.1)
- Protective face and eyewear (ANSI Z87.1)
- Protective headwear (ANSI Z89.1)
- Respirators (ANSI Z88.2 and 42 CFR 84)

There are no national standards for protective garments or gloves except for very specific applications (*e.g.*, emergency response). Employers and end users, therefore, are faced with a variety of choices for PPE selection for meeting regulatory requirements and must use a risk assessment and determination of protection needs (based on PPE design, performance, and service life) in order to decide on the appropriate PPE.

Types of Protective Equipment

Personal protective equipment includes all items worn by a worker that are designed to create a barrier against workplace hazards. Such items would include respirators, protective clothing, and other devices for head, eye and face, hearing, foot, hand, and fall protection, *etc*.

General Use *vs*. Emergency Applications

Personal protective equipment is used in a variety of applications. These applications include protecting workers from sharp objects, flying projectiles, hot surfaces, chemical splash, falling, *etc*. In addition, PPE is used to protect workers from simultaneous hazards (multiple hazards), present in many industrial operations, hazardous waste site operations, confined space operations, and emergency response.

Each application for PPE may present unique challenges dictating different designs and levels of performance. Many industrial operations are associated with hazards that are predictable such as known chemicals, identified confined spaces, *etc*. However, for hazardous waste operations or emergency response situations, a large number of complex issues may need to be considered in both selecting and using the appropriate protection. Unlike in more predictable work environments, hazardous waste site operations and emergency response involve widely ranging conditions and a great deal of uncertainty. Any number of hazards due to the type(s) of operations, environmental conditions, varying chemical mixtures and

concentrations may be encountered. Differences in the performance offered by the various types of PPE could make the difference between adequate protection and hazardous acute or chronic exposure.

Respiratory Protection

The basic purpose of any respirator is to protect the respiratory system from inhalation of hazardous atmospheres. Airborne hazards include dusts, fumes, gases, vapors, mists, aerosols, and smoke, *etc*. Every effort must be made to eliminate airborne respiratory hazards through engineering and administrative control methods. However, when such controls cannot eliminate a hazard or reduce its danger to an acceptable level, adequate respiratory protection is required. Users of respiratory equipment must be in good health and demonstrate competence in the use of the equipment and in the equipment's limitations.

Respiratory protective devices can be categorized into two major types: *air-purifying respirators* and *atmosphere-supplying respirators*. Air-purifying respirators remove contaminants from the ambient air, while an atmosphere-supplying respirator provides air from a source other than the surrounding atmosphere. Respirators are qualified by their purpose: for entry and escape, or for escape only.

Respirators are further differentiated by the types of environments in which they must not be used:

- Not for oxygen-deficient atmospheres (atmospheres containing less than 19.5% oxygen)

- Not for Immediately Dangerous to Life or Health atmospheres (*i.e.,* hazardous atmospheres which may produce physical discomfort immediately, chronic poisoning after exposure, or acute physiological symptoms after prolonged exposure)

Respirators which rely on finite air supplies or filtering capabilities are also classified by their service time ranging from three minutes to four hours as defined in 42 CFR 84, "Approval Of Respiratory Protective Devices."

Air-Purifying Respirators

Air-purifying respirators remove certain contaminants from air by either mechanical or chemical means. Prior to inhalation, ambient air is passed through a filter, cartridge, or canister packed with the appropriate materials to remove or neutralize the contaminants. Air-purifying respirators are of two types: those that are powered with an external power source (powered air-purifying respirator), and those that operate solely through the breathing effort of the wearer.

Filter Respirators. Filter (mechanical) respirators offer protection against airborne particulate hazards such as dust, mists, metal fumes, and radionuclides. They are equipped with either a half or full face facepiece. Directly attached to the facepiece is a mechanical filter, made of an appropriate fibrous material that physically traps the airborne particles and delivers purified air to the user. The specific type of mechanical filter that matches the airborne hazard must be selected, as there are nine different types of mechanical filters: three levels of filtering efficiency (N, R, and P), each with three categories of filtering efficiency degradation, each capable of removing a certain type and size of particulate matter from the air (95%, 99%, and 99.97%). See the section entitled "Selection of Protective Equipment" for more detail on the three levels of filters.

Chemical Cartridge Respirators. These respirators are capable of removing low concentrations of hazardous vapors and gases from breathing air. Cartridges usually attach directly to the respirator facepiece. The removal of air contaminants is accomplished either by adsorption, or chemically by neutralization of the particular contaminants. When chemical cartridges are opened, they begin to adsorb moisture from ambient humidity and air contaminants, which will cause their efficiency and service life to decrease. Cartridges should be discarded after use but if reused they should not be used for longer than the calculated use time. Cartridge change-outs can be determined by end-of-service-life indicators (ESLIs). However, manufacturers may not have an ESLI for a specific cartridge. In this case, appropriate *cartridge use times* must be determined by the employer, prior to being used by the employee. Cartridge use time is based upon many factors such as gas/vapor concentration, use duration, breathing rate, and environmental conditions. A qualified health and safety professional will determine use time as part of the respirator selection process. Many manufacturers of respiratory protection devices as well as OSHA, provide information on calculating use time and cartridge change-out schedule.

Atmosphere-Supplying Respirators

Supplied-air respirators provide breathing air to a facepiece. Two main types of supplied-air respirators are available: Self-Contained Breathing Apparatus (SCBA) and Airline Systems. OSHA 29 CFR 1910.134 requires the employer to provide employees using atmosphere-supplying respirators (supplied-air and SCBA) with breathing gases of high purity.

SCBA. The main SCBA components consist of an air or oxygen supply designed into a harness/backpack-type assembly with attached regulators, hoses, and a facepiece. SCBAs operate by maintaining a positive pressure of breathing air in the user's facepiece or by providing a continuous flow of breathing air to the facepiece. Positive pressure SCBAs represent the highest level of respiratory protection available and are used for Immediately Dangerous to Life or Health (IDLH) conditions. SCBAs usually can provide the user from 20 to 40 minutes of actual breathing time, even though the manufacturer may rate the use time longer. Some forms of SCBAs, especially those designed for mine rescue operations, may be used for extended periods (up to a few hours).

SCBAs can be of either open-circuit or closed-circuit design. In open-circuit devices, the expired air from the user is exhausted directly and is not reused. In closed-circuit equipment, the exhaled air passes through an adsorbent to remove carbon dioxide and water, and breathable air is regenerated. SCBAs provide breathing air that is filtered to a quality as specified by the Compressed Gas Association as Grade D air. OSHA specifies that this quality of air be provided to employees and that the employer document this carefully.

Airline Respirators. Airline respirators are available in pressure demand and continuous flow configurations. This system includes a facepiece component, airline, regulator assembly, escape bottle (for emergency egress, such as in confined space operations) and a breathing supply obtained

7. SCBA Types
were PP & CF

from compressed gas cylinders or an air compressor system. The air quality must be Grade D. The user may wear a standard full or half facepiece, helmet, hood, or complete suit. A pressure demand airline respirator is very similar in operation to a pressure demand open circuit SCBA, except that the air is supplied through a small diameter hose from a stationary source of compressed air rather than from a cylinder of air worn on the user's back. Some important considerations in the use of airline respirators are to ensure that a clean supply of air is available and the air lines do not tangle, puncture, or degrade due to chemical or thermal exposure. In addition, airline systems should not pose an unsafe working condition to the user by restricting their movement or the performance of their work.

For both air-purifying and atmosphere-supplying respirators, OSHA requires frequent inspection, maintenance, and cleaning. SCBAs must be inspected monthly, with written documentation maintained, and the air cylinders hydrostatically tested either every three or five years, depending upon the material of construction of the cylinder.

General Designs and Features

All respirators are equipped with respiratory inlet covers or facepieces to provide a barrier from the hazardous atmosphere and for *connecting* the wearer's respiratory system with the respirator.

The two types of respiratory inlet covers include

- Tight-fitting (facepieces)
  - quarter masks
  - half masks
  - full facepieces
- Loose-fitting
  - helmets
  - hoods
  - blouses
  - suits

General respirator designs include

- Air-purifying respirators (APR)
  - disposable respirators

- particulate filter respirators
- cartridge or canister respirators (gas mask)
- cartridge or canister respirators (gas mask) with particulate filter

! Warning: Many filtering facepiece respirators do not provide an adequate seal on the user's face to prevent inward penetration of atmospheric contaminants and may not easily be evaluated by fit testing. It can also be difficult to train workers on performing a user seal check.

- Powered air-purifying respirators (PAPR)
- Supplied-air respirators (SAR)
  - demand supplied-air respirators
  - continuous flow supplied-air respirators
  - pressure demand supplied-air respirators
- Combination supplied-air/air-purifying respirators
  - continuous SAR/APR
  - pressure demand SAR/APR
- Self-contained breathing apparatus (SCBA)
  - demand self-contained breathing apparatus
  - continuous flow self-contained breathing apparatus
  - pressure demand self-contained breathing apparatus
- Combination supplied-air respirators with auxiliary self-contained air supply (SCBA/SAR)
  - demand SCBA/SAR
  - continuous SCBA/SAR
  - pressure demand SCBA/SAR

Respirators may be either negative pressure or positive pressure respirators. All nonpowered air-purifying respirators are negative pressure respirators. Other negative pressure respirators include:

- Demand supplied-air respirators
- Demand self-contained breathing apparatus
- Combination continuous or pressure demand supplied-air/air-purifying respirator (SAR/APR)

Positive pressure respirators include:

- Powered air-purifying respirators (PAPR)

- Continuous flow supplied-air respirators

- Pressure demand supplied-air respirators

- Continuous flow self-contained breathing apparatus

- Pressure demand self-contained breathing apparatus

- Combination pressure demand supplied-air respirator with auxiliary self-contained air supply (SCBA/SAR)

Respirators have several design and performance features associated with each type, such as the mask material, number of mask sizes, and rating service time.

Respirator Selection Approach

There are a number of regulatory requirements and guidelines that govern the selection of appropriate respiratory protection. In the United States, respirators must be certified by the National Institute for Occupational Safety and Health (NIOSH) to the respective requirements in 42 CFR 84. The selection of general respirator types is specified in OSHA 29 CFR 1910.134 (January 8, 1998). These regulations update previous selection practices specified by the regulation from ANSI Z88.2–1992, "American National Standard for Respiratory Protection."

OSHA 29 CFR 1910, Subpart Z provides for specific selection of respirators for protection against the referenced substances. *Recommended Practices* documents, and specific respirator selection guidance, are available. The guidelines for respirator selection are contained in their *Guide to Industrial Respiratory Protection* (DHHS/NIOSH Publication No. 87–116, 1987).

As discussed earlier, in order to select the appropriate respiratory protection, a hazard assessment must be conducted. The information needed to conduct the specific respiratory hazard assessment includes

- Identification of atmospheric contaminant(s)

- Determination of specific regulations or guidelines which may be available for identified contaminant(s)

- Measurement of concentration(s) for specific contaminant(s)

- Determination of Immediately Dangerous to Life or Health (IDLH) concentrations for contaminant(s). (An IDLH atmosphere poses an immediate threat to life, would cause irreversible adverse health effects, or would impair an individual's ability to escape.)

- Measurement of oxygen concentration in atmosphere. (Oxygen deficiency exists when an atmosphere has an oxygen content below 19.5% by volume.)

- Determination if respirator use is for work or escape

- Determination of chemical and physical state of contaminant(s)

    - gas or vapor

    - particulates (dusts, aerosols, mists, fumes)

The general respirator risk assessment allows for specific types of respirators for IDLH environments and only general respirator types for selection in non-IDLH environments. A more detailed analysis is required to allow decisions between different specific respirator types and features. This analysis consists of

- Determining specific exposure limits and characteristics of the contaminants

- Evaluating workplace factors which affect respirator selection

- Reviewing respirator features related to protection

Specific respirators must be selected for special environments.

Fire Fighting. For fire fighting, select a full facepiece pressure demand self-contained breathing apparatus (SCBA).

Chemical Emergency Response. For chemical emergency response or hazardous waste site cleanup requiring a high level of protection, select

- Full facepiece pressure demand self-contained breathing apparatus (SCBA)

- Combination full facepiece pressure demand supplied-air respirator with auxiliary self-contained air supply (SCBA/SAR)

Counterterrorism Response. For counterterrorism response select

- NIOSH certified for Chemical, Biological, Radiological and Nuclear (CBRN) combination full facepiece pressure demand supplied-air respirator (SCBA)

- NIOSH certified for Chemical, Biological, Radiological and Nuclear (CBRN) full facepiece negative pressure respirator (APR) or powered air-purifying respirator (PAPR).

Airline or Air-Supplied Suits. For airline or air-supplied suits (without internal respiratory inlet covering), select suits which have been approved by the requirements specified by the United States Department of Energy.

Abrasive Blasting. For operations involving abrasive blasting, select respirators approved for abrasive blasting:

- Powered air-purifying respirators

- Type AE, BE, or CE supplied-air respirators

Biological Airborne Pathogens. For protection against biological airborne pathogens (*Mycobacterium tuberculosis* [TB]), choose particulate filter facepiece air-purifying respirators equipped with a high-efficiency particulate air (HEPA) filters. Wear specified respirators when

- Employees enter rooms housing individuals with suspected or confirmed infectious TB diseases

- Employees perform high-hazard procedures on individuals who have suspected or confirmed TB diseases

- Emergency medical response personnel or others must transport, in a closed vehicle, an individual with suspected or confirmed TB diseases

When selecting a respirator, it is also important to consider the potential hazards associated with that respirator:

1) Do respirator materials (especially those in the facepiece) irritate or sensitize the wearer's skin?

2) Is the respirator likely to retain contamination even after cleaning?

3) Should the respirator be protected from exposure to liquids and other contaminants?

4) Does the respirator have a design with loose bands, straps, or material that can be caught in moving machinery?

5) Does the respirator (full facepiece or helmet/hood configurations) provide clear and unobstructed vision for performing required tasks?

6) Is the respirator available in a sufficient number of sizes or can the respirator be adjusted to fit personnel? Has each individual who must wear a respirator been fit-tested?

7) Is the respirator difficult to use and reservice?

8) Is the respirator uncomfortable for the wearer under use conditions?

9) Is the respirator reliable for meeting the intended service life?

! Warning: Surgical masks do not provide adequate respiratory protection.

Protective Clothing

Protective clothing includes specific components of a protective ensemble (*e.g.*, garments, gloves, boots, *etc.*) that provides dermal protection. Dermatological disorders are primarily a result of unprotected exposures to harmful chemical, biologic, and physical agents. Most of these exposure risks can be prevented or reduced through the proper selection and use of protective clothing if engineered or administrative controls are not effective or are inapplicable or unavailable. Personal hygiene practices should always follow use of protective equipment. Firefighting protective equipment is not included in this chapter.

Chemical Protective Clothing

The types of chemical protective clothing (CPC) range from basic work clothes to total encapsulating chemical protective ensembles, with a wide variety of designs in between. Basic items for providing splash protection for specific areas of the body, including the head, torso, and appendages, are available in a wide variety of materials. These materials will be discussed further on in this section.

Chemical protective clothing is used in a variety of operations such as cleanrooms and laboratories, in the manufacture of electronic devices, and for hazardous waste operations and emergency response. When specific chemical protection is required, the specifier of the CPC should research the chemical protection information from the CPC manufacturers. Each manufacturer has its own laboratory data for use in selecting CPC. This information is specific to the manufacturer and should not be used as a reference for other manufacturers' products. It should also be noted that laboratory data from any manufacturer might not directly relate to the use environment of concern to the specifier. Depending on the CPC materials, garment design, and construction, these suits can protect the wearer against a wide range of chemicals, including acids, solvents, oxidizers, alkalis, *etc.*

Chemical protective clothing is generally classified into different types: gas/vapor-resistant and splash/particulate-resistant. The *gas/vapor-resistant clothing* is generally configured as totally encapsulating suits, providing head-to-toe coverage to protect the wearer. These are the large *moon suits* that have special seams and zippers to prevent chemicals from leaking into the suit. The suits have a face shield which is made a part of the hood. *Splash/particulate-protective clothing* provides good protection and is used when less skin protection is needed. Splash/particulate-resistant clothing is available in various designs—some with hood, some with elastic wrists and ankles, *etc.* The hood can either be part of the suit or detached.

All CPC can be either reusable or disposable. *Reusable CPC* would provide the same protection for the second use as it was intended to provide initially. If the CPC cannot meet these criteria, it is considered disposable. Thus performance, not cost, should drive reusability. Unfortunately, because the state-of-the-art in proving reusability of CPC is so poor, many CPC use scenarios require CPC to be disposed of after one or a limited number of uses. All CPC is vulnerable to chemical attack, environmental conditions, and physical abuse. The true useable life of CPC is very difficult to predict, so in many situations it is simply better to err on the side of safety and replace the CPC prior to evidence of failure.

CPC materials and quality of construction also influence the performance of CPC as a barrier to chemicals. CPC is available in a variety of materials and designs. Materials used for protective garments include natural rubber, neoprene, nitrile, polyethylene, chlorinated polyethylene, polyvinyl chloride (PVC), Saran-coated Tyvek or Saranex®, polyurethane, butyl polymers, treated woven fabrics, *etc.* These materials can be supported on cotton, nylon, polyester, and other materials. The most appropriate clothing material will depend on the chemicals present and the task to be accomplished. Ideally, the chosen material should resist permeation, degradation, and penetration. The manufacturers' literature usually provides charts indicating the resistance that various clothing materials have to permeation, subsequent breakthrough, or degradation by certain chemicals. However, no single material can protect against all chemicals or any combination of chemicals, and few currently available materials are effective as barriers to any prolonged high level of chemical exposure beyond 60 minutes. Also, for a given clothing material type, chemical resistance can vary significantly from product to product. And for certain chemicals or combinations of chemicals, there may be no commercially available CPC material that will provide more than an hour's worth of protection following contact.

In recent years, public concerns have been raised regarding civilian exposure to toxic chemical warfare agents with terrorist attacks and activities involving stockpiled weapons, *etc.* Aside from deliberate attacks, there is the potential for exposure from unknown military ordnance dumps. The possibility of the presence of any chemical agent (nerve agents, blister agents, blood agents, choking agents, irritants, and biological agents) may warrant the highest level of personal protection available for initial response efforts. The compatible protective apparel material may vary depending on the specific agent, but the highest precautionary level is imperative until the threat is clearly identified. Also, it is impossible to guarantee 100 percent protection against a chemical agent incident. NFPA has published a PPE standard dealing with these situations: The NFPA–1994, "Standard on Protective Ensembles for Chemical/Biological Terrorism Incidents." Although this standard was published in 2001, it continues to be revised to incorporate new information on the types of threats first responders and HAZMAT teams may encounter.

The design and construction of CPC is also very important for CPC performances. Here are some examples of design and construction factors:

- Stitched seams of clothing may be highly penetrable by chemicals if they are not overlaid with tape or sealed with a coating.

- Lot-to-lot variations do occur, and may have a significant effect on the barrier effectiveness of the CPC.

- Pin-holes may exist in elastomeric or plastic products due to deficiencies or poor quality control in the formulation or in the manufacturing processes.

- Thickness may vary from point-to-point on the clothing item.

- Garment closures differ significantly from one manufacturer to another and within one manufacturer's product line.

The most important criterion in the selection and use of CPC is the effectiveness in protecting against the chemical(s) of interest. However, CPC testing methods are not universal. And manufacturers' testing standards vary substantially. For instance, the American Society for Testing and Materials (ASTM) has numerous standards for testing chemical protective clothing. For example, permeation testing of protective garment materials ASTM, F739–96. This ASTM method determines two critical properties of the CPC material: breakthrough time and steady-state permeation rate. The ideal CPC material should have a very long breakthrough time and a very low steady-state permeation rate.

Thermal Protection

The thermal conditions in the work environment have a great impact on workers' physical conditions as well as work performances. Extreme environmental temperatures can cause heat or cold stress. Common heat disorders may include heat cramps, heat exhaustion, and heat stroke. Cold stress can cause hypothermia and frostbite. Besides good work practices for preventing heat or cold stress, protective clothing can make a big difference in protecting workers from extreme cold or heat.

In hot environments, it is important to ensure that clothing keeps workers cool and prevents dehydration. Clothing that is light in color and fabric, and fits loosely to allow sweat to evaporate is recommended. Cooling vests are also available which can absorb the extra body heat, keeping worker's internal temperatures within a safe range. Studies done by the United States Navy have shown that crewmen using cooling vests can safely work in hot environments for twice as long as those without them. There are two basic types of cooling vests available: passive and active. *Passive devices* generally involve water-based or liquid chemical solutions packaged in sealed sectional plastic strips that can move with a worker. Once frozen, the packs are inserted into insulated vests. *Active cooling devices* usually circulate cool water over the body using a power-generated pump. There are tubes that carry chilled water through the vest and recirculate water warmed by the body to an ice-water reservoir where it is cooled.

In cold environments, one of the ways to stay warm is to dress in layers. An outer layer of a waterproof windbreaker material may be worn—acting as a buffer against the wind. A light, airy, dry shirt should be worn next to the skin. It may also be important to have ventilation in the cloth next to the skin so the body can sweat freely. Hands, fingers, feet, ears, and nose should be protected from the cold, since frostbite tends to attack extremities first.

When proper heat or cold stress protection is used, it should help make most environments more tolerable, which is essential for worker protection and productivity.

Head Protection

Hazards associated with the head are impact, falling or flying objects, electrical shock, burns, and scalping, *etc.* Under the OSHA requirements for head protection (29 CFR 1910.135), the employer must determine the needs for protecting workers from head injuries and ensure that the appropriate protection is provided and worn. The protective helmet provided by the employer must provide protection against impact and penetration of falling and flying objects, protection from limited electric shock and burn, as well as meet criteria and requirements contained in ANSI Z89.1–1997 for helmets.

Protective helmets are made in the following types and classes:

- Type I – crown impact

- Type II – crown and lateral impact

Three classes of *hard hats* are recognized:

- Class G–general, limited voltage protection (proof-tested at 2,200 volts)

- Class E–electrical, high-voltage protection (proof-tested at 20,000 volts)

- Class C–conductive, no voltage protection

Other head protection-related items may include *helmet liner* (for insulating against cold), hood (for protecting against chemical splashes, particulate, and rain), and *protective hair covering.*

Eye and Face Protection

Eye and face injuries are typically caused by the following hazards:

- Flying objects, such as dust, metal, or wood chips

- Splashes of toxic or corrosive chemicals, hot liquids, and molten metals

- Fumes, or gases or mists generated by toxic or corrosive chemicals

- Radiant energy and/or intense heat

- Lasers

Thus, eye and face protective equipment are designed for protecting the users from glare, liquids, flying objects, ultraviolet radiation, or a combination of the above hazards. The OSHA requirements for eye and face protection, which require the employer to provide eye and face protection where there is a reasonable likelihood that injuries could be prevented by use of the protective equipment, are listed in 29 CFR 1910.133. The design, construction, testing, and use of eye and face protective devices must be conducted according to the ANSI standard Z87.1–1989. The OSHA 29 CFR 1910.133 standard also has a chart identifying lens filtering properties. ANSI has recently revised the Z87.1–1989 standard with the Z87.1–2003 standard. At the time of this writing, this standard has not yet been published in the Occupational Safety and Health Act (OSH Act).

Eye and face protective equipment usually includes safety glasses, safety goggles, and face shields. Sometimes, different forms of protection need to be combined to provide better protection.

Safety Glasses. Safety glasses (some are equipped with side shields) are designed for protecting the eyes from flying objects and moderate impacts encountered in operations such as grinding, spot welding, woodworking, scaling, and machine operation, *etc.* Safety glasses normally have hard plastic, clear hardened glass or wire mesh lenses and frames made of plastic, plastic coated wire, wire, or fiber. Safety glasses with metal frames should not be used if there is potential of electrical contact or in an explosive atmosphere where non-sparking tools are required. A face shield needs to be used over the safety glasses if a potential chemical splash hazard exists. Shaded lenses are used when protection from ultraviolet (UV), infared, and laser forms of radiation are present.

Safety goggles. Safety goggles protect the eyes from dust, splashes, flying objects, and sparks from any direction. Some goggles have a cup over each eye, whereas others have a frame that extends over both eyes. Goggles have a variety of designs and forms such as: chemical goggles, leather mask dust goggles, miner's goggles, melter's goggles, welder's goggles, and chipper's goggles. Goggles are appropriate during dusty operations, such as sanding. Welding jobs require their own special helmets, either with stationary or lift front windows, to protect against burns as well as sparks and molten splashes. Shaded lenses are used when protection from UV, infared, and laser forms of radiation are present.

Face shields. Face shields protect the face and neck from splashes, heat, glare, and flying objects. They usually have detachable windows made of plastic, wire mesh, or both. Face shields can be attached to a hard hat. They are also available with infrared absorbers to provide protection against radiation. In potentially explosive atmospheres, nonsparking shields must be used. Face shields do *not* take the place of safety glasses. If safety glasses are required in an area where a face shield is to be worn, the safety glasses are worn under the face shield.

Hearing Protection

Excessive noise can create stress on workers, damage their ability to hear, and reduce their job performance. The OSHA regulations for noise protection (29 CFR 1910.95) require each employer to administer a hearing conservation program whenever employee noise exposures equal or exceed 85 decibels for an 8-hour time-weighted average. For certain work environments involving high impact noise, a 140 decibels level is used. Hearing protective devices are needed when engineering and administrative controls can not reduce noise levels to the permissible noise exposure levels required by OSHA.

The general types of hearing protection include the insert type (earplugs) and the earmuff type. Figure 2 provides examples of various types of hearing protection.

Earplugs. Earplugs are the most common types of hearing protection devices used in industry. They are designed to be inserted into the ear canal. Earplugs come in many different varieties and are made of soft materials. Some devices are made in several sizes to accommodate different-sized ear canals. Others come in one size that can be adapted by their natural expansion when inserted in the canal, or by removing one or more flanges on the unit. Some earplugs are disposable; they are

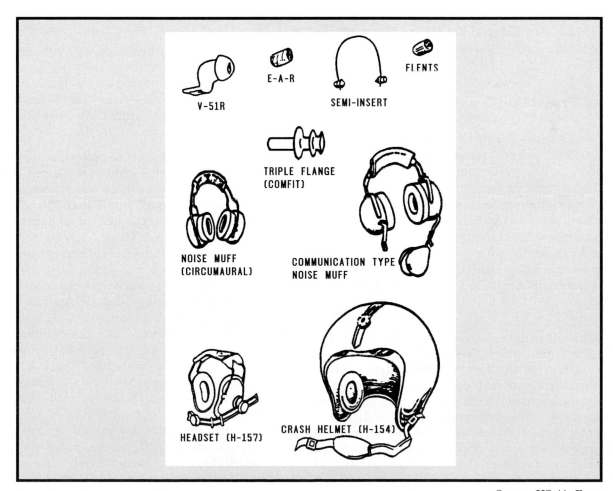

Source: US Air Force

Figure 2. Hearing Protection

normally made of expandable foam. Other earplugs are reusable; they are usually made of a flexible rubber or silicone. They may be flanged or cone-shaped, and are often jointed by a cord so that they are not easily lost.

Earmuffs. Earmuffs consist of a pair of padded plastic shells connected by a flexible band. The shell interior is lined with foam rubber, plastic, or a liquid-filled cushion. Some devices fit only in one position, others are multipositioned and can be worn with the headband over the head, behind the head, or under the chin. Earmuffs can offer good protection if the cushions fit tightly around the ears. Earmuffs cost more initially, but they are cleanable, and replacement parts are available.

Each type of hearing protective device has a noise reduction rating (NRR) which tells how much the protector lessens the noise. The NRR is a key factor for selecting the hearing protective devices. However the selection process is also affected by many other factors, among them comfort, durability, ease of use, hygiene, cost, range or sizes available, care and cleaning requirements, etc. All of these are very important factors.

Foot Protection

Foot protection such as footguards, toe caps, metatarsal guards, safety shoes, or boots are needed for the protection of feet from falling or rolling objects, sharp objects, molten metal, hot surfaces, contaminated materials, and wet slippery surfaces, etc. OSHA 29 CFR 1910.132 has general requirements for the employer to protect workers from hazards that have a potential for causing injury to the foot. OSHA 1910.136 has detailed requirements regarding occupational foot protection.

Boots are available in a wide variety of lengths ranging from hip length to those that cover only the bottom of the foot. Boots constructed of chemical-resistant material are used for protecting feet from contact with chemicals. Chemical protective boots are made of a few different polymers since the boot heel and sole require a high degree of abrasion resistance. The common polymers and rubbers used in chemically resistant boot construction include butyl rubber, nitrile, neoprene rubber, and PVC materials. Disposable shoes or boot covers are also available and made from a variety of materials. Boots constructed with some steel materials (e.g., toes, shanks, and insoles) are used to protect feet from compression, crushing, or puncture by falling, moving, or sharp objects. Safety shoes and boots may also be constructed with fiberglass toes, as a substitute for steel toes in workplaces involving unprotected electrical sources (such as the third rail at a railroad yard).

Safety footwear is classified according to its ability to meet minimum requirements for both compression and impact tests. ANSI standard Z41–1001 is the standard for Personal Protective Footwear. Boots constructed from nonconductive, spark-resistant materials or coatings are used to protect the wearer against electrical hazards and prevent ignition of combustible gases or vapors. ANSI has revised this standard with Z41–1999.

Hand Protection

Hazards to hands may be presented by chemicals, sharp objects, hot surfaces, moving parts of machines or tools, and heavy equipment, etc. Besides the general requirements, OSHA has hand protection requirements in 29 CFR 1910.138.

Gloves. Gloves can be used to protect hands from potential hazards such as burns, cuts, electrical shock, amputation, and absorption of chemicals, etc. There are gloves available that can protect the wearers from any of the individual hazards or any combination thereof. Gloves may be integral, attached, or separate from other protective clothing. Overgloves are sometimes used to provide supplemental protection to the wearer and protect more expensive undergarments from abrasions, tears, and contamination. Disposable gloves are often used to reduce decontamination needs in contamination protection situations. Cloth gloves are often used for light duty materials handling for protection against cuts or abrasions. They may also be used to provide insulation for moderately hot or cold environments. Many glove materials are available for providing chemical protection, such as PVC, nitrile, neoprene, and natural rubber, etc. Breakthrough time and permeation rate are important factors when choosing gloves for chemical protection. When dealing with glove selections, it is important to match the gloves selected to the specific hazards. Comfort, dexterity, glove thickness, glove interface with chemical protective clothing, available sizes, use duration, frequency and degree of exposure, *etc.* are also important factors to be considered.

The health care industry, research laboratories, food service workers, *etc.* commonly use latex gloves. Latex gloves are also used as inner gloves by environmental professionals and emergency response personnel when chemical gloves are required. Latex gloves have proved effective in preventing transmission of many infectious diseases to health care workers. But for some workers, exposures to latex may cause allergic reactions and result in skin rashes, sinus symptoms, asthma, and shock. NIOSH has published an *Alert* publication that recommends employers adopt policies to protect workers from latex exposure and allergy in the workplace.

Fall Protection

Fall protection is needed in many work areas or job activities such as excavations, hoist areas, holes, unprotected sides and edges, roofing work, wall openings, building construction, and other walking/working surfaces. In 1995, two major fall protection-related construction standards took effect: OSHA's Subpart M standard, which relates directly to equipment and systems used for fall protection in the construction industry, and Subpart L, which deals specifically with scaffolds. Residential construction activities are also impacted by these regulations. Other available OSHA fall protection standards include 29 CFR 1926.104 for safety belts, lifelines and lanyards and 29 CFR 1926.105 for safety nets. As required by the OSHA Fall Protection Standard, employers must protect their employees from fall hazards and falling objects whenever an affected employee is 6 feet or more above a lower level. Other OSHA standards will define the requirement for fall protection at different heights (scaffolding, steel erection, roofing of residential construction, *etc.***)**

Fall protection generally can be provided through the use of guardrail systems, safety net systems, personal fall arrest systems, positioning device systems, and warning line systems, *etc.* Canopies and toeboards are methods for protection from falling objects. Employers can select fall protection measures compatible with the type of work being performed. Specific fall protection system criteria and practices required by the fall protection standard must be met when using a system. For construction employees, OSHA's Subpart M standard for construction (29 CFR 1926.500–502) requires the use of full body harnesses as of January 1, 1998 as part of personal fall arrest systems. Locking snap hooks must be used to replace nonlocking snap hooks that took effect at the same time.

Selection of Protective Equipment: Anticipation, Recognition, Evaluation, and Control

The association of potential hazards with modern technology and the increasing use of new biological and chemical reagents requires a positive approach to the anticipation, recognition, evaluation, and control of health hazards, as well as physical stresses in the work place. Each employer and his or her supervisors must be diligent in the recognition of hazards associated with his/her activities. This requires a review of health and physical hazards associated with activities or operations to be conducted. Employers must evaluate the hazards associated with each procedure and process, to determine where exposures exist or may occur; evaluate actual exposure through air sampling, analysis, or other sampling techniques as necessary; conduct medical surveillance programs on employees exposed to hazardous materials as necessary; and control hazards through substitution or elimination of materials, modification of equipment, addition of ventilation, use of personal protective equipment or administrative changes, *etc.*

Hazard Assessment

For each workplace, employers are required to perform a *hazard assessment* to determine if hazards requiring the use of PPE are present or are likely to be present. The hazard assessment usually involves a walk-through survey of the job area to identify sources of hazards, and consideration of the following categories of hazards: impact, penetration, compression, chemical, heat, harmful dust, light radiation, falling, *etc.* During

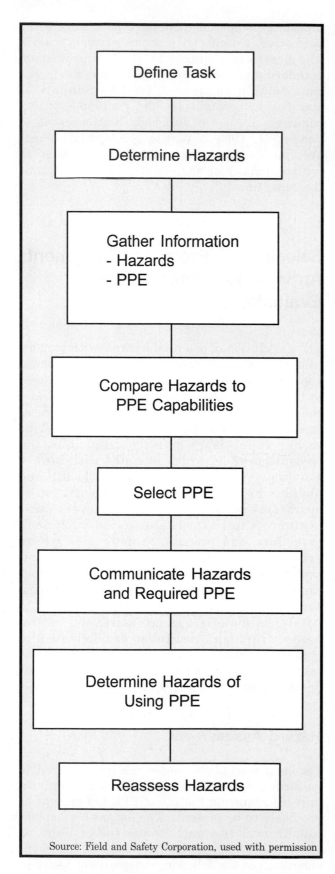

Define Task

Determine Hazards

Gather Information
- Hazards
- PPE

Compare Hazards to PPE Capabilities

Select PPE

Communicate Hazards and Required PPE

Determine Hazards of Using PPE

Reassess Hazards

Source: Field and Safety Corporation, used with permission

Figure 3. Flow Diagram for PPE Hazard Assessment

the walk-through, the sources or potential problem areas for these hazards should be identified. The data and information for use in the assessment of hazards are then recognized and an estimate of the potential for injuries is made. Each of the basic hazards is then reviewed and determinations made as to the type, level of risk, and seriousness of potential injury from each of the hazards. The hazard assessment should be documented in writing, and a reassessment of the hazards should be performed as necessary. A flow chart summarizing the PPE hazard assessment process can be found in Figure 3.

OSHA Requirements for Performing a Hazard Assessment

OSHA 29 CFR 1910.132 requires that employers conduct a hazard assessment to determine the need for and then to select PPE. Appendix B to Subpart I of OSHA 29 CFR provides nonmandatory guidelines for conducting hazard assessments and for selecting personal protective equipment. The following subjects are addressed:

- Controlling hazards

- Assessment guidelines

- Selection guidelines

- Fitting the devices

- Devices with adjustable features

- Reassessment of hazards

- Selection guidelines for eye and face protection

- Selection guidelines for head protection

- Selection guidelines for foot protection

- Selection guidelines for hand protection

- Cleaning and maintenance

The principal source of information for conducting a hazard assessment comes from an inspection of the workplace with actual observation of specific tasks being carried out. Additional information can be obtained by interviewing the affected employees and asking about

- The types and frequency of hazards encountered in the tasks

- Specific instances in which hazards have been encountered in the past

- The past effectiveness or ineffectiveness of any PPE used in the tasks

Other sources of information such as the log, first aid, near miss reports, *etc.* could be used. The specific hazard and nature of any accidents or exposures should be evaluated to determine the possible preventative role of using PPE or improving PPE if involved. In some cases, it will be necessary to measure hazard levels using special instrumentation such as portable sampling devices to measure airborne concentrations of chemicals or noise-monitoring equipment.

Recommended Risk Assessment Approach

The risk assessment based-approach presented in this chapter for selecting PPE uses the following steps:

- Conduct a hazard assessment of the workplace

- Determine the risk of exposure, and rank protection needs

- Evaluate available PPE designs, performance, and applications against protection needs

- Specify appropriate PPE

Conducting the Hazard Assessment. The hazard assessment consists of the following steps:

1) Define the workplace and tasks to be evaluated

2) Identify the hazards in the workplace

3) Determine areas of the body or body systems that are affected by the hazards

4) Estimate the potential for employee contact with hazards in the workplace

5) Estimate the consequences of employee contact with hazards

The specific steps of this process are described in the following sections.

Define Each Workplace and Tasks to Be Evaluated. The *workplace* includes the area that encompasses the range of hazards that may be encountered. Examples of a workplace include

- The specific work locations for a particular employee

- A laboratory

- A part of a production process

Work tasks should be defined as those worker activities that

- Involve unique hazards

- Are accomplished by a single individual or group of individuals within a given period of time

Identify the Hazards Associated with Each Work Task. General hazard categories include

- Physical

- Environmental

- Chemical

- Biological

- Thermal

- Electrical

- Radiation

- Person–position

- Person–equipment

Determine Each Affected Body Area or Body System. For each hazard, determine which portion of the body can be affected by the hazard. General body areas and body systems typically affected by workplace hazards include

- Head

- Eyes and face

- Hands

- Arms

- Feet

- Legs

- Trunk or torso

- Entire body

- Respiratory system

- Hearing

Estimate the Likelihood of Employee Exposure to Identified Hazards. For every identified hazard affecting a specific portion of the body (or the whole body), indicate the likelihood of exposure. One method of doing this is to use a rating scale of 0 to 5 based on both the risk and the frequency of exposure:

0:   Exposure cannot occur

1:   Exposure very unlikely

2:   Exposure possible, but unlikely

3:   Exposure likely

4:   Multiple exposures likely

5:   Continuous exposure likely

Estimate the Possible Consequences of Exposure to Identified Hazards. For every identified hazard affecting a specific portion of the body (or the whole body), indicate the consequences of exposure. A rating scale of 0 to 5, based on the *worst case* effects on the potentially exposed worker, can be used:

0:   No effect

1:   Temporary effect on employee (such as discomfort) with no long-term consequences

2:   Exposure results in temporary, treatable injury

3:   Exposure results in serious injury with loss of work time

4:   Exposure results in permanent debilitating injury

5:   Exposure results in likely death

A completed hazard assessment will provide a list of hazards and show which parts of the worker body may be affected, how likely exposure will occur, and what the probable consequences of exposure might be.

Determining Relative Risk and Establishing Protection Needs. The risk of exposure is determined by the hazard assessment. Protection needs are ranked by the relative risk. For determining relative risk, establish a risk assessment form for listing

- Hazards identified for the specific workplace/task

- Body areas or body systems affected by the respective hazard

- The rating associated with the likelihood or frequency of the respective hazard

- The rating associated with the severity or consequences of the respective hazard

Using risk determinations from the risk assessment form, rank all hazards associated with the workplace/tasks. Those hazards with the highest amount of risk should be assigned higher priority for prevention or minimization. Those hazards with zero risk or low risk should be assigned lower priority for prevention or minimization.

Examine possible engineering or administrative controls for those hazards with the highest risk. Engineering controls can encompass changes in the task and process, use of protective shields, or other designed measures that eliminate or reduce possible exposure to hazards. Administrative controls can include changes in tasks or work practices to eliminate or limit employee exposure time to a hazard. If engineering or administrative controls are not possible, examine different types of PPE for elimination or reduction of exposure to hazards.

From information about affected body area or body systems, decide which type of PPE can be used to eliminate or minimize the hazard. In many cases, the type of PPE to be used will be obvious and limited to a single general type (for example, inhalation hazards can be protected against with a respirator). In other cases there may be several types of PPE that can be used to provide the needed protection.

General Approach for Evaluating PPE Designs, Design Features, Performance, and Applications

The evaluation of PPE designs, design features, performance, and applications encompasses the following steps:

- Understand and choose the types of PPE available for protection

- Understand and choose relevant performance properties of PPE to consider during PPE selection

The types of PPE available in the marketplace and thus the choices available to the end user are rapidly increasing. PPE exists in a variety of designs, materials, and methods of construction, each having advantages and disadvantages for specific protection applications. End users should have an understanding of the different types of PPE and their features in order to make appropriate selections.

> **! WARNING: PPE that are similarly designed may offer different levels of performance. Examine PPE performance in addition to design and features.**

PPE must be properly sized to provide adequate protection.

> **! WARNING: Improperly sized or ill-fitting PPE may reduce or eliminate protective qualities of PPE.**

PPE may be classified by

- Design

- Performance, or

- Intended service life

Design. The classification of PPE by its design usually reflects the configuration of the item or the parts of the body area or body systems that it protects. For example, footwear provides protection to the wearer's feet.

The classification of PPE by design may also provide an indication of specific design features that differentiate PPE items of the same type. For example, closed-circuit self-contained breathing apparatus is configured with significant design differences when compared to open-circuit self-contained breathing apparatus. Some designs of PPE may offer varying protection against hazards in different parts of the PPE item. For example, the palm material in a glove palm may provide a better grip surface than the glove's back material.

> **! WARNING: PPE coverage of a specific body area, in and of itself, does not guarantee protection of that body area.**

Performance. The classification of PPE by performance indicates the actual level of performance to be provided by the item of PPE. This may include a general area of performance or a more specific area of performance. For example, while two items of PPE might be considered to be chemical protective clothing, one item may provide an effective barrier to liquids but not to vapors while the other item provides an effective barrier

to both liquids and vapors. The classification of PPE by performance is best demonstrated by actual testing or evaluations of PPE with a standard test.

> **! WARNING: Intended or manufacturer-claimed performance does not always match actual performance.**

Service Life. The classification of PPE by expected service life is based on the useful life of the PPE item. PPE may be designed to be

- Reusable

- Used a limited number of times (limited use)

- Disposable after a single use

The classification of PPE by expected service life is based on:

- Durability

- Life-cycle cost, or

- Ease of reservicing

Durability is determined by evaluating how the item of PPE maintains its original performance properties following the number of expected uses. The *life-cycle cost* of PPE is the total cost for using an item of PPE and is usually represented as the cost per use for a PPE item. The following costs should be considered in determining the life-cycle cost:

- Purchase cost

- Labor cost for selection/procurement of PPE

- Labor cost for inspecting PPE

- Labor and facility cost for storing PPE

- Labor and materials cost for cleaning, decontaminating, maintaining, and repairing PPE

- Labor and fees for retirement and disposal of used PPE

The total life-cycle cost is determined by adding the separate costs involved in the PPE life cycle and dividing by the number of PPE items and number of uses per item.

If an item of PPE cannot be *reserviced* to bring it to an acceptable level of performance, then it cannot be reused.

! WARNING: Expected service life does not always equal actual use life.

Additional detail for selection factors for different types of PPE is provided later in this chapter.

Risk Assessments and PPE Selection

As discussed earlier, in order to select the PPE needed for a specific task, it is very important that the needs be assessed for the particular job, performance criteria be developed, and a hazard/risk assessment be conducted. The OSHA PPE standard requires the employer to perform a hazard assessment at the workplace to determine if hazards that require the use of head, eye, face, hand, or foot protection are present or are likely to be present. 29 CFR 1910.132 includes a non-mandatory Appendix B that offers compliance guidelines for hazard assessment and PPE selection.

The hazard assessment usually involves a walk-through survey of the job area to identify sources of hazards, and consideration of the following categories of hazards: impact, penetration, compression, chemical, heat, harmful dust, light radiation, and falling, etc. During the walk-through, the sources or potential problem areas for these hazards should also be identified. The data and information for use in the assessment of hazards are then organized, and an estimate of the potential for injuries is made. Each of the basic hazards is then reviewed and a determination is made as to the type, level of risk, and seriousness of potential injury from each of the hazards.

Once it is determined that certain types of hazards exist or potentially exist and the level of risk, and the seriousness of any potential injury analyzed, then the environmental health and safety professional making the PPE selection should become familiar with the types of PPE that are available for the specific hazards. The hazards associated with the environment they exist in are compared with the capabilities of the available PPE. The PPE that ensures a level of protection greater than the minimum required to protect employees from the hazards should be selected. The minimum level of protection required will depend on the performance standard required or selected, such as the Threshold Limit Value (TLV) or Permissible Exposure Limits (PEL), break-

through time, *etc.* Besides performance criteria, the selection may also be affected by the need for decontamination, ergonomic constraints presented, the cost, *etc.* Once the individual PPE items are selected, they should be assembled according to previously established ensemble configuration criteria, and fitted to the user. It is also very important that the users are instructed in the use and maintenance of the PPE, and are made aware of all warning labels and limitations of their personal protective equipment.

In summary, the risk-based PPE selection process should involve: defining work task, determining workplace hazards (type and source of hazards) by using a job safety analysis, analyzing potential risks, determining type of PPE needed for the specific hazard, and comparison of PPE capabilities with performance standard or action level criteria. If the performance standard can be met by the PPE, and other miscellaneous factors including economic constraints are satisfied, then the PPE is selected for the ensemble, configuration, and fitting phases.

The Selection Process

Respiratory Protection. The selection of a specific respirator must be made by individuals knowledgeable about the limitations associated with each class of respirators and acquainted with the actual workplace environment, including the job task(s) to be performed. Many factors may influence the respirator selection, such as: adequate warning, type of hazard, concentration of contaminant, acuteness of hazard, time spent in contaminated atmosphere, nature of the working environment, activity of the wearer, mobility of the wearer, and whether the use is for routine or emergency application, *etc.*

NIOSH Certification. In 1995, NIOSH established new testing procedures and performance requirements for nonpowered, air-purifying respirators in its new certification regulation (42 CFR 84). NIOSH has been approving respiratory products using the new rules since then. The 42 CFR 84 approval procedure uses a letter and number system to differentiate products. There are three types of filters: N–series for protection against solid and water-based particulates; R–series for protection against any particulates, including oil-based materials with eight-hour maximum usage; and P–series for protection against any particulates, including oil-based materials, with no specific time limit. Manufacturers will be able to sell only those products certified under the new procedures after June 10, 1998. Distributors and employers will be able to exhaust their old supplies before switching over to the new ones.

Personal Protective Clothing and Equipment Selection. Besides the selection of respiratory equipment, the PPE selection process involves the selection of other individual items, based on needs, including but not limited to protective equipment for: eye and face, head, foot, hand, torso, and hearing. Many of the factors that affect the selection of individual items were discussed in earlier sections of this chapter. The factors affecting chemical protective clothing (suits, gloves, boots) selections for skin protection are emphasized here.

Several factors have to be considered when making a chemical protective clothing selection. These factors include: body coverage needed, physical properties for avoiding chemical penetration, prior use experience, permeation resistance, protection period required, chemical toxicity, severity of potential chemical contact, temperature of chemicals, multiple chemical exposures, degradation conditions, and decontamination methodology, *etc*.

Whenever exposure to vapors of a chemical is considered unacceptable, permeation resistance data should be used. The permeation resistance performance for protective clothing is particularly important for chemicals that pose known health hazards through irritation, reaction with, or absorption into the skin. Whenever the workplace conditions indicate the likelihood of chemical exposure, such as direct contact with solids or particulate-based chemicals, direct liquid contact through immersion, or contact with liquid through splashing, spraying, or misting, and vapor contact, permeation data should also be considered.

The most common practice for using permeation resistance data is to compare the breakthrough time with the intended period for using the relevant PPE garments. Many users select a chemical protective garment when the garment materials of interest show breakthrough times greater than the longest anticipated use period.

However, according to PPE experts, using this method alone can provide an inadequate PPE selection, resulting in both underprotection and overprotection.

It is recommended that the use of permeation data be based on a risk assessment that identifies the hazards of the chemicals in the work environment, combined with estimates for likelihood of exposure and the possible consequences of exposure. However, unlike respiratory protection, there is little data available for defining acceptable exposure limits for skin to chemicals, which makes it more difficult to define an acceptable risk for selecting PPE. The two available measures may be the *toxic dose low* (TD$_{LO}$) (the lowest concentration of a substance introduced by any route, other than inhalation, over any given period of time and reported to produce any toxic effect in humans or to produce teratogenic or reproductive effects in animals) and the *toxic concentration low* (TC$_{LO}$) (the lowest concentration of a substance in air to which humans or animal have been exposed for any given period of time that has produced any toxic effect in humans or to produce teratogenic or reproductive effects in animals).

One alternative approach recommended by some experts for selecting protective clothing on the basis of chemical permeation resistance data is determining the potential of exposure to chemicals through the permeation rate or minimum detectable permeation rate. The cumulative permeation through the protective clothing is based on a number of assumptions and is calculated using the permeation rate of the chemical together with the exposed clothing surface area and exposure time.

Simultaneous Hazards. Simultaneous hazards may be present under certain conditions. The PPE selection process under these conditions may be even more complicated. The selected PPE should not only protect against each individual hazard, but also against the combination of those simultaneous hazards, if any synergistic effects exist.

Levels of Protection. The components of personal protective equipment may be assembled into a protective ensemble that not only protects the worker from site-specific hazards but also minimizes the hazards and drawbacks of the PPE ensemble itself. The Environmental Protection Agency (EPA) has defined four levels of protection:

Level A, B, C, and D. These levels are widely referenced especially for hazardous waste site operations and emergency response applications.

Level A is required where there is the greatest potential for exposure o skin, respiratory, and eye hazards. Level A includes respiratory protection with positive pressure, full facepiece self-contained breathing apparatus (SCBA), or positive pressure supplied-air respirator with escape SCBA; totally encapsulated chemical-and-vapor-protective suits; inner and outer chemical-resistant gloves; and disposable protective suits, gloves, and boots.

Level B protection includes the highest level of respiratory protection but a lesser level of skin protection. At most abandoned outdoor hazardous waste sites, ambient atmospheric vapors or gas levels are not high enough to warrant Level A protection and Level B often is adequate. Level B includes respiratory protection with positive pressure, full facepiece self-contained breathing apparatus (SCBA) or positive pressure supplied-air respirator with escape SCBA; inner and outer chemical-resistant gloves; faceshield; hooded chemical-resistant clothing, coveralls, and outer chemical-resistant boots.

Level C is required where the concentration and type of airborne substances are known and the criteria for using air-purifying respirators are met. Typical Level C equipment includes full face air-purifying respirators, inner and outer chemical-resistant gloves, hard hat, escape mask, and disposable chemical-resistant outer boots.

Level D protection is the minimum protection required. Level D may be sufficient when no contaminants are present or work operations preclude splashes, immersion, or the other potential for unexpected inhalation or contact with hazardous chemicals. Appropriate Level D protective equipment may include gloves, coveralls, safety glasses, faceshield, and chemical-resistant, steel-toe boots or shoes.

All ensemble components should be specified with regard to manufacturer, model number and item technical, physical as well as chemical resistance characteristics.

Figure 4 provides examples of the levels of protection. *Note that these levels of protection do not provide specific information to the user regarding the specific ensemble components. The specific ensemble components must be specified based upon a site- or workplace-specific risk assessment.*

Validating the Selection Process

Once the PPE is selected, the selection process should be validated. PPE should be fitted to the specific user. For example, respirator fit-testing needs to be performed to decide what size of a particular air-purifying respirator should be assigned to a user. Medical surveillance may be needed for a particular PPE user.

Documenting the Selection Process

In the OSHA PPE standard at 29 CFR 1910.132, the employer is required to provide written certification that the workplace hazard assessment has been performed. The certification shall identify the workplace evaluated, the person certifying that the evaluation has been performed, and the date(s) of the hazard assessment. It is recommended that the whole PPE selection process be documented to include not only the hazard assessment performed but also the PPE selection criteria used, the PPE selected and assigned (including personnel and type of task), and the PPE training performed (including the type and date of training).

Various Factors Affecting PPE Performances

The performances of PPE are affected by many factors, including physical environment conditions, ergonomics and human factors, the types of PPE selected, *etc.*

Adverse physical environments such as extreme temperature conditions can not only cause heat or cold stress to the PPE users, but may also affect the performance of the PPE itself, potentially exposing the worker unexpectedly. For example, low temperatures may fog respirator lenses, impeding the worker's ability to see what he or she is doing. In addition, many elastomeric materials (PVC, butyl, neoprene, and viton rubber) are not designed for use in extremely cold or hot environments and will crack, puncture, and

LEVEL A PROTECTION
Totally encapsulating
vapor-tight suit with full-
facepiece SCBA or
supplied-air respirator

LEVEL B PROTECTION
Totally encapsulating suit
does not have to be
vapor-tight. Same level of
respiratory protection as
Level A.

LEVEL C PROTECTION
Full-face canister air-
purifying respirator.
Chemical protection suit
with full body coverage

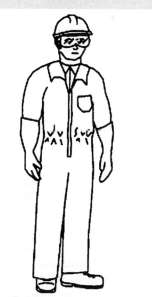

LEVEL D PROTECTION
Basic work uniform; *i.e.,*
longsleeve coveralls,
gloves, hardhat, boots,
faceshield or goggles.

Source: US Air Force

Figure 4. Levels of Protection

degrade more readily than at normal room temperature. The PPE user should be made aware of the limitations of PPE they are assigned, and use them only under the assumed conditions and tasks the PPE was originally selected for.

In certain cases, the use of personal protective equipment could increase workers' discomfort, cause heat stress, and decrease mobility, communications, dexterity, tactility, strength, and endurance, and affect productivity. For example, when workers use more than one layer of gloves, the ability to perform simple motor functions such as trying to grip an object becomes increasingly difficult and muscle fatigue occurs more rapidly. These *ergonomic factors* should be considered when PPE is selected and used. The use of protective clothing may also affect the quality of a worker's performance and increase the chance for human error.

Wearing personal protective equipment can impose some physiological and psychological stress on the user. The weight of the equipment, for example, increases the energy requirement for a given task. The use of PPE may also affect the human response and endurance, especially in hot environments. Various human factors may not only affect the PPE performance but may also affect the safety of the PPE user. These factors may include training, experience, stress, height, weight, false sense of security, *etc.* The mobility, tactility, dexterity, and visibility can also be limited due to PPE usage.

The following practices are recommended for reducing adverse effects caused by various factors:

- Select the lightest-weight protective ensembles and respiratory protective devices that adequately protect the worker. This will minimize the physiological demands placed on the worker that are associated with carrying the weight of this equipment. The size of the PPE should fit the user

- If available, select protective clothing made of material that will allow evaporation of water vapor, while providing skin protection from the contaminant

- When PPE is used during intensive work, reduce the work rate by adjusting work/rest schedules, using automated procedures and/ or mechanical assistance where possible, and minimize the work intensity

- Educate workers on symptoms and prevention of heat illness, and schedule periodic fluid replacement breaks

- Reduce heat or cold stress by scheduling work accordingly and using engineering control methods

Behavior Modification and the Human Factors

Adequate education for PPE users is essential to its effective use. The OSHA PPE standard requires that employees be trained to know when PPE is necessary, what type is necessary, how it is to be worn, and what its limitations are, as well as to know its proper care, maintenance, useful life, and disposal procedures. This must be accomplished before any work that requires the use of PPE is assigned. Retraining may be required if the workplace changes, if the types of PPE to be used change, or if inadequacies are identified which indicate that employees have not retained the necessary understanding or skills. By educating the PPE user, one may be able to improve or control the human factors and achieve a better PPE performance goal.

Chemical Protective Clothing Decontamination

Decontamination of CPC is the process of removing, isolating or reducing contaminants that are known or suspected to be present on the protective clothing. Decontamination can be employed to:

1) Protect the wearer from becoming exposed to the contaminants of concern

2) Minimize the effect contaminants may have on chemical protective clothing and avoid cross-contamination

3) Return chemical protective clothing to service

Effective decontamination of CPC is crucial no matter whether the chemical protective clothing is to be worn once and discarded or is for multiple uses.

Type of CPC Contamination

CPC contamination may include surface contamination, penetration, and or permeation through CPC materials. Factors that can affect the extent of CPC contamination include contact time, the concentration of the contaminant(s), temperature (ambient and contaminant[s]), size of the contaminant molecules and pore spaces within the CPC, and the physical state of contaminant(s).

Decontamination Method and Equipment

The selection of decontamination method depends on many variables including but not limited to

- The type of contamination (solid, liquid or gas/vapor)

- Its physical, chemical and toxicological properties

- The type of contamination permeability of the contaminant through the skin

- Delivery dose

- The location and size of CPC area affected

- The number of CPC users requiring decontamination

- The physical location or facility where decontamination is to be performed

For specific situations, especially outdoor locations, the environmental conditions will have a significant influence on the decontamination process. In general, decontamination methods should control how all contaminated CPC (including equipment, tools, *etc.*) are *left behind* in contaminated areas. These controls may include removal methods, administrative procedures and engineered systems (work zone delineation).

Typically, contamination removal methods are employed when the contaminants can be

1) Physically removed

2) Rendered harmless by chemical detoxification or disinfection/sterilization

3) Removed by a combination of methods involving both physical and chemical means.

In some instances, the type of contamination may be such that removal may be accomplished by dislodging, displacement, rinsing off, wiping off or from evaporation. These removal methods may utilize hand tools (brushes, towels, wipes, *etc.*) and mechanized devices such as portable hand-pressurized pump sprayers or spray/shower-type systems (some of these can also be heated).

Gross decontamination is analogous to kicking mud off boots before rubbing them on a door mat, or showering at the beach before showering inside. The concept is straight forward—get as much off as possible before contaminating other areas unnecessarily, and before beginning the cleaning or decontamination process. This will extend the use life of decontamination equipment and washing/rinsing agents and avoid tracking contamination into other locations.

In some instances there may be a requirement for dry decontamination. Situations employing dry decontamination methods include but are not limited to

- Contamination from water reactive substances

- The inability to contain liquid decontamination run off

- The lack of available wet decontamination substances

- Weather conditions cause water soluble decontamination liquids to freeze

Dry decontamination may be performed using brushing, wiping, blotting, vacuuming techniques (like through the use of a High Efficiency Particulate Air [HEPA] filter vacuum), or dry powders (such as soap, detergents, earth, or flour).

When physical removal of contaminants may not be effective to decontaminate CPC, additional removal methods would be required. Washing and rinsing methods involving water and other chemicals may be used to

1) Dissolve contaminants

2) Reduce adhesion forces between contaminants and the CPC surface being cleaned

3) Solidify liquid or gel contaminants

4) Rinse and dilute and

5) Disinfect/sterilize

The selection of decontamination equipment depends upon several factors. These factors may include economics, available space, available resources (such as water, electricity, *etc.*), as well as contaminants of concern, number of personnel, environmental conditions, and duration of tasks—just to name a few.

Selection of Decontamination Methods by Type of Contamination

Surface contamination can be removed by physical means such as brushing, spraying, washing, and scraping. If the contaminant is water soluble, washing is effective. If the contaminant is marginally water soluble, detergents and wetting agents can enhance removal (*e.g.*, the use of an emulsifier for oils). Some contaminants, such as acids and bases, may require neutralizing or complexing.

Protective clothing that has *pore contamination* usually cannot be decontaminated and must be handled as hazardous waste.

CPC that has been permeated must be decontaminated if feasible and not discarded. Several methods are currently available. In research performed by Schlatter, Berardinelli, Perkins, and Stull, aeration was determined to be as effective or more effective than traditional water washing, dry cleaning, Freon cleaning, and other methods (Schlatter 1988, Perkins 1991, Stull 1996). Aeration is effective when aeration temperatures are above 100°F (hot-air aeration). Research performed by Perkins and others demonstrated the effectiveness of this technique for the removal of various volatile solvents from butyl rubber using 50°C air temperatures (Perkins 1987, Smith 1996). For polar and other water-soluble chemicals, the use of hot water, detergents, and other additives can increase the efficiency of decontamination. Nevertheless, multiple washings may be necessary.

For nonpolar and nonvolatile contaminants, decontamination options are limited. One approach is to use a *wash* solvent with a high affinity for the contaminant. The problem with this approach is that the solvent used to extract the contaminant may in the process damage the protective barrier by removing essential plasticizers or other compounding ingredients. The decontaminating solvent could simply replace the contaminant in the barrier, resulting in a barrier that now is contaminated with the cleaning solvent.

Dry cleaning (using perchloroethylene) is of limited value, as reported by Schlatter (Schlatter 1990). The dry cleaning method could degrade the barriers (Garland 1988). Studies of Freon 113™ washing of butyl, neoprene, and Viton™ suits contaminated with nitrobenzene showed efficiencies of 45%, 67%, and 83%, respectively for an initial treatment (Smith 1996). These efficiencies were increased upon subsequent washing.

Research clearly demonstrates that the standard boot rinse or suit wash used by many hazardous waste site workers and emergency responders is simply not effective except in rare circumstances (Garland 1988 and Mansdorf 1989).

Measure the Effectiveness of Decontamination

The effectiveness of CPC decontamination can be measured many ways and guidelines or procedures should be established in order to assure that the desired results from CPC decontamination are obtained. If the effectiveness of CPC decontamination cannot be determined, then the decontamination process should be revised. CPC decontamination can involve nondestructive testing including visual observation, air monitoring, wipe sampling and chemical solution analysis. Destructive testing on contaminated CPC can be performed as well. In many cases, CPC decontamination should *not* be determined by visual inspection alone. The effectiveness of a decontamination program can be assessed in a variety of ways, such as the collection of wipe samples on decontaminated equipment and on surfaces in clean areas, analyzing the final decontamination rinse water for the presence of contaminants, or visual inspection of PPE for signs of leakage or failure.

Disposal of Decontamination Waste

All decontamination waste, including disposable PPE and rinsate should be disposed of in accordance with all local, State, and Federal regulations. Requirements to consider include waste labeling, packaging, treatment, and manifesting.

Management Approaches to Personal Protection Strategies

Personal protective equipment should not be used as a substitute for engineering controls, work practice, and/or administrative controls. The workplace should be designed, engineered, modified, improved, or controlled by reasonable means to eliminate hazards requiring PPE. PPE should be used in conjunction with these controls—as part of the *big picture* to provide for employee safety and health in workplace. Management must commit its financial, human, and equipment resources towards establishing and maintaining an effective program within which the employees are actively participating. In many organizations, personal protective equipment programs are an integral part of the daily implementation of the corporate environmental health and safety (EHS) program. The corporate EHS program encompasses all strategies (including personal protective equipment) to maintain a healthy and safe workplace. The following section discusses overall workplace health and safety strategies as part of an organization's EHS program.

Environmental Health and Safety Management Program

In order to provide work environments that maintain and protect employee health and safety, organizations must develop and maintain a comprehensive and proactive program. Organizations must be committed to developing and maintaining an environmental, health, and safety (EHS) program that prevents injury and controls loss by minimizing occupational injuries and illnesses; monitoring the workplace environment (*e.g.*, dust, vapor, chemical hazard, radiation, and noise); and using this data as the basis for engineering and work practice controls as well as personal protective equipment selection.

To be effective, this effort must have the strong commitment and support of management. The following elements are important components of an effective EHS management plan:

- Management leadership
- Assignment of responsibility and accountability
- Design and maintenance of safe working conditions
- Accident investigation and analysis
- Safe operating rules and procedures
- Safety training and education
- Recognition, evaluation, and control of occupational hazards
- EHS administration

Management Leadership. The organization must realize that the attitude and commitment of upper management are invariably reflected in the attitude of the supervisory force towards environment, safety, and health. Therefore, management must demonstrate a sincere interest in the EHS program if employee cooperation and participation are to be achieved. Management must issue clear statements of policy for the guidance of supervisors and employees. If safety is a shared responsibility, then management must do its share.

Assignment of Responsibility. While the prime responsibility for the safety and health of all employees is, by law, vested in the Chief Executive, the day-to-day responsibility rests with supervisors. This means that all supervisors have the responsibility to monitor the EHS performance of all employees that report to them. Each employee is responsible for following all of the safety rules and requirements that are applicable to his or her assigned responsibilities. Management should encourage employee participation in the development of EHS promotional programs, goals, and objectives. Employees have the responsibility to make others aware of environmental, health, and safety problems.

Design and Maintenance of Safe Working Conditions. The supervisor or worker is responsible for checking out all new equipment and processes as well as initiating the development of standard operating procedures (including relevant safety precautions) before authorizing use of such equipment. Workplace inspections are essential not only for the maintenance of safe work conditions and operating practices, but also for the discovery of causes of accidents and harmful exposures. Comprehensive inspections of the entire facility should be conducted periodically and at least annually. Self-audits should be conducted daily—before and at the end of the workday. Written reports should be prepared after inspections, and appropriate corrective action should be initiated to correct all deficiencies that are identified. Follow-up inspections by the person responsible for employee safety (usually the Safety Officer) should be conducted to evaluate the corrective action taken.

Accident Investigation and Analysis. Employees must be encouraged to report all near-misses, accidents, injuries, and occupational illnesses. These events should be investigated to determine the cause, and to establish corrective measures to prevent reoccurrence. It is essential that an accident investigation and injury report be completed for all work-related injuries or illnesses. Each supervisor is responsible for investigating all incidents, accidents, and injuries that occur within their area(s) of supervision.

Safe Operating Rules and Procedures. Safe operating rules and procedures must be established as a guide to all employees for the prevention of accidents, injuries, illness, or exposure to harmful substances. These rules and procedures need to be tested and proven to work and reviewed periodically by employees with their supervisors. It may be necessary, on occasion, to establish new safety rules to cover new equipment or operations, or to revise existing rules to improve conditions or procedures. When any safe operating rule or procedure is violated or disregarded, appropriate disciplinary action must be taken, immediately. Employees must be advised of and required to comply with these rules and procedures. This would apply to the management of toxic chemicals, infectious agents, radiation exposures, *etc.*

Safety Training and Education. OSHA has come to the realization that adequate protection of the safety and health of employees goes beyond the provision of personal protective equipment and safe working conditions. Human factors must be considered and action must be taken to encourage proper work practices. Education, training, and safety promotional programs are the means of developing a spirit of safety consciousness and good attitudes in the workplace. OSHA and EPA include a worker training section as part of every standard that they promulgate.

All new and transferred employees must be oriented and trained in their jobs. This basic orientation is usually followed by frequent on-the-job safety instructions by supervisors during their first few days on the job. Potential hazards, if any, in the area are identified, and precautions to avoid injury are defined. Information on fire and emergency procedures, reporting of injuries and accidents, and available health care, should be covered as well. Attention to the integration of safe and healthy work practices into daily tasks is an important factor in this follow-up training. Safety Teams composed of representatives of senior management, employees, and staff should conduct safety reviews periodically to assess the *environment of safety*.

Developing and Managing PPE Programs

Written programs for PPE, respiratory protection, fall protection, confined space entry and rescue, as well as a hearing conservation program should be developed if PPE is needed in the workplace. These programs usually include policy statements, procedures, and guidelines. A risk assessment methodology for selecting the PPE; an evaluation of other control options to protect the worker; PPE selection criteria and procedures; PPE performance criteria; user training requirements; PPE storage, maintenance, and decontamination requirements; and an auditing or program re-evaluation procedures are normally included in the programs. By implementing formal written programs, the chance for error is reduced, worker protection is increased, and a companywide, consistent approach for the selection and use of PPE is established. The PPE program should be reviewed at least annually.

Corporate management and employees should make diligent and dedicated efforts to ensure that corporate respiratory and PPE programs meet their standard goals. The person responsible for administering the program must have the appropriate technical and professional background. It is important that one member of management have final responsibility as well as the necessary management support for the company's respiratory and PPE program; with appropriate staff specialized in all needed areas of respirator and PPE maintenance and use.

PPE Inspection, Cleaning, Maintenance, Storage and Repair. PPE maintenance should be made an integral part of the overall PPE program. Manufacturer's instructions for inspection, cleaning, and maintenance of PPE should be followed to ensure that the PPE continues to function properly. Wearing poorly maintained or malfunctioning PPE may be even more dangerous than not using it at all. The worker wearing a defective device may falsely assume that protection is being provided. Emergency escape and rescue devices are particularly vulnerable to inadequate inspection and maintenance. Although they generally are used infrequently, they are used in the most hazardous and demanding circumstances. The possible consequences of wearing a defective emergency escape and rescue device may be lethal. An adequate PPE maintenance program tailored to the type of workplace and the type of hazards is very important.

PPE Selection Reevaluation. Normally, the EPA levels of protection (A, B, C or D) are used as a starting point for ensemble creation. Each ensemble is then tailored to a specific situation in the selection process in order to provide the most appropriate level of protection. As the amount of information about the specific operation or site increases, the overall level of protection and PPE selected are validated to make sure proper and effective selections were made. The level of protection may also need to be upgraded or downgraded based on the new evaluation.

Reasons to upgrade PPE may include

- Known or suspected presence of additional hazards

- Changes in work task that will increase exposure or potential exposure to hazardous materials

- Request of the individual performing the task

Reasons to downgrade PPE may include

- New information indicating that the situation is less hazardous than was originally thought

- Change in work conditions or work tasks that decreases the hazard

Trends in Biological and Chemical Personal Protection

The trends in personal protection can be described based upon an assessment of the gaps that exist within the collective knowledge of the allied health and safety professions. A national workgroup, spearheaded by NIOSH, established priorities to focus research in a variety of areas of personal protection. This workgroup, the National Organization Research Agenda (NORA), has identified some key areas for study. More specifically, biological and chemical protection research efforts are needed to close the gaps in the areas discussed below.

Dynamics of Biological and Chemical Dermal Exposure

- Research the need for conducting dermal exposure risk assessments and surveillance as part of Biological and Chemical Protective Clothing (BCPC) use.

- Develop state-of-the-art dermal monitoring equipment or techniques.

- Advance biological monitoring practices.

- Establish task-based worker behavior assessment where BCPC is used.

- Study the adverse impact of BCPC on the wearer; *e.g.*, biocompatibility (dermatitis, allergy, sensitization), physical impairments, and ergonomic limitations.

- Investigate the impact of dermal expiration on BCPC performance; *e.g.*, synergetic and inhibition factors that affect the BCPC performance and the establishment of surveillance procedures to monitor this phenomenon.

- Develop approaches and parameters for determining acute and chronic dermal exposure (for the purpose of setting permissible exposure levels).

Improvement of Laboratory and Field Testing Methodologies

- Develop standardized tests for key BCPC performance areas not addressed by industry.

- Identify improvements in laboratory testing methodology, for easier end-user interpretation of results.

- Develop surveillance system for monitoring the selection, use, limitations, and failure of specific BCPC.

- Establish research to validate BCPC and use of end-of-service-life indicators (ESLI).

- Advance real-time biological and chemical monitoring technologies, such as microsensors, colorimetric techniques, and other analytical techniques, as well as field detectors.

Improvement of BCPC Human Factors and Ergonomics

- Investigate procedures for reporting BCPC sizing and techniques for determining correct fit.

- Establish techniques for measuring BCPC comfort and impact on worker productivity and acceptance.

- Develop specific workplace evaluation procedures for assessing the working environment with respect to its effect on BCPC use.

- Investigate BCPC use applications and examine ergonomic factors.

Development of BCPC Decision Logic

- Develop a BCPC management system and practices for its implementation.

- Establish decision logic for BCPC selection that accounts for a range and combination of biological/chemical hazards.

- Integrate ergonomics and human-factor engineering in establishing worker BCPC fit, comfort, functionality, task requirements, physical environment, and contamination avoidance.

- Incorporate feedback for decision logic from dermal exposure and risk assessment data.

- Increase cooperation among small business, trade associations, government agencies, and academia for BCPC use; additionally, establish a partnership among these organizations for ongoing BCPC applications.

Promotion of Education and Training on Selection, Use, and Limitations of BCPC

- Identify ways of reaching users, especially small businesses through trade associations,

unions, government public services, and volunteers.

- Establish methods for communicating hazards to the users using available training techniques; *e.g.*, adult education, distance learning, Internet, *etc.*

- Develop approaches for promoting student learning of BCPC selection and use.

- Establish a model motivation program on proper use and care of BCPC, using organizational reward programs and occupational health and safety programs.

- Evaluate approaches for modifying worker behavior with respect to BCPC use.

- Create a surveillance program for recording problems and successes with use of BCPC.

Investigation of Physiological and Psychological Factors Associated with the Physical Environment

- Investigate practices for reducing the impact of heat stress from BCPC use in specific work applications.

- Determine BCPC factors for protection from extreme cold *(frostbite and hypothermia).*

- Examine increasing effects of nonionizing radiation for impact on workers and BCPC.

- Establish techniques to determine appropriate levels of exertion while wearing BCPC.

- Establish techniques to determine criteria for evaluating BCPC user phobias.

- Evaluate in-service procedures used to evaluate physiological and psychological factors of BCPC users prior to, during, and after mission/task performance.

Encouragement of Engineering Technology

- Identify areas where new BCPC material would provide benefit for different industries.

- Examine aspects of BCPC design which maximize protection and minimize physical stresses on the wearer.

- Establish BCPC human factors and ergonomic design principles for improvement of BCPC.

- Determine procedure for evaluating new BCPC materials with respect to potentially adverse effects before marketing.

Development of BCPC Decontamination and Disposal Methods

- Conduct research to determine when decontamination is possible and effective.

- Establish techniques for evaluating effectiveness of decontamination techniques.

- Investigate novel decontamination approaches for BCPC use.

- Develop decision logic for BCPC decontamination and disposal.

Bibliography

American National Standards Institute. *Industrial Head Protection*. ANSI Z89.1–1997. New York, NY: ANSI, 1997.

American National Standards Institute. *Personal Protection—Protective Footwear*. ANSI Z41–1991. New York NY: ANSI, 1991.

American National Standards Institute. *Personal Protection—ProtectiveFootwear*. ANSI Z41–2003. New York NY: ANSI, 2003.

American National Standards Institute. *Practice for Occupational and Educational Eye and Face Protection*. ANSI Z87.1–1989. New York, NY: ANSI 1989.

American National Standards Institute. *Practice for Occupational and Educational Eye and Face Protection*. ANSI Z87–1999. New York, NY: ANSI, 1999.

American Society for Testing and Materials. *Standard Test Method for Resistance of Protective Clothing Materials to Permeation by Liquids or Gases Under Conditions of Continuous Contact*. ASTM F739–96. West Conshohocken, PA: ASTM, 1996.

Collert, J. *Environmental Health and Safety CFR Training Requirements*. Rockville, MD: Government Institutes, Inc., 1995.

Garland, C. E, and A. M. Torrence, "Protective Clothing Materials: Chemical Contamination and Decontamination Concerns and Possilbe Solutions." In *Performance of Protective Clothing*. S. Z. Mansdorf, R. Sager, and A. P. Nelson, Eds. STP 989. West Conshohocken, PA: ASTM, 1998.

Kavianian, H. R., *et al. Occupational and Environmental Safety Engineering and Management*. New York, NY: Van Nostrand Reinhold, 1990.

Mansdorf, S. Z. "Chemical Protective Clothing Use in U.S. Hazardous Waste Operations." In *Proceedings of the Third Scandinavian Symposium on Protective Clothing Against Chemicals and Other Health Risks*. Gausdal, Norway:1989.

National Institute for Occupational Safety and Health. *NIOSH Guide to Industrial Respiratory Protection*. NIOSH #87–116. Washington, DC: NIOSH, 1987.

National Institute for Occupational Safety and Health. *NIOSH Guide to the Selection and Use of Particulate Respirators Certified Under 42 CFR Part 84*. NIOSH #96–101. NTIS No: PB 96-191–937/A03. Washington, DC: NIOSH, 1996.

National Institute for Occupational Safety and Health. *NIOSH Respirator Decision Logic*. NIOSH # 87–108. Washington, DC: NIOSH, 1987.

National Institute for Occupational Safety and Health. *Occupational Safety and Health Guidance Manual for Hazardous Waste Site Activities*. NIOSH 85–115. Washington, DC: NIOSH, 1985.

"Occupational Exposure To Bloodborne Pathogens, Final Rule." *Federal Register*. 56 (6 December 1991), pp. 64004–64122.

Occupational Safety and Health Administration. *Fall Protection In Construction*. OSHA 3146. Washington, DC: OSHA, 1998.

Occupational Safety and Health Administration. *Protect Yourself with Personal Protective Equipment*. Fact Sheet OSHA 92–08. Washington, DC : OHSA, 1992.

"Occupational Safety and Health Standards." *Code of Federal Regulations*. Title 29. Part 1910.

Perkins, J. L., J. S. Johnson, C. R. Sackett, *et. al.* "Residual Spilled Solvents on Butyl Protective Clothing and Usefulness of Decontamination Procedures." In *Applied Industrial Hygiene.* 2:179. 1987.

Perkins, J. L. "Decontamination of Protective Clothing." In *Applied Occupational and Environmental Hygiene.* 6:29–35. 1991.

Raouf, A. and B. S. Dhillon. *Safety Assessment.* Boca Raton, FL: CRC Press/Lewis Publishers, 1994.

Roland, H. E. and R. B. Moriarty. *System Safety Engineering and Management.* 2nd ed. New York, NY: John Wiley and Sons, 1990.

"Safety and Health Regulations for Construction." *Code of Federal Regulations.* Title 29. Part 1926.

Schlattler, C. N. "Decontamination of Protective Clothing." In *Chemical Protective Clothing.* Vol. 1, Chapter 8. J. S. Johnson and K. Anderson, Eds. Fairfax, VA: AIHA Press, 1990.

Schlattler, C. N. "Effects of Water Rinsing on Subsequent Permeation of Rubber Chemical Protective Gloves." In *Performance of Protective Clothing.* S. Z. Mansdorf, R. Sager, and A. P. Nelson, Eds. STP 989. West Conshohocken, PA: ASTM, 1998.

Schwope, A. D., *et al. Guidelines for the Selection of Chemical Protective Clothing,* 3rd ed. Cincinnati, OH: ACGIH, 1987.

Smith, I. D. and K. E. Burke. "Decontamination of Protective Suit Materials." In *Performance of Protective Clothing.* J. L. Perkins and J. O. Stull, Eds. STP 1037. West Conshohocken, PA: ASTM, 1996.

Stull, J. O., C. R. Dodgen, M. B. Connor, and R. T. McCarthy. "Evaluating the Effectiveness of Different Laundering Approaches for Decontaminating Structural Fire Fighting Protective Clothing." In *Performance of Protective Clothing.* J. L. Perkins and J. O. Stull, Eds. STP 1037. West Conshohocken, PA: ASTM, 1996.

Ziskin, M., *Dermal Protection Strategy for Response to Chemical and Biological Terrorism Incidents.* American Industrial Hygiene Conference and Exposition. San Diego, CA: AIHA, 2002.

Ziskin, M., *Personal Protective Equipment Programs for Unknown Encounters at Unknown Incidents.* American Industrial Hygiene Conference and Exposition. Toronto, Canada: AIHA, 1999.

Ziskin, M., *et al. Chemical Protection: Practical Selection and Use in Hazardous Waste Operations and Emergency Response.* Supplemental materials for Professional Development Course No.4, American Industrial Hygiene Conference and Exposition. Anaheim, CA: AIHA, 1994.

Ziskin M., J. Stull, and J. Zvetan. *Risk-based Assessment for the Selection of Personal Protective Equipment.* American Industrial Hygiene Conference and Exposition–Professional Development Course. Atlanta, GA: AIHA, 1998.

Michael H. Ziskin is the founder and executive vice president of Field Safety Corporation, an environmental, health and safety consulting firm providing risk management, regulatory compliance, training and field services. He has completed undergraduate and graduate studies in Environmental Health Science and Industrial Hygiene. Mr. Ziskin holds certifications as a Certified Hazardous Materials Manager (CHMM) and as a Hazard Control Manager (CHCM). He has received specialized training from various governmental and industrial organizations including: The USEPA, The National Institute for Occupational Health and Safety, and E. I. DuPont de Nemours and Company. Mr. Ziskin has 29 years of experience in the environmental and health and safety industries. He has managed and directed projects including: air pollution assessments, hazardous waste site investigations, remedial actions, emergency responses, and industrial facility compliance audits. Mr. Ziskin has designed and implemented a variety of corporate environmental, industrial hygiene and safety programs for businesses ranging in size from small industrial shops to Fortune 100 corporations. Mr. Ziskin is a nationally recognized authority in personal protection and has been appointed to AIHA, NFPA, AESF, and ASTM Committees involved with occupational health and safety issues. He is a Principal on the National Fire Protection Association Technical Committee on Hazardous Materials Protective Clothing and Equipment and a past chairman of the Personal Protective Clothing and Equipment Committee of the AIHA. Since 1991, Mr. Ziskin serves as an adjunct Professor at the University of New Haven, teaching Hazardous Materials Management courses in the Graduate Environmental Science and Biology and Terrorism courses in the Department of Public Safety, Graduate Fire Sciences Program. He has also been a member of the Fairfield County Hazardous Incident Response Team since 1991. Mr. Ziskin has been awarded the Champion of Excellence from ACHMM, and three Special Recognition awards from AIHA. He is also a Fellow of the Institute of Hazardous Materials Management. Mr. Ziskin has over 70 publications and presentations.

Dawn Han has fourteen years experience in environmental and occupational health and safety, and Industrial Hygiene, with specialized expertise in health and safety hazard analysis, data validation and quality control and assurance, pollution control, ventilation system design, and indoor air quality. She has an MS in Industrial Hygiene and a BS in HVAC Engineering. Ms. Han is certified in the comprehensive practice of industrial hygiene. She is also certified in Hazardous Waste Site Safety Supervision, First Aid, and CPR. Ms. Han is licensed as an Asbestos Inspector, and is an Asbestos Project Designer. She has been responsible for the development of site-specific health and safety plans, conducting health hazard studies, performing on-site OSHA compliant inspections and audits, and technical research. She also participates in the development of corporate environmental health and safety programs, and in the performance of comprehensive Industrial Hygiene and safety services. Ms. Han has performed hundreds of hours of worker exposure monitoring for numerous air contaminants including metals, corrosives, carcinogens, and other respiratory toxicants. She has performed numerous worker exposure studies and risk assessments, especially in the metal-finishing industry, hardware, defense and tool-making manufacturing industries. She has also provided her expertise as a third-party auditor in reviewing exposure cases for worker compensation and legal cases. Ms. Han has previously served as an Industrial Hygienist for an environmental laboratory. In this capacity she directed the company's health and safety program and provided technical oversight for the company's field sampling programs at RCRA and CERCLA sites. She has also conducted a variety of occupational hygiene programs, and has managed asbestos abatement, underground storage tank removals, and waste disposal projects for the University of Cincinnati.

CHAPTER 12

Industrial Toxicology

Robert Roy, PhD, DABT
Robert Skoglund, PhD, DABT, CIH

Introduction

Toxicology is the study of the adverse effects of chemical, physical and biological agents on living organisms. *Toxicity* is the ability of a chemical, physical, or biological agent to cause damage to biological material. Hazard has also been used to describe the ability of substances to cause damage to biological material. For example, in the preamble of the Final Rule for the Occupational Safety and Health Act (OSH Act) Hazard Communication Standard, *hazard* is defined as an inherent property of the chemical that would exist no matter what quantity was present. Toxic agents may be classified in terms of

- *Use*–industrial solvent, pesticide, food additive, pharmaceutical, *etc.*

- *Source*–plant and animal agents

- *Health effect*–carcinogen, teratogen, liver damage, lung damage, kidney damage, *etc.*

- *Physical state*–solid, liquid, gas, particulate, mist, *etc.*

- *Labeling requirements*–flammable, oxidizer, corrosive, irritant, *etc.*

183

- *Chemistry*–aromatic amine, halogenated hydrocarbon, inorganic, aliphatic hydrocarbon, aromatic hydrocarbon, metal, *etc.*

- *Biochemical mechanism of action*–enzyme inhibitor, binding/damage to biomolecules such as deoxyribonucleic acid (DNA) and proteins, *etc.*

- *Poisoning potential*–relatively harmless, slightly toxic, moderately toxic, highly toxic, and extremely toxic

Risk is the likelihood (probability) that an adverse effect (injury or harm) will occur in a given situation. OSHA defines risk as a function of both hazard and the amount of exposure (see 59 FR 6126). It is a function of the *toxicity* (hazard) of the agent and *exposure* to the agent:

Risk = f (Toxicity, Exposure)   (1)

or, expressed in a very useful manner:

Risk = Toxicity x Exposure   (2)

Toxicity is an inherent property of all substances. *The toxicity of a chemical cannot be altered or eliminated.*

Exposure can be defined as the amount of an agent available for absorption into the body. Unlike toxicity, exposure to chemical substances can be significantly reduced or completely eliminated. Methods of reducing or eliminating exposure to chemicals include

- Substituting a less toxic chemical for one that has a higher relative toxicity

- Using administrative controls (*e.g.*, limiting access to certain areas)

- Using appropriate ventilation (*e.g.*, passive and mechanical)

- Using appropriate personal protective equipment (*e.g.*, respiratory protection, eye protection, gloves)

Since the toxicity of a chemical (or chemical mixture) cannot be altered, one can see by using Equation (2) that the risk of adverse health effects from the chemical or mixture is directly proportional to the amount of exposure (*i.e.*, as exposure increases, risk increases, and *vice versa*).

Safety is the probability that adverse effects (harm) will *not occur* under specified conditions (the inverse of risk).

Factors Affecting Responses to Toxic Agents

If a chemical agent reaches an appropriate site (or sites) in the body at a high enough concentration and for a sufficient length of time, it will produce adverse (toxic) effect(s). Many factors affect the responses (*e.g.*, adverse effects) that may occur in a given situation. These factors are:

1) **Chemical and Physical Properties of the Substance**

   - The **physical state** (*e.g.*, liquid, gas, fume, mist, dust, vapor, *etc.*) can influence exposure potential, route of exposure, and amount potentially absorbed.

   - The **solubility** in biological fluid/material such as blood and lipids (fat) may affect its absorption into the body, its movement (distribution) within the body, and its potential for storage in the body (*e.g.*, in fat or bone).

2) **Exposure Situation**

   - *Duration of exposure* includes acute (*e.g.*, usually a single dose), subchronic (*e.g.*, days to years), and chronic (*e.g.*, years to a lifetime).

   - *Frequency of exposure* influences the amount of substance available for absorption into the body. It may be expressed as number of exposures per time period.

   - *Routes of exposure* include the gastrointestinal tract (ingestion), lungs (inhalation), and skin (dermal, topical, or percutaneous). The order of effectiveness of the exposure routes into the body (moving from most effective to least effective) is: intravenous, inhalation, intraperitoneal, subcutaneous, intramuscular, oral, dermal. In the workplace, the major routes of exposure to chemical agents are inhalation, dermal, and oral.

   - *Dosage* (dose) is the most critical factor in determining whether a toxic response will take place. It is defined as the unit of chemical per unit of biological system (*e.g.*, mg/kg body weight, mg/body surface area, ml/kg body weight, *etc.*).

3) Individual factors

- *Age* of the exposed person(s) (*e.g.*, neonates have a less developed blood/brain barrier, thus certain chemicals may easily pass into the central nervous system).

- *Genetic background* is very important in determining the variations seen between individuals (*e.g.*, may determine whether allergic reactions occur).

- *General health status* (*e.g.*, persons with preexisting damage to organs such as the liver, kidney, or lungs may be at an increased risk for damage if they are exposed to chemicals which specifically damage these organs).

Toxicokinetics

Toxicokinetics is the movement of toxic substances (chemicals) within the body. This movement is usually divided into four interrelated processes termed absorption, distribution, biotransformation (metabolism), and excretion.

- *Absorption* is the process by which chemicals cross cell membranes and enter the bloodstream. Major sites of absorption are the skin, lungs, gastrointestinal (GI) tract, and parenteral (*c.g.*, intravenous, subcutaneous). The *degree of ionization* and *lipid (fat) solubility* affects how easily a chemical can move through cell membranes. A chemical's degree of ionization depends on its pK_a (the pH at which a chemical is 50% ionized) and the pH of the solution. For example, at low pH (*e.g.*, pH = 2-3), a weak organic acid such as benzoic acid ($pK_a = 4.0$) is usually ***non-ionized*** ($RCOO^-$ + $H^+ \rightarrow RCOOH$), and an organic base such as aniline ($pK_a = 5.0$) is usually ***ionized*** (RNH_2 + $H^+ \rightarrow RNH_3^+$). In general, more of the non-ionized form of a chemical will be absorbed than of the ionized form. Also, the greater the lipid solubility of a chemical the greater its tendency to be absorbed.

- *Distribution* is the movement of chemicals throughout the body after they have been absorbed. It is usually rapid. Anatomical barriers such as the blood/brain barrier, which limits the passage of chemicals to the central nervous system, can impede distribution. The placenta is not as good a barrier as was once thought. Many chemicals and drugs can cross the placenta and reach the fetus. Some chemicals can be stored in body fat (*e.g.*, lipid-soluble compounds such as dichlorodiphenyltrichloroethane [DDT] and polychlorinated biphenyls [PCBs]) and in bone (*e.g.*, lead, fluoride, and strontium).

- *Biotransformation* (metabolism) is the process by which living organisms can chemically change a substance. Biotransformation reactions take place primarily in the liver, but can also occur in other organs such as the kidneys and lungs. The principal biotransformation enzymes of the body are called the cytochrome P-450 monooxygenases (P-450). Biotransformation reactions convert lipid-soluble chemicals into more polar (water-soluble) metabolites and increase the excretion of the chemicals from the body. The biotransformation of chemicals can produce metabolites that have little or no therapeutic or toxicologic activity (called detoxification reactions). Also, biotransformation reactions can produce metabolites that are capable of causing far more cell and tissue damage than the parent chemical alone would have caused. The biotransformation of a relatively nontoxic chemical into one or more toxic metabolites is called *bioactivation*. Examples of occupational chemicals that undergo bioactivation into highly toxic metabolites include:

Chloroform	$\rightarrow$	Phosgene
Carbon Tetrachloride	$\rightarrow$	Trichloromethyl radical
n-Hexane	$\rightarrow$	2,5-Hexanedione
Methyl *n*-Butyl Ketone	$\rightarrow$	2,5-Hexanedione
Vinyl Chloride	$\rightarrow$	Chloroethylene Oxide

- *Excretion* is the elimination of chemicals from the body. Chemicals may be excreted either unchanged (in the chemical form in which they were absorbed) or as metabolites (the products of biotransformation). The primary organs involved in the excretion of chemicals are the kidneys (urine), liver (bile/feces), and lungs. Renal excretion (kidney) is the primary means by which the polar chemicals and polar metabolites of lipid-soluble chemicals are eliminated from the body. Certain chemicals and their metabolites are eliminated by means of biliary excretion (excretion into the bile from the liver). Volatile chemicals and metabolites can be excreted rapidly and efficiently through the lungs in a process called *pulmonary excretion*.

The Dose-Response Relationship

Dose-response is the quantitative (measurable) relationship between the dose of a chemical (*e.g.*, mg chemical/kg body weight) and an effect (response) caused by the chemical. The dose-response relationship is the most fundamental concept in toxicology.

The dose-response curve (Figure 1) is a graphical presentation of the relationship between the degree of exposure to a chemical (dose) and the observed biological effect or response. One can usually identify both very sensitive (hypersensitive) and resistant populations on a dose-response curve.

The following data can be calculated (estimated) from dose-response curves:

- The *median lethal dose (LD$_{50}$)* is the single dose of a chemical that can be expected to cause death in 50% of the exposed population. The LD$_{50}$ is not a biological constant. There are many factors that can influence the estimation of the LD$_{50}$, such as the route of administration of the chemical and the species and strain of animals used.

- The *median effective dose (ED$_{50}$)* is the single dose of a substance that can be expected to cause a particular effect (other than lethality) to occur in 50% of the exposed population.

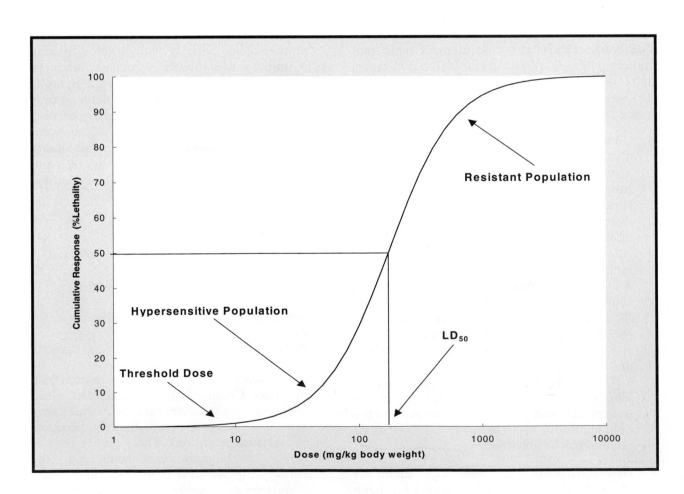

Figure 1. Hypothetical Dose-Response Curve

- The *median lethal concentration (LC$_{50}$)* is similar to the LD$_{50}$ except that the chemical is quantified as an exposure concentration (*e.g.*, concentration in air such as ppm or mg/m^3) rather than a dose (*e.g.*, mg/kg-body weight).

- The *threshold dose* is the lowest dose of a chemical at which a specified measurable effect is observed and below which it is not observed (*e.g.*, No Observed Effect Level [NOEL]).

The dose-response data have a variety of uses. They can be used to:

- Establish a causal relationship between a substance and a particular effect

- Provide an indication of the range of effective dosages (for both toxic and therapeutic effects)

- Provide an indication of the threshold or no-effect-level dosage

- Allow for a quantitative comparison of the toxicities of two substances

- Determine the regulatory classifications (such as Highly Toxic, Very Toxic, Toxic; Packing Group; and Toxicity Category [based on oral LD$_{50}$, dermal LD$_{50}$, and inhalation LC$_{50}$]) of a chemical according to various regulatory and authoritative organizations such as the Occupational Safety and Health Administration (OSHA), Consumer Product Safety Commission (CPSC), Environmental Protection Agency (EPA), Department of Transportation (DOT), and the American National Standards Institute (ANSI).

Chemical Interactions

People are never exposed to only one chemical at a time. We are always exposed to mixtures of chemicals whether we are in the workplace, at home, or in the ambient outdoor environment. Most chemicals do not cause a similar degree of injury in all the tissues or organs they encounter. Major adverse effects usually occur in the *target organs*. For example, benzene usually affects the bone marrow, *n*-hexane affects the peripheral nervous system, and paraquat affects the lungs. The majority of the available toxicological data comes from controlled studies where test subjects have been exposed to only a single substance. There

are little data from studies where test subjects have been exposed to two or more substances simultaneously. Based on the available data and other observations, toxicologists have identified five ways in which chemicals may interact with each other in the body to produce responses. These interactions are called

- *Independent effect*—Substances exert their own toxicity independently of each other.

- *Additive effect*—The combined effect of exposure to two chemicals that have both the same mechanism of action and target organ, is equal to the sum of the effects of exposure to each chemical when given alone (*e.g.*, 3 + 5 = 8). In the absence of any data to the contrary, chemicals are assumed to interact in an additive manner (example: two different organophosphate insecticides and inhibition of acetylcholinesterase at neuromuscular junctions).

- *Synergistic effect*—The combined effect of exposure to two chemicals is much greater than the sum of the effects of each substance when given alone (*e.g.*, 3 + 5 = 30); each substance magnifies the toxicity of the other.

- *Potentiating effect*—One substance, having very low or no significant toxicity, enhances the toxicity of another (*e.g.*, 0 + 5 = 15); the result is a more severe injury than that which the toxic substance would have produced by itself.

- *Antagonistic effect*—An exposure where two chemicals together interfere with each other's toxic actions (*e.g.*, 4 + 6 = 8), or one chemical interferes with the toxic action of the other chemical, such as in antidotal therapy (*e.g.*, 0 + 4 = 2).

General Classification of Toxic Effects

Chemical, physical, and biological agents can produce many general types of toxic effects following exposure:

- *Allergic (hypersensitive, sensitization) reactions* are generally mediated by two mechanisms: those that are mediated via the production of antibodies to the allergen (antigen), (reaction Types I, II, and III), and those mediated via specialized immune cells (Type IV). An example of a Type I reaction is the occupational asthma produced in susceptible individuals following an exposure to certain diisocyanates such as toluene diisocyanate (TDI). A Type IV reaction would be like the allergic contact dermatitis produced in susceptible individuals following an exposure to nickel salts and chromates.

- *Immediate or acute toxicity* occurs rapidly after a single exposure. Examples of acute toxicity include: eye and skin burns from corrosives, or eye and skin irritation; asphyxiation by simple asphyxiants (*e.g.*, propane and methane) which displace oxygen from inspired air; and chemical asphyxiants (*e.g.*, carbon monoxide and cyanide ion) which interfere with oxygen transport or utilization by cells.

- *Delayed or chronic toxicity* manifests itself after a period of latency (may be many years). Chronic toxicity may also occur as a result of long-term exposure to low levels of various chemicals. Examples include cancer, peripheral and central nervous system damage, and liver and kidney disease.

- *Reversible effects* are those adverse effects that wear off (or reverse), given sufficient time after the exposure ceases. Examples include central nervous system depression, skin and eye irritation, upper respiratory tract (*e.g.*, nose and throat) irritation, certain types of liver/kidney damage, and certain types of nervous system damage.

- *Irreversible effects* are those adverse effects that do not reverse after the exposure ceases. The damage is permanent. Examples include neuronal damage in the central nervous system, liver and lung fibrosis, skin and eye corrosion, and birth defects.

- *Local toxicity* occurs at the site of chemical contact. The chemical need not be absorbed to cause this reaction. Examples include skin and eye irritation and corrosion, and upper respiratory tract irritation.

- *Systemic toxicity* occurs at a site or sites distant from the site of chemical absorption.

Examples include liver damage following inhalation of carbon tetrachloride, peripheral nervous system damage following inhalation of *n*-hexane, bone marrow damage following inhalation of benzene, and nervous system damage following dermal exposure to methyl parathion (insecticide). *Most chemicals produce systemic toxicity following absorption.*

Adverse Health Effects, Associated Chemicals, and Other Agents

Some very important adverse health effects and their major symptoms/signs are:

- *Dermal irritation* is a localized, nonimmune, inflammatory response of the skin that is characterized by reversible redness, swelling and pain at the site of contact.

- *Eye irritation* is a localized, nonimmune, inflammatory response of the eye that is characterized by reversible redness, swelling, pain and tearing of the eyes.

- *Dermal and eye corrosion* is an irreversible destruction of tissue with pain, ulcerations, and scarring.

- *Dermal sensitization* is a skin reaction triggered by an immune response to allergens. This reaction is characterized by redness, swelling, crusting/scaling, and vesicle formation.

- *Respiratory sensitization* is a pulmonary (lung) reaction triggered by an immune response to allergens. Pulmonary reactions are characterized by coughing, labored breathing, tightness in the chest, and shortness of breath.

- *Upper respiratory tract irritation* is a reversible inflammatory reaction that occurs in the nose and throat. This reaction is characterized by sneezing, nasal discharge, coughing, hoarseness, the productions of phlegm, and nasal inflammation (rhinitis).

- *Hepatotoxicity* can be caused by cell death (necrosis), accumulation of lipids, damage to the bile ducts, inflammation (hepatitis), and the presence of fibrotic tissue in the liver. Malaise, abdominal pain, nausea/vomiting, jaundice, loose stools, GI bleeding, liver enlargement, and an increase in the presence of liver enzymes in the plasma may be characterized by hepatotoxicity.

- **Nephrotoxicity** can be caused by damage to various portions of nephrons (the functional units of the kidney that produce urine including the glomerulus and the proximal tubule) and may be characterized by decreased urine output, increased blood-urea-nitrogen

Table 1. Adverse Health Effects, and Some of the Chemicals/Agents Associated with Them

Adverse Effect	Chemicals/Agents
Dermal irritation	Acetic acid (<10%), hydrochloric acid (<5%), chloroform, toluene, trichloroethylene, methanol
Eye irritation	Acetone, propylene glycol, sodium hydroxide (<1%), methyl ethyl ketone, xylene, toluene
Dermal and eye corrosion	Acetic acid (>50%), ammonium hydroxide, hydrofluoric acid, hydrochloric acid (>10%), phenol (>5%), sulfuric acid (>10%)
Dermal sensitization	Nickel salts, chromates, epoxy resins, formaldehyde, p-phenylenediamine
Respiratory sensitization	Trimellitic anhydride, toluene diisocyanate (TDI), ethylenediamine, diphenylmethane diisocyanate (MDI), avian proteins, Western red cedar, various bacterial and fungal antigens
Upper respiratory tract irritation	Acrolein, ammonia, hydrogen chloride, formaldehyde, sulfur dioxide, chlorine
Hepatotoxicity (Liver)	Carbon tetrachloride; dimethylnitrosamine; allyl alcohol; dioxane; 1,2,3-trichloropropane; 1,1,2,2-tetrachloroethane; ethanol
Nephrotoxicity (Kidneys)	1,3-dichloropropene; hexachlorobutadiene; cadmium; lead; mercury; chloroform; 1,2-dichloroethane; ethylene glycol; trichloroethylene; tetrachloroethylene; nickel
Neurotoxicity (CNS damage)	Carbon disulfide, lead, manganese, carbon monoxide, toluene
Neurotoxicity (PNS damage)	n-hexane, acrylamide, methyl n-butyl ketone, lead
Neurotoxicity (CNS depression)	Numerous volatile organic compounds (VOCs) including: acetone, benzene, carbon tetrachloride, ethylbenzene, ethyl ether, Stoddard solvent, toluene, trichloroethylene
Pulmonary toxicity (Lungs)	Silica, coal dust, asbestos, ozone, phosgene, paraquat, nitrogen dioxide, beryllium, vanadium, cadmium oxide
Hematotoxicity (Blood)	Benzene, carbon monoxide, cyanide (alkali), arsine gas, aniline, p-nitroaniline, lead, stibine, nitrates/nitrites
Male reproductive toxicity	Chlordecone, dibromochloropropane (DBCP), lead, ethylene glycol monomethyl ether, ethylene glycol monoethyl ether, ionizing radiation
Female reproductive toxicity	Lead, carbon monoxide, ethylene oxide, ionizing radiation, toluene, polychlorinated biphenyls (PCBs)
Developmental toxicity	Mercury (organic), carbon monoxide, lithium, arsenic, PCBs
Cancer	Benzene; vinyl chloride; crystalline silica; arsenic; benzidine; 1,3-butadiene; N-nitrosodimethylamine; acrylonitrile; chromium (VI); asbestos; benzo[a]pyrene

(BUN), electrolyte imbalances, and the presence of protein and glucose in the urine.

- *Central nervous system (CNS) toxicity* affects the brain and spinal cord. CNS toxicity may be characterized by numerous symptoms, both reversible and irreversible, which include depression, irritability, memory disturbances, personality changes, and attention deficits.

- *Peripheral nervous system (PNS) toxicity* affects the sensory and motor nerves of the extremities and often is reversible. PNS toxicity is characterized by numbness and tingling in the hands and feet, loss of tactile sensitivity, fatigue, muscle weakness, loss of coordination, and tremor.

- *CNS depression (narcosis)* is a reversible effect characterized by drowsiness, headache, nausea, slurred speech, difficulty in concentrating, dizziness, loss of coordination, and possibly coma and death in extreme situations.

- *Pulmonary toxicity* can be caused by obstruction of the airways (*e.g.*, by swelling or constriction), damage to the area of gas exchange (alveolar area) in the lungs, and various types of immune reactions. It may be characterized by coughing, shortness of breath, fluid build-up (edema), chest pain, fatigue, radiographic changes, and changes in lung function tests (spirometry).

- *Hematotoxicity* is damage to the formed elements of the blood (*e.g.*, red blood cells, white blood cells, platelets, *etc.*) and/or damage to the bone marrow (area of blood cell formation) and may be characterized by fever, chills, malaise, fatigue, susceptibility to infections, shortness of breath, and an ashen appearance.

- *Male reproductive toxicity* affects the male reproductive system and may be characterized by changes in sexual behavior, the onset of puberty, fertility, sperm production, and hormone levels.

- *Female reproductive toxicity* affects the female reproductive system and may be characterized by changes in sexual behavior, menstrual cycle, fertility (the ability to conceive), length of gestation, lactation, and hormone levels.

- *Developmental toxicity* affects the developing organism (due to the exposure of either parent) and may be characterized by spontaneous abortion, birth defects (*e.g.* teratogenic response), altered growth (*e.g.*, low body weight, *etc.*), and alterations in learning and memory.

- *Genotoxicity* is the ability to cause damage to the genetic material (*e.g.*, DNA). Tests for genotoxicity can be either *in vitro* or *in vivo* and include assays for mutations, chromosomal aberrations, DNA damage and repair, sister chromatid exchange, and cellular transformation.

- *Cancer* is the unrestrained proliferation of immature or abnormal cells that leads to tumor formation and, eventually, to the inhibition of the normal function of the organ or tissue.

See Table 1 for examples of agents that cause these adverse effects.

Exposure Limits for Airborne Chemicals in the Workplace

The exposure concentration limits for airborne chemicals in the workplace are called the *occupational exposure limits* (OELs). The OEL for an airborne substance is the acceptable limit on both the concentration and the duration of an employee's exposure to the substance. OELs are exposure limits to which it is believed that nearly all workers could be repeatedly exposed without an adverse effect. OELs are determined based on data from numerous sources including industrial experience with the chemical, controlled exposure studies involving humans and/or experimental animals, and analogy to chemicals that have a similar structure or are from the same chemical class. Three types of OELs are recognized: (1) the 8-hour time-weighted average (TWA) concentration, (2) the short-term (usually 15 minutes) time-weighted average concentration, and (3) the ceiling (instantaneous) limit.

OELs have been set up by many governmental and other authoritative organizations worldwide. The organizations in the United States that establish OELs include the Occupational Safety and Health Administration (OSHA), the American Conference of Governmental Industrial Hygienists (ACGIH), the National Institute for Occupational Safety and

Health (NIOSH), and the American Industrial Hygiene Association (AIHA).

Bibliography

Ballantyne, B., T. Marrs, and T. Syversen. *General and Applied Toxicology*. 2nd ed. New York, NY: Grove's Dictionaries, Inc., 1999.

Bingham, E., B. Cohrssen, and C. Powell, Eds. *Patty's Toxicology*. 5th ed. New York, NY: John Wiley and Sons, Inc., 2001.

Frazier, L. M. and Hage, M. L., Eds. *Reproductive Hazards of the Workplace*. New York, NY: Van Nostrand Reinhold, 1997.

Hathaway, G. J., N. H. Proctor, and J. P. Hughes. *Proctor and Hughes' Chemical Hazards of the Workplace*. 4th ed. New York, NY: Van Nostrand Reinhold, 1996.

Klaassen, C. D., Ed. *Casarett and Doull's Toxicology–The Basic Science of Poisons)*. 6th ed. New York, NY: McGraw-Hill, 2001.

LaDou, J. *Occupational and Environmental Medicine*. Stamford, CT: Appleton & Lange, 1997.

Rom, W.R., *Environmental and Occupational Medicine*. 3rd ed. Philadelphia, PA: Lippincott-Raven, 1998.

Sullivan, J.B., Krieger, *Clinical Environmental Health and Toxic Exposures*. 2nd ed. Philadelphia, PA: Lippincott, Williams & Wilkins, 2001.

Dr. Robert Roy is a Senior Toxicology Specialist in Corporate Toxicology and Regulatory Services, Medical Department, at the 3M Company in St. Paul, Minnesota. Dr. Roy has over 15 years of experience in the fields of industrial and occupational toxicology, chemical hazard communication and regulatory toxicology. Dr. Roy holds appointments as an Adjunct Professor and graduate faculty member in the Toxicology Graduate Program and the School of Public Health (Environmental and Occupational Health) at the University of Minnesota. Dr. Roy is board-certified in toxicology and is a member of the Society of Toxicology, the American Industrial Hygiene Association, and the Society for Chemical Hazard Communication.

Dr. Robert Skoglund is the Manager of the Regulatory Toxicology group within Corporate Toxicology and Regulatory Services at the 3M Company in St. Paul, Minnesota. In addition, he is an Adjunct Professor at the University of Minnesota where he teaches and advises students in both the Toxicology Graduate Program and the School of Public Health. Dr. Skoglund has been lecturing on regulatory and applied toxicology for more than 10 years and has authored a number of peer-reviewed publications on these topics; including journal articles, book chapters, and scientific abstracts. He is board-certified in toxicology, and industrial hygiene; he is active in the Society of Toxicology and the Society for Chemical Hazard Communication.

CHAPTER 13

Process Safety Management of Highly Hazardous Chemicals

John S. Kirar, CSP, CEA, CHMM*

Introduction

Purpose

The purpose of the Occupational Safety and Health Administration (OSHA) Process Safety Management (PSM) Rule, promulgated in 1992, is to help employers prevent or mitigate episodic chemical releases of highly hazardous chemicals, and to protect workers, the public, and the environment from catastrophic accidents or events. The PSM Rule is codified in the United States Code of Federal Regulations (CFR), Title 29, Part 1910, Section 119, "Process Safety Management of Highly Hazardous Chemicals." For the construction industry, the citation is Title 29, Part 1926, Section 64. The objectives of the performance-based rule are to emphasize the management of hazards associated with highly hazardous chemicals and to establish a comprehensive management program of identification, evaluation, and prevention of chemical releases that could result from failures in processes, procedures, or equipment. These objectives are achieved by first building

---

*Revised version of first edition chapter originally authored by Ken B. Baier, Alan R. Hohl, and John S. Kirar

safety into a process, and then keeping the facility operating safely throughout its life cycle by identifying process hazards and providing necessary controls over the life of the process. PSM requires an ongoing effort to prevent catastrophic accidents involving hazardous process materials and energies. It requires the application of management principles and analytic techniques to reduce risks associated with covered processes during the on-site manufacture, use, handling, storage, and movement of chemicals.

The PSM Rule is a performance-based rule consisting of 14 elements. The rule does not prescribe *how* each of the 14 elements is to be implemented in the management of facilities, technology, and personnel, but instead identifies the minimum requirements that must be met by employers. The 14 elements of PSM are:

- Employee participation
- Process safety information
- Process hazard analysis (PHA)
- Operating procedures
- Training
- Contractor safety
- Pre-startup safety review
- Mechanical integrity
- Hot work permit (authorization for nonroutine work)
- Management of change
- Incident investigation
- Emergency planning and response
- Compliance audits
- Trade secrets

Each of these elements are discussed in this chapter.

Application

The PSM Rule applies to processes rather than facilities. The following criteria are used to determine whether or not an employer must implement the PSM Rule:

- The rule applies to processes involving chemicals at or above threshold quantities (TQs), and processes that involve flammable liquids or gases in quantities of 10,000 pounds or more on-site in one location
- Hydrocarbon fuels are included if the fuel is part of a process covered by the PSM Rule. Hydrocarbon fuels used solely for workplace consumption (*e.g.*, propane used for comfort heating, gasoline for vehicle refueling) are excluded
- The rule does not apply to retail facilities, oil or gas well drilling or servicing operations, or normally unoccupied remote facilities. It also does not apply to flammable liquids stored in atmospheric tanks kept below their normal boiling point without benefit of chilling or refrigeration
- Manufacturers of explosives and pyrotechnics must meet the requirements of the rule

PSM and the Risk Management Program Rule

The Clean Air Act (CAA) Amendments of 1990 place the responsibility for the prevention of accidental chemical releases on both OSHA and the Environmental Protection Agency (EPA). OSHA has the responsibility for the protection of workers, the public and the environment from accidental chemical releases under Section 304 of the Amendments and has promulgated the PSM Rule to satisfy this requirement. The EPA has the responsibility for protection of the general public and the environment from accidental chemical releases under Section 112(r) of the Amendments. The EPA promulgated the Risk Management Program (RMP) Rule in 1996 to satisfy this requirement. The RMP Rule ensures that the public will be properly informed about chemical risks in their communities, and that the Federal, State, and local regulators will have more effective tools to assist with lowering chemical accident risk. The RMP requirements are found in 40 CFR 68, "Chemical Accident Prevention Provisions." The RMP requirements complement related industry standards and practices and build upon the chemical safety requirements established by the PSM Rule. The PSM and RMP programs regulate toxic, reactive, and flammable substances with many substances listed in both rules. As a result, if an employer were required to implement the PSM Rule for a covered process, that same process may also be subject to the RMP Rule. Both the PSM and RMP Rules are important elements of an integrated approach to chemical safety.

Important Terms

Atmospheric Tank—A storage tank that has been designed to operate at pressures from atmospheric through 0.5 pounds per square inch gauge (psig).

Boiling point—The boiling point of a liquid at a pressure of 14.7 pounds per square inch absolute (psia).

Catastrophic release—A major uncontrolled emission, fire, or explosion involving one or more highly hazardous chemicals that presents a serious danger to employees in the workplace.

Facility—The buildings, containers, or equipment which contain a process.

General Duty Clause—The statutory principle that employers are responsible for designing and maintaining a safe plant, identifying the hazards, and preventing or minimizing the consequences of accidental releases of chemicals. Employers operating facilities at which regulated or any other highly hazardous chemicals are present, regardless of the quantity, are subject to the EPA and OSHA general duty clause.

Highly hazardous chemical—A substance possessing toxic, reactive, flammable, or explosive properties specified by the Application section above. Appendix A to the PSM Rule lists 137 highly hazardous chemicals, toxics, and reactives. Also covered by the rule are flammable liquids and gases in quantities of 10,000 pounds or more.

Hot work—Work involving electric or gas welding, cutting, brazing, or similar flame- or spark-producing operations.

Normally Unoccupied Remote Facility—A facility that is operated, maintained or serviced by employees who visit the facility only periodically to check its operation and to perform necessary operating or maintenance tasks. No employees are permanently stationed at the facility.

Process—Any activity involving a highly hazardous chemical in excess of a TQ amount including any use, storage, manufacturing, handling, or on-site movement of such chemicals, or combination of these activities. Any group of vessels that are interconnected and separate vessels that are located such that a highly hazardous chemical could be involved in a potential release is considered a single process.

Replacement in kind—A replacement which satisfies the design specification.

Trade secret—Any confidential formula, pattern, process, device, information, or compilation of information that is used in a particular company, and that gives the company an opportunity to gain an advantage over competitors who do not know or use it.

Employee Participation

The first element of the PSM program is employee participation. Employers are required to include their employees fully in the PSM program. An effective employee participation program provides a cooperative, participatory environment and the necessary flow of information between management and employees. This element requires employee participation during all phases of the program.

At a minimum, employers must have a written plan (action plan) outlining employee participation in the conduct and development of Process Hazard Analyses (PHAs) and in the development of other elements of the PSM Rule. The employers should consult with employees and their representatives about process safety matters, and employees, contractors, and their representatives must have access to PHA information.

Action Plan

The employee participation policy is developed by the employer and should include explicit details

Table 1. Minimum Required Process Safety Information

Pertaining to:	Information Required
Highly Hazardous Chemicals in Process	• Toxicity Information • Exposure Limits (PEL, TLV, IDLH, *etc.*) • Physical Data • Reactivity Data • Corrosivity Data • Thermal & Chemical Stability Data • Compatibility Data
Technology of Process	• Block Flow/Simplified Process Flow Diagram • Process Chemistry • Maximum Intended Inventory • Safe Upper and Lower Limits (temperatures, pressures, flows, compositions, *etc.*) • Consequences of Deviations Outside Safe Operating Limits
Equipment in Process	• Materials of Construction • Piping and Instrument Diagrams (P&IDs) • Electrical Classification • Relief System Design and Design Basis • Ventilation System Design • Design Codes/Standards • Material/Energy Balances • Safety Systems

on employee involvement. Key areas of the policy should incorporate proof of active participation, consultation with affected employees, an *anonymous* means to submit complaints or suggestions, a description of how volunteers are selected (must be nonbiased), and a description of how participation is carried out in the organization.

Employee Consultation

Broad and active employee participation in all elements of the PSM program will enhance the overall program. Participation should include hourly, exempt, nonexempt, and contract employees working together to make their workplace safer. Industry has used different methods to implement the requirements of this element. These methods include (1) management/employee safety committees, (2) management/union representative safety committees, (3) involving hourly operations and maintenance employees in PHAs and development of safe work practices and procedures, (4)

suggestion programs, and (5) safety audits conducted by employees.

Access to Process Hazard Analyses

Employers are required to provide employees, employee representatives, and contractors with access to PHAs and to all other information required to be developed under the PSM Rule. The information should be readily accessible at all times. Employees, employee representatives, and contractors should be told where to find the PSM information.

Process Safety Information

Written process safety information is essential for an effective PSM program and for conducting PHAs. Employers must collect and document the complete and accurate process safety information before any PHA is performed on a process. The employer is required to compile safety information on process chemicals (Material Safety Data Sheets [MSDSs] may be used to comply), process technology, and process equipment (employers must document that existing equipment is designed, maintained, inspected, tested, and operated in a safe manner). The compilation of written process safety information enables the employer and employees involved in operating the process to identify and understand the hazards posed by those processes involving highly hazardous chemicals.

Process safety information should be updated as part of the Management of Change element of the PSM Rule and should be maintained for the life of a process. Process safety information must be sufficient to allow the accurate assessment of toxic, reactive, fire, and explosion hazards; the effects of process chemicals on equipment and instruments; the potential for overpressures or runaway reactions; and the existence of incompatible process materials. Table 1 lists the minimum required process safety information.

Hazards of Highly Hazardous Chemicals in Process

A *hazard* can be defined as an inherent characteristic of a material, system, process, or plant that must be controlled in order to avoid specific undesirable consequences. Typical hazards associated with processes involving highly hazardous chemicals include: combustible/flammable, explosive, toxic, simple and chemical asphyxiant, corrosive, chemical reactant, thermal, potential energy, kinetic energy, electrical energy, and pressure source hazards. The primary purpose of PSM is the prevention of a catastrophic release of highly hazardous chemicals. A *highly hazardous chemical* is defined as a substance possessing toxic, reactive, flammable, or explosive properties that is listed in the PSM Rule. According to PSM regulations, a hazard can be a combination of a highly hazardous chemical, an operating environment (process), and certain unplanned events (accident initiators) that could result in undesirable consequences.

Toxic Chemical Hazards. Toxic chemical hazards involve materials that have a potentially harmful biological effect on surrounding organisms. Toxic chemical hazards include acute and chronic health effects on employees and the public. Toxic effects can also result in additional consequences by disabling operating personnel and/or response personnel. Human health impacts include cancer, nervous system damage, birth defects, lung damage, skin damage, chromosome damage, liver damage, and kidney damage. The primary routes of entry for toxic chemicals are inhalation, ingestion, injection, and dermal absorption.

In order to identify and evaluate toxic hazards, the safety manager must know the material properties; process conditions, concentrations, and quantities; chemical reactions that could produce other toxic materials; industrial hygiene exposure limits; and release and dispersion characteristics of the chemicals involved. Common industrial hygiene exposure limits, also known as *exposure guidelines, levels of concern,* or *toxic endpoints* are published as: American Conference of Governmental Industrial Hygienists (ACGIH) Threshold Limit Values (TLVs), OSHA permissible exposure limits (PELs), National Institute for Occupational Safety and Health (NIOSH) Immediately Dangerous to Life and Health (IDLH) Guidelines, American Industrial Hygiene Association (AIHA) Emergency Response Planning Guidelines (ERPG) and Workplace Environmental Exposure Limits (WEELs), the National Academy of Sciences (NAS) Emergency Exposure Guidance Limits (EEGL) and Short-Term Public Emergency Guidance Levels (SPEGL), and EPA Levels of Concern (LOC).

The data on toxic chemicals that are used in PSM-covered processes can be obtained from a multitude of sources including: MSDSs that meet the requirements of 29 CFR 1910.1200(g); reference textbooks such as Sax's *Dangerous Properties of Industrial Materials,* Lewis's *Hazardous Chemicals Desk Reference,* Meyer's *Chemistry of Hazardous Materials,* National Fire Protection Association (NFPA) Standard NFPA 49, *Hazardous Chemicals Data;* the NIOSH *Pocket Guide to Chemical Hazards;* AIHA *Emergency Response Planning Guidelines and Workplace Environmental Exposure Limits Guidelines;* and ACGIH *Threshold Limit Values (TLVs) for Chemical Substances and Physical Agents and Biological Exposure Indices (BEIs).*

Reactive Chemical Hazards. Reactive chemical hazards exist when one or more substances have the potential to combine chemically, or self-react, with dangerous side effects such as increased process pressures and temperatures; ignition of combustible, flammable, or explosive material; and generation of toxic, asphyxiating, or corrosive materials. These side effects can lead to equipment damage and subsequent chemical release with adverse impacts on human health and the environment. Out-of-control chemical reactions in processes are typically caused by process irregularities involving pressures and temperatures, the inadvertent mixing of incompatible materials, material contamination, and material handling and storage errors.

The chemical characteristics necessary for identifying and evaluating reactive chemical hazards are: the character of reactions between materials or classes of materials associated with a process; reaction energies; reaction rates; material decomposition temperatures; material stability; flashpoints; concentrations; and process temperatures and pressures. To identify reactive chemical hazards for a process, the hazard evaluation team should prepare a chemical interaction matrix that lists all the chemicals or chemical families used or produced by the process. This interaction matrix is used to screen for materials which may pose any unusual and/or dangerous conditions when inadvertently combined. Such a matrix will help to determine whether or not incompatibilities exist near or within the process.

In addition to the previously mentioned information sources, data on reactive chemical hazards can be found in the Federal Emergency Management

Agency's *Handbook of Chemical Hazard Analysis Procedures*; NFPA 491M, *Manual for Hazardous Chemical Reactions*; and Lab Safety's *Pocket Guide to Chemical Compatibility*.

Flammable Chemical Hazards. Flammable chemical hazards exist when there is the potential for one or more materials to rapidly react with an oxidant. Such reactions release energy in the form of heat and light. A flammable liquid has a flash point below 100°F, and has a vapor pressure not exceeding 40 psia at 100°F. Flammable liquids are further subdivided by NFPA 30, *Flammable and Combustible Liquid Code*. The PSM standard also addresses flammable gases, which are defined as: gases that, at ambient temperature and pressure, form a flammable mixture with air at a concentration of 13% or less by volume, and have a flammable range of 1 atmosphere (atm) with air of at least 12% regardless of the lower limit. Fires involving flammable gases or liquids include flash fires, pool fires, fireballs, and jet fires. Consequences of these fires include burns, smoke inhalation, undesired chemical reactions, thermal radiation and damage to process equipment, exposure to toxic by-products from combustion, and environmental impacts.

The chemical necésary for identifying and evaluating flammable chemical hazards include: material flashpoints, flammability limits, auto-ignition temperatures, ignition energies, burning velocities, pyrophoric properties, and process conditions, including temperature, pressure, concentration, and quantity involved.

Information sources available for flammable gases and liquids include: NFPA 325, *Fire Hazard Properties of Flammable Liquids, Gases, and Volatile Solids*; and NFPA 704, *Identification of the Fire Hazards of Materials*.

Explosive Chemical Hazards. Explosive chemical hazards exist when there is a potential for one or more substances to release energy over a short period of time. The behavior of explosions varies depending on temperature, pressure, quantity, properties, and composition of chemicals; characteristics of ignition sources; geometry of surroundings (*i.e.*, confined or unconfined explosion); delayed ignition; and atmospheric mixing prior to ignition. Types of explosions include unconfined vapor cloud explosions, physical explosions, Boiling Liquid Expanding Vapor Explosions (BLEVEs), confined explosions, and

chemical explosions (*i.e.*, runaway reactions). Each of these types of explosions can produce shock wave (overpressure), projectile, and thermal radiation effects resulting in blast injuries, fragmentation injuries, equipment damage, dispersion of toxic materials, damage to nearby processes, and human health and environmental impacts. Flammable gases and liquids, highly reactive chemicals, strong oxidizers, cryogenic liquids, and compressed or liquefied gases are examples of potentially explosive materials.

The chemical characteristics needed for identifying and evaluating explosive chemical hazards include: flammability characteristics, thermodynamic properties, minimum ignition energies, shock sensitivity, ignition source characteristics, dispersion characteristics, and process conditions including temperature, pressure, concentration, and quantity involved.

Technology of the Process

Information on process technology should describe the process chemistry, maximum inventories of process chemicals, and the limits on process parameters. This information is also needed to support a qualitative estimate of the consequences of deviations or process upsets outside the established limits. Process flow diagrams illustrate the flow of the process and typically include

- Equipment sizes and ratings

- Process parameters for each mode of operation

- Limits on chemical levels in process vessels

- Flow and pressure data for pumps and components

- Process temperature and pressure limits for all equipment

Such diagrams may also include the settings for pressure relief valves and alarms, monitoring and surveillance equipment, and batch size information. Therefore, detailed process flow diagrams may contain all of the required process technology information except process chemistry information. Other process information can be obtained from Piping and Instrumentation Diagrams (P&IDs) and written and detailed process descriptions. Process technology information may be developed in conjunction with the PHA.

Equipment in the Process

Process equipment information should describe all of the hardware utilized in the process and provide the *as-built* design, including all codes, standards, or other good engineering practices that the equipment meets. The description must outline the materials of construction; electrical classification; and the design of pressure relief, ventilation, monitoring and surveillance equipment, and other safety systems. The process safety information should contain a functional description of the safety systems (*e.g.,* interlocks, detection or suppression systems) in a process in order to communicate its protective and mitigative features in the event of an emergency. P&IDs should be used to show the relationship between equipment and instrumentation. The information on new processes must include material and energy balances. Process equipment must comply with recognized and generally accepted good engineering practices. For existing equipment designed and constructed in accordance with codes, standards, or practices that are no longer in general use or the design basis is unknown, a documented determination must be made that the equipment is designed, maintained, inspected, tested, and operated in a safe manner.

Safe operation of a process can be demonstrated by (1) conducting engineering analyses or empirical testing to show that a level of protection exists and is equivalent to current codes and standards, (2) changing the design parameters of the process in order to comply with current codes and standards, or (3) using a PHA to demonstrate that the continued use of existing equipment does not significantly increase the probability of a catastrophic release compared to equipment designed to current codes and standards.

Process Hazard Analysis

A PHA is a thorough, orderly, systematic approach for identifying, evaluating, and controlling process hazards and is the major element of the PSM program. PHAs can be used to identify the causes and consequences in the potential accident scenarios that are associated with equipment, instrumentation, utilities, human performance, external events, and natural phenomena. The objective of a PHA is to determine areas of risk where preventive and mitigative measures may be warranted in order to better control the identified hazards. PHAs can help identify accident scenarios that might lead to injuries or fatalities, property or equipment damage, human exposure to highly hazardous chemicals, environmental impacts, or other adverse consequences. The minimum criteria for implementing a PHA include:

- Setting a priority order and conducting analyses according to a defined schedule

- Using the appropriate methodologies to identify and evaluate process hazards

- Addressing process hazards, previous incidents that had catastrophic potential, engineering and administrative controls that apply to the hazards, consequences of the failure of controls, facility siting, human factors, and a qualitative evaluation of the possible safety and health effects on employees should hazard controls fail

- Performing a PHA using a team with expertise in engineering, the process technology and operations, and the PHA methodology

- Establishing a system to address findings and recommendations promptly; including resolution, documentation of corrective actions, schedule for completing actions, and communication of actions to employees who are affected by the process

- Updating and revalidating PHAs at least every five years

- Retaining PHAs and updates for the life of the process

Hazard Identification

Hazard identification involves identifying specific undesirable consequences and the materials, systems, processes, and plant characteristics that could produce such consequences.

A preliminary list of process hazards can be identified systematically by using one or more of the following methods: (1) hazard identification matrix, (2) hazard screening worksheet, (3) hazard identification checklist, or (4) an interaction matrix. (An interaction matrix identifies the interactions between process materials, process conditions, materials of construction, contaminants, human exposure limits, and environmental exposure.) The preliminary results of the hazard identification usually include lists of the process chemicals (toxic, reactive, flammable, and explosive); potentially hazardous reactions with chemicals; system and process equipment hazards; and the conditions that could lead to a runaway reaction. A safety analyst can then use the hazard identification results to define the scope of the subsequent hazard analysis and select the appropriate hazard analysis methodology.

Hazard Analysis Methodologies

The PSM Rule states that employers shall use one or more of the following hazard analysis methodologies to evaluate the hazards that may be present in the workplace. The method(s) should be appropriate for evaluating the hazards of the process under consideration:

- What-If
- Checklist
- What-If/Checklist
- Hazard and Operability Study (HAZOP)
- Failure Mode and Effects Analysis (FMEA)
- Fault Tree Analysis (FTA)
- An appropriate equivalent methodology

Several factors influence the selection of an appropriate method of hazard analysis. These factors include: the reason for performing the hazard analysis, the type of analysis results that are needed, the type and extent of information that is available to perform the hazard analysis, the characteristics of the process that is being analyzed, the perceived risk that is associated with the process, and the available resources.

Usually a PHA is performed in order to comply with corporate policy, function as a risk management tool, or comply with regulations. The result(s) of a PHA could be a simple list of hazards, a list of potential accident scenarios, a list of risk reduction alternatives, identification of areas needing further analysis, and prioritization of results.

The life cycle stage that a process is in and the quality and accuracy of the available documentation define what information is available prior to performing a PHA. The characteristics of a process include the size and complexity of the process, the type of process, the type of process operation(s), the inherent hazards associated with the process, and accident events of concern.

If the risk of a process is perceived to be low and the employer is experienced with the operation of the process, the analyst may chose to use a less exhaustive hazard analysis methodology such as What-If or Checklist. If, on the other hand, the process is perceived as high risk, the use of a more rigorous methodology may be warranted. The resources used for performing a PHA should reflect the availability of skilled and knowledgeable personnel, schedule for performing the analysis, and financial resources.

The safety analyst should refer to appropriate industry references such as the Center for Chemical Process Safety's *Guidelines for Hazard Evaluation Procedures, Second Edition with Worked Examples* for detailed information about the appropriate PHA methodologies.

What-If. The What-If Analysis methodology is an unstructured brainstorming approach that uses a team of people who are familiar with the process under analysis to ask questions about possible undesirable events. The questions are developed based on the experience of the team and are applied to P&IDs, process flow diagrams, and descriptions of the process. The questions should apply to process upset conditions as well as equipment or component failures or process variations. The What-If Analysis primarily addresses single event failures, can be used on any design or procedure, can be performed at any stage of the process's life, and can be led by a relatively inexperienced safety analyst to produce quantitative results.

The process encourages the hazard evaluation team to ask questions that start with "What if." All questions or concerns arising from the analysis should be written down and then divided into specific areas of investigation, such as electrical safety, fire protection, or occupational safety. One or more experts in each area can then address the set of questions relating to his or her field. The results of the What-If Analyses are a list of questions and answers about the process being analyzed. The analysis may also produce organized lists of hazardous situations (potential accident scenarios), consequences, safeguards, and possible ways of reducing risks.

Checklist. The Checklist analysis is a structured question method that is versatile, easy to use, and can be applied at any stage in the life of a process. The Checklist approach can be used by an individual analyst or by a hazard evaluation team, and requires no formal training. A detailed checklist provides the basis for a standard evaluation of process hazards, and can focus on specific areas of concern, such as fire protection, electrical systems, and pressure systems. Checklists are often created by organizing the information from current relevant codes, standards, and regulations. Both the regulations and the Checklists should be reviewed and updated regularly. The Checklist analysis will usually produce a list of hazards associated with the process, and identify deficiencies in the process that could cause accidents. The completed checklist can be used by the analyst or managers to identify alternatives that can improve safety in the workplace. Generic hazard checklists are often combined with other hazard analysis techniques.

What-If/Checklist. This analysis method combines the What-If and Checklist techniques. It can identify hazards, predict the general types of accidents that can occur in a process, evaluate the effects of these accidents, and determine which controls would be adequate to prevent or mitigate these accidents.

Hazard and Operability Study. The Hazard and Operability (HAZOP) analysis methodology is a systematic way to examine how process variations affect a system. Process variations occur as a result of equipment failures, human errors, and process upsets such as localized chemical reactions. The technique can be used for systems with continuous processes as well as batch processes. The use of the HAZOP analysis methodology requires detailed information about the design and operation of the process. The HAZOP methodology is most effective during the design phase of a process or for existing processes.

In the HAZOP analysis, a hazard evaluation team composed of experts from different areas systematically examines every part of the process to discover how process design deviations can occur. The hazard evaluation team leader systematically guides the team through the process design, using a fixed set of *guide words*. These guide words are applied at crucial points or *nodes* of the process.

The guide words include *no, more, less, as well as, part of, reverse,* and *other than.* They are combined with a condition, such as *flow* or *pressure*, to define the deviation. For example, "What is the effect of *low flow* on the process?" Typical deviations include leaks or ruptures, loss of containment, ignition sources, and chemical reactions. The HAZOP analysis should identify hazards and operating problems, and enable the HAZOP team to recommend design or procedural changes that will improve the safety of the process. The results of the HAZOP analysis are documented in a tabular format with a separate table for each segment of the process under study.

Failure Mode and Effects Analysis. The Failure Mode and Effects Analysis (FMEA) tabulates the ways in which equipment and components can fail, and the effects of these failures on a system, process, or plant. Failure modes describe the ways in which equipment can fail (such as open, closed, on, off, leaks, *etc.*). The analyst lists all of the components of the system under review and all the failure modes for these components. The FMEA identifies the individual failure modes that can either cause or contribute to an accident. This method of analysis does not address multiple failures. An FMEA analysis should produce a qualitative, systematic list of equipment and components, a list of associated failure modes, and a list of the effects of the failure modes on the system. The list of effects should include a worst-case estimate of the consequences of each failure mode. The information produced by an FMEA analysis can be used to support recommendations for increased equipment and component reliability that would improve safety.

Fault Tree Analysis. Fault Tree Analysis (FTA) is a deductive analysis technique that allows the analyst to determine the combinations of failures that are necessary to achieve an event defined as the *top* or *undesired* event. FTA is well suited for the analysis of highly redundant systems. The fault tree is a graphic model that displays the various combinations of equipment/component failures and human errors that can give rise to the top event. The FTA provides a means to qualitatively or quantitatively identify the frequency of the top event. It is a deductive technique that employs Boolean Logic (the use of AND and OR gate logic) to relate the top event to a combination of basic events that must occur in order for the top event to happen. The fault tree, once constructed, can be quantified by using the failure rate data for the basic events (*i.e.*, those events at the bottom of the tree). A quantified fault tree projects the rate of occurrence for the top event.

Performing a Process Hazard Analysis

During the Process Hazard Analysis (PHA), the hazard evaluation team must

1) Identify process hazards

2) Review the accident history of the process in order to identify process hazards, accident precursors, lessons learned from previous incidents, and safety trends

3) Consider the influence of human factors

4) Analyze engineering and administrative control measures and their interrelationships

5) Determine the full impacts and consequences that will arise if the control measures fail, taking facility siting into consideration

6) Determine the qualitative range of safety and health effects on the employees at the worksite

The PHA team must also consult with any subcontractor's employees who are involved in the operation or maintenance of the process.

The hazard identification process includes listing all of the obvious hazards, examining the hazardous characteristics of each process chemical, examining all of the parameters for the process (*e.g.*, pressure, temperature, flow rate, *etc.*), analyzing the material interactions for any incompatibilities, and documenting the identified hazards.

Previous accidents and incidents must be reviewed as part of the PHA. Incidents indicate what could happen if protection systems, which are not totally reliable, fail to work. Thorough investigations may reveal the primary cause(s) of initiating events and/or failures of the protective systems. With this information, the safety analyst can suggest action items that will improve the systems of safety management. Incident records also help demonstrate the probability of failures and operational errors.

Several elements must be taken into account when trying to determine the influence of human factors.

These include the degree to which process safety depends on human performance, and whether or not the workers can reasonably be expected to perform the tasks they have been assigned and also judge whether or not the procedures and training provided by the employer adequately guide and prepare employees to perform their tasks correctly.

Engineering and administrative controls that keep the parameters of each process within a safe operating range and prevent threats to the system's integrity must be in place. A PHA addresses the engineering and administrative controls that are applicable to the process hazards. It also explores the interrelationship of these controls by identifying and documenting the safety levels of the process (*e.g.*, temperature and pressure limits, process chemical inventory limits, pressure levels, *etc.*).

Facility siting is the physical location of the covered processes on the plant's property. The hazard evaluation team should consider the proximity of the covered process to workers and the nearest exit routes, in order to evaluate the potential safety and health effects of a chemical release. The team must also consider the influence of vehicle traffic and any nearby operations on the safety of the process. One siting issue is the location of containers of highly hazardous chemicals and their proximity to other equipment, control rooms, maintenance shops, and administration buildings.

The hazard evaluation team must qualitatively evaluate the full range of possible employee safety and health effects in the event of the release of a hazardous chemical. This evaluation may be performed more explicitly by assigning a qualitative term to each scenario. Terms such as *negligible, low, moderate, severe,* and *catastrophic* can be used.

The critical results of the PHA are provided as action items. The action items indicate that additional effort is needed to further analyze a specific accident scenario, eliminate the hazard, or reduce the risks. Action items are not usually specific corrective actions. Rather, they alert the management to potential problems that require attention. Action items might suggest procedural alternatives or recommend safety improvements.

Hazard Evaluation Team

The hazard evaluation team should be composed of personnel who possess expertise in engineering and process operations. The team must include at least one employee who has experience with and knowledge of the specific process that is being evaluated and one member who is knowledgeable and experienced in the specific PHA method that is being used. A hazard evaluation team is usually composed of two to five members and may include a safety engineer or analyst, a process engineer, a maintenance supervisor, an operations supervisor, a facility engineer, or other members with whatever expertise is deemed necessary.

Management System

The PHA is not an end in itself. It is a method of identifying areas of excessive risk. Therefore, management must develop and implement a tracking system to address the findings and recommendations of the hazard evaluation team. This system must ensure that the PHA team's findings and recommendations are resolved and documented, and that actions are completed as soon as possible. A schedule for all resolutions should be established and followed, and actions must be communicated to the employees who are affected by any changes.

Update of Hazard Analysis

The PHA must be updated and revalidated by a team meeting the requirements that were previously discussed at least every five years after the completion of the initial PHA. These updates assure that the PHA remains consistent with the current process.

Recordkeeping Requirements

Written PHAs, updates, revalidations, and the documentation of the resolutions to recommendations must be kept on file by the employer for the life of the process.

Operating Procedures

The employer must provide clear instructions for the activities associated with covered processes. These instructions should be consistent with the information on process safety. Employers should develop and implement written operating procedures in order to fulfill this requirement. The procedures outline the steps for each phase of the operation, the operating limits of the process, the safety systems and their functions, and safety and health considerations. Copies of the procedures are to be kept in a place that is readily accessible to the employees who work with or maintain the process. The procedures should be reviewed as often as is necessary to ensure that they reflect current operating practices, including changes that result from changes in process chemicals, technology, equipment as well as changes to facilities. The employer must certify annually that these practices are current and accurate. Safe work practices should also be outlined for such activities as lockout/tagout, entry into a confined space, opening process equipment, and access control.

Written Operating Procedures

The operating procedures should describe initial startup, normal operations, temporary operations, emergency shutdowns (including the conditions under which emergency shutdowns are required), emergency operations, normal shutdown, and startups following a turnaround or emergency shutdown. The objective in developing operating procedures is to ensure that the actual operations match the written operating procedures. To meet this objective, the safety manager should do the following during the initial development of operating procedures:

- Write procedures that will ensure that various workers perform these tasks the same way, and that the workers know what the employer expects of them

- Write procedures on the assumption that new, inexperienced workers will use them

- Write in a manner that allows for the most effective communication (training) possible

- Include discussions of the desired operating ranges for temperature, pressure, flow, *etc.*

- Describe how to respond if an upset occurs, and include any pertinent alarms and equipment

- Provide a troubleshooting guide that addresses upsets which occur during the normal operating mode

- Include safety precautions and information on safety implications

- Describe the safety systems as they are defined in the process safety information

- Walk down and/or monitor operations to ensure that the actual operations match the written operating procedures

Accessibility of Procedures

The employer must keep the written procedures in a place that is readily accessible to employees who work in or maintain a process. *Readily accessible* means that the employees know where the procedures are located and are encouraged to refer to the procedures if they have questions or concerns during the conduct of operations.

Review and Update

Appropriate personnel should occasionally review the procedures in order to make sure that the operating procedure matches the actual operations and that the appropriate safety features and safety implications have been identified. The review of the procedure ensures that the procedure contains all of the elements that are required by OSHA. The review also ensures that the procedure is accurate and the instructions are clear and understandable. Having the process owner and operator review the procedure helps ensure the procedure accuracy and clarity of instructions.

Equally important as the initial review of the procedure is ensuring that any changes to the process are incorporated into the written procedure. The Management of Change element of the PSM program requires the employer to update any changes to a procedure before operations resume.

Development and Implementation of Safe Work Practices

Employers and managers must show by their attitude and actions that safety is important. The employer must demonstrate to employees and contractors that stopping work whenever they feel conditions are unsafe is the right thing to do, and that management will support the employee's decision if they do stop work. Management has to be committed to promptly resolving any unsafe work conditions and to encouraging the employees to ensure the safety of operations.

Training

The training element is required in order to help employees understand the nature and causes of problems that arise from process operations. Training also increases employee awareness with respect to the specific hazards associated with a process. The process owner or operator is required to train and periodically retrain the employees who are involved in operating processes on the hazards of the process and the routine and nonroutine tasks that are necessary to safely perform their jobs.

The development of a training program provides the employer with an excellent opportunity to demonstrate a commitment to providing a safe working environment. Consultation with employees during development of the training program uses their direct experience with the processs to build an effective training program. All applicable elements of the PSM program should be discussed during the training session.

The employer must determine the initial and refresher training requirements for employees, and implement a process for documenting the training.

Initial Training

The initial training for employees who are new to a process must emphasize the importance of safe work practices. The trainer should discuss the safe work practices that are appropriate to all operating phases of the process. The trainer should describe the hazardous chemicals that are present in the process, the safety and health hazards that are inherent in the process, emergency operations including shutdown, safe work practices applicable to the employee's job tasks, and the controls that have been implemented to prevent exposure to the hazardous chemicals. During the initial training, the employee should learn about the operating limits of the process, the consequences of deviating from these limits, and the ways to avoid deviation. Emergency drills (how to handle upset conditions and emergencies) should be discussed in detail. Every employee should be given the history of any accidents or near-misses that have occurred, along with the lessons that were learned from the incident and the corrective actions that have been taken to prevent similar incidents. This history helps to emphasize the importance the employer places on safe work practices.

Refresher Training

Refresher training shall be provided to each employee at least every three years. Employers and employees should cooperate to determine the necessary frequency for refresher training. This training should review all of the areas that are addressed in the initial training. Any changes to the process and operating procedures should be covered, including why these changes were necessary.

Training Documentation

Employers are required to ascertain that each employee has received and understood the training. A written test is one method of measuring comprehension, but it is not the only acceptable method. A demonstration of the necessary skills is another acceptable method, but the results need to be well documented. Training records should show the date of the employee's most recent training, the type of training provided (classroom, on-the-job, or a combination), and the type of competency test used to measure comprehension.

Contractors

This element requires employers to hire and use only those contractors who accomplish their tasks without compromising the safety and health of other employees at a facility.

Application

Contractors are affected by these requirements if they perform maintenance, repair, turnaround, major renovation, or specialty work on or adjacent to covered processes. Contractors who provide incidental, nonsafety-related services (*e.g.*, janitorial, food and drink service, laundry, delivery services) are not subject to these regulations.

Employer Responsibilities

In order to implement this element, employers should evaluate a contractor's safety performance prior to making a selection, and then periodically reevaluate the safety performance of the contractor. The employer is also responsible for informing contractors of the known potential for fire, explosion or toxic chemical release that are related to the contractor's work, as well as the facility's safety rules and the provisions of the emergency response plan. The contractor must be trained in the work practices that will allow them to safely perform their job responsibilities at the site. The employer or the contractor can administer the training. A contract employee injury and illness log must be maintained by the employer.

There are different methods the employer can use to make sure that contract employees abide by the safety rules of the facility. These include:

- Purchase requisition clauses requiring pre-award submission and approval of the contractor safety program.

- Identification of a technical representative that interfaces with the contractor and is responsible for ensuring that all contract employees receive a safety orientation before they are allowed unescorted access to facilities.

- Periodic evaluation of the performance of contract employers in fulfilling their obligation.

- Maintenance of contractor employee injury and illness logs related to contractors' work in process areas.

- A permit system or work authorization system for activities on or near covered processes.

- Documentation that each contract employee has received and understood the required training.

Contract Employer Responsibilities

Contract employers are required to assure that their employees are trained in all applicable work practices and safety rules of the facility, and that they know about the potential fire, explosion or toxic chemical release hazards of the process they will be working on. Contract employers are also responsible for documenting that their employees were trained and that they understood the training. Any unique hazard that is presented by the contractor's work and any hazards that are revealed by the contractor's work shall be presented to the employer by the contractor.

Pre-Startup Safety Review

The pre-startup safety review is designed to ensure that safety requirements have been fulfilled prior to the introduction of highly hazardous chemicals to a process. The review verifies that

- New or modified facilities and equipment are built and installed in accordance with design requirements

- Process procedures and operator training are adequate and completed prior to the introduction of hazardous materials into the process

- Adequate safety reviews are conducted

- PHA safety recommendations have been implemented prior to startup

This element provides the employer with an opportunity to prove that all of the safety requirements have been implemented before workers are exposed to highly hazardous chemicals during operations.

Requirements for Performing

The employer must perform a pre-startup safety review for new facilities and for modified facilities when the modification requires a change in the process safety information. A pre-startup safety review should also be completed before restarting a process that was shut down for safety-related reasons.

Items Covered in Review

The pre-startup safety review must confirm that

1) Construction and equipment are in accordance with design specifications

2) Adequate safety, operating, maintenance, and emergency procedures are in place

3) A PHA has been performed for new facilities, and recommendations were resolved or implemented

4) Modified facilities meet the requirements of the management of change element

5) Training of each employee involved in the process has been completed

Depending on the complexity of the new or modified process, different methods may be used to conduct the pre-startup safety review. A qualified team should be assembled to conduct each pre-startup safety review. A formal checklist can be used by the team to ensure that the process is ready for startup. The review could include interviews with key personnel, a physical examination of the process and its required safety features, a review of the employee training, and reviews of the documentation (procedures, drawings, *etc.*) Formal documentation should be maintained showing the process used in conducting the pre-startup safety review.

Mechanical Integrity

This element requires the implementation of an equipment integrity philosophy that ensures that all process equipment and instrumentation are designed, constructed, installed, and maintained so as to minimize the risk of hazardous releases. A proactive rather than reactive approach, encompassing all process equipment from installation through retirement, is necessary in order to ensure the effectiveness of the safety program. Equipment in contact with highly hazardous chemicals forms the first line of defense against any uncontrolled catastrophic releases of these chemicals.

An effective mechanical integrity program begins with the compilation of a list of the process equipment and instrumentation included in the program. The process equipment and instruments are assigned priorities based on their importance to the process. The list is then expanded to include the important mitigation system components (*e.g.*, fire protection system components, dikes, drainage systems, *etc.*). The minimum requirements of the mechanical integrity element are

1) The proper application to specific types of process equipment

2) The development of written maintenance procedures

3) Training of maintenance personnel

4) The performance of periodic inspections and tests *Thickness ??*

5) Prompt identification and correction of equipment deficiencies

6) Implementation of a Quality Assurance (QA) program for fabrication, installation, and materials

Application

The mechanical integrity program, at a minimum, applies to pressure vessels and storage tanks, piping systems, relief and vent systems and devices, emergency shutdown systems, controls (including monitoring devices, sensors, alarms, and interlocks), pumps, and other equipment and systems. This should not be considered to be an exhaustive list of equipment. Each facility has to determine which equipment prevents, detects, controls and/or mitigates releases of highly hazardous chemicals. Equipment such as fire protection equipment, ammonia detectors, ventilation systems and electrical systems are subject to this element if the PHA has identified this equipment as necessary to detect, control, or mitigate releases.

Written Procedures

Written procedures help ensure the integrity of process equipment and instruments. The procedures ensure that tests, inspections, and preventive maintenance activities are conducted properly and consistently, even when different employees may be involved. Some components of the maintenance procedures are:

- Identification of safe work practices when working around highly hazardous chemicals

- Development of preventive maintenance plans

- Implementation of a maintenance work control system

- Use of manufacturers' manuals

- Incorporation of job safety analyses for maintenance tasks

- Use of detailed maintenance procedures for accomplishing the task

Training for Process Maintenance

Employees who are responsible for maintaining the process equipment should be trained in an overview of the process, the hazards of the process, and the procedures and equipment applicable to their job. Appropriate training is required to ensure maintenance personnel understand the procedures they will be working to, implement safe work practices in the performance of their task, and understand the proper use of special equipment or unique tools. The training provided to personnel who maintain process equipment and instruments is different from the training provided to the personnel who operate a process. Formal classroom training, reviews of the mechanical integrity of the procedure, and on-the-job training with qualified personnel are all acceptable methods of training maintenance employees.

Inspection and Testing

All process equipment must be inspected and tested in accordance with the manufacturer's recommendations and good engineering practices, or more frequently if experience warrants it. Employers shall certify that inspections and tests have been performed and shall document the test procedures and results. Employers must correct any deficiencies that are outside of acceptable limits or malfunctions before further use of the equipment (or in a safe and timely manner when necessary means are taken to ensure safe operation). Employers must also assure that fabricated equipment is suitable for use in the process, and is installed properly (maintenance materials and spare parts are included in this requirement).

Equipment Deficiencies

When equipment deficiencies that are outside of acceptable limits are found (as defined by the process safety information), the employer is responsible to correct promptly the deficiency before allowing further use of the equipment. This may include such actions as correcting the deficiency immediately, removing the equipment from service, following preapproved temporary operating procedures, or conducting a management of change review to guarantee that safe operation can be continued until the deficiency is corrected.

Quality Assurance

This subsection of the mechanical integrity element requires the employer to implement a quality assurance (QA) program for equipment fabrication, equipment installation, and the use of maintenance materials, spare parts, and equipment. The QA program should focus on reducing the possibility of unwanted chemical releases from process equipment and ensuring that the features that are designed to control or mitigate releases will function when required. The QA program should verify that the proper materials of construction are used in fabrication, that inspection procedures are proper, that as-built drawings are developed, and that there are certifications of coded vessels and other equipment. The QA program for the installation of equipment ensures that the equipment is installed properly, is consistent with design specifications and manufacturer's instructions, and that qualified craftsmen have been used to perform the installation work. For the maintenance procedures, the QA program ensures that maintenance materials, spare parts, and equipment are suitable for the process application.

Hot Work Permit

This element of the PSM Rule requires employers to control uniformly all nonroutine work that is conducted on or near covered processes and that might initiate or promote a release of highly hazardous chemicals. Nonroutine work authorizations include hot work permits, radiation work permits, and confined space entry permits. Hot work permits cover welding, cutting, and other spark-producing operations. Routine work is covered by approved operating procedures and training. The hot work permit element outlines the requirements of the permit and its issuance.

Issuance

Employers shall issue a permit for all hot work (temporary or permanent) conducted on or near a covered process. The permit documents the fire protection provisions, indicates the authorized date(s), and identifies the item which requires the hot work. The permit is kept on file until the hot work is completed.

Items to consider when issuing nonroutine work authorizations include controlling nonroutine work in a consistent manner and communicating the known hazards to those who perform the work and to the affected operating personnel. Authorization of the permit/notice should include a procedure describing the steps that the maintenance supervisor, contractor representative, or others must take to obtain clearance before starting their work. The work authorization procedure should also provide clear steps for closure so personnel know that the equipment can be returned to normal. In addition, prior to welding or cutting activities, supervisors shall ensure that all combustibles present in the hot work area are protected from ignition. Combustibles should be moved or shielded during the time when welding occurs.

Permit Requirements

Hot work permits are required to document compliance with the fire prevention and protection requirements of 29 CFR 1910.252(a). The minimum requirements needed to ensure that the hot work element is implemented by the employer include

- Establishing areas and procedures for safe welding and cutting based on fire potential

- Designating an individual who will be responsible for authorizing cutting and welding in process areas

- Ensuring that welders, cutters, and their supervisor(s) are trained in the safe operation of their equipment

- Advising any subcontractors about the hot work permit program

Some of the items that should be identified on the hot work permit are:

1) The date the hot work is authorized

2) The object which requires the hot work

3) Identification of openings, cracks, and holes where sparks may drop onto combustible materials below

4) Description of fire extinguishers that are available to handle fires if they occur

5) Assignment of fire watchers in locations where more than a minor fire could develop

6) A description of the precautions associated with combustible materials

7) A warning prohibiting welding or cutting in unauthorized areas, in buildings with impaired sprinkler systems, in explosive atmospheres, and in storage areas with large quantities of readily ignitable materials

8) Relocation of combustibles where practicable, and covering with flameproof covers where removal is not practicable

9) Identifying and shutting down any ducts or conveyors by which sparks may reach distant combustibles

Management of Change

The management of change element requires all modifications of equipment, procedures, raw materials, and processing conditions other than *replacement in kind* to be identified and reviewed prior to implementing the change. Process changes that should be included under this element include

- Changes in process technology

- The addition or removal of process equipment or piping

- Changes in process parameters

- Changes in utilities

- Changes in procedures

- Changes in facilities

- Personnel changes (according to OSHA, the presence of personnel are implied in the term *facilities*)

This element is a critical part of the PSM Rule because it integrates many of the other elements of the rule.

The minimum requirements for the management of change element include establishing written procedures to manage change and procedure considerations. For the management of change program to be effective, personnel at all levels should be trained to recognize and understand the ramifications of proposed changes to the safe operation of a chemical process, including the interdependencies and relationships among facility functions, processes, and activities.

Written Procedures

All changes should be identified and reviewed prior to implementation, and the impact of design, operational, and procedural changes on process safety should be examined. Written management of change procedures should address employee responsibilities, the basis for the change, and the impacts of the change. In addition, the written procedure should designate who is responsible for requesting changes to existing systems, processes, and procedures; who can approve changes (and the criteria for approving changes); and who is responsible for implementing the approved changes.

Procedure Considerations

An effective management of change program includes an assessment procedure to determine the importance of the change to process safety, and a procedure to manage each proposed change. The procedure describing the management of change program enables management to

1) Determine the level of effort required for review and implementation of a change

2) Update process safety information and PHAs, and address any resulting recommendations

3) Modify existing operating and maintenance procedures

4) Inform and retrain affected employees and subcontractors

5) Update emergency plans

6) Develop a schedule and a list of required authorizations

7) Update pre-startup procedural changes

8) Modify pre-startup inspection and testing procedures

9) Verify mechanical and system integrity prior to startup

Incident Investigation

The incident investigation element aims to prevent the recurrence of incidents that have the same nature or the same root cause. Employers must investigate every incident that results in, or could reasonably have resulted in, a catastrophic release of a covered chemical in the workplace. The investigation shall be started no later than 48 hours following the incident. An investigation team is established and must have at least one person who is knowledgeable in the process. A contract employee is included on the team if the incident involved a contractor's work. The team investigates the incident and prepares a report on the incident. The report should be reviewed with all of the affected personnel who work in the facility. The employer should have a process in place to address and respond to the report's findings and recommendations. The incident investigation team's recommendations must be implemented, unless it can be documented that an alternative will address the concerns as effectively and efficiently as the team recommendation. Incident investigation reports are to be retained for five years.

The incident investigation reports must record the date the incident occurred, the date the inspection began, a description of the incident, the factors contributing to the incident, and recommendations resulting from the investigation. A *lessons learned* program should be developed, to share the results of the incident investigation with other operations personnel at the site and with operations personnel at other company locations.

A thorough analysis of all incidents or near-miss incidents is important, since the analysis will generally reveal a number of deeper factors that allowed or even encouraged an employee's action. Such factors may include inadequate equipment,

a work practice that is difficult for the employee to carry out safely, or a supervisor allowing or pressuring the employee to take shortcuts in the interest of production. An effective analysis will address each of the causal factors in an accident or *near-miss* incident.

Emergency Planning and Response

This element addresses the actions employees are required to take when there is a release of highly hazardous chemicals. Emergency planning and response are required under the PSM Rule in order to mitigate the consequences of catastrophic releases. Emergency plans form the last line of defense in protecting workers from such events.

Employers shall establish and implement an emergency action plan in accordance with 29 CFR 1910.38(a). 29 CFR 1910.120(a), (p), and (q) may also be applicable—OSHA's Hazardous Waste Operations Rules, or HAZWOPER. The emergency action plan shall address both small and large releases.

The emergency plan should describe escape routes and procedures and the best means for reporting emergencies. The duties and procedures of employees who remain to operate critical equipment and those employees who perform rescue and medical duties need to be described in the emergency plan. The names of persons or locations to contact for more action plan information, and employee alarm systems, must also be provided in the plan.

The emergency plan shall be reviewed with each employee covered by the plan. The plan should be reviewed when it is initially developed, whenever employees' responsibilities or designated actions in the plan change, and whenever the plan is changed.

Training requirements differ according to the responsibilities of employees. Employees who are likely to discover hazardous substance releases are trained and should demonstrate competency in the provisions listed in the awareness level for first responders. Employees who will be required to take defensive action in containing and controlling a release as part of the response are trained as, and should demonstrate knowledge of the operations required of a first responder. Employees who will be responsible for taking offensive action in containing and controlling a release as part of the response are trained as and should demonstrate the competencies required of, a hazardous materials (HAZMAT) technician.

Compliance Audits

The compliance audits element requires employers to self-evaluate the effectiveness of their PSM programs by identifying any deficiencies and taking corrective and preventive actions. This element ensures that the program is operating in an integrated and effective manner. The audit team provides an independent assessment of the degree of compliance with the PSM Rule, even though one member may by necessity be involved in the operation of the process.

Compliance audits have two major objectives. First, they assess whether the management system in place adequately addresses all elements of the PSM Rule. Second, the audits assess whether the management system has been adequately implemented for every facility or process.

Employers must conduct a PSM compliance audit at least every three years. The audit evaluates all elements of the PSM program. The audit team must include at least one person who is knowledgeable in the process. The team will develop a report of its findings, and the employer must promptly respond to each finding and document that any deficiencies have been corrected. The employer must keep the two most recent audit reports on file.

Trade Secrets

Regardless of whether a process has trade secret status, the PSM Rule requires employers to provide all necessary information to

1) Personnel who are responsible for compiling the process safety information

2) Any personnel who are assisting in the development of the PHA

3) Personnel who are responsible for developing the operating procedures

4) Personnel who are involved in incident investigations, emergency planning and response, and compliance audits

A *trade secret* is any confidential formula, pattern, process, device, information, or compilation of information that is used in an employer's business, and that gives the employer an opportunity to obtain an advantage over competitors who do not know it or use it. Appendix D of 29 CFR 1910.1200 sets out the criteria to be used when evaluating trade secrets. Employers may require confidentiality agreements with personnel who receive trade secret information.

Summary

The PSM Rule was promulgated to help employers prevent or mitigate the episodic releases of highly hazardous chemicals and to protect workers, the public, and the environment from catastrophic accidents or events. The rule applies to individual processes rather than to plants. Processes involving chemicals at or above TQs, and processes which involve flammable liquids or gases in quantities greater than or equal to 10,000 pounds on-site in one location, are required to implement the PSM Rule. In addition, manufacturers of explosives and pyrotechnics must also adhere to the requirements of the rule. The PSM Rule provides exclusions for hydrocarbon fuels that are used solely as a fuel for workplace consumption, for retail facilities, for oil or gas well drilling or servicing operations, for facilities that normally are unoccupied, and for flammable liquids that are kept below their normal boiling point without benefit of chilling or refrigeration.

The PSM program provides a way for employers to build safety into their processes and then keep the processes operating safely throughout their life cycles by identifying hazards and providing the necessary controls. The program requires the application of management principles and analytic techniques to be applied in order to reduce the risks associated with covered processes during the manufacture, use, handling, storage, and movement of highly hazardous chemicals. Employers must hold worker safety and health to be a fundamental value of their organization and apply this commitment to safety and health protection with vigor. The management can accomplish this by doing the following:

- Clearly state a work-site policy on safe and healthful work practices and working conditions

- Establish and communicate the goal of the safety and health program and the objectives for meeting that goal

- Provide visible top management involvement in implementing the program

- Provide for and encourage employee involvement in the structure and operation of the program, and in decisions that affect their safety and health

- Assign and communicate responsibility for all aspects of the program

- Provide adequate authority and resources to responsible parties

- Hold managers, supervisors, and employees accountable for meeting their responsibilities

- Review program operations at least annually to evaluate their success in meeting the goal and objectives

- Provide a reliable system wherein employees, without fear of reprisal, can notify management personnel about conditions that appear hazardous; provide employees with timely and appropriate responses to such notices; and encourage employees to use the system

The hazard evaluation and control techniques described in PSM are also useful for minimizing risks in operations involving less than TQ amounts of listed chemicals, or other chemicals not listed in Appendix A of 29 CFR 1910.119. The principles of PSM should be utilized at all facilities where highly hazardous chemicals are used in any other than an incidental manner.

Bibliography

American Conference of Governmental Industrial Hygienists. *Threshold Limit Values (TLVs) for Chemical Substances and Physical Agents and Biological Exposure Indices (BEIs)*. Cincinnati, OH: ACGIH, 2004.

American Industrial Hygiene Association. *Emergency Response Planning Guidelines and Workplace Environmental Exposure Level Guides Handbook*. Fairfax, VA: AIHA, 1996.

American Institute of Chemical Engineers. *Guidelines for Chemical Process Quantitative Risk Analysis*. New York, NY: AIChE–Center for Chemical Process Safety, 1989.

American Institute of Chemical Engineers. *Guideline for Hazard Evaluation Procedures, Second Edition with Worked Examples*. New York, NY: AIChE–Center for Chemical Process Safety, 1992.

"Compliance Guidelines and Recommendations for Process Safety Management ." *Code of Federal Regulations*. Title 29, Pt. 1910.119, Appendix C.

Cote, Arthur E. *Fire Protection Handbook*, 18th ed. Quincy, MA: NFPA, 2003.

"Definition of 'Trade Secret.'" *Code of Federal Regulations*. Title 29, Pt. 1910.1200, Appendix D.

Department of Energy. *Chemical Process Hazards Analysis*, DOE-HDBK-1100-96. Washington, DC: Office of Scientific and Technical Information, 1996.

Department of Energy. *Process Safety Management for Highly Hazardous Chemicals*. DOE–HDBK–1101–96. Washington, DC: Office of Scientific and Technical Information, 1996.

Department of Health and Human Services. Center for Disease Control and Prevention. National Institute for Occupational Safety and Health. *Pocket Guide to Chemical Hazards*. Atlanta, GA: Government Printing Office, 2004.

"Employee Action Plans and Fire Prevention Plans." *Code of Federal Regulations*. Title 29, Pt. 1910.38(a).

Federal Emergency Management Agency. *Handbook of Chemical Hazard Analysis Procedures*. Washington, DC: Government Printing Office, 1987.

"General Requirements for Welding, Cutting and Brazing." *Code of Federal Regulations*. Title 29, Pt. 1910.252(a), Subpart Q.

Government Institutes, Inc. *EPA Technology Handbook.* Rockville, MD: Government Institutes, Inc., 1992.

Government Institutes, Inc. *Process Safety Management Standard Inspection Manual.* Rockville, MD: Government Institutes, Inc., 1993.

"Hazardous Waste Operations and Emergency Response." *Code of Federal Regulations.* Title 29, Pt. 1910.120 (a), (p), and (q).

Lab Safety Supply. *Pocket Guide to Chemical Compatibility.* Janesville, WI: Lab Safety Supply, 1995.

Lewis, Richard J. *Sax's Dangerous Properties of Industrial Materials*, 11th ed. Hoboken, NJ: J. Wiley & Sons, 2004.

Lewis, Richard J., Sr., *Hazardous Chemicals Desk Reference*, 5th ed. Hoboken, NJ: J. Wiley & Sons, 2002.

"List of Highly Hazardous Chemicals." *Code of Federal Regulations.* Title 29, Pt. 1910.119, Appendix A.

Meyer, Eugene. *Chemistry of Hazardous Materials*, 4th ed. Englewood Cliffs, NJ: Brady Prentice Hall, 2005.

National Fire Protection Association. *Hazardous Chemicals Data*, NFPA 49. Quincy MA :NFPA, 1994.

National Fire Protection Association. *Fire Hazard Properties of Flammable Liquids, Gases, and Volatile Solids*, NFPA 325. Quincy, MA: NFPA, 1994.

National Fire Protection Association. *Standard for the Identification of Fire Hazards of Materials for Emergency Response*, NFPA 704. Quincy, MA: NFPA, 2001.

National Fire Protection Association. *Guide for Hazardous Chemical Reactions*, NFPA 491. Quincy, MA: NFPA, 1997.

Plog, Barbara A., Ed. *Fundamentals of Industrial Hygiene*, 5th ed. Itasca, IL: National Safety Council, 2002.

Process Safety Institute. *Performing Hazard Assessments to Comply with EPA's RMP Rule.* Resource Materials for Course #302. Knoxville, TN: ABS Groups, Inc. (formerly JBF Associates Inc.), 1997.

"The Process Safety Management Approach for Compliance." *OSHA Regulation 29 CFR 1910 .119* presented by the American Institute of Chemical Engineers in conjunction with The Process Safety Institute and JBF Associates, Inc. Knoxville, TN, 1994.

"Process Safety Management of Highly Hazardous Chemicals." *Code of Federal Regulations.* Title 29, Pt. 1910.119.

Internet Resources

<http://ull.chemistry.uakron.edu/erd/> (The Department of Chemistry at the University of Akron. The Chemical Database)

<http://www.abs-jbfa.com> (ABS Consulting. Home Page)

<http://www.access.gpo.gov/> (Government Printing Office. Homepage)

<http://www aiche.org/ccps/> (American Institute of Chemical Engineers Center for Chemical Process Safety)

<http://www.aiche.org/safetyprogress> (American Institute of Chemical Engineers. Publications, Process Safety Progress)

<http://www.atsdr.cdc.gov/ >(Agency for Toxic Substances and Disease Registry, Homepage)

<http://www.eh.doe.gov/chem_safety/> (US Department of Energy. Chemical Safety Program)

<http://www.ehso.com/ProcessSafety.htm> (Environment, Health and Safety Online. Process Safety Management)

<http://www.epa.gov/swercepp> (Emergency Prevention, Preparedness and Response. Homepage)

<http://www.osha.gov/SLTC/process safetymanagement/> (US Department of Labor, Occupational Safety and Health Administration. Process Safety Management)

<http://www.sba.gov> (US Small Business Administration. Homepage)

John S. Kirar is a Nuclear Safety Manager with Bechtel Jacobs Company LLC in Oak Ridge, Tennessee. Mr. Kirar has 23 years experience in safety engineering and risk management, systems engineering, project management, environmental health and safety management, and regulatory compliance. He has worked as a System Safety Engineer in the aerospace industry, as a Nuclear Safety Engineer/ Manager supporting the Department of Energy, and as Vice President and Operations Manager for his own safety engineering and environmental management consulting firm. He has worked in the hazardous materials management field for ten years evaluating public, worker, and environmental risks associated with the accidental release of chemicals and radiological contaminants.

CHAPTER 14

Bloodborne Pathogen Program

Frank Pfeifer, CSP, CHMM
Martha Boss, CIH, CSP

Introduction

Part 1910.1030 of Title 29 of the *Code of Federal Regulations* (CFR), was published in the *Federal Register* on December 6, 1991, (29 CFR 1910.1030) and became effective on March 6, 1992. This standard originally sought to protect workers in hospitals, funeral homes, nursing homes, clinics, law enforcement agencies, emergency responders, human immunodeficiency virus/hepatitis B virus (HIV/HBV) research laboratories, and dentists. In reality, however, *all workers* who potentially could be *occupationally* exposed to bloodborne pathogens in the workplace environs are covered.

On November 6, 2000, President Clinton signed the Needlestick Safety and Prevention Act, (P.L. 106–430). The Act required the Occupational Safety and Health Administration (OSHA) to revise the Bloodborne Pathogen (BBP) standard. The revisions to OSHA's BBP standard (required under the Needlestick Safety and Prevention Act) can be broadly categorized into four areas: modification of definitions relating to engineering controls, revision and updating of the Exposure Control Plan, solicitation of employee input, and recordkeeping. These revisions to the BBP standard became effective April 18, 2001. Exposure Control Plans that are reviewed and updated on or after this effective date must reflect the requirements of the revised standard. A summary of the changes to the Bloodborne Pathogens Standard is in the following text box.

Summary of the Changes to the Bloodborne Pathogens Standard from the Needlestick Safety and Prevention Act.

New Definitions

- Engineering controls to include "Safer medical devices, . . . engineered sharps injury protections and needleless systems"
- Sharps with engineered sharps injury protection
- Needleless system

Exposure Control Plans

- Reflect changes in technology
- Document annual review and considerations
- Employer must solicit and document in the exposure plan input from direct patient care employees (nonmanagement) on engineering and work practices controls

Records

- Must keep sharps injury log, including:
  - Device brand and name
  - Work area of exposure
  - How the incident occured
- Employee's confidentiality must be protected

OSHA's BBP standard, including the amendments, is applicable to general industry and shipyard employment (as referenced in 29 CFR 1915.1030).

The Bloodborne Pathogens Standard is one of the regulations that specify that the employer will cover the cost of personal protective equipment (PPE), 29 CFR 1910.1030 (d)(3)(v).

The phrase, "but are not limited to," is extremely important and often overlooked and ignored. Remember, this standard applies to all bloodborne pathogens, not just HBV and HIV. For example, Hepatitis C is increasingly being considered a workplace health hazard and is considered to be a bloodborne pathogen.

This Occupational Safety and Health Administration (OSHA) Bloodborne Pathogen standard gave the Centers for Disease Control and Prevention's (CDC's) universal precautions the force of law. However, this standard does not apply to hospital patients or any other exposure situation outside of the workplace. *Good Samaritan* acts that result in exposure to blood or other potentially infectious materials that could cause exposures are not regulated by this standard. Exposures that may occur when assisting a fellow employee (*i.e.*, assisting a co-worker with nosebleed, giving Cardiopulmonary Resuscitation [CPR] or first aid) are only regulated by this standard if such duties are in the job's task descriptions. OSHA, however, encourages employers to offer post-exposure evaluation and follow-up in such cases.

Exposure Control

OSHA's rule applies to all persons *occupationally exposed* to blood or other potentially infectious materials. Blood means human blood, blood products, or blood components (see Figure 1). *Other potentially infectious materials (OPIM)* include

- Human body fluids: semen, vaginal secretions, cerebrospinal fluid, synovial fluid, pleural fluid, pericardial fluid, peritoneal fluid, amniotic fluid

• Saliva in dental procedures

• Any body fluid visibly contaminated with blood

• All body fluids in situations where differentiation between body fluids is difficult. This would include waste mixtures such as vomit, toilet overflow, sewage, and leachate associated with refuse containers that contained potentially contaminated items

Written Exposure Control Plan

The standard requires the development of a written exposure control plan. At a minimum, the exposure control plan must include plan requirements for

• Exposure determination (without regard for personal protective equipment [PPE])

• Procedures used in evaluating the circumstances surrounding an exposure incident

• Scheduling and methods for implementing sections of the standard covering the methods of compliance

• Hepatitis B vaccination and postexposure follow-up

• Hazard Communication for employees and recordkeeping

• Annual plan review schedules

Paragraph (c)(1)(iv) of the standard has been revised to add new requirements to the annual review and update of the Exposure Control Plan. The review and update of the plan is now required to:

• Reflect changes in technology that eliminate or reduce exposure to bloodborne pathogens

• Annually document consideration and implementation of appropriate commercially

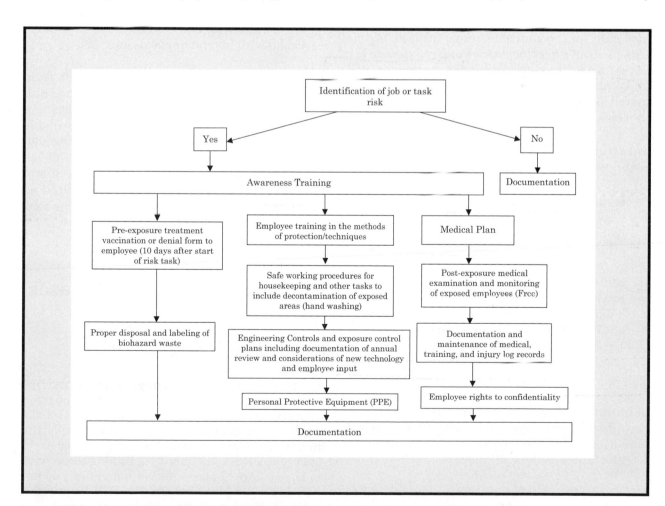

Figure 1. Flow Chart of Exposure Control Plan Development

available and effective safer medical devices designed to eliminate or minimize occupational exposure

Thus, the additional provisions require that employers, in their written Exposure Control Plans, account for innovations in procedure and technological developments that reduce the risk of exposure incidents. Consideration and implementation of safer devices could be documented in the Exposure Control Plan by describing the safer devices identified as candidates for adoption, the method or methods used to evaluate devices and the results of evaluations, as well as justification for selection decisions. This information must be updated at least annually.

The revised Exposure Control Plan requirements make it clear that employers must implement the safer devices that are appropriate, commercially available, and effective. For the purposes of this standard, an *appropriate safer medical device* includes only devices whose use, based on reasonable judgment in individual cases, will not jeopardize patient or employee safety or be medically contraindicated. For purposes of this standard, an *effective safer medical device* is a device that, based on reasonable judgment, will make an exposure incident involving a contaminated sharp less likely to occur in the application in which it is used.

Paragraph (c)(1)(v) of the revised standard now requires that an

> employer, who is required to establish an Exposure Control Plan shall solicit input from nonmanagerial employees responsible for direct patient care who are potentially exposed to injuries from contaminated sharps in the identification, evaluation, and selection of effective engineering and work practice controls and shall document the solicitation in the Exposure Control Plan.

This change represents a new requirement, which is performance-oriented. No specific procedures for obtaining employee input are prescribed. This provides the employer with flexibility to solicit employee input in any manner appropriate to the circumstances of the workplace.

For example, an employee who uses a needled syringe to collect blood from patients in a nursing home, or an employee who administers flu vaccinations in a factory employee health unit, would both be considered to be involved in direct patient care and engaged in activities that put them at risk of direct exposure due to needlestick injuries. Employers may also choose to include other employees in the request for input, such as laboratory technicians, housekeeping staff, maintenance workers, and management-level personnel who may be at risk of injury involving contaminated sharps.

The revised standard requires that solicitation of input from employees be documented in the Exposure Control Plan. Employers can meet this obligation by identifying the employees who were involved and describing the process by which input was requested. Employers should also describe the input obtained with regard to identification, evaluation, and selection of controls. Evidence that employee input has been sought can include, for example, meeting minutes, copies of documents used to request employee participation, or records of responses received from employees such as reports evaluating the effectiveness of a safer medical device in trial applications.

The requirement for solicitation of input from employees has been designated as paragraph (c)(1)(v) in the revised standard. The requirement that the Exposure Control Plan be made available to the Assistant Secretary of Labor for Occupational Safety and Health and the Director of the National Institute for Occupational Safety and Health upon request, previously designated as paragraph (c)(1)(v), has been moved and is now paragraph (c)(1)(vi) in the revised standard.

Bloodborne Pathogenic Diseases

Human Immunodeficiency Virus

Acquired immune deficiency syndrome (AIDS) is caused by a virus. Technically, the viral infection is human immunodeficiency virus (HIV) and the resultant illness is AIDS. The HIV attacks the immune system and thus, the symptoms of AIDS emerge. AIDS is ultimately a fatal disease with no known cure. Many infected individuals do not even know they are infected! HIV requires a narrow temperature–time period environment to survive and is thus very fragile outside of the human body.

Hepatitis B Virus

Hepatitis B (HBV) is a serious public health problem that affects people of all ages in the United States and around the world. The disease is caused by a highly infectious virus that attacks the liver. HBV infection can lead to severe illness, liver damage, and, in some cases, death. Liver failure may be related to HBV and HBV is the most common cause of liver cancer worldwide. Liver cancer is one of the three most common cancers in the world. The best way to be protected against HBV is prevention. The best prevention is to be vaccinated with hepatitis B vaccine, a vaccine that has been proven safe and effective.

People who do not clear the hepatitis B virus from their blood have not fully recovered, and are called *hepatitis B carriers*. An HBV carrier is someone who has had hepatitis B virus in his/her blood for more than six months. While about 10 percent of adults who acquire HBV infection become carriers, children have a greater risk. The younger the child is at the time of infection, the greater the risk that the child will become a lifelong carrier. Many babies born to carrier mothers will also become carriers of HBV unless the babies are given special shots in the hospital and during the six months after birth to protect them from the infection. A carrier usually has no signs or symptoms of HBV but remains infected with the virus for years or for a lifetime and is capable of passing the disease on to others. Sometimes HBV carriers will spontaneously clear the infection from their bodies, but most will not. Although most carriers have no serious problems with hepatitis B and lead normal healthy lives, some carriers develop liver problems later. Hepatitis B carriers are at significantly higher risk than the general population for liver failure or liver cancer.

Hepatitis C Virus

Hepatitis C (HCV) is a viral illness that affects the liver. In 1990 an antibody to the hepatitis C virus was identified, but before that the illness was known in the United States as, *non-A, non-B hepatitis*. Hepatitis C is spread by blood-to-blood contact, and is therefore a bloodborne pathogen.

Some of the most common ways of spreading the virus are

- Transfusion of blood products
- Intravenous drug use
- Tattooing
- Body piercing
- Sharing needles

Menstrual blood can also contain the virus.

Additional Pathogens

Other pathogen diseases should also be considered in a Bloodborne Pathogen Program or a Biological Protection Program, besides the usually covered HIV and HBV. Examples of other bloodborne pathogens include HCV, the bacterium that causes syphilis, and the parasite that causes malaria. A related disease is tuberculosis, which, while not considered a bloodborne disease, is transmitted by contact with body fluids and liquids (*i.e.*, OPIM). Tuberculosis should be considered for addition to the other bloodborne pathogens in a comprehensive Bloodborne Pathogen Program. Separate regulatory requirements are also in effect for tuberculosis.

Training

In determining exposure, you may consult the standard as to employees who are always at risk versus employees who are at risk only in extraordinary situations. Be sure to document the decision logic for inclusion or exclusion of employees from the Bloodborne Pathogen Program. All employees with defined potential exposure risk will need information and training. Through awareness training, assessment of actual risk and the exposure determination may be made from a more educated platform.

Additional training is needed for those who have been determined to be exposed and at risk of acquiring bloodborne pathogen infections. When existing tasks are modified or new tasks that involve occupational exposure to bloodborne pathogens affect the employee's exposure, decision logic as to employee inclusion in the program may also have to be altered.

Training must be accomplished by trainers with knowledge of both the standard and the implications of the standard given current employee exposure. Thus, training must be site- or facility-specific. Information as to routes of exposure and preventative measures, including postexposure follow-up, must include the epidemiology and symptoms of bloodborne diseases. Given the potential to encounter labeled biohazards and unforeseen biohazards when handling waste, the training should include discussions of *what-if* situations.

Training Records

Accurate training records must be kept for 3 years and include the following:

- Training dates
- Content or a summary of the training
- Name(s) and qualification(s) of trainer(s)
- Names and job titles of trainees

Upon request, both medical and training records must be made available to the Director of the National Institute for Occupational Safety and Health (NIOSH) and to the Assistant Secretary of Labor for Occupational Safety and Health. Training records must be available to employees or employee representatives upon request.

Vaccination

Hepatitis B Virus

Fortunately, a vaccine is available to protect employees from HBV prior to exposure and also to provide prophylactic treatment postexposure. Employees who decline the vaccination must sign a declination form. The employee may request and obtain the vaccination at a later date. The vaccination must then be provided by the employer at no cost—despite the prior declination statement by the employee.

The hepatitis B vaccine and vaccination series must be offered within 10 working days of initial

assignment to employees who have occupational exposure to blood or other potentially infectious materials. Any booster doses of the hepatitis B vaccine recommended by the United States Public Health Service must also be offered.

Despite proven occupational exposure, a physician may determine and provide recommendations about which employees should be precluded from receiving the vaccine. The employer must obtain and provide the employee with a copy of the health care professional's written opinion stating whether a hepatitis B vaccination is indicated for the employee and whether the employee has received such vaccination.

HBV Vaccination Declination Statement

In the event an employee elects not to receive the HBV vaccine, he or she should sign and date a declination statement to this effect. An example declination statement is:

> *I understand that due to my occupational exposure to blood and other infectious materials I may be at risk of acquiring hepatitis B virus (HBV) infection. I have been given the opportunity to be vaccinated with the HBV vaccine at no charge to myself. I decline the HBV vaccine at this time. However, I understand that by declining the HBV vaccine, I may continue to be at risk of acquiring HBV. If in the future I continue to have occupational exposure to blood or other potentially infectious materials and I later want the HBV vaccine, I can receive the vaccination series at no charge to me.*

If a declination statement is made and accepted, the employer must also document that the employee had appropriate training to make an informed decision. This training need not be a full program training sequence; however, minimum awareness training is required.

New Definitions and Revised BBP Standard

The revised standard adds two additional terms to the definition section.

- ***Sharps with Engineered Sharps Injury Protections*** is defined as "a nonneedle sharp or a needle device used for withdrawing body fluids, accessing a vein or artery, or administering medications or other fluids, with a built-in safety feature or mechanism that effectively reduces the risk of an exposure incident."

- *Needleless System* is defined as "a device that does not use needles for: A) the collection of bodily fluids or withdrawal of body fluids after initial venous or arterial access is established; B) the administration of medication or fluids; or C) any other procedure involving the potential for occupational exposure to bloodborne pathogens due to percutaneous injuries from contaminated sharps."

Engineering and Work Practice Controls

Engineering and work practice controls are the primary methods used to prevent occupational transmission of HBV and HIV. The term *engineering controls* includes all control measures that isolate or remove a hazard from the workplace, encompassing not only sharps with engineered sharps injury protections and needleless systems but also other medical devices designed to reduce the risk of percutaneous exposure to bloodborne pathogens. Examples include blunt suture needles and plastic or mylar-wrapped glass capillary tubes, as well as controls that are not medical devices, such as sharps disposal containers and biosafety cabinets.

The definition of engineering controls has been modified in the revised BBP standard to include as examples "safer medical devices, such as sharps with engineered sharps injury protections and needleless systems." This change clarifies that safer medical devices are considered to be engineering controls under the standard.

Personal protective equipment (PPE) is necessary when occupational exposure to bloodborne pathogens remains even after instituting engineering controls.

Handwashing is necessary, and handwashing facilities must be provided. All personnel, upon doffing gloves and other PPE, must immediately wash their hands. In the event that an exposure incident has occurred, gloves and other PPE should be disinfected prior to doffing. If the PPE has already been breached, measures to prevent further worker exposure as PPE is doffed must be determined on a situation-specific basis.

Proper work practice controls alter the manner in which a task is performed. In work areas where a reasonable likelihood of occupational exposure exists, work practice controls include restricting eating, drinking, smoking, applying cosmetics, and handling contact lenses, as well as prohibiting mouth pipetting. Foods, including stored food and drink, should be excluded entirely from areas where bloodborne pathogens may be present. This preclusion includes storage of foods and drinks in sample refrigerators.

Personal Protective Equipment

Personal protective equipment (PPE) must prevent blood and/or OPIM from passing through or reaching employees' work clothes, street clothes, undergarments, skin, eyes, mouth, or other mucous membranes. The PPE must remain intact under normal conditions of use and for the duration of time used. Thus, PPE provides a limited barrier between the user and infectious materials. As with any barrier, breakthrough, molecular penetration, and mechanical degradation of PPE will all lessen the barrier's effectiveness.

Gloves, while providing an effective barrier form of PPE, should not be thought of as a foolproof mode of protection. Proper donning and doffing of gloves will lessen worker exposure to surficial contamination, especially after gloves have been used. The practice of reusing gloves may not be appropriate and glove reuse must be discussed thoroughly during training exercises and in the Bloodborne Pathogen Program. *If gloves cannot be reused without increased exposure to the workers, gloves should be disposed of during the initial doffing interval.*

Glove use will not protect the worker if that worker touches his or her eyes, nose, or mouth with a contaminated gloved hand. Consequently implementation of the Bloodborne Pathogen Program must include training and oversight to prevent inadvertent transfer of infective materials on a gloved hand to a worker's bodily orifices.

Some people have an allergy to latex, and thus alternative gloves should be considered in a PPE program. Alternate disposal locations for spent gloves may also be required to protect these employees during glove disposal from exposure to latex gloves worn by others and the resultant latex dusts.

Housekeeping

Normal housekeeping may not be sufficient to deal with bloodborne hazards. In all cases, any housekeeping that provides a way to handle materials without directly touching contaminated surfaces should be encouraged. The use of mechanical means (*e.g.*, tongs, forceps, or a brush and a dustpan to pick up contaminated broken glassware) is an example of good housekeeping procedures.

Scientific and lay publications provide varying time-period discussions as to the continued virulence of bloodborne pathogenic materials. Currently, the HIV virus is thought to exist in virulent numbers or status for only 30 minutes outside of the human body. HBV can, however, remain infective on dry surfaces for 7 days, and in raw sewage for up to 21 days within a *wet* suspension. For housekeeping purposes, you may not know the time or conditions under which the initial spill occurred. So during housekeeping, as in any other exposure situation, assume the materials remain virulent and take required precautions. Reducing splash during cleanup is desirable, and may be accomplished by placing a disposable cloth over the spill and then carefully pouring the disinfectant over the cloth.

Housekeeping protocol development, and the training for housekeeping staff should cover such issues as:

- Handling of floor wash waters and washing tools (mops, booms, squeegees, rags). If blood or OPIM is mopped up—do you continue to use that wash water for mopping other areas? Is this process followed by disinfection?

- Storage of unwrapped medical equipment (swabs, cotton balls, paper products) in areas where blood or OPIM could contaminate these items. An example of such storage is the

practice of placing unwrapped cotton tipped swabs for use in pap smears directly under the location where women are examined. The storage location is essentially a drawer under the examining table that is opened during the examination. If infective materials from the woman could contaminate the swab so stored, successive handling of the swabs can infect workers and future patients.

- Handling of equipment obviously covered with dried blood or OPIM. Phlebotomy kits and containers for sharps are often surficially contaminated with dried blood. What procedures are in place to decontaminate these and other locations where dried blood is present?

- Disposal bag storage locations. Do you store bags containing contaminated items in general use areas?

- Do workers routinely reach into wastebaskets? Despite the presence of foot activated waste baskets and closed refuse containers, do workers often reach into refuse containers to compact garbage or dispose of items?

- How is overflow from toilets handled? Is equipment used to stem the toilet overflow and absorb toilet contents adequately disinfected? If disposed of, is the material marked as potentially a biohazard and/or are workers alerted to the fact that raw sewage contaminated items are being disposed of?

- Although not specifically addressed by the OSHA Standards, how are refuse containers for feminine hygiene products handled? Are these containers placed so that women can enter and exit a toilet stall facility without touching the containers and the container linings?

- Do workers routinely carry items contaminated with bloodborne pathogens (*e.g.*, disposal bags, bed pans, spent medical equipment, soiled bedding and towels)? If so, what items are used to carry this equipment? Is a canvas bag-draped cart used to pick up the soiled hotel linens, and the same cart used to deliver the clean linens? Are briefly washed bedpans routinely placed on patient eating trays between uses?

- Does your workplace have garbage chutes? If so, are the garbage chutes routinely cleaned with disinfectant?

- Does your facility have conjoined storm and sanitary sewer outfall lines from the city? If so, does a major rainstorm cause untreated raw sewage to back up into your facility? How do workers clean this spillage?

Disinfection

All surfaces, reusable PPE, tools, and other devices that come in contact with bloodborne pathogens must be disinfected as soon as possible. A solution of 5.2% sodium hypochlorite (unscented household bleach) diluted between 1:10 and 1:100 with water may be used (read the label to confirm). The recommended dilution is 1:10 (1/4 cup per gallon of water) whenever practicable. The resident time for this solution is also important and varies between 10 to 30 minutes depending on the original solution concentration and the porosity of the materials being disinfected.

Many disinfecting solutions may pose an inhalation or dermal risk for a workforce. The Bloodborne Pathogen Program must discuss employee monitoring when such chemicals are used. Keep in mind that the OSHA Permissible Exposure Limit (PEL) for chlorine is only 1 ppm.

For surfaces, such as the neoprene in respirator harnesses, chlorine is not a recommended disinfecting agent in most cases—the chlorine degrades the neoprene. *When respirator parts must be disinfected, consult the manufacturer about appropriate disinfection solutions.*

Remember that not all disinfecting agents are appropriate or effective in these situations. To obtain information specific to your disinfection needs, contact the EPA Antimicrobial Division at (703) 308–0127 or check the web page listed at the end of this chapter. This EPA office telephone has replaced the National Antimicrobial Information Network. Remember also that disinfection is not sterilization of the surfaces—you are reducing the number of infectious agents, not entirely eliminating all infectious organisms.

Labeling

The standard requires that fluorescent orange or orange-red warning labels be attached to containers of regulated waste, to refrigerators and freezers containing blood and other potentially infectious materials, and to other containers used to store, transport, or ship blood or other potentially infectious materials. The warning label must be fluorescent orange or orange-red, contain the biohazard symbol and the word BIOHAZARD, in a contrasting color, and be attached to each object by string, wire, adhesive, or another method to prevent loss or unintentional removal of the label. The labels are not required when

- Red bags or red containers are used

- Containers of blood, blood components, or blood products are labeled as to their contents and have been released for transfusion or other clinical use

- Individual containers of blood or other potentially infectious materials are placed in a labeled container during storage, transport, shipment, or disposal

If an Exposure Incident Occurs

For employees who have had an exposure incident, the standard requires that the postexposure medical evaluation and follow-up be made immediately available. At a minimum, the evaluation and follow-up must include the following elements:

- Document the routes of exposure and how exposure occurred.

- Identify and document the source individual, unless the employer can establish that identification is infeasible or prohibited by state or local law. (Keep in mind that local regulations and legal interpretations should be consulted in the development of the program, rather than making a random last-minute decision to question the source individual.)

- Obtain consent and provide HBV, HCV, HIV, or other bloodborne pathogen serological testing for the source individual as soon as possible.

    - If the source individual is known to be infected with either HIV or HBV, testing of that individual need not be repeated for those known pathogens.

        ◆ Provide the exposed employee with the source individual's test results and information about applicable disclosure laws and regulations concerning the source individual's identity and infectious status.

        ◆ If, during the collection of blood for baseline testing, the source individual does not give consent for HIV serological testing, preserve the baseline blood sample for at least 90 days. Should the employee test positive for HIV within that 90-day time frame, you may have to revisit the question of serological testing for the source individual.

- Provide HBV, HCV, and HIV serological testing, counseling, and safe and effective postexposure prophylaxis. The employer must give the health care professional evaluating the employee after an exposure incident and responsible for the employee's hepatitis B vaccination as well as post-exposure evaluation and follow-up

    - A copy of the OSHA standard. A description of the employee's job duties relevant to the exposure incident, documentation of the route(s) of exposure and circumstances of exposure. Results of the source individual's serological tests, if available, and all relevant employee medical records, including vaccination status.

Within 15 days after evaluation of the exposed employee, the employer must provide the employee with a copy of the health care professional's written opinion. The required written opinion is limited to whether the vaccine is indicated and has been received. The written opinion for postexposure evaluation must document that the employee has been informed of the results of the medical evaluation and of any medical conditions resulting from the exposure incident that may require further evaluation or treatment. All other diagnoses must remain confidential and not be included in the written report of the postexposure incident.

Recordkeeping

Occupational Exposure

The employer also must preserve and maintain for each employee an accurate record of occupational exposure according to the OSHA rules governing access to employee exposure and medical records (29 CFR 1910.20).

Medical records must include the following information:

1) Employee's name and social security number

2) Employee's hepatitis B vaccination status including vaccination dates and any medical records related to the employee's ability to receive vaccinations

3) Results of examinations, medical testing, and postexposure evaluation and follow-up procedures

4) Health care professional's written opinion

5) A copy of the information provided to the health care professional

Medical Records

Medical records must be kept confidential and maintained for at least the duration of employment plus 30 years. An employee's medical records can be obtained by that employee or anyone having that employee's written consent. Also, if the employer ceases to do business, medical and training records must be transferred to the successor employer. If no successor employer is available, the employer must notify the Director, National Institute for Occupational Safety and Health (NIOSH), United States Department of Health and Human Services, for specific directions regarding disposition of the records at least 3 months prior to intended disposal.

The recordkeeping requirements of the standard at paragraph (h) have been amended by adding paragraph (h)(5) to require that employers maintain a sharps injury log to serve as a tool for identifying high risk areas and evaluating devices. Paragraph (h)(5)(i) now states, "The employer shall establish and maintain a sharps injury log for the recording of percutaneous injuries from contaminated sharps. The information in the sharps injury log shall be recorded and maintained in such manner as to protect the confidentiality of the injured employee. The sharps injury log shall contain, at a minimum:

- The type and brand of device involved in the incident,

- The department or work area where the exposure incident occurred, and

- An explanation of how the incident occurred. The sharps injury log must be maintained for the period required by 29 CFR 1904. The requirement to establish and maintain the log only applies to employers who are otherwise required to maintain a log of occupational injuries and illnesses under 29 CFR 1904 (OSHA's Recordkeeping rule)."

The sharps injury log must include the specified minimum information regarding the device involved (if known), the location of the incident, and the description of the events that resulted in the injury. The level of detail presented should be sufficient to allow ready identification of the device, location, and circumstances surrounding an exposure incident so that the intended evaluation of risk and device effectiveness can be accomplished.

Information in the sharps injury log must be recorded and maintained in a manner that protects the privacy of the injured employee. If data from the log are made available to other parties, any information that directly identifies an employee or information that could reasonably be used to identify indirectly a specific employee must be withheld.

The format of the sharps injury log is not specified. The employer is permitted to determine the format in which the log is maintained (*e.g.*, paper or electronic), and may include information in addition to that required by the standard, so long as the privacy of injured workers is protected. Existing mechanisms for collecting these reports will be considered sufficient to meet the requirements of the standard for maintaining a sharps injury log, provided that the information gathered meets the minimum requirements specified in the standard, and the confidentiality of the injured employee is protected.

Under newly published revisions to OSHA's Recordkeeping rule (29 CFR 1904), employers are required to record sharps injuries involving contaminated objects on the OSHA 300 Log of Work-Related Injuries and Illnesses and the OSHA 301 Injury and Illness Incident Report (the new forms replace the current 200 and 101 forms). The employer must

- Enter the type and brand of the device on either the 300 or 301 form

- Maintain the records in a way that segregates sharps injuries from other types of work-related injuries and illnesses, or allows sharps injuries to be easily separated

Summary

The Bloodborne Pathogen Standard requires that a written program be developed and implemented by employers when their employees may be exposed to these pathogens at work. Before a program can be implemented, a task/job risk identification or hazard assessment must be documented. Awareness training should then be offered to all affected personnel within the work force, including any decision-makers who oversee program implementation. For those personnel judged to be at risk, additional training is needed and must include engineering controls, housekeeping, personal protective equipment (PPE), waste disposal, medical procedures, confidentiality, and documentation requirements. Some states have regulations pending that will add additional requirements for their jurisdictions, so be sure to check with local and state regulatory agencies for additional requirements. Many resources are available to provide additional information on Bloodborne Pathogen Programs, in book form and on the Internet. Some are listed in the following section.

Additional Resources

Many resources are available in printed form and electronically, on the Internet. OSHA, CDC, the

Environmental Protection Agency (EPA), and universities have web sites that provide example programs and other valuable information as to requirements and workplace implementation strategies. Often, grant monies are used to fund phone-number information resources and web pages. When grant resources are altered (*i.e.*, grants are placed with new institutions), the listed phone numbers may change unexpectedly. Be very specific about the information you are seeking, and query the information source as to how they disseminate information. What information do they disseminate? For example, if you are looking for disinfectants and ask for "recommended disinfectants," you may receive the reply that "they do not recommend disinfectants." However, if you ask for a copy of the EPA's "List of Recommended Disinfectants," you will be provided with a list of recommended disinfectants and with guidance to read the labels.

EPA's Antimicrobial Division:
  (703) 308-0127

CDC's HIV and AIDS Hotline:
  (800) 342-2437

OSHA's Emergency Number:
  (800) 321-6742

OSHA's Technical Support:
  (202) 693-2300

Internet Resources

<http://www.cdc.gov/> (Centers for Disease Control and Prevention.Homepage.)

<http://www.cdc.gov/ncidod/hip/Needle/needle.htm> (Centers for Disease Control and Prevention. Division of Healthcare Quality Promotion. Issues in Healthcare Setting.)

<http://www.cdc.gov/niosh/topics/bbp/safer/> (Centers for Disease Control and Prevention. National Institute for Occupational Safety and Health. Safer Medical Devices Implementation in Health Care Facilities.)

<http://www.epa.gov/epahome/Offices.html> (Environmental Protection Agency. Programs. Regional Offices.)

<http://www.epa.gov/oppad001 chemreg.indes.htm> (Environmental Protection Agency. Pesticides: Regulating Pesticides. Microbiological Division.)

<http://www.osha.gov> (Occupational Safety and Health Administration. Homepage.)

<http://www.osha.gov/SLTC/> (U. S. Department of Labor. Occupational Safety and Health Administration. Technical Links to Safety and Health Topics.)

Frank Pfeifer has a degree in Environmental Studies from the University of Kansas. Mr. Pfeifer has worked in several environmental positions since graduation in 1976. Some of these positions include: Water and Wastewater Plant Operator, Sanitarian ("Health Inspector" at city, county, and state levels), Food and Drug Inspector, Asbestos Course Auditor under an EPA Grant, Program Specialist for the Nebraska Department of Health (Water and Asbestos Programs), Industrial Hygienist Consultant for a regional engineering firm, a Safety / Environmental Engineer for 3M and a writer. Today Mr. Pfeifer is a contractor to the Federal Aviation Administration in Kansas City for the Oklahoma firm of Advancia Corporation. Mr. Pfeifer is the past Founding President of the Midwest Plains Chapter of the ACHMM and a past member of the Board of Directors and currently a member of the Heartland Chapter of ACHMM in Kansas City.

Martha Boss is a Certified Industrial Hygienist and a Certified Safety Professional specializing in hazardous materials management, hazardous waste abatement and remediation, OSHA process safety, and EPA risk management program development, risk assessment, biological risk evaluations, due diligence, and OSHA-type compliance and ventilation design. Ms. Boss has been active in these endeavors for over 14 years, during which time she has overseen hazardous materials management at major Environmental Protection Agency, CERCLA, and Department of Defense and Department of Energy sites throughout the nation. These experiences have resulted in published works in Applied Toxicology, Environmental Protection and Compliance magazines. Ms. Boss is currently a Principal Toxicologist for URS performing industrial hygiene, safety, and security audits throughout the nation.

CHAPTER 15

Industrial Hygiene Basics

David M. Trayer

Introduction

The American Board of Industrial Hygiene (ABIH) defines industrial hygiene as "the science and practice devoted to the anticipation, recognition, evaluation and control of those environmental factors and stresses arising in or from the workplace that may cause sickness, impaired health and well-being, or significant discomfort among workers and may also impact the general community" (ABIH 2002). This chapter will focus on health hazards to workers.

The agents that cause health hazards can be chemical, physical, biological, or ergonomic in nature. In its standard on hazardous waste operations and emergency response, the United States Occupational Safety and Health Administration (OSHA) defines a health hazard in terms of chemical and biological agents. The OSHA definition can be broadened to include physical and ergonomic hazards by substituting the words *agent or mixture of agents*:

Health hazard means [*an agent or mixture of agents*] for which there is statistically significant evidence based on at least one study conducted in accordance with established scientific principles that acute or chronic health effects may occur in exposed employees (29 Code of Federal Regulations (CFR) 1910.120).

A more comprehensive discussion of health hazards as defined by OSHA is found in Appendix A of the OSHA Hazard Communication Standard (29 CFR 1910.1200).

The risk that someone will develop an illness from exposure to a specific agent is a function of the dose rate, the frequency of exposure episodes, and the duration of the exposure episodes. However, other factors are also important. These include the biological variability of the workers: age, whether female or male, reproductive status (*e.g.*, the presence of a fetus), body weight, individual genetic characteristics, previous exposures, life style (*e.g.*, smoking and use of alcohol or other narcotics), and their overall health status, including the use of pharmaceuticals. Moreover, workplace conditions can involve simultaneous exposure to multiple agents whose combined effect is unknown. Off-the-job exposures, often unrecognized, may also impact the worker's health. Exposure can also be complicated by ambient conditions, such as heat and pressure extremes. Further complicating assessment of health risks is the fact that many of the symptoms of occupational illness may also occur in nonoccupational illnesses. The ability to attribute symptoms to specific agents is a challenge for occupational physicians. These complexities demand that the industrial hygienist work cooperatively as part of a multidisciplinary team of specialists.

Such a team can include senior and line managers, workers, design and plant engineers, occupational physicians and nurses, safety specialists, chemists and physicists, environmental specialists, human resource managers, lawyers, industrial trainers, and statisticians. As needed, other specialists, such as health physicists, toxicologists, and epidemiologists, may be added to the team. The workers themselves can be one of the most valuable resources. They are closely associated with the work environment, the processes, the procedures, the materials, and the equipment. They observe these on a day-by-day basis and are likely to be able to offer valuable ideas. The suggestions of workers and their representatives should be added to the alternatives under consideration.

What is the role of industrial hygiene in hazardous materials management? Obviously, one role is to protect the workforce from excessive exposure to those hazardous materials being managed. But hazardous materials are managed in a wide variety of industrial operations where workers might also encounter other hazards, including physical hazards, radiation, and ergonomic hazards. The industrial hygienist must deal with all occupational health hazards. For example, at a hazardous waste remediation site, workers may encounter heat stress, particularly if they are *dressed out* for skin and respiratory protection. Biological hazards may also be present at the site in the form of poisonous plants, insects, and infectious agents in the soil. Ergonomic stressors might occur in materials handling operations or simply from the added stress of working in protective gear. This chapter will attempt to address this wider spectrum of potential hazards associated with hazardous waste management.

This chapter covers the overall practice of industrial hygiene, which involves four general functions: anticipation of potential hazards, recognition of potential hazards, evaluation of potential hazards, and control of unacceptable hazards. One other function: the evaluation of the effectiveness of control methods is also mentioned. Finally, there are a few comments concerning the usual qualifications expected of an industrial hygienist.

Anticipation of Workplace Health Hazards

The word *anticipation* implies that a prior action can be taken that might forestall a later action. In the industrial hygiene sense this means that health hazards can often be anticipated and preventive actions taken early to avoid overexposure at some later time. An example of this is the involvement of a professional industrial hygienist in the planning, design, and start-up of a new industrial process. In the early planning phase, the industrial hygienist's knowledge of various industrial processes and their related exposure potentials can be a valuable resource to design engineers. Health hazards can thus be prevented before they become a reality.

Occupational health hazards are difficult to recognize in an operating facility. It is even more difficult to predict what hazards might occur in the future start-up of a new facility. Nevertheless, the application of knowledge and experience can increase success in predicting future health hazards. It has been suggested that the industrial hygienist start the process by acquiring information on definitive features in the occupational environment, namely: the materials present, the process itself, the apparent worker exposure patterns, and the hazard controls in use (Burgess 1995). As this information is brought together potential hazards will start to emerge.

In order to identify health hazards in an occupational environment, it is necessary to have a working knowledge of the hazardous agents and the corresponding effects of exposure. The agents that cause health hazards can be classified into four categories: chemical, physical, biological, or ergonomic. Emotional stressors in the workplace are also recognized. However, these fall more naturally into the realms of management and medical specialists, and so will not be addressed here.

Chemical Hazards

Since almost all hazardous materials are ultimately composed of chemicals, this class of hazard is of keen interest. Toxicity is of basic concern. In the industrial hygiene context, *toxicity* has been defined as the capacity or ability of a chemical to harm or injure a living organism by other than mechanical means (Cohen and Balzer 1996).

Exposures are broadly described as being either acute or chronic. *Acute exposures* are characterized by brief exposures to high concentrations with rapid onset of symptoms. An example of an acute exposure is the inhalation of high concentrations of solvent vapors. Within minutes, depression of the central nervous system will occur and the exposed person will experience dizziness, confusion, drowsiness, and possibly unconsciousness. On the other hand, *chronic exposures* are typically characterized by repeated exposure to low concentrations of a substance over a long period of time, perhaps years, with symptoms of illness developing slowly. An example of chronic exposure is the gradual development of silicosis after frequent, long-term inhalation of very low concentrations of airborne silicon dioxide (silica) dust.

Chemicals can enter the body by several routes, including inhalation, direct tissue contact, ingestion, and occasionally by accidental injection. The most common route of entry of toxic substances in industry is by inhalation, followed by skin or mucous tissues absorption and ingestion. Of these, inhalation of airborne air contaminants is the most important in terms of the seriousness of resulting illness. The lung tissues are in intimate contact with the circulatory system, thereby providing an almost direct path to the blood and thus to all body organs. Furthermore, lung tissue is vulnerable to the direct action of many substances, such as acid vapors, asbestos, and nitrogen dioxide.

The amount of air contaminant inhaled and retained in the lung depends largely on the physical form of the airborne chemical. Airborne contaminants are classified as: gases, vapors, or aerosols. *Gases* are broadly defined as substances that are in the gaseous state at room temperature (25° C) and one atmosphere pressure (760 mm Hg). *Vapors* are the gaseous phase of a substance that is normally a liquid or solid at room temperature and pressure. Thus, a liquid solvent will generate airborne vapor from its surface in concentrations proportional to its vapor pressure. *Aerosols*, as understood by industrial hygienists, are microscopic solid or liquid particles dispersed in the air. Typical industrial aerosols occur as dusts, fumes, mists and fogs, and smoke. *Dusts* are solid aerosols that are typically generated from a bulk solid by some mechanical action, such as crushing, drilling, or grinding. *Fumes*, contrary to common usage, are solid particles formed by condensation of vapors generated from evaporating (*e.g.,* molten) substances. Thus, in welding, metal fumes are generated from the molten electrodes and base metals. *Mists* and *fogs* are suspended droplets of liquid and may be formed by mechanical action, such as spraying (mists) or by condensation from the vapor state (fogs). *Smokes* are produced by the combustion of a bulk material. Smoke can be pure, as when magnesium is burned in air to form magnesium oxide, or it can be a complex mixture of gases, vapors, fumes, and ash, as in the combustion of coal.

Direct tissue exposures can occur when corrosive substances contact the skin or mucous tissues of the eyes and upper respiratory tract. The effect can range from irritation to chemical destruction depending on the corrosiveness of the chemical and the degree of exposure. A number of substances also have the ability to absorb into the bloodstream through intact skin or mucous tissues. For some substances, tissue absorption can be a route to the internal organs. Notorious among chemicals that will absorb rapidly through the skin are organic phosphate insecticides and chemical warfare agents, which can rapidly enter the bloodstream through the skin and affect the central nervous system.

In industrial toxicology, substances are categorized according to the effect they have on the body. The more common categories are shown in Table 1. Some affected organs, symptoms, and examples of specific chemicals are shown for each category. For more complete listings consult the professional literature.

Physical Hazards

The major industrial physical hazards are noise, temperature extremes, radiation, and, in some types of operations, pressure extremes.

Noise. *Noise* has been defined as unwanted sound. Excessive exposure to noise, wanted or not, can cause permanent hearing loss. This noise-induced hearing loss typically results from chronic exposure to high sound levels. In time, this can irreversibly damage the auditory nerves and lead to permanent impairment of hearing. Occupational hearing loss is so serious and widespread that the Occupational Safety and Health Administration (OSHA) regulates it with a separate standard (29 CFR 1910.95).

The ability of noise to damage human hearing is determined primarily by two properties: the loudness of the noise entering the ears and length of time the person is exposed. *Loudness* is referred to as the sound level, and the unit of measurement is the decibel. The sound level of a quiet room is about 40 decibels, a person speaking about 65 decibels, a vacuum cleaner about 75 decibels, a power lawn mower about 95 decibels, and a gunshot above 120 decibels. The OSHA limit for continuous noise exposure for a normal 8-hour work shift is 90 decibels. Anyone exposed above 85 decibels during a work shift must be placed in an employer's hearing conservation program including periodic medical audiometric hearing tests, exposure monitoring, and protective measures. For shorter exposure periods, equivalent limits apply.

Besides hearing loss, excessive noise can interfere with communications, which may result in errors, accidents, or failure to respond to audible emergency alarms. Noise is also recognized as a source of emotional distress.

Temperature Extremes. It is possible for humans to work in a wide range of temperatures from below freezing to above 100° F (38° C). However, there are limits, and both hot and cold ambient conditions can become occupational hazards.

Excessive exposure to heat can lead to conditions ranging from heat rash to fatal heat stroke. Some heat disorders with symptoms and causes are shown in Table 2 (adapted from Bernard 1996).

It is important to note that heat stroke is a life-threatening medical emergency. The victim should be removed immediately from the hot area and his or her outer clothing removed. The victim must be cooled quickly. Medical assistance should be summoned at once. Heat stroke might occur without prior symptoms of heat illness.

Heat exhaustion is more common, and recognition of early signs of onset is important in prevention.

Personal protective gear can exacerbate the effects of heat by decreasing cooling to the skin and by increasing the physical load of work. In hot environments, special precautions are required to assure protection against heat illness for persons wearing protective clothing.

Conversely, work in cold environments, indoors or out, can produce cold-related conditions. Chemical, fire, or radiological protective clothing alone might not be adequate for protection against cold. Exposure to cold can lead to the conditions shown in Table 3 (adapted from Bernard 1996).

Radiation. Radiation is divided into two broad classes: *ionizing radiation* and *nonionizing radiation*. For more information on both classes of radiation, see the chapter in this book entitled "Radiation Safety Principles" or the references by (McCarthy and Thomas 2003) and (Hithcock, *et. al.* 2003).

Ionizing Radiation. One form of ionizing radiation is nuclear radiation (the most common being alpha particles, beta particles, and gamma rays) that is emitted by radioactive atoms. Ionizing radiation also occurs as cosmic radiation, X-rays, neutrons, high-velocity electrons, and protons. Ionizing radiation is invisible and must be detected with

Table 1. Categories of Hazards in Industrial Toxicology

Class of Hazard	Affected Organs	Possible Signs and Symptoms	Selected Examples
Irritants	Exposed tissues (*e.g.*, mucous tissues)	Pain, fluid accumulation	Acids and acid vapors, sulfur dioxide, ozone, ammonia, chlorine
Simple Asphyxiants	Body cells (O_2 is blocked from the lungs)	Confusion, collapse, unconsciousness	Nitrogen, argon, helium, carbon dioxide, methane (natural gas)
Chemical Asphyxiants	Body cells (interferes with oxygenation of body cells)	Confusion, headache, collapse, unconsciousness	Carbon monoxide, hydrogen sulfide, inorganic cyanides
Anesthetics or CNSDs*	Central nervous system	Dizziness, drowsiness, collapse, unconsciousness	Liquids and vapors of many organic solvents (*e.g.*, alcohols, ethers, esters, chlorinated hydrocarbons, toluene, xylene, benzene)
Agents that can cause lung illnesses (*e.g.*, fluid accumulation, tissue scarring, cancer)	Lungs, linings of either the lungs or the abdomen	Breathlessness, chest pain, cough, weakness	Asbestos, crystalline silica (*e.g.*, quartz), coal, radioactive substances, beryllium and its compounds, welding fumes, cotton fibers, arsenic and its compounds, hydrogen fluoride, phosgene, nitrogen dioxide
Carcinogens (agents that are known or suspected of causing cancer in humans)	Various organs, depending on the agent	Pain, coughing, tumors, various other symptoms	Confirmed carcinogens include: asbestos, radioactive substances, polycyclic aromatic hydrocarbons (PAHs), arsenic and its compounds, benzene, hexavalent chromium compounds, coal tars and pitches, vinyl chloride Suspect carcinogens include: acrylonitrile, benzidine-based dyes, benzo[a]pyrene, beryllium and its compounds, cadmium and its compounds, carbon tetrachloride, creosote, ethylene oxide, formaldehyde gas, 2,3,7,8-tetrachloro-dibenzo[p]dioxin (TCDD), trichloroethylene, tetrachloroethylene, and crystalline silica dust
Nephrotoxins	Kidneys	Symptoms vary for different agents	Most heavy metals and their compounds (*e.g.*, lead, mercury, chromium, uranium), some halogenated hydrocarbons (*e.g.*, trichloroethylene, chloroform, carbon tetrachloride), 2,4,5-trichlorophenoxyacetic acid (2,4,5-T), polychlorinated biphenyls (PCBs)
Hepatotoxins	Liver	Symptoms vary for different agents	Some halogenated hydrocarbons (*e.g.*, carbon tetrachloride, chloroform, trichloroethylene and tetrachloroethylene), ethyl alcohol, allyl alcohol, urethane monomer, hydrazine, cerium and its compounds, beryllium and its compounds, and some pharmaceuticals
Chemical Allergens (sensitizers)	Various tissues, especially skin and eyes	Itching, swelling, inflammation	Formaldehyde, beryllium and its compounds, toluene-2,4-diisocyanate (TDI), creosote, some acrylates, epoxy resins and components, coal tar and its derivatives, some organic dyes, turpentine, some woods, poison ivy and oak, white sumac, some pharmaceuticals
Genotoxic and fetotoxic agents	Genotoxic: affects the genetic material of reproductive cells Fetotoxic: affects a fetus	Genotoxins: may be few immediate signs Fetotoxins: deformity or loss of a fetus	Benzene, toluene, xylene, ethyl alcohol, carbon disulfide, carbon monoxide, lead and its compounds, mercury and its compounds, arsenic and its compounds, cadmium and its compounds, radiation and radioactive substances, chlorinated phenoxyacetic acids, paraquat, diquat, PCBs, TCDD, ethylene oxide, dinitrobenzene, and some pharmaceuticals

*Central Nervous System Depressants

special instrumentation. Chronic overexposure to ionizing radiation can cause serious threats to health, including cancer. Acute exposures to high levels of ionizing radiation can be dangerous and possibly fatal. Radiation is mutagenic and may harm fetuses.

The customary workplaces where ionizing radiation is encountered are nuclear reactors, radioisotope preparation facilities, medical and dental facilities, uranium mines, uranium purification and fuel fabrication plants, uranium enrichment plants, nuclear weapons plants and

Table 2. Symptoms and Causes of Heat Illness

Heat Illness	Possible Signs and Symptoms	Possible Causes
Heat Stroke **(Emergency! The body temperature is high and rising dangerously fast!)**	Onset might be sudden, without warning – Confusion, disorientation – Hot, dry, skin (usually) – Sweating might have stopped – Chills, shivering – Restlessness – Skin color changes (face red) – Erratic behavior, irritability, euphoria – Collapse – Convulsions – Unconsciousness – Body temperature ≥ 104° F (40° C) and rising	– Excessive heat exposure – Inadequate acclimation – Subnormal physical tolerance (genetic or acquired) – Alcohol/drug abuse
Heat Exhaustion	– Weakness, fatigue – Dizziness, headache – Blurred vision – Profuse sweating – Irregular gait – Paleness – Collapse – High pulse rate – Low blood pressure – Body temperature normal to slightly elevated	– Inadequate water intake – Dehydration from fever, diarrhea, or vomiting – Inadequate acclimation – Distribution of blood to the periphery – Poor physical fitness – Alcohol/drug abuse
Dehydration	Might be no early signs – Fatigue, weakness – Dry mouth – Lowered work capacity – Slow response time	– Excessive fluid loss – Inadequate water intake – Dehydration from fever, diarrhea, or vomiting – Alcohol consumption
Heat Syncope (fainting or feeling faint)	– Brief fainting or faint feeling – Blurred vision – Body temperature normal	– Pooling of blood in the legs and skin from prolonged static posture and heat exposure – Inadequate water intake
Heat Cramps	– Painful muscle cramps, especially in the abdominal or fatigued muscles of the limbs – Incapacitating muscle pain	– Electrolyte (salt) imbalance caused by prolonged sweating without adequate water and salt intake.
Heat Rash ("prickly heat")	– Itching skin – Reduced sweating – Skin eruptions	– Prolonged, uninterrupted sweating – Inadequate personal hygiene

(Bernard 2001) Used with the permission of the National Safety Council.

Note: Salting of foods is encouraged as both treatment and prevention of some heat-related disorders. Workers on salt-restricted diets should consult their physicians.

handling sites, nuclear test sites, radiation waste storage and disposal sites, and scientific laboratories. However, many ordinary manufacturing plants use radiation sources for radiography, thickness gauges, depth gauges, and a host of other industrial uses. Some types of conventional military artillery shells are made from *depleted* uranium, which is radioactive. The presence of ionizing radiation at any work site indicates the need for the specialized services of a professional health physicist.

Nonionizing Radiation. More commonly, nonionizing radiation occurs in industrial workplaces. Nonionizing radiation includes ultraviolet rays, laser beams, infrared rays, microwaves, and low frequency waves. Typically nonionizing radiation is less energetic than ionizing radiation. Nevertheless, overexposure can be hazardous. The energy of all types of electromagnetic radiation is proportional to its frequency.

Among the nonionizing radiations, the one of greatest health concern is ultraviolet (UV) radiation. UV rays are invisible and must be detected by specialized instrumentation. High energy UV is only slightly less energetic than low energy gamma rays. Even lower energy UV, such as that from the sun, can cause burns to the skin and conjunctiva of the eyes. Overexposure to UV radiation can cause malignant melanoma, a cancerous skin tumor. Sunlight, a source of wide-spectrum UV, can be an occupational hazard to outdoor workers. Electric arc welding, a source of intense UV, occurs in many work environments. All welders are familiar with *flash burn* and the measures that are necessary to protect their eyes and skin. Particular care must be taken to protect both welders and others who are in the vicinity of electric arc welding.

Laser beams of sufficient energy can damage the skin and retina of the eyes. The degree of risk

Table 3. Symptoms and Causes of Cold-Related Conditions

	Symptoms and Signs	Possible Causes
Hypothermia (low body temperature)	– Chills, shivering – Pain in the extremities Fatigue, drowsiness – Euphoria – Slurred speech – Collapse – Unconsciousness – Slow, weak pulse – Body temperature $\leq 95°$ F ($35°$ C)	– Excessive exposure to cold – Exhaustion – Dehydration – Subnormal tolerance (genetic or acquired) – Alcohol or drug abuse
Frostbite (frozen body tissue)	– Burning sensation at first – Coldness, numbness, tingling – Skin discoloration – Skin blisters – Response to touch depends on the depth of freezing	– Exposure to freezing cold – Vascular disease
Frostnip	– Possible itching or pain – Skin color lightens	– Exposure to cold (can be above freezing)
Trench Foot	– Severe foot pain – Feet tingling, itching – Swelling in feet – Skin blisters – Response to touch depends on the depth of affected tissue	– Exposure to cold (can be above freezing) – Exposure to dampness (wet feet)
Chilblain	– Recurrent, localized itching – Painful inflammation – Swelling – Severe spasms	– Inadequate clothing – Exposure to cold and dampness – Vascular disease
Raynaud's Disorder	– Tingling in extremities (*e.g.*,fingers) – Fingers intermittently redden and blanch	– Exposure to cold and vibration – Vascular disease

(Bernard 2001) Used with the permission of the National Safety Council.

Note: Hypothermia is related to systemic cold stress. The other disorders are related to tissue cooling.

depends on the type of laser as well as its wavelength, frequency, output power, pulse frequency and the divergence of the beam with distance from the source. Safeguards should be implemented in areas where laser beams are operated.

Infrared (IR) exposures become important in preventing excessive heat exposures, which can lead to heat disorders. Additionally, chronic exposure of the eyes to intense IR in some occupations, such as smelting, furnace operations, glassblowing, cooking, and laundry work can cause eye disorders (Hitchcock, *et. al.* 2003). Properly selected dark lenses can provide good eye protection.

Microwaves are generated by various industrial heating systems, cooking ovens, communication systems, radar, and navigational systems. The recognized health hazard from microwaves is simple heating of tissue. Knowledge of the hazards and avoidance are major factors in protection.

There is also concern about possible health effects of exposure to the low frequency fields generated by electric power lines, video display terminals (VDTs), cell phones, and similar devices. All electric lines and appliances have attendant electric and magnetic fields, which means that people in the United States are continuously bathed in low frequency (60 Hertz) electromagnetic fields. Whether or not there are serious hazards from the fields near power lines and cell phones is still under study. VDTs do generate some X-radiation, but modern units are shielded to protect viewers.

Pressure Extremes. Workers in certain occupations can encounter abnormally high or low barometric pressures. High pressures are routine in deep water diving and submarine operations. Workers in these occupations are trained to take the routine precautions necessary to avoid health consequences. Construction of underwater tunnels is done in sealed chambers in which the air pressure is increased to prevent the entry of water. Medical workers in hyperbaric chambers are subject to elevated barometric air and oxygen pressures. The health effects range from *barotraumas* to the ears, eyes, sinuses, and teeth to nitrogen narcosis and potentially serious decompression illness. Decompression illness occurs when a person who has worked under high pressure for a period of time is returned to atmospheric pressure (decompressed) too rapidly. The resulting condition often referred to as the **bends**, can affect several organs including the lungs, blood, muscles, and nervous system. Controlled, slow decompression procedures are followed to prevent decompression illness. Replacing compressed breathing air with a mixture of helium and oxygen prevents nitrogen narcosis.

Conversely, persons working at lowered barometric pressure can experience oxygen deficiency and traumatic effects similar to those experienced in decompression. Early aviators were thus restricted. Compressed breathing air and pressurized aircraft cabins have minimized health problems for aircraft crews as well as passengers.

Healthy persons working or living at high altitudes will, to some extent, undergo naturally protective physiological changes.

Biological Hazards

Biological hazards (*biohazards*) refer to hazards from living organisms and their toxins. Contact with biological hazards can occur in work settings such as construction, maintenance outdoors or in crawl spaces and attics, hazardous waste abatement and disposal, medical operations, embalming, biological research, naturalist and conservation work, and agriculture. Reference (Ryan 2003) discusses occupational biohazards in greater detail. Most biological hazards can be grouped into four classes as presented in Table 4.

Ergonomic Hazards

Ergonomics, a word based on a combination of the Greek words for *work* and *management*, has been defined as the discipline that examines the capabilities and limitations of people (Kohn *et. al.* 1996). It deals with the interactions of people with the work that they do. Some of the disorders that can arise from ergonomic stresses are back injuries, muscle sprains and strains, and cumulative trauma disorders (*e.g.*, carpal tunnel syndrome and tendonitis, and Raynaud's disease). Ergonomic

Table 4. Biological Hazards and Possible Effects of Exposure

Group	Examples	Possible Effects of Exposure
Microorganisms and their toxins	– Bacteria – Viruses – Molds and their products – Yeasts and their products	– Infection – Poisoning by toxins – Allergic reactions – Transmission of infection to others
Arthropods	– Spiders – Ticks – Mites – Fleas – Mosquitoes – Flies – Lice – Scorpions – Bees, hornets, and wasps	– Bites and stings with resulting toxic reactions – Transmission of infectious agents – Allergic reactions
Higher Plants	– Poison ivy, poison oak, and white sumac – Some hardwoods – Other plants if worker is previously sensitized	– Dermatoses (skin rashes) – Asthma, runny nose if particles or smoke are inhaled
Animals, their protein allergens and venoms	– Body secretions (urine, feces, blood, saliva, *etc.*) and their dry deposits – Hair – Dander – Bites and scratches	– Allergic reactions – Infection – Toxic reactions

Table 5. Phases of The System Safety Cycle

Phase	Health and Safety Control Point	Desired Result
Concept	Concept design review	Establish design for general development
Definition	Preliminary design review	Establish general design for specific development
Development	Critical design review	Approve specific design for production
Production	Final acceptance review and testing	Approve the plant for deployment (operation)
Deployment	Monitor and audit operations & maintenance	Control health and safety during operations & maintenance
Disposition	Review hazard consequences of disposition	Control hazards during and after disposition

(Adapted from Kohn, *et al.* 1996). Used with the permission of Government Institutes.

hazards are arguably the leading cause of occupational illness (Kohn *et. al.* 1996). Good introductions to ergonomics are presented in Kohn, *et. al.* 1996 and Kroemer 1996.

Recognition of Workplace Hazards

Typically, the industrial hygienist is responsible for managing health hazards in an existing, fully operational industrial plant. The term *recognition of health hazards* is used in reference to existing hazards in an operating facility. Specialized instrumentation is widely used to detect the presence of potentially hazardous agents. In many cases the senses, especially sight, smell, and hearing, are the first indicators of possible hazard. A visible dust cloud near an ore crusher, the smell of rotten eggs near a chemical reactor, or a noisy steam valve are obvious early warnings. However, these indicate only potential hazards. The industrial hygienist must objectively determine if overexposures are occurring. For example, a high sound level in one area of a plant doesn't necessarily mean workers are excessively exposed to noise. It is easy to recognize that the high sound level is potentially hazardous, but is it a real hazard that should be controlled? Are there workers in the noisy area? More information is obviously needed. Once recognized, a potential hazard must

be evaluated to determine whether or not it is a genuine hazard and, if so, how serious the hazard is. This analysis will include finding answers to several questions. How many people are overexposed, how frequently, and for what duration? What are the health consequences of overexposure? Where and when (*e.g.*, which shift) are they overexposed? Are certain craft groups at risk? What operations are related to overexposure? Do medical data confirm overexposure? What are the economic consequences of overexposure to the employer and the employee? What control options are available? These facts, and others, help to determine if implementation of controls is merited. A systematic approach is needed. It so happens that anticipation and recognition of possible hazards are neatly tied together in a logical and proven process known as *system safety*.

The System Safety Approach

The control of industrial health hazards lends itself to the system safety discipline. This is a successful method of managing safety hazards that has evolved over a period of about sixty years. Without going into the details of system safety, we can get some idea how it can be useful in control of health hazards during the entire life cycle of a manufacturing plant. The system safety approach functions through a six-phase cycle as shown in Table 5 (adapted from Kohn, *et al.* 1996).

The Concept Phase. In the concept phase, a decision has been made to build a general type of facility. Detailed design has not yet started. Only the concept, some preliminary views of design, exists. Hazard identification efforts should start at this time. Interfacing as a team with project and design engineers, safety staff, environmental engineers, and occupational physicians, the industrial hygienist can begin to get a picture of what might transpire: the materials to be used, the types of industrial equipment that are to be linked in the process, the desired production rate, the expected types of energy sources, the approximate number of workers required, the support services that will be necessary, and the by-products and wastes that will be produced. As these questions are explored some idea of possibly hazardous exposures begins to develop. A Preliminary Hazard Analysis report is prepared, ideally in concert with safety staff, and transmitted to project managers.

The Definition Phase. As shown in Table 5, a preliminary design review will be initiated in this phase. At this point the industrial hygienist and safety specialists will identify control systems for inclusion in final design. For example, industrial hygiene might recommend local exhaust ventilation systems to control airborne chemical emissions. Shielding could be recommended for radiation sources. Industrial hygiene should also provide design goals to design engineers for controlling anticipated health hazards. One kind of design goal could be the limits on concentrations of air contaminants in the work environments of the plant when it becomes operational. The goal might be set at some prudent fraction of the *Threshold Limit Value* (TLV). Recommendations can also include equipment specifications, such as the maximum acceptable sound levels generated by noisy equipment at specified distances. At this time planning will begin on a performance-testing program to verify that the design goals and specifications are achieved when the plant becomes operational.

The Development Phase. Critical review of actual design will occur in this phase. Process descriptions, flow diagrams, and engineering drawings of the entire process will be reviewed. The industrial hygienist must work closely with design engineers and safety staff to ensure that the hazard control goals recommended in the definition phase are incorporated into the final design. The skill of anticipation of possible workplace hazards comes to full maturity in the development phase. Ideally, the industrial hygiene manager would be expected to approve the final design. The plans for performance testing should be well evolved by this time.

The Production Phase. This is the phase in which the plant has been constructed and start-up begins. When initial operation becomes stable, performance tests will determine if the facility performs according to design. Industrial hygiene testing will focus on those hazard control goals and specifications included in design. The safety staff will conduct similar reviews and will prepare a System Safety Engineering Report to document the hazards identified in the operational facility. Industrial hygiene findings and recommendations should be included in this report.

The Deployment Phase. After the plant reaches stable operation, some conditions will require periodic monitoring or surveillance. Additionally, unforeseen problems will invariably occur: systems fail, equipment wears out, process and production changes are made, accidents occur, or workforce levels change. Hazards can creep in almost undetected. An on-going effort to recognize, evaluate, and control hazards is necessary. Inspection, monitoring, and sampling for hazardous conditions become routine. The skill of recognition of potential workplace hazards reaches full maturity in the deployment phase. Program safety and health audits are conducted. The industrial hygienist must spend a lot of time *in the plant*. In addition to the system safety program, the industrial hygienist should take the following actions in order to foster successful hazard control.

- Develop good working relationships with plant managers, production and support engineers, and supervisory personnel

- Develop good relations with the people of the work force, their crafts, and with the jobs they perform

- Pay attention to worker suggestions, including the job safety analyses and feedback from worker training sessions

- Gain a thorough knowledge of the process, all unit operations, and all support activities

- Become familiar with the total materials inventory, including feedstocks, additives, intermediates, by-products, support materials, and wastes

- Conduct frequent *walk-through* inspections of all work operations, noting abnormalities and needs

- Conduct routine surveys of known health hazards plus special evaluations as needed

- Study and analyze current and previous sampling and monitoring results for exposure patterns and evidences of unrecognized hazards

- Study the summarized results of medical monitoring and of employee visits to the medical station

- Conduct data analyses to detect possible relationships between exposure monitoring and medical surveillance

- Coordinate activities and findings with the safety department

- Review injury and illness reports

- Investigate reported cases of possible occupational illness

- Develop a written health hazard inventory for the plant

- Stay familiar with applicable governmental regulations

- Stay current with ethical good practice in industrial hygiene (above and beyond the mandatory requirements)

- Carefully consider the results of safety audits and inspections

The Disposition Phase. This phase is sometimes referred to as the termination phase. Perhaps an old plant is to be shut down and put up for sale. Or it might have outlived its productive life and is to be removed from service and demolished. A careful review should be made of potential hazards associated with this decommissioning process, which often involves greater hazards than production. Hazardous chemical residues might remain in process systems. Plant equipment and buildings might contain substances that could pose a hazard if removal or demolition is planned (thermal asbestos insulation, for instance). Radiation sources or radioactive contamination might require special attention, even after removal from the site. Chemically contaminated soil and

chemical storage tanks could require abatement. The industrial hygienist has responsibility for employee safety to the very end of the decommissioning process.

Evaluation of Health Hazards

Once a potentially hazardous agent has been identified, a scientific determination must be made of the extent of the hazard. This determination will permit intelligent decisions concerning the need for control or for compliance actions. This usually calls for the collection of monitoring data by sampling employee exposures or taking environmental measurements for the agent in affected areas of the facility. A good working knowledge of current instrumentation and sampling equipment, their capabilities and limitations, is critical to success. Monitoring is expensive and time-consuming, so careful planning is important to maximize effectiveness and minimize costs.

For further detailed guidance on evaluating potentially hazardous chemical agents see references (Perkins 1997) and (Ness 1991).

Occupational Exposure Limits

The word *evaluation* implies that something is to be measured against some standard of attainment. In occupational hygiene the reference standards are usually some body of scientifically established and professionally accepted occupational exposure limits (OELs). In the United States the major sources of OELs are the American Conference of Governmental Industrial Hygienists (ACGIH), OSHA, the National Institute for Occupational Safety and Health (NIOSH), and the American Industrial Hygiene Association (AIHA).

Hundreds of thousands of chemicals are used in United States workplaces, with more being introduced every year. There is no single listing of OELs for all, or even most, industrial chemicals, because of the lack of toxicological data. A similar lack of evidence exists for physical agents. However, relevant toxicological data are available on over 650 of the chemical and physical agents commonly found in industrial environments. This has enabled professional organizations and government agencies to establish some well-documented exposure limits. It is essential to keep in mind that application of any exposure limit is constrained by unanticipated factors, such as the possibility that workers may be exposed to more than one agent or that exposures can occur under different environmental conditions than those under which the data for the exposure limit was acquired. Moreover, most OELs are based on specified exposure durations, typically 8 hours per day and 40 hours per week. It is obvious that some adjustment is needed for extended work hours. For these and other reasons, it is recommended that interpretation and application of any exposure limit be done under the direction of a person trained in that subject. This discussion will cover the major types of limits used in the United States.

Current chemical exposure limits are summarized in two valuable published sources, one from the NIOSH and the other from ACGIH. The NIOSH summary is entitled *Pocket Guide to Chemical Hazards* (NIOSH 2003). The NIOSH Guide lists the occupational exposure limits of NIOSH and OSHA and the concentrations of a number of chemicals that are immediately dangerous to life or health (IDLH). Routes of entry, symptoms of overexposure, target organs, and first aid are listed for each agent. It designates those chemicals that are carcinogenic and those that are prone to absorb through the intact skin. It also includes synonyms, structural formulas, and physical and chemical properties for each substance. Other useful information includes methods of measurement and recommendations for personal protective equipment. Where applicable, Department of Transportation (DOT) identification number and guide number are also shown.

The ACGIH publication is the *Guide to Occupational Exposure Values* (ACGIH 2004a). It includes the latest ACGIH Threshold Limit Values (TLVs), OSHA Permissible Exposure Limits (PELs), NIOSH Recommended Exposure Limits (RELs), and the Federal Republic of Germany's Maximum Acceptable Concentration Values in the Workplace (MAKs). Carcinogenicity categories are listed and include information from the United States Environmental Protection Agency (EPA), the International Agency for Research on Cancer (IARC) and the National Toxicology Program (NTP).

ACGIH Threshold Limit Values. ACGIH was the pioneer in the development of OELs in America. The ACGIH TLVs are probably the most widely recognized and respected industrial exposure limits in the world. Currently over 700 chemicals and physical agents are listed in the TLVs. ACGIH is a not-for-profit professional organization made up of occupational health specialists and industrial hygienists. It is not a government agency. ACGIH publishes annual updates of their lists for both chemical substances and physical agents (ACGIH 2004b). Included in the TLV booklet are Biological Exposure Indices (BEIs), which are recommended guidelines for concentrations of chemical substances or their indicators in the biological media of the body, *e.g.*, urine, blood, exhaled air, and tissue.

An ACGIH policy statement on the use of TLVs and BEIs states that they

> are developed as guidelines to assist in the control of health hazards. These recommendations or guidelines are intended for use in the practice of industrial hygiene, to be interpreted and applied only by a person trained in this discipline. They are not developed as legal standards and ACGIH does not advocate their use as such (ACGIH 2004b).

The TLVs apply only to industrial workers exposed in occupational settings, and they should not be used or applied to the general public or to the general environment. Before using the TLV or BEI tables, it is important to read and understand the introductory sections to each table. For example, it is pointed out that the chemical TLVs and BEIs do not represent fine lines between safe and dangerous conditions, because of individual human differences and the other limiting factors discussed earlier.

ACGIH TLVs for Chemical Substances. Air concentration limits for gases and vapors are given in units of parts per million (ppm). This refers to the number of unit volumes of the contaminant per million unit volumes of contaminated air. For aerosols, concentration limits are given in milligrams of the aerosol per cubic meter of air (mg/m^3).

The chemical TLVs are based on three sources of information: exposure and health data from industrial experience, experimental human and animal studies, and, when possible, combinations of these. The TLVs are developed using the best available data and are recommended, with any revisions, to ACGIH annually by a professional committee made up of industrial toxicologists, occupational physicians, scientists, and industrial hygienists.

There are three categories of TLVs: the ***Threshold Limit Value—Time-Weighted Average*** (TLV-TWA), the ***Threshold Limit Value—Short Term Exposure Limit*** (TLV-STEL), and the ***Threshold Limit Value—Ceiling*** (TLV-C).

ACGIH defines the TLV-TWA as

> the time-weighted average concentration for a conventional 8-hour workday and a 40-hour workweek, to which it is believed nearly all workers may be repeatedly exposed, day after day, without adverse effect (ACGIH 2004b).

Since the TWA is an 8-hour average value, excursions above the average are allowed within limits. A formula for estimating the recommended excursion limits for the great majority of substances is given in the introduction to the chemical TLV table.

The TLV-STEL is

> the concentration to which it is believed that workers can be exposed continuously for a short period of time without suffering from 1) irritation, 2) chronic or irreversible tissue damage or 3) narcosis of sufficient degree to increase the possibility of accidental injury, impair self-rescue, or materially reduce work efficiency, and provided that the TLV-TWA is not exceeded. It is not a separate independent exposure limit: rather, it supplements the time-weighted average (TWA) where there are recognized acute effects from a substance whose toxic effects are primarily of a chronic nature. STELs are recommended only where toxic effects have been reported from high short-term exposures in either humans or animals (ACGIH 2004b).

The TLV-C is

> the concentration that should not be exceeded during any part of the working exposure (ACGIH 2004b).

Since it is not always possible to monitor instantaneous exposures, ACGIH provides some general air sampling guidelines for use in applying the TLV-C.

Another feature of the TLV listing is the *skin* notation for chemicals that might absorb through the skin or mucous membranes. The *skin* notation calls attention to the fact that measures should be implemented to protect the skin as well as the lungs of persons potentially exposed. The TLVs are designed to protect against inhalation exposures, not skin absorption exposures.

For substances known to cause allergic reactions, a sensitizer (*SEN*) notation is shown with the caveat that the lack of the *SEN* notation does not necessarily mean that the substance is not a sensitizer.

A valuable feature of the TLV list is that it designates those chemicals that are known or suspect carcinogens. Four categories of carcinogenicity are provided: confirmed human carcinogen, suspected human carcinogen, confirmed animal carcinogen, and not suspected as a human carcinogen. Appendix A in to the table explains each of these categories in detail.

Three other appendices are included: Appendix B) Substances of Variable Composition, *i.e.*, welding fumes and polytetrafluoroethylene decomposition products; Appendix C) Threshold Limit Values for Mixtures; and Appendix D) Particle Size-Selective Sampling Criteria for Airborne Particulate Matter.

For each substance listed in the chemical TLVs the following information is provided:

1) Chemical Name and Chemical Abstracts Services (CAS) number

2) TLV-TWA, TLV-STEL, or TLV-C values

3) Notations, *e.g.*, carcinogenicity category, skin designation, SEN designation, and if there is a corresponding BEI

4) The molecular weight (used in converting concentration units)

5) The basis for the listed TLV, that is, the critical effects of overexposure

ACGIH Biological Exposure Indices (BEIs). As mentioned earlier, the ACGIH ***Biological Exposure Indices*** (BEIs) are included in the TLV list. The BEIs are useful to medical specialists in monitoring personal exposures by direct measurement of chemical determinants in body fluids and tissues. This procedure is known as biological monitoring and is typically a part of a medical surveillance program if indicated by information on worker exposure. According to ACGIH, "The BEI generally indicates a concentration below which nearly all workers should not experience health effects" (ACGIH 2004b). For example the BEI for exposure to lead (Pb) and its compounds is 30 micrograms of Pb per 100 milliliters of blood (30 µg/100ml). Blood lead concentrations below this value would be considered safe for most healthy adult workers.

Biological monitoring is a valuable supplement to air monitoring in assessing health effects, especially for substances that might have entered the body by tissue absorption or ingestion. Off-the-job exposures might also be detected by biological monitoring. Since biological monitoring results are obtained after exposure has occurred, they should not be used as primary indices of exposure. BEIs should be used, interpreted, or applied in accordance with the information in the introduction to the table and only by a knowledgeable occupational health professional.

ACGIH TLVs for Physical Agents. ACGIH also recommends TLVs for physical agents (ACGIH 2004b). A committee of professional experts develops these by consensus after careful study of available scientific data. As in the chemical TLVs, the Physical Agents Committee recommends limits and revisions to ACGIH annually for approval by the membership. The TLVs for physical agents include limits for noise, ergonomics, ionizing radiation, nonionizing radiation and associated fields, lasers, and thermal stress (both heat and cold). The formats for presentation of the TLVs for the different physical agents vary due to the differences in the agents and conditions of exposure.

ACGIH Documentation of the TLVs and BEIs. ACGIH publishes a separate document that summarizes the scientific evidence and rationale behind each TLV and BEI value. Included are the potential health risks that each TLV and BEI is designed to minimize. The publication is entitled Documentation of the Threshold Limit Values and Biological Exposure Indices and is published in both printed and electronic format (ACGIH 2001).

OSHA Standards and Permissible Exposure Limits (PELs). OSHA addresses hazardous agents in several sections of its general industry standards. OSHA standards are available through the OSHA web page (<http://www.osha.gov>). Subpart H of these standards, Hazardous Materials, deals with substances that can cause fire and explosion, process safety management of highly hazardous materials, hazardous waste operations and emergency response, and several hazardous industrial operations. Subpart I covers Personal Protective Equipment. The subjects in Subparts H and I are addressed elsewhere in this book. Subpart Z, Toxic and Hazardous Substances, is of particular interest in industrial hygiene.

Within Subpart Z are nineteen substance-specific standards detailing the regulatory requirements for specific hazardous substances, including asbestos, vinyl chloride, inorganic arsenic, lead, cadmium, benzene, bloodborne pathogens, ethylene oxide, formaldehyde, 1,3-butadiene, and ionizing radiation. One standard covers thirteen carcinogenic organic compounds. Also included in Subpart Z are standards on Hazard Communication; Access to Employee Exposure and Medical Records; Occupational Exposure to Hazardous Chemicals in Laboratories; and Retention of DOT Markings, Placards, and Labels. All of these are significant to the practice of industrial hygiene. Space will not allow discussion of each of these in this chapter. Some of these subjects are addressed in other chapters of this book. The one paragraph we will discuss here is the one dealing with air contaminants, the source of the OSHA Permissible Exposure Limits (PELs) (29 CFR 1910.1000).

OSHA PELs for Chemical Agents. When the OSHA Act became effective in 1971 there were no Federally approved occupational exposure limits against which to measure compliance. OSHA filled this information gap by adopting the 1968 ACGIH TLV list. The OSHA list became known as **Permissible Exposure Limits** (PELs), and, unlike the TLVs, the PELs are mandatory.

The PELs reflect the toxicological knowledge of 1968. This has provoked cries for revisions to modernize the PELs in the light of more recent toxicological evidence. An extensive revision was done in the early 1990s, but the revised values were legally challenged and subsequently revoked by the courts. However, some states, operating under state OSHA plans, did not adopt the revocation.

In such cases, the state PELs are based on more current science and are more protective and extensive than the old OSHA values.

OSHA PELs are presented in three tables:

1) Table Z–1, "Limits for Air Contaminants," is the primary table of PELs, listing some 500 substances. TWA, STEL, and C values are given. Additional information includes the chemical name, the Chemical Abstracts Service (CAS) number, and a skin designation. In some cases, users are referred to the OSHA carcinogen standard for thirteen organic compounds. Ten clarifying footnotes are provided. A typical listing is the one for aniline and its homologues which lists the CAS number as 62–53–3, the 8-hour TWA as 5 ppm or 19 mg/m³, and a skin designation. Where a full OSHA standard has been promulgated, the user is referred to that standard. For example, the listing for benzene refers the user to 29 CFR 1910.1028, the OSHA benzene standard.

2) Table Z–2, not titled, lists 20 selected substances. In addition to the 8-hour TWA, it includes an Acceptable Ceiling Concentration, and an Acceptable Maximum Peak Above the Acceptable Ceiling Concentration for an 8-hour shift. This latter value lists both a concentration limit and a time of exposure limit. In 29 CFR 1900.1000(b)(2), OSHA defines the *Acceptable Ceiling Concentration* as follows:

> An employee's exposure to a substance listed in Table Z–2 shall not exceed at any time during an 8-hour shift the acceptable ceiling concentration limit given for the substance in the table, except for a time period, and up to a concentration not exceeding the maximum duration and concentration allowed in the column under "acceptable maximum peak above the acceptable ceiling concentration for an 8-hour shift."

3) Table Z–3, "Mineral Dusts," lists six mineral dusts: crystalline silica, amorphous silica, silicates, graphite, coal dust, and so-called *inert* or *nuisance* dust. The concentration limits are in units of mg/m³ or mppcf (million airborne particles per cubic foot of air). The ppm unit of concentration is not applicable to aerosols.

The OSHA Exposure Action Level (AL). It is not ethically adequate to wait until worker exposures equal or exceed the occupational exposure limit before taking some preventive action. OSHA addressed this by defining a typical *action level* (AL) as one-half of the PEL. When exposures equal or exceed the AL, OSHA requires implementation of additional protective actions ranging from increased exposure monitoring to inclusion in a medical monitoring program. The AL is used specifically in some of the later OSHA standards such as those for lead, cadmium, benzene, ethylene oxide, acrylonitrile, and formaldehyde. Many employers have adopted the AL as a trigger point for initiation of controls for agents not specifically regulated by OSHA.

OSHA PELs for Physical Agents. There are no OSHA tables of exposure limits for physical agents. These are addressed in individual agent-specific standards. Currently there are three such standards:

29 CFR 1910.95–Occupational Noise Exposure

29 CFR 1910.97–Nonionizing Radiation

29 CFR 1910.1096–Ionizing Radiation

There is no OSHA standard for temperature extremes. Occasionally the OSHA website (<http://www.osha.gov>) offers some tips for heat protection.

The OSHA Ergonomics Document. There is no OSHA standard on ergonomics at this time. Some helpful recommendations are made in the OSHA document, "Safety and Health Topics: Ergonomics,"(<http//www.osha.gov/SLTC/ergonomics>). This document addresses musculoskeletal disorders (MSDs) in the workplace. Therein OSHA offers to ". . . develop industry—or task specific—guidelines for a number of industries based on current incidence rates and available information about effective and feasible solutions." Outreach and enforcement assistance, along with some helpful resources, are also offered.

NIOSH RELs and IDLH Values. NIOSH is an agency of the Federal government that conducts research, trains professionals, informs the public, certifies respiratory protection equipment, and provides some types of on-site health evaluations upon request. The full range of resources and services available from NIOSH can be accessed through its website homepage (<http://www.cdc.gov/niosh/homepage.html>). NIOSH also recommends to OSHA information on hazards based purely on the risks without regard for the feasibility or economic impacts of implementation. Among these recommendations are the **Recommended Exposure Limits (RELs)**.

RELs are occupational exposure limits recommended by NIOSH as being protective of worker health and safety over a working lifetime. The REL is used in combination with engineering and work practice controls, exposure and medical monitoring, labeling, posting, worker training, and personal protective equipment. This limit is frequently expressed as a time-weighted average (TWA) exposure for up to 10 hr/day during a 40-hr workweek. The REL may also be expressed as 1) a short-term exposure limit (STEL) that should never be exceeded and is to be determined in a specified sampling time (usually 15 min), or 2) a ceiling limit that should never be exceeded even instantaneously unless specified over a given time period (<http://www.cdc.gov/niosh/92-100.html>).

RELs are given for both chemical and physical agents.

NIOSH Chemical RELs. Over 650 chemicals are listed in the REL table. TWA, STEL, and Ceiling values are given, along with the NIOSH carcinogen and skin absorption designations. A valuable feature of the REL table is the listing of health effects for each substance. Where appropriate, reference is made to specific OSHA standards. The chemical name, the Chemical Abstracts Service (CAS) number, and the NIOSH Registry of Toxic Effects of Chemical Substances (RTECS) number positively identify each agent.

NIOSH RELs for Physical Agents. RELs are listed for electrical energy and electrocutions, hand-arm vibration, hot environments, radon progeny in underground mines, noise, radiofrequency (RF) sealers and heaters, and ultraviolet radiation. Health effects for overexposure to each hazard are listed (<http://www.cdc.gov/niosh/92-100.html>).

NIOSH Immediately Dangerous to Life or Health (IDLH) Values. The OSHA definition of an IDLH concentration is

[a]n atmospheric concentration of any toxic, corrosive, or asphyxiant substance that poses an immediate threat to life or would interfere with an individual's ability to escape from a dangerous atmosphere (29 CFR 1910.120).

NIOSH is currently revising older IDLH values. In the meantime, NIOSH offers a list of original and revised IDLH limits for over 380 substances (<http://www.tricornet.com/nioshdbs/idlh/intridl4.htm>).

AIHA ERPGs and WEELs. The American Industrial Hygiene Association (AIHA), a professional society for industrial hygienists and other occupational health specialists, publishes a set of documents featuring Emergency Response Planning Guidelines (ERPGs) and **Workplace Emergency Exposure Limits** (WEELs) (AIHA 2004). Currently ERPG and WEEL guides are available for 106 chemicals. AIHA describes the ERPG series on its website: "This series provides values intended as estimates of concentration ranges where one might reasonably anticipate observing adverse effects as a consequence of exposure to a specific substance" (<http://www.aiha.org/PublicationsAdvertising/html/Poerpgweels.htm>).

According to AIHA,

Each WEEL guideline represents the workplace exposure levels to which it is believed nearly all individuals could be exposed repeatedly without experiencing adverse effects. Information used to establish each guideline is documented in an easy-to-read brochure that identifies the agent by chemical name, synonyms, Chemical Abstracts Service number, molecular formula, and structural formula. Also, information is provided on the agent's chemical and physical properties, uses and volume, toxicology data, and human use and experience (<http://www.aiha.org/PublicationsAdvertising/html/Poerpgweels.htm>).

Selecting the Right OEL. At some point a decision must be made concerning which of the various OEL values to use for specific applications. In the United States, for purely compliance purposes, the OSHA PELs carry the weight of law. This doesn't preclude the use of the more modern NIOSH or ACGIH values, provided the selected values are as protective, or more so, than the PELs. In cases where no OSHA PEL has been promulgated, the NIOSH and ACGIH lists should be consulted. In emergency situations, the AIHA list could be helpful. In all cases good professional judgment should be exercised.

Planning Field Surveys

A logical plan should be developed before sampling begins. This will include determinations of the sampling method to be used as well as any required analytical laboratory analyses. "The sampling strategy needs to answer the following questions:

- Where to sample?

- When to sample?

- How long to sample?

- Whom to sample?

- How many samples to collect?

- How should the samples be obtained?" (Milz, *et. al* 2003)

A good working relationship is necessary between the industrial hygienist and laboratory analysts. The sampler and the analyst should have a mutual understanding of:

- The types of samples that will be submitted

- The sampling method to be used (sometimes this is specified in regulations)

- The specific analyses desired

- Presence of any possible interfering agents

- The accuracy and precision of the analyses

- Any specifications on the analytical method to be used. Regulations often require specific methods of analysis; the lab might need copies of such regulations

- The time and resources the lab might need to establish new analytical methods

- Need for supplemental samples, for example bulk samples or surface samples

- Sampling data sheets, requisite information for the lab and the sampler

- Chain-of-custody requirements for submitted samples. Chain-of-custody should start when the samples are taken and continue into data management

- How individual samples will be identified (labeled) and tracked

- Special sample requirements, such as need for culture media, sterilized containers, or preservatives to prevent degradation of the samples

- Any time constraints, such as the need for prompt culturing of biological agents

The purpose of the survey should be established before monitoring begins. What questions will the survey data answer? The purpose of the survey will dictate the overall design of the survey plan. Survey results may be used for several purposes, for example to:

- Support litigation

- Determine regulatory compliance

- Make *side-by-side* measurements during government inspections

- Investigate compensation claims

- Collect information for design of control methods

- Evaluate the effectiveness of existing controls

- Investigate evidence of industrial illness or other medical findings

- Further characterize the hazardous agents themselves

- Investigate employee complaints or reports

- Meet the requirements of insurance contracts

- Test the performance of new systems

- Conduct special research studies

Some of these will require extensive sampling, perhaps of multiple agents. Others will only require limited measurement of only one agent. The development of rational survey plans consistent with the purpose of the survey will optimize data quality, save time and resources, and minimize errors.

A quality assurance program should be established. It should include both the collection of samples in the field and their analysis in the laboratory. The better analytical laboratories have now adopted reliable quality assurance programs. Selecting an accredited laboratory will promote observance of good quality assurance. The Industrial Hygiene Laboratory Accreditation Program of AIHA should be considered.

Quality assurance measures for field sampling and monitoring includes standardization of all sampling and calibration procedures, standardization of procedures for recording field data, development of criteria for rejecting samples and results, development of chain-of-custody procedures for samples and data, training of personnel, and development of data management and reporting procedures. Good quality assurance is essential in cases involving litigation or regulatory citation.

Standard Methods of Sampling and Analysis

OSHA regulations often specify methods for both field sampling and laboratory analysis. When doing compliance monitoring the OSHA methods should be followed. When such regulatory direction is not given, other resources can be consulted. Foremost among these is the *NIOSH Manual of Analytical Methods*, which includes both sampling and analytical methods for hundreds of chemical air contaminants (Schlect and O'Connor 1994, 1996, 1998, and 2003). The American Society for Testing Materials (ASTM) publishes procedures for air sampling and for measurements of some physical agents (*e.g.*, noise and vibration). Of particular value in industrial hygiene practice is an ASTM guide for air sampling (ASTM 2002), which, according to the ASTM website " . . . provides criteria to be used in defining air sampling strategies for workplace health and safety monitoring or evaluation, such as: duration, frequency, number, location, method, equipment, and timing" (<http://www.astm.org/>). The International Organization for Standardization (ISO) also offers methods for several hazardous agents. The United States Mine Safety and Health Administration (MSHA) provides procedures for sampling and analysis of agents in mines. Procedures for indoor air quality and general environmental agents are available from the Environmental Protection Agency (EPA).

Data Management

Sampling and monitoring data should be analyzed and conclusions drawn according to scientific standards. Reports, including any recommendations for control, should be made to operating management, medical staff, and employees in a timely manner. With modern computer-assisted capabilities, industrial hygiene data management has become more useful and efficient. Integration of personal exposure results with personal medical records can provide more complete information for occupational physicians. It also facilitates the preparation of coordinated reports by medical and industrial hygiene. Personal monitoring results should be protected with the same attention to privacy as personal medical information.

Informing Workers of Personal Exposure Results

As new technology has developed, personal exposure monitoring in the actual breathing zones of the workers has become increasingly commonplace. Continual sampling or monitoring in the breathing zones of workers, as they go about their normal work routines, more clearly defines the dose received than does the older procedures of *area* monitoring data combined with time-motion studies. A successful program of personal exposure monitoring is invaluable in hazard control. Since the workers are personally involved, they become a part of the monitoring team. Typically they are glad to cooperate. They deserve to be informed of what to expect when an industrial hygienist wants to *hang a pump* on their belt and clip a sample collector to their lapel. To achieve this, and to minimize tampering with the sampling equipment, a short briefing meeting should be held with employees prior to the surveys.

OSHA requires that employers inform employees of the results of personal exposure measurements that indicate overexposure. This requirement also applies to other employees who have had exposures *assigned* because of the work conditions they share with those who were monitored. Beyond this requirement, it is an ethical responsibility to inform all monitored and *assigned* workers of all their monitoring results, excessive and otherwise. With automated data managing capabilities, this is relatively simple.

Determination of Risk

Necessarily included in any determination of risk are scientifically determined data on the health status of the workforce. Both medical and exposure data should be analyzed together in arriving at an overall estimate of risk.

At some point, enough data should be available for an analysis of risk and perhaps some estimate of the total cost of the unabated hazard. Field monitoring and medical data can be used together to establish the extent and seriousness of overexposure. The safety profession defines risk as the product of the probability and the severity of injury or loss (Kohn, *et. al.* 1996). The process is more complicated in industrial hygiene. When is an occupational health event equivalent to a traumatic injury? Is a measured overexposure equivalent to an injury? This criterion is used for ionizing radiation exposures. Certainly a confirmed case of occupational disease linked to confirmed overexposure would be equivalent to an injury. But, even then a valid estimate of overall workforce risk requires further information: the total number of workers at risk, the number of those workers who are actually overexposed, the frequency and duration of their overexposures, and information on the number of workers showing medical evidences of overexposure. The severity analysis includes the individual and collective health effects of the overexposures found in the field and medical data. Should severity go further and also include the monetary cost of the uncontrolled exposures to the employer plus the cost to the employees and their families? Whatever estimate is made it must ultimately be weighed against the costs of control of the hazard.

Control of Health Hazards in the Workplace

When careful evaluation shows that a risk is unacceptable and must be controlled, the industrial hygienist must be able to shift into the engineering disciplines. Four general principles of control of health hazards have been offered (Talty 1988):

1) All hazards can be controlled in some manner and to some extent

2) There are usually alternate methods of control

3) Some methods are better than others

4) Some conditions may require more than one method of control

The industrial hygienist must apply these principles to the process of selecting alternative control methods. The best approach involves teamwork with managers, engineering specialists, medical staff, employees and their representatives, human resource managers, and perhaps specialized consultants. Ultimately equipment vendors may be added.

It helps to utilize some criteria as trigger points for implementation of controls. The action level, typically one-half of the OEL, is often used. In some jurisdictions control measures for airborne contaminants must be instituted when any of the following atmospheric conditions exist:

1) The concentration of airborne contaminants exceeds applicable occupational exposure limits, or

2) The lower explosive limit (or lower flammable limit) of flammable gases or vapors is exceeded, or

3) The oxygen concentration is below 19.5%.

Control methods fall into three broad categories: engineering controls, administrative controls, and personal protective equipment. It is not uncommon for effective control programs to involve a combination of all three of these categories.

Industrial exposures involve three related entities: a hazard source, a path of travel for the agent, and a receiver (Raterman 2001). The goal of hazard control is to protect the receiver (the worker). Generally control efforts focus on one of these three entities: contain the source, block the path of the agent, or shield the receiver (the worker). Engineering controls might eliminate or contain the hazard source or block its path of travel. Engineering can also protect the worker with environmental enclosures. Administrative controls can limit or prevent exposure by managing the work force (the receivers). Personal protective equipment blocks the exposure path, thereby enclosing and protecting the receiver.

Engineering Controls

The engineering control category has been divided into sub-categories: substitution, isolation, and ventilation. For more comprehensive information on engineering control of health hazards see (Raterman 2001).

Substitution. Substitution can be applied to the hazard source itself, to the process that generates the hazard, or to the equipment responsible for exposures.

Substitution of a less hazardous material for the hazardous material can be an effective control strategy. An example is the substitution of low-toxicity titanium dioxide for toxic lead oxide as a paint pigment. Another example is the use of mineral wool and fibrous glass to replace more toxic asbestos in thermal and electrical insulation. A word of caution is merited: substitute materials are usually not hazard-free. Some control may still be required after the substitution is made. There are many historical examples of successes (as well as blunders) in substitution of materials.

Substitution of a less hazardous process for a more hazardous one can be a successful control scheme. In the chemical industry, for example, converting from batch pouring operations to enclosed, piping-and-pump transfer operations has reduced both exposures to air contaminants and loss of materials. Hot riveting of structural steel was replaced by welding long ago, thereby eliminating the hearing-loss hazard to riveters. Brush application of paint produces less aerosol and solvent vapor than spray painting. Dipping and electrostatic spraying can be even less hazardous.

Substitution of less hazardous equipment can also reduce exposures. Replacement of manual trans-fers of materials with mechanical conveyor systems has reduced ergonomic stresses. Enclosed screw conveyors for moving dusty solids can replace open conveyor belts. Dust emission is reduced, and the enclosure facilitates the application of local exhaust ventilation for more positive dust control. Replacement of small, high-rpm ventilation fans with larger, lower-rpm fans can reduce ventilation noise without diminishing the airflow rate.

Isolation. The isolation of either the source or the receiver simply breaks the path of travel. It has other advantages as well. Source isolation in the chemical industry has the advantages of increased process efficiency as well as control of exposures. The evaporation of volatiles and generation of aerosols can be reduced at material transfer points. Source isolation can range from total system containment of chemical transfers and reactions to installing lids on chemical vats, or simply keeping existing lids closed during idle periods. Source isolation is widely used in health physics to limit exposure to radiation sources. The similar isolation of sources of intense noise with acoustical enclosures reduces noise exposure.

Workstations are sometimes enclosed to reduce exposures to process noise, heat, or cold. This also permits localized application of heating ventilating and air conditioning (HVAC) to work spaces, locker rooms, lunchrooms, *etc*. Dust, heat, and cold exposures to heavy equipment operators have been reduced by addition of enclosed cabs equipped with HVAC systems.

Isolation in time is sometimes used. In office buildings, pesticides are often applied at night or on weekends when fewer employees are present. Hot jobs might be scheduled after sundown to reduce heat stress to workers. Typically, such procedures are more administrative than engineering in nature.

Ventilation. Ventilation for control of air contaminants and for comfort is an engineering specialty in itself. Detailed engineering information is available in (ACGIH 2004c, McDermott 2001, and Burton 2004).

Ventilation can be applied either to capture a contaminant before it reaches the work atmosphere (called local exhaust ventilation) or to dilute the concentration of contaminant in the atmosphere (called dilution ventilation).

Of these two, local exhaust ventilation is more protective and efficient and usually less costly to operate. Local exhaust ventilation controls worker exposure to airborne contaminants by exhausting the contaminated air out of the work area and replacing it with clean air. The control principle behind local exhaust ventilation is to capture the air contaminant at its source and keep it from ever reaching the breathing zones of the workers.

The principle behind local exhaust ventilation is different than the principle behind dilution ventilation, which is to leave the contaminant in the air and attempt to dilute it to some safe concentration with clean air. However, there are circumstances where local exhaust ventilation is not practicable and dilution ventilation is the method of choice. Both methods have advantages and disadvantages as shown in Table 6, from (<http://www.lni.wa.gov/Safety/Topics/AtoZ/Ventilation/default.asp>).

Consistently effective design of ventilating systems requires engineers trained in that specialty. A properly designed local exhaust system for control of air contaminants consists of five connected components:

1) An exhaust hood that encloses the emission source to the extent practicable. The purpose of the hood is to capture all of the contaminant before it enters the general workroom atmosphere

2) Ducting to convey the contaminated air through an air cleaner and fan to a remote discharge point

3) An air cleaner to remove contaminants from the air stream prior to its release to the outside air

4) An air fan designed to exhaust, or pull, contaminated air into the hood by creating a negative pressure in the hood. The fan must also convey the dirty air through the ducting and the air cleaner before delivering it to the outside atmosphere

5) A stack to direct the discharged air away from occupied areas

An additional system, not connected to the exhaust system, is essential for effective contaminant control. This is a separate air moving system that supplies fresh air to the workroom to replace the air exhausted by the local exhaust system as pointed out in Table 6. Without good design attention to replacement air (sometimes called *make-up air*) the exhaust system might not provide adequate control.

A dilution ventilating system often consists of a window or wall fan pulling in outside air and blowing it into the work zone. During intemperate weather it might be necessary to heat or cool the incoming air; this is another design consideration. In designing dilution ventilation systems attention must be given to airflow patterns in the workroom. The best arrangement is to place the fresh air source close to the work zone to direct the cleanest air to the breathing zones of the employees. Contaminated air is then removed at some point remote from the work zone. When the contaminated air is recirculated back into the workspace, which is not good practice, it is to be expected that the concentration of air contaminants will increase during continual work periods.

Dilution ventilation works well for oxygen deficient atmospheres, provided a source of fresh air is available, because it can quickly move large volumes of fresh air to restore oxygen levels. Similarly, dilution ventilation can dissipate flammable or explosive atmospheres rapidly. Exhaust ventilation is avoided for control of flammable air mixtures because ignition can occur from electrical sparks in the exhaust ducting and fans. In using dilution ventilation for control of flammable air mixtures, attention must be given

Table 6. Ventilation for Control of Air Contaminants

Dilution Ventilation		Local Exhaust Ventilation	
Advantages	Disadvantages	Advantages	Disadvantages
Usually lower equipment and installation costs	Does not completely remove contaminants from the workplace	Captures contaminant at source and removes it from the workplace	Higher cost for design, installation and equipment
Requires less maintenance	Cannot be used for highly toxic airborne chemicals	Only choice for highly toxic airborne chemicals	Requires regular cleaning, inspection, and maintenance
Effective control for small amounts of low toxicity chemicals	Ineffective for dusts or metal fumes or large amounts of gases or vapors	Can handle all sorts of contaminants, including dusts and metal fumes	
Effective control for flammable or combustible gases or vapors	Requires large amounts of heated or cooled replacement air	Requires smaller amount of replacement air since smaller amounts of air are being exhausted	
Best ventilation for small dispersed contaminant sources or mobile sources	Ineffective for handling surges of gases or vapors or irregular emissions	Less energy costs since there is less replacement air to heat or cool	

Source: Washington State Department of Labor and Industries.

to airflow patterns in the room to avoid blowing flammable air toward ignition sources. The airflow delivery capability of the blowers is critical to rapid restoration of oxygen and to quickly diluting flammable mixtures to below their lower flammable limits. It is necessary to deliver lots of fresh air fast.

Mechanical ventilation is also used to deliver localized *spot cooling* or *spot heating* to work zones for alleviation of heat or cold stresses.

In nonmanufacturing areas, mechanical HVAC systems are used to deliver fresh air to prevent the build-up of contaminants that might cause *indoor air quality* problems. In this sense the process is referred to as general ventilation. The American Society of Heating, Refrigerating, and Air-Conditioning Engineers (ASHRAE) publishes guidelines for supplying fresh air to general use buildings (ASHRAE 2001).

Administrative or Management Controls

Administrative control of health hazards starts at he top of the organizational chart, where management establishes and enforces a promotional culture of employee health and safety and puts it in writing in the form of a corporate policy. This policy is then detailed in a corresponding written corporate program. The corporate program should establish the organizational structure necessary for implementation, which can include the establishment of occupational health, safety, and medical programs. These three programs should be cooperatively aligned. The corporate program should also include divisions of responsibility and provisions for staffing and funding of the program elements. Objective audit functions should also be implemented as well as occupational accident and illness investigation policies.

Administrative controls assume several forms at the staff and operating levels :

- Training employees in the details of the hazards of their workplaces, available medical programs, worker rights and responsibilities, existing hazard control measures, safe work practices, housekeeping requirements, personal hygiene provisions and expectations,

emergency procedures, personal protective equipment, *etc.*

- Scheduling and rotating workers to optimize hazard protection

- Developing of internal control standards for those hazards not included in regulatory standards

- Implementing a preventive maintenance program as a means of preventing exposure, especially as it applies to control systems, such as ventilation, emergency alarms, containment systems, and personal protective equipment

- Implementation of safe work practices for employees to minimize their exposures. An example: required wetting of architectural asbestos to reduce dust generation during removal

Personal Protective Equipment (PPE)

Industrial hygienists are philosophically prone to consider the use of PPE as a rather poor way to control health hazards. PPE becomes necessary when there is a failure to control the hazard at the source or in its travel path. Workers are then equipped with a last-ditch barrier and sent into a hazardous environment where equipment failure could result in overexposure. This is true if PPE is used without consideration for more positive control alternatives. However, there are situations in which PPE is practical and effective and might be the method of choice. Escape from emergency conditions and life rescue situations are two examples, although even in these situations, additional administrative controls are essential. Often PPE is used as an additional measure of protection to engineering or administrative controls. At hazardous waste sites, administrative controls and PPE are used extensively as adjuncts to engineering controls, which can be logistically limited. When it is used, PPE should be administered according to a written program that will optimize and ensure protection. The program should provide for administration, proper selection, ready availability, training, individual fitting, medical surveillance, equipment cleaning and maintenance, exposure assessment, and quality assurance.

Management must recognize that use of PPE can affect productivity by restraining the wearer to some extent and by imposing additional physio-logical and ergonomic burdens. Completion time for projects might be lengthened or workforce requirements increased. PPE can also create hazards by restricting movement, balance, visibility, hearing, and tactile senses. In hot or cold environments, protective clothing can promote thermal stress.

Excellent choices of PPE are available to protect the skin, the lungs, the eyes, the ears, the face, the head, the hands, and the feet. Personal devices are available to facilitate emergency escape, to prevent falls from heights, to provide flotation in water, and for a variety of other purposes. PPE, as it applies to management of hazardous materials, is detailed in the chapter entitled "Personal Protective Equipment."

Evaluation of Control Measures

After hazard control measures are implemented, follow-up evaluations should be conducted to determine their effectiveness. This naturally falls within the purview of program audits. Some systems, such as mechanical ventilation systems, may require periodic testing throughout their useful life to verify their performance. Such testing can be a part of a preventive maintenance program, although an industrial hygienist is often called upon to conduct the specialized tests.

Qualifications of an Industrial Hygienist

The American Board of Industrial Hygiene defines a *professional industrial hygienist* as

> a person having a baccalaureate or graduate degree from an accredited college or university in industrial hygiene, biology, chemistry, engineering, physics, or a closely related physical or biological science who, by virtue of special studies and training, has acquired competence in industrial hygiene (ABIH 2002).

As in any profession, actual experience is an important additional qualification. Professional board certification is recognized as a positive indicator of competence in the field.

The qualifications of an industrial hygiene technologist or technician are not as well defined. For example a competitive candidate might have an associate degree or higher in occupational safety and health from a college accredited by the Council for Higher Education Accreditation or the United States Department of Education plus several years experience in the field of safety and health. Other combinations of college credit in the physical sciences or engineering could be considered equivalent for the educational qualification. Board certifications are now available for health and safety technologists from the Council on Certification of Health, Environmental and Safety Technologists. Details are available on the Council website (<http://www.cchest.org/>).

Bibliography

"Air Contaminants." *Code of Federal Regulations.* Title 29, Pt. 1910.1000.

American Board of Industrial Hygiene. *Candidate Handbook: Certified Industrial Hygienist.* Lansing, MI: ABIH, March 2002.

American Conference of Governmental Industrial Hygienists. *Documentation of the Threshold Limit Values and Biological Exposure Indices.* 7th ed. ACGIH Publication #0100DocBEI. Cincinnati, OH: ACGIH, 2001.

American Conference of Governmental Industrial Hygienists. *Guide to Occupational Exposure Values.* ACGIH Publication #0382. Cincinnati, OH: ACGIH, 2004a.

American Conference of Governmental Industrial Hygienists. *Threshold Limit Values for Chemical Substances and Physical Agents and Biological Exposure Indices.* ACGIH Publication #0104. Cincinnati, OH: ACGIH, 2004b.

American Conference of Governmental Industrial Hygienists. Industrial Ventilation Committee. *Industrial Ventilation: A Manual of Recommended Practice,* 25th ed. ACGIH Publication #2094. Cincinnati, OH: ACGIH, 2004c.

American Industrial Hygiene Association. *AIHA Complete ERPG and WEEL Sets*. AIHA Stock No. AEAR02–545. Akron, OH: AIHA, 2004.

American Society for Testing and Materials. *Standard Guide for Air Sampling Strategies for Worker and Workplace Protection*. ASTM E1370–96. West Conshohocken, PA: ASTM, 2002.

American Society of Heating, Refrigerating, and Air Conditioning Engineers. *Ventilation for Acceptable Indoor Air Quality*. ASHRAE Standard 62–2001 (ANSI approved). Atlanta, GA: ASHRAE, 2001.

Bernard, T. E. "Thermal Stress." In *Fundamentals of Industrial Hygiene*, 4th ed. B. A. Plog, Ed. Itasca, IL: National Safety Council, 1996.

Burgess, W. A. *Recognition of Health Hazards in Industry: A Review of Materials and Processes*. 2nd ed. New York, NY: John Wiley & Sons, 1995.

Burton D. J. *Companion Study Guide to Industrial Ventilation: A Manual of Recommended Practice*. ACGIH Publication #04–068. Cincinnati, OH: ACGIH, 2004.

Cohen, R. and K. Balzer. "Industrial Toxicology." In *Fundamentals of Industrial Hygiene*, 4th ed. B. A. Plog, Ed. Itasca, IL: National Safety Council, 1996. p 123.

"Hazard Communication." *Code of Federal Regulations*. Title 29, Pt. 1910.1200.

"Hazardous Waste Operations and Emergency Response." *Code of Federal Regulations*. Title 29, Pt. 1910.120.

Hitchcock R. T., C. E. Moss, W. E. Murray, and R. J. Rockwell. "Nonionizing Radiation." In *The Occupational Environment, Its Evaluation, Control, and Management*. 2nd ed. S. R. DiNardi, Ed. Fairfax, VA: American Industrial Hygiene Association, 2003.

Kohn J. P., M. A. Friend, and C. A. Winterberger. *Fundamentals of Occupational Safety and Health*. Rockville, MD: Government Institutes, 1996.

Kroemer K. H. "Ergonomics." In *Fundamentals of Industrial Hygiene*, 4th ed. B. A. Plog, Ed. Itasca, IL: National Safety Council, 1996.

McCarthy M. E. and B. Thomas. "Ionizing Radiation." In *The Occupational Environment, Its Evaluation, Control, and Management*. 2nd ed. S. R. DiNardi, Ed. Fairfax, VA: American Industrial Hygiene Association, 2003.

McDermott, H. J. *Handbook of Ventilation for Contaminant Control*. 3rd ed. ACGIH Publication #01–001. Cincinnati, OH: ACGIH, 2001.

Milz, S. A., R. G. Conrad, and R. D. Soule. "Principles of Evaluating Worker Exposure in the Occupational Environment." In *The Occupational Environment, Its Evaluation, Control, and Management*. 2nd ed. S. R. DiNardi, Ed. Fairfax, VA: American Industrial Hygiene Association, 2003.

National Institute of Occupational Safety and Health. *NIOSH Pocket Guide to Chemical Hazards*. NIOSH Publication #97–140. Springfield, VA: National Technical Information Service, 2003.

Ness, S. A. *Air Monitoring for Toxic Exposures: An Integrated Approach*. New York, NY: Van Nostrand Reinhold, 1991.

"Occupational Noise Exposure.", *Code of Federal Regulations*. Title 29, Pt. 1910.95.

Perkins, J. L. *Modern Industrial Hygiene. Volume I: Recognition and Evaluation of Chemical Agents*. New York, NY: Van Nostrand Reinhold, 1997.

Raterman, S. M. "Methods of Control." In *Fundamentals of Industrial Hygiene*, 5th ed. B. A. Plog, Ed. Itasca, IL: National Safety Council, 2001.

Ryan, T. J. "Biohazards in the Work Environment." In *The Occupational Environment, Its Evaluation, Control, and Management*. 2nd ed. S. R. DiNardi, Ed. Fairfax, VA: American Industrial Hygiene Association, 2003.

Schlecht P. C. and P. F. O'Connor, Eds. *NIOSH Manual of Analytical Methods (NMAM)*. 4th ed.

DHHS (NIOSH) Publication #94–113. Atlanta, GA: NIOSH, 1994. First Supplement Publication #96–135, 1996. Second Supplement: Publication #98–119, 1998. Third Supplement: Publication #2003–154, 2003.

Talty, J. T. *Industrial Hygiene Engineering–Recognition, Measurement, Evaluation, and Control.* 2nd ed. Park Ridge, NJ: William Andrew Publishing/Noyes, 1988.

Internet Resources

<http://www.abih.org> (American Board of Industrial Hygiene. Homepage)

<http://www.acgih.org> (American Conference of Governmental Industrial Hygienists. Homepage)

<http://www.aiha.org> (American Industrial Hygiene Association. Homepage)

<http://www.aiha.org/PublicationsAdvertising/html/POerpgweels.htm> (American Industrial Hygiene Association. AIHA's 2004 ERPGs/WEELs Update Sets. Emergency response planning guidelines (ERPGs) and workplace emergency exposure limits [WEELs])

<http://www.ashrae.org> (American Society of Heating, Refrigerating, and Air Conditioning Engineers, Inc. Homepage)

<http://www.asse.org> (American Society of Safety Engineers. Homepage)

<http://www.astm.org/> (American Society for Testing and Materials. Homepage)

<http://www.bcsp.org> (Board of Certified Safety Professionals. Homepage)

<http://www.cchest.org/> (Council on Certification of Health, Environmental and Safety Technologists. Homepage.)

<http://www.cdc.gov/niosh/homepage.html> (National Institute for Occupational Safety and Health. Homepage.)

<http://www.cdc.gov/niosh/92-100.html> (National Institute for Occupational Safety and Health. "NIOSH Recommendations for Occupational Safety and Health: Compendium of Policy Documents and Statements." DHHS (NIOSH) Publication No. 92–100. 1992)

<http://www.epa.gov> (Environmental Protection Agency. Homepage)

<http://www.hps.org> (Health Physics Society. Homepage)

<http://www.iarc.fr> (International Agency for Research on Cancer. Homepage)

<http://www.iso.org> (International Organization for Standardization. Homepage)

<http://www.lni.wa.gov/Safety/Topics/AtoZ/Ventilation/default.asp> (Washington State Department of Labor and Industries. Industrial Ventilation Guidelines)

<http://www.msha.gov> (U. S. Department of Labor. Mine Safety and Health Administration. Homepage)

<http://www.nsc.org> (National Safety Council. Homepage)

<http://ntp-server.niehs.nih.gov> (Department of Health and Human Services. National Toxicology Program. Homepage)

<http://www.osha.gov/> (Occupational Safety and Health Administration. Homepage)

<http://www.osha.gov/SLTC/ergonomics/index.html> (Occupational Safety and Health Administration. Safety and Health Topics. Ergonomics)

<http://www.tricornet.com/nioshdbs/idlh/intridl4.htm> (National Institute for Occupational Safety and Health. Documentation for Immediately Dangerous to Life or Health Concentrations (IDLHs). NIOSH Chemical Listing and Documentation of Revised IDLH Values, as of 3/1/95)

Before retiring in 2001, **David M. Trayer** *was Associate Professor of Environmental Health and Safety and Director of the Industrial Hygiene / Health Physics academic program at Chattanooga State Technical Community College. Prior to joining the faculty at Chattanooga State, his career spanned four decades as a chemist, physicist, industrial hygienist, research scientist, and manager in various industries, including the chemical, nuclear, aerospace, electric utility, and hazardous waste abatement industries. In addition, he was owner and president of an industrial hygiene consulting firm. He has published numerous articles in the technical literature and has presented many papers at professional conferences. He is the Past General Chairman and Director of the American Conference of Industrial Hygienists (ACGIH), Past General Secretary and Director of the American Board of Industrial Hygiene (ABIH), and Past President and Director of both the Tennessee Valley and Alabama Sections of the American Industrial Hygiene Association (AIHA). He has chaired the program committees for two national professional conferences. He has served on professional committees of the National Safety Council and the American Society of Safety Engineers. Mr. Trayer was the 1993 recipient of the national AIHA Cummings Memorial Award for outstanding contributions to the knowledge and practice of industrial hygiene. He gratefully recognizes his wonderful family, his many colleagues, and his beloved teachers, all of whom prepared him to write this chapter.*

Part III

The Right to Know

CHAPTER 16

Release Reporting and Emergency Notification

Alan A. Eckmyre, CHMM

Introduction

Several Federal environmental laws require that a *release of hazardous substances to the environment* above certain threshold amounts—Reportable Quantities or RQs—be reported in a timely manner. Failure to report certain releases can result in substantial penalties to be imposed on both the facility and its employees.

Hazardous substances are

- Any elements, compounds, mixtures, solutions, or substances designated by the United States Environmental Protection Agency (EPA) under Section 311 of the Clean Water Act (CWA), (40 CFR 116.4) or under Section 102 of the Comprehensive Environmental Response, Compensation, and Liability Act (CERCLA), (40 CFR 302.4)

- Any toxic pollutants listed under Section 307(a) of the CWA

- Any hazardous substances regulated under Section 311(b)(2)(A) of the CWA (40 CFR 110, 117, and 122)

255

- Any listed or characteristic Resource Conservation and Recovery Act (RCRA) hazardous wastes (40 CFR 261)

- Any hazardous air pollutants listed under Section 112(r) of the Clean Air Act (CAA) (40 CFR 68)

- Any imminently hazardous chemical substances or mixtures regulated under Section 7 of the Toxic Substances Control Act (TSCA) (40 CFR 761.120, *et seq.*)

why is this not in table?

Under TSCA, any release, leak, or spill of a hazardous chemical that *seriously threatens humans with cancer, birth defects, mutation, death, or serious or prolonged incapacitation, or seriously threatens the environment with large- scale or ecologically significant population destruction* must be reported immediately to the appropriate EPA Regional Office by telephone. A written follow-up report is required within 15 days of the oral report. If the incident has been reported under the CWA, the facility does not have to submit the *substantial risk report* for the incident (40 CFR 761.120, *et seq.*).

The Emergency Planning and Community Right-to-Know Act (EPCRA) also establishes emergency reporting requirements for *extremely hazardous substances* (40 CFR 355, Appendix A). All of these substances are also CWA and CERCLA *hazardous substances*.

A ***reportable quantity (RQ)*** is the amount of a hazardous substance that, when released to the environment, must be reported to governmental authorities under the CWA, CERCLA, SARA Title III, or RCRA. Many states also require release reporting in addition to that called for by the Federal statutes. Consequently, a complicated maze of notification requirements exists that makes it difficult for responsible parties to determine which requirements are applicable.

The initial release notification usually is required immediately, or within 24 hours of knowledge of the release. In some cases, follow-up written reports are also required. Therefore it is important to establish in advance a release response program that addresses all appropriate release reporting requirements at a particular facility.

In order to assist individuals with notification obligations, a summary of reporting requirements

contained in the CWA Section 311, CERCLA Section 103, Superfund Amendments and Reauthorization Act (SARA) Title III Section 304, and RCRA Subtitle I is provided in Table 1. The table provides a summary of the various reporting requirements, including type of releases subject to reporting, substances subject to reporting, quantities subject to reporting, parties responsible for reporting, when reporting is required, to whom to report, and penalties for failure to notify.

EPA considers a ***release*** to be virtually all conceivable contacts with the environment, including any spilling, leaking, pumping, pouring, emitting, emptying, discharging, injecting, escaping, leaching, dumping, or disposing into the environment. The abandonment or discarding of barrels, containers, and other closed receptacles containing hazardous substances is also considered a release to the environment. However, EPA has indicated that certain administrative exemptions from reporting hazardous substances contact with the environment may be appropriate.

Some releases are excluded, including

1) Releases solely in the workplace

2) Exhaust emissions from vehicles, aircraft, vessels, pumping station engines, *etc.*

3) Normal applications of fertilizer

4) Releases of source, by-product, or special nuclear material subject to Section 170 of the Atomic Energy Act (AEA) or Sections 102(a)(1) or 302(a) of the Uranium Mill Tailings Radiation Control Act (UMTRCA)   *EPCRA*

5) Federally permitted releases

EPA has not formally defined what constitutes a release solely in the workplace. However, in the final rule setting RQs for radionuclides (54 FR 22524; May 24, 1989) EPA makes clear that this exemption applies only to releases that occur within a closed space with no emissions to the ambient environment. Therefore, spills onto concrete floors of an enclosed building or plant would qualify as a release solely within the workplace as long as the hazardous substances do not leave the building or structure by penetrating the floor or any other route. However, for volatile materials with significant vapor pressure at the release temperature, it is assumed that if an RQ of the material goes off-site immediately then this type of volatile substance is a reportable incident. In addition, the stockpiling of a hazardous substance in any unenclosed containment structure—surface impoundment, lagoon, tank, or other holding device that has an open side with the contained materials directly exposed to the ambient environment—is a release to the environment.

The general assumption underlying the exemptions from reporting requirements for Federally permitted releases is that such releases have been evaluated through the permit process and are not considered to be harmful to human health and the environment. Section 101(10) of CERCLA identifies specific types of releases considered to be Federally permitted, including

- Releases of substances and quantities specified in National Pollutant Discharge Elimination System (NPDES) permits, permit applications, or permit administrative records under the CWA

Table 1. Release Reporting Requirements Summary

Reporting Requirements	CWA Section 311	CERCLA Section 103	SARA Title III Section 304	RCRA Subtitle I (UST Program)
Type of release subject to reporting	Discharge to surface water	Releases into the environment (outside enclosed building or structure)	Releases into the environment with potential to result in exposure to persons offsite	Ground water, surface water, or surface soils
Hazardous substances subject to reporting	Oil and hazardous substances listed in 40 CFR 116.4	CERCLA hazardous substances listed in 40 CFR 302.4	Extremely hazardous substances listed in 40 CFR 355.20 and CERCLA hazardous substances	Petroleum and CERCLA hazardous substances (excluding RCRA hazardous wastes)
Trigger amount for reporting	All discharges of oil that form a sheen and discharges of hazardous substances that equal or exceed the CERCLA RQ	Releases that equal or exceed the CERCLA RQ	Releases that equal or exceed the CERCLA RQ, or one pound for EHSs that are not CERCLA hazardous substances	Any suspected or confirmed release, spills that equal or exceed the CERCLA RQ, and spills of petroleum that exceed 25 gallons or that result in a sheen
Facilities subject to reporting	All facilities and vessels	All facilities and vessels, except where consumer products are in consumer use	All facilities that produce, use, or store an OSHA hazardous chemical	Facilities with an underground storage tank system, the volume of which is 10 percent or more beneath the surface of the ground
Parties responsible for reporting	Person in charge	Person in charge	Owner/operator	Owner/operator
When report is required	Immediately	Immediately	Immediately, with written follow-up report	Within 24 hours
To whom to report	National Response Center	National Response Center	Relevant SERCs[1] and LEPCs[2]; for transportation-related releases, the 911 emergency telephone number or the operator	Implementing agency (usually a State agency)
Maximum penalties	$10,000 and/or prison sentence of one year	$50,000 and/or prison sentence of three years	$50,000 and/or prison sentence of three years	$25,000 per day for each day of noncompliance

[1]State Emergency Response Commissions
[2]Local Emergency Planning Committees

- Discharges complying with permits for dredge or fill materials under Section 404 of the CWA

- Releases in compliance with RCRA final permits

- Releases in compliance with enforceable permits under the Marine Protection, Research, and Sanctuaries Act (MPRSA)

- Underground injection of fluids permitted under the Safe Drinking Water Act (SDWA)

- Injection of fluids authorized by State law regulating underground injection of fluids used in petroleum product production or recovery

- Air releases complying with permit or control regulations under specific provisions of the Clean Air Act (CAA)

- Releases to a publicly owned treatment works (POTW) in compliance with a pretreatment standard and program submitted to EPA for review (must be in compliance with local limits that take into account site-specific characteristics)

- Releases of source, special nuclear, or by-product material in compliance with a license, permit, or order issued pursuant to the AEA

In general, in order to qualify as *Federally permitted*, the hazardous substances, quantities released, and activities causing the release must be within the scope of a permit. If a release exceeds permitted levels, the excess is not in compliance with the permit and cannot be Federally permitted. Therefore, if the amount of a release that exceeds a permit level is equal to or exceeds an RQ, the release must be reported.

The following discussion provides a general summary of the major Federal requirements for release notification and reporting. To be in full compliance with release notification requirements, the discharger should contact the proper authorities and provide them with the appropriate information on the required form. Since the response to a substance release is primarily a function of local government response teams, it is important to review local rules and ordinances for any additional notification requirements.

Clean Water Act Reporting Requirements

The CWA Section 311 reporting requirements apply to releases of CWA hazardous substances and oil from vessels and facilities into waters of the United States and the contiguous zone. CWA hazardous substances are listed in 40 CFR 116.4. For purposes of CWA reporting, *oil* is defined as *oil of any kind or in any form, including, but not limited to, petroleum, sludge, oil refuse, and oil mixed with wastes other than dredged spoil,* CWA Section 311(a)(1).

For a CWA hazardous substance, notification is necessary when a quantity at or above the reportable quantity (RQ) is discharged (released) to surface water within a 24-hour period.

Notification is required for oil discharges that

- Cause a sheen

- Violate applicable water quality standards

- Cause a sludge or emulsion to be deposited beneath the water surface or upon the shoreline (40 CFR 110)

Discharges in compliance with NPDES permits are exempt from the CWA notification requirements. However, if a discharge of oil or CWA hazardous substance violates an NPDES permit, the reporting requirements must be met.

In the event of a release of a hazardous substance, if the National Response Center (NRC) cannot be contacted immediately, reports may be made to the Coast Guard or EPA predesignated On-Scene Coordinator (OSC) for the geographic area where the discharge occurs. All reports are then promptly relayed by the OSC to NRC. If it is not possible to notify NRC or OSC, reports may be made immediately to the nearest Coast Guard unit, provided the person in charge of the vessel or onshore or offshore facility notifies NRC as soon as possible.

Oil and hazardous substance releases require that oral reporting be made immediately upon knowledge of a reportable release. A written follow-up report is also required within 30 days and any additional written follow-up within 60 days. If NPDES permit limits are exceeded, an oral report is required within 24 hours of any noncompliance, with written follow-up within 5 days. Follow-up reports are required to be developed and should be forwarded to EPA regional office, State Emergency Response Commission, Local Emergency Planning Committee or fire department, within reporting deadlines.

Regulations specify the contents of the initial oral report for oil and hazardous substance release. The report must include

- Name of person reporting

- Type and amount of substance

- Location, date, time, and duration of release

- Basis for hazard classification

- Reportable quantity; whether release is to ground, water, or air

- Remedial action taken

- Identity of other regulatory authorities

Furthermore, if there is potential for injury, additional newspaper notice is required to notify potentially injured parties. Table 2 provides a summary of emergency notification procedure content to satisfy notification-reporting requirements.

Table 2. Emergency Notification Procedure Content

Emergency Notification Procedure Content

1) Chemical Name (CAS# if available)

2) Chemical an Extremely Hazardous Substance?

3) Estimate of Quantity Released (refine later during follow-up report)

4) Time and Duration of Release

5) Endangered Media (air, water, and/or land)

6) Known Health Risks and Medical Advice

7) Proper Precautions (evacuation, shelter-in-place, personal protective equipment [PPE])

8) Name and Phone Number for Return Calls

9) Actions Taken and Responders On-Scene or Enroute

10) On-Scene Incident Commander and How to Contact

11) Follow-up Schedule Based upon Incident (within 15 days)

Notes:

- Requirements imply that the person constructing the Emergency Notification Procedure is familiar with the Incident Command System.

- A follow-up report to the same agencies is required, detailing the incident, response, cleanup, effects of the spill, and measures taken to prevent the recurrence of a similar incident.

The follow-up written report must include

- Initial oral report contents

- Name and telephone number of person in charge

- NRC or EPA case number

- Dun and Bradstreet facility or company number

- Source and frequency of release

- Population density

- Sensitive populations

- Sensitive ecosystems within one mile

- Releases over past year

- Basis for stating that release is continuous and stable

- Port of registration if release is from a vessel

Additional follow-up reports should include

- Name of person reporting

- Case number

- Information verifying contents of previous reports

Written follow-up report contents for any NPDES permit limit exceedance include

- Description of noncompliance

- Cause of noncompliance

- The period of noncompliance, including dates and times

- If the noncompliance has not been corrected, the anticipated time it is expected to continue

- Steps to reduce, eliminate, and prevent reoccurrence of the noncompliance (40 CFR 122.41, 403.12, and 403.16)

The following civil penalties exist for reporting requirement violations under the CWA:

- Possible $10,000 fine and up to 1 year imprisonment for failure to notify, 40 CFR 117.22(a)

- $5,000 fine per each release or discharge in a 24-hour period exceeding an RQ (For most petroleum products, the RQ is one barrel, with

the amount in gallons or liters.), (40 CFR 117.22(b)

- Additional civil penalty of up to $5,000, or up to $250,000 if the discharge is the result of willful negligence or willful misconduct, 40 CFR 117.22(b)

Comprehensive Environmental Response, Compensation, and Liability Act Reporting Requirements

Under CERCLA, notification is necessary if an amount of a CERCLA hazardous substance greater than or equal to its reportable quantity (RQ) is released into the environment from a vessel or facility within a 24-hour period.

All included in 302.4 Table

CERCLA *hazardous substances* include

- Substances designated under Sections 307(a) and 311(b)(4) of the CWA

- Hazardous air pollutants listed under Section 112 of the CAA

- RCRA hazardous wastes

- Chemicals or mixtures for which EPA has taken action under Section 7 of the Toxic Substances Control Act (TSCA), CERCLA Section 101(14)

The statute also gives EPA the authority to designate additional hazardous substances.

Petroleum Exclusion

CERCLA exempts the following petroleum products from regulation as hazardous substances:

- Petroleum, including crude oil or any fraction thereof which is not otherwise specifically listed or designated as a hazardous substance

- Natural gas, natural gas liquids, liquefied natural gas

- Synthetic gas usable for fuel (or mixtures of natural gas and such synthetic gas), CERCLA Section 101(14)

According to EPA's interpretation, the petroleum exclusion applies to materials such as crude oil, petroleum feedstocks, and refined petroleum products, even if a CERCLA hazardous substance is a constituent of such products or is normally added to them during refining. However, the exclusion does not apply to hazardous substances that are added to petroleum products after the refining process or contamination that occurs during use, such as with used oil.

In order for notification to be required, all of the following criteria must be met:

- A release of a CERCLA hazardous substance must occur from a vessel or facility. A *release* is defined as *any spilling, leaking, pumping, pouring, emitting, emptying, discharging, injecting, escaping, leaching, dumping, or disposing into the environment.* (40 CFR 302.3)

- The release must occur *into the environment*. A release is considered to have entered the environment if it is not completely contained within a building or structure, even if it remains on the plant or facility grounds.

- The hazardous substance must be released in a quantity that equals or exceeds the RQ for that substance over a 24-hour period. RQs are listed in 40 CFR, Table 302.4.

Determination of whether an RQ has been released is more complicated for mixtures. When the hazardous substances in the mixture and their concentrations are known, releases of the mixture must be reported as soon as any hazardous substance is released in an amount equal to or greater than its RQ.

If the concentrations of hazardous substances are unknown, reporting must occur when the amount of the entire mixture released reaches the RQ for the component having the lowest RQ.

Several types of incidents are exempt from CERCLA notification requirements, including

- Federally permitted releases

- Proper application of pesticide products registered under the FIFRA (Accidents, spills, improper application and improper disposal of pesticides must be reported.)

- Releases of solid particles of antimony, arsenic, beryllium, cadmium, chromium, copper, lead, nickel, selenium, silver, thallium, or zinc, when the mean diameter of particles is larger than 100 micrometers (0.004 inches).

- Releases from consumer products in consumer use

- Emissions from the engine exhaust of a motor vehicle, rolling stock, aircraft, vessel, or pipeline pumping-station engine

- Certain releases of source, by-product, or special nuclear material from a nuclear incident

- Normal application of fertilizer

In addition, EPA has reduced the reporting requirements for *continuous releases*.

Following initial notification, additional reporting for continuous releases is only required annually or when there is a statistically significant increase in the quantity of the release.

CERCLA Section 103(f)(2) provides relief from the reporting requirements of Section 103(a) for a release of a hazardous substance that is continuous, stable in quantity and rate, and either is a release from a facility for which notification of known, suspected, or likely releases of hazardous substances has been given under Section 103(c) or is a release for which notification has been given under Section 103(a) for a period sufficient to establish the continuity, quantity, and regularity of such release. Section 103(f)(2) further provides that in such cases, notification shall be given annually or at such time as there is any statistically significant increase (SSI) in the quantity of hazardous substance released.

The *person in charge* of a facility or vessel must make notification of hazardous substance releases to the National Response Center (NRC) as soon as he/she learns that a reportable release has occurred. The person in charge is not defined by CERCLA. Therefore, each company must designate a person to be responsible for reporting.

In the event of a reportable release of a CERCLA hazardous substance, an initial oral report and follow-up report by the facility emergency coordinator are required to be received by the National Response Center (NRC), State Emergency Response Commission, Local Emergency Planning Committee or fire department. The facility emergency coordinator reports immediately

→ only if off-site which makes it SARA-reportable.

following any release of a reportable quantity. Subsequently, a written follow-up report within 30 days and additional written follow-up report within 60 days are required by reporting deadlines (40 CFR 302, *et seq.*; Appendices A and B).

The content of emergency notification information under CERCLA is very similar to that required under the CWA discussed previously. The initial report must include

- Name of person reporting
- Type and amount of substance
- Location
- Date
- Time and duration of release
- Basis for hazard classification
- Reportable quantity
- Whether release is to ground, water, or air
- Remedial action taken
- Identity of other regulatory authorities

If there is potential for injury, additional newspaper notice also is required to notify potentially injured parties.

The first follow-up written report must include

- Initial report contents
- Name and telephone number of person in charge
- NRC or EPA case number
- Dun and Bradstreet facility or company number
- Source and frequency of release
- Population density
- Sensitive populations and sensitive ecosystems within one mile
- Releases over the past year
- Basis for stating that release is continuous and stable
- Port of registration, if release is from a vessel

Additional follow-up reports should include

- Name of person reporting
- Case number
- Information verifying contents of previous reports

The following criminal penalties exist for reporting requirement violations under the CERCLA:

- Possible fines according to Title 18 of the United States Criminal Code and up to 3 years imprisonment/first offense or 5 years imprisonment/subsequent offenses for failure to notify, submitting false or misleading information, or destroying or falsifying evidence, Section 103(b)(2)

Superfund Amendments and Reauthorization Act Title III Reporting Requirements

SARA Title III Section 304 requires notification of State and local response authorities when releases of CERCLA hazardous substances and SARA Title III extremely hazardous substances (EHSs) extend beyond the site boundary. (On-site releases that do not migrate off-site are exempt from this requirement). This reporting requirement is in addition to CERCLA reporting requirements. Therefore, a release may require notification of both the National Response Center (under CERCLA) and the State and local emergency planning bodies (under SARA Title III).

The applicability of the SARA Title III notification requirements is exactly the same as CERCLA, with 4 exceptions:

1) The SARA Title III reporting requirements apply to CERCLA hazardous substances and extremely hazardous substances (EHSs) listed under SARA Title III. Lists of these substances and their RQs are contained in 40 CFR, Table 302.4 and 40 CFR 355, Appendix, respectively.

2) The SARA Title III requirements apply only to facilities—vessels are excluded.

3) SARA Title III does not contain a petroleum exclusion. Therefore, if a petroleum contains

a listed EHS or CERCLA hazardous substance, which is released above its RQ, notification is required.

4) Releases that only result in exposure to persons solely within the boundaries of the facility are exempt from SARA Title III reporting requirements. CERCLA requires notification of a release regardless of the extent of its impact.

For releases of EHSs and CERCLA hazardous substances that equal or exceed their RQs, facility owners/operators must immediately notify the State Emergency Response Commission (SERC) and the Local Emergency Planning Committee (LEPC). If the release involves a CERCLA hazardous substance, the NRC must be notified as well to comply with CERCLA reporting requirements. The initial SARA Title III notification must be followed by a written report that describes the release, response actions, known or anticipated health risks, and recommendations for medical attention of exposed individuals.

For transportation-related releases, and SARA Title III LEPC notification requirement, the notification requirements may be met by providing the required information to the 911 operator, or, in the absence of a 911 emergency operator, to the telephone operator.

Regulations specify that, in the event of a reportable release of SARA Title III extremely hazardous substances (EHSs), an initial report and follow-up report must be received by the National Response Center (NRC), State Emergency Response Commission, Local Emergency Planning Committee or fire department. The facility emergency coordinator reports immediately following releases of a reportable quantity and written follow-up within 30 days and additional written follow-up within 60 days are required by reporting deadlines (40 CFR 355.40, *et seq.*).

Table 2 provides a summary of the contents of the emergency notification that must be provided to appropriate agencies to satisfy requirements for notification. This information is similar to the information required under both CERCLA and CWA notification requirements previously discussed. Similarly, if there is potential for injury, additional newspaper notice is required to notify potentially injured parties.

The first follow-up written report must include

- Initial report contents

- Name and telephone number of person in charge

- NRC or EPA case number

- Facility or company Dun and Bradstreet number

- Source and frequency of release

- Population density

- Sensitive populations and sensitive ecosystems within one mile

- Releases over past the year

- Basis for stating that release is continuous and stable

- Port of registration if release is from a vessel

Additional follow-up reports should include

- Name of person reporting

- Case number

- Information verifying contents of previous reports

The following civil and criminal penalties exist for reporting requirement violations under the SARA Title III (EPCRA):

- Civil penalties up to $25,000 fine for failing to provide emergency notification

- Criminal penalties of up to $25,000 and 2 years imprisonment/first offense or $50,000 and 5 years imprisonment/subsequent offenses for willfully failing to provide emergency notification (40 CFR 355.50)

Resource Conservation and Recovery Act Subtitle I Reporting Requirements

Notification is required for releases from underground storage tank (UST) systems under RCRA Subtitle I. The RCRA regulations define a ***release*** as any *spilling, leaking, emitting, discharging, escaping, leaching, or disposal from an UST into groundwater, surface water, or subsurface soils.*

Regulated substances for which notification is necessary are petroleum (including crude oil, crude oil fractions, and petroleum-based substances, and CERCLA hazardous substances [excluding RCRA hazardous wastes]).

UST systems regulated by the notification requirements include underground storage tanks for which more than 10% of the volume of its tank and associated piping is underground and that contain regulated substances. The notification requirements also apply to associated underground piping and ancillary equipment, and containment systems. Farm or residential tanks (1,000 gallon capacity or less), tanks used to store heating oil for consumptive use on the premises where it is stored, septic tanks, and certain pipeline facilities are excluded from the requirements.

Notification is required for the following situations:

- Suspected releases discovered through release detection methods, unusual operational conditions, or evidence of contamination

- Confirmed releases

- Spills or overfills of a hazardous substance that equal or exceed its RQ, or that are less than the RQ if the owner/operator is unable to clean up the release within 24 hours

- Spills or releases of 25 gallons of petroleum that the owner/operator is unable to clean up within 24 hours

- Spills or overfill of petroleum resulting in a sheen on nearby surface water

When a regulated release occurs, the owner/operator of the UST system must report to the implementing agency (usually a State agency) by telephone or electronic mail within 24 hours, unless otherwise specified by the implementing agency. The NRC must also be immediately notified if a CERCLA hazardous substance is released in a quantity greater than or equal to its RQ, or if a petroleum release has created a sheen on a nearby surface water. A written report summarizing response actions and plans for future remediation must be submitted to the implementing agency within 20 days after the release, unless otherwise specified (40 CFR 280.50).

EPA may issue compliance orders or file civil actions against owner/operators who fail to comply with the notification requirements. Failure to comply with a compliance order may result in penalties of up to $25,000 for each day of non-compliance.

Clean Air Act Reporting Requirements

Release reporting requirements under the CAA include the following:

- Reporting by owners and operators of new stationary sources or changes to existing stationary sources subject to the National Ambient Air Quality Standards (NAAQS)

- Reporting by owners or operators of existing or new sources subject to (NESHAPs) and

- NESHAPs compliance reporting by owners or operators of:

    - Underground uranium mines

    - Federal facilities releasing radionuclides other than radon

    - Federal facilities releasing radon

    - Facilities with fugitive emission sources of hazardous air pollutants from equipment leaks

If a hazardous substance release to air occurs as part of normal operations and is within the limits specified in a NESHAP permit, then the release may be assumed to be federally permitted.

Compliance with Reporting Requirements

As a best management practice to ensure proper notification of the appropriate authorities, it is recommended that individuals/companies

- Determine which statutes regulate the hazardous substances that are on-site

- Maintain records that document where all regulated substances are located at the facility

- Create a list of RQs for substances managed on-site, and post it at all locations where hazardous substances are present

- Determine the constituents of all mixtures managed on-site, the concentrations of regulated constituents in the mixtures, and their RQs

- Determine the RQs for all waste streams

- Designate a person or alternate responsible for reporting releases, and ensure that the designated individual is familiar with proper notification requirements. That person or designated alternate is the only person to notify the NRC and SERC. Calling 911 in the event of an emergency should be at a supervisor's discretion

- Post by the telephone the numbers of all agencies to whom reporting may be necessary

- Check and reconcile product inventory routinely

- If a release occurs, keep detailed records of any actions taken or planned

- If there is any doubt about whether reporting is required, take a conservative approach and consider reporting anyway to avoid potential violations

The advice of counsel should be obtained in the event of a spill, to avoid any penalties for failure to properly report the release. Failure to report releases under the various applicable Federal and State laws and regulations may result in substantial civil and criminal penalties. Therefore preplanning, development, and implementation and testing of notification plans and procedures detailing incident, response, and mitigative measures are imperative.

It is implicit in the requirement to notify *immediately* that the notifier knows that the release occurred. However, EPA has stated that *if the facility owner/operator should have known of the release, then the fact that he or she was unaware of the release will not relieve the owner/operator from the duty to provide release notification.*

Significant fines have been levied involving incidents where responsible parties waited until they could determine if an RQ had been released. If the possibility that a release may be of a RQ, or if it is of a substance with an RQ and the amount is not immediately known, strong consideration must be given to initiating the notification process. However, there are no penalties for notifying the

agencies (NRC, SERC, and LEPC) and then showing in the follow-up report that an RQ was not released.

Fundamentally, requirements for initial notification can be met by calling

- 911 or operator—this obtains emergency assistance and satisfies the requirement to notify the LEPC

- (800) 424–8802—this satisfies the requirement to notify the National Response Center (Duty Officer of the US Coast Guard—the ultimate Incident Commander in the event of a major incident)

- The State Emergency Response Commission

- Any other affected LEPCs or SERCs (if near a State or LEPC boundary)

- CHEMTREC—if it is a transportation incident (800) 424–9300

- The local poison control center, if persons have been exposed

Calling CHEMTREC, or using any of the emergency guides is only a first resort. CHEMTREC and other contracted response agencies will only read the Material Safety Data Sheet. They are not able to give additional information. The poison control center will give medical advice that may be of assistance in making decisions such as evacuation or shelter-in-place.

With today's advances in communication technology, a facility with significant release risks might decide to have a one-to-many broadcast call preprogrammed to all required agencies simultaneously. The call must be initiated at the earliest instant that the sort of information contained in Table 2 is assembled, but well within the deadlines imposed by regulations as previously discussed.

An emergency notification procedure should be included as a component of any environmental risk management program, to ensure that a facility has an effective notification process. A simple but well-designed emergency notification procedure can ensure compliance and assist in preventing or minimizing a hazardous materials incident, thus avoiding or reducing injuries, loss of life, environmental damage, and creation of a public relations disaster. Having developed and implemented a procedure will help ensure appropriate response to the emergency notification requirements of a reportable accidental spill or release of hazardous substances into air, soil, or water under the pressure of a pending notification deadline.

For additional information, questions concerning SARA Title III or Section 112(r) of the CAA can be addressed to the Emergency Planning and Community Right-to-Know Information Hotline

USEPA (5104)
410 M Street, SW
Washington DC, 20460

(800) 424–9346 or (703) 412–9810
TDD: (800) 553–7672

9:00 am to 6:00 pm, EST, M–F

A valuable desk reference is

Environmental Protection Agency, *Title III List of Lists—Consolidated List of Chemicals Subject to the Emergency Planning and Community Right-to-Know Act (EPCRA) and Section 112 (r) of the Clean Air Act, as Amended.* EPA 550–B–96-015.

It is available through the United States EPA:

USEPA/NSCEP
PO Box 42419
Cincinnati, OH 45242

(800) 490–9198

Bibliography

Business and Legal Reports, *Environmental Compliance*, Rev. 3, Washington, DC: BLR, 1997.

"Designation, Reportable Quantities, and Notification." *Code of Federal Regulations*. Title 40. Pt. 302.4.

"Discharge of Oil." *Code of Federal Regulations*. Title 40. Pt. 110.11.

Environmental Protection Agency. "Chemical Accident Prevention Provisions." *Code of Federal Regulations*. Title 40. Pt. 68.

"Emergency Planning and Notification." *Code of Federal Regulations*. Title 40. Pt. 355.

"Immediate Notice of Certain Hazardous Materials Incidents, Detailed Hazardous Materials Incident Report." *Code of Federal Regulations*. Title 49. Pt. 171.15–171.16.

"Polychlorinated Biphenyls (PCBs) Manufacturing, Processing, Distribution in Commerce, and Use Prohibitions." *Code of Federal Regulations*. Title 40. Pt. 761.30(a).

"Requirements for PCB Spill Cleanup." *Code of Federal Regulations*. Title 40. Pt. 761.125.

"Standards Applicable to Transporters of Hazardous Waste." *Code of Federal Regulations*. Title 40. Pt. 263.30–263.31.

"Technical Standards and Corrective Action Requirements for Owners and Operators of Underground Storage Tanks (UST)." *Code of Federal Regulations*. Title 40. Pt. 280.60–280.67.

Thomas F. P. Sullivan, Ed. *Environmental Law Handbook.* 17th ed. Rockville, MD: Government Institutes, 2003.

"Transmission and Gathering System: Incident Report." *Code of Federal Regulations*. Title 49. Pt. 191.15.

Internet Resources

<http://www.epa.gov/ncepihom/orderpub.html> (Environmental Protection Agency, National Service Center for Environmental Publications, Ordering Information)

<http://www.access.gpo.gov/nara/cfr/cfr-table-search.html> (National Archives and Records Administration, Code of Federal Regulations)

Alan A. Eckmyre holds a BS in Business Administration from New York Institute of Technology, a BE in Nuclear Engineering from the State University of New York, and has been a Certified Hazardous Materials Manager since 1991. Additionally he has MBA and MS in Environmental Engineering studies from Emporia State University and the University of Kansas, respectively. He has served in leadership roles as the Secretary and Director of the Heartland Chapter ACHMM, President of the Magnolia Chapter ACHMM, Chair of the National ACHMM Publications and Professional Development Committees, as a member of the Board of Directors, and as President of the National ACHMM. He also holds professional memberships in the American Society of Testing and Materials and the American Nuclear Society. Mr. Eckmyre has over 22 years professional experience in nuclear and environmental engineering, consulting, environmental management training, and project management. His project management experience includes: UST system closures, State UST ground water/soil remediation investigation and design projects, ASTM Phase I and II site assessments, Federal facility-specific and programmatic environmental assessments and audits, RCRA permitting and corrective measures studies, CERCLA preliminary assessments and Remedial Investigation/Feasibility Studies (RI/FS), NPDES permitting, innovative environmental remediation technology R&D, and expert witness testimony. Mr. Eckmyre has performed numerous release reporting and emergency notifications in addition to authoring reports relating to field evaluation, planning, and analysis for the West Valley Demonstration Project, Tar Creek Superfund Site, Paducah Gaseous Diffusion Plant and Savannah River/Oak Ridge Site Environmental Restoration, Calvert Cliffs, Wolf Creek, and Grand Gulf Nuclear Power Plants, and the U.S. Department of Energy's spent nuclear fuel and radioactive waste management programs. He currently is President of Environmental Protection Resources, Inc., a professional environmental consulting company that provides technical consulting service solutions to commercial and Federal agency clients.

CHAPTER 17

Hazard Communication Standard

Charles M. Bessey, CHMM

Introduction

Approximately one in every four workers comes into contact with hazardous chemicals on the job. In many cases, the chemicals may be no more dangerous than those in use in the typical household. But in the workplace, exposure is likely to be greater, concentrations higher, and exposure times much longer. Because worker exposure to chemicals can cause or contribute to many serious safety and health problems, the Occupational Safety and Health Administration (OSHA) issued the Hazard Communication Standard or the Worker Right-to-Know Standard.

aka

The Hazard Communication Standard is different from most OSHA standards that obligate the employer to prevent workplace hazards through such methods as mandatory limitations on exposure to airborne contaminants, or guarding requirements for machinery. The standard does not impose mandatory limitations or requirements to abate hazardous conditions; rather, it requires that information be obtained, developed and provided to employers and employees.

269

The standard, found in the *Code of Federal Regulations* at 29 CFR 1910.1200, establishes uniform requirements to ensure that the hazards of all chemicals imported, produced, or used in the workplace are fully evaluated for possible physical or health hazards, and that this hazard information is transmitted to affected employers and exposed workers. The standard preempts inconsistent State and local laws and provides for a national law to simplify communication of chemical hazards.

All employees need to learn about the chemicals they work with and how to take precautions against the negative effects associated with them. Chemical manufacturers and importers must communicate the known hazard information they learn from their evaluations to downstream companies by means of Material Safety Data Sheets (MSDSs) and container labeling. In addition, all covered companies must have a written hazard communication program and provide this information to their employees.

Currently, all employers are obligated to comply with the standard. When originally adopted in 1983, the Hazard Communication Standard only applied to *manufacturing* industries with Standard Industrial Classification (SIC) codes, beginning with 20 through 39. On August 24, 1987, the standard was expanded to cover all employers (52 *Federal Register* 31852). Be advised that it is OSHA's contention that any company that uses hazardous materials that might release hazardous products in a *foreseeable emergency* or otherwise expose workers to a hazardous substance, are covered by the standard. Consequently, it is hard to imagine any employer that is not covered by the standard. For facilities that are strictly laboratories, OSHA's Occupational Exposure to Hazardous Chemicals in Laboratories (29 CFR 1910.1450) supercedes the Hazard Communication Standard.

Requirements

The basic requirements specifically covered in the standard include

- Hazard determination
- Material Safety Data Sheets
- Labels and labeling

- Written Hazard Communication Program
- Informing and training employees
- Trade secret provisions

Hazard Determination

Prior to the promulgation of the Hazard Communication Standard, both employers and employees were unaware of the dangerous nature of materials in their facilities. Often, a doctor seeking to treat an exposed employee was unable to do so effectively, because the employer was unable or unwilling to identify fully the specific substance in question. Inhabitants of surrounding communities often did not know the nature of chemicals or vapors that might be released by industrial complexes or the possible hazards that such exposure might entail. Public health officials were not be able to advise communities of potential risk because often they, too, did not have the necessary information. Fire departments, likewise, were not able to obtain the precise information they needed to prepare for fighting fires at these facilities.

The standard states first, that chemical manufacturers and importers must evaluate the hazards of chemicals they produce or import by assessing available scientific information or optionally performing laboratory tests, and furnish this detailed information to their downstream customers; and second, that all employers must provide hazard information to their employees by means of a hazard communication program, labels on containers, Material Safety Data Sheets (MSDSs) and access to written records and documents.

Hazardous chemicals are defined by this standard as chemicals that present a physical or health hazard,to employees in the workplace. The Hazard Communication Standard covers all employees who may be exposed to hazardous chemicals under normal working conditions or where a chemical emergency might occur. Manufacturers and importers must evaluate their chemicals by assessing available scientific information or optionally performing laboratory tests.

At a minimum, *hazardous chemicals* include all chemicals listed by OSHA with a Permissible Exposure Limit (PEL) or by the American

Conference of Governmental Industrial Hygienists (ACGIH) with a Threshold Limit Value (TLV) or those listed in the National Toxicology Program (NTP) Annual Report on Carcinogens (latest edition) or that have been found to be a potential carcinogen in the International Agency for Research on Cancer (IARC) Monographs (latest editions), or by OSHA.

The standard does not apply to hazardous waste, tobacco or tobacco products, wood or wood products, food, drugs or cosmetics that are intended for personal use or, *articles.* Articles are man-ufactured items that are formed to specific shapes during manufacture. They have end-use functions that are dependent upon their shapes during end use. They do not release or otherwise result in exposure to a hazardous chemical under normal conditions of use.

The standard has limited requirements for laboratory workers; such as, they must maintain MSDSs; verify that incoming containers are labeled and that employees are trained. For most laboratories, OSHA's Laboratory Standard, "Occupational Exposure to Hazardous Chemicals in Laboratories," (29 CFR 1910.1450) applies depending on the standard's defined criteria and supercedes the Hazard Communication Standard.

The laboratory standard has its own requirements for labeling, MSDSs, and training, *etc.* and applies only to laboratory work. It is important to note that the Hazard Communication standard still applies to non-laboratory types of activities, such as maintenance, janitorial and facility use of hazardous chemicals.

A work-site risk assessment and inventory of chemicals should be the starting point of the written program. Identification of piping system chemicals and potential in-house reactants (like welding fumes, carbon monoxide from combustion sources, and wood and metal dusts from cutting and grinding operations) should be categorized. A determination of nonroutine tasks in the workplace should be identified and evaluated for chemical exposures.

A *physical hazard* means a chemical for which there is scientifically valid evidence that it is

- Flammable liquid or solid
- Combustible liquid
- Compressed gas
- Explosive
- Organic peroxide
- Oxidizer
- Pyrophoric material (may spontaneously ignite in air at 130°F or less)
- Reactive (unstable) material
- Water reactive

A *health hazard* means a chemical for which there is statistically significant evidence, based on at least one study conducted in accordance with established scientific principles, that acute or chronic health effects may occur in exposed workers. Health hazards may not necessarily cause immediate, obvious harm or even make you sick right away. An employee may not always see, feel, or smell the danger.

Health hazards are categorized as

- Toxic or highly toxic
- Reproductive toxins
- Carcinogens
- Irritants
- Corrosives
- Sensitizers
- Hepatotoxins (liver)
- Nephrotoxins (kidney)
- Neurotoxins (nerve)
- Hematopoietic (blood)
- Other agents that damage the lungs, eyes, skin, and mucous membranes

If a material is a mixture of chemicals that has not been tested as a whole, the evaluator may use whatever valid data is available on the con-stituents of the mixture to assess the physical and health hazards. A mixture must be assumed to have the same hazards for carcinogens at 0.1% of the mixture and for other components at 1% of the mixture to have the same hazards.

If components are present in lesser amounts, but could be released in concentrations that would exceed the permissible exposure limit (PEL) or

Threshold Limit Value (TLV), the evaluator must assume that those hazards exist. The procedure used to evaluate chemical hazards must be recorded in writing.

Material Safety Data Sheets

The Material Safety Data Sheet or MSDS, is designed to provide specific safety and health information to emergency personnel and to employers and employees who handle hazardous materials. The information contained in an MSDS may also be used to determine whether a product is regulated under other OSHA standards or by other agencies, like, DOT and EPA.

The MSDS, a centerpiece of the Hazard Communication Standard, serves as the primary vehicle for transmitting detailed hazards information to both employers and employees. Employee training and information requirements are all based on the MSDS.

Material Safety Data Sheets must be prepared or obtained by manufacturers or importers and provided to downstream manufacturers and distributors with the initial shipment and after each MSDS update or revision. Employers must have an MSDS for every hazardous chemical they use and have copies readily available to workers during all shifts.

An MSDS is a technical bulletin, usually about 2 to 6 pages in length, that contains detailed information about a hazardous chemical or a product that contains one or more hazardous ingredients, such as its chemical composition, its health and safety hazards, its physical and chemical characteristics, and the necessary precautions for its safe transportation, storage, handling and use.

There is no format for Material Safety Data Sheets but they must be in English, contain no blank fields, and contain at a minimum the following information:

- Manufacturer/importer identification and phone number
  - The name, address, and telephone number on the manufacturer, importer, or other party who prepared the MSDS

- Identity used on the label
  - The names used must be the same as the names used on the container labels
- Specific and common chemical names
  - The chemical and/or common name of each included element or chemical compound that contributes to its hazardous nature
- Physical and chemical characteristics of the product
  - Melting point
  - Vapor pressure
  - Flash point
- Physical and health hazards
  - The potential for explosion or fire, reactivity, corrosiveness
  - Signs and symptoms that might result from exposure to the product
- Primary routes of entry into a person's body
  - Breathing
  - Ingestion
  - Through the skin
- Exposure limits
  - OSHA Permissible Exposure Limit (PEL)
  - Threshold Limit Value (TLV), if there is one
- Whether it is a carcinogen (cancer causing agent)
  - Actual carcinogen
  - Potential carcinogen
- Emergency and first-aid procedures
  - Practical emergency and first-aid procedures for release and exposure
- Safe handling precautions and use
  - Appropriate hygiene practices
  - Procedures for clean up of incidental spills and leaks
  - Maintenance and repair of contaminated equipment
- Generally applicable control measures
  - Appropriate engineering controls
  - Work practices
  - personal protective equipment

- Last revision date
  - The date the MSDS was prepared or last revised

OSHA does not require MSDSs to have a specific format. However, some manufacturers and organizations choose to use the American National Standards Institute (ANSI) Standard Z400.1–1998, "Hazardous Industrial Chemicals–Material Safety Data Sheet Preparation." The standard recommends a sixteen-section format as follows:

Section 1: Chemical Product and Company Identification

Section 2: Composition and Information on Ingredients

Section 3: Hazards Identification

Section 4: First Aid Measures

Section 5: Fire Fighting Measures

Section 6: Accidental Release

Section 7: Handling and Storage

Section 8: Exposure Controls and Personal Protection

Section 9: Physical Properties and Chemical Properties

Section 10: Stability and Reactivity

Section 11: Toxicological Information

Section 12: Ecological Information

Section 13: Disposal Considerations

Section 14: Transport Information

Section 15: Regulatory Information

Section 16: Other Information

The manufacturer, distributor or importer must provide copies of MSDSs to purchasers of the hazardous product at the time of initial shipment, although it need not be physically included in the shipment. The MSDS can be mailed separately at the time of shipment or it can be transmitted via fax, Email or computer link. Many purchasers have adopted a policy of refusing chemical shipments if an MSDS is not physically present in each shipment.

Employers are responsible for retaining current copies of MSDSs for all of the hazardous materials used at their facilities. MSDSs can be kept in notebooks, computer CD ROM, or on-line (*e.g.*, the Internet or Local Area Network). MSDSs may be maintained for the entire facility, but more generally are maintained for specific work areas or departments. Employees must be able to access MSDSs for chemicals that they may be exposed to at all times in the workplace, *i.e.*, they must be available to all employees during all shifts.

Copies of MSDSs for hazardous materials at facilities may also be required by Local Emergency Planning Committees (LEPCs) and/or local Fire Departments under the Emergency Planning and Community Right-to-Know Act (EPCRA). The Hazard Communication Standard does not require that employers keep MSDSs for products no longer in use, but other regulations, including 29 CFR 1910.1020(d)(1)(ii)(B), require that some MSDS information be retained for at least 30 years.

Labels and Labeling

The purpose of a label is to provide an unencumbered, immediate hazard warning and to remind users that more detailed information is provided in the MSDS and as part of the employee-training program. Labels must be in English and identify the hazardous chemicals with the appropriate hazard warnings as well as the manufacturer. On individual stationary containers, signs, placards, batch tickets, or printed operating procedures may be used in place of labels. An employee is not required to label a portable transfer vessel where the material is intended only for use by the worker during his or her normal work shift.

Containers are defined by OSHA as any bag, barrel, bottle, box, can, cylinder, drum, reaction vessel, storage tank or the like. Any container that holds a hazardous material must be labeled. An employee is not required to label a portable transfer vessel where the material is intended only for use by the same worker during his normal work shift. Pipes and piping systems for purposes of this standard are not considered containers (some State regulations do require pipes to be labeled).

Substances regulated under other agencies, like, pesticides (Environmental Protection Agency [EPA]), food and drugs (Food and Drug Administration [FDA]), alcoholic beverages (Bureau of Alcohol, Tobacco, and Firearms [ATF]) and consumer products regulated by Consumer Product Safety Commission (CPSC) are excluded from the labeling requirement.

The term *appropriate warning* is somewhat ambiguous under the standard. The purpose of the hazard warning is to convey information about physical and health hazards. ANSI Standard Z129.1–2000, "Hazardous Industrial Chemicals–Precautionary Labeling," can be used as guidance.

Written Hazard Communication Program

Employers must develop and implement a hazard communication program for the hazardous chemicals present in the workplace. The program must describe how the employer will meet the standards requirements for labeling, the type of labeling, MSDS management, and a list of known chemicals in the workplace. The program must be in writing and it must be accessible to all employees and the OSHA inspector. It also must contain provisions for meeting the employee information and training requirements, including a list of hazardous chemicals at the facility, the methods used to inform employees of nonroutine tasks, like cleaning reactor vessels, *etc.* and the methods used to advise outside contractors whose employees are working on the premises of the hazardous chemicals that they may be exposed to.

Training and Information

The employer must provide training that explains and reinforces the information already available to employees through the MSDSs and container labels. The employer must inform workers of the requirements of the standard, the operations where hazardous materials are present, and the location and availability of the written program. Employees must be trained at the time of employment and whenever new hazards are introduced to the workplace.

Specifically, training must include these four basic requirements:

1) The methods and observations that may be used to detect the presence or release of a hazardous chemical in the work area, such as a monitoring device, odor, visual appearance, *etc.*

2) Both the physical and health hazards of the particular chemicals to which an employee may be exposed

3) The measures the employee can take to protect himself from these hazards, like evacuation or other emergency procedures, protective clothing and equipment, *etc.*

4) The details of the company's written hazard communication program that includes an explanation of container labels, MSDSs and how employees can obtain and use the appropriate hazard information

Under the program employers must also define how outside contractors will be informed of potential exposure to hazardous materials in their work areas, and suggest the appropriate protective measures that are to be employed.

Even though it is not required by the standard, training programs should be documented by recording the date, time and subject of each training session and maintaining attendance records.

Trade Secrets

A *trade secret* is defined as any formula, pattern, device, or compilation of information used in one's business, which affords an opportunity to obtain an advantage over competitors who do not know it or use it. While trade secrets can be maintained, the specific hazards must be identified and disclosed. The responsible parties must provide the specific chemical identity to a doctor or nurse if requested in an emergency. A confidentiality agreement may be requested later. In non-emergency situations, health professionals must request trade secret identifications in writing and be willing to sign a confidentiality agreement.

If a manufacturer claims trade secret status for one of its products, it must indicate on the MSDS that the product is a trade secret or a proprietary formula. The manufacturer is still required to list the specific hazardous properties and effects for the product. Additionally, while OSHA does not require a company to report all percentages of each hazardous chemical in a mixture, EPA's EPCRA requires this information for Reportable Quantities that might be involved in a spill or release.

The standard strikes a balance between the need to protect exposed workers and the employer's need to maintain the confidentiality of trade secrets. This is achieved by providing (under specified conditions) of need and confidentiality, for limited disclosure to health professionals who are furnishing medical services, or to other employee health service providers and their designated representatives.

For a chemical or product to be considered for trade secret status, the following factors must be considered:

- The extent to which the information is known outside of the business

- The extent to which it is known by employees and others involved in the business

- The extent of measures taken by the business to guard the secrecy of the information

- The value of the information to competitors

- The amount of effort or money expended by the business in developing the information

- The ease or difficulty with which the information could be properly acquired or duplicated by others

Summary

The OSHA Hazard Communication Standard is the most frequently cited violation by OSHA. It is the only standard that applies to all industries and requires that employers alert workers to the existence of potentially dangerous substances in the workplace. It also mandates that employers provide their employees with the proper means and methods to protect themselves against the hazards.

Bibliography

"Hazard Communication, Correction." *Federal Register*. 59 (22 December 1994): 65947–65948. "Hazard Communication, Final Rule." *Federal Register*. 59 (13 April 1994): 17487–17479.

"Hazard Communication Standard." *Code of Federal Regulations*. Title 29. Pt. 1910.1200.

"Office of Management and Budget Control Numbers under the Paperwork Reduction Act, Final Rule." *Federal Register*. 61 (13 February 1996): 5507–5510.

"Toxic and Hazardous Substances." *Code of Federal Regulations*. Title 29. Pt. 1910, Subpart Z.

Internet Resources

<http://www.epa.gov/> (Environmental Protection Agency, Homepage)

<http://www.osha.gov/> (US Department of Labor, Occupational Safety and Health Administration, Homepage)

<http://www.epa.gov/epaoswer/hotline/epcra.htm> (Environmental Protection Agency; RCRA, Superfund & EPCRA Call Center)

<http://www.dot.gov/> (Department of Transportation, Homepage)

<http://hazmat.dot.gov/> (Department of Transportation, Research & Special Programs, Office of Hazardous Materials Safety)

<http://www.osha.gov/pls/oshaweb/owadisp.show _document?p_table=STANDARDS&p_id=10099> (US Department of Labor, Occupational Safety and Health Administration, Hazard Communication Standard)

Charles M. Bessey earned his CHMM in 1984 and has been an active member of the Michigan Chapter of ACHMM since its inception in 1988, serving as President, Vice President and Director. Chuck has also served on the Academy Board of Directors since 1999 and held the post of Academy President in 2002. He has also actively served on the ACHMM Leadership Committee, chaired the Internet Committee and has been an associate editor and author for the 1st Edition of the Desk Reference. He is a Director for the newly formed CyberChapter. Chuck received the Pete Cook Founders Award in 1999 and was named a Fellow of the Institute of Hazardous Materials Management (IHMM) in 2001.

Part IV

Land and Natural Resources

CHAPTER 18

The National Environmental Policy Act

James L. Oliver

Introduction

The National Environmental Policy Act (NEPA), (42 USC §4321, *et seq.*) was signed into law on January 1, 1970. The Act established a national environmental policy and set goals for the protection, maintenance, and enhancement of the environment as well as providing a process for implementing these goals throughout all Federal agencies. NEPA requires all Federal agencies to prepare a *detailed statement* on proposals for major Federal actions "significantly affecting the quality of the human environment." In addition, the Act also established the Council on Environmental Quality (CEQ) to oversee NEPA and advise the President on environmental issues.

In response to widespread and growing public concern regarding the quality of the nation's environment in the late 1960s, Congress passed the National Environmental Policy Act (NEPA) of 1969, which President Nixon signed into law on January 1, 1970. This Act was the first major environmental legislation passed by Congress and has profoundly influenced decision-making by Federal agencies for more than 34 years.

Compliance with NEPA is not discretionary with Federal agencies; rather, compliance is subject to review in Federal courts even though NEPA does not contain provisions for legal review. Through NEPA, Congress required that Federal agencies incorporate environmental factors in decision-making and directed that regulations be promulgated to establish procedures for doing so. Congress legislated a procedure, not specific outcomes, and judicial review of NEPA compliance often comes under the Administrative Procedures Act (5 USC §551–559) as well as NEPA. The legislative history of NEPA (discussed more fully in the next section of this chapter) does not indicate whether legal enforcement was discussed during development of the act. Regardless of whether some form of legal regulatory enforcement was discussed or not, a judicial review process has been established through the Federal courts and the resulting large amount of NEPA case law. Early court decisions held that Federal compliance with NEPA's environmental decision-making responsibilities was legally enforceable, thus making the Federal courts the chief enforcers of NEPA's environmental reporting mandates. The importance of NEPA resides in its role as a basic environmental responsibility of each Federal agency and their implementing regulations. Compliance with an agency's own NEPA implementing regulations does not excuse an agency from compliance with NEPA.

Passage of NEPA has been followed by the implementation of similar legislation by a number of states—commonly called State NEPA acts. Several of the states' legislative policies are identical to NEPA; however, some states (such as California) are considered more restrictive and sometimes require more extensive analysis and documentation. Many of the State statutes require all State agencies, and sometimes local governments, to prepare appropriate environmental impact statements on actions that significantly affect the environment. Like NEPA, State statutes generally do not apply to the private sector; however, some states require impact statements for specific land development projects requiring state permits or authorizations.

NEPA is a concise piece of legislation consisting of just over three pages of text, comprised of only two

sections: Titles I and II. Title I contains a Declaration of National Environmental Policy, which requires the Federal government to use all practicable means to create and maintain conditions under which man and the environment can coexist in productive harmony and fulfill the social, economic, and other requirements of present and future generations of Americans. In order to carry out the policy set forth in the Act, Congress identified in Section 101 the following six purposes for drafting NEPA:

1) Fulfill the responsibilities of each generation as trustees of the environment for succeeding generations.

2) Assure for all Americans safe, healthful, productive, and esthetically and culturally pleasing surroundings.

3) Attain the widest range of beneficial uses of the environment without degradation, risk to health or safety, or other undesirable and unintended consequences.

4) Preserve important historic, cultural, and natural aspects of our national heritage, and maintain, wherever possible, an environment which supports diversity, and variety of individual choice.

5) Achieve a balance between human population and resources which will permit a high standard of living while sharing these resources.

6) Enhance the quality of renewable resources and maximize the recycling of resources.

Section 102 of NEPA requires Federal agencies to

1) Use a systematic, interdisciplinary approach in their planning and decision-making

2) Identify and develop methods and procedures (in consultation with the Council on Environmental Quality—established by Title II of the Act)

3) Include in every report a detailed statement (commonly referred to as an *environmental impact statement*, [EIS]) addressing:

   • The potential environmental impacts of the proposed action

   • Any adverse environmental effects that cannot be avoided

   • Alternatives to the proposed action

- The relationship between local short-term uses of man's environment and the maintenance and enhancement of long-term productivity

- Any irreversible and irretrievable commitments of resources which would be involved in the proposed action should it be implemented

Title II of NEPA establishes the Council on Environmental Quality (CEQ) and requires the President to transmit to Congress, with the assistance of CEQ, an annual Environmental Quality Report on the state of the environment.

The CEQ, which is headed by a full-time chairperson, oversees NEPA with the assistance of a staff. The duties and functions of the Council are listed in Title II, Section 204 of NEPA, and include

- Gathering information on the conditions and trends in environmental quality

- Evaluating Federal programs in light of the goals established in Title I of the Act

- Developing and promoting national policies to improve environmental quality

- Conducting studies, surveys, research, and analyses relating to ecosystems and environmental quality

When Congress enacted NEPA, the intent was to foster better decision-making for all activities that could have a significant impact on the environment. As stated in the CEQ implementing regulations, 40 CFR 1500.1(C), "Ultimately, of course, it is not better documents but better decisions that count. NEPA's purpose is not to generate paperwork—even excellent paperwork—but to foster excellent action. The NEPA process is intended to help public officials make decisions that are based on understanding of environmental consequences, and take actions that protect, restore, and enhance the environment."

It should be remembered that a key component of NEPA is its role as an early planning process. It

> The legislative history of NEPA is limited; however, the birth of NEPA can be placed with the introduction of a bill by Senator James Murray in 1959 and with bills introduced by Senator Henry Jackson and Congressman John Dingell in 1969.

does not prohibit impacts to the environment, does not contain environmental regulatory requirements, and does not amend or pre-empt other Federal regulations. While NEPA forces agencies to take a hard look at the potential impacts of their actions, it was not designed to impede or delay implementation of those actions.

Legislative History of NEPA

The history of NEPA and the creation of the CEQ find their origin in a bill introduced by Senator James Murray in 1959 (Fogleman 1990). This bill was loosely based on an Act passed in 1946 in which a national employment policy was declared. This Act also established a Council of Environmental Advisors to the President. Senator Murray's bill declared a national policy on conservation and the use of natural resources, and likewise created a council of presidential environmental advisors. One of the functions of the council was to prepare an annual report for the President and/or Congress.

Senator Henry Jackson and Congressman John Dingell independently introduced legislative bills (Senate Bill 1075 and House Resolution 6750) in 1969 very similar to Senator Murray's bill. Both bills called for creating a Council on Environmental Quality; however, only the Dingell bill provided a statement of environmental policy.

In April 1969, Senator Jackson's committee held hearings and afterwards, Senator Jackson introduced an amendment which incorporated a declaration of national policy. Another important amendment submitted by Senator Jackson required *findings* by Federal officials on the environmental impact of agency actions. This requirement was replaced in NEPA by the requirement that Federal agencies prepare *detailed statements*. This is the basis for today's environmental impact statement (EIS).

Significant among the many comments made during the various hearings was one made by Professor Lynton Caldwell, an Indiana University professor, who believed the *findings* requirement to be an *action-forcing* component of NEPA, a phrase that is consistently used today in NEPA terminology. These *action-forcing* provisions require Federal decision-makers to take into account the potential consequences of their decisions on the quality of the human environment.

The Senate bill was unanimously adopted in July 1969 without debate. The House adopted its version of NEPA in September 1969, but added an amendment limiting the overall effect of the bill. However, that amendment was dropped in conference. Had this amendment remained, it would have limited NEPA's effect on agency decision-making.

Following passage of bills by both houses of Congress, it was referred back to the Senate, where additional amendments were added before the bill was sent to the Conference Committee. These amendments are known as the *Muskie-Jackson Compromise.* Senator Henry "Scoop" Jackson was the chief sponsor of NEPA in the Senate and Senator Edmund Muskie was the Chairman of the subcommittee responsible for pollution control and other environmental legislation. For some reason, the "compromise" was not well recorded in the legislative history, which may help explain the vague language presented in the compromise amendments. Nevertheless, both houses of Congress agreed to the conference report by the middle of December 1969 and President Nixon signed NEPA into law on January 1, 1970. The Act set the course for a new direction of the entire Federal establishment, requiring all Federal agencies to consider and describe the environmental consequences of major decisions and alternative courses of action. Senator Jackson's description of NEPA at its passage more than 33 years ago as "the most important and far-reaching environmental and conservation measure ever enacted by Congress . . ." still rings true today. The following sections outline the process for implementation of NEPA, a simple act with far-reaching environmental implications.

Implementation of NEPA

Due to considerable uncertainty in what Congress intended by the enactment of NEPA and consistent with Section 102(B) of the act, the CEQ in 1978 developed NEPA implementation regulations (40 CFR 1500–1508) which are binding on all Federal agencies. The regulations address the procedural provisions of NEPA and the administration of the NEPA process. Both NEPA and the CEQ implementing regulations contain *action-forcing* provisions to ensure that Federal agencies consider environmental information prior to making decisions on proposed actions. The NEPA process includes decision points at which the significance of environmental effects is assessed, project alternatives are evaluated, input from the public is obtained, and a decision prepared that publicly states the alternatives considered and the decision reached by the Federal agency.

The CEQ implementing regulations require that each Federal agency review their policies, procedures, and regulations and revise them as necessary to ensure full compliance with the purposes and provisions of NEPA. To this end, most Federal agencies have promulgated their own NEPA regulations and guidance which generally follow the CEQ procedures but are tailored for the specific mission and activities of the agency.

The NEPA Process

Before proceeding with any major Federal action, the responsible Federal agency must assess the potential environmental impacts of the proposed action and reasonable alternatives. The NEPA process can range from one step to many sequential steps requiring extensive technical expertise. The NEPA process employs what has been described as a *sliding scale* approach (see Figure 1). This approach builds from the principles of CEQ guidance by recommending that agencies focus technical expertise on proposals with the potential for significant environmental impacts and by discussing impacts in proportion to their significance. Key principles utilized in this approach include the following:

1) Proposals fall on a continuum with respect to environmental impacts.

2) Greater potential for significant impacts generally requires more detailed analysis.

3) Likewise, small environmental impacts usually require less analysis.

4) Applies the process to identification of alternatives and to analysis of environmental impacts.

Figure 1. The Sliding Scale as Used in the National Environmental Policy Act Process

The NEPA process can be divided into three basic elements for compliance using the sliding scale approach, these consist of (1) identification of Federal action and NEPA documentation determination (*i.e.*, what type of document to prepare), (2) preparation of the appropriate NEPA documentation, and (3) decision-making and NEPA follow-up. This section provides details on each of these three basic elements.

The information presented in this chapter represents a general description of the NEPA process as it applies to Federal agencies. Many Federal agencies have developed detailed procedures and have published these procedures as regulations for implementation of NEPA. See the Internet Resources section of this chapter for an internet address with links about NEPA compliance for most Federal agencies. The purpose of this chapter is to give our audience (primarily hazardous materials managers) a general understanding of the NEPA process, and does not include detailed information that can be obtained from agency specific guidelines or the numerous books prepared on the subject.

The NEPA process consists of an evaluation of the environmental effects of a Federal undertaking including any reasonable alternatives. Therefore, before commencing any project, a Federal agency must determine whether the proposed project is a major Federal action and whether it may affect the quality of the human environment (Figure 2). The NEPA process can range from one step to many sequential developments. Additionally, NEPA evaluations should be initiated with other planning activities at the earliest possible time, to ensure that planning and decisions reflect environmental values, avoid delays later in the process, and head off potential conflicts.

Many Federal agencies have developed *NEPA checklists* to assist in identifying potential environmental consequences that could necessitate more detailed analysis. Outlined below is an example of specific questions identified in the General Services Administration's *NEPA Desk Guide* (GSA 1999) that could serve as a guide in early NEPA determinations.

1) Is the action likely to be inconsistent with any applicable Federal, State, Indian tribal, or local law, regulation, or standard designed to protect any aspect of the environment?

2) Is the action likely to have results that are inconsistent with locally desired socioeconomic or other environmental conditions?

3) Is the action likely to result in the use, storage, release and/or disposal of toxic, hazardous, or radioactive material or in the exposure of people to such materials?

4) Is the action likely to adversely affect one or more elements of the natural environment?

5) Is the action likely to adversely affect one or more elements of the socio/cultural resources environment?

6) Is the action likely to generate controversy based on environmental issues?

7) Is there a high level of uncertainty about the environmental effects of the proposed action?

8) Is the action part of an ongoing pattern of actions that would cumulatively have adverse effects on the human environment?

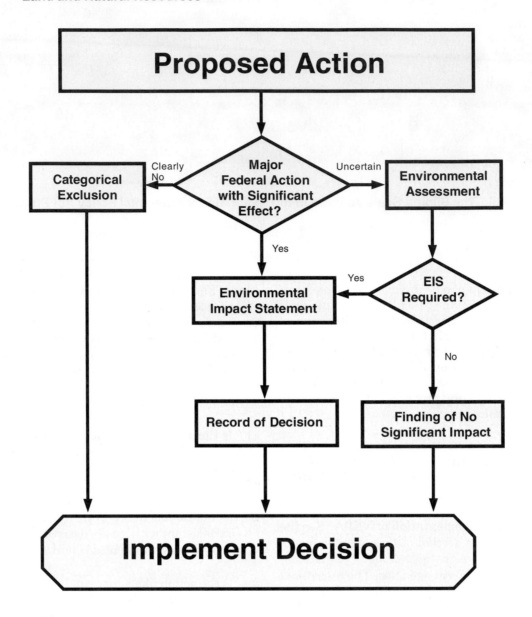

Figure 2. Flow Diagram for the General National Environmental Policy Act

9) Is the action likely to do something especially risky to the human environment?

10) Is the action likely to set a precedent for, or represent a decision in principle about future actions that could have significant effects on the human environment?

11) Is the action likely to have some other adverse effect on public health and safety or on any other environmental media or resources that are not specifically identified in any of the above questions?

Answers to these questions may include a "yes," "no," or an indication that "additional information is needed." Regardless, a clear answer of "yes" to any of these questions could trigger the need for NEPA documentation.

Defining the proposed action is very often the most difficult step in beginning the assessment process. Actions usually begin largely as concepts and in some cases as broad policies or programs whose associated biological, physical, and socioeconomic activities are minimal or unknown at the start. For example, consider a Federal agency contemplating a lease of government-owned land to a private industry to construct and operate a production facility that would serve both the Federal government and industry or the general public. This action on the part of the government is administrative in nature but could result in a range of potential biological, physical, and social impacts to the human environment. Therefore, to assess the environmental consequences of the proposed action, a firm description of the related physical activities must be prepared.

CEQ regulations require the use of *public scoping* (a process in which the agency involves the public and other State and Federal agencies in determining the range of alternatives and actions to be discussed) to identify alternatives or other significant environmental issues that may have been overlooked by the agency in its development of the proposed action. Public involvement is one of the key components of the NEPA process, and scoping is just one method utilized to involve the public.

Identification of alternatives forms another key component in NEPA. An agency must identify and develop real alternatives as opposed to merely looking at options that speculation might suggest. On the other hand, NEPA does not require that all possible alternatives be evaluated, only the *reasonable* alternatives. In addition to these reasonable alternatives, NEPA also requires that agencies include the *no action* alternative. The *no action alternative* is defined as the action that would happen to the environment if the Federal agency's proposed action was not implemented.

There are three levels of analysis, depending on whether or not a proposed Federal action could significantly affect the quality of the human environment. Under NEPA, the term *human environment* encompasses the natural and physical environment (air, water, geography, and geology) as well as the relationship of people with that environment including health and safety, socioeconomics (jobs, housing, schools, transportation), cultural resources, noise, and aesthetics. These three levels include

1) Categorical exclusion determinations,

2) Preparation of an environmental assessment and its associated finding of no significant impact (EA/FONSI), or

3) If there is a potential for significant impacts, preparation of an environmental impact statement (EIS).

Although general guidance on the most appropriate level of NEPA documentation has been developed by many Federal Agencies who have identified classes of action that generally fall within one of the three levels for NEPA analysis, a modification of the sliding scale approach (Figure 3) illustrates the level of NEPA analysis required and the type of NEPA documentation necessary for a proposed action. If the proposed action will

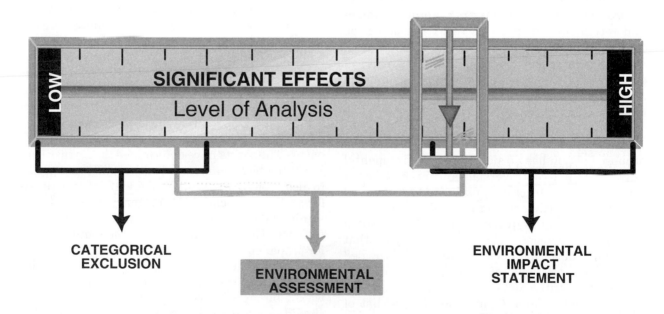

Figure 3. Use of the Sliding Scale in NEPA Documentation

clearly have a significant effect, then the scale slides to the right and an environmental impact statement is required. On the other end of the scale lie actions with only insignificant effects that can be categorically excluded from further NEPA documentation. As depicted in the figure, there are areas of overlap where the effects of the proposed action are not clearly known. In those cases, it is generally more conservative to prepare the next higher level of NEPA documentation.

Categorical Exclusions

A Federal agency may *categorically exclude* an action from detailed environmental analysis if it falls within a class of action that has been previously determined as having no significant environmental impact. CEQ regulations require Federal agencies to develop lists of actions, which normally are categorically excluded from environmental evaluation under their NEPA regulations. These are actions demonstrated individually or cumulatively not to have a potentially significant effect on the quality of the human environment. For example, the routine maintenance (*e.g.*, oil changes) of vehicles for a Federal agency could impact the environment if not handled properly. However, other environmental precautions are in place to ensure that the used oil is disposed of correctly, and this recurring action was previously discussed in a *Federal Register* notice available to the public. In this notice, the Federal agency outlined the environmental precautions that would be taken and recommended that this recurring action be categorically excluded from NEPA documentation. Prior to the proposed action becoming a categorical exclusion, the agency must weigh the comments received by all commentors including individuals and State and Federal regulators.

Therefore, if an agency determines that the proposed action has no significant environmental impacts, is not controversial, and is on a list of agency actions categorically excluded from detailed analysis, no further action is needed. Although NEPA does not require documentation of a categorical exclusion, some agencies require that some form of formal documentation be provided for this step. Documentation, if prepared, usually consists of a written determination containing the proposed action and some type of checklist of environmental conditions that is generally

reviewed by more than one NEPA professional. The determination is filed, and the proposed action can proceed.

Environmental Assessments

If a Federal agency has identified a major action but is not sure if there is a potential for significant environmental impacts, it may decide to prepare an *environmental assessment* (EA) (See Figure 2). An EA is a concise public document prepared to determine whether an *environmental impact statement* (EIS) or a *finding of no significant impact* (FONSI) is needed. Federal agencies typically list classes of actions that normally require the preparation of an EA. An EA is a public document that briefly provides the evidence and analysis necessary to make a threshold determination of environmental significance. There is no defined methodology to be used in the preparation of an EA, but the selected method must be justifiable. An EA must include brief discussions of the need for the proposed action, alternatives to the proposed action, environmental impacts of the proposed action and alternatives, and a list of agencies and private parties consulted. The analysis presented in the EA is less rigorous than that performed for an EIS, and the analysis does not have to be as detailed. The EA should not form conclusions but should present sufficient information to reach a conclusion.

Specific page lengths for EAs are not presented in the CEQ regulations, but CEQ guidance recommends from 10 to 15 pages, with sufficient background data incorporated by reference. However, the page length should be proportional to the complexity of the action under consideration. Over the past few years, the tendency for agencies is to prepare EAs with significantly greater number of pages, sometimes numbering more than 100 pages. The courts have determined that larger EAs might not be adequate and may require an agency to also prepare an EIS. An EA will not substitute for an EIS, especially if the agency has identified significant environmental effects for the proposed action and has not completed all the requirements for preparing an EIS, such as involving the public or other agencies in the process as defined by NEPA. In other words, if an agency believes there would be significant environmental effects, it should prepare an EIS rather than a lengthy EA.

Findings of No Significant Impact. Based on the EA, a Federal agency must either prepare an EIS if it has determined that its proposed action may have a significant impact on the environment or it must prepare a finding of no significant impact (FONSI) if it has determined that the action will not have significant environmental impacts. Should it be determined that an EIS is required, the process outlined in the next section is followed. However, if a FONSI is prepared it must identify the reasons in some detail for the agency's determination. If certain factors used in the analysis are given greater weight than others, the agency must explain those reasons and present the information. Procedurally, the EA may be attached to the FONSI and incorporated by reference or it may be summarized in the FONSI. Other documents noted in the EA must be referenced completely.

Each EA and FONSI must be made available to the public. Each Federal agency may choose the most appropriate method of accomplishing this goal, as long as they ensure that all interested or affected parties are notified. Most Federal agencies maintain a list of interested individuals, agencies, organizations, *etc.*, that are interested in activities of that agency, and therefore the agency automatically sends each a copy of all EAs and FONSIs. In addition, CEQ recommends that each agency also place a notice of availability in the *Federal Register* and in national publications for proposed actions with a national scope. For regional or site-specific actions, a notice of availability may also be published in local newspapers.

Under limited circumstances, the CEQ recommends that FONSIs be published 30 days before an agency's final decision not to prepare an EIS. These circumstances are for two reasons: (1) the proposed action is, or is closely similar to, one which normally requires the preparation of an EIS or (2) the nature of the proposed action is one without precedent.

Environmental Impact Statements

If a Federal agency proposes an action that does not qualify for a categorical exclusion or FONSI, it must prepare an environmental impact statement (EIS). This constitutes the other end of the sliding scale or those actions that could significantly affect the environment. As the sliding scale implies, EISs are more formal than EAs and contain considerations of the environmental effects of the proposed action that include: adverse effects that cannot be avoided; alternatives to the proposal; the relationship between the short-term and long-term uses of the environment; and irreversible and irretrievable commitments of resources as outlined in CEQ regulations.

The major steps in the NEPA process are outlined in Figure 4. This figure illustrates all three levels of NEPA analysis and provides additional detail on the steps in the preparation of an Environmental Impact Statement.

Once a decision has been made to prepare an EIS, the first step in the NEPA process is the public notification through publication of a *Notice of Intent* (NOI) in the *Federal Register*. The NOI describes the proposed action, possible alternatives the agency is considering, background information on issues and potential impacts, and the proposed scoping process including whether, when, and where any scoping meeting will be held. The NOI also contains a contact point within the agency.

After publication of the NOI, the agency generally begins the scoping process. As noted under EAs, scoping is the public process whereby an agency involves the public to determine the scope of issues to be addressed in an EIS and identifies the significant issues. Comments are solicited in a number of ways including in writing, voice mail, email, fax, and at public meetings and, possibly, public workshops.

The EIS is prepared in two stages: a draft EIS and a final EIS. The draft EIS describes, analyzes, and compares the potential environmental impacts of the alternatives that could be chosen to accomplish the purpose and need identified by the Federal agency. A draft EIS is issued to allow the public to review and comment on the proposed action and alternatives before any decisions are made. If the Federal agency has a preferred alternative at this stage, it will be identified in the draft EIS.

EIS Format. The CEQ regulations recommend that Federal agencies use a format for EISs which will encourage good analysis and clear presentation of the alternatives including the proposed action. The following standard format should be used in

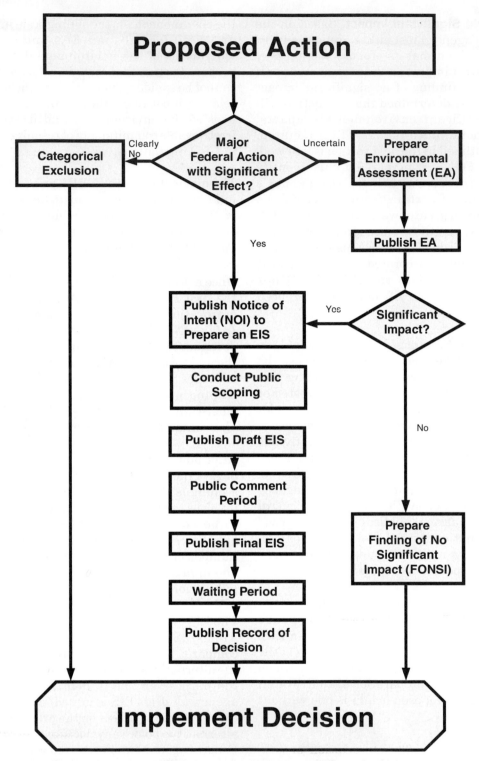

Figure 4. National Environmental Policy Act Process Flow Path

developing the EIS, unless the agency determines that there is a compelling reason to do otherwise:

- Cover sheet
- Summary

- Table of contents
- Purpose of and need for action
- Alternatives including proposed action
- Affected environment

- Environmental consequences

- List of preparers

- List of agencies, organizations, and persons to whom copies of the statement are sent

- Index

- Appendices (if any)

Cover Sheet. The cover sheet lists: the agency preparing the EIS; the title of the proposed action; the location of the proposed action; the name, address, telephone, fax, and email address (if available) of an individual from the agency who can supply additional information; whether the EIS is a draft or final; a one-paragraph abstract of the EIS; and the date by which all comments must be received.

Summary. The summary should normally not exceed 15 pages, and should emphasize the major conclusions in the EIS, and identify any controversial areas (including those identified during the public scoping period), as well as the issues to be resolved, such as choosing between alternatives.

Table of Contents. Consists of a listing of material presented in the EIS, including all tables and figures.

Purpose of and Need for Action. This statement briefly specifies the underlying purpose and need to which the agency is responding in proposing the alternatives including the proposed action.

Alternatives. This section provides an objective evaluation of all reasonable alternatives as well as a discussion of all alternatives considered and eliminated from detailed study, identifies the preferred alternative if one exists, includes the alternative of no action, and presents a comparison of alternatives.

Affected Environment. The affected environment is the area affected or created by the alternatives presented in the EIS. The description of the affected environment must be sufficient for a reader to understand the alternative's environmental effects. The CEQ regulations state that this section be brief, with less important material being summarized, consolidated, or referenced.

Environmental Consequences. This section presents the scientific and analytic basis for the comparisons identified in the alternatives section. The discussion includes the environmental impacts of the alternatives including the proposed action, any adverse environmental effects that cannot be avoided should the proposal be implemented, and the relationship between short-term productivity and any irreversible or irretrievable commitments of resources which would be involved in the proposal should it be implemented. Duplication of information presented in the alternatives section should be avoided unless repetition is needed to increase clarification. In addition, direct and indirect effects and their significance should be presented as well as means to mitigate adverse environmental impacts.

List of Preparers. The names and qualifications of people who were primarily responsible for preparing the EIS or other significant support documentation must be included in the EIS. Where possible, the particular person responsible for preparing a specific section or analysis should be identified.

Appendices (if any). The appendices should not contain analyses and information on environmental effects and alternatives; rather they should supplement information as appropriate to understanding the proposed action and alternatives. Appendices are for amplification or support of critical analyses in the EIS. They are not a data bank or library for total reference support. They should contain only major substantiating data, essential relevant descriptions of environmental components, important professional reports, responses to comments received on the draft EIS, copies of major legislative and executive documents, agency agreements, or other information necessary for analytical or decision-making purposes. If an appendix is prepared, it should be circulated with the EIS or be available upon request.

In addition to the items listed above, the EIS must also present a list of the agencies, organizations, and persons to whom the agency sent a copy of the EIS and an index. Many EISs frequently contain additional information to assist the reader in understanding the proposed action and may include maps, tables, listing of abbreviations, glossaries, *etc.*

Draft EIS. Once the Draft EIS is filed with the Environmental Protection Agency (EPA), a minimum of 45 days is provided for Federal agencies, State and local governments, Native American tribes, and stakeholders to comment on the Draft EIS. However, comment periods of 60 to 90 days or longer are not uncommon among Federal agencies. The public comment period begins upon publication of a Notice of Availability (NOA) for the Draft EIS in the *Federal Register*. The EPA will publish the NOA in the *Federal Register;* however, the agency may also publish its own NOA at its discretion. Generally, at least one public meeting is held to solicit public input on the Draft EIS. Other methods for submission of comments for the EIS include written comments, fax, telephone, email, *etc.* All comments received by the Federal agency are considered to the extent practicable depending on whether they are received by the date indicated in the NOA and the EIS.

Final EIS. Following the public comment period, a Final EIS is published and distributed similar to the Draft EIS. The Final EIS reflects consideration of all comments received on the Draft EIS, contains the agency's responses to those comments, and provides revised EIS text. The Final EIS must also identify the preferred alternative or alternatives. Following distribution and filing with the EPA, the availability of the Final EIS is announced by an NOA in the *Federal Register*, published by the EPA.

Record of Decision. Once the Final EIS is published, a minimum 30-day waiting period (or 90 days after publication of the Draft EIS) is required by NEPA before a Federal agency can issue a *Record of Decision* (ROD), generally with an announcement in the *Federal Register*. The time periods are calculated from the date of publication of the Notices of Availability by the Environmental Protection Agency in the *Federal Register*. The ROD notifies the public of the agency's decision on the proposed action and the reasons for that decision. The ROD may also include consideration of other decision factors such as costs, technical feasibility, agency statutory mission, and/or national objectives in addition to environmental impacts.

The Federal agency must identify all alternatives considered by the agency in reaching its decision and must specify the alternative or alternatives which were considered to be environmentally preferable. The Federal agency is not required to select the environmentally preferable alternative; however, a discussion must be presented to support the selection of agency's preferred alternative. The agency's preferred alternative and the environmentally preferable alternative are often the same.

Finally, the ROD must state whether all practicable means to avoid or minimize environmental harm from the alternative selected have been adopted, and if not, why. Where applicable for mitigation (refer to the "Mitigation" section for a definition relative to NEPA), a monitoring and enforcement program must be adopted and summarized.

Implement Action. Once the Federal agency has prepared a Record of Decision and met the time requirements, it is free to implement the action. Federal agencies may provide for monitoring to ensure that the decision(s) made are carried out in accordance with their Record of Decision. Mitigation and any other conditions established during the course of the EIS or during its subsequent review and committed as part of the ROD must be implemented by the agency.

Mitigation

Federal agencies shall mitigate actions to reduce otherwise significant environmental effects to a reduced level. NEPA requires that mitigation measures be subject to public comment. CEQ defines *mitigation* to include

- Avoiding the impact altogether by not taking a certain action or parts of an action

- Minimizing impact by limiting the degree or magnitude of the action and its implementation

- Rectifying the impact by repairing, rehabilitating, or restoring the affected environment

- Reducing or eliminating the impact over time through the use of appropriate preservation and maintenance operations during the life of the action

- Compensating for the impact by replacing or providing substitute resources or environments

The Benefits of Using NEPA in Decision-Making

The passage of NEPA has resulted in Federal agencies incorporating environmental values in their everyday decision-making process. For most agencies, conducting NEPA reviews is now an integral part of their program planning process. Numerous Federal agencies have developed multidisciplinary staffs to oversee and assist with NEPA compliance for their agency.

The primary benefit of implementing NEPA has been more protection for the environment in which Federal activities are undertaken. This protection has been enhanced because the NEPA review process resulted in positive environmental changes to the proposed projects before they were implemented. Specifically, these changes have been in alternatives to the project design, location of the proposed action or operation, review of a greater range of alternatives presented by the Federal agency, implementation of mitigation measures, enhanced opportunity for public involvement in the decision-making process, and in some cases, reduced costs because of changes made in projects before implementation.

Finally, the NEPA process can assist other Federal agencies by allowing them to address regulatory compliance issues with other environmental laws as part of a single review process rather than as separate reviews under each law, thereby reducing the amount of paperwork, staff time, and effort.

NEPA Impact Assessment Areas and Implications for Hazardous Materials Management

As a result of case law and the issuance of Executive Orders, a number of impact assessment areas directly relevant to hazardous materials management have received considerable attention in NEPA documents. Three of the more relevant impact assessment areas for hazardous materials managers include:

- Cumulative Impacts

- Environmental Justice

- Pollution Prevention/Waste Minimization

A short summary of these areas and how they can be assessed in NEPA documents is provided in the following paragraphs.

Cumulative Impacts

Human activities have resulted in numerous, complex, and detrimental effects on the human environment. Many of these effects are immediately visible and direct (such as the construction of a new interstate highway or a landfill for municipal waste). Other effects are not directly visible and may take considerable time to unfold (such as groundwater contamination leaking into a major river). A single large project and its associated activities often have severe impacts on the environment. However, a large number of small projects over time may have an even more serious environmental impact.

Cumulative effects on the human environment are defined by CEQ regulations (40 CFR 1508.7) as:

> the impact on the environment which results from the incremental impact of the action when added to other past, present, and reasonably foreseeable future actions regardless of what agency (Federal or non-Federal) or person undertakes such other actions.

The regulations further explain that "cumulative impacts can result from individually minor but collectively significant actions taking place over a period of time." Other Federal, State, and local development programs all have the potential to contribute to cumulative impacts on any project. CEQ regulations implementing NEPA require that Federal agencies analyze the cumulative effects of their actions on the environment. This means that cumulative effects must be addressed in an EA or EIS, and in the screening of projects that are normally categorically excluded from further NEPA review.

Finally, in the simplest everyday terms, the analysis of cumulative effects means the consideration of the impacts of a proposed action in the context of everything else that is going on, has gone on, or to the best of one's knowledge, will go on in the vicinity of the proposed action.

Based on the broad definition provided by CEQ, many Federal agencies developed procedures and methods to analyze cumulative effects, all with mixed results. Therefore, in January 1997, CEQ published the handbook, *Considering Cumulative Impacts under NEPA* in order to provide a framework for advancing environmental impact analysis. This handbook introduces the complexities of cumulative effects, outlines general principles, presents useful steps, and provides information on methods of cumulative effects analysis and data sources.

Based on the CEQ handbook, cumulative impact analysis has three main components: (1) scoping, (2) description of the affected environment, (3) determining the environmental consequences of the proposed action. The CEQ handbook further outlines eleven *steps* that make up these three components of cumulative effects analysis. Following and accurately answering these questions should ensure that cumulative effects are analyzed appropriately in the NEPA document.

1) Identify the significant cumulative effects issues associated with the proposed action and define the assessment goals

2) Establish the geographic scope for the analysis

3) Establish the time frame for the analysis

4) Identify other actions affecting the resources, ecosystems, and human communities of concern

5) Characterize the resources, ecosystems, and human communities identified in scoping in terms of their response to change and capacity to withstand stresses

6) Characterize the stresses affecting these resources, ecosystems, and human communities and their relation to regulatory thresholds

7) Define a baseline condition for the resources, ecosystems, and human communities

8) Identify the important cause-and-effect relationships between human activities and resources, ecosystems, and human communities

9) Determine the magnitude and significance of cumulative effects

10) Modify or add alternatives to avoid, minimize, or mitigate significant cumulative effects

11) Monitor the cumulative effects of the selected alternative and adapt management

In summary, cumulative impacts analysis involves the prediction of effects arising from multiple interacting sources over relatively long periods of time. It is more complicated and uncertain than the analysis of direct or easily foreseeable indirect impacts, but it can be done. Completion of the cumulative effects analysis is important to do in order to address the fundamental requirements of NEPA.

Environmental Justice

The environmental impacts of a proposed action are not equally distributed to everyone in society. Evidence of this can be seen in the location and operation of various facilities. For example, chemical manufacturing plants, hazardous waste landfills, highways and other developments with negative environmental consequences have historically been more common in low-income and minority communities. Therefore, low-income and minority populations have been more likely to be exposed to physical displacement and adverse impacts on their cultural institutions, traditional forms of land use, community cultural character, religious practices, and financial well-being. The basic precept behind environmental justice is to recognize these disproportionate impacts and try to avoid them. Thus, *environmental justice* (EJ) is the pursuit of equal justice and equal protection for all people under the environmental statutes and regulations, including NEPA. In everyday language, EJ means ensuring that low-income and minority populations (*i.e.*, the *EJ Community*) are not exposed to unjustly high and adverse environmental impacts from any proposed action pursuant to NEPA. Specifically, an *EJ Community* is any aggregated or dispersed population that

1) Is a low-income population based on the Bureau of the Census Current Population Reports (Series P–60 on Income and Poverty),

2) Is over 50 percent minority, or

3) Contains a minority population percentage meaningfully greater than the minority population percentage in the general population or other appropriate unit of geographic analysis. For example, Federally Recognized Indian Tribes or groups within tribes, which

are made up of minority individuals, may be identified as EJ Communities.

EJ was brought to the forefront of national attention in 1982 when approximately 500 demonstrators gathered in Warren County, North Carolina to protest the siting of a PCB landfill in a predominately African-American and low-income community (GAO 1983). Similar instances were subsequently identified and in the late 1980s and early 1990s a number of conferences were held which further increased awareness. As a result, Federal and State policy-makers became increasingly aware and involved in environmental equity discussions. Therefore, in February 1994, President Clinton issued Executive Order 12898, *Federal Actions to Address Environmental Justice in Minority Populations and Low-Income Populations*. In the memorandum issued with the Executive Order, President Clinton specifically recognized the importance of procedures under NEPA to identify and address EJ concerns. As a result of this Executive Order in 1994, the Office of Environmental Equity within EPA was renamed the Office of Environmental Justice.

In April 1998, EPA issued *Guidance for Incorporating Environmental Justice Concerns in EPA's NEPA Compliance Analyses* (EPA 1998). In this document, EPA defined environmental justice as:

> The fair treatment and meaningful involvement of all people regardless of race, color, national origin, or income with respect to the development, implementation, and enforcement of environmental laws, regulations, and policies. Fair treatment means that no group of people, including racial, ethnic, or socioeconomic group should bear a disproportionate share of the negative environmental consequences resulting from industrial, municipal, and commercial operations or the execution of Federal, State, local, and Tribal programs and policies.

NEPA provides a major planning context in which EJ issues can be and are addressed. In December 1997, CEQ issued *Environmental Justice Guidance under the National Environmental Policy Act* (CEQ 1997). The Presidential Memorandum identifies four important ways to consider EJ under NEPA, which are summarized in the CEQ guidance as follows:

1) Each Federal agency should analyze the environmental effects, including human health, economic, and social effects of Federal actions, including effects on minority populations, low-income populations, and Indian Tribes, when such analysis is required by NEPA.

2) Mitigation measures identified as part of an EA, FONSI, EIS, or a ROD, should, whenever feasible, address significant adverse environmental effects of proposed Federal actions on minority populations, low-income populations, and Indian Tribes.

3) Each Federal agency must provide opportunities for effective community participation in the NEPA process, including identifying potential effects and mitigation measures in consultation with affected communities and improving the accessibility of public meetings, crucial documents, and notices.

4) Review of NEPA compliance (such as EPA's review under Section 309 of the Clean Air Act) must ensure that the lead agency preparing the NEPA analyses and documentation has appropriately analyzed environmental effects on minority populations, low-income populations, or Indian Tribes, including human health, social, and economic effects.

In practical terms, the application of EJ should be performed as part of a normal NEPA review process. This means considering the potential for disproportionate adverse health or environmental effects on EJ communities at each stage of NEPA review and analysis. The following are decision points or activities in which EJ should be considered:

- Screening a potential categorical exclusion to ensure that no unique circumstances exist that would require preparation of an EA or EIS

- Formal scoping for an EIS, and informal scoping for an EA

- Conducting NEPA analyses

- Circulating reports for review and comment

- Designing mitigation measures

- Implementing mitigation

The incorporation of EJ into NEPA documents is an ever-evolving process. However, a number of

Federal agencies are seeing significant progress and a growing list of *success stories* relevant to the Hazardous Materials Manager are occurring each year. For example, EPA's Office of Solid Waste and Emergency Response publish a yearly report on compliance with EJ. The most recent report, entitled *Environmental Justice Success Stories Report (FY 1999 – 2001)* (EPA 2002), lists 48 success stories and is organized into five different sections:

1) Brownfield's Training and Revitalization

2) Superfund

3) Resource Conservation and Recovery Act (RCRA)

4) Environmental Justice Awareness Training

5) Community Involvement, Outreach, and Planning

These success stories highlight projects that demonstrate EPA's success in integrating environmental justice into its programs. A review of these stories would be beneficial for the NEPA professional.

Pollution Prevention/Waste Minimization

Pollution prevention is a multimedia approach that reduces waste generation and the emission of pollutants released to land, air, and water without transferring the pollutant from one medium to another. Pollution prevention, referred to as P2, is defined as practices that reduce the amount and/ or toxicity of pollutants in waste streams or emissions to the environment. If less hazardous or toxic pollutants are produced, then there will be less hazardous and toxic wastes that require disposal or are released to the environment. The key principle in pollution prevention is that it is much less expensive and considerably easier to prevent pollution than it is to capture, store, transport, and neutralize the material.

Several Federal laws, Executive Orders, and Federal guidance documents that promote pollution prevention include:

• The Pollution Prevention Act of 1990

• Council on Environmental Quality, *Guidance to Federal Agencies on Incorporating Pollution*

Prevention Principles, Techniques, and Mechanisms into their Planning and Decision-making Processes and Evaluating and Reporting Those Efforts in Documents Prepared Pursuant to NEPA (58 FR 6478)

• Executive Order 12856, *Federal Compliance with Right-to-Know Laws and Pollution Prevention Requirements* (August 3, 1993)

• Executive Order 12873, *Federal Acquisition, Recycling, and Waste Prevention* (October 20, 1993)

Many strategies have been developed and used to reduce pollution and therefore protect environmental resources. Pollution prevention techniques can include the following:

• Modifying equipment or technology

• Modifying processes or procedures

• Reformulating or redesigning products

• Substituting raw materials

• Improving housekeeping, maintenance, training, or inventory control

• Incorporating demand-side management when designing or renewing projects

• Integrating resource planning into project planning

NEPA provides an excellent opportunity for pollution prevention in project siting, design, construction, operation, and decommissioning. Recognition of these opportunities in NEPA documents allows the Federal agency to promote the very essence of NEPA—protection of the human environment.

Bibliography

"Administrative Procedures Act." PL(89-554), 60 *Statutes* 237. US Code. Title 5, Sec. 551-559.

Bear, D. "NEPA at 19: A Primer on an 'Old' Law with Solutions to New Problems." *Environmental Law Reporter, News & Analysis.* 19: 10060; 1989.

Council on Environmental Quality. *Code of Federal Regulations.* Title 40. Pts. 1500–1508.

Council on Environmental Quality. *Considering Cumulative Effects Under the National Environmental Policy Act.* Washington, DC: CEQ January 1997.

Department of Energy, Office of NEPA Oversight. *Recommendations for the Preparation of Environmental Impact Statements.* Washington, DC: DOE, May 1993.

Environmental Protection Agency. Office of External Affairs, Office of Federal Activities. *Policies and Procedures for the Review of Federal Actions Impacting the Environment.* Washington, DC: EPA, 3 October 1984.

Environmental Protection Agency. Office of Federal Activities. *Guidance for Incorporating Environmental Justice Concerns in EPA's NEPA Compliance Analyses.* Washington, DC: EPA, April 1998.

Environmental Protection Agency. Office of Solid Waste and Emergency Response. *Environmental Justice Success Stories Report (FY 1999 – 2002).* Washington, DC: EPA, September 2002.

"Filing System Guidance for Implementing 1506.9 and 1506.10 of the CEQ Regulations." *Federal Register* 54 (1989): 9592.

Fogleman, V. M. *Guide to the National Environmental Policy Act: Interpretations, Applications, and Compliance.* Westport, CT: Quorum Books, 1990.

"Forty Most Asked Questions Concerning CEQ's National Environmental Policy Act Regulations." *Federal Register* 51 (25 April 1986): 15618.

General Accounting Office. *Siting of Hazardous Waste Landfills and Their Correlation with Racial and Economic Status of Surrounding Communities.* RCED-83-168. Washington, DC: GAO, 14 June 1983.

General Services Administration. *National Environmental Policy Act NEPA Desk Guide.* Washington, DC: GSA, October 1999.

Office of the President. *Federal Actions to Address Environmental Justice in Minority Populations and Low-Income Populations,* with accompanying *Memorandum.* Executive Order 12898. 11 February 1994.

"Scoping Guidance." *Federal Register* 46 (7 May 1981): 25461.

Internet Resources

In addition to the numerous books and articles published yearly regarding NEPA, it is recommended that anyone interested in learning more about NEPA and its implementation, visit NEPAnet, a website maintained by the President's Council on Environmental Quality, for additional detail regarding policies and guidance regarding NEPA. The URL for the website is: <http://ceq.eh.doc.gov/nepa/nepanet.htm>.

James L. Oliver is a Senior Project Manager with Tetra Tech NUS, Inc., in Aiken, South Carolina. Mr. Oliver has a BS in Biology from Murray State University. He has over 32 years professional experience in the management of a broad range of environmental and regulatory projects including: 13 years as a Fishery Research Biologist with the US Fish and Wildlife Service and over 19 years in the private environmental consulting field. Mr. Oliver has extensive experience with the National Environmental Policy Act process and, since 1994, has successfully managed or provided technical input and direction to over a dozen major environmental impact statements. He has experience with the implementing requirements of the Council on Environmental Quality and the NEPA public involvement process. The projects he has participated in include environmental impacts associated with construction and operation of reservoirs and associated infrastructure (e.g., roads, bridges, and utilities), pumped storage hydroelectric operations for peaking electrical usage, small-scale hydroelectric redevelopment in rural and remote locations, environmental studies in large reservoirs, winter navigation in the Great Lakes and interconnecting river systems, environmental impacts of operating wastewater treatment plants as well as nuclear production and generation facilities.

Mr. Oliver would like to thank Mr. Andrew R. Grainger, J. Peyton Doub, and Kent T. Cubbage for their willingness to review and improve this chapter on NEPA compliance for Hazardous Materials Managers.

Their thoughtful insight and comments contribute to the improvement and usefulness for all NEPA professionals. In addition, Mr. Oliver would like to thank Dr. Bruce H. Bradford for his technical review, comments, and guidance in the preparation of the 1999 version of this Chapter.

CHAPTER 19

CERCLA Liability and All Appropriate Inquiry

Lawrence J. (Sandy) Horan III, MBA, JD

Introduction

While *Superfund* does not appear often in headlines, the Comprehensive Environmental Response, Compensation, and Liability Act (CERCLA, also known as *Superfund*) remains a viable and pivotal piece of legislation controlling the business and environmental decisions of lenders, property owners, facility operators and their consultants and contractors. CERCLA entered the environmental regulatory arena in 1980 and has been amended three times since then. Its initial purposes were to mandate cleanup of abandoned hazardous disposal sites and to allocate responsibility for that cleanup response. More recently, the *Brownfields Amendments* (as defined below) clarified formerly uncertain areas such as the scope of an environmental site assessment necessary to meet CERCLA's *Innocent Landowner* defense. This chapter will examine just these matters—how CERCLA came about, liability and defenses under the Act, as well as significant aspects of the new *Brownfields Amendments* and the status of the United States Environmental Protection Agency's (EPA) *All Appropriate Inquiries* Rule.

CERCLA: Its Importance Today

CERCLA, commonly referred to as Superfund, has been in effect since 1980 (PL 95–510, December 11, 1980) and is, the pivotal statute responsible for the environmental industry as we know it today. Since its promulgation, CERCLA has been amended three times to address deficiencies or to clarify the scope of its coverage. The basic goals of CERCLA have been to protect human health and the environment and, through the Brownfields portion of the legislation, to return severely environmentally impacted properties to the stream of commerce. CERCLA appears to have become more benevolent over time, evolving from a primarily enforcement-related focus to that of a more equitable allocation of cleanup responsibility and increased economic redevelopment of impacted properties. Recent changes in CERCLA brought about by the Small Business Liability Relief and Brownfields Revitalization Act (the *Brownfields Amendments*, PL 107–118, January 11, 2002) clarified the scope of the *All Appropriate Inquiries* requirements for CERCLA's *Innocent Landowner* defense as well as adding new landowner liability protections. The *Brownfields Amendments* also provide for funding and guidance for cleanup of Brownfields sites. On August 26, 2004, EPA published its proposed rule on *All Appropriate Inquiries* in the Federal Register (69 FR 52542). It is expected that EPA will promulgate the final rule in late 2005.

History of CERCLA

CERCLA was originally promulgated in response to the public outcry in 1978 over the infamous and highly publicized Love Canal site, an uncontrolled hazardous waste landfill located in Niagara Falls, New York. CERCLA created a fund (commonly referred to as Superfund) and process for governmental cleanup of abandoned toxic waste sites and mandated recovery of governmental cleanup costs from parties potentially responsible for the creation of and/or disposal of *hazardous substances* (CERCLA's definition of *hazardous substance* is discussed in a later section). CERCLA quickly earned draconian status based upon its strict, joint and several liability scheme which extended liability to any *potentially responsible party*

(PRP), whether or not they caused or directly contributed *hazardous substances* to the site.

CERCLA was amended with the passage of the Superfund Amendments and Reauthorization Act (SARA) of 1986 (PL 99–499, Oct. 17, 1986). SARA overhauled some of CERCLA's provisions, increased its fund and penalty amounts and added the Emergency Planning and Community Right-to-Know Act (EPCRA) provisions of the law. EPCRA (42 USC §§11001–11050) is often referred to as SARA Title III. EPCRA imposes certain reporting, emergency planning and emergency response obligations on manufacturers and users of both CERCLA *hazardous substances* and *extremely hazardous substances*.

CERCLA was amended a second time in 1996 as part of the *Asset Conservation, Lender Liability, and Deposit Insurance Protection Act* (PL 104–208, September 30, 1996) in order to clarify the scope of CERCLA liability with respect to lenders and trustees. These so-called *Lender Liability Amendments*, discussed later in this chapter, made it clear that a secured creditor or lender will not fall within the definition of **owner or operator**. The lender is protected where it holds only an indicia of ownership in the property and acts primarily to protect its security interest (*e.g.*, through foreclosure or post-foreclosure acts) but does not participate in the management of the facility. See CERCLA §9601 (20)(E–G).

Potentially Responsible Parties

CERCLA §9607(a) identifies four classes of potentially responsible parties (PRPs) liable for cleanup which include: (i) the (current) owner and operator of a facility; (ii) any person who at the time of disposal of any hazardous substance owned or operated any facility at which such *hazardous substances* were disposed of; (iii) any person who by contract, agreement, or otherwise arranged for disposal or treatment or transport of *hazardous substances*; and (iv) any person who accepts or accepted any hazardous substances for transport to a disposal or treatment facility selected by such person.

The third round of CERCLA amendments come into play with the Small Business Liability Relief and Brownfields Revitalization Act (the *Brownfields Amendments*), which became law in 2002. Importantly, the *Brownfields Amendments* help define what constitutes *All Appropriate Inquiries* for purposes of establishing the **Innocent Landowner Defense** and the **Contiguous Property Owner Protection** and the **Bona Fide Prospective Purchaser Protection** from CERCLA liability. The *Brownfields Amendments* also address Brownfields redevelopment and establish federal funds for that purpose. The term **Brownfields** has been coined to mean properties that have been affected by releases of *hazardous substances*, petroleum or other pollutants.

Definition of CERCLA Hazardous Substances

CERCLA liability accrues when there has been a release or threatened release of a **hazardous substance.** CERCLA broadly defines the term *hazardous substance*, 42 USC §9601(14)(A–F), by incorporating the definitions of various pollutants, wastes, substances and materials regulated under the Clean Water Act, the Clean Air Act, the Resource Conservation and Recovery Act, the Toxic Substances Control Act, as well as CERCLA §9602. CERCLA specifically excludes petroleum from the definition of *hazardous substance*, which includes crude oil or any fraction thereof, that is not

Definitions of CERCLA Hazardous Substances

CERCLA §9601(14)(A) defines the term *hazardous substance* to include pollutants and wastes from other regulatory programs (see below) but specifically excludes natural gas, natural gas liquids, liquefied natural gas, or synthetic gas usable for fuel (or mixtures of natural gas and such synthetic gas) from the definition of hazardous substances.

Clean Water Act

42 USC §9601(14)(A) and (D): "Substances designated pursuant to Sections 1321(b)(2)(A) or Section 1317(a) of Title 33."

Clean Air

42 USC §9601(14)(E): "[A]ny hazardous air pollutant listed under Section 112 of the Clean Air Act [42 USC §7412]."

Resource Conservation and Recovery Act

42 USC §9601(14)(C): "[A]ny hazardous waste having the characteristics identified under or listed pursuant to Section 3001 of the Solid Waste Disposal Act [42 U.S.C. §6921] (but not including any waste the regulation of which under the Solid Waste Disposal Act [42 U.S.C. §6901 *et seq.*] has been suspended by Act of Congress)." The Solid Waste Disposal Act of 1980 amended the Resource Conservation and Recovery Act (RCRA).

Toxic Substances and Control Act

42 USC §9601(14)(F): "[A]ny imminently hazardous chemical substance or mixture with respect to which the [EPA] has taken action pursuant to Section 2606 of Title 15."

otherwise specifically listed or designated as a *hazardous substance*. Despite CERCLA's petroleum exclusion, most, if not all, petroleum substances continue to be regulated under other Federal, State and local environmental laws, such as those applicable to petroleum storage tanks or spill/release reporting and response.

CERCLA's Liability Scheme

Who Can Be Liable? Clients, Consultants and Others

CERCLA's liability scheme has received mixed reviews over the years because it is strict, joint and several. Four factors must exist before a *potentially responsible party* (PRP) may be found liable for response costs at a site:

1) The site must be a *facility*, as defined by CERCLA §9601(9)

2) A *release* or threatened release of a *hazardous substance* from the site occurred

3) The release or threatened release caused the incurrence of *response costs*

4) The defendants fall within at least one of the four classes of PRPs identified in CERCLA §9607(a)

The four classes of PRPs are:

1) The (current) *owner and operator* of a facility

2) Any person who at the time of disposal of any *hazardous substance* owned or operated any facility at which such *hazardous substances* were disposed of

3) Any person who by contract, agreement, or otherwise, arranged for disposal or treatment or transport of *hazardous substances*

4) Any person who accepts or accepted any *hazardous substances* for transport to a disposal or treatment facility selected by such person

Avoiding CERCLA Liability—Defenses and Protections

Fortunately, CERCLA, as amended, offers PRPs several defenses, exclusion or protections from liability. CERCLA's so-called third-party defenses, are listed in §9607(b) and would act to defend a PRP from liability where the release or threat of release of a *hazardous substance* (and resulting damages) were caused solely by: (1) an act of God; (2) an act of war; or (3) an act or omission of a third party, other than an employee or agent of the defendant or a third party whose act or omission occurs in connection with a contractual relationship existing directly or indirectly, with the defendant. Note: CERCLA §§9601(35)(A) defines the term *contractual relationship* to include, but not be limited to, land contracts, deeds, easements, leases or other instruments transferring title or possession. This last defense is commonly referred to as the CERCLA *Innocent Landowner* defense. CERCLA also contains the *Lender Liability Exclusion* and protections for contiguous property owners and *bona fide* prospective purchasers, each of which is discussed below.

Innocent Landowner Defense and All Appropriate Inquiries

Under CERCLA's *Innocent Landowner* defense, a defendant must establish by a preponderance of the evidence that the defendant: (a) exercised due care with respect to the *hazardous substance* concerned, and (b) took precautions against foreseeable acts or omissions of any such third party and the consequences that could foreseeably result from such actions or omissions. Congress recognized early on that the presence of a *contractual relationship* would essentially abrogate the *Innocent Landowner* defense. The *Innocent Landowner* defense could be asserted so long as the *hazardous substance* release or threatened release occurred on the site prior to the owner (defendant) acquiring the property and the owner (defendant) "did not know and had no reason to know of the *hazardous substance*" with respect to the property. Congress further clarified that the owner (defendant) must have undertaken *All Appropriate Inquiries* in order to establish that the owner (defendant) "did not know and had no reason to know of the *hazardous substance*" See CERCLA

Important Definitions Found in CERCLA

Facility

A) Any building, structure, installation, equipment, pipe or pipeline (including any pipe into a sewer or publicly owned treatment works), well, pit, pond, lagoon, impoundment, ditch, landfill, storage container, motor vehicle, rolling stock, or aircraft.

B) Any site or area where a hazardous substance has been deposited, stored, disposed of, or placed, or otherwise come to be located; but does not include any consumer product in consumer use or any vessel.

Release

Any spilling, leaking, pumping, pouring, emitting, emptying, discharging, injecting, escaping, leaching, dumping or disposing into the environment (including the abandonment or discarding of barrels, containers and other closed receptacles containing any hazardous substance, or pollutant or contaminant), §9601(22).

Response costs

Indirectly defined at §9601(25) to mean costs related to both removal actions, §9601(23), and remedial actions, §9601(24).

Owner or Operator

Any person owning or operating a facility or the person who owned, operated or otherwise controlled activities at a facility immediately prior to such facility's transfer to a unit of state or local government due to bankruptcy, foreclosure, tax delinquency, abandonment or similar means. The term *owner* or *operator* does not include a person, who, without participating in the management of a facility, holds indicia of ownership primarily to protect his security interest in the facility (this exemption is commonly referred to as the *secured creditor* exemption), §9601(20)(A) and §9601(E).

§9601(35)(B). What scope was required to meet the *All Appropriate Inquiries* standard? This uncertainty led to lively debate in the environmental arena for many years. The industry, without regulatory guidance, did its best to develop various industry-wide environmental site assessment protocols to meet this undefined and illusive standard. See, for example, the American Society of Testing and Materials (ASTM) E–1527 Standard Practice for Environmental Site Assessments: Phase I Environmental Site Assessment Process.

When the *Brownfields Amendments* became law in 2002, the environmental industry finally received some direction for *All Appropriate Inquiries*. The Amendments set forth interim standards to meet *All Appropriate Inquiries* and required that the Environmental Protection Agency promulgate regulatory standards and practices no later than January 11, 2004 "for the purpose of satisfying the requirement to carry out all appropriate inquiries under §9601(35)(B)(i)." To assist EPA in meeting its mandate, Congress identified 10 criteria forming the foundation for the regulatory standards and practices to be established by EPA. These ten criteria are:

1) The results of an inquiry by an *environmental professional*

2) Interviews with past and present owners, operators, and occupants of the facility for the

purpose of gathering information regarding the potential for contamination at the facility

3) Reviews of historical sources (such as chain-of-title documents, aerial photographs, building department records, and land use records) to determine previous uses and occupancies of the real property since the property was first developed

4) Searches for recorded environmental cleanup liens against the facility that are filed under Federal, State, or local law

5) Reviews of Federal, State and local governmental records, waste disposal records, underground storage tank records, and hazardous waste handling, treatment, disposal and spill records, concerning contamination at or near the facility

6) Visual inspections of the facility and of adjoining properties

7) Specialized knowledge or experience on the part of the defendant

8) The relationship of the purchase price to the value of the property, if the property was not contaminated

9) Commonly known or reasonably ascertainable information about the property

10) The degree of obviousness of the presence or likely presence of contamination at the property, and the ability to detect contamination by appropriate investigation

Recognizing that it would take some time for EPA to promulgate regulatory standards and practices, Congress provided two sets of interim standards and practices, with one set applicable to properties purchased prior to May 31, 1997 and the other set applicable to commercial real estate transactions occurring on or after May 31, 1997.

Congress specified a single criterion for meeting *All Appropriate Inquiries for transactions occurring on or after May 31, 1997*:

> the procedures of the American Society for Testing and Materials, including the document known as standard E1527–97, entitled 'Standard Practice for Environmental Site Assessment: Phase I Environmental Site Assessment Process.

In June 2003 EPA promulgated a final rule that became effective June 9, 2003, entitled *Clarification to the Interim Standards of Practice for All Appropriate Inquiries Under CERCLA*. This rule allows the interim use of the ASTM E1527–00 standard to meet *All Appropriate Inquiries* (68 FR 24888–24891, May 9, 2003). While its regulatory significance is not entirely clear at this time, Congress, in the *Brownfields Amendments*, also provided for a third, more relaxed standard for meeting *All Appropriate Inquiries* which was applicable only to certain residential properties. This standard only applies to properties for residential use or other similar use purchased by a nongovernmental or noncommercial entity. Under this reduced standard, a facility inspection and title search that do not reveal a basis for further investigation would satisfy *All Appropriate Inquiries*. On August 26, 2004, EPA published its proposed rule on *All Appropriate Inquiries* (69 FR 52542), which is discussed in more detail later in this chapter.

The Five Elements of *All Appropriate Inquiries*

The interim Standard and Practice applicable to commercial properties *purchased prior to May 31, 1997* sets forth five elements to be considered by a court in determining whether a defendant conducted *All Appropriate Inquiries*:

(i) any specialized knowledge or experience on the part of the defendant

(ii) the relationship of the purchase price to the value of the property if the property were not contaminated

(iii) commonly known or reasonably ascertainable information about the property

(iv) the obviousness of the presence or likely presence of contamination at the property

(v) the ability of the defendant to detect the contamination by appropriate inspection

Lender Liability Exclusion

When Congress promulgated CERCLA, it recognized potential hardships that CERCLA liability could place on holders of security interests in property (*e.g.*, lenders) where those parties were not responsible for acts or omissions of others that caused or contributed to property contamination. In an effort to ease these burdens, Congress created the so-called *secured creditor* exemption within the definition of *owner or operator*. Lenders avoided CERCLA liability if they held an "indicia of ownership primarily to protect his security interest" so long as they did not participate in the management of the facility. In 1992, EPA sought to further clarify the scope of the exemption through its *Lender Liability* rule (57 FR 18344, April 29, 1992). In 1994, the courts struck down the *Lender Liability* rule[1]. Subsequently, in September 1996, Congress acted to address lenders' concerns and passed the *Lender Liability Amendments* (PL 104–208, §§2501–2505, 110 Stat. 3009, September 30, 1996) to clarify the scope of both the *secured creditor* exemption and the fiduciary liability exemption.[2] The *Lender Liability Amendments* state that a secured creditor or lender will not fall within the definition of *owner or operator* (and, therefore, be potentially liable under CERCLA) when the lender merely holds an indicia of ownership and acts primarily to protect its security interest in a facility (*e.g.*, through foreclosure or post foreclosure acts) but does not

participate in the management of the facility. See §9601(20)(E–G). Participation in management was defined to mean actual participation in the management or operational affairs of a vessel or facility and does not include merely having the capacity to influence, or the unexercised right to control, vessel or facility operations. These amendments also state that a person who is a lender holding an indicia of ownership primarily to protect a security interest in a vessel or facility will be considered to "participate in management" where the lender exercises environmental decision making authority or management control while the borrower is in possession.

Contiguous Property Owner Protection

The *Contiguous Property Owner* (CPO) protection, CERCLA §9607(q), offers another way for *owners* or *operators* to avoid CERCLA liability. A property owner is protected from liability even if the subject property was impacted by a release from an adjacent site, so long as the property owner conducted *All Appropriate Inquiries* prior to purchase, did not cause or contribute to the release, and does not have any affiliation with the party that is potentially liable for such release.

In addition to meeting these two threshold criteria for *All Appropriate Inquiries* and non-affiliation, the successful CPO would have to meet certain

---

Lenders as Owners or Operators

42 USC §9601(F)(i)(I)(ii)(I)(II)(aa) states that a lender would be deemed an *owner* or *operator* if, while the borrower is still in possession of the vessel or facility encumbered by the security interest, the person:

1) Exercises decision making control over the environmental compliance to the vessel or facility, such that the person has undertaken responsibility for the hazardous substance handling or disposal practices related to the vessel or facility; or

2) Exercises control at a level comparable to that of a manager of the vessel or facility, such that the person has assumed or manifested responsibility for the overall management of the vessel or facility encompassing day-to-day decision making with respect to environmental compliance.

---

[1]See *Kelley v. EPA,* 15 F.3d 1100 (DC Cir 1994), reh'g denied 25 F.3d 1108 (DC Cir. 1994).

[2]A discussion of the Superfund liability exemptions applicable to fiduciaries such as trustees, receivers and

conservators as a result of the 1996 Lender Liability Amendments is presented in "Fiduciary Liability: A New Safe Harbor Under CERCLA" Lawrence J. Horan III, *Environmental Regulation and Permitting*, Spring 1997, John Wiley & Sons.

Basic Conditions for Establishing Contiguous Property Owner Protection

The *Contiguous Property Owner* protection is intended to benefit "a person that owns real property that is contiguous to or otherwise similarly situated with respect to, and that is or may be contaminated by a release or threatened release of a hazardous substance" from contiguous real property owned by someone else, so long as

1) The *Contiguous Property Owner* did not cause, contribute, or consent to the release or threatened release; and

2) The *Contiguous Property Owner* is not

   a) Potentially liable, or affiliated with any other person that is potentially liable, for response costs at a facility through any direct or indirect familial relationship or any contractual, corporate, or financial relationship (other than a contractual, corporate, or financial relationship that is created by a contract for the sale of goods or services); or

   b) The result of a reorganization of a business entity that was potentially liable.

---

continuing obligations to maintain the liability protection. The five continuing obligations are:

1) The person takes reasonable steps to

   a) stop any continuing release;

   b) prevent any threatened future release;

   c) prevent or limit human, environmental, or natural resource exposure to any hazardous substance released on or from property owned by that person.

2) The person provides full cooperation, assistance, and access to persons that are authorized to conduct response actions or natural resource restoration at the vessel or facility from which there has been a release or threatened release (including the cooperation and access necessary for the installation, integrity, operation, and maintenance of any complete or partial response action or natural resource restoration at the vessel or facility).

3) The person

   a) Is in compliance with any land use restrictions established or relied on in connection with the response action at the facility;

   b) Does not impede the effectiveness or integrity of any institutional control employed in connection with a response action;

4) The person is in compliance with any request for information or administrative subpoena issued by the President under this Act;

5) The person provides all legally required notices with respect to the discovery or release of any *hazardous substances* at the facility.

In order to qualify for the *Contiguous Property Owner* protection a person must establish, by a preponderance of the evidence, that the conditions in clauses (i) through (viii) of subparagraph §9607(q)(1)(A) have been met. The CPO protection makes it clear that at the time the person acquired the property, the person conducted *All Appropriate Inquiries* within the meaning of CERCLA section 101(35)(B) with respect to the property and, based upon such inquiry, did not know or have reason to know that the property was or could be contaminated by a release or threatened release of one or more *hazardous substances* from contiguous real property not owned or operated by the person.

Bona Fide Prospective Purchaser Protection

The *Bona Fide* Prospective Purchaser protection (BFPP) See CERCLA §9607(r) for a limitation on CERCLA §9607(a)(1) liability for persons meeting the definition of a **bona fide *prospective purchaser.*** The prospective purchaser must meet all of the criteria in CERCLA §101(40) when potential liability for a release or threatened release is based solely on the purchaser's status as an owner or operator of a facility. BFPP status assumes that the prospective purchaser was not responsible for the release of *hazardous substances* at the property. In taking advantage of this protection, the prospective purchaser would have to undertake *All Appropriate Inquiries,* demonstrate nonaffiliation with liable parties and meet continuing obligations and other criteria set forth in CERCLA §101(40). In contrast to the *Innocent Landowner* and *Contiguous Property Owner* protections, the BFPP protection allows a purchaser to avoid CERCLA liability even if the property was purchased with knowledge of contamination. The BFPP protection only applies to properties purchased after January 11, 2002.

All Appropriate Inquiries Rulemaking

On August 26, 2004, EPA's *All Appropriate Inquiries* (AAI) proposed rule was published in the Federal Register, thus opening the 60-day public comment period. Upon completion of the public comment process and revisions to the proposed rule, the final rule will be published in the Federal Register for subsequent incorporation into the Code of Federal Regulations at 40 CFR Subchapter J, Part 312. Because the proposed rule was the culmination of a lengthy negotiated rulemaking process between EPA, governmental authorities, the environmental industry and the regulated community, the final AAI rule will most likely be only slightly different from the proposed rule. Given the history and status of the proposed rule, it appears likely that the final AAI rule will be published in 2005.

The proposed AAI rule mirrors the February 17, 2004 Negotiated Rulemaking Committee Final Consensus Document, which can be found on EPA's docket website, and defines the standards and practices necessary to meet CERCLA's AAI requirements. The proposed AAI standards and practices are more rigorous than the current ASTM E1527–00 standard, which has been generally adopted by the environmental and real estate industries as the threshold standard for conducting a Phase I environmental site assessment that satisfies CERCLA's *Innocent Landowner* defense.

Guidance on Meeting the *Bona Fide* Prospective Purchaser, Contiguous Property Owner, and Innocent Landowner Liability Limitations

EPA's March 2003 *Interim Liability Common Elements* guidance addresses the criteria landowners must meet in order to qualify for CERCLA's *Bona Fide Prospective Purchaser* (BFPP), *Contiguous Property Owner* (CPO) and *Innocent Landowner* (ILO) liability limitations. The guidance makes it clear that to be eligible, BFPPs, CPOs, and ILOs must conduct *All Appropriate Inquiries* before property purchase and that BFPPs and CPOs must also demonstrate *nonaffiliation* with a liable party. The guidance also discusses BFPPs', CPOs', and ILOs' responsibility to meet five continuing obligations:

1) Complying with land use restrictions and institutional controls

2) Taking reasonable steps with respect to hazardous substance releases

3) Providing full cooperation, assistance, and access to persons that are authorized to conduct response actions or natural resource restoration

4) Complying with information requests and administrative subpoenas

5) Providing legally required notices

See 42 USC §101(40)(H), and 42 USC §107(q)(1)(A)(ii), respectively. EPA's Common Elements guidance document is available at <http://www.epa.gov/compliance/resources/policies/cleanup/superfund/common-elem-guide.pdf>.

ASTM is in the process of revising its E1527–00 standard to match the proposed AAI regulatory changes. The rule, because of the additional requirements to meet AAI, will be more performance-based than the prescriptive methodology used historically in performing environmental assessments.

The proposed rule, which is subject to change in its final version, adds definitions and standards and practices to 40 CFR 312, and is entitled *Innocent Landowners, Standards for Conducting All Appropriate Inquiries.* The proposed rule would also require AAI environmental assessments to be conducted by an ***environmental professional*** the requirements for which designation may significantly impact firms conducting environmental site assessments.

As set forth in proposed 40 CFR 312.10, an *environmental professional* is a person who possesses sufficient specific education training and experience necessary to exercise professional judgment to develop opinions and conclusions as to the environmental condition of a property. Persons qualifying as an environmental professional would include:

- A Professional Engineer or Professional Geologist with three years of full-time relevant experience

- An individual licensed by the government to perform environmental inquiries who has three years of full-time relevant experience

- A person that has a baccalaureate or higher degree in a relevant discipline of engineering, environmental science or earth science plus the equivalent of five years of full-time relevant experience

- A person having a baccalaureate or higher degree in any field with ten years of full-time relevant experience

The rule would allow persons not meeting the qualifications of an *environmental professional* to assist in the conduct of *All Appropriate Inquiries* under the supervision of an *environmental professional.*

Under the rule, environmental reports would be considered stale and fall short of meeting AAI unless prepared within one year and updated within 180 days prior to the transaction date. The rule, as proposed, would require the following inquiries to be updated to within 180 days of the transaction date:

1) Interviews with past and present owners, operators and occupants

2) Searches for recorded environmental cleanup liens

3) Reviews of Federal, Tribal, State and local government records

4) Visual inspections of the facility and of adjoining properties

5) A declaration by the environmental professional

Inquiries conducted in accordance with the proposed AAI rule are similar to but more detailed than the current ASTM E1527–00 Standard Practice for Phase I Environmental Site Assessments and would require the *environmental professional* conducting the environmental assessment to perform to a higher investigative standard. The rule would require the *environmental professional* to identify data gaps, opine in the implications of such data gaps and provide an explanation of the steps taken, or to be taken to address and/or remedy such data gaps. The proposed §312.10 definition of data gap is "a lack of or inability to obtain information required by the standards and practices listed in Subpart C of proposed Part 312 despite good faith efforts by the *environmental professional* or persons identified under §312.1(b), as appropriate, to gather such information pursuant to §312.20(d)(1) and §312.20(d)(2)."

In its present proposed form, the rule would also require a written opinion by the *environmental professional* as to the thoroughness and reliability of data gathered and require an affirmative declaration to that effect in the *environmental professional's* written report. The *environmental professional* will be required to include two written statements in the AAI report

1) [I, We] declare that, to the best of [my, our] professional knowledge and belief, [I, we] meet the definition of *environmental professional* as defined in §312.10 of 40 CFR 312.

2) [I, We] have the specific qualifications based on education, training and experience to assess a property of the nature, history, and setting of the subject property, [I, We] have developed and performed the all appropriate inquiries in

conformance with the standards and practices set forth in 40 CFR Part 312.

The rule would also expand AAI to include recorded environmental cleanup liens as well as an evaluation of the relationship of the purchase price to the fair-market-value of the subject property if the property were not contaminated. (See the consensus document draft rule §312.29. It appears that this requirement would go primarily to the party seeking to qualify for the particular defense or exemption and not to the *environmental professional*.)

While not new to users of the ASTM E1527 standard practice, the rule also expands the scope of AAI investigations beyond the strict CERCLA definition of *hazardous substance* to include petroleum and petroleum products and controlled substances. (See 69 FR 52577). The rule would appear to require AAI compliant investigations to include petroleum and petroleum products that are otherwise excluded from the definition of hazardous substance as a result of the CERCLA §101(14) petroleum exclusion as well as *controlled substances* as defined in 21 USC §802. At the present time, the scope and intent of requiring investigation of *controlled substances* in the context of conducting *All Appropriate Inquiries* is unclear.

Summary

Contrary to popular belief, CERCLA is alive and well. It remains the impetus behind the environmental assessment and remediation industry as we know it today. The *Brownfields Amendments* clarify what steps are required for *All Appropriate Inquiries* sufficient to meet the various landowner protections available under CERCLA. While still in draft stage, EPA's AAI rule (eventually to be promulgated as 40 CFR 312) will mandate changes in the scope of environmental due diligence and qualifications for *environmental professionals*, which are required to meet CERCLA's new AAI standards and practices.

Lawrence J. ("Sandy") Horan III is a partner with the North Texas firm of Horan & Horan, a law practice focusing on environmental and OSHA/health and safety compliance. He has practiced environmental and regulatory law for more than 14 years and provides ongoing compliance and risk reduction counseling to industry, contractors, consultants, environmental professionals, engineers and laboratories. Prior to forming Horan & Horan, Mr. Horan was Environmental and Health & Safety Counsel for MCI/Worldcom and worked in private law practice prior to MCI. Sandy holds a law degree as well as an MBA degree from University of Tulsa. His technical background began with undergraduate studies in geology, anthropology/archeology and biochemistry at University of California–Santa Cruz and was supplemented in the field with several research positions in geology. Following the Brownfields Amendments, he was asked by the American Society for Testing and Materials to assist in the preparation of a new draft of the Legal Appendix to E1527, Standard Practice for Phase I Environmental Site Assessments, including updates regarding the Asset Conservation, Lender Liability, and Deposit Insurance Protection Act of 1996 and the Small Business Liability Relief and Brownfields Revitalization Act of 2001.

CHAPTER 20

Human Health Risk Assessment

Frank Phillips CET, CIAQP, CHMM

Background and History

For the hazardous materials manager, the principal type of risk assessment is the human health and ecological risk assessment associated with remedial activities at sites contaminated with chemical pollutants. This chapter includes a discussion of Superfund human health risk assessments, as well as other applications of risk assessment.

Statutes, Regulations, Guidance and Studies

In 1980 Congress enacted the Comprehensive Environmental Response, Compensation, and Liability Act (CERCLA) (42 USC 9601 *et seq.*), commonly called *Superfund*, in response to the dangers posed by sudden or otherwise uncontrolled releases of hazardous substances, pollutants, or contaminants into the environment. CERCLA authorized funding for a comprehensive program to clean up the worst abandoned or inactive waste sites.

The reauthorization of CERCLA is known as the Superfund Amendments and Reauthorization Act (SARA), and was signed by the President on October 17, 1986. Under SARA, Congress

309

strengthened the Environmental Protection Agency's (EPA) mandate to focus on permanent cleanups at Superfund sites, to involve the public in decision processes, and to encourage states and Federally recognized Indian tribes to participate actively as partners with EPA. SARA expanded research, development in the area of alternative technologies, and training responsibilities. Section 121 of CERCLA, "Cleanup Standards," states a strong preference for remedies that are highly reliable and provide long-term protection. Remedies must be protective of both human health and the environment.

Section 121(d)(2)(A) of CERCLA incorporates the CERCLA compliance policy, which specifies that remedial actions must meet any Federal standards, requirements, criteria, or limitations that are determined to be legally applicable or relevant and appropriate requirements (ARARs). ARARs guidance is found in EPA's *CERCLA Compliance with Other Laws Manual.* Under CERCLA section 104(I)(6), the Agency for Toxic Substances and Disease Registry (ATSDR) is required to conduct a health assessment for every site included or proposed for inclusion on the National Priorities List. Other environmental laws that deal with remedial actions include the Resource Conservation and Recovery Act, Clean Water Act, and Clean Air Act (EPA 1989f).

Human Health Evaluation in Superfund Remedial Investigations/Feasibility Studies

The primary concern of Superfund's human health risk assessment (HHRA) is the health effects of chemical exposure. The goal of the Superfund human health evaluation process is to provide a framework for developing the risk information that is used for decision-making at remedial sites. Specific objectives of the process are to:

- Provide an analysis of baseline risks and help determine the need for action at sites

- Provide a basis for determining levels of chemicals that can remain on-site and still be adequately protective of public health

- Provide a basis for comparing potential health impacts of various remedial alternatives

- Provide a consistent process for evaluation and documenting public health threats at sites

The three basic parts of the Remedial Investigation/Feasibility Study (RI/FS) human health evaluation are:

Part A: Baseline Risk Assessment

Part B: Refinement of Preliminary Remediation Goals

Part C: Remedial Alternatives Risk Evaluation

There are seven documents addressing Risk Assessment Guidance for Superfund, commonly known as the RAGS documents:

RAGS I-A for Baseline Risk Assessments

RAGS I-B: Development of Risk-Based Preliminary Remediation Goals (PRGs)

RAGS I-C: Risk Evaluation of Remedial Alternatives

RAGS I-D: Standardized Planning, Reporting, and Review of Superfund Risk Assessments

RAGS I-E: Supplemental Guidance for Dermal Risk Assessment

RAGS II for Environmental Evaluation (Ecological Risk Assessment)

RAGS III: Process for Conducting Probabilistic Risk Assessment

These documents are a revision of EPA's Superfund Public Health Evaluation Manual, published in 1986.

Key Concepts

Hazard and Risk

Hazard is a property of a material or a site that may pose health or safety concerns. Chemical hazards include ignitability and corrosivity. Physical hazards include boiling point and evaporation rate. Biological hazards include poison plants and poison animals. Physiological hazards include chemical exposure, toxicity, heat stress, cold exposure, noise, and oxygen deficiency. Safety hazards include electricity, slippery surfaces, tripping and falling, and sharp objects.

Vulnerability is the susceptibility of life, property, and the environment to injury or damage. *Risk* is the likelihood (probability) that injury to life, or damage to property and the environment, will occur. (Note: Outside of the United States and Canada, the term *hazard* refers to the probability of an adverse outcome.)

Superfund Risk Assessment Process

This chapter will cover the human health risk assessment principles involved in the baseline risk assessment part of the HHRA. The human health evaluation process is part of the Superfund remedial process as shown in the Figures 1 and 2.

Baseline Risk Assessment

The four steps in the baseline risk assessment are shown in Figure 3 and include data collection and evaluation, exposure assessment, toxicity assessment, and risk characterization.

Step 1: Data Collection and Data Evaluation. The types of data needed for a baseline risk assessment include

- Contaminant identities

- Contaminant concentrations in the key sources and media of interest

- Characteristic of sources, especially information related to release potential

- Characteristics of the environmental setting that may affect the fate, transport, and persistence of the contamination

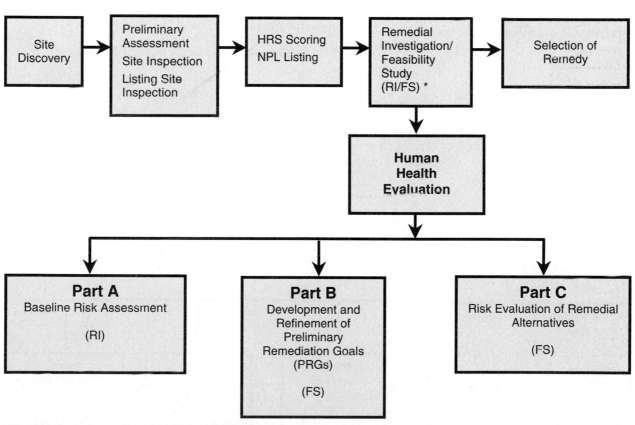

*The RI/FS can be undertaken prior to NPL Listing

Figure 1. Role of the Human Health Evaluation in the Superfund Remedial Process

The RI/FS has four primary data collection components:

1) Characterization of site conditions

2) Determination of the nature of the wastes

3) Risk assessment

4) Treatability testing

The site-scoping meeting is one of the earliest stages of the RI/FS at which risk assessment data needs can be addressed. The scoping meeting allows development of a comprehensive Sampling and Analysis Plan (SAP). Data Quality Objectives (DQO) guidance provides information on the review of site data and the determination of data quality needs for sampling.

Data Quality Objectives are qualitative and quantitative statements established prior to data collection that specify the quality of the data required to support agency decisions during remedial response activities. The DQOs for a particular site vary according to the end use of the data (*i.e.*, whether the data are collected to support preliminary assessments/site inspections, remedial investigations/feasibility studies, remedial designs, or remedial action.

The DQO process consists of three stages:

Stage 1: Identify Decision Types. All available site information is compiled and analyzed in order to develop a conceptual model of the site. The model describes suspected sources, contaminant pathways, and potential receptors. The outcome of Stage 1 is a definition of the objectives of the site investigation and an identification of data gaps.

Stage 2: Identify Data Uses/Needs. The data necessary to meet the objectives set in Stage 1 is specified. The sampling approaches and the analytical options for the site are selected and multiple-option approaches are considered in order to allow more timely or cost-effective data collection and evaluation.

Stage 3: Design Data Collection Program. The methods used to obtain data of acceptable quality are specified in such products as the SAP or the workplan.

A preliminary identification of potential human exposure provides much of the information needed for the SAP. This activity involves the identification of

1) Media of concern

2) Areas of concern

3) Types of chemicals expected at the site, and

4) Potential routes of contaminant transport through the environment

The **media of concern** are any currently contaminated media to which individuals may be exposed or through which chemicals may be

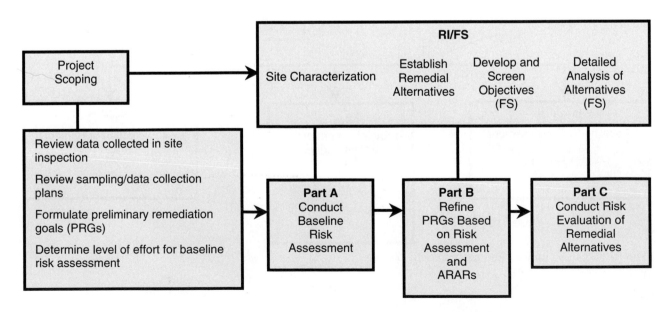

Figure 2. Risk Information Activities in the RI/FS Process

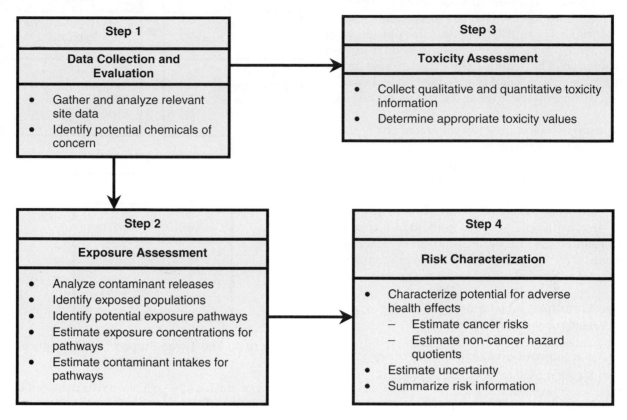

Figure 3. The Four Steps of a Baseline Risk Assessment

transported to potential receptors and any currently uncontaminated media that may become contaminated in the future due to contaminant transport. Media includes soil, groundwater, surface water and sediment, air, as well as biota. **Biota of concern** are organisms that are likely to be consumed by humans. This includes animals such as commercial and game fish (*e.g.*, salmon, trout, catfish), shellfish (*e.g.*, oysters, clams, crayfish), fowl (*e.g.*, pheasant, duck), and terrestrial animals (*e.g.*, rabbit, deer), as well as plants such as grains (*e.g.*, wheat, corn), vegetables (*e.g.*, spinach, carrots), and fruit (*e.g.*, melons, strawberries). **Areas of concern** refer to the general locations at or near the site. For large sites, areas of concern may be treated in the RI/FS as *operable units*. Areas of concern can also be thought of as the locations of potentially exposed populations (nearest residents) or biota (wildlife feeding areas).

The following nine steps should be followed to organize the data into a form appropriate for a baseline risk assessment:

1) Gather all data available from the site investigation and sort by medium

2) Evaluate the analytical methods used

3) Evaluate the quality of data with respect to sample quantitation limits

4) Evaluate the quality of data with respect to qualifiers and codes

5) Evaluate the quality of data with respect to blanks

6) Evaluate tentatively identified compounds

7) Compare potential site-related contamination with background

8) Develop a set of data for use in the risk assessment

9) If appropriate, further limit the number of chemicals to be carried through the risk assessment (*e.g.*, select the chemicals of potential concern)

Step 2: Exposure Assessment. The objective of the exposure assessment is to estimate the type and magnitude of exposures to the chemicals of potential concern (COPCs) that are present at or migrating from a site and are selected for further evaluation. The results of the exposure assessment are subsequently combined with chemical-specific toxicity information to characterize potential risks.

Exposure is defined as the contact of an organism (humans in the case of health risk assessment) with a chemical or physical agent. The ***magnitude of exposure*** is determined by measuring or estimating the amount of an agent available at the exchange boundaries (*i.e.*, the lungs, gut, skin) during a specified time period. ***Exposure assessment*** is the determination or estimation (qualitative or quantitative) of the magnitude, frequency, duration, and route of exposure.

There are three steps conducted in the exposure assessment, as shown in Figure 4:

1) Characterization of exposure setting

2) Identification of exposure pathways

3) Quantification of exposure

The exposure setting must be characterized with respect to general physical characteristics such as climate, vegetation, groundwater hydrology, and the presence and location of surface water, and with the characteristics of populations such as location relative to the site, activity patterns, and the presence of sensitive subpopulations. ***Receptors*** are those humans who are potential recipients of chemical contaminants by way of one of the pathways. ***Sensitive subpopulations*** are those receptors that have pre-existing medical or physical conditions that may make them more sensitive to the health effects of chemical exposure.

An ***exposure pathway*** describes the course that a chemical or physical agent takes from the source to the exposed individual. An exposure pathway generally consists of four elements:

1) A source and mechanisms of chemical release

2) A retention or transport medium

3) A point of potential human contact with the contaminated medium (exposure point)

4) An exposure route at the contact point

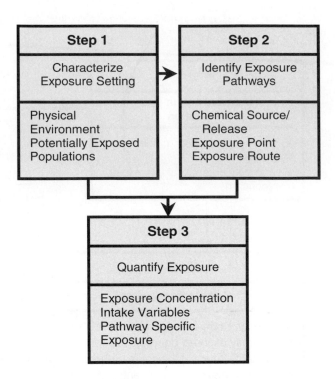

Figure 4. The Three Steps of an Exposure Assessment

Exposure pathways are identified based on: consideration of the sources, releases, types, and locations of chemicals at the site; the likely environmental fate (including persistence, partitioning, transport, and inter-media transfer) of these chemicals; and the location and activities of the potentially exposed populations. ***Exposure points*** (points of potential contact with the chemical) and ***routes of exposure*** (inhalation, ingestion, dermal absorption) are identified for each exposure pathway. Table 1 contains a summary of exposure pathways.

The concentrations of chemicals that will be contacted over the exposure period are estimated using monitoring data and/or chemical transport and environmental fate methods. Chemical specific exposure estimates for each pathway are expressed in terms of the mass of substance in contact with the body per unit body weight per unit time (*e.g.*, milligrams of chemical per kilogram body weight per day [mg/kg-day]). These exposure estimates are termed ***intakes***, and represent the normalized exposure rate. Actions at Superfund sites should be based on an estimate of the reasonable maximum exposure expected to occur under both current and future land-use conditions. ***Reasonable maximum exposure*** (RME) is defined as the highest exposure that is reasonably

Chemical Contaminants	Selected COPCs[a] (Examples)	Media	Sources (Examples)	Release Mechanisms	Transport Mechanisms	Receptors (Examples)	Exposure Points (Examples)	Exposure Routes
Inorganics								
Toxic metals and elements (As, Ba, Cd, Cr, Pb, Hg, Se, Ag)	Cadmium Chromium	Surface soil					Handling drum at site	Inhalation
Toxic light metals	Beryllium	Subsurface soil	Waste pile	Volatilization	Air volatilization	Site workers	Walking near site boundary	Ingestion
Toxic air contaminants	Alpha quartz silicates	Groundwater	Contaminated soil	Soil leaching	Air contaminants attached to particulates	Nearby residents		Dermal absorption
Organics regulated by CWA, RCRA, CERCLA								
Aliphatic solvents	Methyl ethyl ketone (MEK)	Surface water[b]	Leaking drum	Spill	Surface water	Sensitive subpopulations	Drinking water from a contaminated well	
Aromatic solvents	Benzene	Storm water	Contaminated floor	Disturbance of contaminated media	Groundwater	Animals	Incidental ingestion of dust	
Halogenated solvents	Tetrachloroethylene	Sediment			Storm water runoff	Plants		
PCBs, dioxins, dibenzofurans	Aroclor 1254 TCDD	Air						
Others								

[a]Chemicals of Potential Concern (COPCs) are those chemicals selected for full study in the HHRA.
[b]Surface water includes lotic waters (fast-moving waters such as rivers and streams) and lentic waters (slow-moving waters such as lakes, ponds, and impoundments.)

Table 1. Exposure Pathways

expected to occur at a site. RMEs are estimated for individual pathways. If a population is exposed via more than one pathway, the combination of exposures across pathways also must represent an RME.

After a chemical is released to the environment, it may be

- Transported (*e.g.*, convected downstream in water, on suspended sediment, or through the atmosphere)

- Physically transformed (*e.g.*, volatilization, precipitation)

- Chemically transformed (*e.g.*, photolysis, hydrolysis, oxidation, reduction, *etc.*)

- Biologically transformed (*e.g.*, biodegradation) and/or

- Accumulated in one or more media (including the receiving medium)

The quantification of the magnitude, frequency and duration of exposure for the populations and exposure pathways selected for evaluation is usually conducted in two stages. First, exposure concentrations are estimated, then pathway-specific intakes are quantified. There are three categories of variables used to estimate intake:

1) Chemical-related variables such as exposure concentrations

2) Variables that describe the exposed population—contact rate, exposure frequency and duration, and body weight

3) Assessment-determined variables such as averaging time

The concentration term in the intake equation is the arithmetic average of the concentration that is contacted over the exposure period. Because of the uncertainty associated with any estimate of exposure concentration, the 95 percent upper confidence limit on the arithmetic average will be used for this variable. Contact rate reflects the amount of contaminated medium contacted per unit time or event. The upper-bound value of 30 years can be used for exposure duration when calculating reasonable maximum residential exposures. In some cases, however, lifetime exposure (70 years by convention) may be a more appropriate assumption. For pathways where contact rate-to-body weight ratios are fairly

constant over a lifetime, (*e.g.*, drinking water ingestion), a body weight of 70 kg is used.

The averaging time selected depends on the type of toxic effect being assessed. When evaluating exposures to developmental toxicants, intakes are calculated by averaging over the exposure event (*e.g.*, a day or a single exposure incident). For acute toxicants, intakes are calculated by averaging over the shortest exposure period that could produce an effect, usually an exposure event or a day. When evaluating longer-term exposure to noncarcinogenic toxicants, intakes are calculated by averaging intakes over the period of exposure (*i.e.*, subchronic or chronic daily intakes). For carcinogens, intakes are calculated by prorating the total cumulative dose over a lifetime (*i.e.*, chronic daily intakes, also called lifetime average daily intake, LADI).

For exposure pathways, monitoring data generally provide the best estimate of current exposure concentrations.

For a given residence in the vicinity of a contaminated site, the following residential exposures would be estimated:

- Intake of chemicals from ground water and surface water
  - In drinking water
  - In surface water while swimming
  - Dermal contact with chemicals in water

- Intake of chemicals from soil, sediment, and dust
  - Incidental ingestion
  - Dermal contact

- Intake of chemicals from air
  - Inhalation of vapor-phase chemicals
  - Inhalation of particulate-phase chemicals

- Intake of chemicals from food
  - Ingestion of fish and shellfish
  - Ingestion of vegetables and other produce
  - Ingestion of meat, eggs, and dairy products

The generic equation for calculating chemical intakes is:

$$I = \frac{C_m \times CR \times EFD}{BW \times AT} \tag{1}$$

Where:

I = Intake, the amount of chemical at the exchange boundary, expressed in mg/kg body weight-day

C_m = Concentration of chemical in the affected medium, the average concentration contacted over the exposure period (*e.g.*, mg/liter water). This concentration is a chemical-related variable. For water exposure, C_m becomes C_w (or CW), the chemical concentration in water.

CR = Contact rate, the amount of contaminated medium contacted per unit time or event (*e.g.*, liters/day). For the ingestion route of exposure, CR is called IR (ingestion rate).

EFD = Exposure frequency and duration; describes how long and how often exposure occurs. Often calculated using two terms, EF and ED where EF is the exposure frequency in days/year and ED is the exposure duration in years.

BW = body weight, the average body weight over the exposure period (kg).

Note: CR, EFD, and BW are variables that describe the exposed population.

AT = averaging time, the period over which exposure is averaged (days). AT is an assessment-determined variable.

As an example, assume that for residential exposure by ingestion, the groundwater contained benzene at 0.0053 mg/L (the exposure concentration). The contaminated groundwater impacted a nearby drinking water well. What would be the intake for a person drinking water from the contaminated well?

$$\text{Intake} = \frac{CW \times IR \times EF \times ED}{BW \times AT} \quad (2)$$

$$I = \frac{0.0053 \times 2 \text{ L/d} \times 365 \text{ d/yr} \times 30 \text{ yrs}}{70 \text{ kg for an average adult} \times 365 \text{ d/yr} \times 30 \text{ yrs}} \quad (3)$$

= 0.00015 mg/kg-day benzene

For noncarcinogens, and for the noncarcinogenic effects of carcinogen compounds, the chronic daily intake (CDI) is calculated. Since the exposure duration for carcinogens is considered to be 70 years, CDI may be referred to as lifetime acceptable daily intake, LADI. Table 2 is an example format that can be used for summarizing the results of the exposure assessment.

Population	Exposure Pathway	Chemical	Chronic Daily Intake (mg/kg-day)	
			Carcinogenic Effects	Noncarcinogenic Effects
	Ingestion of groundwater that has migrated from the site to downgradient local wells.	Benzene	0.00015	---[b]
		Chlordane	0.00025	
		Phenol	---[c]	
		Cyanide	---[c]	
		Nitrobenzene	---[c]	
	Inhalation of chemicals that have volatilized from groundwater during use	Benzene	0.000013	---[b]
	Ingestion of fish that have accumulated chemicals in nearby lake	Chlordane	0.00008	0.00019
		MEK	---[c]	0.005
		Phenol	---[c]	0.08

[a]Similar tables should be prepared for all subchronic daily intake (SDI estimates as well as for all CDI and SDI estimates under future land use conditions.
[b]CDI for noncarcinogenic effects not calculated for benzene because it does not have an EPA-verfied chronic reference dose.
[c]CDI for carcinogenic effects not calculated for chemicals not considered byEPA to be potential human carcinogens.

Table 2. Example of Table Format for Summarizing the Results of the Exposure Assessment Current Land Use[a]

Step 3: Toxicity Assessment. The purpose of the toxicity assessment is to weigh available evidence regarding the potential for particular contaminants to cause adverse effects in exposed individuals and to provide an estimate of the relationship between the extent of exposure to a contaminant with the increased likelihood and/or severity of adverse effects.

The first step in toxicity assessment, *hazard identification*, is the process of determining whether exposure to an agent can cause an increase in the incidence of a particular adverse health effect (*e.g.*, cancer, birth defect) and whether the adverse health effect is likely to occur in humans. Hazard identification involves characterizing the nature and strength of the evidence of causation.

The second step, *dose-response evaluation*, is the process of quantitatively evaluating the toxicity information and characterizing the relationship between the dose of the contaminant administered or received and the incidence of adverse health effects in the exposed population. From this quantitative dose-response relationship, toxicity values (e.g., reference doses and slope factors) are derived that can be used to estimate the potential adverse effects as a function of human exposure to the agent.

Toxicity Assessment for Noncarcinogenic Effects. A *reference dose*, RfD, is the toxicity value used for evaluating noncarcinogenic effects resulting from exposures. A *chronic RfD* is defined as an estimate of a daily exposure level for the human population, including sensitive subpopulations, that is likely to not result in appreciable risk of deleterious effects during a lifetime. RfDs are generally provided in the Integrated Risk Information System (IRIS) (see below) rather than being derived on a project level.

For many noncarcinogenic effects, protective mechanisms of the human body are believed to exist that must be overcome before an adverse effect is manifested. In developing a toxicity value for evaluating noncarcinogenic effects (*i.e.*, an RfD), the approach is to identify the upper bound of this tolerance range, the maximum subthreshold level. Because variability exists in the human population, attempts are made to identify a subthreshold level protective of sensitive individuals in the population. The RfD is generally considered to have uncertainty that spans an order of magnitude or more.

In the development of *oral RfDs*, all available studies examining the toxicity of a chemical following exposure by the oral route are gathered and judged for scientific merit. If adequate human data are available, this information is used as the basis of the RfD. Otherwise, animal study data are used. The effect characterized by the **lowest observed adverse effect level** (LOAEL) after dosimetric conversions to adjust for species differences is referred to as the critical toxic effect.

After the critical study and toxic effect have been selected, the experimental exposure level representing the highest level tested at which no adverse effects (including the critical toxic effect) were demonstrated. The highest **no observed adverse effect level** (NOAEL) is the key datum obtained from the study of the dose-response relationship. The NOAEL is selected based in part on the assumption that if the critical toxic effect is prevented, then all toxic effects are prevented.

The RfD is derived from the NOAEL (or LOAEL) for the critical toxic effect by consistent application of uncertainty factors (UFs) and a modifying factor (MF). For the chemical not explicitly addressed by uncertainty factors, a modifying factor ranging from greater than 0 to 10 is included to reflect a qualitative professional assessment of additional uncertainties in the critical study and in the entire database. The default value for the MF is 1. Uncertainty factors generally consist of multiples of 10, with each factor representing a specific area of uncertainty inherent in the extrapolation from the available data. A UF of 10 is used:

- To account for variation in the general population and is intended to protect sensitive subpopulations (*e.g.*, elderly, children)

- When extrapolating from animals to humans

- When a NOAEL derived from a subchronic instead of a chronic study is used

- When a LOAEL is used instead of a NOAEL

Oral RfDs are typically expressed as one significant figure in units of mg/kg-day.

For the derivation of *inhalation RfDs* (RfD$_I$), methods similar in concept to those used for oral RfDs are applied.

Toxicity Assessment for Carcinogenic Effects. The mechanism hypothesized for carcinogens is referred to as *nonthreshold* because there is believed to be essentially no level of exposure that does not pose a finite possibility of generating a carcinogenic response. For carcinogenic effects, EPA uses a two-part evaluation in which the substance first is assigned a weight-of-evidence classification, and secondly a slope factor (SF) is calculated.

Evidence from human and animal studies are combined, and based on the extent to which the agent has been shown to be a carcinogen, the agent is given a provisional weight-of-evidence classification. The weight-of-evidence classification system for carcinogenicity, shown in Table 3, is used.

Group	Description
A	Human Carcinogen
B1	Probable human carcinogen. Limited human data are available.
B2	Probable human carcinogen. Sufficient evidence in animals and inadequate or no evidence in humans.
C[a]	Possible human carcinogen.
D	Not classified as to human carcinogenicity.
E	Evidence of noncarcinogenicity for humans.

[a]Calcuation for slope factors for Group C chemicals proceeds on a case-by-case basis.

Table 3. Weight-of-Evidence Classification System for Carcinogenicity

The *slope factor* is a plausible upper-bound estimate of the probability of a response per unit intake of a chemical over a lifetime. The slope factor is used in risk assessments to estimate an upper-bound lifetime probability of an individual developing cancer as a result of exposure to a particular level of a potential carcinogen.

There exists a hierarchy of toxicological information data sources. The Integrated Risk Information System (IRIS) is an EPA database containing up-to-date health risk and EPA regulatory information for numerous chemicals.

IRIS contains only those RfDs and slope factors that have been verified. Other sources should be consulted only if information is not available in IRIS for the chemical being evaluated.

The second tier of toxicological information is EPA's Health Effects Assessment Summary Tables (HEAST), a tabular presentation of information and values for chemicals for which Health Effects Assessments (HEAs), Health and Environmental Effects Documents (HEEDs), Health and Environmental Effects Profiles (HEEPs), Health Assessment Documents (HADs), or Ambient Air Quality Criteria Documents (AAQCDs) have been prepared. Other sources include criteria documents, toxicological profiles, and EPA's Environmental Criteria and Assessment Office. EPA criteria documents include drinking water criteria documents, drinking water health advisory summaries, ambient water quality criteria documents, and air quality criteria documents. The Agency for Toxic Substances and Disease Registry (ATSDR) has developed over 250 toxicological profiles for substances found at Superfund sites.

Step 4: Risk Characterization. Risk characterization involves summarizing and integrating toxicity and exposure information into quantitative and qualitative expressions of risk. A risk characterization cannot be considered complete unless the numerical expressions of risk are accompanied by explanatory text interpreting and qualifying the results. The steps in risk characterization are shown in Figure 5.

For carcinogens, CDI is the chronic daily intake averaged over 70 years and expressed as mg/kg-day; SF is the slope factor expressed in $(mg/kg-day)^{-1}$

For carcinogens:

$$Risk = CDI \times SF \text{ (or, LADI} \times SF) \tag{4}$$

Total carcinogenic risk is a summation of all individual carcinogenic risks:

$$\text{Total Risk, Risk}_T = \Sigma \text{ Risk}_T = (CDI_1 \times SF_1) + \tag{5}$$
$$(CDI_2 \times SF_2) + \ldots (CDI_i \times SF_i)$$

For noncarcinogens and for the noncarcinogenic effects of carcinogens:

$$Risk = CDI/RfD = \text{Hazard Index (HI)} \tag{6}$$

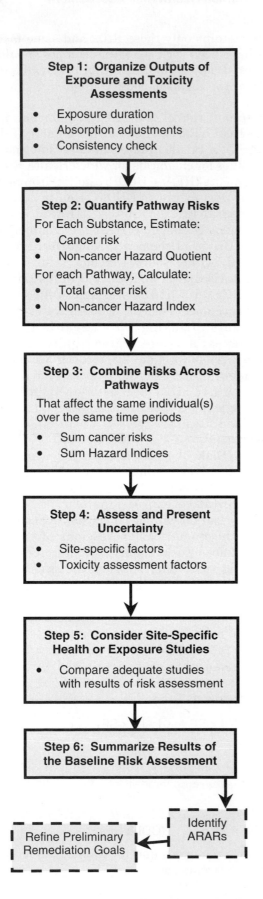

Figure 5. Steps in Risk Characterization

Total noncarcinogenic risk is a summation of all individual noncarcinogenic risks:

$$\text{Total Risk} = \text{Hazard Quotient (HQ)} = \qquad (7)$$
$$\Sigma \, HI = CDI_1/RfD_1 + CDI_2/RfD_2 + \ldots$$
$$+ CDI_i/RfD_i$$

Ecological Assessment

Basics of Ecological Assessments. Ecologists generally study three levels of organization: populations, communities, and ecosystems. A ***population*** is a group of organisms of the same species, generally occupying a contiguous area, and capable of interbreeding. A ***community*** is a complex association in which populations of different species live together.

Ecosystems are areas that vary with climactic, topographical, geological, chemical, and biotic factors. Types of ecosystems include tundra, deciduous forests, coniferous forests, deserts, mountain ranges, freshwater systems, and saltwater systems. The ecological assessment looks at the effects of contaminants on impacted areas and their inhabitants. The principles of site characterization, data collection and evaluation, contaminant evaluation, and potential for exposure that were used in the human health risk assessment apply to environmental evaluations. (EPA 1989g)

An ***ecological assessment*** is a qualitative and/or quantitative appraisal of the actual or potential effects of a hazardous waste site on plants, animals, and domesticated species. Environmental evaluation at Superfund sites should provide decision makers with information on threats to the natural environment associated with contaminants or with actions designed to remediate the site. Not all sites will require environmental evaluations since many sites are in industrial areas with little, if any, wildlife.

Other Applications of the Risk Assessment Process

RCRA Corrective Action

The RCRA corrective action process is similar to the Superfund remediation process. See the chapter entitled "RCRA Corrective Action," in this book or the Environmental Protection Agency website <http://www.epa.gov/correctiveaction> for more information and guidance.

Corrective Action for Underground Storage Tank Releases

Risk-Based Corrective Action (RBCA) for Leaking Underground Storage Tank (LUST) Sites. Remediation of soil and ground water contamination caused by leaking underground storage tanks (LUSTs) is generally regulated by states. Most state programs are based on the risk management objective embodied in the ASTM E–1739 "Standard for Risk-Based Corrective Action (RBCA) Applied at Petroleum Release Sites." The ASTM RBCA process is designed to facilitate the efficient allocation of corrective action resources based upon site-specific evaluation of human health and environmental risks. The ultimate endpoint of the RBCA planning process is the closure of sites in an expedient, protective, and cost-effective manner. State regulatory programs customize the RBCA process to meet State requirements. Some states apply modified approaches such as Illinois' Tiered Approach to Corrective Action (TACO).

Bibliography

Barcelona, Michael J., J. P. Gibbs, J. A. Helfrich, and E. E. Garske, *Practical Guide for Ground-Water Sampling.* EPA–600/2–85–104. Champaign, IL: Illinois State Water Survey, 1985.

"Chemical Carcinogens: A Review of the Science and Its Associated Principles." *Federal Register* 50 (14 March 1985) 10372.

Environmental Protection Agency. *A Compendium of Superfund Field Operation Methods.* EPA–540/P–87–001, OSWER Directive 9355.0–14. Washington, DC: Office of Emergency and Remedial Response, 1987a.

Environmental Protection Agency. *Air Superfund National Technical Guidance Series: Interim Final. Volume I: Applications of Air Pathway Analysis for Superfund Activities.* EPA–450/1–89–001. Research Triangle Park, NC: Office of Air Quality Planning and Standards, 1989a.

Environmental Protection Agency. *Air Superfund National Technical Guidance Series: Interim Final. Volume II: Estimation of Baseline Air Emissions at Superfund Sites.* EPA–450/1–89–002. Research Triangle Park, NC: Office of Air Quality Planning and Standards, 1989b.

Environmental Protection Agency. *Air Superfund National Technical Guidance Series: Interim Final. Volume III: Estimations of Air Emissions from Cleanup Activities at Superfund Sites.* EPA–450/1–89–003. Research Triangle Park, NC: Office of Air Quality Planning and Standards, 1989c.

Environmental Protection Agency. *Air Superfund National Technical Guidance Series: Interim Final. Volume IV: Procedures for Dispersion Modeling and Air Monitoring for Superfund Air Pathway Analysis.* EPA–450/1–89–004. Research Triangle Park, NC: Office of Air Quality Planning and Standards, 1989d.

Environmental Protection Agency. *Data Quality Objectives for Remedial Response Activities: Development Process.* EPA–540/G– 87– 004, OSWER Directive 9355.0–7B. Washington, DC: Office of Emergency and Remedial Response and Office of Waste Programs Enforcement, 1987b.

Environmental Protection Agency. *Data Quality Objectives for Remedial Response Activities: Example Scenario (RI/FS Activities at a Site Contaminated Soils and Ground Water).* EPA–540/G–87–004, OSWER Directive 9355.0–7B. Washington, DC: Office of Emergency and Remedial Response and Office of Waste Programs Enforcement, 1987c.

Environmental Protection Agency. *Ecological Assessment of Hazardous Waste Sites: A Field and Laboratory Reference Document.* EPA–600/3–89–013. Corvallis, OR: Environmental Research Laboratory, 1989e.

Environmental Protection Agency. *EPA Approach for Assessing the Risk Associated with Chronic Exposure to Carcinogens (Background Document 2).* Washington, DC: Integrated Risk Information System, 1992.

Environmental Protection Agency. *Exposure Factors Handbook, Volumes 1–3.* EPA –600/P–95/002Fa, EPA–600/P–95/002Fb. Washington, DC: Office of Research and Development,

National Center for Environmental Assessment, 1997.

Environmental Protection Agency. *Field Manual for Grid Sampling of PCB Spill Sites to Verify Cleanup*. EPA–560/5–86–017. Washington, DC: Office of Toxic Substances, 1986a.

Environmental Protection Agency. *Guidance for Conducting Remedial Investigations and Feasibility Studies Under CERCLA: Interim Final*. EPA/540/G–89/004. OSWER Directive 9355.3–01. Washington, DC: Office of Emergency and Remedial Response, 1988.

Environmental Protection Agency. *Guidance for Coordinating ATSDR Health Assessment Activities with the Superfund Remedial Process*. OSWER Directive 9285.4–02. Washington, DC: Office of Emergency and Remedial Response, Superfund Docket, March 11, 1987d.

Environmental Protection Agency. *Methodology for Characterization of Uncertainty in Exposure Assessments*. EPA–600/8–85–009. Washington DC: EPA, 1985a.

Environmental Protection Agency. *Methods Manual for Bottom Sediment Sample Collection*. EPA–905/4–85–004. Chicago, IL: Great Lakes National Program Office, 1985b.

Environmental Protection Agency. *Quality Assurance Field Operations Manual*. Washington, DC: Office of Solid Waste and Emergency Response, 1987e.

Environmental Protection Agency. *Reference Dose (RfD): Description and Use in Health Risk Assessments. Background Document 1A*. Washington, DC: Integrated Risk Information System 1993.

Environmental Protection Agency. *Risk Assessment and Management: Framework for Decisionmaking*. EPA–600/9–85–002. Washington, DC: EPA, 1984.

Environmental Protection Agency. *Risk Assessment Guidance for Superfund (RAGS): Volume 1–Human Health Evaluation Manual (HHEM) (Part A, Baseline Risk Assessment)*. Interim Final. EPA–540/1–89–002. Washington, DC: Office of Emergency and Remedial Response,

1989f. (Volume 1 primarily addresses concerns of risk assessors and risk assessment reviewers.)

Environmental Protection Agency. *Risk Assessment Guidance for Superfund (RAGS): Volume 1–Human Health Evaluation Manual (HHEM) (Part B, Development of Risk-Based Preliminary Remediation Goals)*. Interim Final. EPA–540/R–92/003. OSWER Directive 9285.7–01B. Washington, DC: Office of Research and Development, 1991.

Environmental Protection Agency. *Risk Assessment Guidance for Superfund (RAGS): Volume 1–Human Health Evaluation Manual (HHEM) (Part C, Risk Evaluation of Remedial Alternatives)*. Interim Final. EPA–540/R–92/004. OSWER Directive 9285.7–01C. Washington, DC: Office of Research and Development, 1991.

Environmental Protection Agency. *Risk Assessment Guidance for Superfund (RAGS): Volume 1–Human Health Evaluation Manual (HHEM) (Part D, Standardized Planning, Reporting and Review of Superfund Risk Assessments)*. Final. Publication 9285.4–47. Washington, DC: Office of Research and Development, 2001.

Environmental Protection Agency. *Risk Assessment Guidance for Superfund (RAGS): Volume 1–Human Health Evaluation Manual (HHEM) (Part E, Supplemental Guidance for Dermal Risk Assessment)*. Interim Review Draft–For Public Comment. Washington, DC :Office of Research and Development, 2001.

Environmental Protection Agency. *Risk Assessment Guidance for Superfund (RAGS): Volume II–Environmental Evaluation Manual*. Interim Final. EPA–540/1–89–001. OSWER Directive 9285.7—01. Washington, DC: Office of Solid Waste and Emergency Response, 1989g. (This volume primarily addresses Remedial Project Managers (RPMs) and On-Scene Coordinators (OSCs) who are responsible for ensuring a thorough evaluation of potential environmental effects at remediation sites.)

Environmental Protection Agency. *Risk Assessment Guidance for Superfund (RAGS): Volume II. (Part A, Conducting Probabilistic Risk Assessment)*. Washington, DC: Office of Research and Development, 2001.

Environmental Protection Agency. *Road Map to Understanding Innovative Technology Options for Brownfields Investigation and Cleanup, 2nd ed.* EPA–542/8–99–009. Washington, DC: Office of Solid Waste and Emergency Response, 1999.

Environmental Protection Agency. *Superfund Exposure Assessment Manual.* EPA–540/1–88–001. OSWER Directive 9285.5–1. Washington, DC: Office of Emergency and Remedial Response, 1988.

Environmental Protection Agency. *Superfund Public Health Evaluation Manual.* EPA–540/1–86–060. OSWER Directive 9285.4–1. Washington, DC: EPA, 1986b. (Predecessor to RAGS documents).

Environmental Protection Agency. *Technical Assistance Document for Sampling and Analysis of Toxic Organic Compounds in Ambient Air.* EPA–600/4–83–027. Research Triangle Park, NC: Environmental Monitoring Systems Laboratory, 1983.

Environmental Protection Agency. *SW–846, Test Methods for Evaluating Solid Waste: Physical/ Chemical Methods.* 3rd ed. Washington, DC: Office of Solid Waste, 1998.

Environmental Protection Agency. *The Endangerment Assessment Handbook.* TR–693–24B. Washington, DC: Office of Waste Programs Enforcement, 1985c.

Environmental Protection Agency. *The Risk Assessment Guidelines of 1986.* PB–88–123977; EPA–600/8–87–045. Washington DC: Office of Health and Environmental Assessment, 1987f.

Environmental Protection Agency. *Toxicology Handbook: Principles Related to Hazardous Waste Site Investigations.* TR–693–21A. Washington, DC: Office of Waste Programs Enforcement, 1985e.

Environmental Protection Agency. *Transport and Fate of Contaminants in the Subsurface.* EPA–625/4–89–019. Technology Transfer Seminar Publication. Cincinnati, OH: Center for Environmental Research Information, 1989h.

Frantzen, Kurt A., PhD; J. Vangalio; and C. Williams, PhD. "Assessing Risk." In *Managing Hazardous Materials: A Definitive Text,* Jack E. Leonard, Ed. Rockville, MD: Institute of Hazardous Materials Management, 2002.

Gilbert, R. O. *Statistical Methods for Environmental Pollution Monitoring.* New York, NY: Van Nostrand Reinhold, 1987.

"Guidelines for Carcinogen Risk Assessment." *Federal Register* 51 (24 September 1986) 33992.

"Guidelines for Exposure Assessment." *Federal Register* 51 (24 September 1986) 34042.

"Guidelines for Health Risk Assessment of Chemical Mixtures." *Federal Register* 51 (24 September 1986) 34014.

"Guidelines for the Health Assessment of Suspect Developmental Toxicants." *Federal Register* 51 (24 September 1986) 34028.

"Guidelines for Mutagenicity Risk Assessment." *Federal Register* 51 (24 September 1986) 34006.

Klaassen, Curtis D., Ed. *Casarett and Doull's Toxicology: The Basic Science of Poisons,* 6th ed. New York, NY: McGraw-Hill, 2001.

Library of Congress, Congressional Research Service. *A Review of Risk Assessment Methodologies.* Washington, DC: US Government Printing Office, 1983.

National Academy of Sciences. *Risk Assessment in the Federal Government: Managing the Process.* Washington, DC: National Academy Press, 1983.

"National Oil and Hazardous Substances Pollution Contingency Plan." *Code of Federal Regulations.* Title 40, Pt. 300.

Pao, E. M., Fleming, K. H., Guenther, P. M., and Mickle, S. J. *Food Commonly Eaten by Individuals: Amount Per Day and Per Eating Occasion.* Washington DC: US Department of Agriculture, 1982.

"Proposed Amendments to the Guidelines for the Health Assessment of Suspect Developmental Toxicants." *Federal Register* 54 (6 March 1989) 9386.

"Proposed Guidelines for Exposure-Related Measurements." *Federal Register* 53 (2 December 1988) 48830.

Verner, S. *Sampling and Analysis of Toxic Organics in the Atmosphere.* STP 721. West Conshoshocken, PA: ASTM, 1981.

Internet Resources

<http://www.epa.gov/iriswebp/iris/index.html> (Environmental Protection Agency. Integrated Risk Information System. IRIS Database for Risk Assessment)

<http://www.epa.gov/superfund/programs/risk/index.htm> (Environmental Protection Agency. Superfund Risk Assessment)

<http://www.epa.gov/superfund/resources/radiation/radssg.htm> (Environmental Protection Agency. Superfund. Soil Screening Guidance for Radionuclides)

<http://toxnet.nlm.nih.gov> (National Library of Medicine. Specialized Information Systems. TOXNET)

<http://www-nehc.med.navy.mil/HHRA/> (US Navy. Navy Guidance for Conducting Human Health Risk Assessments)

<http://fda.gov/nctr> (US Food and Drug Administration. National Center for Toxicological Research)

<http://www.niehs.nih.gov> (National Institute of Environmental Health Sciences. Homepage)

<http://www.atsdr.cdc.gov> (Agency for Toxic Substances and Disease Registry. Homepage)

<http://www.epa.gov/correctiveaction/> (Environmental Protection Agency. RCRA Corrective Action)

Frank A. Phillips is the Principal Consultant with Phillips Environmental. Mr. Phillips holds a BA in Physiology from Southern Illinois University at Carbondale, graduate studies in Chemistry from the University of Houston, and an MBA from Lindenwood University in St. Charles, Missouri. He has been a CHMM since 1986 and was selected as the 1995 Hazardous Materials Manager of the Year. In addition to environmental consulting and training, he has project management experience in the areas of regulatory compliance, waste management, environmental restoration, as well as RCRA, air, and wastewater treatment permitting. He has presented more than thirty 3-day, 5-day, and 10-day CHMM certification review courses and has presented Pollution Prevention Initiatives training courses in the United States, Eastern Europe, and Africa. Mr. Phillips has been a Committee Chair in the Gateway (St. Louis) Chapter, and a member of the Professional Development Committee of the ACHMM. He is also a Certified Environmental Trainer, a Registered Environmental Manager, and a Certified Indoor Air Quality Professional.

Property Assessments

Keith Liner, MCE, CHMM

CERCLA Liability

The Comprehensive Environmental Response, Compensation, and Liability Act (CERCLA) was originally passed in 1980 to provide a response mechanism for uncontrolled release of hazardous substances to the environment. CERCLA provides authority for State and Federal governments to respond to release of hazardous substances into the environment. In order to provide funds for the cleanup actions a trust fund called *Superfund* was established by Congress. CERCLA includes the right for the State and Federal government to initiate cleanup and to seek reimbursement from the primarily responsible parties. The money collected from the responsible parties is intended to replenish the *Superfund*. CERCLA places liability on the present site owner and operator. One way for landowners to protect themselves from liability is to invoke the *Innocent Landowner Defense* when purchasing property. This chapter describes the process that landowners must use to invoke this defense.

CERCLA includes two basic types of response actions: removal actions and remedial actions. A ***removal action*** is an immediate action taken over the short term to address a release or threatened release of a hazardous substance. A ***remedial action*** selects remedies that are protective of human health and the environment, that maintains protection over time and minimizes untreated wastes. A remedial action takes a longer time to implement than a removal action.

A *release* is defined in CERCLA as

> any spilling, leaking, pumping, pouring, emitting, emptying, discharging, injecting, escaping, leaching, dumping, or disposing of hazardous substances to the environment.

CERCLA defines *hazardous substances* as

> such elements, compounds, mixtures, solutions, and substances which when released into the environment may present substantial danger to public health and welfare or the environment.

Hazardous substances under CERCLA include

- Any elements, compounds, mixtures, solutions, or substances designated by the United States Environmental Protection Agency (EPA) under Section 311 of the Clean Water Act (CWA), (40 CFR 116.4), or under Section 102 of the Comprehensive Environmental Response, Compensation, and Liability Act (CERCLA), (40 CFR 302.4)

- Any toxic pollutants listed under Section 307(a) of the CWA

- Any hazardous substances regulated under Section 311(b)(2)(A) of the CWA (40 CFR 110, 117, and 122)

- Any listed or characteristic Resource Conservation and Recovery Act (RCRA) hazardous wastes (40 CFR 262)

- Any hazardous air pollutants listed under Section 112(r) of the Clean Air Act (CAA) (40 CFR 68), or

- Any imminently hazardous chemical substances or mixtures regulated under Sections 7 of the Toxic Substances Control Act (TSCA) (40 CFR 761.120, *et seq.*)

CERCLA defines the *environment* as

> (A) the navigable water, the waters of the contiguous zone, and the ocean waters of which the natural resources are under the exclusive management authority of the United States under the Magnuson Fishery Conservation and Management Act, and (B) any other surface water, ground water,

drinking water supply, land surface or subsurface strata or ambient air within the United States or under the jurisdiction of the United States.

CERCLA imposes strict liability. The EPA and private parties can seek recovery of cleanup costs associated with releases of CERCLA hazardous substances from the potentially responsible party. The *potentially responsible party* is an

> individual or company potentially responsible for, or contributing to the contamination problems at a Superfund site.

The EPA can use appropriate administrative and legal actions to require primarily responsible parties to clean up contaminated sites.

Under strict liability, any defense claiming that negligence did not occur because the activities were consistent with standard industry practice is no defense at all. CERCLA liability is joint and several. This means that if more than one party has disposed of hazardous substance in a common location, all are responsible. The EPA can divide the cleanup costs among all responsible parties regardless of their contribution to the problem. CERCLA liability is also retroactive. This means that parties may be found liable for actions taken long before passage of CERCLA, even if the disposal of the hazardous substance was lawful at the time of disposal.

CERCLA places liability on the present site owner and operator. Liability is a condition for land purchasers. One way for land purchasers to protect themselves is to invoke the *Innocent Landowner Defense*. In order for the landowner to use the *Innocent Landowner Defense* to CERCLA liability,

> *All Appropriate Inquiry* must be made into the previous ownership and uses of property consistent with good commercial or customary practice.

Appropriate inquiry is made by conducting an environmental site assessment in accordance with the American Society for Testing and Materials (ASTM) Practices E1527–00, "Environmental Site Assessment Transaction Screen," E1528–00, "Environmental Site Assessment: Phase I Environmental Site Assessment Process," and E1903–97, "Environmental Site Assessments: Phase II Environmental Site Assessment Process." (These standard practices can be found at <http://www.astm.org>) In court, the landowner can use the *Innocent Purchaser* defense. If the landowner uses the ASTM standards, he has exercised **due diligence**. *Due diligence* states that

> at the time of land acquisition, *All Appropriate Inquiry* was made into the previous ownership and use of the property was consistent with good commercial or customary practice.

Transaction Screen Process

The Transaction Screen Process is intended to permit a user to satisfy one of the requirements to qualify for the *Innocent Landowner Defense* to CERCLA liability. The Transaction Screen Process is intended to establish a customary practice for conducting an environmental site assessment of a parcel of land or property. The customary practice identifies recognized environmental conditions. **Recognized environmental conditions,** as defined by CERCLA, means

> the presence or likely presence of any hazardous substances or petroleum products on a property under conditions that indicate a release, a past release, or a material threat of any hazardous substances or petroleum products into structures on the property or into the ground, ground water, or surface water of the property

Recognized environmental conditions as defined under CERCLA do not include *de minimus* conditions that generally do not present a material risk or harm to public health or the environment and that generally would not be subject to an enforcement action if brought to the attention of appropriate governmental agencies.

The customary practice is designed to (1) synthesize and put in writing good commercial and customary practice for environmental site assessments for commercial real estate, (2) to facilitate high-quality standardized environmental site assessments, (3) to ensure that the standard appropriate practice is practical and reasonable, and (4) to clarify an industry standard for appropriate inquiry in an effort to guide legal interpretation of CERCLA's *Innocent Landowner Defense*.

The customary practice assists the user in developing the information about the environmental condition of a property and has utility for a wide range of persons, including those who may have no actual or potential CERCLA liability and as such may not be seeking the *Innocent Landowner Defense*.

The Transaction Screen Process is conducted by the user or by an environmental professional. An environmental professional must perform a Phase I and Phase II Assessment. The most important qualification for the environmental professional is the number and size of properties previously assessed.

Completion of the Transaction Screen Process in accordance with the ASTM standards may allow the user to conclude that no further inquiry is needed to assess the environmental conditions of the property. This will allow the user to invoke the *Innocent Landowner Defense* without performing a Phase I or II Assessment. The Transaction Screen can be used in a residential transaction, but at least a Phase I Assessment is required by lending institutions for commercial transactions. Completion of the Transaction Screen Process concludes that (1) no further inquiry into recognized environmental conditions of the property is needed for purposes of appropriate inquiry, or (2) further inquiry is needed to assess recognized environmental conditions appropriately for purposes of appropriate inquiry. If no further inquiry is needed, the user has completed appropriate inquiry into the property.

The process is not an exhaustive assessment of a clean property. A balance is established at a point at which the costs outweigh the benefits. The same level of inquiry will not be required for all properties. The type of property will guide the type and depth of inquiry.

The Transaction Screen Process consists of asking questions contained within the Transaction Screen Questionnaire. This questionnaire is for owners and occupants of the property with direction provided by the Transaction Screen Process. The questionnaire is then used to conduct a limited records review of government records and certain historical sources. The owners and occupants are asked the same questions.

The questionnaire in the standard is divided into three sections:

1) Guide for Owner and Occupant Inquiry

2) Guide to Site Visit

3) Guide to Government Records/Historical Sources Inquiry

The guide and process uses these steps: (1) inquiry into owners/occupants, (2) site visit, (3) inquiry into governmental records.

The questionnaire should be used to ask questions of the (1) current owner of the property (2) any major occupants of the property or if more than one occupant at least 10% of the occupants of the property, and (3) in addition to the current owner and occupants above, any who are likely to be using, treating, generating, storing, or disposing of hazardous substances or petroleum products on the property.

The evaluator uses the *site visit column* during the observation of the property including any buildings and other structures on the property. The questions on the questionnaire profile the property and ask about

- Current use and past use of the property

- Stored items on the property including drums, car batteries, paints

- The presence of ponds, pits, or lagoons

- Stained soil or foul-smelling drains

- The presence of hazardous substances, poly-chlorinated biphenyls (PCBs), among others

The respondents answer the questions *Yes*, *No*, or *Unknown* to the best of their knowledge.

The historical sources inquiry answers if the property is listed on the

- National Priorities List (NPL) (<http://www.epa.gov>)

- RCRA Corrective Action Report System (CORRACT) facility list

or is near any of the following facilities:

- Hazardous waste sites being investigated for remediation

- Leaking underground storage tanks (USTs)

- Solid waste/landfill facilities

The guide and information obtained during the Transaction Screen Process should be used to conclude that no further inquiry is needed. If the user cannot conclude that no further inquiry is required based on their best business judgement and the questionnaire answers, then further inquiry may be required and the user should proceed to a full Phase I Environmental Site Assessment.

Phase I Assessment

The Phase I Assessment is a continuation of the Transaction Screen Process. The purpose of this practice is identical to the Transaction Screen. It is intended to define good commercial and customary practice in the United States for conducting an environmental assessment.

The Phase I Assessment purpose is to identify, to the extent feasible pursuant to the process prescribed herein, recognized environmental conditions in connection with the property.

A Phase I Environmental Site Assessment has four components:

- Records review

- Site reconnaissance

- Interviews

- Evaluation report

There is no sampling involved with the practice. The first three phases are intended to be complementary, in that if during a records review it is found that the property was used for a particular purpose, the site visit inspections should try to identify the previous use. An environmental professional must perform the interviews and the site visit. The environmental professional must also oversee the writing of the report and must review and interpret any information on which the report is based. The records review can be done by governmental agencies, through freedom of information requests, the user, occupants of the property, *etc.*, and should be done under the supervision of an environmental professional. The environmental professional is not required to independently verify the information provided by others unless the professional knows by actual knowledge that certain information is incorrect. Phase I Assessments are used in cases of significant liability. The environmental professional must remember that the Phase I Assessment is a forensic-type of investigation.

Records Review

The records review is intended to help identify recognized environmental conditions in connection with the property. The records should be obtained from reasonably ascertainable and standard sources. The records are reasonably ascertainable if they can be obtained with reasonable time and cost within 20 days of a written, verbal, or in-person request. The records should provide information that is relevant to the property. The records review should also include a review of property records for property adjacent to the property in question. A minimum reach distance is defined in the ASTM standard. This is intended to identify situations in which hazardous substances or petroleum products might migrate into the property in question. The approximate minimum reach distance may be reduced due to the (1) density of setting that the property is located, (2) distance hazardous or petroleum substances might migrate based on geological data, (3) other reasonable factors. The reduction should be documented in the final report. Typical minimum reach distances are

Federal NPL Site List	1.0 mi
State Leaking USTs	0.5 mi
Federal RCRA CORRACTS TSD List	1.0 mi
Federal RCRA Non-CORRACTS TSD List	0.5 mi

The Federal NPL site list and Federal RCRA Treatment, Storage and Disposal (TSD) list state that the minimum reach distance may not be reduced.

Typical local records include

- Lists of landfill/solid waste disposal sites
- Lists of underground storage tanks
- Records of contaminated public wells

A current United States Geological Survey (USGS) 7.5 Minute Topographic Map or equivalent showing the area that the property is located shall be reviewed. The map will provide information about geologic, hydrogeologic, or topographic characteristics of the site and is the only standard physical setting resource that is required to be evaluated. An equivalent map can be used if necessary.

In order to judge the past property use, historical resources should be used from the present back to the property's first obvious developed use, or back to 1940, whichever is earlier. Records should be used to develop a history of the property and surrounding properties. Some standard historical resources are

- Aerial photographs
- Fire insurance maps
- Property tax files
- Title records

Site Reconnaissance

The site reconnaissance is intended to obtain information and likelihood of identifying environmental conditions. An environmental professional must conduct the site reconnaissance. It is not expected that more than one site visit will be necessary. The environmental professional must visually and physically survey the property and any buildings on the property. The visit must be documented in the final report and include the method used for evaluation. The exterior of buildings as well as the periphery of the property must be inspected for any evidence of present or past contamination of hazardous substances or petroleum products. Exterior inspections should include observations for vent tubes, fill tubes for under-ground storage tanks, pipes leading into the ground, past spill sites, *etc.* The interior of buildings must be visually and physically observed including commonly accessible areas. Knowledge of building materials is essential to determine if asbestos-containing materials (ACMs), lead paint, lead solder or polychlorinated biphenyls (PCBs) may be present.

Any physical limitation of the inspection must be noted in the final report including physical obstructions, bodies of water, asphalt, snow, and rain. A digital camera may be used to document findings. Occupants and past occupants must be questioned in accordance with the standard.

The current use of the property must be identified in the report. Any current uses likely to involve the use, treatment, storage, disposal, or generation of hazardous substances or petroleum products must be identified. The property must be inspected for past use in areas that the record review may have identified. A general description of buildings, roads, topography, water supply, sewage, and storage tanks must be included. Any odors, pools of liquid, or container storage must be identified and evaluated in the visit and documented in the report. Any equipment with PCBs must be identified in the report. Soil and pavement must be inspected for stains and evaluation completed. Vegetation shall be examined to see if it is stressed. Any drains, sumps, wells on the property must be documented in the report. The environmental professional must assess the entire property and surrounding area during the site visit.

Interviews with Owners and Occupants

Interviews must be conducted with owners and occupants in an attempt to identify recognized environmental conditions with the property. Questions may be asked in person during the site visit, in writing, or by telephone. A key site manager must be interviewed. This individual should have a good knowledge of the uses and physical characteristics of the property. A reasonable number of occupants of the property must be interviewed. A representative number of individuals should be interviewed in order to assess any recognized environmental conditions. The report must document the individuals interviewed and the duration of their occupancy. Prior to the site visit the key site manager, property owner or user should be asked if the following documents exist and copies should be requested

- Environmental audit reports
- Environmental site assessment reports
- Environmental permits
- Update on geological conditions
- Hazardous waste generator notices
- Any other applicable aspects of information

Interviews with Local Government Officials

At least one staff member from the local fire department, local health agency, or regional office of the State agency, and one from the local agency or regional office of State agency having jurisdiction over hazardous waste disposal or other environmental matters in the area in which the property is located, should be interviewed. The interviews with local officials are to obtain information on the property's environmental conditions. Questions may be asked by telephone or person to person. The content of the questions is at the discretion of the environmental professional and is aimed at gaining insight into current and past uses of the property.

Evaluation and Report Preparation

The final report should include documentation to support the analyses, opinions, and conclusions found in the report. All sources including those that revealed no findings should be documented to facilitate reconstruction at a later date. The report should follow the format contained in the standard and should state if the user or property owner revealed that the property has an environmental lien encumbering the property. The report shall name the environmental professionals involved in conducting the Phase I Assessment. One of two options should be used to document qualifications of the persons involved: (1) the report shall include a qualification statement of the environmental professionals responsible for the assessment and preparation of the report and individual and correlate qualification or (2) a written qualification statement for the environmental professional responsible for the Phase I Assessment and preparation of the report shall be delivered to the user. All evidence of recognized environmental conditions shall be described in full. The report shall include the environmental professional's opinion of the impact of the recognized environmental conditions in connection with the property. The report shall include a findings and conclusions section that states one of the following:

> We have performed a Phase I Environmental Site Assessment in conformance with the scope and limitations of ASTM Practice

E1527 of the property. Any exceptions to or deviations from this practice are described in Section [ ] of this report. This assessment revealed no evidence of recognized environmental conditions in connection with the property

or

We have performed a Phase I Environmental Assessment in conformance with the scope and limitations of ASTM Practice E1527 of the property. Any exceptions to or deviations from this practice are described in Section [ ] of this report. The assessment revealed no evidence of recognized environmental conditions in connection with the property except for the following list . . . .

The environmental professional then signs the report and transmits it to the user.

Phase II standards are under development and will probably require sampling. Remediation techniques, liability/risk evaluation recommendations are outside the scope of the current standards.

Phase II Assessment

The Phase II Assessment is conducted in order to evaluate the recognized environmental conditions identified in a Phase I Assessment or the Transaction Screen Process.

The purpose of the Phase II Assessment is to provide sufficient information regarding the nature and extent of contamination about the property being assessed. Sufficient information is needed to make business decisions about the property and to satisfy the innocent landowner's defense under CERCLA.

The Phase II Assessment may need to be performed more than once. The Phase II Assessment guide allows the user to determine when there is sufficient data to terminate the process.

At the completion of the Phase II Assessment the environmental professional should be able to conclude that there is no basis to suspect the presence of hazardous substances or that there are

hazardous substances present on the property. If hazardous substances are present, steps must be taken to remediate. The environmental professional completes the process as many times as needed to determine the nature and extent of contamination.

The components of a Phase II Assessment are as follows:

- Development of the scope of work
- Assessment activities
- Evaluation and interpretation of data
- Presentation of findings and conclusions

Scope of Work

The environmental professional first develops a scope of work. The environmental professional establishes the tasks necessary to conduct the Phase II Assessment. The environmental professional uses the information from the Phase I Assessment to determine sample locations and the required chemical analyses. The scope of work should include sampling locations and depths where highest contamination is likely, testing parameters, and appropriate Quality Assurance/ Quality Control (QA/QC) measures. The potential distribution and mobility of hazardous substances must be analyzed in order to determine sample locations based on the Phase I Assessment and Transaction Screen Process. A laboratory with appropriate certifications should be used to conduct testing. Analytical methods, data deliverables, QA/ QC methods, minimum detection level, and chain-of-custody requirements are to be specified by the environmental professional. The environmental professional is responsible for anticipating physical and logistical impediments, which interfere with the sampling. This should be done by conducting a physical inspection of the property and may include marking of sample locations.

Assessment Activities

Both intrusive (*e.g.*, sampling) and nonintrusive (*e.g.*, field observation) activities are used to assess the property. Field screening and testing is used to map the distribution of contaminants and to identify sampling locations. Field measurements can be used to provide qualitative and quantitative information. This information can then be used to direct more extensive sampling efforts. Common field screening methods include portable flame and photoionization detectors, field gas chromatographs, colorimetric wet chemistry methods, and use of ion-selective electrodes. Field screening can be used to specify monitoring well locations.

All samples must be collected according to a specified protocol. The protocol must include a chain-of-custody process to verify that tampering of samples did not occur. The sampling activities must also be reproducible. All sample hold times must be satisfied for validity of data.

Evaluation and Interpretation of Data

The sample data that is obtained must be evaluated in order to qualify the adequacy of the Phase II Assessment. The first step is to verify the results of the tasks that were established during the scope of work. Sample locations and depths must be verified to ensure that they represent the most probable contamination locations. Monitoring well locations and depths must be verified to ensure that the collected data is representative of the property's condition. If any of the results are found to be invalid the process may need to be repeated. The second step is to evaluate the quality of the sample data. The data must be verified to ensure that QA/QC measures were taken, sample hold times were satisfied, minimum detection levels have been achieved, and samples were not compromised.

The results of the sampling and testing should be interpreted to determine the significance of the data. The data must be evaluated to determine if other sources of contamination are present at the site or if more highly contaminated media is present. The data must be evaluated to determine if the identified chemicals are naturally occurring or have been introduced as part of a processing operation.

Elimination of Recognized Environmental Conditions

If sampling and site evaluations find no presence of hazardous substances or petroleum products, the environmental professional has a basis to draw a conclusion. If there is no reasonable basis for suspecting the disposal or release of hazardous substances at the site, then no further work is necessary and *All Appropriate Inquiry* has been made in order to invoke the *Innocent Landowner Defense*.

A recognized environmental condition that has been identified in a Phase I Assessment or the Transaction Screen Process may be eliminated by obtaining further information. The new information may eliminate the need for further Phase II tasks. Also the conformation of an off-site condition that influences the property may be identified and Phase II tasks may be omitted.

Confirmation of Recognized Environmental Conditions

If the Phase II Assessment was conducted in accordance with the ASTM guide and the presence of hazardous substances or petroleum products were identified at the property, the *Innocent Landowner Defense* may not be supportable. The data must be further interpreted to determine if further work is required to determine the extent of the release and contamination. The environmental professional may recommend an iteration of the Phase II process to further characterize the contamination. The data shall be compared to the appropriate requirements in order to identify where requirements have been exceeded.

Presentation of Findings and Conclusions

As in the Phase I process, a formal report is normally prepared to document the findings of the Phase II Assessment. It should be noted that a written report is not required for Phase II Assessments. The formal report should describe the work performed and provide documentation of the data obtained. The data evaluation constitutes the factual findings, supports the conclusion of the environmental professional, facilitates decisions about the transactions, and documents the basis for the decision regarding the need for further assessment. The report is prepared in accordance with the ASTM standard. The report has the components of a scientific report: good technical writing and an accurate presentation of the results and conclusions. The report consists of introduction, background, Phase II activity, evaluation, and conclusion sections. Appropriate tables, figures, and appendices are also included. The report is intended to stand on its own.

The findings and conclusion section of the report includes the environmental professional's interpretation of the data and the professional's conclusions. A statement is included which states that

> in the judgement of the environmental professional, the data provides sufficient information to support a professional opinion that there is no reasonable basis for suspecting the disposal or release of hazardous substances or petroleum products at the site with respect to the environmental conditions assessed, and that no further assessment is necessary

or

> with respect to the recognized environmental conditions assessed, hazardous substances or petroleum products have been released or disposed of at the property.

The environmental professional then signs the report and transmits it to the user.

Bibliography

American Society for Testing and Materials, "Standard Practice for Environmental Site Assessments: Phase I Environmental Site Assessment Process." ASTM Practice E 1527–00. Westconshohocken, PA: ASTM, 2000.

American Society for Testing and Materials, "Standard Practice for Environmental Site Assessments: Transaction Screen Process." ASTM Practice E 1528–00. Westconshohocken, PA: ASTM, 2000.

American Society for Testing and Materials, "Standard Guide for Environmental Site Assessments: Phase II Environmental Site Assessment Process." ASTM Practice E 1903–97. Westconshohocken, PA: ASTM, 1997.

DOE/Westinghouse. "DOE/Westinghouse School for Environmental Excellence Manual, CERCLA Chapter." Hanford, WA: DOE/Westinghouse, 1993.

"Designation of Hazardous Substances." *Code of Federal Regulations.* Title 40, Part 302.4, 1997.

Keith Liner *is currently employed with the Westinghouse Savannah River Company, in Aiken, South Carolina. He is an Environmental Engineer and works at the Saltstone and Defense Waste Processing Facility within the Closure Business Unit. Mr. Liner is a Certified Hazardous Materials Manager and holds a BS in Chemical Engineering from the University of Pittsburgh and an MCE in Environmental Engineering from Auburn University. He would like to thank his wife, Chris, and his children, C.J. and Paul, for their love and support during the writing of this chapter.*

CHAPTER 22

Brownfields

John E. Milner, JD
Charles A. Waggoner, PhD, CHMM

Introduction

What Is a Brownfield?

Perhaps the most succinct general definition of **brownfields** can be found in *Superfund: Barriers to Brownfield Redevelopment*:

> abandoned, idled or under-utilized industrial and commercial facilities where expansion or redevelopment is complicated by real or perceived environmental contamination (GAO, 1996).

Historically, brownfields laws have typically targeted urban and heavily industrialized areas where there is significant contamination of extensive areas. However, brownfields are not limited to the classic *rust bucket* districts of major cities. They include small rural properties like gas stations where underground storage tanks may have leaked. Indeed, the brownfields concept has even expanded to include areas where there is only the perception of contamination due to a property's proximity to areas known to be contaminated.

Brownfields are often contrasted to **greenfields**, which are generally defined as uncontaminated properties outside of urban areas that have not previously been sites of industrial or commercial uses. It is easy to understand why development of a greenfield property is a competing alternative to brownfield redevelopment. Greenfield properties do not require removal of old industrial or commercial structures and they demand little or no cleanup cost. Additionally, the time line for greenfield development does not include delays resulting from environmental investigation and remediation activities. Brownfield laws have been developed in an attempt to provide legal and economic incentives to encourage brownfield redevelopment as will be discussed below.

What Are the Problems Caused by Brownfields?

The General Accounting Office estimates indicate a range of 150,000 to 450,000 brownfield sites in the United States. This wide range of estimates is based on the varying definitions of brownfields and the properties that fit within those definitions. Left unremediated, brownfields pose significant potential problems. First, actual environmental contamination at brownfield sites obviously can create human health risks to industrial and commercial facility workers. More broadly, contamination can pose widespread risks through ground water to a broad scope of persons who live in the area of the contaminated properties, whether urban or rural. Second, the existence or even the perception of environmental contamination can depress property values of land in the area surrounding the brownfield. Third, local governments suffer on a variety of levels. The aesthetics can be a defining issue for the city and dramatically reduce the potential for bringing in new business interests. The loss of tax revenues due to reduced property values and the absence of ongoing economic activities compounds the problems associated with the increased overhead of providing infrastructure to nonproductive areas.

What Are the Sources of these Problems?

The primary sources of the problems creating the brownfield dilemma are Federal environmental laws imposing liability for the contamination that exists on these properties. Paramount among these laws is the Comprehensive Environmental Response, Compensation, and Liability Act (CERCLA), also known as Superfund. It is appropriate to recall that CERCLA has a broad scope of liability for potentially responsible parties (PRPs), who are all persons having a contractual relationship with the contaminated site. This liability extending to PRPs under CERCLA is more authoritative and threatening than under any other Federal environmental statute. PRPs are exposed to liability which is strict, joint and several, and also retroactive to the time that the contamination occurred on the property.

The categories of PRPs under CERCLA who are potentially liable for cleanup costs are much broader than just the person(s) who caused the contamination. A current site owner can be compelled to clean up the property or completely underwrite the cost of site remediation, even if he/she has made no contribution to the contamination. Other categories of PRPs include site operators whether or not they have owned the property, generators of hazardous substances contaminating the site, and even individuals who arranged for transportation or disposal of the hazardous substances that ended up at the site.

In addition to CERCLA, sites that are not serious enough to be included on CERCLA's National Priorities List (NPL) may fall within the scope of the Resource Conservation and Recovery Act (RCRA). RCRA creates a *cradle-to-grave* regulatory scheme for management of hazardous wastes and also regulates underground storage tanks (USTs). The Environmental Protection Agency (EPA) has statutory authority to compel *corrective actions* to redress environmental contamination which has resulted from releases of hazardous wastes by RCRA regulated activities.

The Federal Clean Water Act and Clean Air Act can also impact brownfield properties. Both of these acts create stringent pollution control requirements applicable to new sources as well as modifications to existing sources. The reader should recognize that remediation of a brownfield property can be viewed as a new source of air emissions and regulated as such. Beyond these Federal laws, State environmental laws can also create obstacles for brownfield redevelopment. Many states have enacted their own *Superfund* laws that parallel the Federal CERCLA statute.

Voluntary cleanup of contaminated property has always been an option, but the degree of rigor required to obtain an official acknowledgment that effective cleanup has been accomplished has been the same for brownfields as for NPL sites. Clearly, the costs associated with obtaining such *clearance* can easily dwarf the cost of a small piece of property. Most regrettable is the fact that there is little incentive to clean up a site without the possibility of obtaining some sort of official recognition of the benefits. Consequently, these disincentives have led to abandonment or under-utilization of these sites because voluntary cleanup has not been economically feasible in many instances.

What Has EPA Done to Help Resolve the Brownfields Dilemma?

In the last several years, EPA has specifically targeted brownfield redevelopment through its *Brownfields Action Agenda*. The following components of the Agenda are significant.

The *kiss of death* for efforts to clean up a brownfield property has been the listing of it on EPA's NPL. Even listing of the site on EPA's much larger list of sites targeted for investigation and potential listing has been an obstacle to brownfields, although to a lesser extent. This larger investigatory list is called the Comprehensive Environmental Response, Compensation, and Liability Information System (CERCLIS). In an attempt to remove this stigma from undeserving sites, EPA has reviewed CERCLIS and deleted many of its archived listings, which has included 30,000 sites. (See <http://www.epa.gov/superfund/sites/products/archinv.pdf>.) A Statement of Company Removal from the list is also provided to reinforce the fact that EPA has no further interest in the delisted sites.

EPA has also changed its policy so that it will not seek to impose cleanup obligations on persons having an interest in property adjoining a contaminated site where the contamination has migrated under the adjoining property. Therefore, many properties that previously would have been within the CERCLA liability scheme are now excluded.

Another important component of the Brownfields Action Agenda is EPA's effort to provide liability waivers called prospective purchaser agreements (PPAs) to a number of prospective purchasers of brownfield properties. Additionally, EPA has developed a guidance document regarding the issuance of *comfort letters* to sellers and buyers conducting voluntary cleanups. In these letters, EPA provides assurance that it does not intend to take enforcement action at the remediated site. EPA has also recently promulgated a directive allowing future land uses to be considered in selecting the appropriate remedial action at NPL sites.

Moreover, at least one EPA Region has entered into Memoranda of Understanding (MOU) with State environmental agencies under CERCLA. These memoranda provide assurances that EPA will not take enforcement action at sites where private parties have conducted cleanup under the state's direction or pursuant to State voluntary cleanup acts. At this point, MOUs do not appear to contain similar assurances under RCRA. EPA is continuing to refine and pursue MOUs with State environmental agencies.

Information concerning EPA's Brownfield initiatives is accessible over the Internet at

<www.epa.gov/brownfields>.

What Has the Federal Government Done to Impact Brownfields?

On January 11, 2002 President Bush signed into law the *Small Business Liability Relief and Brownfields Revitalization Act* (the Act). The Act consists of two titles. Title I addresses liability exemptions for parties who generate and transport small quantities of hazardous substances and certain generators of municipal solid waste. Title I also provides for expedited settlements with certain parties that can demonstrate a limited ability or inability to pay their share of response costs. The Title II amendments focus on facilitating the responsible cleanup and re-use of contaminated properties. The amendments provide specific statutory authority for EPA's brownfields program and authorize appropriations to fund brownfields grants and grants for State and Tribal response programs. Title II also provides conditional exemptions from CERCLA liability for contiguous property owners and *bona fide* prospective purchasers and clarifies the *All Appropriate Inquiry* requirement of the pre-existing innocent landowner defense. Finally, the amendments place certain limits on EPA's use of its enforcement and cost recovery authorities at low-risk sites where a person is conducting a response action in compliance with a state program and authorizes grants for the development of state level response programs.

What Are the Key Provisions of the New Federal Brownfields Act?

The Liability Provisions of the Act

Title I: *De Micromis* and Municipal Solid Waste Liability Relief and Ability-to-Pay Settlements.
Title I, §102 of the Act adopted, with some modification, three existing EPA policies. For a decade, EPA has maintained a policy of not pursuing, and providing contribution protection for, parties who generated or transported a minuscule (*de micromis*) amount of waste to a site. Similarly, prior to passage of the Act, EPA had a policy to handle the liability of generators of municipal solid waste (MSW). In 1997, EPA issued guidance on making ability to pay determinations in Superfund cases. Thus, it is not probable that EPA's policies will change, to the extent they are consistent with the Act. However, the *de micromis* and MSW provisions, in particular, contain notable deviations from these existing EPA policies as explained below.

De Micromis. Section 102(a) of the Act added new §107(o) to CERCLA and exempts generators and transporters of *de micromis* quantities of hazardous substances from response-cost liability. The Act requires a person seeking the exemption to demonstrate that "the total amount of the material containing hazardous substances they contributed was less than 110 gallons of liquid materials and 200 pounds of solid materials" and that "all or part of disposal, treatment, or transport occurred before April 1, 2001." This exemption is subject to the following exceptions

1) If the materials contribute significantly, either on their own or in the aggregate, to the cost of the response action or natural resource restoration

2) If the person fails to comply with an information request

3) If the person impedes a response action or natural resource restoration, or

4) If the person has been convicted of a criminal violation for conduct to which the exemption would apply.

The Act provides significant protection for generators and transporters of *de micromis* amounts of hazardous substances at NPL sites where disposal, treatment or transport occurred after April 1, 2001. While EPA is not directed to provide contribution protection to these parties, the Act includes substantial disincentives for litigation by private party plaintiffs. First, the exemption shifts the burden of proof to private party plaintiffs to show that the exemption does not apply. Second, the new law makes private party plaintiffs liable for the defendant's costs and fees if a court finds the defendant to be exempt under this provision.

Municipal Solid Waste. Section 102(a) of the Act also added §107(p) to CERCLA which exempts certain generators of municipal solid waste (MSW) from Superfund response cost liability at NPL sites. The persons covered by this exemption are: owners, operators, and lessees of residential property; small businesses; and certain nonprofit organizations. This exemption is subject to all but one of the same exceptions as found in the *de micromis* exemption. The new law defines MSW in the following two ways

1) As waste generated by a household

2) As waste generated by a commercial, industrial, or institutional entity that is essentially the same as waste generated by a household, is collected as part of normal MSW collection, and contains no greater amounts of hazardous substances than that contained in the waste of a typical single-family household.

Similar to the *de micromis* exemption, the MSW exemption has burden-of-proof and fee-shifting provisions to discourage litigation against exempt parties. The Act provides further protection for residential property owners by barring private parties from contribution actions against them.

Ability to Pay. Section 102(b) of the Act amended §122(g) and grants EPA the authority to enter into expedited settlements with persons who demonstrate an inability or limited ability to pay response costs. The Act directs EPA to consider whether the person can pay response costs and still maintain basic business operations, which includes consideration of financial condition and ability to raise revenues. Section 122(g) prior to the new act provided for settlements with *de minimis* parties and some changes apply to these settlements as well.

Title II: Contiguous Property Owners, *Bona Fide* Prospective Purchasers, and Innocent Landowners.

The Act creates two new conditional exemptions from CERCLA *owner/operator* liability for contiguous property owners and *bona fide* prospective purchasers (BFPP). Again, these exemptions embody aspects of pre-existing EPA policies. The Act also modified the existing innocent landowner defense by clarifying the meaning of *All Appropriate Inquiries*. All three provisions embody some common elements for persons to maintain nonliable status while also including unique provisions and requirements.

Contiguous Property Owners. Section 221 of the Act adds new §107(q) which exempts from owner or operator liability persons that own land contaminated solely by a release from contiguous, or similarly situated property owned by someone else. In the case of a contiguous property owner, the owner must not have known, or had reason to know, of the contamination at the time of purchase and must not have caused or contributed to the contamination. The section also modifies what constitutes appropriate care/reasonable steps for contiguous property owners by clarifying that the requirement does not obligate a contiguous property owner to conduct groundwater investigations or remediate groundwater contamination except in accordance with EPA's pre-existing policy.

The Act generally provides greater protections for contiguous property owners than EPA's existing policy on owners of contaminated aquifers. The Act does not limit the exemption to properties contaminated by groundwater but may also apply to soil contamination resulting from neighboring properties. The Act also grants EPA the authority to provide assurances that the Agency will not take action against a person as well as protection from third party suits. As in EPA's Contaminated Aquifer Policy, a person who purchases with knowledge of the contamination cannot claim the exemption; however, the Act notes that a party who does not qualify for the exemption for this reason may still qualify as a BFPP.

Bona Fide Prospective Purchasers. The most notable aspect of the BFPP provision is that, for the first time, Congress has limited the CERCLA liability of a party who purchases real property and knows that it is contaminated. The caveats to this exemption, in addition to the common elements, include requirements that

1) All disposal takes place prior to the date of purchase

2) The person does not impede a response action

3) The property may be subject to a ***windfall lien***

The windfall lien provision provides for a lien on the property of a BFPP if EPA has unrecovered response costs and the response action increased the fair market value of the property. The lien arises as of the date the response cost was incurred and the amount cannot exceed the increase in fair market value attributed to the response action.

To address the status of Prospective Purchaser Agreements (PPAs), on May 31, 2002, EPA issued new guidance entitled *Bona Fide Prospective Purchasers and the New Amendments to CERCLA.* This guidance states that "EPA believes that, in most cases, the Brownfields Amendments [Act] make PPAs from the Federal government unnecessary." Therefore, in the majority of cases EPA intends for the law to be self-implementing. However, the guidance does recognize the following two exceptions where EPA may enter into an agreement with the purchaser: (1) there is likely to be a significant windfall lien needing resolution and (2) the transaction will provide significant public benefits and a PPA is needed to ensure the transaction will take place.

Common Elements and Innocent Landowners. The contiguous property owner exemption, the definition of what constitutes a BFPP, and the innocent landowner defense, found in CERCLA §107(b)(3), and the definition of *contractual relationship* in §101(35), all contain the following common obligations which persons seeking these exemptions must meet:

- Conduct *All Appropriate Inquiry* prior to purchase of the property

- Not be potentially liable or affiliated with any person potentially liable

- Exercise appropriate care by taking reasonable steps to "stop any continuing release; prevent any threatened future release; and prevent or limit any human, environmental, or natural resource exposure to any previously released hazardous substance"

- Provide full cooperation, assistance, and access to persons undertaking a response action or natural resource restoration

- Comply with all governmental information requests

- Comply with land use restrictions and not impede the performance of institutional controls

- Provide all legally required notices regarding releases of hazardous substances

Changes to CERCLA §101(35)(B) now define *All Appropriate Inquiries* for purposes of all three provisions. First, the Act directs EPA to promulgate regulations based on statutory criteria within two years of date of enactment, establishing standards for all appropriate inquiry. For purchases prior to issuance of these regulations, the Act utilizes two standards based on date of purchase. For purchases prior to May 31, 1997 the Act sets forth a narrative standard, directing courts to consider such factors as specialized knowledge of the defendant, the obviousness of the contamination, and relationship of purchase price to property value. For purchases after May 31, 1997 the Act states that procedures set forth in the American Society for Testing and Materials, Standard Practice E 1527–97—"Environmental Site Assessment: Phase I Environmental Site Assessment Process" (ASTM E 1527–97) shall satisfy the requirement. EPA, in its negotiated rulemaking on All Appropriate Inquiries has established that the revised version, ASTM E 1527–00, satisfies the statutory requirements. The section also provides that for purchasers of property for residential use or similar use by a nongovernmental or noncommercial entity a facility inspection and title search shall fulfill the requirements.

Title II: Limitations on EPA CERCLA Enforcement and Cost Recovery Authority and Expanded Brownfield Definition.
Section 231 of the Act amends CERCLA by adding a new §128.27. Section 128(b) sets forth limitations on EPA's enforcement authority under §106(a) and cost recovery authority under §107(a). These limitations apply to actions against persons who have conducted or are conducting response actions at *eligible response sites* in compliance with a "State program that

specifically governs response actions for the protection of public health and the environment." The limitations only apply to response actions commenced after February 15, 2001 and in states that maintain a public record of sites being addressed under a State program in the upcoming year and those addressed in the preceding year. Additionally, these limitations are subject to specified exceptions.

The definition of an *eligible response site* is found in new CERCLA §101(41). The definition includes *brownfield sites* as defined in §101 (39)(A) and (B). The definition of a brownfield site has been expanded and specifically includes the following:

- Chemicals identified as *Controlled Substances*

- Petroleum and petroleum products otherwise excluded from CERCLA

- Mine-scarred land

The Act further specifies entities that are eligible for Brownfield Grants and expands funding options. As stated, the definition of a brownfield site is very broad in that it essentially captures any real property with real or perceived contamination but excludes facilities that are

- Subject to a planned or ongoing CERCLA removal

- Listed or proposed for listing on the national priorities list

- Subject to a unilateral administrative order, court order, administrative order on consent, or consent decree under CERCLA

- Subject of a unilateral administrative order, court order, administrative order on consent, consent decree, or permit under the Resource Conservation and Recovery Act (RCRA, 42 USC. §6901 *et seq.*), the Clean Water Act (CWA, 33 USC §1251, *et seq.*), the Toxic Substances Control Act (TSCA, 15 USC §2601, *et seq.*), or the Safe Drinking Water Act (SDWA, 42 USC §300[f], *et seq.*)

- Subject to Corrective Action under RCRA §3004(u) or 3008(h), to which a corrective action permit or order has been issued or modified requiring the implementation of corrective measures

- A land disposal unit with closure notification submitted and a closure plan or permit

- On land subject to the custody, jurisdiction, or control of a department, agency, or instrumentality of the United States, except for land held in trust by the United States for an Indian Tribe

- A portion of a facility contaminated by PCBs subject to remediation under TSCA

- A portion of a facility receiving assistance from the Leaking Underground Storage Tanks Trust Fund (LUST Fund sites)

EPA may also include sites excluded under the fourth, fifth, sixth, and eighth bullets on a site-by-site basis. The definition of eligible response site contains an additional exclusion for sites at which EPA has conducted a Preliminary Assessment (PA) or Site Investigation (SI) and after consulting with the state has determined that the site achieves a preliminary score sufficient for, or otherwise qualifies for, listing on the NPL.

Brownfields Grants and State and Tribal Funding

In addition to the Contiguous Property Owner, *Bona Fide* Prospective Purchaser, and Innocent Landowner Provisions, Title II for the first time provides explicit statutory authority for EPA's brownfields program. Title II also authorizes EPA to provide grants to states and tribes to develop response programs. Generally, brownfields are considered properties that have real or perceived contamination that discourages redevelopment or reuse due to the potential liability of those persons associated with the site. The Act authorized annual appropriations of $200 million for the brownfields grant program for fiscal years 2002 through 2006. EPA is using appropriations to provide brownfield characterization and assessment grants, to capitalize revolving loan funds, and for the first time to provide direct grants for brownfields cleanup. The Act also provides an expanded list of persons eligible for these funds that include states, local governments, state chartered redevelopment agencies, tribes, land clearance authorities, and, for certain funds, nonprofits and other private entities. The Act provides ranking criteria for grant distribution and directs EPA to provide guidance for grant applicants.

Title II also authorizes $50 million annually from 2002 through 2006 to provide assistance for State and Tribal response programs, to capitalize a revolving loan fund for brownfield remediation, or purchase insurance/create a risk sharing pool, an indemnity pool, or insurance mechanism to help fund response actions. To receive grants state and tribal programs must meet or be working towards several criteria or the state or tribe must have a memorandum of agreement for voluntary response programs with EPA. States receiving funds must also maintain and annually update a public record of sites going through the states' response programs.

What Have States Done to Resolve the Brownfield Problem?

Many states have developed and are continuing to develop legislation and regulations that narrow the scope of liability under State law, particularly regarding lenders, purchasers, and residential homeowners. Some states are attempting to provide greater certainty and flexibility in identification of cleanup standards, including allowing future land uses to be considered in selecting a remedy. These State laws consistently enact voluntary programs that provide brownfields cleanup incentives.

The two primary incentives that are the cornerstones of the State brownfields voluntary cleanup laws are

1) Utilization of risk-based cleanup criteria that are more specific to the risks encountered at a particular property

2) Liability protection against having to do further cleanup beyond the scope of the risk-based cleanup that is voluntarily agreed upon with the State agency

The utilization of risk-based cleanup criteria in most instances provides an opportunity for a less extensive and therefore, less expensive, cleanup. Integral to this risk-based process is an examination of the current and future land uses of the brownfield property. These land uses are often incorporated into the remediation plan since the land uses may eliminate or restrict the environmental risk associated with the contamination. These future land uses can then be legally incorporated into *institutional controls* such as deed restrictions and other legal agreements.

Deed restrictions provide public notification of use constraints and grant a variety of options for enforcing compliance with them. For example, if an owner of industrial property will agree through deed restrictions and other necessary legal devices that the property will only be used for industrial purposes in the future, he may select target cleanup criteria that are reflective of this intended use. Many states use less stringent concentration levels for industrial sites as compared to residential ones. By opting for these less stringent criteria, a less expensive cleanup may be designed which will not be less protective of human health and environment under the restricted use, so long as the use restrictions are honored.

The second lynch pin of these State brownfields laws is liability protection. Without legal limitation of liability, a brownfields cleanup would always be subject to agency action. The continuing ability to require additional cleanup in the future is an obvious detriment to redevelopment. In addition to future agency action, there is the potential liability to landowners and citizens for *third-party liability,* which includes personal bodily injury, diminution of property value, and destruction of natural resources. State brownfields laws, in most instances, strive to provide some measure of liability protection to the parties performing the agreed risk-based brownfield cleanup.

Although these State brownfields cleanup programs are important and laudable, it must be remembered that they are not binding upon EPA. Therefore, the existence of an MOU between the state and EPA that will bind EPA to the brownfields cleanup approved by the State agency is important. If a state does not have such an MOU, parties considering a voluntary cleanup under a State brownfields law must seek approval from EPA in conjunction with the State agency in order to have assurance that the agreed-upon risk-based cleanup will be approved without further additional activity in the future.

Analysis of State Brownfields and Voluntary Cleanup Laws

Due to the fact that Congress has not enacted Federal brownfields legislation, State governments have taken the initiative to enact laws to provide incentives for cleanup of brownfields properties. Without a Federal pattern for states to follow, every State law is different. We have attempted in this section to briefly analyze and compare these laws. The following categories are utilized for comparison:

1) Does the State law require fees and payment of agency oversight costs?

2) What is the extent of eligibility of properties and applicants for inclusion in the brownfields program?

3) Is risk-based analysis applied in the program?

4) Is liability protection provided by the State law?

5) Is a no further action letter or other similar documentation of acceptance of the cleanup by the State agency provided?

6) Does the program provide reopeners that could require additional cleanup under certain circumstances?

7) Does the program provide economic incentives to help pay for the cleanup of the brownfield property?

A table, located at the end of this chapter, identifies the states which currently have established a brownfields program. This table also contains attendant contact information, including Internet web sites, where available. A brief summary of the information found in each of the seven categories of analysis described above has been included. Finally, the table contains a synopsis of any unique features of the laws that did not fit into one of these seven categories. Please understand that this table has been developed for the purpose of providing a general *snapshot* of the current status of State brownfields programs.

The reader should note that State brownfields programs are currently undergoing a significant amount of change and it is impossible for this text to be completely accurate by the time that it becomes available. With that in mind, the authors have attempted to include in the summary table web page locations for State agency analogues to EPA, even if the State did not have a brownfield program at the time of submission for publication. Additionally, it is in the reader's best interest to download up-to-date information about a particular State program of interest.

The following subsections attempt to summarize trends that can be seen in each of the seven categories of analysis. The conclusions reached are very general in nature and therefore we encourage review of the tabular information for individual states. This is particularly true for states in which there is a vested interest. Web sites have been provided for nearly all states, but may be changed without notice. If interested in a particular state and the listed site is not found, a simple search can be initiated from the general State web page. The generic address of State home pages will follow the format:

<www.state.xx.us> (e.g., <www.state.ny.us> for New York State)

Most State home pages will have an *Agencies* icon. Click on this icon to get the listing or directory. EPA- related regulations are most commonly handled by the department of environment; however, they are administered by the department of natural resources or even the department of health in a few states.

Fees and Oversight Costs

The majority of the State brownfields voluntary cleanup programs require that the State environmental agency oversight costs be paid by the program applicant. These costs will normally consist of the agency's cost of processing and administration applicable to the particular brownfield project. Eight states require payment of agency oversight costs but have no specific application or other fees. Twelve states require both fees (ranging from $250 to $10,000) as well as payment of agency oversight costs. Twelve states do not require agency oversight costs, but do require some type of application or program fee ranging from $500 to $7,500. Only seven states require neither fees nor agency oversight costs.

Eligibility

The great majority (27) of the surveyed State programs allow anyone, including PRPs who caused or contributed to the contamination, to make application for inclusion into the program. Only six State programs do not allow PRPs to become an applicant while three states restrict eligibility to only potential purchasers of brownfield properties. The scope of most programs is broad with regard to the types of properties that may be included in the program, although most exclude NPL sites and sites that are under Federal orders requiring either RCRA corrective action or CERCLA cleanup. This is an important trend since it indicates a relatively common desire to include active industrial and commercial properties owned by persons that could be deemed to either have caused or contributed to the contamination under existing environmental laws. This indicates a trend toward encouraging as many properties to be cleaned up in the state as possible rather than restricting the brownfields incentives to prospective purchasers or innocent landowners.

Risk-Based Cleanup

Most of the states provide for risk-based cleanup of brownfields properties. There appears to be a trend towards allowing more emphasis on the cost effectiveness of the cleanup. Many states are utilizing institutional controls as part of the risk analysis in order to reduce the risk and therefore to reduce the cost of cleanup. This trend confirms that most states are utilizing risk-based cleanup in conjunction with institutional controls to provide significant incentives to clean up brownfield properties.

Liability Protection

Most states provide liability protection against further requirements by the State environmental agency for additional cleanup. Only three surveyed states do not provide for liability protection and only one state limited liability protection to prospective developers. Five states do not provide liability protection to PRPs. At the other end of the spectrum, six states not only provide that PRPs could obtain liability protection, but also extend liability protection to cover third-party liability.

No Further Action Letters

All of the surveyed State brownfields voluntary cleanup programs provide for documentation of approval of the risk-based cleanup through no further action letters (NFAs) or certificates of completion (CoCs). The programs were fairly evenly divided between these two types of approvals. This indicates the importance of NFAs and CoCs for brownfields redevelopment to prospective purchasers and lenders. Documentation of the completion of the brownfield cleanup process and approval by the State agency provides a meaningful level of comfort for transactions involving these properties. It should also be pointed out that business owners who are not buying, selling, or lending also need this documentation in order to reactivate construction and use of these previously dormant properties.

Reopeners

Reopeners are legal requirements setting forth the bases on which additional cleanup of the brownfield property can be required in addition to what was originally agreed upon with the State agency. These reopeners vary from state to state, but in many states the following are included:

1) Fraudulent or misrepresented information has been provided to the agency.

2) An imminent threat to human health or the environment occurs on the property.

3) A previously unknown condition or new information comes to the agency's attention.

4) The risk on which the agreed-upon cleanup was based significantly changes so that additional cleanup to prevent endangerment to human health and the environment is required.

These reopeners are *chinks in the armor* of liability protection. However, it should be understood that reopeners can benefit the landowner, as well as call for increased levels of treatment. Although none of the stakeholders of a cleanup initiative wants to consider the possibility of reopening a completed project, inspection of factors that states have identified as triggering such action has obvious merit. State programs must provide necessary flexibility to meet both the land user's needs and also be protective of risks to human health and the environment that were not contemplated by the initial agreed-upon risk-based cleanup.

Economic Incentives

A significant segment of the surveyed State programs, 13 states, do not provide economic incentives. Of the remaining states that do, 17 states provide tax exemptions, abatements or credits to encourage development of brownfields properties. 11 states provide monetary grants while the same number provide for low-interest loans to infuse capital into brownfields projects.

It is expected that in the future, more states will enact brownfields tax deductions due to the momentum provided by the passage by Congress in 1997 of legislation allowing eligibility for immediate tax deduction of environmental remediation expenditures for brownfields sites located in high poverty areas targeted for Federal empowerment zones or enterprise community efforts and announced as a brownfields pilot project by EPA. This tax treatment is scheduled to expire at sunset on December 31, 2000. It applies to neither rural brownfield sites nor to CERCLA NPL sites.

This summary analysis of State brownfields laws is only intended to provide a broad perspective on existing and developing trends in these State enactments. As stated earlier, we encourage the reader to review the attached table for clarification of any specific state's brownfields program and to further research the state's program by getting in touch with the State agency contact person and utilizing, if available, the State program's web site.

Implementation of State Brownfield Programs

State Brownfield Programs Just Extend CERCLA and RCRA to Less Contaminated Sites, Right?

Brownfield projects are voluntary efforts. The enabling statutes for State brownfields programs do not grant authority to mandate compliance unless the site is enrolled in the program. Individual states vary in the incentives offered property owners to increase the number of eligible sites and enrollment. To view brownfields programs as an attempt to extend the authority of RCRA and CERCLA is to lose sight of the incentive packages, a potentially costly mistake for many sites.

The differences between State programs preclude blanket statements being made, and that fact should have significant impact on how the prudent environmental professional evaluates potential brownfield programs. Be sure to establish as first priority the thorough review of the brownfield program in the state containing the project. This review includes the eligibility requirements, the process and paperwork to be submitted, an estimate of the amount of time that regulators will need to review proposals and the results of sampling or modeling, the expected fees, the professional requirements called for by the agency, the liability protection offered and whether or not the state has signed a MOA with its EPA regional office, and, of course, the reopeners. For the purpose of discussing how Certified Hazardous Materials Managers (CHMMs) will likely interface with brownfield programs, we will assume that the state of interest has one of the more comprehensive statements of eligibility.

The first section of this chapter outlines the factors that have given rise to the numerous State brownfield programs that exist—predominantly the need to facilitate returning idle industrial and commercial property to productive use. This material has also indicated the individuality of the State programs. Even so, it is easy to note the similarity between elements of brownfields programs and the more established concepts of due diligence and CERCLA/RCRA-directed remediation efforts. Specifically, the determination of the extent of contamination that exists at a site is virtually synonymous with a Phase I and Phase II environmental property assessment or a rigorous site assessment under CERCLA/RCRA. The evaluation of technologies that may be used to remediate a brownfield site is very similar to what takes place in a CERCLA remedial investigation/feasibility study (RI/FS). It is, in fact, very desirable to conform to the requirements of these as much as possible. The more closely EPA, CERCLA, or RCRA protocols and methodology are followed in the characterization and remediation of a brownfield site, the higher the confidence level for mitigation of long-term liability.

It is important to point out that there are at least three subtle differences between State brownfields programs and the older Federally mandated ones. These differences can have a significant impact on the decision to conduct the project under oversight of a State brownfield program. The first of these differences is so obvious that it is easy to overlook. Brownfields projects are voluntary cleanup activities. Keep in mind that there is a wide range of quality in voluntary cleanup efforts. There is a tendency to associate brownfields projects with redevelopment of derelict industrial sites, but voluntary cleanup efforts at active facilities can qualify for many of the State brownfields programs.

The absence of a regulatory mandate to remediate a site typically reduces the level of commitment to initiate a cleanup effort. This bias is one of the major factors that has motivated states to provide incentives for cleanup through brownfields programs. Consider the level of difficulty for convincing management of a marginally profitable industrial facility to undertake the expense of remedial activities that are not mandated. The reticence to initiate a voluntary cleanup project will be much stronger when there are homeowners near property boundaries that may become alarmed upon learning of the contamination.

The lack of a regulatory mandate removes the necessity to keep to a time line and it is easy for projects to bog down. Property redevelopment ventures are particularly susceptible to failure from this. The potential for all parties simply to walk away or defer action indefinitely kills many initiatives. It is prudent to go into any brownfield project with a heightened sensitivity to the need to provide compelling data that the proposed course of action is both economically and environmentally beneficial. Project initiation is facilitated by stressing the advantages of being proactive, clearly identifying economic benefits, emphasizing brownfield program incentives, providing concrete data regarding liability reduction, and presenting a realistic expectation for the reduction of excess risk to the general population.

The two remaining ways State brownfield restoration efforts differ from CERCLA/RCRA programs are best discussed together. These are: (1) the liability protection offered by State program oversight and (2) State program flexibility. Both of these result from the lack of a Federal statute requiring EPA to provide regulatory oversight of State programs. Absence of a requirement for equivalence provides states the flexibility to design a program with unique features to best serve the concerns of their constituents. But it also dramatically lessens the technical support they can receive from their EPA regional offices in these unique areas.

Federally mandated programs, although normally delegated to the same State agency overseeing the brownfield program, are still Federal programs and subject to oversight by EPA. It is currently impossible to determine the likelihood that a cleanup appropriately completed under a State brownfield program may be reopened under a Federal program (CERCLA or RCRA) because of the novelty of the State programs. This is especially true when there is not a memorandum of agreement between the state and EPA that includes those circumstances relevant to the site of interest.

One can reasonably expect more latitude for using innovative technologies in brownfield cleanups as compared to the more rigid RCRA or CERCLA allowances, but of course this will vary from state to state. Another way that some State programs differ from the Federal ones is by not requiring a public hearing to review the project before implementation.

Since brownfield initiatives are voluntary efforts, most States require the user to finance administrative costs via a fee structure. There are opportunities to take advantage of this and use State regulators as pseudoconsultants. Seek their input regarding reasonable measures that have proved effective in limiting the costs or time required for the completion of similar projects. As the site progresses through the process of characterization and assessment, significant time and cost reductions may be achieved by judiciously consulting the regulatory person reviewing the project.

What If the State Does Not Have a Brownfields Program?

In all likelihood, the state will still have a mechanism for handling voluntary cleanups in spite of the lack of a formal brownfields program. Contact the State environmental agency and provide a description of the site, its history, and the expected use upon completion of the remediation. The most likely places to start will be the Superfund or RCRA branches. Distill the facts regarding the site to a terse set of the most significant considerations. This should include whether the intended use of the remediated site will be residential, commercial, or industrial. Determine if there are sensitive receptors in the area such as drinking water wells, daycare centers, or hospitals. Have an inventory of the activities and chemicals that were used on the site. Review also the most typical cleanup targets that would be established by CERCLA or RCRA. If specific, insightful questions are asked, there is a much greater probability of obtaining the information necessary for decision making. A final recommendation: while discussing the brownfield project with regulators, ask questions, don't debate the issues. If information provided during the conversation does not appear to correlate with other data that have been collected, put that data in writing and submit it for review.

In the absence of brownfields guidance or process at the State level, follow CERCLA or RCRA cleanup policies and guidance as much as possible. The general rules of thumb for deciding which program will have jurisdiction over the site can be given as: (1) if the contamination originated from underground tank systems (either petroleum or chemical), it is probably a RCRA Subtitle I site; (2) if the contamination originated from industrial activity on a site which is currently regulated under RCRA Subtitle C (site has a hazardous waste generator identification number), then it will probably be a RCRA Corrective Action; otherwise, (3) the site is most likely a CERCLA site.

The best way to ensure long-term liability protection is to follow protocols equivalent to CERCLA/RCRA schemes. This is particularly true during the data-gathering stage. Even if the state has a voluntary cleanup program, all the site assessment data generated and the effectiveness of control measures implemented may ultimately be measured relative to CERCLA/RCRA yardsticks. Consider carefully the dangers associated with not doing an aggressive job of characterizing the site, designing the site sampling plan, implementing the sampling plan, using Quality Assurance/Quality Control (QA/QC) measures to ensure data quality, or using an analytical lab capable of producing Contract Laboratory Program (CLP) quality analytical data. A certain reopener for any project is to miss areas of contamination during the site investigation.

Data quality is a very important to EPA. Superfund program activities are particularly likely to require development and use of data quality objectives. If they are not employed from the outset of the project, State program approval of a site sampling plan is unlikely. The data generated by activities which were not developed consistent with data quality objectives may be deemed unusable by a regulatory agency or subjected to a very high degree of scrutiny.

What Are Data Quality Objectives and Why Are They Significant?

Over the past decade EPA has begun promoting and even requiring the use of Data Quality Objectives (DQOs) as a guiding principle for ensuring the defensibility of environmental data. In a document entitled *Data Quality Objectives Process for Superfund: Interim Final Guidance* (EPA, 1993), the agency sets forth a seven-step process for explicitly establishing acceptance and rejection criteria for information generated by each activity involved in the process of generating data. Details about DQOs and a number of useful tools can be obtained by searching the Office of Solid Waste and Emergency Response (OSWER) documents for DQOs from the EPA brownfield web site:

<www.epa.gov/swerosps/bf/>

The American Society for Testing and Materials (ASTM) has developed two standards related to the DQO process (the titles are included in the bibliography). The DQO process can be briefly summarized thus:

Step 1 State the problem that requires new environmental data.

Step 2 Identify the decision that must be resolved to address the problem.

Step 3 Identify the informational inputs (data) required to address the problem.

Step 4 Specify the spatial and temporal circumstances that are covered by the decision.

Step 5 Integrate the information developed in Steps 1–4 into a statement that describes the logical basis for choosing from among the alternate actions.

Step 6 Specify the acceptable limits on decision errors and the corresponding performance goals limiting uncertainty in the data.

Step 7 Design the most resource-effective sampling and analysis plan for generating the data expected to satisfy the DQOs.

DQOs are developed in the earliest stage of the project. They serve as the basis for judging both the appropriateness and the veracity of the data which will be generated.

What Tools Can I Use for the Site Evaluation Process?

The introduction of the concept of an *innocent landowner* in the 1986 Superfund Amendments and Reauthorization Act has given rise to the *due diligence investigations* of property prior to transfer of title. The environmental site assessment industry has matured to the point that there are now two ASTM standards describing the process. One describes the general Phase I Environmental Site Assessment process (E 1527–00) and the other is designed to address commercial real estate (E 1528–00). From a professional standpoint, one of the best protections against charges of negligence is to be proficient in the application of all applicable professional codes of practice and to follow them faithfully.

An environmental site assessment conducted in accordance with the two ASTM standards will provide a good basis from which to develop a site sampling plan. ASTM also has a set of standards on environmental sampling that can be purchased collectively (03–41–8097–38). These standards, in conjunction with guidelines set forth in SW–846 (EPA, 1997) and other EPA publications like the Region IV Environmental Investigation Standard Operating Procedures and Quality Assurance Manual (EISOPQAM), will be extremely helpful in planning for and conducting site sampling. This document can be easily downloaded from the web site:

<www.epa.gov/region04/sesd/eisopqam/eisopqam
.html>

All of these activities will be selected and conducted in a manner sufficient to achieve all DQOs. The list of activities will include

1)   Identifying the analytes of interest

2)   Targeting the size and types of samples to be taken

3)   Developing a sampling scheme identifying the location of all samples to be collected

4)   Establishing requirements for sampling tools, sample containers, and sample preservation for each type sample to be collected

5)   Ensuring appropriate QA/QC measures are included in the sampling protocols

6)   Providing forms for the necessary paperwork for documenting all samples, establishing chain of custody, and submitting the samples to an analytical laboratory for their appropriate analysis

States that have brownfields programs will have established forms and processes to be followed. It is highly likely that DQOs will be required as part of the process. It goes without saying that the development of a sampling plan followed by collection of environmental samples is an expensive process. No regulatory official wants to be put into a position of telling a property owner that the data they have paid for was collected incorrectly or is inappropriate for characterizing their site. By requiring DQOs to be included in the initial site description and Phase I characterization, an added measure of comfort can be provided to all parties that the approved scope of work detailed in subsequent stages will be adequate to achieve success.

Finally, there are a variety of software packages and guidance documents to assist in the development of a site safety and health plan. A commonly employed tool is the Health and Safety Plan (HASP) software available from EPA and OSHA. HASP can be downloaded from the web site:

<www.osha.gov/dep/etools/ehasp/index.html>

and technical support can be obtained by calling (800) 999–6990. Keep in mind that the HASP will need to be updated or modified as the brownfield project moves from the initial screening stages through final remediation. It will also be necessary to ensure that all individuals involved in these activities have undergone the appropriate degree of Hazardous Waste Operations and Emergency Response (HAZWOPER) training.

What Kind of a Team Should Be Assembled for a Brownfield Project?

For purposes of discussion, it is probably best to divide the brownfield team into two groups, an administrative group to deal with financial and business considerations and a technical group to address issues related to site investigation and cleanup. The administrative team members would include the owner/site manager, capital source/chief financial officer, attorney, environmental professional, and a public relations person.

The technical team members will be equivalent to those that would be involved in a CERCLA cleanup. A CHMM needs to be involved to ensure that all applicable environmental regulations are properly taken into account. Many states require that a registered professional engineer submit the documentation associated with brownfield investigations and remediation. This engineer should be an expert in either the designing or construction of environmental remediation systems, or possibly both. Under the new Federal Act, an inquiry by an *environmental professional* is required for conducting all appropriate inquiry at a site before purchase in order to establish a liability defense as an innocent landowner, *bona fide* prospective purchaser, or contiguous property owner. Also, a Phase I Environmental Site Assessment (ASTM E 1527–00) should be conducted by the qualified environmental professional.

A registered professional geologist may be necessary to assess soil samples and log the wells installed for ground water monitoring. The wells themselves should be drilled by a certified driller who has sufficient environmental experience to guarantee that wells and samples will not be contaminated by the drilling process. A certified industrial hygienist and/or a certified health physicist may be necessary to develop the HASP and assure worker safety. Site assessment may require the services of professionals experienced in the areas of ground water modeling, pollutant migration, or risk assessment. Other experts may be required to address endangered species, archeological considerations, Federal facility requirements, and wetlands.

A thorough discussion of selection of technologies applicable to a given site is beyond the scope of this chapter. The reader is referred to other sections of this text for guidance. It will also be helpful to review the EPA Superfund Office of Research and Development web site:

<http://www.epa.gov/ord/>

and Department of Energy (DOE) Environmental Management web site for information about innovative technologies:

<http://www.em.doe.gov>

Bibliography

"Amendment to the National Oil and Hazardous Substances Pollution Contingency Plan (NCP)." *Federal Register* 60 (29 March 1995): 16053. (Codified at 40 CFR 300).

American Society for Testing and Materials. *ASTM Standards on Environmental Sampling.* 2nd Ed. ASTM Publication Code Number 03–418097–38. West Conshoshocken, PA: ASTM, 1997.

American Society for Testing and Materials. *Standard Practice for Environmental Site Assessments: Phase I Environmental Assessment Process.* E 1527–93. West Conshoshocken, PA: ASTM, 1993.

American Society for Testing and Materials. *Standard Practice for Environmental Site Assessments: Transaction Screening Process.* E 1528–93. West Conshoshocken, PA: ASTM, 1993.

American Society for Testing and Materials. *Standard Practice for Generation of Environmental Data Related to Waste Management Activities Development of Data Quality Objectives.* D 5792–95. West Conshoshocken, PA: ASTM, 1995.

American Society for Testing and Materials. *Standard Practice for Generation of Environmental Data Related to Waste Management Activities Quality Assurance and Quality Control Planning and Implementation.* D 5283–92. West Conshoshocken, PA: ASTM, 1992.

Connor, Paul and Schefski, K. C. "The Small Business Liability Relief and Brownfields Revitalization Act: The Challenge of Implementing Changes to Superfund Liability," in *Proceedings of the American Bar Association Section of Environment, Entergy and Resources 10th Section Fall Meeting.* Chicago, IL: October 9, 2002), 499–513.

Buonicore, A. J., Ed. *Cleanup Criteria for Contaminated Soil and Ground-Water.* DS 64. West Conshoshocken, PA: ASTM, 1996.

Davis, T. S., and K. D. Margolis. *Brownfields, A Comprehensive Guide to Redeveloping Contaminated Property.* Chicago, IL: American Bar Association, 1997.

Environmental Protection Agency. "Memorandum on *Bona Fide* Prospective Purchasers and the New Amendments to CERCLA." Washington D.C.: EPA Office of Site Remediation Enforcement, May 31, 2002.

Environmental Protection Agency. *Contract Laboratory Program National Functional Guidelines for Inorganic Data Review.* EPA/540/R–94/013. Springfield, VA: National Technical Information Service, 1994.

Environmental Protection Agency. *Contract Laboratory Program Statement of Work for Inorganic Analysis—Multi-Media, High Concentration ILM02.1.* EPA/540/R–94/095. Springfield VA: National Technical Information Service, 1991.

Environmental Protection Agency. *Contract Laboratory Program—Statement of Work for Organic Analysis, OLM03.1.* EPA/540/R–94/073. Springfield, VA: National Technical Information Service, 1994.

Environmental Protection Agency. *Contract Laboratory Program—Statement of Work for Turnaround Dioxin Analysis, Multi-Media.* EPA/540/R–94/091. Springfield, VA: National Technical Information Service, 1992.

Environmental Protection Agency. *Data Quality Objectives (DQO) Decision Error Feasibility Trials (DEFT) Version 4.0 (on diskette).* PB95–100418INC. Springfield, VA: National Technical Information Service, 1994.

Environmental Protection Agency. *Data Quality Objectives Process for Superfund.* EPA/540/R–93/071. Washington, DC: US Government Printing Office, 1993.

Environmental Protection Agency. *Environmental Investigations Standard Operating Procedures and Quality Assurance Manual.* Athens, GA: USEPA, Region IV, 1996.

Environmental Protection Agency. *Good Automated Laboratory Practices: Principles and Guidance to Regulations for Ensuring Data Integrity in Automated Laboratory Operations.* 2185. Research Triangle Park, NC: USEPA Office of Information, 1995.

Environmental Protection Agency. "General Policy on Ability to Pay Determinations." Washington D.C.: EPA Office of Site Remediation Enforcement, September 30, 1997.

Environmental Protection Agency. *Health and Safety Plan.* EPA/540/C–93/002. Springfield, VA: National Technical Information Service, 1990.

Environmental Protection Agency. "Methodology for Early De Minimis Waste Contributor Settlements under CERCLA Section 122(g)(1)(A) (1992)." OSWER Directive #9834.7–1C. Washington D.C.: EPA, Office of Solid Waste and Emergency Response. June 2, 1992.

Environmental Protection Agency, *Organic Contract Compliance Screening System (OCCSS) Software (OLM01.8 Version 7).* PB94–504255INC. Springfield, VA: National Technical Information Service, 1994.

Environmental Protection Agency, "Policy for Municipality and Municipal Solid Waste CERCLA Settlements at NPL Co-Disposal Sites." Washington D. C.: EPA, Office of Enforcement and Compliance Assistance. February 5, 1998. (This policy supplements the "Interim Policy on CERCLA Settlements Involving Municipalities and Municipal Solid Waste." Environmental Protection Agency, Office of Site Remediation Enforcement. 1989).

Environmental Protection Agency. "Policy Towards Owners of Property Containing Contaminated Aquifers (1995)." In *Handbook of Tools for Managing Federal Superfund Liability Risks at Brownfields and Other Sites.* EPA 330–B–98–001. Washington, D.C.: EPA , Office of Enforcement and Compliance Assurance. 1998.

Environmental Protection Agency. "Site Remediation Enforcement, Guidance on Settlements with Prospective Purchasers of Contaminated Property (1995)." In *Handbook of Tools for Managing Federal Superfund Liability Risks at Brownfields and Other Sites.* EPA 330–B–98–001. Washington, D.C.: EPA , Office of Enforcement and Compliance Assurance. 1998.

Environmental Protection Agency, *Quality Assurance/Quality Control Guidance for Removal Activities—Sampling QA/QC Plan and Data Validation Procedures.* EPA/540/G–90/004. Springfield, VA: National Technical Information Service, 1990.

Environmental Protection Agency. *Sampler's Guide to the Contract Laboratory Program.* EPA/540/R–96/032. Springfield, VA: National Technical Information Service, 1996.

Environmental Protection Agency. *Test Methods for Evaluating Solid Waste Physical/Chemical Methods, CD-ROM Version 2.* SW–846. Springfield, VA: National Technical Information Service, 1997.

Environmental Protection Agency. *User's Guide to Contract Laboratory Program.* EPA/540/8–89/012. Springfield,VA: National Technical Information Service, 1988.

"Final Policy Toward Owners of Property Containing Contaminated Aquifers." *Federal Register*, 60 (3 July 1995): 34790.

General Accounting Office. *Superfund: Barriers to Brownfield Redevelopment.* GAO/RED–96–195. Washington DC: Government Printing Office, US General Accounting Office, 1996.

Gerrard, M. B., Ed. *Brownfields Law and Practice.* New York, NY: Matthew Bender Publishing Company, 1998.

"Small Business Liability Relief and Brownfields Revitalization Act." PL 107–118, 115 *Statutes* 2356 . *US Code.* Title 42, Sec. 9601–9675.

John E. Milner is a partner in the Jackson, Mississippi law firm of Brunini, Grantham, Grower & Hewes, PLLC. He received his BA from the University of Mississippi in 1975 and his JD from the University of Mississippi Law School in 1978. His practice emphasizes environmental law, real estate due diligence, and contractual matters. Mr. Milner represents business and industrial clients in environmental litigation in State and Federal courts in the southeastern region. He has also had significant experience in environmental permitting and enforcement actions and regulation promulgation proceedings involving the US EPA and the Mississippi Department of Environmental Quality. Mr. Milner is currently serving as Environmental Counsel for the Mississippi Manufacturers Association, and has recently authored and lobbied to enact the Mississippi Brownfields Voluntary Cleanup and Redevelopment Act. He is the Mississippi consultant to Matthew Bender, Inc., for its multivolume reference publication Brownfield Law and Practice. *He has authored numerous articles including "Overview of Major Federal Environmental Acts and Regulations for the General Practioner" (with Dr. Waggoner), for the* Mississippi Law Journal, *and "Environmental Justice," for the ABA's* Natural Resources & Environment.

Dr. Charles A. Waggoner currently serves as the Manager of Safety, Excellence, and Environment for the Diagnostic Instrumentation and Analysis Laboratory at Mississippi State University (MSU). He holds a BS and MS in biochemistry and a PhD in physical chemistry. He has over 15 years experience in environmental management with particular emphasis on hazardous waste management and related issues. Dr. Waggoner's professional activities have included serving as the MSU Hazardous Waste Officer, Technical Director of Environmental Training for the MSU Division of Continuing Education, and Dean of Environmental Science and Technology at Chattanooga State Technical Community College. Dr. Waggoner has served as a member of the IHMM-ACHMM Advisory Committee, ACHMM Board of Directors, and as General Chairperson for the 1994 National Conference in Chattanooga, Tennessee. He has authored numerous articles, including, "Overview of Major Federal Environmental Acts and Regulations for the General Practioner" (with Mr. Milner), and the asbestos chapter in the Handbook on Hazardous Materials Management, *5th edition, published by IHMM in 1995.*

The authors would like to express their appreciation to Gene Wasson and Richard Cirilli of the Brunini, Grantham, Grower, and Hewes law firm, for their assistance in the preparation of materials contained in this chapter.

Summary of State Brownfields Programs

State	Alabama	Alaska	Arizona	Arkansas
Program	Informal policy-based program only	Has discretion to allow alternative cleanup levels	Greenfields Pilot Program (GPP), 1997 Arizona Session Laws, Ch. 296 12. 4/30/97 and Voluntary Remediation Program (VRP), Arizona Revised Statutes Ann. 49-282.05, 4/29/97	Arkansas Code Ann. 8-7-110 *et seq.*, 4/2/97
Contact Information	Dept. of Environmental Management (334) 271-7711 <www.state.al.us>	Dept. of Environmental Conservation (907) 766-3184 <www.state.ak.us/local/>	Arizona Dept. of Environmental Quality (ADEQ) 3033 N. Central Ave. Phoenix, AZ 85012 (602) 207-0833 <www.azleg.state.az.us>	Superfund Brownfields Branch Arkansas Dept. of Environmental Quality (ADEQ) PO Box 8913 Little Rock, AR 72219-8913 (501) 682-0744 <www.adeq.state.ar.us>
Fees			ADEQ's costs	
Eligibility			GPP: first qualified sites – No groundwater impact – No UST sites – No site subject to current enforcement – No permitted hazardous waste site with a release to soil in violation of its permit VRP: anyone	Sites where no PRP can be found
Risk-Based Analysis			Predetermined risk-based levels based on future use of property or site specific standards based on risk assessment	Cleanup standards on case-by-case basis
Liability Protection				No
No Further Action (NFA)			Yes	CNS for past contamination
Reopeners			If audit shows site not cleaned in accordance with NFA letter	No
Economic Incentives			None	Loan fund
Unique Features				1997 statute provides for petition process to ease water quality standards for certain long-term improvement projects, including brownfields

State	California	Colorado	Connecticut	Delaware
Program	Dept. of Toxic Substances Control adopted a policy document in 1995	Voluntary Cleanup and Redevelopment Program (VCRP), 1994	Two programs: 95-183 and 95-190 Connecticut General Statutes 22a-133a *et seq.*, 1995	1995
Contact Information	California Environmental Protection Agency Dept. of Toxic Substances Control (510) 540-3827 <www.state.ca.us/s/environ/>	Superfund/Voluntary Cleanup Unit Leader Colorado Dept. of Public Health and Environment (CDPHE) HazMat/Waste Management Div. 4300 Cherry Creek Dr. South Denver, CO 90222-1530 (303) 692-3300 <www.cdphe.state.co.us/hm/rpbrownfields.asp>	Urban Sites Remedial Action Program Connecticut Dept. of Environmental Protection (CDEP) 79 Elm St. Hartford, CT 06106-5127 (860) 424-3800 <www.state.ct.us/agency.htm>	Manager Dept. of Natural Resources and Environmental Control (DNREC) Div. of Air and Waste Management SIRB 715 Grantham Lane New Castle, DE 19720 (302) 323-4540 <www.dnrec.state.de.us/>
Fees		$2000 filing fee plus costs	95-193: $2000 fee	$5000 oversight deposit
Eligibility		Owners of property that are not subject to any other government authority	95-183: 1) Sites on Connecticut's hazardous waste disposal site list 2) Groundwater class GA or GAA sites, and "Establishments" under the Connecticut Property Transfer Act 95-190: Groundwater class GB and GC sites	Persons other than PRPs, numerous site exceptions
Risk-Based Analysis		Depends on future land use		State developed screening levels—varies with commercial and residential use
Liability Protection		No	No	Release from liability to DNREC for future release attributable to conditions existing before certification issued. Contribution protection under State CERCLA
No Further Action (NFA)		Yes	CNS if not a PRP	CoC or remedy
Reopeners		Failure to comply with cleanup plan	Cleanup not completed or land use restriction not filed or complied with	If work under plan is not complete
Economic Incentives		None	Loans	Matching grant to $25,000, tax credits, loans
Unique Features			CNS may in some cases cost 3% of the value of uncontaminated property	

See end of Table for list of abbreviations.

Summary of State Brownfields Programs (Continued)

State	District of Columbia	Florida	Georgia	Hawaii
Program	None	Brownfields Redevelopment Act Florida Statutes 288.107 and 376.77, *et seq.*, 5/30/97	1996 Amended 1998	Voluntary Cleanup Program (VCP) 7/7/97
Contact Information	Dept. of Consumer and Administration Regulatory Affairs Environmental Regulation 2100 Martin Luther King Jr. Ave, SE, Room 203 Washington, DC 20020 (202) 645-6080 Fax: (202) 645-6622	Florida Dept. of Environmental Protection (DEP) 2600 Blair Stone Road MS 4505 Tallahassee, FL 32399-2400 (850) 488-0190 <www.dep.state.fl.us>	Georgia Dept. of Natural Resources (GDNR) Environmental Protection Div. (EPD) 205 Butler St., S.E., Suite 1462 Atlanta, GA 30334 (404) 657-8600 <www.ganet.org/dnr/environ/>	Hawaii Dept. of Health (HDH) Hazard Evaluation and Response Office, Rm 206 919 Ala Moana Blvd. Honolulu, HI 96814 (808) 586-4248 <www.state.hi.us/doh>
Fees				$1000 filing fee plus costs
Eligibility		Any person who has not contributed to contamination after 7/1/97; sites under active Federal enforcement and hazardous waste TSDs or post closure are excluded	Potential purchasers of sites on Hazardous Sites Inventory or State Superfund list – PRPs are excluded	Sites subject to current enforcement excluded
Risk-Based Analysis		Default cleanup standards with alternative of site-specific risk-based standards	Based on future use, then standard or site-specific risk assessment within the case classification	Yes
Liability Protection		From State enforcement and from third-party contribution while cleanup is ongoing	Limits third-party liability for contribution or damages; release of liability to the state	Liability protection from subsequent enforcement actions
No Further Action (NFA)		Yes	EPD will respond in writing as to whether it concurs with party's compliance status report	CoC
Reopeners		Fraud, new information of threat to environment or public health, cleanup not complete, increase in risk such as change in site use, new release occurs	No	No
Economic Incentives		Tax credit and loans	None	Tax exempt
Unique Features				

State	Idaho	Illinois	Indiana	Iowa
Program	VCP Enactment of statute, 3/14/95 Promulgation of regulations, 2/97	VCP 1989, amended 1995	Indiana Code 13.25-5-1 *et seq.*, 1992 Brownfields Financial Incentives, 1997	VCP Enactment of statute 1997 No regulations as of 1/1/99
Contact Information	Dept. of Health and Welfare (DHW) Division of Environmental Quality (DEQ) 1410 N. Hilton Boise, ID 83706 (208) 373-0276 <www.state.id.us/>	Brownfields Coordinator Illinois Environmental Protection Agency (IEPA) Bureau of Land 1001 North Grand Ave F Springfield, IL 63702 (217) 782-6761 <www.epa.state.il.us/>	Brownfields Coordinator Indiana Dept. of Environmental Management (IDEM) 2525 N. Shadeland PO Box 6015 Indianapolis, IN 46202-6015 (317) 234-0966 <www.state.in.us/idem>	Iowa Dept. of Natural Resources (IDNR) Environmental Protection Div. 900 E. Grand Ave. Des Moines, IA 50319 (515) 242-5817 <www.legis.state.ia.us>
Fees	Costs of review and oversight $250 filing fee	IEPA's oversight costs unless applicant retains and Illinois licensed professional engineer to oversee	$1000 application fee and pay costs of oversight	Review costs up to $7500
Eligibility	Sites subject to current enforcement excluded	Anyone • Specific site exceptions such as NPL sites	Excludes various sites such as imminent threat, current enforcement, *etc.*	Excludes NPL sites, USTs and animal feeding operations as well as sites subject to State or Federal enforcement
Risk-Based Analysis	Yes	Yes	Can either use standard or site-specific risk assessments	Standard or site-specific risk assumptions • Site-specific include future land use
Liability Protection	Liability protection from subsequent enforcement actions	Neither Illinois nor EPA will bring future enforcement actions under CERCLA or RCRA	CNS that protects against all public and private claims under State environmental laws	CNS that protects against further enforcement or liability for response actions – Exempt from liability under state environmental laws to the state or other parties
No Further Action (NFA)	CoC	Yes	CoC	Yes
Reopeners	No	Site is not managed in accordance with site plan	Conditions not known to IDEM	Imminent and substantial threat – Fraud or material misrepresentation – Corrective controls fail
Economic Incentives	Tax exempt	Grants, tax credits	Loans, grants, loan guarantees, *etc.* for local grants – Tax abatements for private entities	Fund for financial assistance – Local governments may provide tax relief
Unique Features				

See end of Table for list of abbreviations.

Summary of State Brownfields Programs (Continued)

State	Kansas	Kentucky	Louisiana	Maine
Program	VCP Enactment of statute, 1997 Promulgation of regulations, 1998	Brownfields Program 1996	VCP Enactment of statutes 7/1/96 No regulations as of 1/1/99	VCP 1993
Contact Information	Kansas Dept. of Health and Environment (KDHE) Bureau of Environmental Remediation Forbes Field, Bldg. 740 Topeka, KS 66620 (785) 296-1675 <www.kdhe.state.ks.us>	Superfund Branch Kentucky Natural Resources and Environmental Protection Cabinet (NREPC) Div. of Waste Management 14 Reilly Road Frankfort, KY 40601-1990 (502) 564-6716 <www.state.ky.us>	Louisiana Dept. of Environmental Quality (LDEQ) Inactive and Abandoned Sites Div. PO Box 82282 Baton Rouge, LA 70884-2282 (504) 765-0487 <www.deq.state.la.us/remediation>	Voluntary Response Action Program Maine Dept. of Environmental Protection (MDEP) Bureau of Remediation and Waste Management 12 State House Station Augusta, ME 04333-0017 (207) 287-2651 <www.state.me.us/dep>
Fees	$200 application fee and pay oversight costs		Agency costs	$500 application fee and oversight costs
Eligibility	Excludes various sites, such as NPL, imminent threat, current enforcement, etc.	Limited to public entities	PRPs are eligible but must remove all contaminants of concern Non-PRPs rely on easement restrictions, etc.	Anyone
Risk-Based Analysis	Site-specific, may include institutional controls, such as use restrictions	Yes	Standard and site-specific	Site-specific, including institutional controls
Liability Protection		Protection for public entity and any successor or assign from further remediation liability	Release from liability under State Superfund law − Does not extend to damage to third parties	Release of liability to state and protection against third party contribution
No Further Action (NFA)	Yes	Yes	CoC	CoC
Reopeners	Fraud or misrepresentation, failure to complete and maintain	No	Fraud or misrepresentation	No
Economic Incentives		None	None	None
Unique Features				

State	Maryland	Massachusetts	Michigan	Minnesota
Program	VCP Enactment of statute, 2/97	New law passed in 1998 No data available as of 1/1/99	Informal VCP that includes Brownfield financing—otherwise, no specific statute	Enactment of statute and promulgation of regulations in 1992
Contact Information	Maryland Dept. of the Environment Waste Management Administration 2500 Broening Hwy. Baltimore, MD 21224 (410) 631-3437 <www.mde.state.md.us/programs/landprograms/errp_brownfields/home/index.asp>	Massachusetts Dept. of Environmental Protection (617)727-2200 <www.state.ma.us/dep/bwsc/files/bfhdout2.htm>	Chief, Site Reclamation Unit Michigan Dept. of Environmental Quality <www.michigan.gov/deq>	Minnesota Pollution Control Agency (MPCA) Site Response Section 520 Lafayette Rd. St. Paul, MN 55155-4194 (612) 296-9707 <www.pca.state.mn.us/cleanup>
Fees	$6000 application fee and oversight costs			
Eligibility	Excludes sites such as NPL, current enforcement, and sites contaminated after 10/97, unless innocent purchaser or site-specific	Anyone	Local governments	Excluded sites include NPL sites and sites with drinking water contamination
Risk-Based Analysis	Standard or site-specific			Standard or site-specific
Liability Protection	Release from liability for further remediation under State law; protection from third party contribution	Yes		Release from state of responsibility for further remediation under State Superfund law
No Further Action (NFA)	CoC			CoC is available to non-PRPs
Reopeners	Imminent threat, fraud or misrepresentation, conditions previously unknown, etc.			New information
Economic Incentives	Loans, grants and tax abatement	Loans and tax credits	Loans and tax credits	Loans, grants and tax credits
Unique Features				

See end of Table for list of abbreviations.

Summary of State Brownfields Programs (Continued)

State	Mississippi	Missouri	
Program	Mississippi Brownfields Voluntary Cleanup and Redevelopment Act (MBVCRA), 1988 Mississippi Laws, Chapter 528 Regulations are being promulgated as of 1/1/99	VCP 1993 Brownfields Redevelopment Program (BRP) 1995	
Contact Information	Brownfields Coordinator Mississippi Dept. of Environmental Quality (MDEQ) PO Box 10385 Jackson, MS 39289-0385 (601)961-5171 <http://www.welcome.to/brownfields>	VCP: Chief, Voluntary Cleanup Section Missouri Dept. of Natural Resources (MDNR) PO Box 176 Jefferson City, MO 65102 (573) 526-8913 <www.dnr.state.mo.us/deq/hwp/program.htm>	BRP: Manager, Finance Programs Missouri Dept. of Economic Development (MDED) PO Box 118 Jefferson City, MO 65102 (573) 751-0717
Fees	$2000 application fee and pay MDEQ's processing and administration costs	VCP: $200 application fee and initial deposit to cover oversight costs	
Eligibility	Anyone, including PRPs, except 1) Existing or proposed CERCLA NPL sites unless CoC has been issued 2) Sites under current CERCLA or RCRA orders and 3) RCRA sites undergoing RCRA corrective action unless it has been completed The commission on Environmental Quality has the discretion to determine qualifying projects	VCP: any person and most nonresidential property BRP: only certain types of limited projects	
Risk-Based Analysis	Risk-based cleanup criteria specific to the property mandated	BRP: allows for risk-based cleanups	
Liability Protection	Liability protection from further remediation – No third-party liability protection	BRP: liability protection consistent with the level of risk remaining at the site – Immunity from third-party civil action – Immunity from tort liability prior to issuance of NFA letter	
No Further Action (NFA)	Yes	Yes	
Reopeners	None, unless 1) Developer provides false information or fails to provide information 2) Previously unreported contamination 3) Changes in exposure 4) New information raises risk 5) Failure to file notice of Bronwfields Party 6) Owner violates land use restrictions		
Economic Incentives	None, but MBVCRA requires MDEQ to propose incentives to the Mississippi legislature	BRP: Direct loans, guarantees, grants, and tax credits	
Unique Features			

State	Montana	Nebraska	Nevada	New Hampshire
Program	Voluntary Cleanup and Redevelopment Act (VCRA), 1995	Remediation Action Plan Moderating Act (RAPMA); 1/1/95	No VCP – Party may submit proposed remediation plan to the Nevada Dept. of Conservation and Natural Resources (NDCNR) for review and comment	New Hampshire Brownfields Program (NHBP), 7/1/96 No regulations as of 1/1/99
Contact Information	Montana Dept. of Environmental Quality (MDEQ) Remediation Division 2209 Phoenix PO Box 20091 Helena, MT 59620 (406) 444-0478	RAPMA Program Coordinator Nebraska Dept. of Environmental Quality (NDEQ) The Atrium 1200 North Street, Suite 400 Lincoln, NE 68509 (404) 471-2214 <www.deq.state.ne.us/>	NDCNR, Div. of Environmental Protection Waste Management and Corrective Action 33 West Nye Lane Carson City, NV 89706 Superfund Branch Supervisor: (702) 687-5872 Remediation Branch Supervisor: (702) 687-5872	Supervisor of State Sites New Hampshire Dept. of Environmental Services (DES) PO Box 95 6 Hazen Drive Concord, NH 03302-0095 (603) 271-2456 or Brownfields Coordinator (603) 271-6778 <www.state.nh.us/des>
Fees	Oversight costs	Applicant must submit payment plan and schedule for reimbursement along with application fees totaling $10,000		$500 application fee and $3000 initial program fee
Eligibility	Any person, but not sites subject to UST laws, agency orders, court actions or consent decrees; or sites proposed for the NPL	Any "entity"		Any person who did not cause or contribute to the contamination; NDES has discretion
Risk-Based Analysis	Yes	No		Yes
Liability Protection	Yes	No		Yes, but not responsible parties
No Further Action (NFA)	Yes	Yes		CoC
Reopeners	New information	If contamination is recurring, additional contamination is present which was not previously identified or remedial action was not taken		
Economic Incentives	None	No		Municipalities may grant tax abatements
Unique Features	Controlled Allocation of Liability Act (ALA) significantly modified State Superfund law. – Prospective purchaser agreements available			One of two states to receive $250,000 in Superfund program monies to undertake emergency removal work without direct EPA involvement

See end of Table for list of abbreviations.

Summary of State Brownfields Programs (Continued)

State	New Jersey	New Mexico
Program	VCP; Brownfields Act, 1/6/98	Voluntary Remediation Act (VRA), 3/21/97
Contact Information	New Jersey Dept. of Environmental Protection (DEP) Bureau of Field Operation Case Assignment PO Box 434 Trenton, NJ 08625-0434 (973)669-3960 <www.state.nj.us/dep/srp/index.htm>	New Mexico Environment Dept. (NMED) Ground Water Quality Bureau Harold Runnels Bldg, Ste. N2300 1190 St. Francis Dr. Santa Fe, NM 87502 (505) 827-2754 <www.nmenv.state.nm.us>
Fees	Applicant must pay oversight costs	Application fee and oversight costs
Eligibility	Most contaminated properties and all parties	Current and prospective owners and operators – Excluding certain types of sites
Risk-Based Analysis	Yes	No
Liability Protection	CNS – However, liable parties under the Spill Compensation and Control Act are not eligible for a covenant not to sue	CNS releases purchaser from direct and future liability for claims to NMED, but does not protect against liability to Federal government, other State agencies, or third parties
No Further Action (NFA)	Yes	CoC
Reopeners	Contamination that has migrated – Negligent acts that aggravate or contribute to the contamination – Future noncompliance with environmental laws or – Noncompliance with the NFA	Unreasonable threat to human health or the environment, noncompliance with VRA or work plan, fraud or contamination not previously identified
Economic Incentives	Loans and loan guarantees – Real property tax exempts – Grants to municipalities and innocent parties – Corporate tax revenues allocated to site remediation – Reuse of sites for retail purposes is funded – Cost reimbursement development agreements	None
Unique Features		

State	New York	North Carolina	North Dakota	Ohio
Program	Articulated in various papers and speeches by officials of the New York State Dept. of Environmental Conservation (DEC) and subject to change without formal administrative process	Brownfields Property Reuse Act (BPRA), 10/1/97 VCP, State cleanup law was amended in 1994-5	No formal program, private party proposing a VCP would have to submit plan to North Dakota Dept of Health (NDDOH) for review and comment	Voluntary Action Program (VAP) Statute, 7/94 Regulations, 12/96
Contact Information	50 Wolf Road Albany NY 12233-7010 (518) 457-5861 <www.nysgis.state.ny.us>	Dept. of Environmental and Natural Resources (DENR) Div. of Waste Management Superfund Branch 401 Oberlin Rd. Raleigh, NC 27605 (919) 733-2801 <www.ehnr.state.nc.us>	Coordinator of Hazardous Waste Program PO Box 5520 Bismark, ND (701) 328-5166 <www.ehs.health.state.nd.us/ndhd/environ/wm/index.htm>	VAP Div. of Emergency and Remedial Response Ohio Environmental Protection Agency PO Box 1049 1800 Watermark Dr. Columbus, OH 43216-1049 (614) 644-2279 <www.odod.state.oh.us/ud>
Fees		BPRA: $1000 initial fee plus $500 when developer submits final report	Site assessment cost	
Eligibility	All persons – Limited participation by PRPs	BPRA: only prospective developers or innocent landowners who did not cause or contribute to contamination VCP: any responsible party	Businesses, local governments, private entities	All properties, unless specifically excluded
Risk-Based Analysis	No			Yes
Liability Protection	Yes	Prospective developers, but not responsible parties		Ohio EPA may issue CNS after receiving NFA from certified professional engineer
No Further Action (NFA)	Yes	BPRA: CNS VCP: a responsible party or developer my receive NFA from DENR for $500		Certified professional may issue the parties a NFA
Reopeners	Response plan proves insufficient to protect health and environment; site use changes to require more cleanup; fraud discovered; unknown onvironmental conditions discovered	Previously unreported contamination, changes in exposure, new information raises risk, failure to file Notice of Brownfields Party or owner violates land use restrictions		None
Economic Incentives	Funding is available to municipalities	None		None
Unique Features	1996 Environmental Bond Act – Municipalities can receive reimbursement up to 75% of costs – Municipality afforded liability protection – Urban renewal projects New York City has Brownfields Initiative			State oversight not required

See end of Table for list of abbreviations.

Summary of State Brownfields Programs (Continued)

State	Oklahoma	Oregon	Pennsylvania	Puerto Rico
Program	Brownfields Voluntary Redevelopment Act (BVRA), 1996	VCP, 1991 Oregon Recycled Lands Act (7/18/95)	VCP 7/18/95	
Contact Information	Waste Management Div. Oklahoma Dept. of Environmental Quality (ODEQ) (405) 702-5127 <www.deq.state.ok.us>	Oregon Dept. of Environmental Quality (ODEQ) 811 S.W. Sixth Ave. Portland, OR 97204 VCP: (503) 229-6834 or 1 (800) 452-4011 ODEQ: <www.deq.state.or.us> Portland Brownfields Initiative: <www.brownfield.org>	Director Land Recycling and Cleanup Program Pennsylvania Dept. of Environmental Protection (PDEP) PO Box 8471 Harrisburg, PA 17105-8471 (717) 783-7120 <www.dep.state.pa.us/>	Chief, Superfund Core Puerto Rico Environmental Quality Board PO Box 11488 Santure, PR 00910 (787) 767-8181
Fees	Oversight costs	$5000 deposit to cover ODEQ's review and oversight costs, but if site will likely not need remediation, applicant can pay $2000 oversight fee to have ODEQ issue NFA		
Eligibility	Almost any individual or entity with some relationship to the property	Any person, including responsible parties	Responsible persons can participate	
Risk-Based Analysis	Yes	Yes	Parties may use site-specific standards	
Liability Protection	Applicant, lender, lessee, successor or assign are released from liablity; also protection from third party liability; responsible parties also eligible	CNS	Current or future owners; protection extends to citizen suits and contribution actions under state law	
No Further Action (NFA)	Either a CoC or a Certificate of No Action Necessary	Yes	If DEP approves the report, the developer and DEP will enter into an agreement that outlines the cleanup liability for the property	
Reopeners	Noncompliance with consent order or NFA		Fraud, new information, remediation fails to attain the selected standard, change in use of property creates unacceptable level of risk, remedy has becom technically and economically feasible	
Economic Incentives	Businesses which locate their principal operations on certain contaminated properties quality for the incentive payments under the state Quality Jobs Act	Loans and grants are available	Two funds which are awarded on a competitive basis	
Unique Features	Sales tax exemption for purchases used in reducing volume or toxicity of hazardous waste		The American Legislative Exchange Council adopted the Pennsylvania program as the national model for industrial site recycling	

State	Rhode Island	South Carolina	South Dakota	Tennessee
Program	VCP, 1995	No statute but VCP for responsible parties was established in 1988 and expanded in 1995 to include nonresponsible party cleanups	South Dakota has a planned voluntary cleanup program (as of 1/1/99)	Voluntary Oversight and Assistance Program (VOAP), 1994
Contact Information	Rhode Island Dept. of Environmental Management (DEM) Div. of Site Remediation 291 Promenade Street Providence, RI 02908 (401) 222-2797 <www.riedc.com/infrastructure/sites/brownfields/brownfields.htm>	Bureau of Land Waste Management South Carolina DHEC 2600 Bull Street Columbia, SC 29201 (903) 800 4009 <www.myscgov.com/>	Dept. of Environment and Natural Resources Foxx Building 523 East Capitol Ave Pierre, SD 57501-3182 (605) 773-5868 <www.state.sd.us>	Manager Voluntary Oversight and Assistance Program Tennessee Dept. of Environment and Conservation (TDEC) Div of Superfund 401 Church St. L&C Annex, 4th Floor Nashville, TN 37243 (615) 532-0912 <www.state.tn.us/environment>
Fees		Oversight costs		$5000 initial participation fee
Eligibility	Any person not a responsible party	NPL sites are not eligible		All parties are eligible, but only inactive hazardous substance sites are eligible to enter the VOAP
Risk-Based Analysis	Yes	Yes		Yes
Liability Protection	Person will not be considered a responsible party under the Industrial Property Remediation and Reuse Act; also, DEM may issue a CNS; additional protections provided for cleanups of CERCLIS sites	Responsible party: CNS, but no release for past contamination that is discovered at a later date. Nonresponsible party will receive full liability protection for all past contamination		VOAP parties protected from liability for further TDEC-mandated cleanups
No Further Action (NFA)	Letter of Compliance	CoC		Yes, in form of a letter of completion
Reopeners	No	No		If new or different information becomes known that questions the effectiveness of the selected remedial response
Economic Incentives	Investment tax credit, business tax credits and an interest income credit in terms of State income taxation and authorization for localities to grant property tax exempts to qualifying properties	None		None
Unique Features	Expedited environmental permit process available for projects of critical economic concern			

See end of Table for list of abbreviations.

Summary of State Brownfields Programs (Continued)

State	Texas	Utah	Vermont
Program	VCP, 9/1/95	VCP, 3/17/97	Redevelopment of Contaminated Properties Program (RCPP), 1995
Contact Information	Project Manager Voluntary Cleanup Section Texas Natural Resource Conservation Commission (TNRCC) PO Box 13087 Austin, TX 78711-3087 (512) 239-2252 or (512) 239-2498 <www.tnrcc.state.tx.us/>	Coordinator Voluntary Cleanup Program Div. of Emergency Response and Remediation Dept. of Environmental Quality 168 North 1950 West Salt Lake City, UT 84114-4810 (801) 536-4100	Chief Sites Management Section Dept of Environmental Conservation (DEC) Vermont Agency of Natural Resources (VANR) 103 S. Main Street Waterbury, VT 05671-0404 (802) 241-3491 <www.anr.state.vt.us>
Fees	$1000 application fee and costs	$2000 application fee and costs	Applicants must pay $500 fee and, following acceptance into the RCPP, must submit a $5000 fee
Eligibility	All persons and any contaminated property, subject to certain exceptions	Most sites and most parties	Only parties who are not responsible for the contamination; certain sites are excluded
Risk-Based Analysis	Yes	Yes	No
Liability Protection	Yes, but responsible parties will not be released from liability; CoC protects subsequent owners and lenders	Yes, for nonresponsible parties	No liability under the State hazardous waste management law
No Further Action (NFA)	CoC	CoC	CoC
Reopeners		Fraud, misrepresentation, or the knowing failure to disclose material information	When the eligible person or a successor engages in activities that are inconsistent with the approved correction action requirements or causes the release or contamination to become worse
Economic Incentives	Municipal tax abatements are available in reinvestment zones	None	None, but some are proposed
Unique Features	The TNRCC VCP has expanded its program to offer a limited number of federally funded brownfields site assessments at selected brownfields properties owned by qualifying governmental entities		

State	Virginia	Washington
Program	Voluntary Remediation Program (VRP), 1995	Person may undertake voluntary cleanup with formal, informal or no agency oversight under VCP of Department of Ecology (DOE)
Contact Information	Manager Voluntary Remediation Program Virginia Dept. of Environmental Quality (VDEQ) PO Box 10009 Richmond, VA 23240 (804) 698-4201 <www.deq.state.va.us/>	Department of Ecology PO Box 47775 Olympia, WA 98504-7775 (360) 407-7187 <www.wa.gov/ecology>
Fees	$5000 fee or 1% of the cost of cleanup, whichever is less	For informal consultation, party must pay for agency service – $50 to $100 per hour and for more complex sites, the agency offers the option of entering into a prepayment agreement – Minimum deposit of 25% of estimated costs
Eligibility	Any persons who own, operate, have a security interest in or enter into a contract for the purchase or use of an eligible site; any property as long as remediation has not been mandated	Any person; however, where discussion or negotiations have already commenced, a potentially liable party cannot take remedial action unless 1) Such action does not foreclose negotiations or the selection of a cleanup action; and 2) The party has provided notice of the proposed action to DOE without objection
Risk-Based Analysis	Parties may select published, media specific cleanup levels or may develop site-specific cleanup levels through a risk assessment	No
Liability Protection	Immunity is limited to site conditions at the time of issuance of the certificate	Contribution protection and may contain CNS
No Further Action (NFA)	Certificate of Satisfactory Completion	Yes
Reopeners	If contamination posing an unacceptable risk to human health or the environment is rediscovered on the site, or if the parties supplied DEQ with false, inaccurate or misleading information	NFA does not preclude the DOE from requiring other further action based on reevaulation of the site or additional information
Economic Incentives	None	Limited "mixed funding" is available on a discretionary basis
Unique Features		Remedial Action Grants are available to municipalities

See end of Table for list of abbreviations.

Summary of State Brownfields Programs (Continued)

State	West Virginia	Wisconsin	Wyoming
Program	Voluntary Remediation Program (VRP), 7/1/96	Voluntary Party Exemption Program (VPEP)	Voluntary Corrective Action Order Program (VCAOP)
Contact Information	Chief West Virginia Div. of Environmental Protection (DEP) Office of Environmental Remediation Brownfields and LUST Remediation Programs 1356 Hansford Street Charleston, WV 25301 (304) 558-2508 <www.dep.state.wv.us/oer/index.html>	Wisconsin Dept. of Natural Resources (DNR) 101 S. Webster St. Box 7921 Madison, WI 53707-7921 (608) 261-6422 <www.dnr.state.wi.us>	Program Manager, VCAOP Wyoming Dept. of Environmental Quality (WDEQ) Solid and Hazardous Waste Div. Herschler Building 122 West 25th St. Cheyenne, WY 82202 (307) 777-7752 <www.state.wy.us>
Fees	Applicant must pay $1000-$5000 fee (based on a point system) upon filing	$250 application fee and must pay either $1000 or $3000 to cover administration and oversight costs	
Eligibility	Any person not causing or contributing to contamination; sites not subject to unilateral Federal or State enforcement actions or listed on NPL	Persons who are not deemed responsible for the contamination	Generators and transporters of hazardous waste and nonresponsible parties – Site conditions and hazardous waste release circumstances determine eligibility – TSD hazardous waste facilities are not eligible
Risk-Based Analysis	Yes	No	Yes
Liability Protection	Yes	Yes	No
No Further Action (NFA)	CoC which may be subject to a land use covenant	NFA at sites that don't need remediation – CoC affords protection against future State enforcement action	Yes
Reopeners	Fraud – New information – Level of risk has increased significantly or – Remediation method failed to meet standards	Failure to maintain the property as required by DNR; activities inconsistent with maintenance of the property	Subsequently discovered contamination
Economic Incentives	Loan fund	1) Agricultural Chemical Cleanup Program 2) Petroleum Environmental Cleanup Fund Act 3) Brownfields Environmental Assessment Program 4) State trust fund loan program 5) Tax credits 6) Business Improvement Districts 7) Tax-increment financing for municipalities	No

Abbreviations

CERCLA	Comprehensive Environmental Response, Compensation and Liability Act	**MOA**	Memorandum of Agreement	**TSD**	Treatment, Storage and Disposal Facility
CERCLIS	Comprehensive Environmental Response, Compensation and Liability Information System	**NFA**	No Further Action letter	**USEPA**	United States Environmental Protection Agency
CNS	Covenant Not to Sue	**NPL**	National Priorities List	**UST**	Underground Storage Tank
CoC	Certificate of Completion	**PRP**	Potentially Responsible Party	**VCP**	Voluntary Cleanup Program
IRRP	Industrial Property Remediation and Reuse Act	**RCRA**	Resource Conservation and Recovery Act	**VRP**	Voluntary Remediation Program

Part V

Management of Hazardous Materials and Hazardous Substances

CHAPTER 23

Department of Transportation Hazardous Materials Regulations

Dorothy Christman, CHMM
Michael Eyer, CHMM

Department of Transportation Hazardous Materials Regulations

Introduction

The hazardous materials regulations (HMR) of the United States Department of Transportation (DOT) are promulgated with the goal of establishing shipping practices and ensuring the secruity of hazardous materials, thereby allowing the safe movement of hazardous materials without incident in the national and international transportation systems.

DOT hazardous materials regulatory authority is divided between several administrations: the Federal Motor Carrier Safety Administration (FMCSA), Federal Railroad Administration (FRA), Pipeline and Hazardous Materials Safety Administration (PHMSA), Federal Aviation Administration (FAA). Since September 11, 2001, post 9/11 regulatory changes have been made by the government to secure the safety of our hazardous materials while in transportation. Other agencies have been created that have regulatory authority; some have moved from the USDOT and other previously extant agencies have added transportation regulation. These agencies include the Department of Homeland Security, United States Coast Guard; Transportation Security Administration; Bureau of Alcohol, Tobacco, and Firearms; and the United States Customs Service.

Although some hazardous materials regulations are written by the modal agencies, most of the rules are generated by the PHMSA. Additionally, any hazardous materials moving by the United States Postal Service must meet the Postal Service rules. Private carriers, such as UPS and FedEx may impose requirements more stringent than DOT's rules.

The hazardous materials/dangerous goods regulations that are used worldwide are based on suggestions made by the United Nations Committee of Experts and found in the "Orange Book," *Recommendations on the Transport of Dangerous Goods*, 11th Edition. Regulations for radioactive materials are developed separately by the International Atomic Energy Agency and are published in *Regulations for the Safe Transport of Radioactive Materials, Safety Series TS-R-1*. DOT regulations apply to all modes of transport, but can be superseded by other nations' regulations and regulations issued by the International Maritime Organization and the International Civil Aviation Organization. To competently prepare a shipment of hazardous materials, a hazardous material manager must be familiar with all of the possible regulatory agencies' rules, particularly if the movement will be multimodal or international.

Definitions and Regulatory Authority

It is important to understand that DOT's definition of the words *hazardous materials* applies to those materials in pre-transportation, transportation, transloading and storage for the purpose of transport in commerce. By definition, all Environmental Protection Agency (EPA) *hazardous wastes* and *hazardous substances* are DOT hazardous materials. However, the Occupational Safety and Health Administration (OSHA), the Department

of Agriculture, the Department of Health and Human Services, and the National Fire Protection Association (NFPA) define *hazardous materials* much more broadly than does the DOT. Unlike the hazardous waste regulations, under which states can adopt their own waste codes, the DOT's definitions preempt all local, State, Tribal, and regional definitions and codes. Both the EPA and OSHA are free to regulate to the full extent of their authority in areas where the DOT has no authority. However, where DOT does regulate, the other agencies have only limited authority.

The principal exception to DOT's authority is that for noncommercial movement. This exception exempts Federal and State government agencies, school districts, *etc.* from most of these rules unless a state has specifically placed them under the authority of the regulation. This exemption applies only to the *Hazard Communication System* (HCS) parts of the regulations and does not extend to issues such as driver's licenses and highway cargo tank packaging.

Regulations

The DOT regulations that address hazardous materials are found in the *Code of Federal Regulations*, Title 49, Parts 100–500 (49 CFR 100–500). The majority of the rules are in 49 CFR 170–180. In 49 CFR 171.8, the DOT defines a ***hazardous material*** as

> a substance or material, that the Secretary of Transportation has determined is capable of posing an unreasonable risk to health, safety, and property when transported in commerce, and has designated as hazardous under Section 5103 of Federal hazardous materials transportation law (49 USC 5103). The term includes hazardous substances, hazardous wastes, marine pollutants, elevated temperature materials, materials designated as hazardous in the Hazardous Materials Table (see 49 CFR 172.101), and materials that meet the defining criteria for hazard classes and divisions in Part 173 of Subchapter C of this Chapter.

The Secretary of Transportation can add or delete materials to the list at any time. For example, the Secretary added the entire category of *marine pollutants* following a major train incident in 1991 that pollluted the Sacramento River in Dunsmuir, California. The products released were DOT regulated if shipped by water. When such changes occur, notices are provided through the *Federal Register*. If other agencies change their listings, (*i.e.*, the Comprehensive Environmental Response, Compensation, and Liability Act [CERCLA] designations in the EPA's hazardous substances table), the changes are automatically effective for the DOT, even though the change may not appear in Title 49 until the next printing. (Government titles are printed on an annual basis.) Title 49 has a cover date of October 1, and usually appears about mid-March. Without an update service of some kind, a shipper and/or carrier will always be at least five months out of date, even if they have the latest *official* edition. It is the responsibility of the shipper and the carrier to be aware of all changes.

Hundreds of other regulations and publications are *incorporated by reference* in the DOT regulations. These publications and regulations are indexed in 49 CFR 171.7. If a commercial company is shipping or carrying hazardous materials, the company is required to know the applicable regulations issued by the EPA, OSHA, the Department of Energy, the Nuclear Regulatory Commission, the Consumer Product Safety Commission, the Food and Drug Administration, *etc*. The shipper must also know the regulations promulgated by departments of the DOT, *i.e.*, Federal Motor Carrier Safety Administration.

Historically, DOT regulations have been based on safety in transportation and have been developed independently from other nations' concerns. In the early 1980s, the DOT began to issue preliminary notices of its intent to harmonize with the United Nations (UN) rules used by the international community. Major changes were mandated beginning in 1992 and are continuing as of this writing. The entire Hazard Communication System (HCS) commodity classifications and ancillary information, labeling, marking and placarding, have been and are continuing to be substantively altered. Packaging moved from individualized safety-engineered packaging to performance oriented generic requirements. The DOT is one of the most fluid regulatory bodies.

The DOT's hazardous materials regulations assume that all of the materials listed in the hazardous materials table of 49 CFR 172.101 and its two appendices, hazardous substances and marine pollutants, are fully regulated in all

quantities. The 49 CFR regulations give the shipper the option of removing specific commodities and/or groups of materials from the rules: *small quantities* are in 49 CFR 173.4, *limited quantities* are referenced in their specific hazard classes, *materials of trade* are discussed in 49 CFR 173.6. Specific commodities (*i.e.*, batteries 49 CFR 173.159) are also eligible for exception. PHMSA, the principal rule-writing branch of the DOT, issues exemptions which release a commodity or package from various regulatory requirements. As of late spring 2005, there were over 7,000 active exemptions. Exemptions are valid for two years and may be renewed on a continuing basis.

Shippers and carriers must know the DOT Hazard Communication System (HCS) in order to legally move a shipment of hazardous materials. The HCS requires each covered shipment to have a properly prepared shipping invoice, some form of package marking, some form of class symbols on the package (either labels or placards), and packaging that is properly designed to prevent the release of its contents during normal transportation.

The company must certify that all employees who handle hazardous materials meet the training requirements of 49 CFR 172.700, *et seq.*, which includes general awareness, safety, security, and function-specific areas. The training requirement is designed to increase safety awareness and to improve emergency preparedness for employees who must respond to transportation incidents and accidents. Testing and recordkeeping are mandatory. Retraining is required every three years, except for certain radioactive materials that require training every two years. Anyone who directly affects hazardous materials transportation safety is a ***hazmat employee***.

Before any hazmat employee performs a function specific to the HMR, the person must receive initial training in the performance of the function. If a new regulation is adopted, or an existing regulation is changed, affected employees must first be instructed in those new or revised requirements before carrying out their duties. An employee may perform a required function under the direct supervision of a properly trained and knowledgeable employee for 90 days, or until the training is provided.

The DOT requires a hazardous materials endorsement on a Commercial Driver's License for those drivers who haul certain quantities of hazardous materials as well as a cargo tank endorsement, if applicable. OSHA's hazard communication training may be used to fulfill the safety training portion of DOT's requirement.

Training is one of the most frequently violated sections of the HMR. The maximum DOT penalties go up to $27,500 per day/per violation, and if criminal sanctions are awarded in a criminal trial, up to 5 years in jail. These penalties can be levied in addition to any penalty from another agency, *i.e.,* a hazardous materials/waste transporter is subject to enforcement under both sets of regulations.

Hazardous Materials Table 172.101

The heart of the DOT hazardous materials regulations is found in 49 CFR 172.101, the Hazardous Materials Table, its two appendices and list of special provisions. A portion of the table is reproduced in Figure 1. This table gives the shipper the information needed to ship a hazardous material in commerce.

172.101 Column 1

In Column 1 there are 6 possible symbols. The "+" fixes the proper shipping name, hazard class, and packing group, even though it might belong elsewhere. "A" and "W" indicate that the material is only regulated by *Air* or *Water*, unless the material is a hazardous substance or waste. "D" means the shipping name is allowable only for *Domestic* shipments. "I" is for *International* movements and the product is required to use this shipping name; the "I" is allowable for domestic use as well. "G" indicates that the technical names of the materials in mixtures or solutions are required in parentheses. (If there are multiple hazardous materials in the mixture, then the two materials which have the largest constituents must be listed on the shipping manifest.

172.101 Column 2

Column 2, *proper shipping name* (PSN), is the most important item in the DOT hazardous

materials regulations. The PSN determines whether the material is legal to move, how to package, label, mark, and placard the shipment, whether special provisions apply, *etc.* It is the shipper's responsibility to determine the proper name; failing to properly identify a material can result in penalties, injuries, and deaths. A major contributing factor in the 1996 Valujet crash in which more than 100 people were killed, was failure to properly identify the "oxygen generators chemical, spent" and to provide proper shipping papers.

There are about 2800 proper shipping names in the hazardous materials table. This list is insufficient to cover the tens of thousands of materials which are regulated (the current Chemical Abstract Service database lists nearly 2 million chemicals), so the DOT has also created approximately 170 generic names, like "solids containing corrosive liquid, n.o.s." on the chart. The term "n.o.s.," means *not otherwise specified* (*i.e.,* the material meets the definition of a DOT hazard class but is not listed by a specific name in the 172.101 table).

If an n.o.s. entry is selected by the shipper as most accurately representing the hazard(s) of the commodity, the shipper must enter either the common or technical name in parentheses following the letters n.o.s.—*i.e.,* "Amines, liquid, corrosive, n.o.s., (cobaltammine, hydrochloric acid)"—unless the entry is "hazardous waste, liquid or solid, n.o.s.", Class 9, in which case the appropriate waste code may be used in lieu of the technical name in accordance with 49 CFR 172.203(k)(4)(i). Certain materials in Classes 6.1 and 2.3 (poisons and poison gases) also require additional technical information.

Only the names shown in **bold** type are legal shipping names The names in *italics* cannot be used as proper shipping names, but will refer you to a proper name; *e.g., "storage batteries, wet"* refers to **"batteries, wet."** In the example table this can be seen with *"Aminopropyldiethanoliamine, see Amines, etc."* Material which is italicized following a proper shipping name may be used as supplemental information.

When deciding if a given shipment contains a hazardous material, remember that you cannot assume that simply because a material is not listed by specific name, or does not fit into a hazard class n.o.s. description, that the product is not a

§ 172.101 HAZARDOUS MATERIALS TABLE—Continued

Symbols (1)	Hazardous materials descriptions and proper shipping names (2)	Hazard class or Division (3)	Identification Numbers (4)	PG (5)	Label Codes (6)	Special provisions (§172.102) (7)	Packaging (§173.***) Exceptions (8A)	Non-bulk (8B)	Bulk (8C)	Quantity limitations Passenger aircraft/rail (9A)	Cargo aircraft only (9B)	Vessel stowage Location (10A)	Other (10B)
				II	8, 3	IB2, T11, TP2, TP27	None	202	243	1 L	30 L	A	
G	Amines, liquid, corrosive, n.o.s. or Polyamines, liquid, corrosive, n.o.s..	8	UN2735	I	8	A3, A6, B10, N34, T14, TP2, TP27	None	201	243	0.5 L	2.5 L	A	
				II	8	B2, IB2, T11, TP1, TP27	154	202	242	1 L	30 L	A	
				III	8	IB3, T7, TP1, TP28	154	203	241	5 L	60 L	A	
G	Amines, solid, corrosive, n.o.s., or Polyamines, solid, corrosive n.o.s..	8	UN3259	I	8	B7, IP1	None	211	242	1 kg	25 kg	A	
				II	8	IB8, IP2, IP4	154	212	240	15 kg	50 kg	A	
				III	8	IB8, IP3	154	213	240	25 kg	100 kg	A	
	2-Amino-4-chlorophenol	6.1	UN2673	II	6.1	IB8, IP2, IP4	None	212	242	25 kg	100 kg	A	
	2-Amino-5-diethylaminopentane	6.1	UN2946	III	6.1	IB3, T4, TP1	153	203	241	60 L	220 L	A	28, 36
	2-Amino-4,6-Dinitrophenol, wetted with not less than 20 percent water by mass.	4.1	UN3317	I	4.1	23, A8, A19, A20, N41	None	211	None	1 kg	15 kg	E	
	2-(2-Aminoethoxy) ethanol	8	UN3055	III	3	IB3, T4, TP1	154	203	241	5 L	60 L	A	
	N-Aminoethylpiperazine	8	UN2815	III	8	IB3, T4, TP1	154	203	241	5 L	60 L	A	
+	Aminophenols (o-; m-; p-)	6.1	UN2512	III	6.1	IB8, IP3, T4, TP1	153	213	240	100 kg	200 kg	A	12
	Aminopropyldiethanolamine, see Amines, etc.												
	n-Aminopropylmorpholine, see Amines, etc.												
	Aminopyridines (o-; m-; p-)	6.1	UN2671	II	6.1	IB8, IP2, IP4, T7, TP2	None	212	242	25 kg	100 kg	B	12, 40
I	Ammonia, anhydrous	2.3	UN1005		2.3, 8	4, T50	None	304	314, 315.	Forbidden	25 kg	D	40, 57
D	Ammonia, anhydrous	2.2	UN1005		2.2	13, T50	None	304	314, 315.	Forbidden	25 kg	D	40, 57
D	Ammonia solution, relative density less than 0.880 at 15 degrees C in water, with more than 50 percent ammonia.	2.2	UN3318		2.2	13, T50	None	304	314, 315.	Forbidden	25 kg	D	40, 57

122

Figure 1. Excerpt from the DOT Hazardous Materials Table 172.101

hazardous material. It may still be listed in either of the appendices. If the material exceeds the reportable quantity for a hazardous substance as found in Appendix A, or is to be placed in bulk (greater than 450 liters) packaging, or will move in part by water and is listed in Appendix B for marine pollutants, then the material is fully regulated.

172.101 Column 3

Column 3, hazard class or division, refers to classes of materials developed under the aegis of the UN "Orange Book." The United Nations (UN) recognizes 9 hazard classes, and the United States (US) adds two additional classes: "combustible liquids" and "other regulated materials/ORM–D/consumer commodities." Some of the classes have subsets, called divisions. It is the shipper's responsibility to determine into which class/division a material falls.

All materials have at least *one* class/division; if they meet the technical requirements for a second class/division, they must show the subsidiary class/division in parentheses following the PSN. The subsidiary class can usually be surmised if labels for two or more different classes are required. If a product meets the definition of more than one class, a hazard precedence table, found in 49 CFR 173.2(a), determines which class is dominant. The essential order of precedence is: explosives, radioactive materials, poison gas, flammable gas, non-flammable gas, poison liquid, organic peroxide, and all others. Those materials which represent the greatest hazard in a possible transportation emergency are given precedence.

Note that although the DOT does sometimes show degrees of risk in transportation through sequential numbering (*i.e.*, the Packing Groups I, II, and III go from great to minor risk), the divisions do not represent any specific ranking. One exception to this is Class 1 explosive materials. For Class 1 materials, 1.1 is a much greater explosive risk than a 1.6.

Materials which are listed as "forbidden" in column 3, like *sodium tetranitride,* cannot be shipped. (Note: The name is italicized, therefore it is not a PSN.)

Figure 2 shows class numbers, division numbers, class or division names, and those sections of the subchapter which contain definitions for classifying hazardous materials, including forbidden materials.

Class No.	Division No. (if any)	Name of class or division	49 CFR reference for definitions
None	....	Forbidden materials	173.21
None	....	Forbidden explosives	173.54
1	1.1	Explosives (with a mass explosion hazard)	173.50
1	1.2	Explosives (with a projection hazard)	173.50
1	1.3	Explosives (with predominately a fire hazard)	173.50
1	1.4	Explosives (with no significant blast hazard)	173.50
1	1.5	Very insensitive explosives; blasting agents	173.50
1	1.6	Extremely insensitive detonating substances	173.50
2	2.1	Flammable gas	173.115
2	2.2	Non-flammable compressed gas	173.115
2	2.3	Poisonous gas	173.115
3	....	Flammable and combustible liquid	173.120
4	4.1	Flammable solid	173.124
4	4.2	Spontaneously combustible material	173.124
4	4.3	Dangerous when wet material	173.124
5	5.1	Oxidizer	173.127
5	5.2	Organic peroxide	173.128
6	6.1	Poisonous materials	173.132
6	6.2	Infectious substance (Etiologic agent)	173.134
7	....	Radioactive material	173.403
8	....	Corrosive material	173.136
9	....	Miscellaneous hazardous material	173.140
None	....	Other regulated material: ORM–D	173.144

Figure 2. DOT Hazardous Materials Classes and Divisions

Because the Orange Book and recommendations from the UN Committee of Experts are advisory, individual countries are allowed a degree of freedom within the UN system and may create their own additional classes and divisions as long as they do not supersede or differ substantially from the international standards. In the United States, the DOT changed the definition of Class 3, flammable liquid materials. If the shipper so chooses, any non-waste hazardous substance, non-marine pollutant Class 3 material with a flashpoint between 38°C and 93°C can be reclassified as a combustible liquid in accordance with 49 CFR 173.120 and 173.150(f). The international standards define Class 3 materials as those with a flashpoint of 60.5°C and below, and have no regulation for materials with flashpoints above 60.5°C. This change allows (domestic only) shippers to remove themselves from some or all of the Hazard Communication Standards (HCS) requirements; *i.e.*, fuel oil haulers and paint manufacturers are exempt from some packaging requirements. Other countries also have changes: Anhydrous ammonia is a "2.3, poison gas" everywhere in the world except the US, where it is a "2.2, non-flammable gas." Canada and other countries divide Class 9, miscellaneous materials into three divisions. Many countries divide Class 8, corrosives into two divisions for acids and bases. The US has not yet adopted these latter two modifications of the basic system.

The US has also carried forward from pre-UN days "other regulated material-D/consumer commodities." Most hazard classes have sections identifying what requirements must be met to take advantage of the ORM-D exceptions, *e.g.*, 49 CFR 173.150 for Class 3 materials. Both are subsets of the nine classes and can be used optionally by shippers if all qualifications are met. Both allow the shipper and carrier to comply with fewer requirements. Consumer commodities are a subset of "limited quantities" and apply to those items intended for household use (*e.g.*, cosmetics which would normally be classified as flammables or corrosives could carry no hazard identifications of any kind if reclassified). Charcoal briquettes in packaging of up to 30 kilograms (66 pounds) are another example of a material which is frequently reclassified. Briquettes which would normally require shipping papers, labeling, and appropriate packaging are exempt from those portions of the HCS under 40 CFR 173.151(c), provided they are not a hazardous substance, hazardous waste, or marine pollutant.

Although other agencies use terminology similar to the DOT's, always remember that DOT terminology is preeminent in transportation. EPA waste manifests are required to list the DOT's proper shipping names. The DOT terminology sometimes differs from the EPA's. For example, EPA's "corrosivity" is pH-based, but DOT's Class 8, corrosives are based on several different criteria (found in 49 CFR 173.136), none of which involves pH. EPA's "ignitability" and DOT Class 3, "flammable liquids" are both determined by flashpoint, but use different flashpoints. In addition, the DOT's definition applies only to flammable liquids; other materials (gases and solids) covered in the EPA's definition are found in DOT Classes 2, 4, and 5.

172.101 Column 4

Column 4, *identification number* (ID number), refers to a 4-digit number assigned to the commodity, or group of similar commodities, by the United Nations or the United States. If the material is identified in Column 1 with a "D," the PSN is allowed only for use in domestic transportation and in most cases the number will be prefaced "NA," North America. All other numbers are prefaced with a "UN," or United Nations. It is important not to confuse the 4-digit DOT hazardous material ID number with the 3-digit EPA waste code, since the waste code can appear as part of the PSN, see 49 CFR 172.203(c)(1). The ID number is not necessarily commodity-specific. See, for example, the ID number 1993 in Figure 3. The ID number, in addition to being required on shipping papers, is also a requirement for package marking.

The ID number is most critical to emergency response. It is used by responders to determine the chemicals' identities and what initial emergency steps to take. This information is found in the official DOT *North American Emergency Response Guidebook* (ERG), which is a compilation of emergency response guides. The Guide for flammable liquids is shown in Figure 3. The official DOT *North American Emergency Response Guidebook* (2004 edition), or an equivalent such as a Materials Safety Data Sheet (MSDS), must accompany every shipment in every mode. Information can be found in the *ERG* by looking up the ID number or the PSN. The *ERG* is issued every three years. It is published in English, French, and Spanish, and Russian for use throughout North America.

ID No.	Guide No.	Name of Material
1993	128	Combustible liquid, n.o.s.
1993	128	Compound, tree or weed killing, liquid (flammable)
1993	128	Compounds, cleaning, liquid (flammable)
1993	128	Cosmetics, n.o.s.
1993	128	Diesel fuel
1993	128	Disinfectant, liquid, n.o.s.
1993	128	Drugs, n.o.s.
1993	128	Ethyl nitrate
1993	128	Flammable liquid, n.o.s.
1993	128	Fuel oil
1993	128	Heater for refrigerator car, liquid fuel type
1993	128	Medicines, flammable liquid, n.o.s.
1993	128	Refrigerating machine

GUIDE 128   FLAMMABLE LIQUIDS (NON-POLAR/WATER-IMMISCIBLE)   NAERG 96

POTENTIAL HAZARDS

FIRE OR EXPLOSION
- **HIGHLY FLAMMABLE: Will be easily ignited by heat, sparks or flames.**
- Vapors may form explosive mixtures with air.
- Vapors may travel to source of ignition and flash back.
- Most vapors are heavier than air. They will spread along ground and collect in low or confined areas (sewers, basements, tanks).
- Vapor explosion hazard indoors, outdoors or in sewers.
- Some may polymerize **(P)** explosively when heated or involved in a fire.
- Runoff to sewer may create fire or explosion hazard.
- Containers may explode when heated.
- Many liquids are lighter than water.
- Substance may be transported hot.

HEALTH
- Inhalation or contact with material may irritate or burn skin and eyes.
- Fire may produce irritating, corrosive and/or toxic gases.
- Vapors may cause dizziness or suffocation.
- Runoff from fire control or dilution water may cause pollution.

PUBLIC SAFETY
- **CALL Emergency Response Telephone Number on Shipping Paper first. If Shipping Paper not available or no answer, refer to appropriate telephone number listed on the inside back cover.**
- Isolate spill or leak area immediately for at least 25 to 50 meters (80 to 160 feet) in all directions.
- Keep unauthorized personnel away.
- Stay upwind.
- Keep out of low areas.
- Ventilate closed spaces before entering.

PROTECTIVE CLOTHING
- Wear positive pressure self-contained breathing apparatus (SCBA).
- Structural firefighters' protective clothing will only provide limited protection.

EVACUATION
Large Spill
- Consider initial downwind evacuation for at least 300 meters (1000 feet).
Fire
- If tank, rail car or tank truck is involved in a fire, ISOLATE for 800 meters (1/2 mile) in all directions; also, consider initial evacuation for 800 meters (1/2 mile) in all directions.

Page 204

Figure 3.   DOT Hazardous Material ID No. 1993 and Its Emergency Response Guide

172.101 Column 5

Column 5, "PG," refers to packing groups, identified as I, II and III. The numbers I, II, and III represent great, medium and minor risks, respectively. Classes 2, gases; 7, radioactive materials; infectious substances and consumer commodities do not have packing groups. Gases and radioactive materials have specific packaging which is determined by other agencies. Consumer commodities theoretically represent a very low risk of hazard and are excepted from UN performance packaging. The other seven classes and combustible liquids are divided into three groups according to their degree of danger. Any one PSN may have up to three packing groups and the shipper is responsible for determining which packing group is correct for each shipment. *The*

packing group determines the proper packaging of a shipment. Packing group criteria vary by hazard class, *i.e.*, for 6.1, poison liquids, it is based on LD_{50} data; for Class 3, flammable liquids, the following criteria are used:

I   greatest danger, flashpoint (fp) and boiling point (bp) less than 35°C

II   medium danger, fp less than 23°C, bp greater than 35°C

III   minor danger, fp greater than 23°C, less than 60.5°C, bp greater than 35°C

Non-bulk packages are cross-indexed to the packing groups. They will show an "X" for those able to handle PG I (II and III), "Y" for PG II (and III), and "Z" for PG III only.

Non-bulk packages are defined as follows:

- Liquids–a maximum capacity of 450 liters or less

- Solids–a maximum net mass of 400 kg or less and capacity of 450 liters or less

- Gases–water capacity of 454 kg or less

172.101 Column 6

Column 6, labels, show by hazard class number the type(s) of labels that are required to be on each package in that class. See Figure 4 for example labels. Many products, such as Anhydrous Ammonia, require more than one label (in this case, 2.3 and 8 for international, "I," shipments). Label sizes and placement requirements are found in 49 CFR 172.407. Class 7, radioactive packages, require two labels; all other classes require one label per package per class. In general, labels are applied to non-bulk packages and placards to bulk packages; however, numerous exceptions do apply.

The labels must appear near the marked PSN if the non-bulk package dimensions allow. Labels may be on a tag attached by a wire or other means if needed. Cylinders may be labeled and marked in accordance with the Compressed Gas Association's *Pamphlet C-7* (1996). EPA regulations cross-reference the DOT requirements. A package may display the EPA and/or the OSHA Hazardous Materials Information System (HMIS) required labels while in transportation, but it must display the DOT label if not exempted.

Sample labels and placards with color and dimensional requirements can be found at the end of 49 CFR 172.400 and 172.500. DOT PHMSA also supplies copies of the guide chart, currently chart 12, and the placards are shown (not the correct size) in the *ERG*.

Whenever inner containers of different classes or materials are placed in the same outside container, or overpack, the outside container must be labeled for each different class represented within.

172.101 Column 7

Column 7 details any special provisions that may be applicable to the commodity. Such provisions

may be found in 49 CFR 172.102, following the table's two appendices. These provisions can supplant, supplement, or change any of the table's or packaging section's requirements. If the special provision is a straight numeric designation, *e.g.*, 47 for "solids containing flammable liquid, n.o.s.,"

Figure 4. Examples of DOT Labels

the provision applies to *all* modes of transportation. If the designation is a combined alpha-numeric, (*e.g.*, B2, T8, or T26) it applies only in restricted circumstances (*e.g,* IB8, IP2, IP4, T7, TP2 for aminopyridines):

- A = air only

- B = only bulk packages (except intermodal tanks)

- H = highway

- N = non-bulk packages

- R = rail

- T = intermodal tanks

- W = water

The IP listings are found in Table 3 of the special provisions and these reference IBC (Intermediate Bulk Containers) packagings. The most common designator will be a straight numeric, 1–6 and 13, (which identifies the material as an inhalation hazard, requiring additional shipping paper entries, labeling, marking, possibly placarding, handling/stowage, driver's training, etc.). Be sure to read any listed special provisions before preparing hazardous materials for shipment. As an example, "cord detonating, flexible" is classified as a 1.1D, where Division 1 represents the greatest risk of explosion. Special provision 102 allows the material to be reclassified as a 1.4D, a much lower risk category. The *D* refers to compatibility group D, an alpha designator that only applies to Class 1 materials and is used to determine which Class 1 materials can be transported together.

172.101 Column 8

After the HCS requirements are met, the proper packaging is selected utilizing Column 8 of the Table and any special provisions found in Column 7. Column 8 is subdivided into three sections: 8A covers any exceptions (how the material could avoid the packaging requirements, *e.g.*, limited quantities or consumer commodities), 8B covers non-bulk packages, and 8C, bulk packages.

Shipping Papers

For a shipping paper to be legal, the proper shipping information must be provided by the shipper, and, to the extent that common sense allows, checked by the carrier. Shipping papers must show the following basic description and be in this sequence:

- Proper shipping name
- Hazard class/division
- Identification number
- Packing group (if appropriate)
- Total quantity by weight or volume
- Emergency response information
- Shipper's certification (if required)

[handwritten margin note: This is what I learned to be the DOT basic description.]

The international community requires the UN identification number be shown first, before the PSN. It is expected that DOT will adopt this change by 2008. Shipping papers must show the appropriate packing group Roman numerals (*e.g.*, II). However, for Class 7, radioactive materials, the shipping papers may also be required to show other Roman numerals that mean the opposite of DOT's PGs (*e.g.*, where "I" is the lowest risk). Additional information on other commodities, such as pesticides, may contain potentially conflicting

numbers and cannot be included in the basic description: PSN, hazard class/division, ID number, and packing group (if required). For example, pesticides use *signal words* like "Caution" which cannot be included in the basic description but are not precluded from appearing elsewhere on the shipping paper.

Additional shipping descriptions which are required by 49 CFR 172.203 can include

- Reportable Quantity (RQ) for EPA hazardous substances
- The technical names of the chemicals for most n.o.s. entries
- The wording "marine pollutants" for those materials in Appendix B to 49 CFR 172.101
- "Poison [or toxic]" for certain materials meeting Division 6.1 criteria and not otherwise identified
- "Poison [or toxic] inhalation hazard" and the appropriate hazard zone for material meeting the poison or inhalation criteria
- "Hot" for elevated-temperature materials (*i.e.*, some asphalts), *etc.*
- Transportation-mode specific entries (*i.e.*, flashpoint for water shipments)
- DOT exemption numbers

Shipping papers must be retained for 375 days, unless they are also an EPA hazardous waste manifest prepared in accordance with 40 CFR 262.20. In this case, there is a three-year retention rule. Under 49 CFR 172.205, an EPA form 8700–22/22A waste manifest can be used as a DOT shipping paper if it meets all of the DOT requirements.

Marking, Labeling, and Placarding

Packages must remain marked and labeled until the container is cleaned and purged of all hazardous material, unless it is filled with a nonhazardous material. This regulation is unlike the EPA's, which defines *empty* as less than 3% for nonbulk packages or .3% for bulk packages.

Marking

Package marking is another way to communicate the nature of hazardous contents. Markings, like labels and placards, are integral parts of HCS. All of the HCS indications should indicate the same commodity/class.

Markings should convey the PSN, ID number, and hazard class. This information readily identifies a package that contains a hazardous material, and is used by carriers to ensure compliance with loading and stowage requirements.

Each person who offers a hazardous material for transportation must mark each package, freight container, and transport vehicle as required. Marking requirements vary depending upon package size, bulk/non-bulk packaging, commodity, and type of package.

Some examples of non-bulk markings which may be required are

- Proper Shipping Name
- ID number
- Package specification markings (including the X, Y, or Z that reflects the packing group)
- Shipper or consignee name and address
- International Organization for Standardization orientation arrows, for liquids packed in a container inside an outer package
- Hazardous substance RQ notation
- Marine pollutant ("dead fish"/"fish and chips"). See Figure 5.
- "Inhalation Hazard"
- The embossed word, "poison"

Marking on bulk containers might display some or all of the following:

- Proper Shipping Name
- ID number
- Package specification numbers (without the "X, Y, Z")
- Elevated temperature (HOT)

Figure 5. DOT Marine Pollutant Marking

- Commodity/class name (inhalation hazard)

On bulk packages, the ID number is normally displayed on the placards. If a shipment contains more than 4000 kg of any one non-bulk commodity, the container's exterior must show that ID number; if a bulk package is inside an enclosed outer container, the outer container must show the ID number. Bulk containers may display ID numbers on orange panels or white-square-on-point display configurations that are the same size as placards. The display configurations may also be used for any HOT or inhalation hazard markings. Specific bulk packages such as portable tanks, cargo tanks, and tank cars may also require the commodity name.

Labeling

Labels are not placards. Although the symbols and colors are the same, labels and placards differ in size and the number required to be placed on the package/vehicle. Unless excepted, labels are 100 mm x 100 mm, and placards are 273 mm x 273 mm. There are many exceptions from placarding; however, these exceptions do not apply to labels. In most cases, neither labels nor placards require the name, *e.g.*, corrosive, of a class. Usually, only the class icon and division/class/compatibility group letter are required. The exceptional cases that do require class names differ. For example, in keeping with the restrictive requirements noted above for shipping papers and labeling, Class 7, radioactive labels must have the class name shown in accordance with 49 CFR 172.405(a). The United States DOT rules differentiate between labels and placards; however, for shipments that move by water or have a vessel segment the regulatory agency, the International Maritime Organization, defines placards as oversize labels.

Labels and markings help prevent the potentially dangerous situations which may occur when incompatible materials are loaded near each other; *e.g.*, poisons with foodstuffs, or certain Class 8s, corrosives, with Class 3s, flammables. The information aids in commodity identification for emergency responders, especially if the shipping papers have been destroyed. Markings must be in English, durable, and unobscured by other information.

Table 1-Placard Any Amount		
Category of Material	**Placard Name**	**Placard Section**
1.1	Explosives 1.1	172.522
1.2	Explosives 1.2	172.522
1.3	Explosives 1.3	172.522
2.3	Poison Gas	172.540
4.3	Dangerous When Wet	172.548
5.2 (Organic peroxide, Type B, liquid or solid, temperature controlled)	Organic Peroxide	172.552
6.1 (Inhalation hazard, Zone A and B)	Poison Inhalation Hazard	172.555
7 (Radioactive Yellow III label only)	Radioactive	172.556
Table 2-Placard When the Amount Transported Exceeds 1000 Pounds		
Category of Material	**Placard Name**	**Placard Section**
1.4	Explosives 1.4	172.523
1.5	Explosives 1.5	172.524
1.6	Explosives 1.6	172.525
2.1	Flammable Gas	172.532
2.2	Non-Flammable Gas	172.528
3	Flammable	172.542
Combustible Liquid	Combustible	172.544
4.1	Flammable Solid	172.546
4.2	Spontaneously Combustible	172.547
5.1	Oxidizer	172.550
5.2 (Other than Organic peroxide, Type B, liquid or solid, temperature controlled)	Organic Peroxide	172.552
6.1 (Other than Inhalation hazard, Zone A and B)	Poison	172.554
6.2	(None)	(None)
8	Corrosive	172.558
9	Class 9	172.560
ORM-D	(None)	(None)

Figure 6. Tables 1 and 2 from 49 CFR 172.504

Placarding

Placards provide a visible warning that hazardous materials are present. Placards are normally what emergency responders first see when approaching an incident. Both placards and labels use the color, symbol, and hazard class to indicate the contained danger.

The Departments of Transportation and Homeland Security concluded a review in spring of 2005 which determined that keeping placards and markings on packages was best for the transportation and emergency response communities and did not represent a significant security risk.

Placards convey information about the hazardous material in several ways:

- Color (red for flammable liquids/solids/gases/combustibles)

- Hazard class/division/compatibility group letter (1.1A for an explosive)

- Symbols (skull/crossbones for poisons, skull/crossbones with a black background for inhalation hazards)

Additional information may include

- Name text (if required; *e.g.*, radioactive)

- ID number (1830 on a Class 8 for sulfuric acid)

Cargo tanks, rail cars, and certain portable tanks must be placarded on both the sides and the ends, and must remain placarded until cleaned and purged.

The shipper must provide the carrier/driver with the appropriate placards if they are not already displayed. In certain instances, subsidiary placarding may be required per 49 CFR 172.505, for inhalation hazards, and dangerous when wet materials. *Permissive* placarding is allowed as long as the placard correctly represents the hazard(s).

Bulk shipments must be placarded for all classes of materials, other than certain exceptions listed for domestic movements for Class 9. The hazard class/division of non-bulk shipments determines whether or not they must be placarded. See Figure 6. Materials listed in Table 1 of 49 CFR 172.504 must be placarded for any quantity. These materials include 1.1, 1.2, 1.3, and certain types of commodities in 2.3, 4.3, 5.2, 6.1, and 7. Any materials not meeting the 49 CFR 172.504, Table 1 definitions fall into Table 2. Table 2 allows up to 454 kg *aggregate gross weight* (material and its packaging) to be shipped without placards. This means most freight forwarders, *e.g.*, UPS or FedEx, can carry hazardous materials without external identification.

If a shipment contains two or more 49 CFR 172.504 Table 2 classified materials, and no single class weighs more than 1000 kg, the vehicle may be required to display a "Dangerous" placard. If any single class exceeds 1000 kg, placarding for the specific class is mandated.

Placarding is the final segment of the HCS: shipping papers, labeling, marking, and placarding. All of the elements should be identical, so that all personnel and any emergency responders in the transport loop are fully aware of the hazards that they are facing.

UN Performance Packaging

Proper packaging is the first line of defense in ensuring that hazardous materials will not be released during transportation. A poorly packaged commodity may not be offered for transportation, accepted, or transported. The HMR specify various performance levels for the packing used with hazardous materials based on the nature and levels of risk the hazards pose. All packing must be designed to ensure that there will be no releases under the normal conditions of transportation. Except for packaging designed for Class 2, 7, and some 6.1 materials, all DOT UN non-bulk performance packaging has to pass a series of performance oriented tests: stacking, bumping, dropping, *etc*. The tests are designed to be progressively more challenging for each packing group. If the packaging passes the tests, the DOT allows the shipper some flexibility in actual package design.

Training

Subpart H, 49 CFR 172.200, *et seq.*, of the regulations details the requirements of the mandatory US DOT training. Every *person* who in any way handles, moves, bills, loads, transports, or is responsible for any of those actions, in association with hazardous materials, must be trained at least every three years. The training is divided into three sections: general awareness/familiarization, function-specific, and safety. Employees are not allowed to perform their job functions unless they are trained or under the direct supervision of someone who is trained. However, in all cases, the training must be completed within 90 days. Any time an employee changes job functions, the employee must be trained in the new job's requirements.

Each employee must also be tested in the three areas. Employers are required to keep copies of tests, training materials, and employee training records for as long as the employee is with the company plus 90 days. The section does not specify who will do the training, what the trainers' qualifications should be, what kind of test is required, or what is a passing score. This section of the regulations is one of the most frequently cited by regulators; any exception to other sections can also be construed as a failure to properly train.

Security

RSPA has created regulations for the security of hazardous materials. On March 25, 2003 the final rule was issued as an addition to 49 CFR regulations. The new Subpart I–Security Plans, 49 CFR 172.800 through 172.804, was added and became mandatory immediately. The training requirements in 172.704 have been revised to include Security awareness training. Each hazmat employee must receive training that provides an awareness of the security risks associated with hazardous materials transportation and methods designed to enhance transportation security.

The security training must include components covering how to recognize and respond to possible security threats. After March 25, 2003 new hazmat employees must receive the security awareness training required by 49 CFR within 90 days and in-depth security training by December 22, 2003. In-depth security training includes training on the organization's security plan and its implementation. Security training must include:

- Company security objectives
- Specific security procedures
- Employee responsibilities
- Actions to take in the event of a security breach
- Organizational security structure

The security plan must be in writing and must be retained for as long as it remains in effect. Copies of the plan, or portions thereof, must be available to the employees who are responsible for implementing it, consistent with personnel security clearance or background investigation restrictions and a demonstrated need-to-know. The security plan must be revised and updated as necessary to reflect changing circumstances. When the security plan is updated or revised, all copies of the plan must be maintained as of the date of the most recent revision. Each security plan must have a written disclaimer on the first page and each page must be stamped "security sensitive information," per 172.1520.

Reporting and Penalties

The DOT regulations also contain ancillary requirements for shippers and carriers. These ancillary provisions deal mainly with incident reporting, national registration, and penalties for noncompliance. Modal administrations may have additional requirements, such as FMCSA's safety permitting rules.

Companies that are responsible for the movement of certain classes/quantities of materials (defined in 49 CFR 107.601) are required to pay a $300 annual Federal registration fee. A copy of the registration certificate must be carried at all times by affected highway carriers. This program is administered by PHMSA, and the majority of the money ($250) is sent to the states for the purpose of training emergency responders. Some states and local jurisdictions frequently have their own registration and/or permitting program if the program is not in conflict with Federal governance.

If an incident occurs involving hazardous materials, or one in which a hazardous materials package is involved (even when not leaking or breached), a report must be filed with the Federal government.

Certain circumstances require immediate telephone reporting. All incidents require written follow-up according to the requirements outlined in 49 CFR 171.15 and 49 CFR 171.16. Failure to report, even though all corrective action was successfully accomplished, has resulted in severe financial penalties. If a hazardous material is involved in a spill and the commodity is also a hazardous substance and an amount greater than the reportable quantity is spilled, EPA must also be called immediately. The DOT reporting call will not satisfy the EPA or State/local requirements. Separate calls must be made.

DOT penalties are established by PHMSA and are periodically adjusted for cost of living. The penalties are found in Appendix A to 49 CFR 107. As an example, the baseline penalty assessment is $3,700 for "using a shipping name and hazard class that is incorrect." If, using the above description, the "material is mis*classified*," the baseline assessment is $6,200. The penalties are per shipment/per day. If willful intent to avoid the law is determined, criminal penalties (including up to 5 years in prison) are assessable.

Summary

Shippers and carriers have the following responsibilities:

- Shipping documents must include the PSN, hazard class, ID number, packing group (except Classes 2 and 7), shipper certification, proper count and weight, as well as emergency response phone number and information. Additional information may be required depending upon the PSN, class, and special provisions.

- Proper packaging must be selected.

- Packages must be properly closed and show no evidence of leakage.

- Packages and/or vehicles must be properly labeled, marked, and placarded.

- Incompatible materials must not be packaged together in the same packaging.

- All required training must be accomplished and documented for everyone involved at each step.

- Proper emergency response information must accompany the shipment.

- Personnel must be aware of any other agencies' rules which may affect transportation; *e.g.*, EPA spill reporting requirements.

- Highway shippers may need to ensure that drivers have a Commercial Driver's License with appropriate endorsements and that background checks have been conducted.

- Shippers, carriers, and brokers need to be registered under the DOT registration programs, depending on the type and quantity of material shipped and/or carried.

- Some materials may require route plans, copies of exceptions or exemptions.

The DOT regulations are dynamic. They have undergone constant change since they were first promulgated 100 years ago. If all affected parties comply in full, the nation will continue to experience the excellent safety record and benefits the commodities bring.

Resource Information

Companies providing 24-hour phone response (note these are subscription services; companies can provide their own response, if qualified):

CHEMTREC: (800) 424–9300

PERS: (800) 728–2482

CHEMTELL: (800) 255–3924

INFOTRAC: (800) 535–5053

National Response Center for reporting a spill of hazardous substances greater than the RQ:

(800) 424–8802 (24 hours)

Internet Resources

<http://faa.gov/> (Federal Aviation Administration. Homepage)

<http://hazmat.dot.gov> (Research and Special Programs Administration, Office of Hazardous Materials Safety. Hazmat Safety Homepage)

<http://www.epa.gov> (US Environmental Protection Agency. Homepage)

<http://www.fmcsa.dot.gov> (US Department of Transportation, Federal Motor Carrier Safety Administration. Homepage)

<http://www.fra.dot.gov> (US Department of Transportation, Federal Railroad Administration. Homepage)

<http://www.hmac.org> (Dangerous Goods Advisory Council. Homepage)

<http://www.osha.gov> (US Department of Labor, Occupational Health and Safety Administration. Homepage)

<http://www.uscg.mil> (US Coast Guard. Homeland Security Homepage)

<http://www.vohma.com> (Internationa Vessel Operator's Hazardous Material Association. Homepage)

Other Resources

Bureau of Explosives Publications
PO Box 1020
Sewickley, PA 15143

Telephone: (412) 741–1096
Fax: (412) 741–0609

Environmental Protection Agency
Ariel Rios Building
1200 Pennsylvania Avenue, NW
Washington, DC 20460

Telephone: (202) 260–2090

Federal Aviation Administration
800 Independence Avenue, SW
Washington, DC 20591

Telephone: (202) 267–5885

Federal Motor Carrier Safety Administration
US Department of Transportation
400 7th Street, SW
Washington, DC 20590

Telephone: (202) 366–7908

Federal Railroad Administration
US Department of Transportation
1120 Vermont Ave., NW
Washington, DC 20590

Telephone: (202) 493–6230

International Air Transport Association
Customer Service Publications
PO Box 113
Montreal, Quebec, Canada H4Z 1M1

Telephone: (1) (514) 390–6726
Fax: (1) (514) 874–9659

Occupational Safety and Health Administration
200 Constitution Avenue, NW
Washington, DC 20210

Pipeline and Hazardous Materials Safety Administration
US Department of Transportation
400 7th Street, SW
Washington, DC 2059

Telephone: (800) 467–4922

(Hazardous Materials Information Center)

United States Coast Guard
2100 Second Street, SW
Washington, DC 20593

Telephone: (202) 267–1217

Dorothy Christman *is the President of her own company, Pacific Training, a consulting firm for the transportation of hazardous materials. She has been presenting DOT regulatory seminars for over 10 years. She has over 24 years of experience in the chemical industry, with 10 years as Shipping Supervisor for Atofina N.A. Atofina manufactured and shipped approximately 1000 tons of chemicals a day. Ms. Christman has an AA in Chemistry, BS in Business Management, and has been a Certified Hazardous Materials Manager since 1990. She is Past President of the Willamette Columbia Chapter in Portland, Oregon, Past President of the Transportation Association of Portland and Portland's Transportation Person of the Year in 1997.*

Michael Eyer *is currently the Hazardous Materials Specialist, Rail Division for the State of Oregon. He has over 27 years of experience in the hazardous materials management field, including 12 years as a District Inspector with the Bureau of Explosives, three years with Oregon's Department of Environmental Quality managing the spill response and illegal drug lab cleanup programs, as well as eight years with the Oregon PUC/DOT as a Transportation Specialist. Mr. Eyer is a Certified Hazardous Materials Manager, US DOT-certified Highway and Rail Vehicle Inspector/Trainer, US DOT Hazardous Materials Inspector/Trainer and US DOE Radioactive Materials Inspector/Trainer. He has also served as National Chair of the Cooperative Hazardous Materials Enforcement and Development (COHMED) program. Mr. Eyer has been a guest instructor at UCLA, Oregon State University, and University of Michigan. He founded the Willamette Columbia Chapter of CHMM in Portland, Oregon and was its first President. He has been a Master Level CHMM since 1989. Mr. Eyer has a BS in K-12 education and an MBA.*

CHAPTER 24

Underground Storage Tanks

Alan A. Eckmyre, CHMM

Introduction

Underground tanks that contain either petroleum or hazardous substances are subject to Federal Underground Storage Tank (UST) regulations. These regulations, issued by the Environmental Protection Agency (EPA) under authority of Subtitle I of the Resource Conservation and Recovery Act (RCRA) (Section 9003 of the Hazardous and Solid Waste Amendments [HSWA] of 1984), established standards for installation, operation, release detection, corrective action, repair, and closure of USTs and attached piping. EPA also authorized individual states to implement their own UST regulatory programs in place of the Federal requirements. To receive this authorization, the State program must be *no less stringent* than the Federal requirements. In authorized states, the UST requirements may be more stringent than the Federal requirements. When a State program receives authorization, it becomes the *implementing authority* for the UST regulations. This means that the State agency has primary enforcement responsibility for its UST program. Parties in these states must comply with State requirements that may be more stringent than Federal regulations.

Federal regulations govern roughly 1.1 million active USTs. About 96 percent of these contain petroleum products, including used oil. Fewer than

1 percent contain hazardous materials, and about 2 percent are empty. Petroleum or hazardous substance releases from USTs can occur during tank filling. They can also occur from leaks in tanks and piping that result from corrosion, structural failure, or faulty installation. As of September 1996, EPA has reported nearly 318,000 confirmed releases at Federally regulated USTs. More are expected. These releases can contaminate soil and groundwater and cause fires or explosions.

Identification and Classification

The UST regulations differentiate between existing USTs and new USTs and between petroleum USTs and hazardous substance USTs. The regulations also exclude certain USTs and defer requirements for others. Therefore, correct application of the UST regulations requires accurate identification and classification of regulated tanks and piping.

An **underground storage tank** is defined by Subtitle I as any tank or combination of tanks (including connected underground pipes) used to contain an accumulation of regulated substances, the volume of which (including the volume of connected underground pipes) is 10 percent or more beneath the surface of the ground (40 CFR 280.12).

Connected piping means all buried piping, including valves, elbows, joints, and flexible connectors, attached to tank systems through which regulated substances flow. For the purpose of determining how much piping is connected to any individual UST system, the piping that joins two UST systems should be allocated equally between them (40 CFR 280.12).

The regulations hold owners and operators responsible for compliance. A UST owner is

- Any person who owns a UST system on November 8, 1984, or who brought the system into use after that date

- In the case of any UST system in use before November 8, 1984, but no longer in use on that date, any person who owned a UST immediately before the discontinuation of its use

An **operator** is any person in control of or having responsibility for the daily operation of the UST system (40 CFR 280.12).

RCRA Subtitle I gave EPA the authority to distinguish types (storing petroleum or hazardous substances), classes (excluded, deferred, or fully regulated), and age.

Categories of USTs

There are two broad categories (types) of USTs: petroleum USTs and hazardous substance USTs. **Petroleum USTs** contain petroleum or a mixture of petroleum with *de minimis* quantities of other regulated substances. These systems include tanks containing motor fuel, jet fuel, distillate fuel oil, residual fuel oil, lubricants, petroleum solvents, or used oil. **Hazardous substance USTs** contain either

1) Hazardous substances as defined in Section 101(14) of the Comprehensive Environmental Response, Compensation, and Liability Act (CERCLA) (40 CFR 302.4), but not including any of the substances regulated as a hazardous waste under RCRA Subtitle C

2) Any mixture of such CERCLA-listed substances and petroleum that is not a petroleum UST system (40 CFR 280.12)

In order to determine whether a tank system contains a regulated substance under Subtitle I, the following steps should be taken:

- First, determine if the substance belongs to one of the seven general categories of regulated petroleum substances (*i.e*, motor fuel, jet fuel, distillate fuel oil, residual fuel oil, lubricants, petroleum solvents, and used oil).

- Second, determine whether the stored material is included within the *production process and physical properties* description for petroleum products (*i.e.*, petroleum-based substances comprised of a complex blend of hydrocarbons derived from crude oil through the processes of separation, conversion, upgrading, and finishing, or any fraction of crude oil that is liquid at 60°F and 14.7 lbs/in^2 absolute, standard temperature and pressure).

- Third, determine whether the substance is listed as a hazardous substance under Section 101(14) of CERCLA and is not a hazardous waste under Subtitle C of RCRA.

If the substance meets any of these three criteria, then it is a regulated substance.

Hazardous substance USTs have more stringent release detection, secondary containment, and interstitial monitoring requirements than petroleum USTs. All other technical requirements are the same for UST systems storing regulated substances.

UST Exclusions and Exemptions

In identifying UST classes, there are two ways a tank can be excluded from the UST regulations. One way is for the tank to be excluded from the statutory definition of a UST, RCRA Section 9001 (1)(A – I). The other way is for the tank to be excluded from the applicability section of the regulations, 40 CFR 280.10(b). Changes in the statutory exclusions must be made by Congress, while changes in the regulatory exclusions may be made by EPA. For example, USTs used for storing heating oil for consumptive use on the premises were exempt by the statute, as were septic tanks and stormwater collection systems. Tanks excluded from the regulations by EPA include hydraulic lift tanks and tanks that have a capacity of less than 110 gallons.

Some tanks were excluded because they pose a negligible risk to human health and the environment. These USTs were excluded to allow Federal, State, and local agencies as well as UST owners and operators to focus their limited resources on those USTs that pose a greater risk. Other tanks were excluded because they were sufficiently regulated under other statutes.

Excluded USTs are not regulated by the Federal UST regulations, but they may be subject to State laws, other Federal laws, or industry codes or practices. States may write regulations for tanks that have been excluded from the Federal UST regulations. This has been the case in some states that have regulated tanks containing heating oil. Federal laws, other than RCRA Subtitle I, may

apply to excluded tanks depending on their function. For example, any UST system holding hazardous wastes listed or identified under Subtitle C of the Solid Waste Disposal Act is exempt from Subtitle I but regulated by RCRA Subtitle C.

The following categories of tanks have been excluded from the definition of a UST:

- Farm or residential tanks of 1,100 gallons or less capacity used for storing motor fuel for noncommercial purposes

- Tanks used for storing heating oil for consumptive use on the premises where stored

- Septic tanks

- Pipeline facilities regulated under the Natural Gas Pipeline Safety Act of 1968 or the Hazardous Liquid Pipeline Safety Act of 1979, or that are intrastate pipeline facilities regulated under State laws comparable to the provisions of these acts

- Surface impoundments, pits, ponds, or lagoons

- Storm water or wastewater collection systems

- Flow-through process tanks

- Liquid traps or associated gathering lines directly related to oil or gas production and gathering operations

- Storage tanks situated in an underground area (such as a basement, cellar, mineworking, drift, shaft, or tunnel) if such tanks are situated upon or above the surface of the floor

The term *underground storage tank* does not include any pipes connected to any tank that is described above.

In addition to the statutory exclusions, EPA excluded the following tanks from the RCRA Subtitle I regulations:

- Any UST system holding hazardous wastes listed or identified under Subtitle C of the Solid Waste Disposal Act or a mixture of such hazardous waste and other regulated substances

- Any wastewater treatment tank system that is part of a wastewater treatment facility regulated under Section 402 or 307(b) of the Clean Water Act

- Equipment or machinery that contains regulated substances for operational purposes such as hydraulic lift tanks and electrical equipment tanks

- Any UST system whose capacity is 110 gallons or less

- Any UST system that contains a *de minimis* concentration of regulated substances

- Any emergency spill or overflow containment UST system that is expeditiously emptied after use

The types of tanks excluded because they are considered equipment or machinery includes any tank that is part of a piece of equipment or machinery (*e.g.*, hydraulic lifts and electrical equipment) and that meets two criteria:

1) The equipment or machinery contains small amounts of regulated substances solely for operational purposes.

2) Faulty operation of the equipment or machinery will cause a loss of regulated substances.

In addition, EPA does not specify a maximum time a tank may hold an emergency spill or overflow material, but intends this exclusion to apply to many types of sumps and secondary barrier tanks that are rarely used and are emptied shortly after use. The purpose of this exemption is to allow immediate response to emergency situations. It is analogous to the exclusion for emergency response treatment and containment under RCRA Subtitle C (40 CFR 264.1 and 265.1). The exclusion does not include sumps designed to store petroleum or hazardous substances during periodic cleaning or maintenance of machinery or equipment (*e.g.*, turbine oil sumps that are used during maintenance of electric power generation turbines), 40 CFR 280.10(b)(6).

Any UST system holding a mixture of hazardous waste identified under Subtitle C of the Solid Waste Disposal Act and petroleum or non-petroleum substances regulated by Subtitle I is excluded from the Federal UST regulations. EPA excluded these tanks from Subtitle I regulation because USTs containing this kind of mixture would be subject to dual jurisdiction from Subtitle C and Subtitle I.

Very small, *de minimis*, concentrations of residual contaminants can occur in a UST accidentally (through contamination) or by design (for example, underground tanks storing potable water that has been treated with chlorine). EPA has not defined a specific percentage as the *de minimis* cutoff because of the many difficulties with measuring tank contents for low concentrations of regulated substances. Instead, implementing agencies determine on a case-by-case basis if tanks that hold very low concentrations of regulated substances are excluded via *de minimis* amounts, (40 CFR 280.10 (b)(5).

Radioactive mixed waste (RMW) contains both a hazardous component regulated under RCRA and radioactive material regulated under the Atomic Energy Act. The applicability of Subtitle I to RMW depends on whether those USTs are regulated under RCRA Subtitle C. If a UST containing RMW is regulated under Subtitle C, it is exempt from Subtitle I in accordance with 40 CFR 280.10 (b)(1).

To determine if a UST is subject to Subtitle C regulation, it is necessary to know the authorization status of a particular state's hazardous waste program. In most states, RMW is regulated as hazardous waste under RCRA Subtitle C either because the state has an authorized RCRA program and has received a modification of their authorization to cover RMW, or because the state does not have RCRA authorization and therefore the hazardous waste component of the mixed waste is subject to the Federal RCRA Subtitle C program. If a UST located in one of these states contains RMW, it is excluded from the Subtitle I regulations.

On the other hand, if the UST is located in a state that has an authorized RCRA program but has not yet received a modified authorization to cover RMW, then the RMW is not recognized or regulated as a hazardous waste under Subtitle C. In these circumstances, the UST is regulated under Subtitle I.

Also, states without mixed waste authorization may regulate underground storage tanks containing RMW pursuant to their State regulations. In these cases, the wastes may be regulated by both EPA and the state.

Tanks containing radioactive and other materials (not hazardous wastes) fall under the deferred tank classification.

Deferred USTs

A *deferred UST* refers to a UST for which EPA has deferred the Subpart B (design, construction, installation, and notification), Subpart C (general operations requirements), Subpart D (release detection), Subpart E (release reporting, investigation, and confirmation), and Subpart G (closure) regulations. Until EPA decides how to regulate these USTs fully, the only regulations that apply are Subpart A (interim prohibition) and Subpart F (release response and corrective action). Examples of deferred tanks include underground, field-constructed, bulk storage tanks, and UST systems that contain radioactive wastes.

UST systems that store fuel solely for use by emergency power generators are deferred from Subpart D (release detection) requirements because those requirements currently mandate frequent monitoring that may be unworkable. These tanks often are used to store diesel fuel as a source of backup power in unmanned, remote locations (*e.g.*, telephone switching locations). The other Subtitle I requirements apply fully to these USTs.

Tanks containing radioactive wastes and other radioactive materials at commercially licensed nuclear facilities are regulated under the Atomic Energy Act of 1954 (AEA) and by the Nuclear Regulatory Commission (NRC). EPA deferred these systems because they are already subject to stringent regulation.

New and Existing USTs

EPA classifies tanks for which installation commenced on or before December 22, 1988, to be *existing USTs*. Any UST for which installation commenced after this date is a *new tank system*. All new tank systems must meet the requirements of Subparts B, C, and D before they can commence operation (40 CFR 280.12).

Installation is considered to have commenced if

- The owner or operator has obtained all Federal, State, and local approvals or permits necessary to begin physical construction or installation

- Either a continuous on-site physical construction or installation program has begun

- The owner/operator has entered into contractual obligations (which cannot be canceled or modified without substantial loss) for physical construction at the site or installation of the tank system

New USTs have stringent installation requirements that must be met before the UST may be used. Existing USTs were required to be upgraded to meet the requirements of Subparts B and C (for corrosion protection, overfill controls, and operating requirements) by December 22, 1998. To do this, they either had to be replaced with tanks that met these standards or upgraded in place. Upgrades must include overfill controls and corrosion control (an interior lining, cathodic protection, or another acceptable method of protecting the tank system from corrosion and structural failure). The release detection requirements for existing USTs were phased in on a schedule based on the age of the tank and took effect December 22, 1993.

New USTs must prevent releases due to structural failure, corrosion, or spills and overfills. Spill and overfill controls must be installed with each new UST, and the installation must be properly conducted and certified by at least one of several methods. By December 22, 1998, all existing USTs must have met the new UST standards by being replaced or upgraded with lining and/or cathodic protection and must have complied with the new UST spill and overfill control requirements (40 CFR 280.20 and 280.21).

New UST systems must be designed and constructed to provide protection for buried components from corrosion by using either noncorrodible materials or a cathodic protection system. EPA requires that the installation be conducted in accordance with a code of practice developed by a nationally recognized association or independent testing laboratory and in accordance with the manufacturer's instructions. In addition, the installation must be certified, tested, or inspected by one of six procedures provided in the regulation. These are:

1) The installer has been certified by the tank and piping manufacturers.

2) The installer has been certified or licensed by the implementing agency.

3) The installation has been inspected and certified by a registered professional engineer with training and experience in tank installation.

4) The installation has been inspected and approved by the implementing agency.

5) All work listed in the manufacturer's installation checklist has been completed.

6) The owner/operator may use another method if approved by the implementing agency.

Anyone bringing a UST system into use after May 8, 1986, must within 30 days of bringing such tank into use, submit the "Notification for Underground Storage Tanks" form (EPA form 7530–1) or the corresponding State form to provide notice of the existence of the tank to the administering agency. This notification also includes a certification of compliance with the installation certification requirement; 40 CFR 280.20(a), (d), and (e), and 280.22(a) and (b).

Existing tanks may meet the new tank performance standards or they may be retrofitted with an internal lining, cathodic protection, or an internal lining combined with cathodic protection. In addition, EPA has established inspection requirements for these upgraded tanks. If an existing tank does not meet the upgrading requirements by December 22, 1998, it must be replaced or closed.

UST Procedures and Operating Requirements

In order to meet the day-to-day operating requirements of UST systems (40 CFR 280.30–34), spill and overfill procedures must be followed, and corrosion protection must be operated and maintained, USTs must be compatible with their contents, reports must be made and records must be kept, and any repairs must be performed in accordance with the regulations. In addition, before a transfer is made, owner/operators must ensure that the volume in the tank is greater than the volume of product to be transferred. The transfer operation also must be monitored continuously to prevent overfilling and spilling.

The following UST reporting to appropriate agencies is mandatory:

- Notification for all UST systems, which includes certification of installation for new UST systems

- Reports of all releases including suspected releases, spills, and overfills, and confirmed releases

- Notification of corrective actions planned or taken including initial abatement measures, initial site characterization, free product removal, investigation of soil, groundwater cleanup, and corrective action plans

- Notification before permanent closure or change in service, 40 CFR 280.34(a)

All of the following records must be kept, if applicable:

- A corrosion expert's analysis of site corrosion potential if corrosion protection equipment is not used

- Documentation of corrosion protection equipment operation

- Documentation of UST system repairs

- Recent compliance with release detection requirements

- Results of the site investigation conducted at permanent closure, 40 CFR 280.34(b)

Leak detection methods used by the owner/operator must be able to detect a release from any portion of the tank and piping system that routinely contains product. Allowable methods of release detection include

- Monitoring for vapors in the excavation area

- Monitoring for petroleum floating on the water table

- Secondary containment with interstitial monitoring

- Continuous product level gauging

- Tank system integrity (or tightness) testing

- Inventory control

Monitoring for vapors or liquids in the environment around the tank or in the interstitial space of secondary containment can be done manually or automatically. If done manually, the sampling activity must be done once every 30 days. Tank tightness testing, however, is required only once every five years if the tank meets the corrosion protection and overfill requirements. If the tank does not meet these requirements, testing must be done once each year. In both cases, tank inventories must be recorded daily and reconciled monthly.

Whichever method is selected, the release detection system must be installed, calibrated, operated, and maintained in accordance with the manufacturer's instructions. In addition, the method(s) used must meet EPA performance standards specified for each type. Performance standards have been promulgated for each type of release detection method (40 CFR 280.43 and 44).

Owners/operators are required to maintain all written performance claims for release detection systems for five years. In addition, the following release detection records must be maintained. The results of any sampling, testing, or monitoring must be maintained for at least one year except that the results of tank tightness testing must be retained until the next test is conducted. Written documentation of all calibration, maintenance, and repair of release detection equipment permanently located onsite must be maintained for at least one year after the servicing work is completed. Any schedules of required calibration and maintenance provided by the release detection equipment manufacturer must be retained for five years from the date of installation. The implementing agency is authorized to modify recordkeeping time limits. However, prudent recordkeeping that entails record retention for the life of the UST system is recommended to assist with compliance enforcement mitigation and/or penalty avoidance.

Release Reporting

The following would be considered cause to suspect a release:

- Discovery of released regulated substances at the UST site or in the surrounding area (such as the presence of vapors in soils, basements, or sewer and utility lines, or emanating from nearby surface water)

- Unusual operating conditions (such as the erratic behavior of product-dispensing equipment, the sudden loss of product from the UST system, or an unexplained presence of water in the tank)

- Monitoring results from a release detection method indicating that a release may have occurred. Suspected releases must be reported to the implementing agency within 24 hours

The following types of spills and overfills must be reported and are subject to corrective action:

- Spills or overfills of petroleum that result in the release of 25 gallons or that cause a sheen on nearby surface water

- Spills and overfills below 25 gallons if cleanup of the spill or overfill cannot be accomplished within 24 hours

The implementing agency has the authority to establish reasonable quantities or time periods different from those listed above. If they do, then an owner/operator should follow the limits established by the implementing agency.

When a release from a UST has been confirmed, the UST owner/operator must perform

- Initial response actions

- Initial abatement measures

- A site check

- A site characterization

- Free product removal if necessary

- Investigation for soil and ground water cleanup if certain conditions exist

In addition, upon request of the implementing agency or by the decision of the UST owner or operator, a corrective action plan may need to be developed. For each confirmed release that requires a corrective action plan, the implementing agency provides for public participation.

The following initial response actions must be taken within 24 hours of a release or within another reasonable period of time determined by the implementing agency:

- The release must be reported to the implementing agency (*e.g.*, by telephone or electronic mail)

- Immediate action must be taken to prevent any further release of the regulated substance into the environment

- Fire, explosion, and vapor hazards must be identified and mitigated (40 CFR 280.61)

After a confirmed release, the owner/operator must

- Remove as much of the regulated substance from the UST system as is necessary to prevent further release to the environment

- Visually inspect any above-ground or exposed below-ground releases and prevent further migration of the released substance into surrounding ground water and soils

- Continue to monitor and mitigate fire and safety hazards

- Remedy hazards posed by soils and, if necessary, treat and dispose of soils according to applicable State and local requirements

- Measure for the presence of a release where contamination is most likely to be present at the UST site, unless the presence and source of the release has already been confirmed

- Investigate to determine the possible presence of free product and begin free product removal as soon as practicable. Within 20 days after release confirmation, submit a report to the implementing agency summarizing the initial abatement steps taken

Owners and operators are encouraged, in the interest of minimizing environmental contamination and promoting effective cleanup, to begin cleanup of soil and ground water before the corrective action plan is approved by the implementing agency, provided that they

- Notify the implementing agency of their intention to begin cleanup

- Comply with any conditions imposed by the implementing agency, including halting cleanup or mitigating adverse consequences from cleanup activities

- Incorporate these self-initiated cleanup measures in the corrective action plan that is submitted to the implementing agency for approval (40 CFR 280.66)

If there is a release from a UST located at a RCRA-permitted hazardous waste treatment, storage, and disposal (TSD) facility and the UST contained hazardous waste, then the corrective action must be performed in accordance with the hazardous waste regulations under Subtitle C of RCRA found in 40 CFR 264.100 and 264.101.

UST Change in Service and Closure

If a facility stops using a UST, the UST must undergo temporary closure, a change in service, or permanent closure. A change in service occurs when a UST system is no longer used to contain a regulated substance. If a UST is closed for longer than 12 months, it must be permanently closed (40 CFR 280.70 and 71).

For a UST to remain temporarily closed, the owner or operator must continue operation and maintenance of corrosion protection and release detection. However, if the UST system has been emptied, then release detection is not required. (The UST system is empty when all materials have been removed using commonly employed practices so that no more than 2.5 cm [1 inch] of residue or 0.3% of the weight of the total capacity of the UST system remain.) When a UST is temporarily closed for three months or more, the vent lines must be left open and functioning, and all other lines, pumps, manways, and ancillary equipment must be capped and secured. Any UST system temporarily closed for more than 12 months must be permanently closed unless it meets the new UST performance standards (40 CFR 280.20 and 280.21). Under this upgrading provision, an owner/operator of an operating existing UST had until December 22, 1998, to meet the new tank requirements. Therefore, the owner/operator could have postponed upgrading his or her temporarily closed UST until December 22, 1998. After December 22, 1998, any tank that has been temporarily closed for more than 12 months must be permanently closed unless it meets the new UST standards of 40 CFR 280.20 or the technical upgrading requirements under 40 CFR 280.21 (See 40 CFR 280.70).

Continued use of a UST system to store a nonregulated substance is considered a change in service. Before a change in service, the UST must be emptied and cleaned by removing all liquid and accumulated sludge, and a closure site assessment must be performed. At least 30 days before beginning a change in service, or within another reasonable time period determined by the implementing agency, the implementing agency must be notified of the intent to perform a change in service. Closure records also must be maintained.

To permanently close a tank, it must be emptied and cleaned by removing all liquids and accumulated sludges. All tanks taken out of service permanently must either be removed from the ground or filled with an inert solid material. (Note: Many State regulations require that closed USTs must be removed unless the removal would endanger a building, road, or other structural foundation.) At least 30 days before beginning permanent closure, or within another reasonable time period determined by the implementing agency, the implementing agency must be notified of the intent to close the UST. Before permanent closure is granted by the implementing agency, owners and operators must perform a closure site assessment. If during the assessment a release is confirmed, then corrective action would need to be commenced.

Records demonstrating compliance with the closure requirements must be maintained, in addition to the results of the excavation zone assessment, for the closure or change in service site assessment for at least three years after completion of permanent closure or change in service. Records may be maintained by the owner or operator who took the UST system out of service or by the current owner or operator of the UST system. The records may be mailed to the implementing agency if they cannot be maintained at the closed facility (40 CFR 280.74).

UST Upgrade Requirements

As of December 22, 1998, all existing petroleum and hazardous substance USTs must be equipped with spill protection, overfill protection, and corrosion protection devices. Owners and operators have three choices for complying with these requirements. These are:

* Add spill, overfill and corrosion protection. (USTs that never receive more than 25 gallons

at a time are not required to meet the spill and overfill protection requirements.)

* Close the existing UST

* Replace the closed existing UST with a new UST. (When new USTs are installed, they must have spill, overfill, and corrosion protection, and leak detection devices.)

The basic upgrading requirements for existing USTs are presented below.

Spill Protection. Spills cause releases at many UST sites. Generally, spills occur at the fill pipe when a delivery truck hose is disconnected. Such spills usually are small, but repeated small releases can lead to significant environmental problems. The regulations require that by December 22, 1998, existing tanks must have catchment basins to contain spills from delivery hoses.

Overfill Protection. Overfilling a tank can lead to large releases at the fill pipe and through loose fittings on the top of the tank. Existing USTs must have overfill protection devices after December 22, 1998, that will do one of the following:

* Automatically shut off flow into the tank when the tank is no more than 95 percent full

* Alert the operator when the tank is no more than 90 percent full

* Restrict for 30 minutes prior to overfilling, alert the operator 1 minute prior to overfilling, or automatically shut off flow so that none of the fittings on the top of the tank is exposed to product

Corrosion Protection. Corrosion occurs when bare metal, soil, and moisture combine to produce an underground electric current that destroys metal. Because unprotected steel USTs can corrode and release product through corrosion holes, Federal regulations require owners or operators to install corrosion protection in existing tanks by December 22, 1998. Existing tanks may already meet the corrosion protection requirements if one of the following performance standards is satisfied:

* The tank and piping are made entirely of noncorrodible material, such as fiberglass

* The tank and piping are made of steel having corrosion-resistant coating and having cathodic protection

- The tank is made of steel and clad with a thick layer of noncorrodible material

Because it is impractical to coat or clad unprotected steel USTs, owners or operators of such tanks must choose one of the three following methods to provide corrosion protection:

- Add cathodic protection

- Add interior lining to the tank

- Combine cathodic protection interior lining

The regulations also require that existing piping have one of the following characteristics:

- Uncoated steel piping has cathodic protection

- Steel piping has corrosion-resistant coating and cathodic protection

- Piping is made of, or enclosed in, noncorrodible material (*e.g.*, fiberglass)

Besides the spill, overfill, and corrosion protection upgrades required of all existing petroleum and hazardous substance USTs, hazardous substance USTs must meet additional leak detection requirements.

The UST regulations are intended in part to ensure that releases or leaks from USTs are discovered before contamination can spread. EPA has found that hazardous substances that have leaked into the soil are more difficult to detect and to clean up than petroleum leaks. Consequently, leak detection requirements for new hazardous substance USTs are more stringent than those for new petroleum USTs. Thus, while new petroleum USTs can meet leak detection requirements by selecting one of several specified leak detection methods (these methods include secondary containment and interstitial monitoring, automatic tank gauging systems, vapor monitoring, groundwater monitoring, statistical inventory reconciliation, manual tank gauging, and tank tightness testing, as well as inventory control), new hazardous substance USTs must be equipped with secondary containment systems with monitoring devices. All existing hazardous substance tanks must meet the more stringent leak detection requirements for new hazardous substance USTs.

If an existing petroleum or hazardous substance UST system has not been upgraded by December 22, 1998, it must be properly closed. After the existing system has been closed, it may be replaced by installing a new UST that meets the new tank performance standards.

Bibliography

Environmental Protection Agency. *Must for USTs*, EPA/530/UST–88/008. Washington, DC: EPA, 1991.

Grace H. Weaver. *Strategic Environmental Management.* New York, NY: John Wiley and Sons, Inc., 1996.

"Technical Standards and Corrective Action Requirements for Owners and Operators of Underground Storage Tanks." *Code of Federal Regulations.* Title 40, Pt. 280.

The Superfund Amendments and Reauthorization Act of 1986. PL 99–499, 100 Stat.1613 (codified in various sections of 42 USC §§9601–9675, 1988).

Thomas F. P. Sullivan, Ed. *Environmental Law Handbook.* 13th ed. Rockville, MD: Government Institutes, 1995.

Internet Resources

<http://www.epa.gov/swerust1/> (Environmental Protection Agency. Underground Storage Tanks)

<http://www.steeltank.com> (Steel Tank Institute. Homepage)

<http://www.aee.hq.faa.gov/aee-200/FSTQAG/ustq.html> (Federal Aviation Administration. Underground Storage Tanks, Index of Questions)

Alan A. Eckmyre *earned his BS in Business Administration from New York Institute of Technology, a BE in Nuclear Engineering from the State University of New York, graduate MBA studies from Emporia State University and MS in Environmental Engineering from the University of Kansas, and has been a Certified Hazardous Materials Manager since 1991. He has served in leadership roles as the Secretary and Director of the Heartland Chapter ACHMM, President of the Magnolia Chapter ACHMM, Chair of the National ACHMM Publications and Professional Development Committees, member of the Board of Directors and has served as President of the National ACHMM. He also holds professional memberships in the American Society of Testing and Materials' and the American Nuclear Society. Mr. Eckmyre has over 22 years professional experience in nuclear and environmental engineering, consulting, environmental management training, and project management. His project management experience includes: UST system closures, State UST ground water/soil remediation investigation and design projects, ASTM Phase I and II site assessments, Federal facility-specific and programmatic environmental assessments and audits, RCRA permitting and corrective measures studies, CERCLA preliminary assessments and Remedial Investigation/Feasibility Studies (RI/FS), NPDES permitting, innovative environmental remediation technology R&D, and expert witness testimony. Mr. Eckmyre has authored numerous UST closure reports and plans in addition to authoring reports relating to field evaluation, planning, and analysis for the West Valley Demonstration Project, Tar Creek Superfund Site, Paducah Gaseous Diffusion Plant and Savannah River/Oak Ridge Site Environmental Restoration, Calvert Cliffs, Wolf Creek, and Grand Gulf Nuclear Power Plants, and the US Department of Energy's spent nuclear fuel and radioactive waste management programs. He currently is President of Environmental Protection Resources, Inc., a professional environmental consulting company that provides consulting services and solutions to commercial and Federal agency clients.*

CHAPTER 25

Toxic Substances Control Act Basics

Valentino P. De Rocili, PhD, CHMM

History and Overview of the Toxic Substances Control Act

The Toxic Substances Control Act (TSCA) of 1976 was enacted by Congress in order to test, regulate, and screen all chemicals produced or imported into the United States. It was designed as a regulatory framework to deal with the risks posed by the manufacture, distribution, processing, use and disposal of certain chemical substances. Many thousands of chemicals and chemical compounds are developed each year with unknown toxic or other dangerous characteristics. To prevent unreasonable risk of injury to health or the environment, TSCA requires any chemical that reaches the consumer marketplace to be tested for possible toxic effects before commercial manufacturing begins. TSCA requires corrective action in cases of cleanup of toxic materials contamination. TSCA was also designed to supplement other Federal statutes, including the Clean Air Act and the Toxic Release Inventory under the Emergency Planning and Community Right-to-Know Act (EPCRA).

The enactment of TSCA brought about the following basic changes to the environmental regulatory requirements:

- Created a screening mechanism for the production of new chemicals and new uses of existing chemicals

- Prescribed Environmental Protection Agency (EPA) control actions in the manufacture, use, and disposal of chemicals

- Conferred upon EPA extraordinary authority to address imminent hazards

- Banned the manufacture and use of polychlorinated biphenyls (PCBs)

- Gave EPA the power to require the testing of chemical substances that present a risk of injury to health and the environment

- Regulated the production and distribution of new chemicals and governed the manufacture and use of existing chemicals

- Regulated the cleanup, disposal, and record-keeping of asbestos and PCBs (Lee, 1996)

Any existing chemical that poses health and environmental hazards is tracked and reported under TSCA.

Even before the EPA was created in 1970, political pressure to develop this regulation focused on several issues, including the perceived need to regulate chemicals. In 1962, *Silent Spring* by Rachel Carson publicized the misuse of chemicals. According to Carson, this misuse of chemicals threatened to upset the balance of nature and allowed chemicals to enter the food chain. The book was so powerful that some feel it marked the beginning of the environmental movement in the United States.

Congress' intent in creating TSCA was to provide a comprehensive *catch-all* law to close the loopholes that existed in previous chemical laws, such as the Federal Food, Drug, and Cosmetics Act (FFDCA) of 1938, and the Federal Insecticide, Fungicide, and Rodenticide Act (FIFRA) of 1947.

Today, the United States is involved in a major drive toward international cooperation in the control of chemicals. Whenever international agreement is reached on this issue, the EPA has indicated that it would be prepared to modify its policy, if necessary, in order to conform to international standards. The agency believes that the international harmonization of efforts in the control of chemicals will protect health and the environment, while fulfilling its obligations under the Trade Agreements Act of 1979, 40 CFR 707.20(b)(3).

TSCA Authority

The principal authority of TSCA was provided by the Congress in 1976 as stated in the *United States Code* (USC, Title 15 [Commerce and Trade], Chapter 53 [Toxic Substances Control], Subchapter I [Control of Toxic Substances]). In this statute, Congress stated three important findings:

- Human beings and the environment are exposed each year to many chemical substances and mixtures,

- There are some chemical substances and mixtures that may present an unreasonable risk of injury to health or the environment, and

- Regulation of both interstate and intrastate commerce is required.

From these findings, Congress established the policy of the United States as follows:

- Develop and collect adequate data regarding the effect of chemical substances and mixtures on health and the environment from those who manufacture and process chemical substances and mixtures,

- Provide regulatory authority regarding chemical substances and mixtures that present an unreasonable risk of injury to health or the environment, and

- Require that regulatory authority not impede unduly or create unnecessary economic barriers to technological innovation.

The definition of *chemical substances* does not include pesticides (as defined by the Federal Insecticide, Fungicide, and Rodenticide Act); any source material, special nuclear material, or by-product material (as defined in the Atomic Energy Act of 1954); any article the sale of which is subject to the tax imposed by the Internal Revenue Code of 1986; and any food, food additive, drug, cosmetic, or device (as defined by the Federal Food, Drug, and Cosmetic Act). In addition, TSCA does not regulate tobacco, any tobacco product, firearms, or ammunition, because other laws regulate these articles.

When it created TSCA, Congress' intent was that the Administrator should carry out his/her responsibilities in a reasonable and prudent manner, considering the environmental, economic, and social impact of any action taken (15 USC §2601). In 1978, under Executive Order No. 12088, provisions for Federal compliance with pollution control standards were introduced, making the head of each executive agency responsible for that agency's compliance with any applicable standards of pollution control (43 FR 47707).

The current TSCA regulations are found in Title 40, *Code of Federal Regulations*, Parts 700–799 (40 CFR 700–799). The statutes behind the regulation can be found in 15 USC §§2601–2629. Notable changes to TSCA requirements have been made from 1980 through 1998. In 1986, the Asbestos Hazard Emergency Response Act was enacted.

Regarding enforcement, in 40 CFR 710, Inventory Reporting Regulations, EPA says that it "does not intend" to concentrate its enforcement efforts on insignificant clerical errors in reporting, but rather on the overall goal of TSCA. However, the potential penalty for incomplete or missing PCB Annual Reports as required by 40 CFR 761 is a fine of $10,000 per year.

How TSCA Works

Under TSCA, EPA has the authority to approve all chemical substances used for manufacture, importation, or processing in commercial applications before they are introduced into commerce in the United States.

Manufacturers and importers must notify the EPA at least 90 days in advance of manufacturing a new chemical or importing a new chemical in bulk for commercial purposes. The EPA has 90 days to complete its review, and either approves the production of the chemical substance or acts to ban its manufacture. EPA may extend this review period for an additional 90 days. If additional time is needed, the review may be interrupted to develop additional data.

The Toxic Substances Control Act is intended to be comprehensive, and ensure the protection of

health and the environment from unreasonable risks associated with the use of chemicals. For this reason, TSCA includes importation in the Act's definition of the term *manufacture*: "manufacture means to import, produce, or manufacture," 15 USC §2602(7). Thus, importers are responsible for making sure that their methods of importing chemicals comply with TSCA just as domestic manufacturers are responsible for ensuring that their methods for manufacturing chemicals comply with TSCA, 40 CFR 707.20(b).

The Toxic Substances Control Act supplements other Federal statutes, including the Clean Air Act and the Toxic Release Inventory, under the Emergency Planning Community Right-To-Know Act (EPCRA) (EPA, 1997). The disposal of PCBs is regulated by TSCA. Note that hazardous wastes mixed with PCBs can be regulated under

- both TSCA and the Resource Conservation and Recovery Act (RCRA), or

- the most stringent standards of either TSCA or RCRA, or

- a specific exemption that may apply.

See, for example, 40 CFR 261.8 for details concerning RCRA exempt waste regulated by TSCA and 40 CFR 268.45(a)(5) for details concerning waste regulated by both TSCA and RCRA. Note also that disposal of a waste could be subject to both TSCA and RCRA regulations.

Under Section 6 of the Act, specific chemical substances are regulated because they pose unreasonable risk. These chemicals include lead, asbestos, tetrachlorodibenzo-*p*-dioxin (TCDD), chlorofluorocarbons (CFCs), PCBs, and any other listed substances.

Section 5(a)(2) of the Act defines the uses of chemical substances that EPA considers to be significant new uses. EPA imposes the Significant New Use Rule (SNUR) after the chemical is approved for manufacture. Under the SNUR, the use or production volume of the chemical substance may be restricted. In September 1984, the first SNUR was issued. It required manufacturers to notify the EPA if the use of the specified chemical substance exceeded 5 percent of a consumer product. Additionally, this rule requires manufacturers and importers to notify the EPA within 90 days prior to commencing the manufacture or import of listed chemical substances for the significant new uses as defined by TSCA. Listed chemical substances are updated periodically. The SNUR also specifies the procedures that manufacturers, importers, and processors must use in order to report on any significant new uses.

Under TSCA, a Premanufacture Notification (PMN) must be filed with the EPA for chemical substances that are not already listed on the inventory. The PMN must include chemical identification, information on use, method of disposal, production levels, work exposure, potential by-products or impurities, and health and environmental effects. The inventory of chemical substances is contained in 40 CFR 721. Exemptions from the PMN included in 40 CFR 723, Subpart B are:

- Chemical substances manufactured in quantities of 10,000 kilograms or less per year

- Chemical substances with low environmental releases and human exposures

- Some high molecular weight polymers

- Chemical substances used for the manufacture or processing of instant photographic and peel-apart film articles have special requirements

TSCA Regulatory Requirements

The Toxic Substances Control Act was designed by the Federal government to provide the following twenty-one basic functions:

1) **Collection of Fees and Cost Reimbursement.** Fees are required from manufacturers, importers, and processors who submit notices and applications to EPA under Section 5 of the Toxic Substances Control Act (15 USC §2604) in order to defray part of EPA's cost of administering the Act, 40 CFR 700.40(a), Subpart C. 40 CFR 791, Data Reimbursement, establishes procedures and criteria to be used in determining fair amounts of reimbursement for the costs of testing incurred under Section 4(a) TSCA, 15 USC §2603(a).

2) **Mechanism for Civil Actions.** Section 20(a)(1) and (2) of TSCA authorizes any person to begin a civil action to compel the EPA to perform TSCA nondiscretionary acts or duties; to restrain any violation of TSCA, or of any rule promulgated under Sections 4, 5, or 6, or of any order issued under Section 5 of TSCA. The purpose of this regulation is to outline the procedures for submitting a notice of intent to file suit as required by Section 20(b) of TSCA before beginning civil actions (40 CFR 702.60, Subpart C).

3) **Reporting and Recordkeeping Procedures.** 40 CFR 704 specifies reporting and recordkeeping procedures under Section 8(a) of TSCA for manufacturers, importers, and processors of chemical substances and mixtures. The reporting and recordkeeping provisions are chemical-specific (7 USC §§136, *et seq.*). There are also reporting and recordkeeping requirements under 40 CFR 761.180.

4) **Important Definitions.** Title 15, Section 2602 of the USC includes the following important definitions:

Administrator means Administrator of the Environmental Protection Agency.

Chemical substance means any organic or inorganic substance of a particular molecular identity, including

- Any combination of substances occurring in whole or in part as a result of a chemical reaction or occurring in nature

- Any element or uncombined radical

Chemical substance *does not* include

- Any mixture

- Any pesticide (as defined by the Federal Insecticide, Fungicide, and Rodenticide Act) when manufactured, processed, or distributed in commerce for use as a pesticide (7 USC §§136, *et seq.*)

- Tobacco or any tobacco product

- Any source material, special nuclear material, or by-product material (as such terms are defined in the 1954 Atomic Energy Act)

- Any article the sale of which is subject to the tax imposed by the 1986 Internal Revenue Code

- Any food, food additive, drug, cosmetic, or device as defined by the Federal Food, Drug, and Cosmetic Act

Mixture means any combination of two or more chemical substances if the combination does not occur in nature and is not, in whole or in part, the result of a chemical reaction. There are two exceptions to this definition: (1) the combination is *not* a mixture if it occurs as the result of a chemical reaction in which there are no new chemical substances, and (2) the combination is *not* a mixture if it could have been manufactured for commercial purposes without a chemical reaction at the time the combination's chemical substances were combined.

New chemical substance means any chemical substance that is not included in the chemical substance list compiled and published under Title 15, Section 2607(b) of the *United States Code*.

5) **General Import Requirements and Restrictions.** TSCA addresses aspects of the regulation promulgated by the United States Customs Service (Customs), Department of the Treasury (19 CFR 12.118–12.127, 127.28 [amended], 15 USC §2612). Section 13 requires the Secretary of the Treasury to refuse entry into the Customs territory of the United States of any chemical substance, mixture, or article if it does not comply with the rules that are in effect under TSCA (40 CFR 707.20, Subpart B).

6) **EPA Enforcement Procedures.** The EPA and Customs monitor chemical imports to determine if imported shipments comply with the certification requirements and the substantive mandates of TSCA. Customs is authorized to refuse entry to any shipment until the certification is properly submitted, and is allowed to detain a shipment if reasonable grounds exist to believe that such shipment or its import violates TSCA's regulations or orders. A shipment that is in violation must either be brought into compliance, exported, destroyed, or voluntarily abandoned within the time periods prescribed in 19 CFR 12.124 of the Section 13 rule. When EPA determines

that a shipment should be detained, EPA will identify the reasons for the detention and the actions required of the importer in order to bring the shipment into compliance with TSCA, 40 CFR 707.20(c), Subpart B.

7) **Inventory Reporting Procedures.** Those who manufacture, import, or process chemical substances for commercial purposes under Section 8(a) of the Toxic Substances Control Act must report according to regulations, 15 USC §2607(a). Section 8(a) authorizes the Administrator to require reporting of information necessary for administration of the Act, and requires EPA to issue regulations that allow it to compile an inventory of the chemical substances manufactured or processed for a commercial purpose. Following the initial reporting period, EPA published an initial inventory of chemical substances manufactured, processed, or imported for commercial purposes. The EPA periodically amends the inventory to include the new chemical substances reported under Section 5(a)(1) of the Act. The agency also revises the categories of chemical substances and makes other amendments as appropriate. Under Section 15(3) of TSCA, it is unlawful for any person to fail or refuse to submit the information that is required under these reporting regulations. In addition, Section 15(3) states that it is unlawful for any person to fail to keep, and allow access to, the records that are required by these regulations. Section 16 states that any person who violates a provision of Section 15 is liable to the United States for a civil penalty and may be criminally prosecuted. Pursuant to Section 17, the Government may seek a court order to compel submission of Section 8(a) information and to otherwise restrain any violation of Section 15, 40 CFR 710.1, (a), (b).

In January 2003 the EPA promulgated an amendment to TSCA Section 8(a) regarding the Inventory Update Rule (IUR). Accordingly, the EPA is requiring the reporting of additional data for certain listed chemical substances to assist EPA and other agencies in accessing the potential risks, including exposures that result from industrial chemical operations as well as commercial and consumer uses of TSCA-listed chemical substances.

Additionally, the amendment modified the EPA's procedure for making Confidential Business Information claims (68 FR 848 January 7, 2003).

8) Chemical Information Rules. Procedures are outlined by which chemical manufacturers and processors must report production-, use-, and exposure-related information on listed chemical substances. The rules stipulate the requirements that apply to all reporting (40 CFR 712.1, Subpart A). 40 CFR 750 establishes procedures for all rulemakings under authority of Section 6 of the Toxic Substances Control Act (TSCA), 15 USC §2605.

9) Requirements for Health and Safety Data Reporting. TSCA requires manufacturers, importers, and processors to submit lists and copies of health and safety studies on the chemical substances and mixtures selected under Section 4(a), and on other chemical substances and mixtures for which EPA requires health and safety information.

10) Records and Reports for Adverse Chemical Substance Reactions. Section 8(c) of TSCA requires manufacturers, processors, and distributors of chemical substances and mixtures to

- Keep "records of significant adverse reactions to health or the environment, as determined by the Administrator by rule, alleged to have been caused by the substance or mixture"

- "Allow inspection and submit copies of such records," upon request of any designated representative of the Administrator

This rule implements Section 8(c) of TSCA. It describes the records to be kept and prescribes the conditions under which certain firms must submit or make the records available to a duly designated representative of the Administrator; 40 CFR 717.1 (a) and (b), Subpart A.

11) Rules for Reporting New Chemical Substances. 40 CFR 720 establishes the procedures by which new chemical substances must be reported by manufacturers and importers under Section 5 of the Toxic Substances Control Act (15 USC §2604). The rule defines the persons who are subject to the reporting requirements, and the chemical substances that must be reported. It prescribes the contents of Section 5 notices, and establishes procedures for submitting notices. The rule also outlines the EPA's policy regarding claims of confidentiality for, and public disclosure of, various categories of information that are submitted about Section 5 notices. A complete list of chemicals is located in 40 CFR 721.

12) Specific Use Requirements for Certain Chemical Substances. 40 CFR 747 provides specific requirements for metal-working fluids including mixed mono- and diamides of an organic acid (40 CFR 747.115), triethanolamine salt of a substituted organic acid (40 CFR 747.195), and triethanolamine salt of tricarboxylic acid (40 CFR 747.200). 40 CFR 749.68 furnishes the requirements for water treatment chemicals in air-conditioning and cooling systems, such as hexavalent chromium-based water treatment.

13) Prohibitions of, and Requirements for, the Manufacture, Processing, Distribution in Commerce, Use, Disposal, Storage, and Marking of PCBs and PCB Items. 40 CFR 761 applies to all persons who manufacture, process, distribute in commerce, use, or dispose of PCBs or PCB Items. Substances regulated by this rule include, but are not limited to, dielectric fluids, contaminated solvents, oils, waste oils, heat-transfer fluids, hydraulic fluids, paints, sludges, slurries, dredge spoils, soils, materials contaminated because of spills, and other chemical substances or combinations of substances, including impurities and by-products and any by-product, intermediate, or impurity manufactured at any point in a process. Most of the provisions of this part apply to PCBs only if PCBs are present in concentrations above a specified level. For example, Subpart D applies generally to materials at concentrations of 50 parts per million (ppm) and above. Also, certain provisions of Subpart B apply to the PCBs that are inadvertently generated in manufacturing processes at concentrations specified in the definition of PCB under 40 CFR 761.3. No provision specifying a PCB concentration may be avoided because of dilution, unless otherwise specifically provided (40 CFR 761.1, Subpart A).

With certain exceptions, TSCA Section 6(e)(3) bans the manufacture, importing, processing, and distribution in commerce of PCBs. However, the EPA does have the authority to grant petitions through the rulemaking process. For example, in 2001 the United States Defense Logistics Agency (DLA), an agency of the Department of Defense (DoD), submitted petitions to the EPA to import foreign-manufactured PCBs that the DoD owns in Japan and Wake Island for the purposes of disposal in the United States. In a final rule promulgated in January 2003, the EPA amended its rules to grant DLA's petitions allowed them to engage in the import of PCBs for disposal (68 FR 4934; January 31, 2003).

14) **PCB Spill Cleanup Policy.** In 1987, EPA promulgated a national PCB spill cleanup policy. The policy requires notification and recordkeeping of PCB spills into sensitive areas such as open water, near wells, vegetable gardens, and grazing lands. It requires a specific cleanup and cleanup verification function for any spills of PCB in concentrations of 50 ppm or above. Additional requirements are prescribed for spills of oil containing PCBs at levels greater than 1 pound and 10 pounds (40 CFR 761.120–135).

15) **Asbestos-Containing Materials.** 40 CFR 763 regulates asbestos abatement projects and Asbestos-Containing Materials (ACM) in schools. It also prohibits the manufacture, importation, processing, and distribution in commerce of certain asbestos-containing products and establishes the labeling requirements for these products.

16) **Requirements for Testing for Dibenzo-*p*-Dioxins / Dibenzofurans.** 40 CFR 766 outlines the requirements for testing to ascertain whether certain specified chemical substances may be contaminated with halogenated dibenzodioxins (HDDs) and/or dibenzofurans (HDFs) as defined in 40 CFR 766.3, and requirements for reporting under Section 8 of TSCA (15 USC §2607).

17) **Rules that Govern Testing Consent Agreements and Testing.** TSCA establishes procedures for gathering information, conducting negotiations, and for developing and implementing test rules or consent agreements on chemical substances and mixtures under

Section 4 of TSCA. Section 4 of the Act authorizes the EPA to require the manufacturers and processors of chemical substances and mixtures to test these chemicals in order to determine whether they have adverse health or environmental effects. Section 4(a) empowers the Agency to require such testing. In addition, the EPA has the implied authority to enter into enforceable consent agreements that require testing where the Agency provides procedural safeguards equivalent to those that apply where the testing is conducted by rule rather than by agreement. The EPA uses enforceable consent agreements to carry out testing where a consensus exists between the EPA, the affected manufacturers and/or processors, and interested members of the public concerning the need for testing. If such a consensus does not exist and the Agency believes that it can produce the findings specified in Section 4(a), then the EPA will initiate proceedings to declare test rules that will be codified in 40 CFR 799.

18) **Good Laboratory Practice Standards.** Good laboratory practices for conducting studies relating to health effects, environmental effects, and chemical fate testing are established. The standards are intended to ensure the quality and integrity of the data submitted pursuant to testing consent agreements and test rules issued under Section 4 of TSCA (PL 94–94–469, 90 Stat. 2006, 15 USC §§2603, *et seq.*).

19) **Provisional Test Guidelines.** TSCA provides provisional chemical fate guidelines, environmental effects guidelines, health effects guidelines, and exposure and toxicity guidelines (40 CFR 795–798).

20) **Identifies Specific Chemical Substance and Mixture Testing Requirements.** 40 CFR 799 identifies the chemical substances, mixtures, and categories of substances and mixtures for which data will be developed, specifies the persons who are required to test (manufacturers, including importers, and/or processors), specifies the test substance(s) in each case, prescribes the tests that are required and their standards, and provides deadlines for the submission of reports and data to EPA. This part requires manufacturers and/or processors of the chemical substances or mixtures that are identified in Subpart B to submit letters of

intent to test, exemption applications, and study plans according to the EPA test rule. This part also requires the manufacturers and/or processors of the chemicals identified in Subpart B to conduct tests and to submit data following the test standards contained in this part in order to enable the EPA to develop data on the health and environmental effects and other characteristics of these chemicals. This data is used to assess the risk of injury to human health or the environment that is presented by these chemicals; 40 CFR 799.1 (a), (b), and (c). This includes hazardous waste constituents subject to testing, (40 CFR 799.5055) and drinking water contaminants subject to testing (40 CFR 799.5075).

21) **Lead-Based Paint Poisoning Prevention in Certain Residential Structures.** TSCA requires the disclosure of known lead-based paint and/or hazards upon sale or lease of residential property, and regulates lead-based paint activities (40 CFR 745). On June 1, 1998, the EPA promulgated a final rule that changed the requirements for hazard education before renovation of target housing by requiring that a lead hazard informational pamphlet be provided to owners and occupants of such housing prior to commencing of a renovation. In addition, the rule requires notification on the nature of renovation activities in certain circumstances involved with multifamily housing (63 FR 29908).

In July 2001, EPA revised 40 CFR 745 to include a framework for individuals and firms who engage in lead-based paint activities in target housing and child-occupied facilities. The regulatory framework assists states in developing their regulations, training program requirements, certification, recordkeeping, and work practice standards.

Highlights of Regulatory Changes for the Disposal of PCBs

On June 29, 1998 in the *Federal Register*, the Environmental Protection Agency promulgated its final rule under TSCA for the disposal of PCBs (63 FR 35383–35474). Changes made to the existing regulations became effective on August 28, 1998.

The changes affected requirements under both 40 CFR 750 and 40 CFR 761.

The EPA amended the portion of its rules under TSCA which addresses the manufacture, processing, distribution in commerce, use, cleanup, storage, and disposal of PCBs. The rule provides some flexibility regarding selection of disposal technologies for PCB wastes and expands the allowable procedures for decontamination of PCB on surfaces and water. The rule also modifes the requirements regarding the use and disposal of PCB equipment. It also codifies policies that EPA has developed and implemented over the 19 years prior to this ruling.

Regulatory changes that affect PCB concentration assumptions for electrical equipment are as follows:

- The PCB concentration assumption rule was changed, allowing any person to assume that electrical transformers, circuit breakers, reclosers, oil-filled cable, and rectifiers containing less than 1.36 kg (3 lbs) of fluid whose PCB concentration has not been established contain less than 50 ppm of PCBs, and therefore non-PCB rated equipment (63 FR 35436).

- Any person may assume that mineral oil-filled electrical equipment, including transformers, that was manufactured before July 2, 1979, and whose PCB concentration is not established, is PCB Contaminated Electrical Equipment. It will be assumed that the equipment will contain 50 ppm or greater PCBs, but less than 500 ppm PCBs (63 FR 35436).

- Pole-top and pad-mounted distribution electrical transformers manufactured before July 2, 1979, are assumed to be mineral oil–filled and PCB-Contaminated Electrical Equipment while in use, unless the concentration has been established (63 FR 35436).

- If the date of manufacture of mineral oil-filled electrical equipment is unknown, any person must assume it to be PCB-Contaminated Electrical Equipment (63 FR 35437).

- Any person may assume that oil-filled electrical equipment, including transformers, that was manufactured after July 2, 1979, and whose PCB concentration is not established, is Non-PCB Rated Equipment, containing less than 50 ppm of PCBs (63 FR 35437).

- Any person must assume that an electrical transformer manufactured before July 2, 1979, that contains 1.36 kg (3 lbs) or more of fluid other than mineral oil, and whose PCB concentration has not been established, is a PCB Transformer, containing 500 ppm or greater PCBs (63 FR 35437).

- Any person may assume that a capacitor manufactured after July 2, 1979, is Non-PCB Rated Electrical Equipment, containing less than 50 ppm PCBs (63 FR 35437).

- Any person may assume that a capacitor manufactured before July 2, 1979, whose PCB concentration is not established, is a PCB Capacitor, containing 500 ppm or greater of PCBs (63 FR 35437).

- If the date of manufacture is unknown, any person must assume that a capacitor contains 500 ppm or greater of PCBs (63 FR 35437).

- Any person may assume that a capacitor marked at the time of manufacture with the statement "No PCBs" in accordance with the regulations is Non-PCB Rated Equipment (63 FR 35437).

Assumption policies do not apply when electrical equipment is being disposed of. At the time of disposal, the owner or operator of PCB equipment must know its actual PCB concentration and use the proper disposal method (63 FR 35389).

In addition to changes in assumption policies for electrical equipment, the EPA required that registration of PCB Transformers be completed no later than December 28, 1998. This new registration requirement includes PCB Transformers in use or in storage for reuse, even if a specific PCB Transformer was registered under the previous regulatory requirements (63 FR 35440).

If an electrical transformer owner who assumes that a transformer is PCB Contaminated, and discovers after December 28, 1998 that it is in fact a PCB Transformer, the owner of the transformer must register the newly identified PCB Transformer, in writing, with the EPA no later than 30 calendar days after it is identified as such. This requirement does not apply to transformer owners who have previously registered with the EPA PCB Transformers located at the same location as the newly identified PCB Transformer (63 FR 35440).

The new rule also addresses persons who take possession of a PCB Transformer after December 29, 1998. For this condition, the owner is not required to register or re-register the transformer with the EPA (63 FR 35440).

Owners of PCB Transformers are required to maintain, with an annual log, proof of registration with the EPA, local fire response, and/or building owners (63 FR 35440).

PCB cleanup levels for soil have changed in this new ruling. The soil cleanup level for high occupancy (*e.g.*, residential areas) is less than 1 ppm, or less than 10 ppm if the contaminated soil is capped (63 FR 35390). For PCB-contaminated soil in low occupancy (*e.g.*, electrical substations), the soil cleanup level is less than 25 ppm to less than 100 ppm, depending upon site conditions (63 FR 35390).

Decontamination standards for PCB-contaminated surfaces are as follows:

- Nonporous surfaces in contact with liquid PCBs destined for reuse: less than 10 micrograms of PCBs per 100 square centimeters (63 FR 35390).

- Nonporous surfaces in contact with nonliquid PCBs destined for reuse: as required by the National Association of Corrosion Engineers (NACE) Visual Standard No. 2, Near-White Blast Cleaned Surface Finish (63 FR 35390).

- Concrete surfaces containing fresh PCB spills: less than 10 micrograms of PCBs per 100 square centimeters (63 FR 35390).

- PCB spills to water: less than 5 micrograms of PCBs per liter for unrestricted use; 63 FR 35390, 40 CFR 761.79(b)(1)(ii).

The handling of PCB wastes was addressed in this new rule as follows:

- If the PCB component of a waste is approved for disposal at a facility, the approval for the disposal of the other regulated waste components must be addressed by all other statutes or regulatory authorities (See, related discussion in the section entitled, "How TSCA Works.")(63 FR 35390).

- Unless otherwise noted in the regulations, references to weights or volumes in 40 CFR 761 apply to the total weight or volumes of the PCB-containing material (*e.g.*, oil, soil, *etc.*), not to the calculated weight or volume of only the

PCB fraction within that substance (63 FR 35390).

- Restrictions regarding manufacturing, processing, distribution in commerce, and use of PCBs were addressed in the new ruling. The EPA also revised the definition of PCB remediation waste and addressed sewage sludge containing PCBs (63 FR 35392).

New marking requirements were provided in the ruling requiring the M_L mark for storage units, PCB Large Low Voltage Capacitors, and PCB Equipment (including equipment in use) that contain PCB Transformers, PCB Large High or PCB Large Low Capacitors (63 FR 35426).

For the first time, natural gas pipeline systems are included under the PCB regulation. The EPA has initiated a compliance monitoring program for companies with greater than 50 ppm PCBs in their pipelines, to address contamination issues in natural gas pipelines and associated equipment (63 FR 35395).

Where to Get More Information

In support of Title 15, Section 2625, the EPA Office of Prevention, Pesticides, and Toxic Substances (OPPTS) provides a TSCA Assistance Information Service. The service provides information and assistance to chemical manufacturers, processors, users, storers, disposers, importers, and exporters, concerning the regulations under TSCA.

As of August 2003, OPPTS could be reached at (202) 554–1404 or at the following Internet address:

<tsca-hotline@epamail.epa.gov>

Also, check for TSCA information on the EPA homepage:

<http://www.epa.gov>

Bibliography

"Agriculture." *US Code*. Title 7, Secs. 136, *et seq.*

"Chemical Fate Testing Guidelines." *Code of Federal Regulations*. Title 40, Pt. 796.

"Chemical Import and Exports." *Code of Federal Regulations*. Title 40, Pt. 707.

"Chemical Information Rules, General Provisions." *Code of Federal Regulations*. Title 40, Pt. 712, Subpart A.

"Citizen Suit." *Code of Federal Regulations*. Title 40, Pt. 702, Subpart C.

"Control of Toxic Substances, Definitions." *US Code*. Title 15, Sec. 2602.

"Control of Toxic Substances, Findings, Policy, and Intent." *US Code*. Title 15, Sec. 2601.

"Disposal of Polychlorinated Biphenyls (PCBs), Final Rule." *Federal Register* 63:124. (29 June 1998) 35383–35474.

"Entry into Customs Territory of the United States." *US Code*. Title 15, Sec. 2612.

"Environmental Effects Testing Guidelines." *Code of Federal Regulations*. Title 40, Pt. 797.

Environmental Protection Agency, Office of Public Affairs. "Toxic Substances Control Act (TSCA) Assistance Information Service." Washington, DC: EPA, 13 March 1997.

"Fees." *Code of Federal Regulations*. Title 40, Pt. 700, Subpart C.

"General Import Requirements and Restrictions." *Code of Federal Regulations*. Title 40, Pt. 707, Subpart B.

"General Reporting and Recordkeeping Provisions for Section 8(a) Information-Gathering Rules." *Code of Federal Regulations*. Title 40, Pt. 704, Subpart A.

"Health and Safety Data Reporting, General Provisions." *Code of Federal Regulations*. Title 40, Pt. 716, Subpart A.

"Health Effects Testing Guidelines." *Code of Federal Regulations*. Title 40, Pt. 798.

"Identification of Specific Chemical Substance and Mixture Testing Requirements." *Code of Federal Regulations*. Title 40, Pt. 799.

"Inventory Reporting Regulations." *Code of Federal Regulations*. Title 40, Pt. 710.

Lee, C. C. *Dictionary of Environmental Legal Terms*. New York, NY: McGraw-Hill, 1996.

"Manufacturing and Processing Notices." *US Code*. Title 15, Sec. 2604.

"Metal Working Fluids." *Code of Federal Regulations*. Title 40, Pt. 747.

"Polychlorinated Biphenyls (PCBs) Manufacturing, Processing, Distribution in Commerce, and Use Prohibitions." *Code of Federal Regulations*. Title 40, Pt. 761.

"Premanufacture Notification." *Code of Federal Regulations*. Title 40, Pt. 720.

"Premanufacture Notification Exemptions." *Code of Federal Regulations*. Title 40, Pt. 723.

"Provisional Test Guidelines." *Code of Federal Regulations*. Title 40, Pt. 795.

"Public Health and Welfare." *US Code*. Title 42, Secs. 2011, *et seq.*

"Records and Reports of Allegations That Chemical Substances Cause Significant Adverse Reactions to Health or the Environment, General Provisions." *Code of Federal Regulations*. Title 40, Pt. 717, Subpart A.

"Reporting and Retention of Information." *US Code*. Title 15, Sec. 2607.

"Testing of Chemical Substances and Mixtures." *US Code*. Title 15, Sec. 2603, *et seq.*

"Water Treatment Chemicals." *Code of Federal Regulations*. Title 40, Pt. 749.

Valentino P. De Rocili *is the President of Compliance Environmental, Inc., an environmental health and safety consulting firm located in Dover, Delaware. He has managed over $60 million of environmental and safety-related projects in more than 24 years of hands-on work experience in areas including hazard and risk assessment, PCBs, lead-based paint inspection and abatement, waste management, underground storage tanks, indoor air quality, wastewater treatment plants, solid waste landfills, and compliance requirements. He is currently an Assistant Professor at the University of Delaware, and the co-founder of the Delaware Chapter of Hazardous Materials Managers. He serves on several technical committees including the Environmental Technical Review Committee for the United States Air Force at Dover Air Force Base, and the Lead Advisory Group for the State of Delaware Department of Health and Social Services. In 1996, he received the Champion of Excellence Award from the National Academy of Certified Hazardous Materials Managers.*

Federal Insecticide, Fungicide, and Rodenticide Act

Keith Trombley, CIH, CSP, CHMM

Introduction

The Federal Insecticide, Fungicide, and Rodenticide Act (FIFRA) was first passed in 1947. Its primary goal was to protect consumers from misbranded, adulterated, and ineffective pesticides.

Original jurisdiction for this law was given to the United States Department of Agriculture (USDA), but this was transferred to the United States Environmental Protection Agency (EPA) when it was created in 1970. FIFRA has been amended many times by Congress over the years, most recently through the Food Quality Protection Act (FQPA) in 1996 (Public Law [PL] 104–170).

One important distinction between FIFRA and most of the other environmental protection laws is that it was originally a *registration* rather than *reporting* standard (however, more and more reporting requirements have been added to the act). The registration concept tends to limit the amount of liability incurred by the industry once their products are legally on the market. This benefit is often offset because the registration process has become expensive and difficult. Most products that make any pesticidal claims on their label must go through a far more extensive testing and approval process than most of the other chemicals we may use in our daily lives. This affects not only a user's cost, but also the variety of chemicals that are available to consumers.

The text of FIFRA can be found under the reference 7 *United States Code* (USC) §§136, *et seq*. The regulations promulgated from this law are found in the *Code of Federal Regulations* at 40 CFR 150–189 (Subchapter E, Pesticide Programs). However, knowing the law and regulations is only the beginning step to compliance and getting a pesticide registered and on the market. At the Federal level there are guidance manuals, interpretation documents, and many specific bureaucratic procedures that must be followed to negotiate successfully the registration process. Nearly every state has its own level of regulations, some of which are just as detailed as those at the Federal level. The following text is an overview of some of the more notable issues of the pesticide regulation process.

The Law

FIFRA can trace its legislative lineage as far back as 1906 to the Pure Food Act. It is still closely linked to the present-day Federal Food, Drug, and Cosmetic Act (FFDCA). The text of the act is broken down into several sections, the most important being: Sections 3 and 4 on registration and reregistration, Section 7 on registrations of establishments, Section 10 on protection of trade secrets and other information, and Section 11 on use of restricted-use pesticides and applicators.

As with some of the other environmental laws presently being enforced, it is worthwhile to be familiar with both the law and the regulations. References to the act, the law (*i.e.*, *United States Code*), and the regulations are interchanged frequently.

Definitions and Exceptions

As with any law and subsequent regulations, certain terms must be specifically defined so everybody understands and accepts what

everybody else is talking about. Listed below are some of the more key definitions and notable exceptions to the rules.

Pest—An organism deleterious to man or the environment if it is: any vertebrate animal other than man; any invertebrate animal, including but not limited to any insect, other arthropod, nematode, or mollusk such as a slug and snail, but excluding any internal parasite on living man or other animals; any plant growing where not wanted, including any mosses, alga, liverwort, or other plant of any higher order, and any plant part such as a root; or any fungus, bacterium, virus, or other microorganism, except those on or in living man or other living animals and those on processed food or processed animal feed, beverages, drugs, and cosmetics; as defined under FFDCA Sections 201(g)(1) and 201(i).

Pesticide—Any substance or mixture of substances intended for preventing, destroying, repelling, or mitigating any pest, or intended for use as a plant regulator, defoliant, or desiccant, other than any article that is a new animal drug under the FFDCA Section 201(w); an animal drug that has been determined by regulation of the Secretary of Health and Human Services not to be a new animal drug; or an animal feed under the FFDCA Section 201(x) that bears or contains any substances described above.

Pesticide product—A pesticide in a particular form (including composition, packaging, and labeling) in which the pesticide is, or is intended to be, distributed or sold. The term includes any physical apparatus used to deliver or apply the pesticide if distributed or sold with the pesticide.

End use product—A pesticide product whose labeling: includes directions for use of the product (as distributed or sold, or after combination by the user with other substances) for controlling pests or defoliating, desiccating, or regulating the growth of plants; and does not state that the product may be used to manufacture or formulate other pesticide products.

Manufacturing use product—Any pesticide product that is not an end use product.

Label—The written, printed, or graphic matter on, or attached to, the pesticide or device or any of its containers or wrappers.

Labeling—All labels and other written, printed, or graphic matter which: accompanies the pesticide or device at any time; or reference is made on the label or in literature accompanying the pesticide or device, except to the current official publications of the EPA, the USDA, Department of the Interior (DOI), Department of Health and Human Services (DHHS), state experiment stations, state agricultural colleges, and other Federal or State institutions or agencies authorized by law to conduct research in the field of pesticides.

Some products that are not considered pesticides, even though the above definitions seem to include them, are: drugs; fertilizers; deodorizers, bleaches and cleaning agents (if they make no pesticide label claims); barriers that contain no toxicants (such as screens or sheet metal); treated articles or substances (such as treated lumber); natural cedar; and a listing of 31 specific *minimum-risk pesticides* (*e.g.*, cinnamon, garlic, peppermint, zinc metal strips, *etc.*).

Many things that are not directly part of the product's label are still considered labeling. For example, Material Safety Data Sheets (MSDSs), while not directly regulated by the EPA, are considered product labeling under FIFRA and should include the same directions and precautions as found on the product label.

The Regulated Community

The main groups of people or businesses directly regulated by FIFRA fall into two basic categories: manufacturers and formulators. A manufacturer is a company that actually produces the chemical that is the active ingredient in a pesticide. These companies typically are very large chemical firms, such as Dow, Dupont, or Monsanto. There are probably less than 30 or so major companies and about 100 smaller companies in the United States that fall into the category of manufacturer. Conversely, there are thousands of pesticide formulators in the United States. A formulator is a firm that mixes active ingredient(s) with various inert ingredients, such as diluents, carriers, propellants, *etc.*, to create a product for an end user. Consequently, pesticides are categorized for manufacturing or end use. While most pesticide manufacturers make both manufacturing use and end use products, formulators focus almost entirely on end use products. Since the majority of the regulated community falls into the category of formulator, this chapter will mainly focus on compliance from the formulator's point of view.

The Registration Process

When registering a pesticide, there are three main items that will be reviewed by the EPA before the product is allowed to be sold: the label, the formula, and the supporting data. All of the required documents and forms must be grouped together in an application that is submitted to the EPA for review and, hopefully, approved.

The Paperwork

There are numerous applications, forms, and documents that must be submitted in the correct amount, format, and order. Failure to meet these administrative requirements will result in immediate rejection of the application. Once the registration application is determined to be administratively correct, then all submittals, especially the label and formula, will be reviewed in detail. Depending on the type of product and the length of the label, this process can be quite time-consuming, and there is always the chance that something that was accepted during a first review will not be accepted on a subsequent review. The review process for a registered pesticide is never really over. Sometimes products that have been in use for years will be required to have their label changed because something that was accepted in the past is now "unacceptable."

Some of the documents that will have to be submitted with a registration application are

- Application for Pesticide Registration (EPA Form 8570–1)

- Confidential Statement of Formula (CSF) (EPA Form 8570–4)

- Formulator's Exemption Statement (EPA Form 8570–27)*

---

* Only needed when using a registered pesticide as an ingredient in the formula.

- Certification with Respect to Citations of Data (EPA Form 8570–34)

- Data Matrix (EPA Form 8570–35)

- Summary of Physical/Chemical Properties (EPA Form 8570–36)

- Self-Certification Statement for the Physical/Chemical Properties (EPA Form 8570–37)

- Product labeling

- Supporting product data

These forms can be found on EPA's Office of Pesticide Programs Internet site at

<http://www.epa.gov/pesticides/registrationkit/>

The EPA publishes a very helpful guidance document, the *Label Review Manual*, which is availble on-line and is indispensable to even the most experienced applicant. It gives detailed guidance for correctly submitting applications, amendments, notifications, and other various documents. The label regulating process is also in an almost constant flux and new guidance is published periodically through the Pesticide Registration Notice (PR–Notice) system. PR–Notices are sent directly to all pesticide registrants and are available on-line.

The Label

The EPA must approve all pesticide labels. There are very specific requirements on what and where required language must appear on a pesticide's label. The product label is usually the only source of instructions and precautions given to a user. While most of the FIFRA requirements for labels are straightforward, some requirements are less clear and sometimes interpreted differently by the registration applicant than by the EPA. The root of this "conflict" is usually due to the registrant's desire to provide user-friendly instructions that do not meet the EPA's specific statements for directions and precautions. Both parties have an interest in developing a *good* label, but finding a happy medium can result in a lengthy review process and a delay in getting a product approved and on the market.

As anyone who has ever read the label of a pesticide will profess, it is not something that is read unless necessary. Pesticide labels are typically very long,

often complicated, and not easy to understand. While both the EPA and the regulated community are trying to make labels less difficult to read, this will not be corrected overnight. Pesticide registration applicants should keep in close contact with the regulators that will be providing the approval. Early communication can eliminate later misunderstandings.

All pesticide labels must include the following items:

- Ingredient statement

- Restricted use pesticide statement*

- "Keep Out of Reach of Children" statement

- Precautionary statements with signal word

- Skull and crossbones symbol and the word "Poison"*

- First aid statements ("statement of practical treatment")

- Environmental hazard statements

- Physical or chemical hazard statements

- Directions for use

- Re-entry statement

- Product name

- Storage and disposal statements

- Registrant name and address

- Net contents statement

- EPA registration and establishment numbers

There are also requirements regarding where on the label most of these items must be placed, the order in which the statements must appear on the label, and the size of the text. While this may seem rather restrictive, it does allow for a somewhat standardized format and easy retrieval of information once the user is familiar with it. This can be very handy in an emergency.

The label section that is usually the hardest to get approved is the ***directions for use*** statements. This is the part of the label where the registrant describes how much of the product to use, for what applications it can be used (*e.g.*, which crops, pests, locations, *etc.*), and how to apply it. This is a key portion of the product label and will always start

---

* Required only when applicable to that pesticide.

with the statement "It is a violation of Federal law to use this product in a manner inconsistent with its labeling." This is the EPA's method of putting all users on notice that they must follow the label directions.

The directions for use statements are also where most companies' marketing departments get involved and try to make performance claims. One person's acceptable claim is another person's outrageous claim, and this difference of opinion often occurs between the registrant and the regulator. Even the proposed product name can become a bone of contention, because of perceived or implied claims made by the name. Again, communication with the regulators is the key to avoiding roadblocks and delays.

Formula

All pesticides must have a specific written formula with certifiable concentration limits of active ingredients. A Confidential Statement of Formula (CSF) must list the names of all the ingredients, the suppliers of the ingredients, the amount (by weight and percentage of total formula) of each ingredient in the final formula, and the reason for adding each ingredient to the formula. In addition, any registered pesticide used in the formula must include the EPA registration number. Including registered pesticides in formulae is a cost-efficient way of making an end use product. This is the method used by most pesticide formulators to avoid thousands of dollars in costs for supporting data. The subject of supporting data will be discussed in the next section.

While the EPA does allow for substituting different ingredients in a formula, all of these substitutions must be spelled out in the statement of formula. The statement of formula goes back to one of the original reasons behind FIFRA, i.e., the protection of consumers from adulterated products. A pesticide that does not conform to its specified statement of formula is considered adulterated and illegal to sell.

Product formulae are considered Confidential Business Information (CBI) and very tightly controlled by businesses as well as the EPA. Product formulae are exempt from the provisions of the Freedom of Information Act (FOIA).

Supporting Data

Supporting data are all of the scientific and clinical data required before a product is considered safe enough to be registered. Areas where a registrant could be required to submit supporting data to the EPA are:

- Product properties
- Product performance
- Fate, transport, and transformation
- Health effects
- Occupational and residential exposure
- Spray drift
- Ecological effects
- Residue chemistry

There are also specific testing procedures for biochemical and microbial pesticides.

Determining which supporting data must be submitted is dependent on the use pattern of the pesticide. Typically, a formulator will need product property data and the *6-pack* of acute toxicity studies:

1) Acute oral toxicity
2) Acute dermal toxicity
3) Acute inhalation toxicity
4) Primary eye irritation
5) Primary dermal irritation
6) Dermal sensitization

Products that make claims to protect human health (*e.g.*, sanitizers and rodenticides) will usually have to submit product performance data also.

Supporting data can be either submitted or *cited*. If a product is identical or similar to an existing registered product, permission to reference these data that are already on file with the EPA can be given. There is also a provision in the law for an applicant to cite another registrant's data, or even "cite-all" data on file, without the other registrants' immediate permission, by making an *offer to pay* for these data references. Using this method opens an applicant to potential arbitration procedures to determine the actual amount to be paid to the data holders.

Most manufacturers of active ingredients have developed numerous end use formulae for their manufacturing use products. The manufacturer will usually supply a formulator with the formulae and permission to cite the supporting data already on file with the EPA, as long as the active ingredient is purchased from them. In fact, the majority of all data are collected and submitted by pesticide manufacturers in support of their widely used active ingredients. Supporting data are where the bulk of the pesticide industry's financial investment is found. The cost and time involved for a chemical manufacturer to discover, develop, and test a new active ingredient can be staggering. Consequently, additional protections have been built into FIFRA to protect a manufacturer's investment. There is a 15-year window where the first submitter of supporting data for an active ingredient is given *exclusive use* protection and other applicants cannot cite their data without specific permission.

As with the unending label revisions, all registrants can look forward to eventually being tasked with a Data Call-In (DCI) notice. The EPA has the authority to require registrants to submit additional supporting data for their products as new issues arise. When this happens, registrants are faced with deciding to generate the new data (either alone or with other registrants), or canceling their product registration.

Adverse Effects Reporting

One of the reporting requirements of FIFRA is in the area of unreasonable adverse effects, found under Section 6(a)(2) of the law (40 CFR 159). This requirement is very similar to the reporting required under the Toxic Substances Control Act (TSCA), Section 8(c). Registrants must report to the EPA when they have knowledge of unreasonable adverse effects to humans or the environment. There are specific reporting procedures and deadlines, depending on the actual adverse effect. Failure to follow this reporting requirement could result in very costly enforcement actions.

Reregistration

FIFRA went through a major revision in 1988, which started a process called *reregistration.* The EPA systematically categorized and grouped all active ingredients in the formulae of all registered pesticides. Active ingredients that had been initially registered before 1984 are put through a process of complete reevaluation. This evaluation covers labels, formulae, and especially supporting data. A determination is made whether or not an active ingredient should be eligible for reregistration, and what additional supporting data, if any, are needed to complete the cost-benefit picture. The Re-registration Eligibility Document (RED) for that active ingredient is published quantifying the results of the evaluation. DCIs are issued for any missing or inadequate supporting data. If registrants do not meet the requirements of the RED within the set time periods, then that product's registration is canceled.

One outgrowth of this program has been the registration maintenance fee. Each registrant must pay an annual fee to the EPA based on the number of registrations they have. This money is used to fund the reregistration program. The EPA's original goal was to complete the reregistration process for all active ingredients by 1997, at which time their authority to collect the maintenance fee would expire. However, the reregistration program is still in progress, and the authority to collect fees has been extended (as part of the Food Quality Protection Act [FQPA], see below).

The reregistration program has been a massive task for the EPA, but once completed, all active ingredients will be essentially *up-to-date* in terms of labels, formulae, and supporting data.

Applicators and Worker Protection

A *restricted use pesticide* is a pesticide whose toxicity is high enough that the EPA restricts its use. Applicators of restricted use pesticides must be certified. This certification process is handled at the State level, usually by a state's Department of Agriculture. Most states also require that anybody applying pesticides as part of a business operation also be certified as an applicator. Applicators are tested and certified in the techniques and hazards of pesticide application. Applicators fall into two general categories: commercial and private. Commercial applicators are those who apply pesticides for a living (*e.g.*, exterminators). Private applicators apply pesticides only to their own property (*e.g.*, farmers). Most states have specialized certification tests for different applications, such as structural pest control, pools, turfgrass, *etc.*

The EPA has also developed the Worker Protection Standard (WPS) for pesticide application. While the EPA does not usually regulate occupational hazards, they took the lead when it came to occupational exposures to pesticides in the agriculture industries. This standard requires employers in agriculture (farms), silvaculture (forests), and horticulture (nurseries and greenhouses) that use pesticides to follow some basic procedures in hazard communication, first aid and emergency medical treatment, and personal protective equipment. It also requires employers to restrict workers from entering treatment areas during a pesticide's Restricted Entry Interval (REI).

The Food Quality Protection Act

As everyone should recognize, a pesticide is a poison. In fact, early legislation actually referred to them as *economic poisons*. When supporting data first started being submitted for review, analysis was done on a cost-benefit basis. Applying a poison to our environment has a certain cost to the environment. The benefit of applying this poison might be increased crop yields, or decreased health hazards. Up until 1996, all pesticides were subjected to this cost-benefit analysis when they were registered.

However, when Congress passed the FQPA in 1996, analysis shifted from a cost-benefit to a health-based analysis. This changed the *tone* of the law, even though the EPA was already using many of the procedures mandated by the new law. It also fixed many discrepancies in the law that could have eventually caused some major problems for the agriculture industry.

Under FQPA, the benefits of a pesticide could only be used to sway a registration decision in specific situations or when certain conditions were met. Specifically, if the health effects of using a pesticide are less than the health effects of not using it, or if not using it would jeopardize the domestic food supply, then a pesticide's benefits can be used to influence registration decisions. An example of this could be if using a certain pesticide was the only presently available way to combat a certain pest on a certain crop (*e.g.*, blueberries), then the environmental cost of using that pesticide would be weighed against the possibility of having no blueberries.

One of the major *problems* corrected by FQPA was with the ***Delaney clause***, which was part of the FFDCA. This clause was added to the law in 1958 and basically stated that carcinogens could not be purposely added to food. Prior to passage of the FQPA, the Delaney clause prohibited the setting of pesticide residue tolerances for carcinogens in processed foods, even if a tolerance may already have existed for the raw agricultural commodity from which the processed food was derived. This system functioned adequately at first, but as time went on, scientific detection methods improved and more toxicological data were collected. Subsequently, analytical methods were developed that detected pesticide residues at lower and lower levels and research began to show that many of these residues were potentially carcinogenic (typically at higher levels). In order to handle this situation, an interpretation of the Delancy clause was developed that allowed for residue tolerances of carcinogens in processed foods when they posed negligible risk. However, in the early 1990s environmental groups sued EPA in Federal court and were successful in demanding strict enforcement of Delaney's zero carcinogen level on residue tolerances. Congress then passed the FQPA (after several years of debate), which created a residue tolerance procedure for food that is more compatible with the advances of science and the realities of agriculture.

The FQPA also requires the EPA to evaluate the pesticide tolerances for all pesticides using the new health-based risk analysis. All active ingredients that had already gone through the reregistration process based on the 1988 amendments to FIFRA will need to have their tolerances reevaluated using the new risk analysis scheme. There is also a requirement under FQPA to review periodically all registrations on a 15-year cycle, to ensure that accurate and complete data are maintained. This also resulted in extending indefinitely the requirement to pay annual registration fees.

The States

Each state has its own pesticide registration requirements. While this usually only means submitting copies of the EPA approvals, labels, formula, *etc.*, along with a fee, some states, particularly California, have a registration process that nearly duplicates the EPA's. In fact California's supporting data requirements are often more involved and difficult to maneuver than EPA's. It is standard to require product performance data with all pesticide registration applications in California (something the EPA requires only for certain types of products). Some states may not accept certain label claims, or may prohibit the sale of a product's active ingredient. This can be very important to know before marketing a product nationally.

Also regulated at the State level are products that are not pesticides under the Federal rules but are often associated with pesticides (*e.g.*, fertilizers, soil amendments, seeds, *etc.*) The labeling and formula requirements for these types of products are just as stringent as those for pesticides. Some states may even require supporting data for some label claims made on these products.

Finally, there are the additional costs for registering products with the states. While the annual registration maintenance fees required by the EPA under the reregistration program are very high (easily in the five-digit range for even a small formulator), also paying a fee to each state (remember, there are 50) for each product can easily add up to a significant amount of money.

Conclusion

Pesticides are a reality of our modern world. There probably isn't a household in the United States that doesn't have at least one pesticide in the garage, bathroom, or under the kitchen sink. Pesticides are used for sanitation and vector control, as well as insect and weed control in agricultural and residential locales. We can debate the value, the costs, and the benefits of different pesticide uses. Deciding what is safe, acceptable, or beneficial will continue to be debated in the scientific, regulatory and political arenas. FIFRA provides an adjustable process for evaluating and controlling these useful but potentially hazardous chemicals, while still protecting our environment.

Internet Resources

<http://www.epa.gov/pesticides> (Environmental Protection Agency. Office of Pesticide Programs, Homepage)

<http://www.epa.gov/pesticides/registrationkit> (Environmental Protection Agency. Office of Pesticide Programs. Pesticide Registration Kit)

<http://www.epa.gov/pesticides/regulating/index.htm/> (Environmental Protection Agency. Office of Pesticide Programs. Pesticides: Regulating Pesticides)

Index of the Law and Regulations

Major Legislation Amending Pesticide Regulation	Year
Federal Environmental Pesticide Control Act	1972
Federal Insecticide, Fungicide and Rodenticide Act (FIFRA)	1975
Federal Pesticide Act	1978
FIFRA Amendments of 1988	1988
Food Quality Protection Act	1996

7 USC §§ 136 *et seq.*	Federal Insecticide, Fungicide, and Rodenticide Act as Amended by the Food Quality Protection Act of 1996 (PL 104-170, Enacted August 3, 1996)
Section 1	Short title and table of contents
Section 2	Definitions
Section 3	Registration of pesticides
Section 4	Reregistration of registered pesticides
Section 5	Experimental use permits
Section 6	Administrative review; suspension
Section 7	Registration of establishments
Section 8	Books and records
Section 9	Inspection of establishments, *etc.*
Section 10	Protection of trade secrets and other information
Section 11	Use of restricted use pesticides; applicators
Section 12	Unlawful acts
Section 13	Stop sale, use, removal, and seizure
Section 14	Penalties
Section 15	Indemnities
Section 16	Administrative procedure; judicial review
Section 17	Imports and exports
Section 18	Exemption of Federal and State agencies
Section 19	Storage, disposal, transportation, and recall
Section 20	Research and monitoring
Section 21	Solicitation of comments; notice of public hearings
Section 22	Delegation and cooperation
Section 23	State cooperation, aid, and training
Section 24	Authority of States
Section 25	Authority of Administrator
Section 26	State primary enforcement responsibility
Section 27	Failure by the State to assure enforcement of State pesticide use regulations
Section 28	Identification of pests; cooperation with Department of Agriculture's program
Section 29	Annual report
Section 30	Severability
Section 31	Authorization for appropriations
Section 32	Department of Agriculture minor use program
Section 33	Severability
Section 34	Authorization for appropriations

40 CFR Part	Subchapter E–Pesticide Programs
152	Pesticide registration and classification procedures
153	Registration policies and Interpretations
154	Special review procedures
155	Registration standards
156	Labeling requirements for pesticides and devices
157	Packaging requirements for pesticides and devices
158	Data requirements for registration
159	Statements of policies and interpretations
160	Good laboratory practice standards
162	State registration of pesticide products
163	Certification of usefulness of pesticide chemicals
164	Rules of practice governing hearings, under FIFRA, arising from refusals to register, cancellations of registrations, changes of classifications, suspensions of registrations and other hearing called pursuant to Section 6 of the Act
166	Exemption of Federal and State agencies for use of pesticides under emergency conditions
167	Registration of pesticide and active ingredient producing Establishments, submission of pesticide reports
168	Statements of enforcement policies and interpretations
169	Books and records of pesticide production and distribution
170	Worker protection standard
171	Certification of pesticide applicators
172	Experimental use permits
173	Procedures governing the rescission of State primary enforcement responsibility for pesticide use violations
177	Issuance of food additive regulations
178	Objections and requests for hearing
179	Formal evidentiary public hearing
180	Tolerances and exemptions from tolerances for pesticide chemicals in food
185	Tolerances for pesticides in food
186	Pesticides in animal feed

Keith Trombley is an Industrial Hygienist on staff with the University of Michigan in Ann Arbor, in the University's Department of Occupational Safety and Environmental Health (OSEH). Mr. Trombley has a bachelor's degree in geology from Eastern Michigan University and has been working in the hazardous materials management, occupational safety, and environmental health fields for more than 17 years, in consulting, manufacturing, and service industries. Keith is a Certified Hazardous Material Manager, Certified Industrial Hygienist, and Certified Safety Professional.

CHAPTER 27

Radiation Safety Principles

George D. Mosho, CHMM

Introduction

Radioactive material is a hazardous material. Although obvious, that had to be stated. With that in mind, radioactive material can be understood and safely managed as other hazardous materials are managed.

This chapter presents some basic information in the field of radiation safety, which is commonly known as *health physics*. As basic information, it is given as a primer in radiation safety. It is not the intent to belabor the reader with details concerning some topics such as nuclear theory, biological effects of radiation, radiation-producing devices, regulations, *etc.* However, for the sake of completeness, some of these topics are briefly covered in this chapter. There are many books and documents that have been written that treat those and other topics with the attention they deserve. A bibliography and list of professional organizations are supplied at the end of the chapter for additional information. Some common terms in the field of radiation safety are defined in the Glossary at the end of the book. Glossary words found in the text are ***bold italicized***. Specific questions concerning radiation safety, radioactive materials, and radiation-producing devices should be addressed to the governmental agency that has regulatory jurisdiction for such matters in your state.

ALARA

Radiation is the emission and propagation of energy in the form of particles and waves through space. Radiation can be classified as either ionizing radiation (alpha particles, beta particles, gamma rays, x-rays, neutrons, high-speed electrons, high-speed protons, and other particles capable of producing ions) or nonionizing radiation (sound, radio, microwaves, or visible, infrared, and ultraviolet light).

When radiation or radioactive material is to be incorporated as part of a process or an end product, a basic question should be asked: "Does the *benefit* outweigh the *risk*?" If it does not, the *exposure* (of people and the environment) is unnecessary and should not occur. If, however, the benefit does outweigh the risk, then a review should follow to investigate any potential change in the operation or product that could further minimize that risk while considering the impact such changes may have on the total cost, or the efficacy of the operation, or the quality of the product. This process is a cornerstone of radiation safety programs. It is commonly known as *ALARA*.

ALARA is an acronym for *As Low As Reasonably Achievable*. The goal of radiation protection is to reduce and maintain all necessary exposures (internal and external) to radiation to ALARA levels. Planning and hazard reviews as well as proactive actions are needed for successful implementation. The design of workplaces, equipment, process systems, and procedures needs to be done by proactively integrating ALARA. This proactive approach is also evident in training programs emphasizing ALARA techniques as daily work habits. These habits are better described in the following section on radiation protection principles. Finally, on-the-job surveillance and monitoring for radiological exposure and contamination sources are imperative to adequately define actual workplace conditions and the effectiveness of prejob ALARA engineering.

Obviously, the ALARA process has a cost. The cost may be time, equipment, training, process redesign and reengineering, new materials, or some other parameter. The principal determination of the reasonable and appropriate cost for ALARA is based upon the level of accepted risk. There may also be regulatory drivers stating or inferring these acceptable risk levels. Whatever the case, these elements define ALARA at a workplace or facility.

Radiation Protection Principles

As stated earlier in the introduction, radioactive material is a hazardous material. To better express that statement, Table 1 was extracted from a 1996 *Health Physics* journal article. In reviewing these 10 principles or commandments, it is obvious to anyone who works with hazardous materials and risk management that this list is very applicable to almost all hazardous materials.

"Time, distance, and shielding" had long been the mantra for radiation protection. It is easy to acknowledge that the reduction of time (#1) spent at or near a radiation source would effect a reduction in exposure from that source. It is also easy to understand that the reduction of the concentration (#3) or of the size (#4) of the radiation source or the substitution of a nonradioactive material for the source or adoption of an entirely different process (#9) would consequently reduce or eliminate the exposure. Keeping the material contained (#5) and off your body (#6), as well as quickly and effectively decontaminating personnel who have been contaminated (#7), are also important.

Another time-related exposure-reduction method may be available when dealing with short-lived radionuclides. All radionuclides decay exponentially. *Radioactive decay* describes the process where an energetically unstable atom transforms itself to a more energetically favorable, or stable, state. The unstable atom can emit ionizing radiation in order to become more stable. This atom is said to be *radioactive*, and the process of change is called *radioactive decay*.

Each radionuclide decays at a different rate. The term *half-life* describes the time required to deplete the radioactive source to ½ of its original activity. Radionuclide half-lives range from extremely small fractions of a second to hundreds of thousands of years. It may be possible, if the

Table 1. Principles and Commandments of Radiation Protection

	Principle	Commandment (familiar)	Commandment (technical)
1.	Time	Hurry (but don't be hasty).	Minimize exposure/intake time.
2.	Distance	Stay away from it.	Maximize distance; stay upwind.
3.	Dispersal	Disperse it and dilute it.	Minimize concentration, maximize dilution.
4.	Source Reduction	Use as little as possible.	Minimize production and use of radiation and radioactive material.
5.	Source Barrier	Keep it in.	Maximize absorption (shield); minimize release (contain and confine it).
6.	Personal Barrier	Keep it out.	Minimize entry into the body of radiation and radioactive materials.
7.	Decorporation (Internal and Surface Irradiation only)	Get it out of you and off of you.	Maximize removal or blocking of materials from the body (after intake or skin contamination).
8.	Effect Mitigation	Limit the damage.	Optimize exposure over time and among persons; scavenge free radicals; induce repair.
9.	Optimal Technology	Choose the best technology.	Optimize risk-benefit-cost figure.
10.	Limitation of Other Exposures	Don't compound risks (don't smoke).	Minimize exposures to other agents that may work in concert with radiation (*e.g.*, genotoxic agents or those that may cause initiation, promotion, or progression of tumors).

(Strom 1996) Reprinted from the journal *Health Physics* with permission from the Health Physics Society.

material is one that quickly decays, to wait some length of time before doing the needed task. This would also decrease the overall potential exposure. This relationship of radioactivity and time is described by the following equation:

$$A = A_o \, e^{-\ln 2 \, (t/T)} \tag{1}$$

where:

A = Activity remaining at time = t
A_o = Activity at time = 0
t = Elapsed time
T = Half-life of the radioisotope

Examples are given below that better depict the relationship of specific radionuclides and their activity over time. The activity of a 15 mCi ^{137}Cs source with a 30-year half-life would decrease by about 11 percent to 13.5 mCi after 5 years:

$$
\begin{aligned}
A_o &= 15 \text{ mCi} \\
t &= 5 \text{ y} \\
T &= 30.0 \text{ y } [^{137}\text{Cs}]
\end{aligned}
\tag{2}
$$

Therefore:

$$A = 15e^{-\ln 2 \, (5/30)} = 13.5 \text{ mCi } ^{137}\text{Cs}$$

However, the activity of a 15 mCi ^{60}Co source would decrease to about 7.8 mCi (about 52 percent of the initial amount) afer the same 5-year period:

$$
\begin{aligned}
A_o &= 15 \text{ mCi} \\
t &= 5 \text{ y} \\
T &= 5.26 \text{ y } [^{60}\text{Co}]
\end{aligned}
\tag{3}
$$

Therefore:

$$A = 15e^{-\ln 2 \, (5/5.26)} = {\sim}7.8 \text{ mCi } ^{60}\text{Co}$$

The radioactive decay process can be somewhat more complicated. Often, when a radionuclide decays, it produces one or more *daughter products* that are radioactive too. The daughters and any other subsequent progeny are also subject to the decay process until the result is a stable daughter product. These radioactive progeny may be of greater significance than the original parent.

In the ^{137}Cs example, ^{137m}Ba is produced and at the end of five years and is almost (about 97 percent) in equilibrium or the same value as the remaining ^{137}Cs. The gamma emissions (662 keV) that are used as an identifier for ^{137}Cs are actually emitted from the decay of the daughter ^{137m}Ba. (Note: ^{137m}Ba is ^{137}Ba in a metastable state. This means that final stability will be achieved after the release of excess energy in the form of a photon or gamma ray [662 keV].) Therefore, it is important to note and appreciate the production, presence and significance of these *daughter products* in the decay series of many radioisotopes.

Two other principles of radiation protection involve biological mechanisms:

- Permit the body to heal itself between exposures, and medically assist in that repair if necessary (#8).

- Limit or remove other causal factors (#10) that may work as catalysts or enhancers for the undesired effect such as cancer.

Probably one of the most effective ways to minimize exposure is to maintain a distance from the source. For illustration purposes, assume the source is a *point*. The radiation field about a point source is spherical in shape, similar to light from a light bulb, and therefore follows what is called the *inverse square law*. This physical law is expressed by the formula:

$$I_2 = I_1 (d_1^2/d_2^2) \tag{4}$$

where:

I_1 = Intensity of radiation (exposure rate) at position #1
I_2 = Intensity of radiation (exposure rate) at position #2
d_1 = Distance position #1 is from source
d_2 = Distance position #2 is from source

As an example, the exposure at 2 meters from a 120 mR/h point source, decreases to 30 mR/h when the distance is increased to 4 meters:

I_1 = 120 mR/h   (5)
d_1 = 2 m from the source
d_2 = 4 m from the source

Therefore:

I_2 = 30 mR/h

The importance of this and the other radiation protection principles cannot be overemphasized. They are simple, straightforward, generally easy to employ, and very effective.

Operational Radiation Safety Program

The cornerstone of radiation safety is an effective program. Essential elements in such a program are presented in the following list.

Operational Radiation Safety Program Elements. (In no particular order)

- Establish a radiation safety organization.

- Obtain and maintain a valid radioactive material license or other such documentation of authorization.

- Construct and maintain an inventory of radioactive material sources, or radiation-producing devices.

- Identify responsible users.

- Establish an exposure (external and internal, if needed) tracking and recording program, including external dosimetry and bioassay services.

- Establish an ALARA program as well as a job safety or hazard analysis program to review proposed, current, and completed jobs or tasks with respect to personnel exposure to hazards.

- Develop, institute, and maintain procedures for the purchase, use, transfer, and disposal of radioactive material sources or radiation-producing devices, and emergency response.

- Institute a surveillance and monitoring program using qualified individuals with appropriate instrumentation.

- Maintain pertinent records of surveillance and monitoring activities, source inventory and instrument calibration.

- Perform self-assessments of the radiation safety program elements for quality assurance.

There is much that can be said about each program element listed. As a matter of regulatory compliance, usually these elements are specified further by the governmental agency that has jurisdiction over the use of sources of ionizing radiation.

The size of a radiation safety organization usually is not critical. It can be as small as one *(e.g.,* a dentist) or many people *(e.g.* Argonne National Laboratory has 14 health physicists; 4 chief technicians; and 34 technicians, who are sometimes referred to as radiation technologists). What are important are the qualifications (both knowledge and experience) of the individuals, and the direct support of management in executing their respective duties.

Radiation Safety Training. As implied previously, these radiation safety personnel and the responsible users require training appropriate to their needs. Pertinent topics for such training are listed below (*Note: The depth and detail of these topics are dependent on the specific responsibilities of the individual as well as the scope of work performed with radioactive materials and radiation-producing devices*):

- Review of basic mathematics and science

- Theory of radioactivity

- Sources of radiation

- Interaction of radiation with matter

- Biological effects of ionizing radiation

- Radiation units

- Radiation protection standards and regulations

- Dose assessment

- Radiation detector theory

- Contamination control

- Exposure (external and internal) control

- Waste management

- Emergency response actions

Radiation Theory Overview

This section is a very simple overview of some of the information that would be presented in a radiation safety training program.

Types of Radiation. *Nuclear radiation* is naturally a part of all that is around us and within us. Radiation sources can be either natural (terrestrial and extraterrestrial) or manmade. The radiation emitted by these sources can be any one or a combination of forms of electromagnetic energy: gamma, and x-rays, and particles: alpha, beta, and neutron.

Gamma (γ) rays, x-rays, and *neutrons* are highly energetic and have the capability to cause ionization by penetrating the human body and other materials. Many diagnostic instruments such as moisture density gauges, industrial radiography cameras, and medical x-ray units utilize this feature to provide *in situ* analyses of various materials. Since these types of radiation can penetrate the human body, they are considered as external hazards. That is, they have the potential to harm an exposed individual from outside the body. Shielding with high-Z materials (*i.e.,* lead, steel, *etc.*) for both γ and x-rays can effectively reduce exposure rates. However, similar shielding for neutrons would not be as effective. Fairly large quantities of hydrogenous material (*i.e.,* water, concrete, plastic, *etc.*) are more appropriate to achieve significant attenuation of neutrons.

Alpha (α) particles are rather large on the atomic scale. Each α particle consists of two protons and two neutrons. The mass and electric charge of such a particle precludes it passing through the dead layer of skin on the outside of the human body. These particles can travel about 3 cm in air and <0.003 cm in human skin tissue. When the particle strikes the dead layer of human skin, its energy is transferred to the tissue, causing ionization in the dead skin. Therefore, α particles are not an external hazard. However, if they are inhaled, ingested, or they enter the body in some other manner, they can be deposited directly against sensitive body tissues. These particles have a significant potential for harm within the body and are listed as an internal hazard. A single sheet of paper can effectively stop α radiation. Efforts should be taken to minimize the inhalation and ingestion pathways when working with α particulate radiation.

Beta (β) *particles* are essentially electrons. This type of particulate radiation can travel to a maximum distance of roughly 5 m in air and 1.5 cm in body tissue. It is considered to be both an internal and external hazard to the body. Although β radiation is more penetrating than α radiation, adequate shielding can generally be accomplished by using plastic, cardboard, wood, or heavy clothing. High-Z materials should not be used as shielding due to the potential to produce secondary radiations from the interaction of the β radiation with those types of materials.

Interaction of Radiation with Matter. What all these types of radiation have in common is that they can interact with atoms causing a loss of electrons and resulting in the creation of ions. In short, they are *ionizing radiation*. Nonionizing radiation cannot do this. Examples of nonionizing radiation include microwave, laser, and radio wave. When the material that ionizing radiation interacts with is human tissue, damage to the tissue can occur.

Many years ago, as a conservative approach to radiation exposure, an assumption was formed from a dose-response model. That model (the Linear No Threshold Hypothesis) depicted that any exposure to radiation incurred a deleterious effect. This assumption did not take into account the duration of the exposure or time between exposures, the repair mechanisms of the human body, and many other parameters. Today, this model is highly debated by radiation safety professionals but is still used as the standard model for radiation protection purposes.

The effect that radiation has on any material is determined by the *dose*. Radiation dose is simply the quantity of radiation energy deposited in a material. There are several additional descriptive terms used in radiation protection which provide precise information on how the dose was deposited, the method used to calculate the dose, and how the radiation energy deposited in tissue will affect humans.

Absorbed dose is the amount of energy deposited in any material by ionizing radiation. The unit of absorbed dose, the rad, is a measure of energy absorbed per gram of material. The unit used in countries other than the US is the *gray*. One gray equals 100 rad.

The concept of *equivalent dose* involves the impact that different types of radiation have on humans. Not all types of radiation produce the same effect in humans. The equivalent dose takes into account the type of radiation and the absorbed dose. For example, when considering beta, x-ray, and gamma ray radiation, the equivalent dose (expressed in rems) is equal to the absorbed dose (expressed in rads). For alpha radiation, the equivalent dose is assumed to be 20 times the absorbed dose.

With that in mind, dose can be received from chronic and/or acute *exposures* to radiation. An *acute exposure* is one where a large exposure (high exposure rate) is received over a very short period of time, usually minutes or seconds. A *chronic exposure* is a long term or possibly constant exposure to low-level radiation. Cell repair mechanisms have demonstrated that cumulative doses to radiation resulting from chronic exposures have less impact than similar doses from acute exposures.

The effect of radiation on the human body can be somatic and/or genetic. The term *somatic* relates to the person exposed. These somatic effects may be early or late depending upon when the effect is evident. *Early effects* occur within hours or days of an acute exposure. Examples of early effects are erythema (reddening of the skin), loss of hair, and, in extreme cases, death. *Late effects* appear many years, possibly 20 or 30, after an acute exposure. Cancer induction is an example of a late effect. Another form of somatic effect is known as teratogenic effects. Children *in utero* who are exposed to radiation may develop and exhibit certain birth defects. Radiation-damaged DNA may cause genetic effects. Such an effect may become evident in future progeny.

Radiation Units. Throughout the world, most countries have adopted radiation units defined by the International System of Units (SI). However, despite efforts to change to SI in the United States, these units seem to be used routinely only in transportation documentation, as prescribed by the United States (US) Department of Transportation. A comparison of the SI and US systems of units is presented in Table 2.

In discussing data with radiation control technicians (RCTs) or health physics technicians (HP Techs), often the term *dose* is incorrectly used interchangeably for *exposure*. Most often, radiation data are expressed as *rates*. Portable survey meters display values in terms such as

Table 2. Radiation Unit Comparison

Type	US	SI	US → SI Multiply by
Activity	curie (Ci)	becquerel (Bq)	3.7 E+10
Absorbed Dose	rad (r)	gray (Gy)	1.0 E-02
Effective Dose Equivalent	rem (rem)	sievert (Sv)	1.0 E-02
Exposure	roentgen (R)	coulomb per kilogram (C/kg)	2.58 E-04

counts per minute (cpm), *disintegrations per minute* (dpm), and *µR/h* or *mR/h*. Contamination measurements are denoted for the type of radiation and for a specific area (*i.e.*, 320 dpm α/100 cm²) that is usually the active area of the survey probe or, if a smear, the area smeared for counting.

Radiation Detection. The whole issue of radiation safety would be irrelevant if there was no practical way to detect radiation. Fortunately, that is not the case. In fact, detecting low-level radiation is usually easier than detecting many hazardous materials. Detectors used routinely by RCTs or HP Techs are either portable or nonportable equipment. Portable detectors or survey meters are designed for a specific purpose such as contamination or exposure monitoring, but not both. They are also specific to the type of radiation that they can detect. For example, a *rem ball* is a neutron-only detector; a ZnS scintillator detects exclusively α contamination; whereas a *pancake* Geiger-Mueller (G-M) is good for β-γ contamination, and so on. Sorry, no magic box yet that can detect, discriminate, and quantify all types of ionizing radiation.

To measure the dose an individual may actually receive from penetrating radiation, there are dosimeters. One of the first discoveries about the effect of radiation was that certain radiations (γ and x-rays) caused fogging on photographic film. This was later advantageously transformed into a film badge with various attenuators to determine the energies of the radiation affecting the film. This type of badge is still used today; however, most facilities have upgraded to a thermo-luminescent dosimeter (TLD). This badge is composed of one or more crystal chips with attenuators. These dosimeters are much better than the film and they are reusable after readout and annealing and therefore more cost-effective in the long run. There are other much newer products such as optically stimulated luminescent badges that are now replacing TLDs. Whether TLD, film or other such device, the badge is worn on the chest to measure

Table 3. Portable Gamma Exposure Detectors

Instrument (Example types)	Detector Description	Measurement Units
"µR meters" Eberline PRM-3; Ludlum 19	Scintillator (internal) NaI 1" x 1"	µR/h
Bicron Microrem	Scintillator (internal) Loaded plastic 1" x 1"	µrem/h
Eberline RO-20, RO-2, RO-2A, PIC-6; Victoreen 450, 450P	Ionization Chamber (internal)	mR/h; R/h
Teletectors, Ludlum 77-3, Eberline 6112B; Xetec 302-B	Geiger-Mueller (G-M) energy compensated	mR/h; R/h

Table 4. Portable Surface Contamination Detectors

Instrument (Example types)	Detector Description	Measurement Units	Radiation Type
NE Technology, Ltd. Electra	Dual scintillator, 100 cm^2 sampling area	cpm; dpm	α and β
Eberline PAC4G-3	Gas proportional, 61 cm^2 sampling area	cpm	α
Ratemeter with Eberline HP-260, HP-210 (T, L; AL); Ludlum Model 44-9	Geiger-Mueller (G-M) "pancake probe" 4.4 cm diameter window	cpm	β-γ
Ratemeter with Eberline AC-3; Ludlum Model 43-5	ZnS 59 cm^2 sampling area	cpm	α
Ludlum Model 3	Air proportional, 50 cm^2 sampling area	cpm	α

the quantity of dose received by the *whole body*. Extremity badges for hands, feet, head, *etc.* may be important in operations where exposure fields are not uniform. In addition, self-reading dosimeters (SRDs) may be used to supplement the *whole body* badge by giving the worker a method to check on his/her exposure during the course of a job.

There are also several types of portable detectors that can be readily used in the field for radiation detection and quantification. There are detectors for contamination that detect either α, β, or β-γ, and some that can do both α and β. Exposure rate meters are designed specifically for x-rays, γ rays, and fast and thermal neutrons. Special detectors exist to perform tasks such as floor monitoring, *in situ* γ spectroscopy, and ^{3}H (tritium) vapor detection. Some of the more common detectors are listed in Tables 3 and 4.

Finally, there are some counting systems that, due to the method of detection used or the precision needed in the resultant data, are nonportable. A few of the typical types of counters are the gross α–β counting system, spectroscopy (α, β, or γ) system, personnel contamination monitors, and continuous air monitors (CAMs).

Radiation Protection Planning

The optimal way to ensure that ALARA, radiation protection principles, and good radiation safety practices, are a routine way of business is by getting in at the work or facility planning stage. Many facilities use a radiation work permit (RWP) process to do just that. The permit process predicates having all interested parties sit down and think the job through before actually doing it. Previous radiation survey data and discussion of the task to be performed help the radiation safety personnel (probably a health physicist) to visualize the job and estimate potential dose received for doing that job. A workplace hazard mitigation plan is developed using engineering techniques and personnel protective equipment if necessary. Considerable thought is placed upon this topic. Sometimes it is found that protecting an individual from one hazard causes him/her to be at greater risk from another hazard (*e.g.*, poly-coated coveralls for radiation protection purposes *vs.* heat stress caused by their use). Once again, does the benefit outweigh the risk? The plan is noted formally in the RWP and the permit is read and signed off by all job participants. After the work has been completed, a review of the lessons learned and the actual dose (depicted from self-reading dosimeters) accumulated during the job aid in future training, and in job planning.

Summary

Despite what reservations one may have had initially concerning radiation, radioactive material and radiation are really very similar to other hazardous materials. The basic philosophies used to minimize exposure (time, distance, concentration, size, optimal technology, containment, personal protection, and decontamination) are the same. Both radioactive and other hazardous materials need to be treated with the appropriate respect, understanding, and care.

Bibliography

American Society for Testing and Materials. "Standard for the Use of the International System of Units (SI): The Modern Metric System." IEEE-ASTM–SI–10; IEEE/ASTM SI–10. West Conshocken, PA: ASTM, 1999.

Cember, H. *Introduction to Health Physics*, 3rd ed. Elmsford, NY: Pergamon Press, 1996.

Eisenbud, M. and T. F. Gesell. *Environmental Radioactivity from Natural, Industrial, and Military Sources*, 4th ed. San Diego, CA: Academic Press, 1997.

Gollnick, D. A. *Basic Radiation Protection Technology*, 4th ed. Altadena, CA: Pacific Radiation Corporation, 2000.

Martin, J. E. and C. Lee. *Principles of Radiological Health and Safety*. Hoboken, NJ: John Wiley and Sons, Inc., 2003.

Shapiro, J. *Radiation Protection. A Guide for Scientists, Regulators and Physicians*, 4th ed. Cambridge, MA: Harvard University Press, 2002.

Shleien, B. *The Health Physics and Radiological Health Handbook*. 3rd ed. Baltimore, MD: Lippincott, Williams & Wilkins, 1998.

Strom, D. J. "Ten Principles and Ten Commandments of Radiation Protection." Rev. 8/6/96. *Health Physics*. Vol. (70) No. (3): pp. 388-393, 1996.

Turner, J. E. *Atoms, Radiation, And Radiation Protection*, 2nd ed. New York, NY: John Wiley and Sons, Inc., 1995.

Internet Resources

<http://www.ans.org/> (American Nuclear Society. Homepage)

<http://www.crcpd.org/> (Conference of Radiation Control Program Directors, Inc. Homepage)

<http://www.hps.org/> (Health Physics Society. Homepage)

<http://www.nrc.gov> (US Nuclear Regulatory Commission. Homepage)

<http://www.nrrpt.org/> (National Registry of Radiation Protection Technologists. Homepage)

<http://www.orau.org/ptp/infores.htm> (Oak Ridge Associated Universities. Professional Training Program. Health Physics Resources)

<http://www.orau.gov/reacts/> (Oak Ridge Associated Universities. Radiation Emergency Assistance Center/Training Site [REAC/TS])

<http://www.umich.edu/~radinfo/> (Radiation and Health Physics Homepage)

George D. Mosho is a senior health physicist at Argonne National Laboratory, near Chicago. He received a BS in Physics at The Citadel: The Military College of South Carolina (1977), and an MS in Radiological Health at the University of Pittsburgh (1985). Previous assignments included Team Captain for the US Department of Energy (DOE) Radiological Assistance Program (RAP) Team and radiological instructor for the US National Domestic Preparedness Program (Weapons of Mass Destruction) NBC Technician and Awareness Courses. He has spent more than 20 years in radiological characterization, decontamination, and decommissioning, and emergency response. He also serves as a Hazmat Officer (Lieutenant) for the Hazmat Division of the Will County Emergency Management Agency (WEMA), in Joliet, IL;, a member of the Health Physics Society's Homeland Security First Response subcommittee; the Illinois (IL) Association of Hazardous Materials Response Techncians and Specialists; and an emergency communicator and official emergency radio station for the Amateur Radio Relay League (ARRL). Mr. Mosho has authored/co-authored several technical reports on radiological characterization and decontamination and decommissioning activities. He has also co-authored and presented papers and training on personnel communication improvements for emergency responders.

CHAPTER 28

Lead

Chris Gunther, CHMM

Background

Lead was considered to be one of the seven metals in antiquity, partially because of an inherent property to bond well with many different types of substrates. Archeologists have found lead-based pigments on buildings that were constructed 5,000 years ago. It is therefore not difficult to understand why lead-based pigments have been used as an additive in paint for centuries.

In the 18th century, however, harmful health effects from exposure to lead paint were noticed. In 1786, Benjamin Franklin wrote a letter to a friend named Benjamin Vaughn. In the letter, Mr. Franklin discussed in some detail his observations regarding "the mischievous effects of lead." The effects outlined in the letter included poisonings, partial paralysis, and severe gastric disorders. The observations included secondhand information that Mr. Franklin collected from conversations with knowledgeable people of his day, as well as from direct personal experience. Mr. Franklin ended his letter by writing a statement that has unfortunately been validated in recent times:

> This, my dear friend, is all I am at present to recollect on the Subject. You will see by it, that the Opinion of this mischievous Effect from Lead, is at least above Sixty Years old; and you will observe with concern how long a useful Truth may be known, and exist, before it is generally receiv'd and practis'd on.

In the twentieth century, lead compounds, such as lead chromate and lead carbonate, have been used widely as pigments in paint and, to a lesser extent, in varnishes and primers. Although the use of lead, particularly on interior surfaces, has declined over the years, most housing units constructed before 1980 have some lead-based paint. Although the paint can be found anywhere in a building, it was used primarily on areas of high impact, friction, or humidity.

Presently, the principal use of lead is in the manufacturing of electrical storage batteries, and as solder in electronics. Other current uses include ammunition, chemicals, and sinkers for fishing. The use of lead as a paint additive and gasoline additive has been greatly reduced (if not eliminated) in the United States, along with lead solder and piping. Unfortunately, the residual effects from past uses are still present.

Routes of Exposure and Health Effects

Although lead occurs naturally in small quantities in the earth's crust, the greatest exposure to the metal stems from manmade processes and products. Lead serves no useful purpose in the body; rather, it is a poison that alters or hinders vital biological reactions. Some of the areas in the body that are impacted by the presence of lead include the brain and central nervous system, kidneys, heart, bones, and liver.

The major sources of lead poisoning in children are surface dust and soil that have been contaminated by deteriorated lead paint. The primary routes of exposure among children are through ingestion (from hand-to-mouth activity), inhalation of the dust, and by drinking water that has passed through plumbing that contains lead solder or brass valves.

In construction and general industry, the primary routes of exposure are still inhalation and ingestion. However, inhalation of lead dust and fumes is more common among workers in these areas than is ingestion. For example, many welders have been lead-poisoned by welding steel containing lead as a primer coat.

Lead is absorbed through the stomach in the same manner as the vital metals (calcium, zinc, iron, chromium, boron, etc.). The absorption of lead into the blood stream appears to be diet-related. The higher the fat content in a person's diet, the higher the rate of lead absorption appears to be. A healthy diet (rich in protein and metals such as calcium, zinc, iron, etc.) tends to decrease the absorption rate of lead.

Exposure to high concentrations of lead can cause retardation, convulsions, coma, and death. Children (especially those under the age of six) are especially vulnerable to lead because of their metabolism, developing nervous systems, and their tendency to absorb nutrients into developing bones and muscles. Even low levels of lead consistently absorbed into a child's body during childhood have been known to slow the child's development. This retarded development can also lead to learning and behavioral problems.

Symptoms of lead poisoning are not readily observed because they are not specific. The most common short-term symptoms are abdominal pain, headaches, constipation, and aches in the joints. Unfortunately, all of these symptoms can be attributed to causes other than lead poisoning, such as the common cold or influenza. The main difference, however, is that these *flu-like* symptoms don't subside in the same manner as a real flu. Instead, the symptoms linger or even become worse if the poisoning continues.

If the poisoning continues over time, then the lead will accumulate in the body, particularly in the bone structure. Even if the exposure to lead is suddenly halted, the detrimental effects of the metal can linger for months afterwards. In some conditions, such as pregnancy or aging, the effects of lead poisoning can recur as bone tissue breaks down and releases the absorbed lead into the bloodstream.

Over the past 20 years, the Centers for Disease Control and Prevention (CDC) has responded to the increasing information about the effects of lead poisoning in children by progressively lowering the blood lead level that requires medical intervention. The current goal is for all children to have lead levels below 10 micrograms per deciliter of blood (μg/dl).

The present level of concern (10 μg/dl) is far above the *natural background* of the blood level of people living in remote areas of the world. The fatal dose for a young child is 100–150 µg/dl, or roughly 10–15 times the level of concern.

Regulations

Regulatory Overview

Today, lead typically is present in small detectable quantities in paints that are for sale both commercially and publicly. In 1976, the Lead-Based Paint Poisoning Prevention Act (LBPPPA) established an upper limit of lead in paint at 600 ppm (.06%). In 1977, the Consumer Product Safety Commission (CPSC) adopted this standard for most residential and commercially available paints, with the intent of reducing lead exposures in facilities where children may be present. However, CPSC has no jurisdiction over worker exposure, and the Occupational Safety and Health Administration (OSHA) does not recognize this arbitrary limit. Instead, OSHA considers any paint with detectable levels of lead to pose a potential exposure to employees who are involved in *trigger tasks*. OSHA interprets a ***trigger task*** as one that may result in occupational exposures above the permissible exposure limit for lead (50 µg/m^3). These tasks include

- Sanding
- Scraping
- Manual demolition
- Heat gun removal
- Spray painting
- Abrasive blasting
- Torch burning
- Welding
- Cutting
- Tool cleaning

The OSHA permissible exposure limit is based upon airborne concentrations of lead dust, not the lead content of the painted surface impacted by an employee. In situations where paint with detectable lead levels is expected to be disturbed, all OSHA worker protection measures and work practices apply during trigger tasks. Since air concentrations of disturbed lead dust or fumes are usually unknown, then the employer is required to protect affected workers with respiratory and body protection, along with engineering controls to control the migration of the lead aerosols.

The presence of lead must be established by recognized sampling protocols and methods of analysis. The most common analytical methods include atomic absorption spectrometry (AAS), inductively coupled plasma-atomic emission spectroscopy (ICP-AES), or x-ray fluorescence analysis (XRF). The use of over-the-counter colorimetric tests is not a valid method for determining the presence of lead in paint.

In addition, the Department of Housing and Urban Development (HUD) has adopted several Environmental Protection Agency (EPA) guidelines for abating lead hazards, and has defined inspection protocols and risk assessment methodologies.

On the Federal level, the following documents regulate lead exposure:

- 29 CFR 1910.1025 (OSHA)
- 29 CFR 1926.62 (OSHA)
- 40 CFR 745 (EPA)
- 40 CFR 50 (EPA)
- 40 CFR 122 (EPA)
- 40 CFR 261 (EPA)
- *Guidelines for the Evaluation and Control of Lead-Based Paint Hazards in Housing* (HUD)

Lead Standard for General Industry

29 CFR 1910.1025. The general industry standard does not apply to the construction industry, even though this standard shares many aspects of the construction industry standard. For example:

- The regulation allows an airborne action level (AL) for lead concentration of 30 µg/m^3 as an 8–hour time-weighted average (TWA).

- The regulation allows an airborne permissible exposure limit (PEL) for lead concentration of 50 µg/m^3 as an 8–hour TWA.

- The regulation requires biological monitoring at all times and medical removal if blood lead becomes too elevated (>50 µg/dl).

- The regulation requires the employer to institute a medical monitoring program for all employees exposed above the AL for more than 30 days per year. The employer must also make available the results of the blood testing to the employees.

Lead Standard in the Construction Industry

29 CFR 1926.62. The construction industry standard applies to construction-related activities including demolition, removal, encapsulation, alteration, transportation, storage, and disposal of lead (metallic lead, inorganic lead compounds, and organic lead soaps). The standard also establishes maximum limits of airborne exposure to lead for all covered workers, including a PEL of 50 $\mu g/m^3$ (TWA) and an AL of 30 $\mu g/m^3$ (TWA).

If the employee's initial exposure to lead is at or above the action level, the employer must implement a site-specific lead compliance manual, and collect samples that represent the *regular daily exposure* of a full work shift, one sample for each shift. In addition, a full medical examination with extensive testing must be available for each employee who has been subject to exposure at or above the action level more than 30 days per year.

The employer must notify all affected employees of the examination and test results within five days of receiving the medical results. If the employee has a final medical determination or detected medical condition that places him/her at increased risk of material impairment from exposure to lead, the employee must be temporarily removed from exposure, with medical removal benefits still in effect. An employee whose blood lead level exceeds 50 $\mu g/dl$ is subject to removal if the employer has no other work under the AL to offer. The employee(s) can return to the job when: (1) two consecutive blood sampling tests indicate a blood level of lead below 40 $\mu g/dl$, and (2) a subsequent medical examination indicates that there is no longer a detectable medical condition that increases risks to health from lead exposure. All medical removals and returns are subject to physician review.

Lead; Requirements for Lead-Based Paint Activities in Target Housing and Child-Occupied Facilities; Final Rule

40 CFR 745. This document became effective on August 29, 1996, and was written to ensure that

- Individuals who conduct activities involving lead-based paint in target housing and child-occupied facilities are properly trained and certified

- Accredited training programs provide instruction in these activities

- These activities are conducted according to reliable, effective, and safe work practices, as presented in *The HUD Guidelines for the Evaluation and Control of Lead-Based Paint Hazards in Housing*

The regulation seeks to ensure that a trained and qualified workforce is available to identify and address the hazards associated with lead-based paint and to protect the public from exposure to these hazards.

Air Programs

40 CFR 50. The portions of the *Code of Federal Regulations* that address the Clean Air Act can be found in 40 CFR Subchapter C, "Air Programs," encompassing Parts 50 through 99. Restrictions on lead emissions can be found in 40 CFR 50.12, "National Primary and Secondary Ambient Air Quality Standards for Lead." This section establishes a limit of 1.5 $\mu g/m^3$ in the ambient air; this is the maximum arithmetic mean averaged over a calendar quarter.

Water Programs

40 CFR 122. A National Pollutant Discharge Elimination System (NPDES) permit must be obtained for the discharge of a pollutant into the waters of the United States. This part of the regulation was written to address pollutants that are piped or channeled into the water from facilities. Construction projects require permits if more than five acres will be disturbed (or less than five acres if the parcel is part of a larger project).

Resource Conservation and Recovery Act

40 CFR 261. The Resource Conservation and Recovery Act of 1976 (RCRA) lists lead as a toxic hazardous waste. The analytical test used to determine toxicity under RCRA is the Toxicity Characteristic Leaching Procedure (TCLP), which is also referenced as EPA Method 1311. Wastes containing lead concentrations greater than 5 ppm by this test are regulated as hazardous wastes. Paint chips and other nonrecyclable painted components are typically regulated as potential hazardous. The regulation and disposal of lead-contaminated wastes is continuing to evolve. The EPA relaxed the disposal of lead-based paint in the spring of 2003 (68 FR 36487–95). However, compliance with RCRA will continue to vary from state to state, and even from landfill to landfill. It is therefore imperative that the hazardous waste manager stay abreast of the regulations.

The HUD Guidelines

Formally known as *The HUD Guidelines for the Evaluation and Control of Lead-Based Paint Hazards in Housing*, this document (the *Guidelines*) provides detailed comprehensive technical information on how to identify lead-based paint hazards and how to control such hazards safely and effectively. The goal is to assist property owners, private contractors, and government agencies in reducing children's exposure to lead without unnecessarily increasing the cost of housing. The *Guidelines* provide more complete guidance than do the regulations on *how* lead abatement activities should be implemented, and *why* certain measures are recommended. Lead exposure that comes from air emissions, Superfund sites, drinking water, ceramics, home (folk) remedies, cosmetics, and foods are *not* the focus of the *Guidelines*.

Instead, the *Guidelines* focus on the amount of lead in paint, dust and soil. Presently, HUD defines *lead-based paint* as any paint, varnish, or shellac that contains a minimum of 1 mg/cm^2 lead (XRF) or more than 0.5% lead in the dried solid (paint chip). The maximum allowable amount of lead in dust depends on where the lead is found. The target areas are window wells (trough), windowsills, and floors, and the concentration of lead is measured in micrograms per square foot (μg/ft^2).

See Figure 1. At the present time, the HUD clearance levels are:

Window wells:	400 μg/ft^2
Windowsills:	250 μg/ft^2
Floors:	40 μg/ft^2

Additional Lead Regulations

Many states and other jurisdictions have recently enforced regulations dealing with the presence of lead-based paint, particularly in residential properties. For example, Maryland has adopted a regulation that allows a limited liability cap for rental property owners. One of the conditions under which the limited liability can occur is if the property can be certified as *lead-free*. Under the *Code of Maryland Regulations,* COMAR 26. 16.02.02(B)(5), *lead-free* means

- Containing no lead paint (<0.7 mg/cm^2 by XRF or <0.5% by paint chip analysis)

- All interior surfaces of the affected property contain no lead-based paint

- All exterior surfaces of the affected property coated with lead-based paint that were chipping, peeling, or flaking have been restored without lead-based paint

- No exterior surfaces coated with lead-based paint are chipping, peeling, or flaking

In most instances, the properties in question have been certified as lead-free by means of inspections with an x-ray fluorescence analyzer.

Related Protocols

The American Society for Testing Materials (ASTM) has issued protocols for collecting samples of dust, soil, paint and air for subsequent analysis for lead. These protocols are summarized below.

E1727–04. *Standard Practice for Field Collection of Soil Samples for Lead Determination by Atomic Spectrometry Techniques.* This protocol deals with the collection of soil samples using coring and scooping methods. The protocol is not suitable for areas that are paved, nor does it address the development of sampling plans such as grid

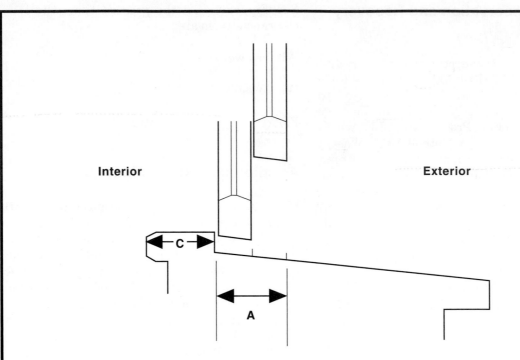

1. Sectional view of window (with no storm window) showing window trough area, A, to be tested. Trough is the surface where both window sashes can touch the sill when lowered. The interior window sill (stool) is shown as area C. Interior window sills and window troughs should be sampled separately.

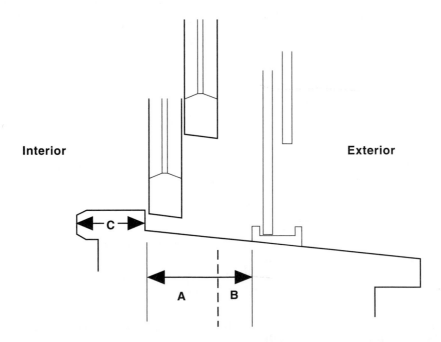

2. Sectional view of window (including storm window) showing window trough area, A and B, to be tested. Trough extends out to storm window frame. The interior window sill (stool) is shown as area C. Interior window sills and window troughs should be sampled separately.

Source: Department of Housing and Urban Development. *The HUD Guidelines for the Evaluation and Control of Lead-Based Paint Hazards in Housing*

Figure 1. Window Locations for Dust Sampling

patterns, *etc*. Lead concentration is measured in ppm.

E1728–03. *Standard Practice for Field Collection of Settled Dust Samples Using Wipe Sampling Methods for Lead Determination by Atomic Spectrometry Techniques.* This protocol covers the collection of settled dust on hard surfaces using the wipe sampling method. The standard does not address criteria for sampling design. Lead concentrations are presented in $\mu g/ft^2$.

E1729–99. *Standard Practice for Field Collection of Dried Paint Samples Using Wipe Sampling Methods for Lead Determination by Atomic Spectrometry Techniques.* This protocol deals with the collection of dried paint samples or other coatings from buildings and related structures. The procedure is used to collect samples for subsequent analysis on an area basis (milligrams of lead/area sampled) or on a concentration basis (milligrams of lead/gram of dried paint solid). The protocol does not include sampling plan criteria that are used for risk assessments or other purposes.

E1973–99. *Standard Practice for Collection of Surface Dust by Air Sampling Pump Vacuum Technique for Subsequent Lead Determination.* This procedure describes the vacuum collection of surface dusts onto filters using portable, battery-powered air-sampling pumps. The protocol is designed for the subsequent analysis for lead on a loading basis (micrograms of lead/area sampled) unless preweighed filters are used. The amount of lead can also be determined on a concentration basis (micrograms of lead/gram of dust collected) if preweighed filters or filter cassettes are used.

Bibliography

American Society for Testing and Materials. *ASTM E1727–04 Standard Practice for Field Collection of Soil Samples for Lead Determination by Atomic Spectrometry Techniques.* West Conshohocken, PA: ASTM, 2004.

American Society for Testing and Materials. *ASTM E1728–03 Standard Practice for Field Collection of Settled Dust Samples Using Wipe Sampling Methods for Lead Determination by Atomic Spectrometry Techniques.* West Conshohocken, PA: ASTM, 2003.

American Society for Testing and Materials. *ASTM E1729–99 Standard Practice for Field Collection of Dried Paint Samples Using Wipe Sampling Methods for Lead Determination by Atomic Spectrometry Techniques.* West Conshohocken, PA: ASTM, 1999.

American Society for Testing and Materials. *ASTM E1973–99 Standard Practice for Collection of Surface Dust by Air Sampling Pump Vacuum Technique for Subsequent Lead Determination.* West Conshohocken, PA: ASTM, 1998.

Department of Housing and Urban Development. *The HUD Guidelines for the Evaluation and Control of Lead-Based Paint Hazards in Housing.* Washington, DC: GPO, 1995.

"Lead in Construction." *Code of Federal Regulations.* Title 29, Pt. 1910.26.

Chris Gunther is the Manager of IH Services at EMG in Hunt Valley, Maryland. Prior to that he was the Environmental Manager of Aerosol Monitoring & Analysis, Inc. (AMA) in Hanover, Maryland. He has been employed in the field of hazardous materials management for more than 15 years, primarily in the disciplines of lead, asbestos, environmental risk assessment, and indoor air quality. Mr. Gunther thanks Tom Bernitt and Julie Henderson for reviewing this chapter.

CHAPTER 29

Asbestos

Margaret V. Naugle, EdD, JD, CHMM
Charles A. Waggoner, PhD, CHMM

Asbestos, what is it? Where is it found? How is it used? What are the health hazards associated with exposure? These are questions with clear, concise answers. But when it comes to asbestos and the regulations, duties, and responsibilities of property owners and employers, the answers are less clear. The information that follows offers a response to the basic background information and addresses the current regulations affecting employers and property owners.

Asbestos

Background Information

Asbestos is a group of naturally occurring fibrous minerals that have been used since the time of the ancient Greeks. Most of the world's asbestos comes from Canada and South Africa. However, it has also been mined in Russia, Australia, Finland, and the United States.

Asbestos is composed predominantly of magnesium silicate and there are six subspecies of asbestiform minerals. These are classified based upon their crystal structure and the presence of contaminating metals (iron, calcium, and sodium) within the mineral matrix. Asbestos includes: chrysotile, crocidolite, amosite, tremolite asbestos, actinolite asbestos, anthophyllite asbestos, and any of these minerals that have been chemically treated and/or altered. Additionally, the precise chemical formulation of each species varies with the location from which it was mined.

433

Ths asbestos minerals are classified into one of two generalized groups: (1) serpentine or (2) amphibole. The serpentine group consists of only one asbestos mineral, chrysotile or white asbestos. Chrysotile accounts for approximately 95% of all asbestos found in buildings in the United States. Serpentine is identified by its layered or sheet-type crystal structure. This crystal structure causes its fibers to be strong, flexible, and straw-like. This makes asbestos an excellent composite material allowing it to be spun and woven into fabrics. The hollow straw-like structure of the fibers contributes to the material's ability to absorb water. This important physical property allows *wet methods* to be an effective engineering control to prevent fiber release during abatement activities.

The amphibole group is characterized by a chain-like crystal structure and the presence of metals other than magnesium. Asbestos minerals included in this group include: amosite (brown asbestos), crocidolite (blue asbestos), and the asbestiform minerals: tremolite, actinolite, and anthophyllite. Amphiboles are more resistant to heat and chemical degradation than is chrysotile. Therefore, amosite and crocidolite are frequently found where high temperature insulation applications are found. The unique crystalline structure of amphiboles makes it more difficult to wet, and requires the addition of surfactant to water when wet methods are used to control fiber releases.

Asbestos has a high tensile strength, is chemically inert, noncombustible, and heat-resistant. Asbestos also has a high electrical resistance and good sound-absorption properties. It can be woven into cables, fabrics, or other textiles, and can be matted into asbestos papers, felts, or mats.

The physical and chemical properties of asbestos coupled with the economics of production led to the manufacture of more than 3,000 products in the United States. Asbestos has been used in the manufacture of heat-resistant clothing, automotive brake and clutch linings, as well as thermal, fireproof, and acoustical insulation. It has even been used in cigarette filters. Floor tiles, roofing felts, ceiling tiles, asbestos cement pipe and sheets, and fire-resistant drywall have also been manufactured with asbestos. It has been used as a strengthening agent in concrete, mortar, grout, and drywall spackling compounds. Still other applications for asbestos include pipe and boiler insulation materials and in sprayed-on decorative materials for surfacing walls, pillars, and ceilings. Asbestos-containing materials (ACM) are found on beams, in crawl spaces, and within the wall cavities of older building, particularly those built before 1980.

Asbestos is a versatile cost-effective material that is ideal for many uses. It is found everywhere. It has been widely used in construction, it occurs naturally in our environment, and, because of its unique properties, has been found in many manufactured products. Why then is it so highly regulated? The answer is related to the potential adverse health effects and the associated liability.

Health Effects

The adverse health effects that cause EPA to regulate asbestos as a toxic substance seem to stem more from particle size and shape more than from its chemical composition. The primary routes of human exposure to asbestos are inhalation and ingestion, with inhalation being considered the most dangerous mode of exposure. Most cases of asbestos-related illness are linked to the inhalation of microscopic asbestos fibers, while exposure via ingestion is believed to be linked to an increased incidence of cancer in the alimentary canal. Dermal exposure is known to cause asbestos warts on the hands of abatement workers; these warts tend to disappear after exposure is ended. Dermal exposure to asbestos is not believed to produce dangerous or irreversible effects.

There are six disorders that are associated with human exposure to airborne asbestos fibers: pleural effusions, pleural plaques, pleural thickening, asbestosis, lung cancer and mesothelioma. The first three of these diseases are frequently asymptomatic. Most of these diseases require extensive exposures over long periods of time and are easily prevented. All have long latency periods and are degenerative diseases. From a liability standpoint, the most significant classification of asbestos is as a known human carcinogen. This is particularly true with regard to mesothelioma, a rare form of cancer that is almost exclusively linked to exposure to asbestos. A final unusual aspect of this disease is that it does not seem to follow a dose-response relationship, a single fiber is theoretically all it takes to cause this always fatal disease.

Lung Cancer. Inhalation of asbestos fibers has been directly linked to the development of all types of lung cancer, a malignancy of the covering of the bronchial tubes. As with most asbestos-related diseases, lung cancer follows a dose-response relationship. Risk to the individual increases as the length of exposure time and/or the level of exposure increases. A latency period of 20 to 30 years can be expected between initial exposure to airborne asbestos fibers and declaration of the disease. It is also important to note that a synergistic effect exists between smoking tobacco and exposure to airborne asbestos fibers. Exposure to industrial concentrations of asbestos fibers increases the likelihood of lung cancer approximately five times whereas smoking in and of itself increases the risk of cancer ten times that of the normal population. Individuals who smoke tobacco and are exposed to asbestos increase their likelihood of contracting lung cancer by as much as 80 to 100 times.

Mesothelioma. *Mesothelioma* is a malignancy of the lining of the chest or abdominal cavity. Pleural mesothelioma is a malignant growth of the pleura, the exterior lining of the lungs. Peritoneal mesothelioma is a malignancy of the peritoneum of the abdominal cavity. Either form of the disease spreads quickly and is always fatal. Pleural mesothelioma gained public notoriety when Steve McQueen was diagnosed and later died of it. Asbestos is the only material linked to this disease. The disease has a latency period of greater than thirty years and represents a severe management problem because it does not follow a dose-response relationship. Lack of a dose-response relationship between exposure and incidence of this disease implies that there is no known safe level of exposure.

Asbestosis. *Asbestosis*, also known as *white lung*, is the scarring of lung tissue that results from an accumulation of asbestos fibers in the lung. Asbestosis is the most common asbestos-related disease and is the most preventable. All forms of asbestos have demonstrated the ability to cause asbestosis, a disease with symptoms that are similar to those of emphysema. The latency period for asbestosis ranges from 15 to 30 years and follows a dose-response relationship. In most cases, individuals will not develop asbestosis unless exposed to high concentrations of airborne fibers for an extended period of time (years). Risk of contracting asbestosis can be reduced by lowering either exposure concentration or exposure time, and therefore asbestosis represents one of the most preventable of the asbestos-related diseases.

Pleural Effusion and Thickening. *Pleural effusion* is a collection of fluid around the lung and is the most common effect of inhalation of asbestos dust. It is probably the only effect which occurs during the first ten years of exposure. Diffuse *pleural thickening* is often associated with the occurrence of pleural effusion. It is a thickening of the visceral (lung) and/or parietal (chest wall) pleura. The thickening can vary from 0.5 to 2 cm in thickness and results in increased difficulty in breathing.

Pleural Plaque. *Pleural plaque* is a thickening of tissue under the parietal pleura, which can become calcified. An associated latency period of 20 years exists and the condition is typically asymptomatic. Pleural plaques are the most important x-ray abnormalities found as a result of asbestos exposure and are used as diagnostic signposts.

The best noninvasive method for monitoring exposure is by radiographic examination. Pleural plaques are more likely to be identified using x-rays. Only fifteen percent of the pleural plaques found in asbestos workers during autopsy were capable of being diagnosed by pre-autopsy x-ray examination. This underscores the fact that in addition to being a known human carcinogen, asbestos exposure leads to physiological changes in a majority of individuals who are significantly exposed.

Asbestos-related diseases are well known for their long latency periods which vary from 10 to 40 years. All asbestos-related diseases are progressive; therefore, treatment is intended to retard the rate at which a patient's condition degrades. It is important to note that most of the asbestos-related diseases are asymptomatic; that is, the patient never demonstrates physical symptoms. This fact coupled with the long latency period cause many workers to become cynical to the danger of exposure. Although not an immediate health risk, asbestos does cause adverse health effects. The best weapon is prevention; therefore, worker education is essential to minimize unwarranted exposure.

The Management Process

The questions of what asbestos is, how it is used, and where it can be found have been addressed. The wide use of asbestos-containing materials (ACM) and their associated health effects explain why it is so highly regulated. So, how does one ensure the health and safety of people, protect the environment, and manage asbestos-containing material? The first step is to identify the presence of asbestos and assess the risks.

One might expect that a person with experience and knowledge about where ACM is located and how it is used could identify materials that contain asbestos. A building owner might turn to the maintenance man for help. Beware! Both the building owner and the maintenance man incur liability if errors are made. The only way to be certain that a suspect material contains asbestos is by laboratory analysis. Think again when you undertake to make your facility a safe workplace, for by law

- Only accredited inspectors may identify and assess asbestos-containing materials

- Only certain laboratories may analyze samples of suspect materials

- Only certain methods of analysis can verify if the material contains asbestos in sufficient quantity to meet the legal definition of ACM

- Only certain response actions are available to the building owner

- Only certain persons may design the appropriate response action

- Only certain contractors may perform the response action

- Only certain supervisors may oversee the management of the response action

- Only certain workers may perform the work

- Only air monitoring can determine if the job is done

The total process of managing asbestos, whether maintaining it in place or removing it, can best be found in the Asbestos Hazard Emergency Response Act (AHERA) regulations, Title II of the Toxic Substances Control Act (TSCA). AHERA, as revised, continues to represent the state-of-the-art in the asbestos abatement industry. The Model Accreditation Plan found in Appendix C of 40 *Code of Federal Regulations* (CFR) 763 defines the qualifications of the various accredited individuals who are required by law to perform the many tasks which are a part of any asbestos-related project. The first rule: *No one does anything unless accredited.*

The process begins with identification of **asbestos-containing materials** (ACM) and **presumed asbestos-containing materials** (PACM), as required by the Occupational Safety and Health Administration (OSHA). This is done by an AHERA-accredited inspector who makes a physical assessment to determine the quantity, the location, and condition of ACM.

A statistically random and scientifically valid sampling scheme must be developed. The sampling scheme describes where and how many samples must be taken from each homogeneous area. The inspector must physically touch each homogeneous area to determine *friability*. The inspector collects the appropriate number of bulk samples. The entire process requires specific documentation, *i.e.*, sample locations on schematic diagrams, and a chain-of-custody form. The samples are properly packaged and shipped to an accredited laboratory for analysis. EPA requires bulk sample analysis by Polarized Light Microscopy (PLM) methods. The inspector signs and dates a written inspection report certifying to the building owner that the entire process was conducted pursuant to the regulations. The inspection report includes all supporting documentation developed during the inspection process, and the analytical report, which is signed and dated by the technician performing the analysis. This document becomes part of the management plan.

Note: The building owner may avoid inspection by assuming that all suspect materials are asbestos-containing and treat them accordingly. However, this management strategy extends potential liability and places a real financial burden on the owner; i.e., quantifying and labeling materials, purchasing and maintaining special equipment, training and monitoring of personnel, and recordkeeping.

Based on this inspection report, an AHERA-accredited management planner makes a hazard assessment. The hazard assessment is based on the type and condition of the ACM and the potential for disturbance from noise, vibration, or contact. Using the hazard assessment the management planner outlines the appropriate response actions to be considered by the building owner. The management plan includes an operations and maintenance program to manage asbestos-containing material remaining in the facility. The plan becomes a *living document*; it remains with the facility being updated as periodic surveillance is performed, the 3-year reinspections are conducted, emergency response actions occur, and abatement activities are completed. The management plan is transferred to new owners.

Note: With the exception of the accredited management planner, the Asbestos School Hazard Abatement Reauthorization Act extended AHERA accreditation requirements to public and commercial building owners who undertake abatement activities. However, OSHA requires building owners to have a written plan to manage the ACM/PACM at their facilities. With so many regulations impacting the decision-making process, it would be prudent to find experienced professionals to assist in the development of the written plan.

In any building, it is the building owner who selects the response actions. Response actions include: enclosure, encapsulation, repair and maintenance, or removal. Removal is required only before demolition or renovation pursuant to the National Emissions Standards for Hazardous Air Pollutants (NESHAPs). The building owner must select from the response actions that *protect human health and the environment*. The building owner may choose that action which is *the least burdensome method* (40 CFR 763.90).

Once the response action has been chosen, an AHERA-accredited project designer prepares the design to accomplish the appropriate response.

An accredited contractor develops an abatement plan. The Asbestos NESHAP requires that a 10-day advance written notification be given to the agency with jurisdiction before abatement work begins. If the project does not start on that date, a new 10-day notice is given. AHERA-accredited supervisors who are *OSHA competent* manage the abatement project and AHERA-accredited workers perform the abatement work. All OSHA health and safety standards are applicable. Each project is unique; *methods of compliance* are specified in the regulations.

Pursuant to AHERA regulations at 40 CFR 763.90 (i)(1–6) response actions require clearance by air monitoring. Clearance testing methods are determined by the size and type project. Transmission Electron Microscopy (TEM) clearance test methods are required in schools for projects greater than 260 linear or 160 square feet. Phase Contrast Microscopy (PCM) clearance test methods are required in most public and commercial building projects.

All ACM/PACM waste must be properly packaged and labeled. It must be shipped with a Waste Shipment Record (WSR) or waste generator's manifest. DOT regulations apply. Waste is stored at an EPA-approved landfill. The landfill covers the waste with six inches of dirt within 24 hours. In keeping with the *cradle-to-grave* concept, waste continues to be the property of the building owner. Any discrepancies in the waste shipment must be reported to EPA.

Note: (1) The building owner should be aware that a conflict of interest exists between the air monitoring function and the abatement contractor. The building owner should consider a third party to verify clearance of the response action. (2) Additional State and local regulations may apply. (3) Most states require asbestos professionals to be licensed in addition to maintaining accreditation training.

Regulatory Overview

For more than three decades, a variety of Federal agencies have overseen the regulation of asbestos, products containing asbestos, asbestos waste and emissions. The Federal, State, and local regulations that address the manner in which asbestos can be used or handled are many and complex. There are numerous references and differing definitions that open the door to various interpretations. In addition, specific regulations often target definite businesses, as is the case with schools, both public and private. Business and industry were caught off-guard by not having monitored the promulgation of regulations under the Asbestos School Hazard Abatement Reauthorization Act which successfully extended AHERA training requirements to public and commercial buildings.

The people impacted by the wide range of regulations are far-reaching. Building owners and occupants, engineers, construction contractors, as well as other service crews such as custodial and maintenance workers, electricians, cable and telephone service personnel, and plumbers are all touched by asbestos regulations. The list goes on to include lawyers, insurance professionals, analytical laboratories, training providers, health care providers, and health and safety equipment suppliers.

The Federal agencies that impact the use of asbestos include the Environmental Protection Agency, the Occupational Health and Safety Administration, the Department of Transportation and the Consumer Product Safety Commission (CPSC). Regulated activities include mining and milling of asbestos ores, manufacturing of asbestos-containing products, construction, removing ACM, disturbing ACM while performing custodial and maintenance activities, repairing automotive brakes and clutches, as well as transporting and disposing of asbestos-containing waste. Anyone who *may* come into contact with ACM is afforded protection by law.

The following information is a broad overview of current Federal regulations. A chronology of the regulations appears in Table 1, and a cross-reference guide to asbestos regulations is shown in Table 2.

The regulations can be explained by examining them according to the agency with oversight. Three Federal agencies have primary regulatory jurisdiction over asbestos: the Department of Transportation (DOT), the Occupational Safety and Health Administration (OSHA) and the the Environmental Protection Agency (EPA). DOT regulations represent a good starting point since they are the most brief.

Department of Transportation

The Hazardous Materials Transportation Uniform Safety Act (HMTUSA) falls under the auspices of DOT. This act specifies packaging, marking, labeling and placarding of materials shipped by rail, aircraft, vessel, and public highway. Under the HMTUSA, asbestos is categorized as Class 9, miscellaneous hazardous material. If the material

is only moving domestically, it may be billed as: Asbestos, 9, NA2212, III, RQ.

If the type of asbestos is known, then the following proper shipping names must be used:

- Blue Asbestos, 9, UN2212, II [RQ optional], if crocidolite

- Brown Asbestos, 9, UN2212, II [RQ optional], if amosite/mysorite

- White Asbestos, 9, UN2590, III [RQ optional], if chrysolite/actinolite/anthophylite/tumolite

One of the latter three names must be used if the shipment is international or includes an air or water leg. Other requirements may also apply if the shipment is going by air or water.

ACM should be described as:

- Other Regulated Substances, Solid, N.O.S., (Asbestos), 9, UN3077, III.

As a waste, ACM should be identified as:

- Environmentally Hazardous Substance, Solid, N.O.S., (Asbestos), 9, UN3077, III.

Note: The RQ is required before or after the shipping name if > 1 lb of pure, friable asbestos is being shipped. If shipped by water, the UN number must be shown first. This will also be true of land shipments after 2007.

Containers appropriate for shipment of asbestos are found in 49 CFR 173.216 for non-bulk packaging and 49 CFR 173.240 for bulk packaging. Containers can be rigid or nonrigid but must be air-tight. Asbestos or ACM which are fixed or immersed in a natural or artificial binder (cement, plastic, asphalt, *etc.*) are exempt (removed) from the DOT regulations.

Transportation personnel must follow the appropriate OSHA regulations when loading, handling, and unloading ACM in order to minimize exposure to airborne particles. For asbestos abatement projects this means ensuring that waste materials are thoroughly wetted prior to transport and that such waste materials are place in DOT-approved containers. Only trained individuals may handle the waste. The level of training is dependent upon

Table 1. Chronology of Asbestos Regulations

Year	EPA	OSHA	Other
1971	Asbestos listed as a hazardous air pollutant	PEL set at 5 f/cc	
1973	Spray application of friable ACM prohibited under NESHAP		
1973	Standard for milling, manufacturing, and building demolition under NESHAP		
1975	NESHAP extended to waste collection and processing industries not previously covered		
1976		PEL lowered to 2 f/cc	
1977			Consumer Product Safety Commission prohibits asbestos in patching compounds
1978	All friable spray on ACM prohibited—demolition and renovation covered by NESHAP		
1979	Technical assistance program to schools to identify and control friable ACM.		DOT regulates ACM
1982	Reporting required for production of products containing asbestos (TSCA)		
1982	Asbestos in School Rule–identification and notification of friable ACM (TSCA)		
1984	Asbestos School Hazard Abatement Act–loan and grant program to help schools eliminate hazard		
1987	Worker Protection Rule–extended OSHA to government employees		
1987	Asbestos Hazard Emergency Response Act–established model accreditation program, extended responsibilities for schools to identify, notify, and respond, added criminal and civil liabilities (TSCA)	General Industry Standard Revised–29 CFR 1910.1001	
1989	Ban and Phase Out Rule	Construction Standard Implemented 29 CFR 1926.58	
1990	NESHAP Revised		
1991	NESHAP Revised –Training Requirements		
1992	Asbestos School Hazard Abatement Reauthorization Act (ASHARA)–extended AHERA training requirements to public and commercial buildings		
1994	ASHARA Revised Model Accreditation Plan	Asbestos Standards Revised–Construction changed from 29 CFR 1926.58 to 29 CFR 1926.1101, Maritime added 29 CFR 1915.1001, General Industry Amended 29 CFR 1910.1001	
1995		Asbestos Standards Compliance Dates Extended 2/21 Revised–6/28, Corrected 9/29	
1998		Respiratory Protection Revised 29 CFR 1910.134	
2001	Worker Protection Rule, Final		
2002	Ban Asbestos in America Act, proposed		
2003	"Asbestos Strategies Process," EPA Final Report		
2003	Asbestos Claims Criteria and Compensation Act of 2003 (S413), proposed		
2005	Fairness in Asbestos Injury Resolution Act of 2005 (S852), proposed		

Table 2. Cross-Reference Guide to Asbestos Regulations

Agency	Reference	Standard
EPA	40 CFR 61, Subpart M	Asbestos NESHAP
	40 CFR 763, Subpart E	Asbestos in Schools (AHERA/ASHARA) Appendix C Model Accreditation Plan
	40 CFR 763, Subpart F	Friable Asbestos-Containing Materials in Schools
	40 CFR 427	Effluent Standards (Asbestos Manufacturing)
	40 CFR 763, Subpart G	EPA Worker Protection Rule
	40 CFR 763, Subpart I	Asbestos Ban and Phase Out Rule
OSHA	29 CFR 1910.1001	General Industry Asbestos Standard
	29 CFR 1915.1001	Shipyard Asbestos Standard
	29 CFR 1926.1101	Construction Industry Asbestos Standard
	29 CFR 1926	General Health and Safety
	29 CFR 1926.59	Hazard Communication Standard
	29 CFR 1910.134	Respiratory Protection Standard
MSHA	30 CFR 57, Subpart D	Surface Mining Asbestos Standard
	30 CFR 57, Subpart D	Underground Mining Asbestos Standard
DOT	49 CFR 171 and 172	Hazardous Materials Transportation Act
CPSC	16 CFR 1304	Consumer Products Bans

the OSHA classification of the work that generated the waste. Workers that handle waste from Class I and Class II activities must have AHERA accreditation.

One of the most common DOT violations during transport of asbestos-containing waste is that the waste has not been properly wetted. This produces a dilemma for the environmental professional when preparing wastes for disposal. The material should be wetted, yet free water should not be present in the containers since free liquids are banned from landfills.

Note: see relevant EPA and OSHA regulations.

Occupational Safety and Health Administration

OSHA's first asbestos standard appeared in 1971. Over the years it has been revised and updated many times. The focus of the Asbestos Standard is on protecting workers from harmful exposure to asbestos fibers. A totally revised Asbestos Standard (in effect, three standards) was published August 10, 1994. The Asbestos Standards focus on protecting workers from harmful exposure to asbestos fibers. A brief description follows.

General Industry. In the past, the General Industry Standard (29 CFR 1910.1001) had been considered to be the *generic* asbestos standard. It covers all activities (except agriculture) that are not covered by the construction or shipyard standards. The two largest segments covered by 29 CFR 1910.1001 are *brake and clutch repair* and custodial workers who are not involved with construction activities. General industry maintenance activities and custodial personnel who may, in the performance of their duties, *disturb* ACM and be exposed to asbestos fibers, have been specifically assigned to and included in provisions of the construction and shipyard standards.

Construction Industry. The Construction Industry Standard at 29 CFR 1926.1101 covers the activities involving asbestos such as demolition, removal, alteration, repair, maintenance, installation, cleanup, emergency response to spills containing asbestos, transportation, storage, and disposal of contaminated debris. Previously identified as 29 CFR 1926.58, this standard was redesignated as 29 CFR 1926.1101 to reflect the reorganization of health standards covering construction made on June 30, 1993 (58 FR 35076).

Shipyards. OSHA received many comments complaining that placing shipyards under the construction standard caused confusion because it was never clear when 29 CFR 1910 applied or when 29 CFR 1926 was correct. Therefore, OSHA produced a *vertical* standard in 29 CFR 1915.1001 for shipyards that is different in some ways but, overall, is meant to be neither more nor less rigorous than the general industry or construction standards.

The 1994 regulatory overhaul was in response to issues raised by the DC Circuit Court of Appeals when it remanded the 1986 Asbestos Standard back to OSHA for reconsideration. The issues raised by the court were: (1) establishment of operation-specific exposure limits, (2) small scale, short duration definition, and (3) extension of reporting and information-transfer requirements. These *new* rules were challenged in the courts and subsequently stayed and amended. At issue were management and work practices involving asbestos-containing roofing and flooring materials.

The final amended rule resulted in many significant changes—some that were not at issue in the initial court's remand. These changes included but are not limited to: a change in permissible exposure levels; a change in the definition of the term *asbestos* to include *presumed asbestos-containing material* (PACM); an expanded responsibility and liability of building owners; and the addition of a classification system for work activities (Class I, II, III and IV) involving the potential contact, possible disturbance, and removal of ACM/PACM.

Exposure Levels. The permissible exposure limit (PEL) for airborne asbestos fibers was lowered to 0.1 fibers per cubic centimeter (cc) of air over a time-weighted average of 8 hours. The action level was eliminated. The short-term exposure of workers to airborne asbestos fibers or excursion limit (EL) is 1.0 fiber/cc on a 30-minute time-weighted average.

Asbestos Defined.

Asbestos includes chrysotile, amosite, crocidolite, tremolite asbestos, anthophyllite asbestos, actinolite asbestos, and any of these minerals that has been chemically treated and/or altered. For purposes of this standard, *asbestos* includes PACM, as defined below.

PACM means *Presumed Asbestos-Containing Material*. Presumed Asbestos-Containing Material means thermal insulation and surfacing material found in buildings constructed no later than 1980. The designation of material as *PACM* may be rebutted pursuant to paragraph (k)(4) of this section.

This definition of asbestos, coupled with the economics of treating all thermal system insulation and all surfacing material as ACM, forces property owners to pursue the *rebuttal criteria* as specified in the Standard. Unless a property owner can prove otherwise through documentation obtained from an inspection performed by an Inspector accredited under AHERA with sample analysis by an accredited laboratory, then any surfacing material and any thermal system insulation that is in a facility built not later than 1980 shall be considered to be asbestos.

Note: See relevant EPA regulations. EPA regulations under ASHARA require that inspections, response actions, and design undertaken by commercial and industrial facilities must be performed by persons who are accredited under the Model Accreditation Plan as described by AHERA (40 CFR 763). This is more stringent than OSHA, which allows a Certified Industrial Hygienist (CIH) to take samples.

Owner Responsibility and Liability. Greater regulatory liability is placed upon the building owner. New and expanded requirements with *specific information conveying and retention duties* are assigned to the building owner. Notification *shall be in writing or shall consist of a personal communication between the owner and the person to whom notification must be given or their authorized representative.* Owner responsibilities include but are not limited to the following:

- Communication about the presence, location, quantity, and condition of all ACM and PACM to employees, to prospective employees, to all employers of employees, to tenants, and to future building owners.

- Communication through signs, labels, training, and site-specific written operations and maintenance plans.

- Confirmation through an *initial exposure assessment* that employees are not exposed to ACM/PACM in the performance of their duties.

- Maintenance of records for the life of the facility. The records will remain with the facility and be transferred to future owners.

- Notification to OSHA if *methods of compliance* involve the use of of work practices other than those in the Standard.

In addition to the changes described above, the Standard specifically addresses *General Contractors* of construction projects. General contractors are held liable over work covered by the standard even though the general contractor may not have specific knowledge of asbestos abatement practices. The contractor *shall ascertain whether the asbestos contractor is in compliance with the standard and shall require such contractor to come into compliance with this standard when necessary.*

Classification of Asbestos Work I-IV. OSHA added four classes of activities to the Construction and Shipyard Standards. These classes trigger different provisions in the standard. OSHA deleted *small scale, short duration* from its final standard.

Note: See related EPA regulations.

The Agency, through its four classes of work, distinguishes high-risk from lower-risk operations. Class I activities represent the greatest risk, with decreasing risk potential associated with each successive class. Work that in the 1986 standard was considered *small scale, short duration* falls into Class II and III in the new standard. The Construction and Shipyard Standards regulate Classes I–III, and all three standards regulate Class IV.

Note: "Small scale, short duration projects" and "major" and "minor" fiber release episodes are defined by EPA. See 40 CFR 763.

Classes I–III are intended to cover the kinds of work which, under the 1986 Construction Standard, were designated *asbestos removal, demolition and renovation operations, including small scale, short duration operations such as pipe repair, valve replacement, installing electrical conduits, installing or removing drywall, roofing and other general building maintenance or renovation.*

By establishing Class IV, OSHA rejected the idea that some activities potentially involving asbestos disturbance would result in a *de minimis* risk, and as such should not be regulated.

Class I–means activities involving the removal of Thermal System Insulation (TSI) and surfacing ACM and PACM.

Class II–means activities involving the removal of ACM that is not TSI or surfacing material (miscellaneous materials). Examples are removal of floor or ceiling tiles, siding, roofing, and transite panels.

Class III–means repair and maintenance operations where ACM, including TSI and surfacing materials, are likely to be disturbed. It includes repair and maintenance activities involving intentional disturbance of ACM or PACM. It is limited to ACM/PACM.

Class IV–means maintenance and custodial work, including cleanup, during which employees contact ACM or PACM.

Note: Class I, II, and III work shall be conducted in a " regulated area". See 29 CFR 1926(b) Definition of "Regulated Area" and (e).

Note: Workers who perform tasks in regulated areas are required by EPA through AHERA/ ASHARA to be accredited under the Model Accreditation Program.

The OSHA standards require that regulated work areas be established where airborne concentrations of asbestos fibers might be expected to equal or exceed the PEL. The establishment and supervision of a regulated area is to be under the direction of a **competent person**. The qualifications of a competent person vary depending upon the classification of work being supervised; *i.e.*, the greater the risk of the work being overseen, the more experience and training the supervisor needs. The responsibilities of the competent person are to

- Establish negative pressure enclosures where necessary

- Supervise exposure monitoring

- Designate appropriate personal protective equipment

- Ensure training of workers with respect to proper use of said equipment

- Ensure the establishment and use of hygiene facilities

- Ensure that proper engineering controls are used throughout the project

Respiratory Protection. OSHA significantly overhauled the Respiratory Protection Standard (29 CFR 1910.134) on January 8, 1998. This regulation called for the development and implementation of a nine-part written program that is overseen by an employer-specified program administrator. Specific qualifications for the program administrator are not identified by the standard, rather this individual is required to possess capabilities commensurate with the degree of hazard(s) associated with the workplace activities. Additionally, a *site-specific* written respiratory protection program must be established for activities that involve the potential exposure to asbestos. The selection of proper respiratory protective equipment is based on the results of area air sampling that is conducted prior to intitiation of the project and personnel monitoring is required throughout the life of the project. Sampling and analysis conducted for this purpose follows the National Institute for Occupational Safety and Health (NIOSH) Method 7400 (PCM). All employees covered by this respiratory protection program are to be notified of the results of personal exposure monitoring either by personal contact or the posting of the test results.

Employers are required to provide respirators to all workers who may be exposed to greater than the PEL of airborne asbestos fibers during their work activities. The employer must ensure that the provided equipment is capable of giving adequate protection to the exposed individuals. The OSHA guidelines listed in 29 CFR 1926.1101(h)

contain specific reuquirements for respirator selection when workers are exposed to asbestos.

Medical Surveillance. Workers who (1) are exposed to concentrations of asbestos fibers at or above the PEL for 30 calendar days or more in a year, or (2) are required to wear a negative pressure respirator, must be included in a medical surveillance program. The medical examinations include: collection of a medical history; completion of a standardized questionnaire contained in Appendix D of 29 CFR 1910.1001, 1915.1001, and 1926.1101; a chest x-ray; examination of the pulmonary and gastrointestinal system; as well as a pulmonary function test by forced vital capacity or forced expiratory volume. Examinations are to be completed yearly, with the cost being borne by employers.

Other OSHA Standards. In general, OSHA standards are directed at protection of workers and ensuring a safe work environment. All general health and safety standards apply. Due to its carcinogenic nature, OSHA considers asbestos a hazardous chemical because of its carcinogenic nature and therefore covered under the Hazard Communication Standard (29 CFR 1910.1200). Other OSHA standards which should be reviewed when undertaking action involving asbestos include: Lock Out/Tag Out, Confined Space Entry, Fall Protection, Ventilation, and General Health and Safety.

Environmental Protection Agency

EPA has promulgated a number of rules intended to limit environmental release of asbestos fibers. The jurisdiction of EPA, as it relates to asbestos, involves the enforcement of various legislative acts.

National Emmissions Standard for Hazardous Air Pollutants

The regulations promulgated pursuant to the Clean Air Act Section on the National Emissions Standard for Hazardous Air Pollutants, better known as the *Asbestos NESHAP*, are found in 40 CFR 61, Subpart M. These regulations are some of the most frequently cited EPA asbestos regulations.

The currently enforced asbestos NESHAP was published in final form on November 20, 1990 (55 FR 48406); some significant revisions were made at that time. A number of definitions were either revised or added (see 40 CFR 61.141), including those for *adequately wet, nonfriable, regulated ACM,* and *waste shipment record.* In addition, the regulations uniformly established a 10-day written notice prior to the commencement of defined abatement activities.

The asbestos NESHAP addresses: (1) fugitive emissions from work sites, (2) required removal before renovation or demolition, (3) notification requirements before disturbing ACM, and (4) disposal of asbestos-containing waste materials in landfills.

No Visible Emissions. The *no visible emissions* statement for releases from mining, milling, and manufacturing processes is probably the most commonly quoted part of the asbestos NESHAP. This restriction extends to renovation and building demolition projects. It is important to distinguish between the OSHA PEL and the EPA *no visible emissions level.* OSHA establishes exposure standards for inside the work space while EPA establishes limits for nonpoint source emissions to the environment. The EPA no visible emissions limit is not intended to serve as a worker protection standard.

Required Removal. A second requirement of the asbestos NESHAP is that all regulated asbestos-containing materials (RACM) must be removed from a building prior to demolition. This is the only place in Federal regulations in which asbestos removal is required.

Notification. Before any renovation, remodeling, or removal activities involving disturbance of RACM can be undertaken, the State agency responsible for Clean Air Act enforcement must be provided written notification 10 days in advance of beginning work. This advance notification is required in the event that 260 linear feet or 160 square feet of RACM will be affected, or if 35 cubic feet of asbestos-containing waste material will be generated. Should the starting date of the removal project change prior to initiation of work, a revised notification form must be submitted and 10 working days must separate submission of this form from the start of work. Finally, the delegated State agency must be provided with project

updates in the event the amount of asbestos affected changes by 20 percent.

Waste Disposal. Asbestos-containing waste materials are hazardous *materials,* not hazardous *waste.* As hazardous materials, asbestos-contaminated waste can be disposed of in EPA-approved landfills. The asbestos NESHAP establishes guidelines for proper disposal of such asbestos wastes. These guidelines include provisions for restricting emissions, adequate wetting of waste materials, use of hazard warning labels, indelible marking of each container with information about the generator, and use of waste shipment records in a fashion analogous to the uniform manifest for hazardous waste disposal. This documentation of waste shipments includes the requirement to submit an *exception report* if written verification of disposal of the asbestos waste is not received from the designated disposal facility within 45 days.

Note: See other relevant EPA regulations and relevant DOT and OSHA regulations.

Toxic Substances Control Act

Asbestos is explicitly addressed in the Toxic Substances Control Act (TSCA) as one of five chemicals specifically regulated under TSCA and found in 40 CFR 763. The Asbestos Hazard Emergency Response Act (AHERA) of 1986 and the Asbestos School Hazard Abatement Reauthorization Act (ASHARA) of 1990 go hand-in-hand. They are Title II of TSCA:

Asbestos Hazard Emergency Response Act (Subpart E)

Asbestos School Hazard Abatement Reauthorization Act (Subpart E)

Appendix A: . . . Mandatory to Determine Completion of Response Actions

Appendix B: Work Practices . . . Operation and Maintenance Activities

Appendix C: Model Accreditation Plan

Appendix D: Transport and Disposal of Asbestos Waste

Appendix E: . . . Bulk Sample Analysis

Worker Protection Rule (Subpart G)

Ban and Phase Out Rule (Subpart I)

AHERA and ASHARA. *AHERA* established state-of-the-art practices for the asbestos abatement industry. It includes the *Model Accreditation Plan* (MAP). This was the first time in our nation's history that government set forth specific training requirements for the work force. Only EPA-approved training providers may conduct accreditation training programs. AHERA initially applied to schools, public and private (see 40 CFR 763, Appendix C).

Definitions. As with any discussion involving environmental regulations, one must begin with *definitions* (40 CFR 763.83). An **asbestos-containing material** (ACM) is any material or product containing greater than 1 percent asbestos. An **asbestos-containing building material** (ACBM) is defined as ACM found in or on interior structural members or other parts of a building. EPA further defines asbestos-containing materials by grouping them into one of three categories: surfacing materials, thermal system insulation, and miscellaneous ACM. Each of these categories can be further described as being either *friable* or *nonfriable*. **Friable ACM** is defined as material which, when dry, may be crumbled, pulverized, or reduced to powder by hand pressure, and includes any damaged nonfriable material. There are also key definitions for removal, enclosure, encapsulation, and repair which define *abatement* activity.

Other important asbestos definitions include:

Surfacing Material—ACM that has been sprayed or troweled on surfaces (walls, ceilings, structural members) for acoustical, decorative, or fireproofing purposes. This includes plaster and fireproofing insulation.

Thermal system insulation—Insulation used to inhibit heat transfer or prevent condensation on pipes, boilers, tanks, ducts, and other components of hot and cold water systems and heating ventilation and air condition (HVAC) systems. This includes pipe lagging and pipe wrap; block, batt, and blanket insulation; cement and *mud*, and other products such as gaskets and ropes.

Miscellaneous materials—Other, mostly nonfriable and friable products and materials such as floor tile, ceiling tile, roofing felt, concrete pipe, outdoor siding, and fabrics.

Model Accreditation Plan—The Model Accreditation Plan (MAP) established five areas of accreditation as the appropriate training requirements for individuals who would: (1) perform inspections, (2) prepare management plans for buildings, (3) supervise abatement projects, (4) serve as workers on abatement projects, or (5) design abatement projects. Accreditation in each of these areas is achieved by attending an EPA-approved course and passing a written examination. To maintain accreditation, individuals must attend annual refresher classes and may be required to pass written examinations. In addition, many states now require asbestos professionals to have a registration or license.

Asbestos School Hazard Abatement Reauthorization Act. This law (Public Law 101–637) was passed on November 20, 1990. The highlights of this act include the following:

- As of April 4, 1994, the Revised Model Accreditation Plan was implemented on an interim basis, to be followed by full implementation (under ASHARA and the Revised MAP) by October 4, 1994.

- Any person who conducts asbestos work in schools as an Inspector, Management Planner, Worker, Contractor/Supervisor, and/or Project Designer must still be accredited.

- Any person who conducts asbestos work in public or commercial buildings as an Inspector, Worker, Contractor/Supervisor, and/or Project Designer must be accredited under the provisions of ASHARA and the Revised MAP.

- The length of training programs for accreditation as a Worker has increased from 3 days to 4 days, with a minimum of 14 hours of hands-on training.

- The length of training programs for accreditation as a Contractor/Supervisor has increased from 4 days to 5 days, with a minimum of 14 hours of hands-on training.

- The extended training requirements of the Contractor/Supervisor course also satisfy the training requirements for Workers.

- The Contractor/Supervisor course no longer meets the accreditation requirements for Project Designers.

- A person must take the refresher course specific to the area in which he or she seeks to maintain accreditation; *i.e.*, Design Update, Inspector Update.

- There are some grandfather provisions in the Revised MAP:

  – Anyone holding valid accreditation in any of the five disciplines as of April 3, 1994, will be accredited (grandfathered) under the Revised MAP.

  – The 12–month grace period for obtaining renewal accreditation is in effect *if* a state allows it.

  – For nonaccredited persons as of April 3, 1994, a person must either take a course that meets the upgraded training requirements noted above, or take a course meeting the old MAP requirements and then take an upgraded course before October 4, 1994. *In effect, if* a person took a course between April 4 and October 4, 1994 that had not been upgraded, that person would need to retake the initial training again before October 4, 1994.

AHERA and ASHARA carry the full enforcement authority of TSCA, with criminal and civil penalties for failure to comply. States were required to adopt the AHERA guidelines or to develop their own that were *at least as stringent as* the Federal guidelines. Because of the far-reaching impact of the expanded regulations under ASHARA, states once again had to take legislative action to adopt guidelines at least as stringent as the new Federal guidelines. These regulations are required reading for anyone who is dealing with asbestos management or abatement projects.

Inspection and Reinspection. 40 CFR 763.85 requires looking at the inspection procedure and floor plans along with record drawings and specifications of construction projects in order to identify locations of suspected ACBM. Homogeneous areas defined as an area of surfacing material, thermal system insulation material, or miscellaneous material which is uniform in color and texture are then established for the purpose of sampling.

Sampling. 40 CFR 763.86 requires that bulk samples be taken from each homogeneous area in a statistically random fashion, with the number of samples collected based upon the square or linear footage present in the homogeneous area. Each sample must be collected by an accredited inspector. Documentation of the entire process is specific and includes a unique numbering system, diagrams of sample location, date, signature, and accreditation number of the inspector, a description of the homogeneous area, and a chain of custody form.

Analysis. 40 CFR 763.87 requires sample analysis using the PLM point count method in a laboratory, which has been accredited by the National Institute of Standards and Technology (NIST). The analytical report must be signed and dated by the individual analyzing the sample. If one sample from a homogeneous area is determined to contain greater than one percent asbestos, the homogeneous area must be classified as ACBM. The results of the analysis must be submitted to the designated asbestos program manager within 30 days of analysis. In lieu of sampling and analyzing suspected ACM, the building owner is allowed to assume the material is ACM and manage it accordingly.

Assessment. 40 CFR 763.88 requires that the final stages of inspecting a building include an assessment of the physical condition of all materials identified or assumed to be ACBM. The inspector indicates the type ACM and the degree to which damage is present (poor, fair, or good). The inspector indicates the potential for disturbance (high, moderate, or low) as probability of human contact, noise, and/or sound vibration. The inspection report submitted to the building owner will include the sampling scheme, sample locations, names of inspectors collecting samples, analysis reports for all samples, classification of homogeneous areas as ACBM or non-ACBM, and physical assessment and description of all homogeneous areas.

Response Actions. According to AHERA (40 CFR 763.90), an accredited management planner will review information contained in the inspection report and conduct a hazard assessment. The hazard assessment serves as an indicator of risk for building occupants. Based upon this hazard assessment, the management planner will recommend a response option for each homogeneous area: removal, or enclosure, encapsulation, repair, and maintenance. In conjunction with these response option recommendations, the management planner will also prescribe an operation and maintenance plan for all ACBM left in the building. The management planner must sign, date, and record their accreditation number on recommendations made to the building owner.

Any response to a *major fiber release* must be completed only by accredited personnel: project designer, project supervisor, and project workers. A *major fiber release* is defined to have occurred when *greater than three square or linear feet of ACBM becomes dislodged from its substrate.*

In the event a major fiber release occurs, the facility environmental manager should take immediate action. The area where the release occurred should be isolated by modifying or shutting off the heating, ventilation, and air conditioning (HVAC) systems. Entry to the affected area should be restricted and signs posted warning of the hazard. An air sampling firm should be contacted to have nonisolated areas tested for airborne asbestos fibers. Finally, an accredited project designer should be contacted to coordinate the response action.

Operations and Maintenance. 40 CFR 763.91 contains specific work practices for operations and maintenance activities: worker protection, initial cleaning, major and minor fiber-release episodes. Maintenance activities involving the disturbance of quantities of ACM greater than three linear feet or three square feet must be designed and conducted by persons accredited under AHERA. More specific work procedures are identified in the regulations.

Training and Periodic Surveillance. AHERA also establishes training requirements for those individuals who carry out the operations and maintenance plan (40 CFR 763.92). Any custodial or maintenance personnel working in a building containing ACBM must be given two hours of awareness training, whether they work with ACBM or not. Those individuals who may *disturb* ACBM during their duties must receive an additional 14 hours of training. Employee training must be site-specific, and include locations of ACBM in each building. Operations and maintenance personnel routinely document periodic surveillance every six months to ensure that no change in condition or use of the ACM has occurred.

Finally, AHERA does not supersede those requirements established by OSHA standards, the Asbestos NESHAP, or the EPA Worker Protection Rule. EPA has begun integrating concepts of AHERA into other asbestos regulations, as is reflected by the updated NESHAP. AHERA has become the *state of the art* in asbestos management and abatement.

Worker Protection Rule. When OSHA was first created, its purview was limited to the private sector. Federal agencies were incorporated into the OSHA sphere of authority in 1979 via executive order of the President. Approximately half the states in our nation have statutes placing their State and local government agencies subject to OSHA standards. EPA addressed this small group of OSHA-exempt workers in something commonly referred to as the *Worker Protection Rule* (40 CFR 763, Subpart G).

The purpose of the EPA Worker Protection Rule is to extend the OSHA worker safety guidelines to employees of State and local governments, especially those who perform asbestos abatement work. The regulations became effective March 27, 1987.

Ban and Phase out Rule. The EPA published the Ban and Phase out rule on July 12, 1989. The purpose of the rule was to *prohibit at staged intervals, the future manufacture, importation, processing, and distribution in commerce of asbestos in almost all products.* The first stages of the rule concentrated on nonfriable forms of ACM such as floor tile, textiles, and asbestos cement products. Implementation was scheduled in three phases. If the restrictive ruling had not been challenged in the courts it eventually would have eliminated 94 percent of all asbestos-containing materials from the United States marketplace by 1997. However, on October 21, 1991, the Federal Appeals Court sent the rule back to EPA and effectively suspended the rule except for those products which were out of production prior to July 12, 1989.

Notifications and reports that must be submitted by miners, primary processors, secondary processors, manufacturers, and importers, are outlined in 40 CFR 763, Subpart D. In certain cases, information must also be submitted to the Consumer Product Safety Commission as well as the EPA.

Asbestos Claims Criteria and Compensation Act of 2003

Asbestos Claims Criteria and Compensation Act of 2003 (S. 413) address problems caused by the enormous number (more than 200,000, with an additional 50,000 cases expected to be filed each year) of nonmalignant asbestos cases currently being litigated in Federal and State ccourts. The bill does not affect workers' compensation claims but will be of interest to the workers' compensation community because many of the asbestos tort claims arose in connection with workplace exposure. Nonmalignant cases are those filed by litigants who:

1) Have been exposed to asbestos

2) May have some physical sign of exposure, but

3) Are not presently suffering any impairment from the exposure

Senate Bill 413 notes that the cost of compensating exposed persons who are not presently suffering any health problems from asbestos exposure

> jeopardizes the ability of defendents to compensate people with cancer and other serious asbestos-related diseases, now and in the future

and

> strains the ability of the courts to manage the deluge of cases involving nonimpaired plaintiffs.

In addition, the Bill notes that more than 60 companies have declared bankruptcy as a consequence of asbestos claims, that an estimated 50,000 to 60,000 workers have lost their jobs as a result of the aforementioned litigation and bankruptcies, that those workers have lost an estimated $25,000 to $60,000 in wages, and that the value of the 401(k) plans of the shareholders of these bankrupt companies will decline by an estimated 25%.

Among other things, the Bill delays the effective date of the statute of limitations in these cases until discovery of an injury caused by exposure to asbestos. It sets forth the *prima facie* for showing a valid claim.

Fairness in Asbestos Injury Act

On May 26, 2005, after years of considering and battling over asbestos reform proposals, the Senate Judiciary Committee moved Senate Bill 852, The Fairness in Asbestos Injury Resolution Act (FAIR)

out of committee. The FAIR Act sets up a $140 billion trust funded by *defendants*. FAIR has been spearheaded by Committee Chairman Arlen Specter, R-PA, and is based in large part on a measure (which died at the end of the 108th Congress) negotiated by former Chairman Orrin Hatch, R-UT, ranking member Patrick Leahy, D-VT, Majority Leader Bill Frist, R-TN, and former Minority Leader Tom Daschle, D-SD. The FAIR Act is an extremely complex bill.

Among the defendants who face asbestos liabilities are: manufacturers, property owners, employers, and insurers. FAIR establishes a *no-fault* liability system in which claimants would be subject to statutory medical criteria and specific claims values, depending on the disease suffered. In most cases, lawsuits based on asbestos exposure would be banned. And, compensation to attorneys would be limited.

After months of work with senators from both sides of the aisle and many stakeholders participating, progress was made toward a compromise. The most controversial issues include how to:

1) Prevent the continuation of claims in the tort system, even as buisinesses are paying billions into the fund

2) Ensure that the most ill claimants, many of whom have a very short life expectancy, are paid as quickly as possible during the *start-up* period of the fund

3) Ensure through medical criteria that all those with diseases likely caused by asbestos exposure, but not others, receive compensation

One important issue that remains is how to treat residents of US cities who face issues similar to Libby, Montana, where mining of asbestos-contaminated vermiculite caused health problems for virtually the entire town.

Labor and victims' groups hold that the total trust funding is inadequate, thus providing a windfall to companies who face hugh liabilities. House Majority Leader Dick Arny, R-TX, representing the conservatives, opposes a trust fund approach as do trial lawyers who favor a medical criteria tort reform approach.

Asbestos Strategies Process Final Report

In May 2003, the Global Environment and Technology Foundation published its final report, *Asbestos Strategies: Lessons Learned about Management and Use of Asbestos*. This report, which was originated and funded by EPA, used the information that was provided by many of the country's top asbestos management experts, stakeholders, and medical experts in asbestos-related diseases to sumarize the state of asbestos oversight, outreach, and education as well as other concerns. Included in the report are ten leading recommendations. These recommendations have been excerpted and, with the permission of the publisher, provided below. This report can be found in its entirety on the Internet at:

<http://www.getf.org/asbestosstrategies/>

Action 1: Update Existing Asbestos-in-Buildings Guidance. Guidance documents provide workers with processes to follow in order to protect their health, protect the health of building occupants, and comply with regulations. EPA should update the *purple book* guidance document to make it the premier technical resource for managing asbestos in buildings and facilities, including industrial settings. The revised resource should include updated *green book* (operations and maintenance) information, and should be consistent with current federal regulations and good practices that have evolved since its release in 1985. The resulting resource, in a form such as an online integrated database of all relevant documents, will facilitate compliance with existing regulations, reducing asbestos exposure among contractors working in buildings. *Lead Agency: EPA; Supporting Agency: OSHA.*

Action 2: Encourage Compliance with Existing Regulations. Regulatory agencies should encourage compliance with existing regulations and good practices for managing asbestos in buildings and conducting response actions. In some cases, businesses do not fully comply with existing regulations because they are not aware of the regulations. In other cases, they do not understand why it is important that the regulations be followed. Both may be addressed through a series of asbestos awareness seminars directed at the regulated community (building owners, contractors, and consultants). The seminars should be

sponsored by EPA and OSHA, and hosted by the resident state asbestos authority. Joint sponsorship would be extremely valuable. Seminars should be held in conjunction with national or regional meetings of professional/trade associations, such as the Environmental Information Association (EIA), the International Facility Managers Association (IFMA), the Building Owners Management Association (BOMA), and the American Institute of Architects (AIA), to encourage participation by the target audience. Regulatory compliance will increase worker and building occupant safety, reduce asbestos exposure, and decrease costs associated with liability. This action should be undertaken in the context of a long-term effort to enforce existing regulations and improve consistency among agencies, as noted in Action 7. *Lead Agency: EPA; Supporting Agencies: OSHA, EPA, and State Regulators.*

Action 3: Clarify the Asbestos Definition to Address Asbestos Contamination in Vermiculite and Other Minerals. Some of the asbestiform amphiboles found in the vermiculite from Libby, Montana were not among the six minerals currently regulated as asbestos. Nevertheless, they were similar enough to regulated forms as to present dangerous health risks. The Libby vermiculite situation should be considered an important lesson, but not be treated as a typical case. A Federal process should be undertaken promptly to clarify the definition of *asbestos*. Many parties recommended that the definition should include all asbestiform amphiboles, in addition to currently regulated amphiboles and chrysotile. EPA, OSHA, and Mine Safety and Health Administration (MSHA) will need to evaluate how such a clarification should be accomplished and what consequences, if any, it would have on other industries. If adopted, this definition would enable federal agencies to address the risk of exposure from minerals such as winchite and richterite. USGS, trade associations, and other organizations can serve as resources for clarifying and understanding the science associated with creating a new definition. *Lead Agency: EPA; Supporting Agencies: MSHA, OSHA, and USGS.*

Action 4: Advance a Federal Legislative Ban on Asbestos. Asbestos continues to be used in products manufactured in the United States and in products imported into the United States. This may present risk to workers or members of the public, and it increases the cost of regulatory compliance for building owners. A clearly defined legislative ban on the production, manufacture, distribution, and importation of products with commercially-added asbestos is the most direct means to address concerns about remaining health risk and reduce future costs for facility owners and managers. Such a ban should be proposed by the Congress, promptly debated, and conclusively resolved. Enabling legislation would eliminate remaining products by a specified date, and installation of those products by a later date. Jurisdictional issues could be addressed in Congressional legislation that might not be achievable by individual agency rulemakings. Exceptions may be necessary for a small number of applications for which substitutes may not be available, and for research purposes. Implementing regulations, and perhaps the enabling legislation itself, could be challenged in the courts. A regulatory ban is within EPA's authority and is also an option. Many see a ban on asbestos, enacted to prevent future exposure, as a complementary action to a litigation resolution process that fairly compensates injuries resulting from past exposure. *Lead Group: Congress; Supporting Agencies: EPA, OSHA, and US Department of Congress.*

Action 5: Develop a National Mesothelioma Registry. A national mesothelioma registry is necessary to facilitate epidemiological studies to evaluate the effects of asbestos exposure and enable public health officials to identify and respond to hazards. Many countries and some states have established mesothelioma registries. The establishment of such a registry would likely be performed by agencies within the Centers for Disease Control (CDC), including the National Center for Health Statistics, National Institute for Occupational Safety and Health, and the National Center for Environmental Health, in conjunction with Agency for Toxic Substances and Disease Registry (ATSDR) and State public health departments. An accompanying effort to connect interested parties with the best experts and data would improve research and treatment of asbestos-related disease. *Lead Agency: CDC; Supporting Agencies: State Public Health Departments, ATSDR.*

Action 6: Update Asbestos Model Training Curricula. There have been substantial changes to Federal regulations and standards since the model training curricula was developed. It is important to ensure that workers understand current regulations and understand why it is important to follow these regulations. EPA should update the model training curricula to ensure that all relevant agencies' priorities are reflected. Updating the training will make the curricula consistent with existing regulations and increase worker safety. The updated versions should cover the revised OSHA asbestos standards, revised EPA asbestos National Emission Standard for Hazardous Air Pollutants (NESHAP) standards, the EPA Worker Protection Rule, new respirator designations/regulations, and other topics. The training providers should also be permitted to vary the course content in refresher courses. *Lead Agency: EPA; Supporting Agencies: State Regulators, OSHA.*

Action 7: Enforce Existing Asbestos Regulations. Existing asbestos regulations have been designed to reduce the adverse effects from asbestos exposure on the health of the public and of workers. Inconsistent interpretation leads to confusion; lax enforcement allows substandard practices. Both can lead to increased health risk as regulations are ignored. EPA, OSHA, Consumer Product Safety Commission (CPSC), and State regulators should focus on more stringent, predictable, and consistent enforcement of these existing regulations, which may offer greater benefit than committing scarce resources to new rulemaking efforts. This recommendation can be implemented immediately; however, such an effort must continue for the long term. Consistent interpretations and streamlining across agencies will lead to increased compliance and potential reduced liability for businesses. Any step that EPA and OSHA can take to encourage the enforcement of existing regulations at the local level will likely prove most effective. To this end, consideration should be given to the use of a form such as the one created by EPA to assure compliance with existing regulations at the time applications are made for building, renovation, or demolition permits. This action ties into Action 2. *Lead Agency: EPA; Supporting Agencies: OSHA, CPSC, State Regulators.*

Action 8: Reduce the Occurrence of Unintended Asbestos in Products. Accidental contamination of mineral products with asbestos can increase risks to the users of these products or the workers who process them, and in turn can result in major liability losses affecting the mineral product companies. Assisting companies in avoiding asbestos in the first place is in the best interest of all parties. Reduction of naturally occurring asbestos in products could be achieved by a program set up by a consortium of mining concerns to develop a sampling and analytical protocol to analyze bulk materials at the mining stage for chrysotile and all asbestiform amphibole forms of asbestos. Oversight of such a program may be provided by EPA and MSHA, with technical assistance by the National Institute for Occupational Safety and Health (NIOSH), the National Institute for Standards and Technology (NIST), and USGS. This program would assist the mining and quarrying industries in avoiding unwanted asbestos in their products. The program would provide a degree of assurance to users of these raw materials that they are not contaminated with asbestos. *Lead Agency: EPA; Supporting Agencies: Mining Industry, MSHA, OSHA, NIOSH, NIST, USGS.*

Action 9: Address Asbestos-Containing Products in Commerce. Consumers, employers, and building owners are in many cases unaware of the inclusion of asbestos in products. Without this knowledge, they cannot take appropriate steps to protect their health. A coordinated effort to educate consumers, employers, and building owners about products with commercially-added asbestos is necessary. Such a program would assist the target audience in making an informed decision about which products are legally available with commercially added asbestos. This education and outreach effort would be performed by EPA, OSHA, and CPSC. These agencies would need to perform research to determine which products actually have commercially added asbestos, which do not, and which are to be phased out voluntarily by manufacturers. Congress should consider amending the Asbestos Information Act of 1988 to require manufacturers and importers to update information on their asbestos-containing products to EPA. *Lead Agency: EPA; Supporting Agencies: CPSC, OSHA, Congress, Bureau of Customs and Border Protection.*

Action 10: Partner with State Agencies in Support of Asbestos Training. Training requirements for contractors must be enforced. Training fraud does exist and is a real concern, particularly with some contractors producing fraudulent certification. If untrained contractors perform asbestos abatement, they put themselves and building occupants at risk. Training providers under the EPA model accreditation plan (MAP) and corresponding State plans should be audited with sufficient frequency to ensure that training is provided, tests are conducted, records are maintained, and certificates are issued. This action, conducted in concert with Action 6, will increase worker safety and the effectiveness of abatement efforts. Reducing the incidence of training fraud will provide greater security to building occupants and owners. Partnering with State agencies will provide better coordination. *Lead Agency: EPA; Supporting Agencies: State Regulators, Training Providers, OSHA.*

Summary

Asbestos is a naturally occurring mineral that has been widely used. It is a known carcinogen that also causes disabling respiratory disease. There is no known safe level of exposure, because all of the illnesses are not dose-response related. There are many regulations that impact the manner with which asbestos is used and encountered in the workplace. The regulations are complex and intertwined; they are cross-referenced one to the other. There are differing definitions that open the door to various interpretations. The regulations often are targeted at specific businesses, as is the case with schools. All public and commercial buildings are regulated. Only accredited individuals may *disturb* ACM. Waste generated that contains asbestos is believed to be the property of the building owner. Property owners and employers should read the regulations and seek the assistance of asbestos professionals.

Asbestos Laws and Regulations

A list of useful asbestos laws and regulations is provided below.

Asbestos Hazard Emergency Response Act of 1986 (AHERA): 15 USC §§2641–2656 (dealing with asbestos in schools), and amended by The Asbestos School Hazard Abatement Reauthorization Act (ASHARA), 15 USC §§2641–2654; 40 CFR 763, Subpart E.

Asbestos labeling: 29 CFR 1910.1001(g)(2)(ii) and 40 CFR 61.149.

Asbestos listed as a hazardous air pollutant: CAA, 42 USC §7412(b)(1).

Asbestos manufacture, importation, processing, and distribution prohibitions, and labeling requirements—Asbestos mining activities: 30 CFR 56, Subpart D; 30 CFR 57, Subpart D.

Clean Air Act (CAA): 42 USC §§7401, 7412, 7414, 7416, and 7601.

Effluent standards for asbestos manufacturing source categories: 40 CFR 427.

Hazardous Materials Transportation Uniform Safety Act of 1990: 49 USC §§5101–5127, Asbestos transportation: 49 CFR 171–172.

National Emissions Standards for Hazardous Air Pollutants (Asbestos NESHAP): 40 CFR 61.140–61.157 (Subpart M); *see also* Asbestos NESHAP Clarification, 58 *Federal Register* (FR) 51784 (10/5/93); 59 FR 542 (1/5/94); 60 FR 38725 (7/28/95); and 60 FR 65243 (12/19/95).

OSHA Construction Industry Standard: 29 CFR 1926.1101.

OSHA General Industry Standard: 29 CFR 1910.1001, 1910.1200.

OSHA Shipyard Employment Standard: 29 CFR 1915.1001.

Safe Drinking Water Act: 42 USC §300(f) (municipal annual water testing for asbestos).

State and Local Employees Worker Protection Rule: 40 CFR 763.

Toxic Substances Control Act (TSCA), Title II: 15 USC §2601.

OSHA and EPA Guidance Documents

Environmental Protection Agency. *A Guide to Normal Demolition Practices under the Asbestos NESHAP.* EPA 340/1–92–013. Washington, DC: EPA, Office of Air Quality Planning and Standards, September 1992.

Environmental Protection Agency. *A Guide to Performing Re-Inspections under the Asbestos Hazard Emergency Resource Act (AHERA).* ("Yellow Book") EPA 700/B–92/001. Washington, DC: EPA, Office of Pollution Prevention and Toxic Substances, February 1992.

Environmental Protection Agency. *A Guide to Respiratory Protection for the Asbestos Abatement Industry.* ("White Book") EPA 560–OPTS–86–001. Washington, DC: EPA, 1986.

Environmental Protection Agency. *Abatement of Asbestos-Containing Pipe Insulation, Asbestos-in-Buildings,* Technical Bulletin 1986–2. Washington, DC: EPA, 1986.

Environmental Protection Agency. *Advisory to the Public: On Asbestos in Buildings.* EPA 745K93014. Washington, DC: EPA.

Environmental Protection Agency. *Asbestos: Waste Management Guidance,* EPA 530SW85007. Washington, DC: EPA.

Environmental Protection Agency. *EPA Guidance for Service and Maintenance Personnel.* EPA 560/5–85–018. Washington, DC: EPA, 1985.

Environmental Protection Agency. *EPA Model Curriculum for Training Asbestos Abatement Contractors and Supervisors.* CX–820760–01–0. Atlanta, GA: Safety, Health, and Ergonomics Branch, Electro-Optics, Environment, and Materials Laboratory, Georgia Tech Research Institute, October 1995.

Environmental Protection Agency. *EPA Model Training Course Materials for Accrediting Asbestos Building Inspectors and Management Planners in Accordance with AHERA.* Washington, DC: EPA, 1995.

Environmental Protection Agency. "EPA's Pilot Study to Estimate Asbestos from Vermiculite Attic Insulation." *Pollution Prevention Fact Sheet.* Washington, DC: EPA, 2003.

Environmental Protection Agency. *EPA Model Curriculum for Training Asbestos Abatement Project Designers Instructor's Manual,* CX–816386–01. Marietta, GA: Georgia Environmental Institute, 1995.

Environmental Protection Agency. *Fact Sheet: Asbestos (HTML),* EPA 745F93007. Washington, DC: EPA.

Environmental Protection Agency. "Fact Sheet: Asbestos-Contaminated Vermiculite." *Pollution Prevention Fact Sheet.* Washington, DC: EPA, 2000.

Environmental Protection Agency. *Guidance for Controlling Asbestos-Containing Materials in Buildings.* ("Purple Book") EPA 560/5–85–024. Washington, DC: EPA, 1985.

Environmental Protection Agency. *Guidelines for Asbestos NESHAP Demolition and Renovation Inspection.* EPA 340190007. Washington, DC: EPA.

Environmental Protection Agency. *Managing Asbestos in Place.* ("Green Book") EPA 20T–2003. Washington, DC: EPA, 1990.

Environmental Protection Agency. *Managing Asbestos In-Place: A Building Owner's Guide to Operations and Maintenance for Asbestos-Containing Material.* EPA 745K93013. Washington, DC: EPA.

Environmental Protection Agency. *Simplified Sampling Scheme for Surfacing Materials.* ("Pink Book") EPA 560/5–85–030a. Washington, DC: EPA, 1986.

Environmental Protection Agency and Agency for Toxic Substances and Disease Registry. *Current Best Practices for Vermiculite Attic Insulation.* EPA 747–F–03–001. Washington, DC: EPA and ATSDR, 2003.

Global Environment & Technology Foundation. *Asbestos Strategies: Lessons Learned about Management and Use of Asbestos.* Annandale, VA: GETF, 2003.

Occupational Safety and Health Administration. *Asbestos Standard for Construction Industry.* OSHA 3096. Washington, DC: OSHA, 1995.

Occupational Safety and Health Administration. *Asbestos Standard for Shipyards.* OSHA 3145. Washington, DC: OSHA.

Occupational Safety and Health Administration. *Chemical Hazard Communication.* OSHA 3084. Washington, DC: OSHA, 1998.

Occupational Safety and Health Administration. *Personal Protective Equipment.* OSHA 3077. Washington, DC: OSHA.

Occupational Safety and Health Administration. *Respiratory Protection.* OSHA 3079. Washington, DC: OSHA, 1998.

Dr. Margaret V. Naugle is President of Environmental Training Corporation of Birmingham, Alabama, is an attorney and member of the Alabama Bar. She has been a consultant to business and industry in the area of environmental training and regulatory compliance for over 20 years. Her experience includes planning, designing and implementing the State of Mississippi's Model Accreditation Plan under the Asbestos Hazard Emergency Response Act; serving on the State of Mississippi Joint Legislative Committee for Environmental Matters; giving presentations at local, state, and national conferences; and publishing articles and training materials about various hazardous materials. Dr. Naugle has served on the National Advisory Board of Business and Legal Reports. She is Past-President of the Academy of Certified Hazardous Materials Managers and the Alabama Society of Hazardous Materials Managers. The Academy recognized Dr. Naugle for her leadership as President with their first honorary lifetime membership. Dr. Naugle is active in the Alambama and American Bar Associations.

Dr. Charles A. Waggoner currently serves as the Manager of Safety, Excellence, and Environment for the Diagnostic Instrumentation and Analysis Laboratory at Mississippi State University (MSU). He holds a BS and MS in biochemistry and a PhD in physical chemistry. He has over 15 years experience in environmental management, with particular emphasis on hazardous waste *management and related issues. Dr. Waggoner's professional activities have included serving as the MSU Hazardous Waste Officer, Technical Director of Environmental Training for the MSU Division of Continuing Education, and Dean of Environmental Science and Technology at Chattanooga State Technical Community College. Dr. Waggoner has served as a member of the IHMM-ACHMM Advisory Committee, ACHMM Board of Directors, and as General Chairperson for the 1994 National Conference in Chattanooga, Tennessee. He has authored numerous articles, including "Overview of Major Federal Environmental Acts and Regulations for the General Practioner," and the asbestos chapter in the* Handbook on Hazardous Materials Management, 5th edition, *published by IHMM in 1995.*

Part VI

Homeland Security

CHAPTER **30**

Chemical and Biological Weapons

Dwight H. Clark CET, CHMM

Introduction

The threat of chemical and biological weapons (CBW) is a growing concern in the world today. The likelihood of a chemical or biological attack is very uncertain. However, several groups, both state and non-state sponsored, are documented in the development or deployment of such weapons. As stated by Ernie Hood in *Environmental Health Perspectives* (1999), "The words *chemical and biological weapons* send a shiver down most spines these days." The effects of a CBW attack, even in a crude form, can be devastating to the affected population. This devastation can be in many forms including casualties, contaminated property, and psychological effects on the population.

There are three basic types of chemical and biological agents used in warfare: chemical agents, infectious agents, and toxins.

Historical Uses of Chemical and Biological Weapons

The history of chemical and biological weapons in warfare is long and sordid. In ancient times, as far back as 2000 BC, toxic fumes were used in battle. Later, the Tartar soldiers used plague-ridden corpses in an attack on Kaffa in 1346 AD. The British Army used smallpox against the Indians in the French-Indian war prior to American independence by distributing two contaminated blankets and a handkerchief to the Indians surrounding Fort Pitt. The British used smallpox again in the American Revolutionary war by sending immunized civilians to infect the Americans.

The modern use of chemical weapons dates to the use of gases (mustard gas, chlorine, and phosgene) in World War I by the German, French, and British armies. There are a number of documented chemical attacks in the period between the two world wars. Britain, Spain and Italy all launched offenses that included chemical attacks in Afghanistan, Iraq, and Northern Africa (Balfour 2002). The documented first modern uses of biological agents are by Japan in northern China during the 1930s. The Japanese used agents such as the plague, anthrax, and cholera.

Other armies throughout the world have developed and many have used chemical weapons. Not many countries will admit that they are developing or that they hold chemical weapons. The Central Intelligence Agency has testified to Congress that over twenty countries have or are developing chemical weapons. Most notable of these are the former Soviet Union, Iraq, Libya, Iran, Syria, and North Korea. Several countries have been documented in the use of chemical weapons in the past half-century. Some of the most notable attacks include: the Egyptian use of mustard gas and phosgene against Yemeni Royalist forces in the mid 1960s, the Iran-Iraq war where chemical weapons were repeatedly used by both sides, the Iraq attacks on the Kurds with mustard and nerve agents, and the 1987 use of chemical agents by Libya against Chad (Hogendoorn 1997).

The use of chemical and biological weapons by terrorist groups has been documented by Sokolski in his article, "Rethinking Bio-Chemical Dangers" (2000): "In the period from 1900 to 2000 there was a documented seventy-one attacks involving the use of CBW." Sokolski continues the data discussion with "That total seems relatively low, however forty-five of the attacks have occurred in the last ten years of the period studied." The most well known terrorist attack involving CBW is the series of seven incidents from 1994 to 1995 by the Shoko Asahara group in Japan. These attacks are most notably characterized by the May 1995 sarin attack in a Tokyo subway which killed 12 and injured thousands. However, the same group had 10 failed biological weapons attacks and attempted a number of other chemical attacks in Japan. The United States has not been immune from CBW attacks by terrorist groups. As early as 1984, the Rajneeshee religious sect in Oregon infected a salad bar with Salmonellosis food poisoning in an attempt to disrupt a local election. This attack injured 751 persons, with no fatalities from the poisoning. In 1994, the FBI investigated and arrested members of a tax protest group in Minnesota for possession of a biological weapon. The evidence presented at the trial indicated that the subjects had discussed the use of ricin to kill public officials (Mefford 1996). Some suggest that the 1993 World Trade Center bombing was laced with cyanide; however, it has never been proven. The most recent attacks in the United States followed the 9/11 tragedy and were the anthrax attacks that were delivered by the US Mail. Those attacks caused injuries to over 25 persons and caused five fatalities.

Chemical Weapons

Definitions

Chemical Weapons. Many definitions exist for chemical weapons. A statutory definition of *chemical weapons* found in the "Chemical Weapons Convention," which was developed by the Organisation for the Prohibition of Chemical Weapons:

(a) Toxic chemicals and their precursors, except where intended for purposes not prohibited under this Convention, as long as the types and quantities are consistent with such purposes;

(b) Munitions and devices, specifically designed to cause death or other harm through the toxic properties of those toxic chemicals specified in subparagraph (a), which would be released as a result of the employment of such munitions and devices;

(c) Any equipment specifically designed for use directly in connection with the employment of munitions and devices specified in subparagraph (b).

The definition of chemical weapons from "Agents of Death" (Moodie 2000) is:

Chemical weapons are poisons that incapacitate, injure, or kill through their toxic effect on the human body. They are generally classified as blister, blood, choking, incapacitating, or nerve agents, depending on which part of the body they are designed to affect. Some chemical agents can be lethal when vaporized and inhaled in amounts as small as a few milligrams.

Agent Types. The United States military publication, *Treatment of Chemical Agent Casualties and Conventional Military Chemical Injuries* describes the types of agents that are used in chemical weapons:

Blister Agent. Blister agents (vesicants) are likely to be used to produce casualties and to force opposing troops to wear full protective equipment. Blister agents are used to degrade fighting efficiency rather than to kill, although exposure to such agents can be fatal. Thickened blister agents will contaminate terrain, ships, aircraft, vehicles, or equipment and present a persistent hazard. Vesicants include sulfur, mustard gases (H and HD), nitrogen mustards (HN), lewisite (L) (this may be used in mixture with HD), and halogenated oximes (example: phosgene oxime [CX]). The properties and effects of halogenated oximes are very different from those of the other vesicants.

Vesicants burn and blister the skin or any other part of the body they contact. They may act on the eyes, mucous membranes, lungs, and skin; mustards may act on blood-forming organs. They damage the respiratory tract when inhaled and cause vomiting and diarrhea when ingested.

Some vesicants have a faint odor; others are odorless. They often have more serious effects than is immediately apparent. Both L and CX cause immediate pain on contact. The mustards are insidious in action, with little or no pain at the time of exposure. In some cases, signs of injury may not appear for several hours. Vesicants poison food and water and make other supplies dangerous to handle.

The severity of a blister agent burn is directly related to the concentration of the agent and the duration of contact with the skin.

Blood Agent. Blood agents produce their effects by interfering with oxygen utilization at the cellular level. Inhalation is the usual route of entry. Hydrogen cyanide (AC) and cyanogen chloride (CK) are the important agents in this group. All blood agents are nonpersistent.

Choking Agent. Chemical agents, which attack lung tissue, primarily causing pulmonary edema, are classified as lung-damaging agents (choking agents). They include phosgene (CG), diphosgene (DP), chlorine, and chloropicrin (PS). Best known of these agents is CG. Agents in this class are called lung-damaging agents because irritation of the bronchi, trachea, larynx, pharynx, and nose may occur and, with pulmonary edema, contribute to the sensation of choking. Blister agents and certain systemic agents also may injure the respiratory tract.

Incapacitating Agent. An incapacitating agent is a chemical agent that produces temporary disabling conditions. The disabling conditions persist for hours to days after exposure to the agent (unlike that produced by riot control agents, which usually are momentary or fleeting in action). Medical treatment, while not essential, may facilitate recovery that is more rapid. In the narrower sense, the term incapacitating agents has come to mean those agents that are:

1) Highly potent (an extremely low dose is effective) and logistically feasible.

2) Able to produce their effects mainly by altering the higher regulatory activity of the CNS.

3) Temporary in duration of action lasting hours or days, rather than of a momentary or fleeting action.

4) Not likely to produce permanent injury in concentrations which are militarily effective.

Nerve Agent. Nerve agents are a group of highly toxic organic esters of phosphoric acid derivatives. These agents have physiological effects (inhibition of cholinesterase) resembling those of the drugs physostigmine and pyrido-stigmine. However, they are more potent, longer acting, and tend to be irreversible after a time, which varies with the agent. Nerve agents are among the deadliest of chemical agents and may produce rapid symptoms. They include the G- and V-agents. *G-agents* are usually volatile liquids and are not persistent in the environment. By contrats, *V-agents* can remain in the environment for a long time. Examples of G-agents are Tabun (GA), Sarin (GB), Soman (GD), and GF. A V-agent is VX.

Several related but somewhat less toxic compounds have proven to be useful in medicine and agriculture, as indicated below. The symptoms and treatment of poisoning by these compounds are similar to those of poisoning by nerve agents.

1) Anticholinesterase agents have been used in the treatment of abdominal distention, urinary retention, and glaucoma.

2) Many of the insecticides currently in use are organophosphates and are chemically related to nerve agents. Although beneficial for arthropod control, their widespread use has caused many accidental poisonings—some fatal. Organophosphate insecticides may have a slower and longer lasting effect as compared to CW organophosphates.

Persistent Agent. Persistent Agents remain hazardous for as long as a month when deposited on soil, vegetation, or objects, and pose mainly a skin contamination threat.

Nonpersistent Agent. Nonpersistent agents dissipate (lose their strength) within a few hours and pose mainly a threat to the lungs.

General Discussion

Chemical weapons are routinely thought of as military weapons. There is indeed a great amount of technology required for optimum dispersal of a chemical agent. The agents are effected by the conditions in which they are released, above all else the meteorological conditions. However, as noted by the recent attacks in Japan, inefficient delivery of the weapons can cause the desired psychological effect on the population. This makes

these weapons attractive to groups wishing to confront large powerful nations, exploiting the vulnerabilities in the population.

The current planning for a chemical weapons attack usually considers a large concentrated population, such as a sporting event or other crowded public place (airport, subway, or high-rise office building). These attacks can make it much harder to contain the contamination given the number of persons involved. Several studies (Fricker, *et. al* 2002; Geiger 2001) have reviewed a number of scenarios, and most have reached the conclusion that preparedness is key to response. The United States has increased funding of local preparedness programs dramatically since 1996, and the most significant funding has come post 9/11.

The production of chemical agents in the world today has been simplified with technological advances and the common use of numerous chemicals in industry. For example, the key precursor chemical for mustard agents is thio-diglycol, which is a key component or chemical intermediate of ballpoint pen ink. The former Soviet Union has been found to have developed new, more deadly and persistent nerve agents in the late 1980s. These new agents are reported to be as much as ten times more deadly than VX. They are of particular concern as they are far easier and less costly to produce than typical nerve agents, as they are made from a combination of benign industrial and agricultural chemicals. This makes them far more difficult to detect in advance of an attack.

Additionally, one should be aware that there are a number of industrial chemicals that, when used in an inappropriate manner, become chemical agents. These chemicals are commonplace in almost every city and town in America. These agents could include: pesticides, chlorine, phos-gene, ammonia, hydrogen cyanide, hazardous wastes, as well as various acids and bases. This type of attack may not necessarily use these directly as chemical agents, but a weapon of opportunity. This has been documented in attacks by the Tamil Tigers using chlorine, when low on ammunition; or in the Balkan war attacks on industrial facilities. The effects of this type of attack can be characteristically similar to most hazardous waste emergencies.

One positive note on the possibility of a chemical agent attack can be found in the actual numbers of casualties. The Tokyo subway attacks killed 12 persons; however, it has been found that all who died were contacted with liquid agent. The efficient delivery of chemical agents has been developed by the world's major militaries; however, documentation by Sokolski (2000) reveals, "Of the 27,000 Iranians reported to have been exposed to Iraqi gas through March 1987, only 265 died." He continues, " The facts should not be used to denigrate any loss of life or suffering caused by chemical weapons." Parachini states in a paper published well after 9/11 and the invasion of Iraq "In cases where terrorists have used unconventional weapons in the past, they mostly have used crude toxic materials, not sophisticated, military-grade weapons."

Physical Effects and Toxicity

The physical effects and toxicity of the agents differ by the agent type and particularly with the nerve agents the toxicity varies by agent. The physical effects and toxicity are shown in Table 1 by class of agent. This information was excerpted with edits from United States Army Edgewood Chemical Biological Center website <http://www.ecbc.army.mil/hld/ip/bca_qr_text_only.htm> and Centers for Disease Control Bio-Terrorism agents pages <http://www.bt.cdc.gov/agent/agentlist.asp>.

Biological Weapons

Definitions

Biological Weapons. As defined by Moodie in "Agents of Death" (2000):

> Biological Weapons are living organisms or the by-products of living organisms used as instruments for waging conflict. In essence, biological warfare is the deliberate spread of disease.

Biological weapons generally are categorized as infectious agents (bacteria, viruses, or fungi) or toxins.

Infectious Agents. "These agents can produce numerous bacteria, viruses, or fungi previously known to science, as well as new genetically engineered organisms" (Mefford 1996). The infectious agents can mutate similar to other living organisms and will reproduce in a host organism. The infectious agents, unchecked in a population, will spread to cause high casualty counts. Examples include anthrax and the plague.

Toxins. "Toxins, unlike infectious agents, cannot reproduce, even though living microorganisms produce them. These poisonous substances require no incubation period, and some can cause incapacitation or death within minutes or hours. Examples of deadly toxins used in biological weapons include botulinum toxins and ricin" (Mefford 1996). Ricin is listed as a chemical agent in the Chemical Warfare Convention.

General Discussion

Biological agents, similar to that of chemical agents, have been historically thought of as military weapons. The incubation period and possibility of transmitting disease from person-to-person make biological weapons, specifically infectious agent weapons—a larger concern for public health.

The scenario of spreading an infectious agent in a crowded airline terminal, shopping mall, or public event could allow the unchecked spread of the infections throughout the country and even the world, within days. The impacts may not be seen immediately, based on the agent used and the incubation periods required. The local medical system may see a small increase in flu-like symptoms over a few days, followed by a large rush on the medical system with advanced stages of the disease.

The production of biological agents is relatively simpler than that of chemical agents. The equipment is similar to that of pharmaceutical industry or of a brewery. The largest technological feat is making the agents in a respirable form. A respirable form would be similar to that of any other contaminant commonly encountered. A particle size of 5–10 microns would be optimal, given that less than 1 micron is unlikely to stay trapped in the alveoli and infect the person, and a particle greater than 10 microns is likely to be

Agent	Signs and Symptoms of Exposure	Physical Effects	Toxicity
Blister Agent (Mustard, Lewisite)	*Skin:* redness and itching of the skin may occur 2 to 48 hours after exposure and change eventually to yellow blistering of the skin. Eyes: irritation, pain, swelling, and tearing may occur within 3 to12 hours of a mild to moderate exposure. A severe exposure may cause symptoms within 1 to 2 hours and may include the symptoms of a mild or moderate exposure plus light sensitivity, severe pain, or blindness (lasting up to 10 days). *Respiratory tract:* runny nose, sneezing, hoarseness, bloody nose, sinus pain, shortness of breath, and cough within 12 to 24 hours of a mild exposure and within 2 to 4 hours of a severe exposure. Digestive tract: abdominal pain, diarrhea, fever, nausea, and vomiting.	Cellular irritant: breaks down cell walls causing open weeping wounds, can damage DNA, and is a known carcinogen.	Low from the agent when in contact, if ingested much higher. The greater danger is from the secondary infections in the open wounds.
Blood Agent(Hydrogen Cyanide, Cyanogen Chloride, Arsine)	People exposed to a small amount of cyanide by breathing it, absorbin itg through their skin, or eating foods that contain it may have some or all of the following symptoms within minutes: rapid breathing, restlessness, dizziness, weakness, headache, nausea and vomiting, rapid heart rate. Exposure to a large amount of cyanide by any route may cause these other health effects as well: convulsions, low blood pressure, slow heart rate, loss of consciousness, lung injury, respiratory failure leading to death.	Impairment of cellular oxygen utilization.	
Choking Agent (Phosgene, Diphosgene)	Smells like freshly mown hay. Symptoms include: coughing, burning sensation in the throat and eyes, watery eyes, blurred vision, difficulty breathing or shortness of breath, nausea and vomiting. Skin contact can result in lesions similar to those from frostbite or burns.	Limits the oxygen exchange in the alveoli. A person may develop fluid in the lungs (pulmonary edema) within 2 to 6 hours.	
Incapacitating Agent (D-lysergic acid diethylamide [LSD], 3-Quinuclidinyl Benzilate [BZ])	Giddiness, restlessness, dizziness, inability to perform simple tasks	Similar to other well-known central nervous system stimulants or depressants.	Toxic only at extremely high doses.
Nerve Agent (VX, Sarin, Soman, Tabun)	People exposed to a low or moderate dose of VX by inhalation, ingestion (swallowing), or skin absorption may experience some or all of the following symptoms within seconds to hours of exposure: runny nose, watery eyes, small pinpoint pupils, eye pain, blurred vision, drooling and excessive sweating, cough, chest tightness, rapid breathing, diarrhea, increased urination, confusion, drowsiness, weakness, headache, nausea, vomiting and/or abdominal pain, slow or fast heart rate, abnormally low or high blood pressure. Even a tiny drop of nerve agent on the skin can cause sweating and muscle twitching where the agent touches the skin. Exposure to a large dose of VX by any route may result in these additional health effects: loss of consciousness, convulsions, paralysis, respiratory failure possibly leading to death.	Inhibits acetylcholinesterase which allows acetylcholine levels to build up, and disrupts the function of muscles (does not allow a muscle to relax).	Highly toxic, as little as 10 mg may kill a fully-grown man.

Table 1. Physical Effects and Toxicity of Chemical Weapons

filtered out. With the expansion of knowledge, and advances in microbiology the threats are very real.

The most difficult problem in responding to a biological attack is difficulty in knowing that one occurred prior to infection of the population. Most biological weapons have no visual or other sensory properties, allowing for little warning. Biological agents are not part of routine tests in medical laboratories unless suspected.

Physical Effects and Toxicity

The incubation, lethality, persistence, and symptoms of biological weapons are summarized in Table 2. This information was excerpted with edits from United States Army Edgewood Chemical Biological Center website <http://www.ecbc.army.mil/hld/ip/bca_qr_text_only.htm> and Centers for Disease Control Bio-Terrorism agents pages <http://www.bt.cdc.gov/agent/agentlist.asp>.

Use of Chemical and Biological Weapons as Weapons of Mass Destruction

The *United States Code*, Title 50, "War and National Defense," defines ***weapons of mass destruction*** (WMD) as

> any weapon or device that is intended, or has the capability, to cause death or serious bodily injury to a significant number of people through the release, dissemination, or impact of (A) toxic or poisonous chemicals or their precursors; (B) a disease organism; or (C) radiation or radioactivity.

The use of a CBW as a weapon of mass destruction or what can be termed "the poor man's nuke" is growing in the world today. Political and religious viewpoints have created serious fanatics throughout the world. The United States being the lone superpower has the attention of most of the worlds groups that are seeking their 15 minutes of fame. This is in addition to the fringe groups or home grown terrorists inside the United States. The need for many of these groups to satisfy revenge for actual or perceived actions by the government or

even business enterprises increases the threat on a daily basis. Some believe that it is not a question of if there will be another attack, only when and where.

Potential Delivery Methods and Tactics

There are several methods of delivery for CBW and the most common will be discussed below. This work does not attempt to cover all possible methods, only some of the methods considered plausible. A detailed analysis of the setting for any attack will lend itself to the evaluation of specific methods that may be employed.

Water Systems Attack. This type of attack would be characterized by the contamination of the water supply with an agent. It has received great attention in the recent past along with increased security measures. It is not considered a large concern, based on the following factors:

- Increased security following 9/11
- Large volume of agents required for a credible threat
- Small number of known waterborne agents

Bombing Attack. Several types of bombing attacks have been employed with conventional bombs and the setting of secondary bombs to injure the rescuers. This type of attack could spread an agent within a small area, generally less than one square kilometer (0.6 mile), and contaminate the area, complicating recovery efforts. An indoor attack is much more serious than an outdoor attack since the air is circulated with minimal dilution.

Placement of Agents. This type of attack is similar to the Tokyo subway incident, in that the agents are placed and allowed to contact persons. The worst-case scenario for this type of attack is in places of high traffic and minimal ventilation.

Spraying of Agents. This type of attack is the hardest to accomplish and can give the most casualties. Recent concerns about this method have led the government to scrutinize the crop dusting industry. The agents could also be sprayed from any kind of spraying device such as a garden sprayer.

Table 2. Characteristics of Biological Weapons

Agent	Incubation Period	Lethality	Persistence	Symptoms
Anthrax, Skin Form (Cutaneous)	1-5 days	Rarely fatal.	Very stable (known to remain virulent in soils for years).	The first symptom is a small sore that develops into a blister. The blister then develops into a skin ulcer with a black area in the center. The sore, blister and ulcer do not hurt.
Anthrax, Intestinal Form (Gastrointestinal)	1-5 days	Fatal in most advanced cases.	Very stable (known to remain virulent in soils for years).	The first symptoms are nausea, loss of appetite, bloody diarrhea, and fever, followed by bad stomach pain.
Anthrax, Inhalation form	1-5 days	3-5 days fatal with no treatment.	Very stable (known to remain virulent in soils for years).	The first symptoms of inhalation anthrax are like cold or flu symptoms and can include a sore throat, mild fever and muscle aches. Later symptoms include cough, chest discomfort, shortness of breath, tiredness and muscle aches.
Cholera	12 hours-6 days	Low with treatment. High without treatment.	Unstable in the environment, except saltwater.	Diarrhea, vomiting, and leg cramps.
Plague	1-3 days	1-6 days fatal.	Extremely stable.	Fever, weakness, and rapidly developing pneumonia with shortness of breath, chest pain, cough, and sometimes bloody or watery sputum. Nausea, vomiting, and abdominal pain may also occur. Without early treatment, pneumonic plague usually leads to respiratory failure, shock, and rapid death.
Ebola	4-6 days	7-16 days fatal. No known direct treatment.	Unstable.	The onset of illness is abrupt and is characterized by fever, headache, joint and muscle aches, sore throat, and weakness, followed by diarrhea, vomiting, and stomach pain. A rash, red eyes, hiccups and internal and external bleeding may be seen in some patients.
Botulinum toxins	Hours to days	High without treatment.	Stable.	Symptoms of botulism include double vision, blurred vision, drooping eyelids, slurred speech, difficulty swallowing, dry mouth, muscle weakness that always descends through the body: first shoulders are affected, then upper arms, lower arms, thighs, calves, *etc*. Paralysis of breathing muscles can cause a person to stop breathing and death.

Table 2. Characteristics of Biological Weapons (cont'd)

Agent	Incubation Period	Lethality	Persistence	Symptoms
Smallpox	10-12 days	Highly lethal. No known direct treatment.	Very stable.	The first symptoms of smallpox include fever, malaise, head and body aches, and sometimes vomiting. The fever is usually high, in the range of 101 to 104 degrees Fahrenheit. At this time, people are usually too sick to carry on their normal activities. This is called the prodrome phase and may last for 2 to 4 days.A rash emerges first as small red spots on the tongue and in the mouth. These spots develop into sores that break open and spread large amounts of the virus into the mouth and throat. At this time, the person becomes most contagious. Around the time the sores in the mouth break down, a rash appears on the skin, starting on the face and spreading to the arms and legs and then to the hands and feet. Usually the rash spreads to all parts of the body within 24 hours. As the rash appears, the fever usually falls and the person may start to feel better. By the third day of the rash, the rash becomes raised bumps. By the fourth day, the bumps fill with a thick, opaque fluid and often have a depression in the center that looks like a bellybutton. (This is a major distinguishing characteristic of smallpox.) Fever often will rise again at this time and remain high until scabs form over the bumps.
Ricin	Hours to days	Fatal in cases less than 5 days, greater than 5 days. No known direct treatment.	Stable.	*Inhalation:* Within a few hours of inhaling significant amounts of ricin, the likely symptoms would be respiratory distress (difficulty breathing), fever, cough, nausea, and tightness in the chest. Heavy sweating may follow as well as fluid building up in the lungs (pulmonary edema). *Ingestion:* If someone swallows a significant amount of ricin, he or she would develop vomiting and diarrhea that may become bloody. Severe dehydration may be the result, followed by low blood pressure. Other signs or symptoms may include hallucinations, seizures, and blood in the urine.

Preparedness Strategies

There are two primary preparedness strategies for the workplace. One is the prevention of unauthorized access and the second is a sound *shelter-in-place* procedure. The prevention of unauthorized access prevents attacks from within. The shelter-in-place planning prevents outside contaminants from coming inside. Without extensive training and costly resources, this is the best possible preparation. In the case of a CBW attack, a mask, or protective clothing may not be helpful, unless it can be properly donned within one minute of the exposure.

The centerpiece of the shelter-in-place strategy is the much criticized *duct tape and plastic sheeting* as recommended by the Department of Homeland Security. However, as hazardous waste professionals, we all understand the benefits of these items in the fabrication of containment areas.

General Response Methodology

Many persons think that the response to a CBW attack, a hazardous waste release, or a nuclear attack is the same. There is some truth in the similarity between a hazardous waste emergency and a chemical agent attack. However, until very recently, most hazmat responders did not have the capability to detect the chemical agents. A biological attack may not be detected until the casualties are within the medical system (Henretig 2001). This will stress the medical system beyond its capabilities. A hospital study in the Pacific Northwest conducted by Wetter, Daniell, and Tresser (2001) concluded that a large proportion of hospitals are not prepared for even small-scale terrorist CBW events. The events reviewed assumed that there were fifty casualties, which is small based on the Tokyo incident. The data may have underrepresented the level of preparedness, however, due to the military antidotes and protective equipment that were stockpiled near to the hospitals surrounding an Army chemical depot. Those hospitals have been provided extensive training and funding for chemical events.

The key to response in a CBW attack is to get clean breathing air very quickly and remove any agents from your body. If an attack is outdoors, immediately go indoors (an unaffected building) or stay indoors and secure all windows, doors, and ventilation. If the attack is indoors, immediately get fresh air by opening a window, or going outside, if safe. Do not venture outside unless directed or the *all clear* is sounded. Once a safe source of breathing air is secured then conduct decontamination to remove any contaminants.

Decontamination

The general decontamination requirements for most CBW agents follow the same guidelines as any other chemical contamination. Remove any contaminated clothing and bag to prevent re-contamination, shower with warm soap and water to remove contamination. Seek medical attention for further decontamination and treatement for the effects of the agents.

Military and medical professionals have specific decontamination methods for each agent. The decontamination agents in some cases are toxic or very corrosive and should not be used without specific training.

Demilitarization

As a result of the "Chemical Warfare Convention" and its implementing organization, the Organisation for the Prohibition of Chemical Weapons, the world is currently destroying the declared chemical weapons. The methods of destruction, or demilitarization, are straightforward. The primary method in the world is some type of incineration, under controlled conditions, with monitoring of exhaust gases. In some situations, chemical neutralization or other reactions are used to break down the agents. These technologies are gaining acceptance in light of the public perception of incineration. Emergency conditions allow weapons to be openly detonated within specified procedures if a direct hazard to movement or storage exists.

References

Balfour, S. "Chemical Warfare in the 1920s & 30s." *History Today* 52(2002.): 2-3.

Davis L. E., T. LaTourrette, D. E. Mosher, L. M. Davis, and D. R. Howell. *Individual Preparedness and Response to Chemical, Radiological, Nuclear, and Biological Attacks.* Santa Monica, CA: Rand Corporation, 2003.

Fricker, R. D., J. O. Jacobson, and L. O. Davis. *Measuring and Evaluating Local Preparedness for a Chemical or Biological Terrorist Attack.* Santa Monica, CA: Rand Corporation, 2002.

Geiger, H. J. "Terrorism, Biological Weapons, and Bonanzas: Assessing the Real Threat to Public Health." *American Journal of Public Health* 91(2001.): 708–709.

Henretig, F. "Biological and Chemical Terrorism Defense: A View From the 'Front Lines.' of Public Health." *American Journal of Public Health* 91(2001.): 718–720.

Hogendoorn, E. J. "A Chemical Weapons Atlas." *The Bulletin of the Atomic Scientists* 53: (September/October 1997): 35-39

Hood, E. "Chemical and Biological Weapons: New Questions, New Answers." *Environmental Health Perspectives* 107(1999): 931

Moodie, M. "Agents of Death." *Forum for Applied Research and Public Policy* 15(2000): 6–12.

Mefford, L. A. "Canaries in Cages: Responding to Chemical/Biological Incidents." FBI Law Enforcement Bulletin 65 (August 1996): 20.

Parachini, J. "Putting WMD Terrorism into Perspective." *Washington Quarterly* 26(2003.): 37–50.

Sokolski. H. "Rethinking Bio-Chemical Dangers." *Orbis* 44(2000): 207.

US Departments of the Army, the Navy, and the Air Force, and Commandant, Marine Corps. *Treatment of Chemical Agent Casualties and Conventional Military Chemical Injuries.* Washington, DC:1995.

Wetter, D. C., W. E. Daniell, and C. D. Treser. "Hospital Preparedness for Victims of Chemical or Biological Terrorism." *American Journal of Public Health* 91(2001): 710–716.

Internet Resources

<http://cns.miis.edu/research/cbw/index.htm> (Center for Nonproliferation Studies. Monterey Institute for International Studies. CNS Subjects: Chemical and Biological Weapons, Chemical and Biological Weapons Resource Page)

<http://www.bt.cdc.gov/index.asp> (Centers for Disease Control. Emergency Preparedness and Response)

<http://www.ecbc.army.mil/hld/index.htm> (Edgewood Chemical Biological Center. Homeland Defense)

<http://www.emergency.com/cbwlesn1.htm> (Emergency Response and Research Institute. Emergency Response to Chemical/Biological Terrorist Incidents)

<http://www.fas.org/nuke/guide/usa/doctrine/dod/fm8-9/toc.htm> (Federation of American Scientists. FM 8–9 NATO Handbook on the Medical Aspects of NBC Defensive Operations AMedP–6 [B])

<http://www.fema.gov/hazards/terrorism/terror.shtm> (Federal Emergency Management Agency [FEMA]. Hazards, Backgrounder: Terrorism)

<http://www.mitretek.org/home.nsf/HomelandSecurity/ChemBioDefense> (Mitretek Systems. Chemcial/Biological Defense)

<http://www.nicsinfo.orgSIP%20plan%20for%20offices%20NICS%20feb2003.pdf> (National Institute for Chemical Studies. Shelter in Place at Your Office: A General Guide for Preparing a Shelter in Place Plan in the Workplace)

<http://www.nti.org/f_wmd411/f1a.html> (Nuclear Threat Initiative [NTI]. WMD411: A Primer on WMD)

<http://www.opcw.org/index.html> (Organisation for the Prohibition of Chemical Weapons. Homepage)

<http://www.rand.org/publications/IP/IP217/IP217/index.html> (Rand Corporation. Issue Paper, Measuring and Evaluating Local Preparedness for a Chemical or Biological Terrorist Attack)

<http://www.rand.org/publications/MR/MR1731/> (Rand Corporation. Publications, Individual Preparedness and Response to Chemical, Radiological, Nuclear and Biological Terrorist Attack)

<http://www.rand.org/research_areas/terrorism/> (Rand Corporation. Terrorism and Homeland Security Research Area)

<http://www.ready.gov> (Department of Homeland Security. Homepage)

<http://www.vnh.org/FM8285/cover.html> (Virtual Navy Hospital. Treatment of Chemical Agent Casualties and Conventional Military Chemical Injuries. NAVMED P–5041, FMFM 11–11, AFJMAN 44–149, FM8–285.)

Dwight H. Clark has more than twenty years of diverse experience in the environmental industry, of which the last seven has been spent as a consultant. His experience includes all sectors of the environmental industry from government to commercial and from treatment operations to site operations consulting. Mr. Clark currently participates as a Director for Thunderbird Chapter of ACHMM, Arizona Emergency Response Association, Environmental Professionals of Arizona, and American Society of Military Engineers. On a national level, Mr. Clark participates in the ACHMM Emergency Response Committee. In addition, Mr. Clark is the educational committee chair for the Thunderbird Chapter and a National Overview Course instructor. He is currently the Compliance Program Manager for Jason Associates Corporation under contract to the U.S. Army at Yuma Proving Ground. His responsibilities at Yuma Proving Ground include: a RCRA Part B permit application for an open burning/open detonation unit, RCRA closures of Solid Waste Management Units (most units with unexploded ordnance hazards in addition to chemical hazards), Title V air permit, NPDES and wastewater programs, as well as drinking water, PCB management, RCRA and OSHA related training programs, and RCRA Large Quantity Generator operations. Prior to his arrival at Yuma Proving Ground, Mr. Clark was involved in several research and development, and commercial operations for waste treatment. He has specialized experience in radioactive and mixed wastes, RCRA, weapons of mass destruction, and oil pollution prevention. Prior posts include: Environmental Manager for a treatment facility in Dugway, Utah, under a RCRA Research Development and Demonstration permit (a facility designed for the treatment of chemical munitions by neutralization); Operations Manager for an experimental chemical weapons treatment demonstration facility at Redstone Arsenal, Alabama; Specialized Waste Services Manager for Teledyne Brown Engineering, a hazardous, radioactive, and mixed waste removal, treatment, and disposal operation; Facility Maintenance and Operations Manager for a mixed waste treatment operation in Oak Ridge, Tennessee; and, while on Active Duty, Nuclear Engineer and Nuclear Operations Trainer, U.S. Navy Nuclear Program.*

CHAPTER 31

Incident Response

Marilyn L. Hau MS, RN-C, COHN-S, EMT-P (Ret'd), OHST, CHMM

Hazardous materials incidents are among the most dangerous situations that hazardous materials managers and emergency responders may face. The combination of chemical and physical threats compounded by the uncontrolled and often unknown nature of emergency events mandate that special precautions be taken to ensure the safety of response personnel and the public. Hazardous materials incidents create conditions that can be hazardous and confusing. The best approach to hazardous materials incidents is prevention.

Decisions at the incident scene must sometimes be made based on limited information and under severe time restrictions. The Hazardous Materials Manager must be able to identify the hazardous material and its properties, evaluate the severity of the incident and the possible consequences, and apply effective decision-making strategies to contain the incident while protecting the responders. This includes an understanding of the various levels of training, capability, response tactics and personal protective equipment of hazardous materials response. In addition, the Hazardous Materials Manager must manage the incident in such a way that human and technical resources are utilized effectively and the needs of incident stakeholders such as the media are addressed. Follow-up of the incident must be performed to ensure restoration of essential functions, compliance with incident regulatory requirements, record keeping and response critique for continual improvement.

Characteristics of Hazardous Materials Incidents

Minor incidents are generally handled on a regular, day-to-day basis through planning and routine procedures, such as cleaning up a small acid spill in a chemical fume hood with a commercial chemical spill kit. The site does not have to be evacuated. The assistance of additional persons is not needed. The consequences of the spill are unlikely to escalate during the time it takes to discover and remediate it. No special personal protective equipment (PPE) beyond the normal work PPE is necessary. However, the Hazardous Materials Manager must still ensure that these incipient-level incidents receive preventive efforts, and are also anticipated and planned-for through periodic inspections, incident investigations, reporting of *near-misses*, employee training and other recognized safety practices.

Handling a more serious incident requires more personnel and resources beyond the routine preparations. These events are less likely to occur, but must still be recognized as possible. For example, the accumulation of carbon monoxide in a warehouse from closed doors and propane forklifts may require evacuation of the facility and ventilation to remove the gas. Equipment such as carbon monoxide detectors may be necessary to determine the amount of carbon monoxide before re-entry is permitted. It is very unlikely that such events could pose a danger to offsite locations and the public, but it could escalate at the facility, such as the failure to recognize the hazard, resulting in fatal overexposures. Identification and mitigation of these potential hazardous materials incidents, with the goal of preventing them, is even more essential. Permitting only electric forklifts indoors during the winter season in this scenario is an example. The Hazardous Materials Manager, however, must still plan for these events. Because of the greater risks and dangers involved, the need for effective incident management is greater. Training of response persons and the purchase of response equipment for an in-house response team may be appropriate recommendations. Routinely evacuating the site, securing the perimeter from entry, and summoning community emergency responders may also be preferred alternatives.

A greater extent or potential impact of a hazardous materials release, results in a greater need for additional trained personnel, equipment and resources, and outside agency response; particularly when the risk for impact on the public increases. For example, the release of ammonia from a pipe inside a refrigeration plant could result in an explosion, fatalities, property damage, and other consequences. The Hazardous Materials Manager must not only identify the possibility for such an event, but must also recognize when the event is beyond the training, ability and resources of employee responders. Planning must be done to ensure that no actions are taken that could escalate the problem, such as an employee operating a forklift in the area in an effort to reach the pipe leak rather than summoning the proper response agencies (such as the fire department). The Hazardous Materials Manager should establish a multidisciplinary committee, including production, research, safety, security, nursing and other key personnel, to develop a written Emergency Action Plan that identifies and plans for the release of all hazardous materials specific to that location. The plan must then be communicated to and practiced by all the employees; a written plan without practice is a deception in preparedness. Also, the plan must be reviewed at least annually to correct outdated telephone numbers, personnel rosters and other information changes. The community emergency response agencies should also be included in the planning and be provided a copy of the final plan. They may also be interested in practicing the plan, such as through a mock hazardous materials release drill.

A disaster necessitates full mobilization of facility and community resources such as law enforcement, fire, medical, hazmat teams and/or emergency response contractors. A disaster has the ability to create significant off-site consequences that almost always impact the public. It may necessitate facility and residential evacuations, public shelters, rerouting of transportation, and mobilization of hospital disaster plans. The assistance of other community agencies and State resources may be needed. The release of the contents of a rail car of chlorine at a repackaging facility is an example. The chlorine plume could harm nearby residents and highway travelers. Its corrosivity could create property and environmental damage. Such a release necessitates the use of specially trained hazmat responders with special rail car equipment to contain the event. The need for effective incident management with coordination of agencies and resources is necessary to ensure a unified and efficient disaster response. Efforts to recognize the potential for such incidents require creative thinking and thorough knowledge of the facility and the hazardous materials used there. Among the best persons to identify the potential effects of incidents are the employees who work closely with these materials. Their observations and experience are essential elements in hazardous materials incident prevention.

Response Decision-Making

The **DECIDE process** is an effective decision-making tool. The six steps of the DECIDE process are depicted in Figure 1. The process requires that the hazardous material first be identified, and then an estimate of the likely harm from the incident be performed. In order to perform this estimate, information about the properties of the material, the conditions such as weather at the site, the type of container involved, and the presence of potential exposures must be taken into consideration. Material Safety Data Sheets and the North American Emergency Response Guide are common initial information sources. They have been found to be less than completely accurate, however. An important rule of thumb in incident response is to use at least three sources of information in decision-making. NEVER rely on just one source. To do so creates the risk of using out-dated information, erroneous data, and inadequate material for safe response. Additional information resources are provided later in this chapter.

After likely harm has been estimated, the objectives for a response must be determined. *The priority in emergency response is: Persons, then Property, and then Environment. Persons* includes protection of the responders, the employees and the community. *Property protection* deals with property at the emergency scene as well as protecting property on which the event may impinge. *Environmental protection* involves reduction and elimination of incident's impact on air, groundwater, surface water, soil and wildlife within and beyond the incident boundaries. Evacuation of a building or shutting off air intakes to prevent building occupant exposure are person objectives. Soaking the side of a building to prevent the spread of fire is a property response objective. Diking or damming a stream to prevent the downstream spread of a hazardous material spilled in the water is an environmental response objective. Although eliminating environmental damage is usually considered the lowest exposure priority, it is still a very important concern. If possible, all released products should be contained and held until their impact on the environment can be determined.

Once the objectives have been chosen, the next step is to identify what response options are available to meet those objectives. There may be many options available or possibly even none. Perhaps only one of the objectives can be accomplished. Training levels and capabilities of the human and technical resources must be recognized and not exceeded. For example, rescue from a confined space may not be possible due to the risk to the rescue personnel. A fire that has spread beyond the facility's available equipment and training may need to be left in the hands of the community fire department.

Risk analysis is an important consideration in response options decision-making. What is the hazard? How vulnerable are the exposures? What is the risk in the proposed action or inaction? This must be a continuous decision-making process because emergency incidents seldom are stable. A hazardous materials release may escalate. An incipient fire may progress to a higher level. A medical emergency may develop at any time.

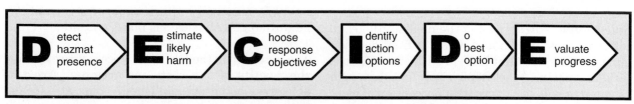

Adapted from (Brenner 1978), used with permission of Starline Software Ltd.

Figure 1. The Six Steps of the DECIDE Process

Mode of response is another important decision to be made while evaluating response options to hazardous materials incidents. A strategic decision that must be made is whether to respond in a defensive or an offensive mode. In a defensive mode, the objectives are to avoid intentional contact with the hazardous material and perform actions that may control or contain the incident. Going upstream to shut of a valve on a leaking sulfuric acid pipeline or placing plastic over a nearby sewer inlet to prevent an oil spill from entering are defensive mode activities. In the defensive mode, no PPE beyond the routine work requirements is needed. In an offensive mode, there may be a need for contact with the hazardous material in order to achieve containment. Plugging a leaking 55-gallon drum of sodium hydroxide or spreading activated charcoal over a large pool of solvent are offensive mode activities. Special chemical suits, gloves and boots and Self-Contained Breathing Apparatus (SCBA) personal protective equipment (PPE) are usually necessary. The defensive mode should be considered first if such activities can be effective. The offensive mode should be considered when defensive actions are insufficient.

Levels of training of responders is another decision factor. The mode of response is dependent on the amount and extent of trained responders and equipment available. First Responder Operations-level training is necessary to perform defensive mode response. It does not provide sufficient training for offensive mode. Hazardous materials technician training is required for offensive mode response and for the ability to use the specialized PPE in emergency response. One other training level is the Awareness level. This enables an employee to recognize a hazardous materials incident, secure the area, and activate the Emergency Action Plan. It does not provide sufficient training to respond to an incident in either a defensive or offensive mode. These levels of training are outlined in detail in the OSHA standard 29 CFR 1910.120. Fire department personnel are also trained according to these various levels.

Selection of PPE is part of the next step—*i.e.*, to select the best option and do it. A final decision must be made on what level of PPE to use for the response action. A lack of physical indicators such as vapor or smoke can create a perception of no or minimal hazard. A safe approach is to react with the highest possible level of response. It is easier to reduce the level of response when additional information indicates that it is safe to do so. It is not feasible to upgrade the response once the exposure has already occurred. It is essential that incident preplanning include the necessary PPE to respond to potential hazardous materials incidents. A written Standard Operating Procedure for each hazardous material on-site should include the type of PPE necessary and the chemical compatibility of PPE cloth/compositions.

Unfortunately, no single type of PPE offers total chemical protection under all conditions. Before a technician responds to a hazardous material incident, he/she must be familiar with the types and levels of protective clothing available. The Occupational Safety and Health Administration has developed a classification scheme for the various levels of chemical protective clothing (29 CFR 1910.120, Appendix B). The levels are defined as follows:

Level A–protection that should be worn when the highest level of respiratory, skin, eye, and mucous membrane protection is needed (for example— SCBA and gas-tight, totally encapsulating chemical suit).

Level B–protection that should be selected when the highest level of respiratory protection is needed with a lesser level of skin and eye protection (for example, SCBA plus an encapsulated suit with an exhaust port or a hooded suit, gloves, and boots). Level B protection is the minimum level recommended on initial site entries until the hazards have been further identified and defined by monitoring, sampling, and other reliable methods of analysis.

Level C–protection that should be selected when the type of airborne substance is known, concentration is measured, criteria for using air-purifying respirators are met, and skin and eye exposures are unlikely. Periodic monitoring of the air must be performed.

Level D–primarily, a work uniform. It should not be worn on any hazardous materials site.

The final step in the DECIDE process is to evaluate the results of the response actions. Are the objectives being accomplished? Should another option be taken? Are additional resources needed?

Are the resources being allocated appropriately? Should the response be halted and the hazardous materials incident allowed to run its course?

Enormous amounts of information must be collected and evaluated. Resources must be identified and collected. Activities must be coordinated and supervised. Leadership must be provided that ensures a united approach and eliminates free-lancing. With these and so many other functions to be performed quickly in incident response, the Hazardous Materials Manager must employ an effective way to manage the incident.

Incident Command System

In order to manage a hazardous materials incident, there must be an ability to handle the smallest incident and expand to a larger one. A method must be employed that is recognized by all response personnel and uses common terminology and procedures. One such incident management method is the *Incident Command System (ICS)*, also known as the Incident Management System. Major wild land fires in Southern California required the involvement of a huge number of resources and the response of local, county, State, and Federal jurisdictions and agencies. Problems such as ineffective communications, lack of a common command structure, lack of accountability, and the inability to coordinate the available resources occurred. FIRESCOPE (Fire Resources of Southern California Organized for Potential Emergencies) was created to identify solutions to these problems. This was the first version of the ICS. It has evolved from wild land fires into an all-risk emergency management system. The National Fire Academy has produced the Model Incident Command System that is used as a model by most emergency response agencies and jurisdictions.

The ICS is based upon basic business management practices, emphasizing the safety of personnel, coordination of incident activities, clear lines of authority and communication, maximizing the effectiveness of resources, unity of command, and a manageable span of control. In a business, leaders perform the basic tasks of planning, directing, organizing, co-ordinating, communicating, delegating, and evaluating. The same is true in incident command. The ICS is divided into five functional areas.

Command

These functional areas are under the overall direction of the Incident Commander (IC). The IC's role is to establish the strategy and tactics needed to control the incident and implement and manage the overall response plan. The IC has the ultimate responsibility for the response outcome and for the safety of the personnel. This position must be established at every incident no matter how small or whether it involves only a single resource. In larger incidents, the Command function is located in a *Command Post*, a structure, room or trailer with communications, information sources and management tools with which to command the incident but away from the immediate site of the incident.

The Command Staff positions are designed to provide assistance to the IC. The Command Staff positions are:

- **Safety Officer.** The Safety Officer is responsible for monitoring and assessing unsafe situations and ensuring personnel safety. The Safety Officer takes immediate action to correct unsafe acts and conditions and to remove responders from any threat of imminent danger.

- **Liaison Officer.** When multiple agencies are involved a Liaison Officer may be appointed to provide the point of contact and coordination for agencies not involved in the Command function.

- **Information Officer.** The Information Officer provides accurate and complete information regarding the incident for the media and other agencies requiring information directly from the incident scene.

Operations

Operations is the function that carries out the tactical activities to implement the strategy that Command develops. With the exception of the Staging area, the Operations function is located at the vicinity of the incident. Staging is the location where the resources report until given an assignment by the Staging Officer. Staging is located close enough to the incident that resources can respond quickly when assigned, but not close enough to crowd or interfere with response activities.

Planning

The purpose of the Planning function is to collect and evaluate information that is needed for the preparation of the response plan. It used to estimate the probable course of events the incident may take and prepare alternative strategies for Command consideration.

Logistics

Logistics provides services and supplies in support of Operations. This may include facilities, transportation, supplies, equipment, fuel, and services for response personnel.

Finance

Finance is usually needed only in long-term large-scale incidents to keep financial records and provide financial planning and advice to the IC.

The functions of Command, Operations, Planning, Logistics, and Finance report directly to Command. Figure 2 is a diagram of the Incident Command System.

The ICS can be implemented on a company, community, state and/or national basis, and under a variety of conditions. It does not require the disruption of existing reporting channels. The OSHA and Superfund Amendments and Reauthorization Act require that organizations that deal with hazardous material incidents respond using an ICS. Most fire, police, and Emergency Medical Services (EMS) departments implement the ICS at fire scenes, hazardous materials responses and in Mass Casualty Incidents. Certain insurance companies and local regulations require implementation of an ICS.

Media Relations

One of the functions that is available through the ICS is media relations. The media have an important role to play in our society. However, emergency responders may forget the importance of the media's role in covering an emergency when they are forced to deal with what they view as hordes of reporters at the site of a crisis. On the other hand, the media also may view emergency responders as difficult to deal with because of the lack information that is given to the press. The media represents the public's First Amendment right-to-know at a news incident. Media representatives feel they have an ethical responsibility to report news to the public, using the means provided by their specific media branch. As such, it is the responsibility of the press to find out what has taken place and to provide objective and responsible reporting to the public based on the best available information that can be obtained.

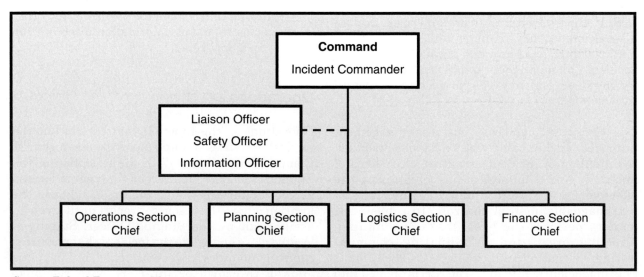

Source: Federal Emergency Management Agency, Emergency Management Institute, 2004

Figure 2. Functional Areas of the Incident Command System

Most reporters take their roles seriously and make sincere efforts to communicate news events responsibly.

Different media outlets have different needs. A single statement issued by a public information officer may not meet the needs of everyone. The television reporter is looking for a good 12-second shot. Radio reporters want good sound bites. Newspaper reporters want details and background information. And specialty services may want to cover "the story behind the story."

The incident site is the first place the press will go. It provides the best source of information for the first-in journalist. The second location where the press will show in force are at command-and-control locations. Command Posts, Emergency Operations Centers (EOCs), police and fire stations, and the offices of public officials are just a few of the locations where reporters may appear. The Liaison Officer must be prepared to monitor and, if necessary, counter misinformation. A good defense during an initial encounter with the media is to have a preselected site for media operations and interviews and to distribute a packaged press kit. This kit, which can be prepared with generic information months in advance, may buy time to gain control of the situation and what is taking place. Sample information contained in package press kits can include

- Telephone numbers for press lines at the emergency operations center
- Background information on emergency service units
- Background information on emergency response teams
- Glossary
- Diagrams of specialized equipment
- Training photographs
- Explanation of procedures, *e.g.*, use of the Chlorine B Kit
- Safety information
- Interview procedures and policies
- Information on past incidents/disasters

Encounters with the press should be planned. Designate persons with media training to provide interface with them. Instruct all others to refer the media to this person or persons. They should avoid saying "No Comment!" as this only fuels media curiosity and doubt.

There are certain rules regarding media interviews. The interviewee does not have the right to *take back* a comment already on the record, or to take it off the record. However, an attempt should be made to correct any misstatement of fact as soon as possible—even if it's after the interview. The interviewee also has no right to review a reporter's story or his or her notes prior to publication. Journalistic ethics and editorial policies of virtually all reputable news organizations forbid it. However, a request should be made to have a (print) reporter read back your quotes. It is important to remain available for later clarification if needed.

Make an effort to control the message:

- Create a short list of bullet points—the main messages to convey
- Make a list of questions that may be asked—including negative questions
- Map out and rehearse transitioning responses to the questions into statements of your messages

Be calm in panel debates and hostile interviews. Maintain composure in voice and appearance even when asked a hostile, unexpected or simplistic question. Avoid attempting to *convert* the reporter. Focus on getting the message to the public. Explain any refusal to answer a question. "It is our policy not to discuss lawsuits currently in litigation," or "I can't answer that because I haven't seen the research paper you are referring to." Do not repeat loaded words in your answer or denial. Also, don't guess. If an unfamiliar fact is brought up, offer to check on it rather than be pressured into uncomfortable estimates or judgments. Correct any misconceptions stated in interview questions. Also, if a reporter states an opinion, and then asks a question based on this *fact*, direct the answer to the opinion, not to the question.

Perceptions and Behaviors

In dealing with both the media and the public, a common problem in incident response is reality versus perception. A serious incident, such as high carbon monoxide levels in air, may have very little physical evidence. By contrast, there may be significant physical indicators suggesting an incident that are actually normal, nonemergency events. A liquid oxygen tank can exhibit frost that could be perceived as a chemical release. A planned stack flare at a refinery can be misinterpreted as an uncontrolled process problem.

Besides physical indicators, the impact on the public can influence the perception of an incident. The longer the public is subjected to disruptions and media coverage, the greater the perceived gravity of the incident. Other influences on perception are *outrage factors*, such as: incidents involving human error versus nature, chemical names *versus* natural substances names for the same material, unfamiliar hazards *versus* familiar ones (sulfuric acid *vs.* battery acid.) It is not the actual hazard that influences behaviors, it is the perception of the hazard. Outrage factors cloud the perception of the technical probability and severity of an incident. Consequently, they must be addressed in order to obtain the hazard recognition and behavioral responses needed for a safe incident response.

Political environments can also influence perceptions. Everyone has his or her own agenda. Ignoring external and governmental representatives can result in a perception of poor incident management. Using technical language instead of clear information suggests an attempt to hide something. Diplomacy and respect are critical when obtaining information. Including a Liaison Officer in the ICS is a helpful solution. The Local Emergency Planning Committee (LEPC) may also be a valuable resource.

The perception and behavior of responders needs to be considered. Some responders have a *Superman* syndrome, feeling that they can handle any incident by freelancing. Others may feel that they are not having their concerns heard, and consequently hesitate to perform in their assigned roles. Buy-in is more likely when responders have a say in the response plan. These problems can be addressed through participatory incident pre-planning and through implementation of the Incident Command System with frequent communications among sections.

When faced with unwanted volunteers, *rubber-neckers*, untrained senior management and other frustrations, be careful to avoid insulting these persons. Try to keep from being overheard by others while explaining why their services are not being solicited or why they must leave the scene. Be careful to document the interaction. If the outcome of an incident response is less than what was planned, scapegoating and hindsight supervision of the Incident Commander by political entities and supervisors can be devastating events. Much of this can be avoided by having their concerns addressed by a Liaison or Planning Section Officer during the incident.

The entire perception process and resulting behavior are based on the belief that a hazard exists, that the source of information is credible, and that the response instructions and rationale are understood. The Hazardous Materials Manager should use a well-managed communications effort in order to ensure that perceptions among responders, employees, the public, as well as community agencies and representatives are accurate.

Sheltering-In-Place

One important perception that must be understood in incident response is that the majority of persons, both employees and the public, feel that evacuation is always the best action to take. This may not be the case, however. Sometimes it is safer to stay in the building and let the release pass by. This is known as *sheltering-in-place.* Lack of adequate warning, rapid release and spread, and the time required to evacuate are all elements that may necessitate sheltering-in-place. A building can be sealed at air entrances and isolated by shutting down the air handling systems, creating an air bubble for in-place protection. In the event of an airborne hazardous material release from a plant, for example, the adjacent corporate or plant office personnel may need to remain sheltered in the office building, rather than evacuated. Some building occupants could sustain more harm from the process of an evacuation than from other options. These could include employees with impaired mobility, hospital patients, nursing home patients, and some school students, as well as large populations, such as an entire production work shift, that would obstruct evacuation routes. Evacuation may not be an option for persons who do not understand instructions due to language barriers, for prisoners, or for persons fearing loss of personal property should they leave. The severity and nature of the emergency and the exposure vulnerability determines the best options. Sometimes a combination of both strategies is feasible. If sheltering-in-place is selected, it is essential that the occupants understand the concept in order to gain their cooperation. Persons unfamiliar with this method of protection will be less compliant.

Recordkeeping

Detailed recordkeeping is an integral part of any incident response. Complete and accurate incident information: provides the ability to evaluate/critique the response and revise response plans based upon lessons learned; provides data for governmental compliance/reporting needs; provides data for management/corporate needs, helps facilitate future financial planning and allocations; and may be of beneficial use in case of litigation. Decisions made by the Incident Commander can be recorded via tape-recorder, then transposed into written form at a later time. The following can be used as a guide for the types of documentation necessary to hazardous materials incidents.

Pre-Incident/Planning Phase

- Medical surveillance records
- Respirator fit testing records
- Training records
- Drills
- Emergency Action Plans
- Standard Operating Procedures

Incident Phase

- Documentation of all decisions, responses and actions—telephone/radio traffic included
- Incident photographs/videotapes

- Hazardous materials documents, *i.e.*, shipping papers, MSDSs, *etc.*
- The ICS that was used, with defined responsibilities and levels of authority
- Documentation of media statements and public announcements

Post-Incident Follow-up. The nature and the extent of the hazardous materials incident will determine the follow-up that is necessary following the incident. A post-incident debriefing with response personnel might be a significant action to take. An incident investigation is more than likely appropriate. Some of the essential steps to consider are to:

- Ensure safety of responders and community
- Prepare an accurate record of the incident
- Revise response plans from lessons learned
- Share experiences with other response organizations
- Organize data for governmental compliance needs
- Organize data for management/corporate needs
- Establish contact persons for further activity needs
- Stimulate financial planning and allocations
- Prevent long-term emotional aftereffects
- File records and reports promptly
- Consult with legal counsel
- Keep any notes that have been made
- Correct noted response deficiencies
- Mitigate identified hazards

Inaccurate information after the incident can result in responder illness; improper cleanup; unsafe disposal; inaccurate public, management, and news media perceptions; and failure to obtain maximum benefit from the incident experience. A Comprehensive Event Analysis should be conducted, with a reconstruction of the incident and the response activities to create a clear picture of everything that occurred. Do not allow this analysis to turn into a fault-finding or finger-pointing exercise. The Analysis is completely independent of any probable-cause investigations for administrative, civil, or criminal proceedings or litigation. A completed report is disseminated to management, department heads, training personnel, and team leaders/coordinators responsible for the revision of Standard Operating Procedures and improvement in response capability.

Reporting Requirements

An essential incident response element is meeting regulatory reporting requirements. This is seldom the first thought at the beginning of an event, but cannot be ignored for long. Local, State, and Federal agencies require incident reporting in prescribed time frames and methods according to the nature of the event, the chemical(s) involved, the extent of injuries, and other incident specifics. For example, OSHA requires certain injury and fatality reports. The EPA has certain hazardous substances, toxic pollutant, and hazardous waste release immediate notification requirements and, in some cases, written report follow-up requirements (*e.g.*, oil spill written reports, wastewater exceedance reports) The United States Coast Guard has waterways release requirements. The United States Department of Transportation has hazardous materials incident written report requirements. Failure to provide timely and accurate notification and follow-up reporting can result in significant fines and adverse publicity. An essential part of preplanning is to identify possible applicable reporting requirements and the persons designated for reporting responsibilities. Have the necessary forms, instructions, and telephone/fax numbers prepared in advance.

Information Resources

An important resource in a hazardous materials emergency is the Chemical Transportation Emergency Center (CHEMTREC)—access via telephone, (800) 424–9300 or (202) 483–7616 in Washington, DC. CHEMTREC is a clearinghouse that provides a 24-hour telephone number for chemical transportation emergencies. It covers more than 3,600 chemicals that have been submitted by manufacturers as the primary materials they ship. The American Chemistry Council sponsors CHEMTREC, although non-members also are served. The emergency telephone number is widely distributed to emergency service personnel, carriers, and the chemical industry. The number usually appears on the bill of lading. When an emergency call is received by CHEMTREC, the person on duty writes down the essential information. As much information as possible is obtained by phone. The person on duty gives the caller information on hazards of spills, fire, or exposure that the manufacturers of the chemicals involved have furnished. The person on duty then notifies the shipper of the chemical by phone. At this point, responsibility for further guidance passes to the shipper. CHEMTREC's function is basically to serve as the liaison between the person with the problem and the chemical shipper and/or the manufacturer, the people who know the most about the product and its properties.

Another important resource is the local poison control center. Many chemical manufacturers in the United States will list the phone number of a poison control center on their Material Safety Data Sheets (MSDSs).

Many government agencies offer information, response plans and chemical data. Some of them are the National Ocean Service Office of Response and Restoration at <http://response.restoration.noaa.gov>. NIOSH offers training materials and information such as the *NIOSH CD-ROM Guide to Chemical Hazards*, #S022CD, released in July of 2002. The Coast Guard provides a chemical response manual at <http://www.chrismanual.com/>. The Federal EPA has resources at: <http://yosemite.epa.gov/oswer/ceppoweb.nsf/content/index.html> and <http://www.epa.gov/enviro/html/emci/chemref>.

Other countries have useful sites such as the prehospital care guide from the United Kingdom at <http://www.publications.doh.gov.uk/epcu/cbr/cbrpdf/prehosp.pdf>.

University professors and websites also provide helpful information, such as the site at the University of Akron at <http://ull.chemistry.uakron.edu/erd/>.

Bibliography

Auf Der Heide, Eric. *Disaster Response: Principles of Preparation and Coordination.* St. Louis MO: C.V.Mosby & Co., 1989.

Benner, L., "D.E.C.I.D.E. For Hazardous Materials Emergencies, Presented Papers." in , *Fifth International Symposium on the Transport of Dangerous Goods by Sea and Inland Waterways.* Vol.II. pp 24-27. Hamburg, Germany: Federal Ministry of Transport, Federal Republic of Germany:April, 1978.

Benner, L., Series of four Investigation Guides to accompany video training films with same names: *Introduction To Investigation, Accident Investigation, Hazmat Investigation And Fire Investigation.* Stillwell , OK: International Fire Service Training Association,Oklahoma State University, 1997.

Hau, Marilyn L. *While Help Is On The Way.* Chicago, IL: Health Products Marketing, 1994.

Kelly, Robert B., Industrial Emergency Preparedness. New York, NY: Van Nostrand Reinhold, 1989.

Rimson, Ira J. and L Benner, "Mishap Investigations: Tools For Evaluating The Quality Of System Safety Program Performance." in *Proceedings of 14th System Safety Conference.* Albuquerque, NM: 1996.

Internet Resources

<http://www.starlinesw.com/lbjr/HMdocs/HME76.pdf.> (A Textbook for Use in the Study of Hazardous Materials Emergencies. Internet Edition. Oakton, VA: Starline Software Ltd, 2000)

<http://www.training.fema.gov/emiweb/IS/is195.asp> (Federal Emergency Management Agency. Emergency Management Institute. IS–195 , Basic Incident Command System, 2004)

<http://www.training.fema.gov/emiweb/IS/is230.asp> (Federal Emergency Management Agency, IS–230, Principles of Emergency Management, 2004)

Marilyn L. Hau has graduate degrees in Occupational Safety and Health and Environmental Health and Safety Management. She is certified as a community health registered nurse, an occupational health nurse specialist, a firefighter/paramedic, an Occupational Safety and Health Technologist, an Associate Safety Professional and a CHMM. Ms. Hau is trained in Incident Command by the National Fire Academy and has 36 years experience in health, safety, and emergency response in communities and industry. She is the Director of Environmental Health and Safety for the University of Illinois at Chicago.

CHAPTER 32

Natural Disasters and Induced Hazardous Materials Releases

Brett A. Burdick, PG, CHMM

Introduction

During the weekend of October 15, 1994, more than 20 inches of rain fell on Southeast Texas. The San Jacinto River in Houston, which normally flows at a depth of two and one-half feet, crested to a record flood level of 23.5 feet on October 21st and forced the evacuation of more than 13,000 residents (Fedarko 1994; National Response Team 1997). Some rivers in Southeastern Texas spread nine miles outside of their levees, impacting homes where flooding had never before been seen. At least 6,000 residences were affected and some 18 persons died as a result of the flooding, prompting the Governor to declare Southeast Texas a disaster area and to seek a Federal Disaster Declaration. The President declared 26 counties in Southeast Texas and the City of Houston a Disaster Area on October 18th (National Response Team 1997). Eventually, 36 counties were included in the Federal Disaster Declaration.

As the storms eased and the San Jacinto River began to subside, two petroleum pipelines, originally buried to a depth of three feet beneath the riverbed, lay exposed. The pipelines may have been damaged by debris or may have simply collapsed, but around breakfast time that October morning they ruptured, releasing about 200,000 barrels of gasoline and diesel fuel into the still swollen stream. Seconds later the fuels ignited, pushing flames more than 100 feet into the air and sending a burning torrent flowing downstream at nearly 80 miles per hour. The inferno engulfed trees, vessels, and more than one house as it sped onward.

The two pipelines carried a huge quantity of petroleum—about one-sixth of the nation's daily fuel consumption—from Texas to New Jersey. The spill occurred within the refining and petrochemical district in Houston, severely impacting fuel availability and fuel prices throughout the east. The Houston Ship Channel was closed for several days. Several other petroleum pipelines were also leaking and discharging oil into Galveston Bay (Fedarko 1994). The fuel spill, in addition to the fire and environmental consequences, resulted in severe financial disruption beyond the devastation already caused by the flooding.

Induced Hazardous Materials Releases

Any natural or man-caused disaster may be the trigger of an induced hazardous materials release (IHR). The IHR may be extremely localized—such as the spillage of household cleaners from a shelf at a local grocery store during an earthquake—or, as illustrated above, a relatively widespread problem that spreads destruction throughout a community and severely impacts communities and economies well outside of the disaster area. It is possible that the hazardous materials component of the incident may become the major factor in terms of actual harm resulting from the disaster. In some emergency situations, as seen in the 1984 release of methyl isocyanate in Bhopal, India, and the 1986 nuclear reactor accident in Chernobyl, the hazardous materials incident is itself the disaster. In other cases, the harm done by the release of hazardous materials is minimal except to those who happen to be in the immediate vicinity of the release. The full spectrum of hazardous materials incidents has been experienced as IHRs.

As a component of the larger emergency situation, the IHR must be managed to a successful and desirable outcome as part of the overall response and recovery operations. The goal of these operations is to alleviate suffering and to protect human health and the environment. These activities may need to be performed under extremely difficult circumstances, such as when electrical power is lacking due to a damaged supply grid, with ongoing adverse weather situations, with the occurrence of additional aftereffects as the disaster continues, and with the potential of public panic and hysteria. There are also the challenges of competing priorities, resources, and personnel availability in the wake of a major disaster response operation. Any IHR associated with a community's response to a disaster situation is, to one degree or another, a critical incident. While the largest IHRs will undoubtedly be a focus of government response activities, a given IHR at a given facility may not rank high enough in priority to warrant government response in comparison to all of the other issues at hand. Yet, the protection of human health and the environment demands that the release be abated.

The response to hazardous materials incidents must be a labor-intensive exercise if it is to be performed safely and effectively. Hazardous materials response is different from other emergency management functions in that it is governed by Federal law and regulation, most notably under the Occupational Safety and Health Act and its regulations at 29 CFR 1910.120. Even the exigencies of a disaster situation do not preclude the need to operate in a safe manner compliant with the governing regulations. These two factors—being labor-intensive and requiring compliance with Federal rules—induce a third factor into the equation of hazardous materials incident response—that of time. The issue of the time required to abate any hazardous materials incident makes dealing with IHRs especially challenging. Just when the community is involved in a full-scale response to the disaster, the response to IHRs requires the community to devote a significant amount of the available resources for a considerable length of time to doing hazardous materials (HAZMAT) management. The need to address IHRs under disaster conditions and to have the mechanism in place to do this should be understood by all Certified Hazardous Materials Managers (CHMMs).

There is a linkage and a synergy between disasters and hazardous materials incidents. This linkage has only recently begun to be studied, to define the degree of association and the true magnitude of the problem. Recent investigations, however, have shown that almost all natural and man-caused disasters involve some hazardous materials component. Understanding this linkage is vital to the ability of private and public safety officials to respond to and recover from natural and man-caused disasters.

The purpose of this chapter is twofold—to introduce CHMMs to the field of Emergency Management as it is practiced in the United States and to examine the IHR problem. Emergency Management has changed significantly over the past few years and is now recognized as a separate and distinct profession that unites and coordinates the traditional public safety areas of firefighting and hazardous materials response, law enforcement, emergency medical services, and mass care. Specifically, we will investigate how hazardous materials management fits into the larger emergency management picture and how hazardous materials incidents might be addressed within this larger context.

The rest of this chapter will introduce the general concepts of managing emergency events through the concept of the emergency management cycle. It will then review the major types of IHRs as the kinds of hazardous materials response challenges IHRs pose. Finally, the chapter will review the Federal response structure and the roles of State and local government and of industry in dealing with IHRs.

The Emergency Management Cycle

The Federal Emergency Management Agency (FEMA) was established as a Federal agency in 1979 and charged with coordinating the national efforts in emergency management. FEMA is currently part of the Department of Homeland Security. FEMA defines the term *emergency* as *any event which threatens to, or actually does, inflict damage to property or people*, and the term *management* as *the coordination of an organized effort to attain specific goals or objectives*. Within this conceptual framework, it is clear that hazardous materials incidents fall under the umbrella of emergency management (FEMA 1993).

Implicit within this concept is the assumption that the natural or man-caused disaster interacts with people or their property to the detriment of people. This important concept is sometimes forgotten. A strong coastal storm or hurricane near a large city can be a disaster. Along an open coastline in an unpopulated area it is just another natural event. It is the interaction of the event with humans and their works that makes it a disaster.

The field of Emergency Management addresses the preparation for, response to, and recovery from any natural or man-caused disaster. This *All Hazards* approach has allowed Emergency Management to evolve from an exercise of "throwing assets at problems as they arise" to a legitimate field of study and endeavor where scientific and managerial principles are applied to the four phases of Emergency Management. These four phases are conceptually laid out as a cycle following an event and are, in order of occurrence, Response, Recovery, Mitigation, and Preparedness. Each of these four phases is briefly discussed below (FEMA 1993).

At the time of this writing (Fall 2004) the Department of Homeland Security (DHS) has issued a draft of the National Response Plan (NRP). The NRP includes a fifth phase of emergency management—that of Prevention. The concept of a Prevention phase is clearly linked to the DHS mission of homeland security and terrorism. Acts perpetrated by humans can, with some effort, be prevented—those of natural origin often cannot. For the purposes of this chapter we will not address the prevention phase of emergency management as envisioned by the NRP. The finalized National Response Plan is expected to be implemented sometime in early 2005.

The Event

Within the context of All Hazards Emergency Management, an event can be anything that precipitates a community-wide response. It could be a natural disaster (flood, hurricane, tornado, or earthquake), a man-caused disaster (hazardous materials release, nuclear power plant accident, act of terrorism), or even a planned event (political rally, concert, State fair, sporting event). For our purposes, the event is viewed as the beginning of the active phase of Emergency Management where significant community resources are or will be committed to intervene in the natural course of events resulting in successful and more desirable outcomes than would otherwise be expected.

It is usually assumed that the event is of such importance that both governmental and private resources must be involved in the resolution of the event to avoid undesirable outcomes. This may be a result of the scale of the event being outside of those normally encountered or a result of some particular complexity that requires unusual resources to be involved. The event is not defined by normal, day-to-day activities within the routine capabilities of public safety agencies and the private sector. The scale of the event, therefore, is such that its resolution may involve the coordination of public and private assets and capabilities, multiple legal authorities, and possibly multiple levels of government. The coordinated response to and recovery from this type of event is the mainstay of Emergency Management.

Response

Response activities occur during and immediately after the event and are designed to provide emergency assistance to victims of the event and to reduce the likelihood of secondary damage. In the case of response to a disaster, the traditional life-saving activities, law enforcement actions, and environmental protection measures come into play during this phase.

Response involves the effective and efficient application of assets and activities to resolve the immediate impacts of an event. In the case of a planned event, response activities include the application of sufficient resources to ensure that the event occurs without undue or unexpected undesirable outcomes.

Recovery

Recovery activities occur until all community systems return to normal or nearly normal conditions. This includes both short-term and long-term recovery actions. *Short-term recovery* is aimed at returning vital life-support systems to minimum operating standards, while *long-term recovery* continues until the entire disaster area is completely redeveloped, either as it was in the past or for entirely new purposes that are less disaster-prone. This may and frequently does take many years to accomplish. Recovery involves those assets and activities designed to return the community to normalcy following an event.

It is important to note that government recovery activities will not restore a community or individuals within that community to 100 percent of their preevent status. It is more involved with ensuring that a community and its citizens have the opportunity to recover through their own efforts. Recovery is a community undertaking and may involve such diverse fields as housing, economic development, and community investment.

Mitigation

Mitigation refers to those actions and activities taken to reduce or eliminate the chance of occurrence or the effects of a disaster. These include restricting development in flood plains, requiring building codes that will increase the likelihood of surviving a given wind load, and providing secondary containment for the storage of oil and hazardous materials. FEMA (1993) professes that much can be done to either prevent a major emergency or disaster from ever happening or, at least, to reduce the impact of such an event.

Preparedness

Preparedness is planning how to respond in case an emergency or disaster occurs and working to increase the resources that are available to respond effectively. The concept of preparedness is intended to address the capabilities of a community to respond to the next disaster in a safer, more efficient, more effective manner. Preparedness activities are designed to help save lives and minimize damage by preparing people to respond appropriately when an emergency is imminent. This involves planning, exercising of the plans, identifying hazards and risks, and public education through outreach and awareness.

Preparedness is the process of preparing for the next event, whether the event is planned or unexpected.

The phases of the Emergency Management Cycle often overlap and co-occur. Mitigation and Preparedness, for instance, go hand in hand before the event occurs. The transition from Response to Recovery is seldom clean, and in fact this transition may occur at different times in different geographical areas impacted by the same event (such as when a flood event works its way downstream into new areas). The utility of the Emergency Management Cycle model, however, lies in its ability to help us conceptualize the major aspects of dealing with any emergency or disaster.

It is appropriate for Certified Hazardous Materials Managers to understand the Emergency Management System as it exists in the United States today and how that system is designed to respond to hazardous materials releases associated with disasters. Disasters of all kinds will continue to involve hazardous materials releases. CHMMs are uniquely positioned to provide the linkage between disaster activities and protection of the public from the release of hazardous materials.

Disasters and IHRs—Some Examples

The model of the Emergency Management Cycle can be applied with great success to hazardous materials incidents, and specifically to those incidents precipitated by natural or man-caused disasters. In this section we will examine how natural disasters can give rise, often unexpectedly and improbably, to hazardous materials incidents. Later, we will examine how the field of Emergency Management and the programs supporting the Emergency Management Cycle can assist in resolving these incidents as part of the emergency management system.

The Federal Emergency Management Agency (FEMA) has identified at least 15 kinds of natural and man-caused hazards that may impact local communities. These include severe thunderstorms, floods and flash floods, landslides and mudflows, tornadoes, hurricanes, winter storms, drought and extreme heat, wildfire, earthquake, tsunami, volcanic eruption, dam failure, structural

fires and explosions, radiological accidents, and hazardous materials releases (FEMA 1994). Many other hazards exist that are within the domain of emergency management. These include transportation incidents, mass casualty incidents, and public health incidents, for example.

Several of these 15 natural and man-caused hazards can and have resulted in a secondary release of hazardous materials. These secondary or induced hazardous materials releases (IHRs) compound the problems facing emergency managers and, in fact, sometimes become the most significant hazard encountered during the disaster.

One review of the occurrence of IHRs caused by natural disasters in the United States over the period of 1980 through 1989 was accomplished by surveying the states and asking them to respond to a questionnaire (Showalter and Myers 1994). The survey revealed that of 311 incidents identified in 20 states, the vast majority of IHRs were the result of earthquakes (73 percent). This might be expected due to the large area of impact an earthquake can have and the fragility of hazardous materials storage and transportation systems when exposed to significant ground shaking and displacement. Earthquake-related IHRs were followed in descending order of frequency by hurricanes (8.3 percent) and floods (5.1 percent). The remaining 14 percent of IHRs were attributed to lightning, winds, storms, dam breaks, fire, fog, ice storms, tornadoes, and landslides. It follows from this that any natural event could result in the release of hazardous materials, but that the most common causes of IHR are earthquakes, hurricanes, and floods.

The authors do not claim that this analysis is all-inclusive. It is evident that their results may be biased by over-reporting by states prone to earthquakes and by poor recordkeeping among the states in general. It is also difficult to understand what exactly the states meant, for instance, by a "flood-induced hazardous materials incident." If a flood resulted in the dislocation and subsequent recovery of 100 hazardous materials containers over a wide area throughout the flood plain, is this one incident or 100? If an earthquake causes 100 separate IHRs in the impacted area, how are these tallied? (For example, the Loma Prieta Earthquake in 1989 resulted in 300 separate IHRs; see below.) Nevertheless, the Showalter and Myers (1994) study is instructive in that it is an initial quantification of the number and geographic extent of IHRs. At least 311 incidents in 20 states over a period of 10 years indicate that the occurrence of IHRs is not a trivial problem.

Results from this study suggest a correlation between the number of IHRs experienced during an event and the magnitude of the causative event, although this general correlation must be tempered to consider the degree of industrialization in the affected area. In a large event in an urban setting, the cumulative problem of IHR would predictably be quite serious. The authors also conclude that when communities and commercial facilities are simultaneously impacted by a natural disaster, response agencies will first become involved with assisting the citizenry directly, at the expense of responding to damaged facilities. This means that hazardous materials facility response plans that rely on the full cooperation of public fire, police, and other emergency response departments are inherently unworkable during a natural disaster. The ability of any individual community to respond to a HAZMAT incident varies. CHMMs involved in IHR planning must consider the local capabilities and those of industry within the community when formulating realistic response plans.

The above discussion suggests that three phenomena—earthquakes, hurricanes, and floods—result in the majority of IHRs. Each of these phenomena results in a different pattern of IHR that should be understood by all emergency and hazardous materials managers. The rest of this section looks at each of these natural events and the kinds of IHR they may generate.

Earthquakes

The release of hazardous materials caused by earthquakes is the most studied of all IHR events. Many authors conclude that this event is the most likely kind of natural disaster to result in an IHR, due in part to the widespread impacts of ground shaking over a large geographical area and the proximity of some major metropolitan and industrialized areas to active faults (Los Angeles, San Francisco, Mexico City, and Tokyo, as examples). The occurrence of strong aftershocks tending to follow major earthquakes may also result in IHRs among already damaged structures or in otherwise undamaged communities miles away from the original epicenter and for months following the original earthquake (Hough and Jones 1997).

The risk posed by earthquake-induced hazardous materials releases (EIHRs) can be explored from an historical standpoint (Lindell and Perry 1996 and 1997). The EIHR experience in recent earthquakes in this country includes the following:

1) The 1971 San Fernando earthquake (magnitude 6.6) resulted in 100 fires requiring fire department response and 18 documented hazardous materials releases.

2) The 1983 Coalinga earthquake (magnitude 6.7) resulted in many natural gas leaks and oil pipeline ruptures and 9 documented hazardous materials releases. In addition, chlorine tanks at the local sewage treatment plant slid 10 inches and threatened to release.

3) The 1987 Whittier Narrows earthquake (magnitude 6.1) resulted in 1,411 natural gas line ruptures and 30 hazardous materials releases, one of which involved the release of chlorine (see below). Another event involved the toppling of a container containing metallic sodium under kerosene at a college science laboratory. A water leak from a safety shower reacted with the sodium to produce sufficient heat and hydrogen gas to cause a fire. The fire resulted in the vaporization of mercury elsewhere in the laboratory, and firefighting activities exposed asbestos incorporated into the building construction. The cleanup of this laboratory cost nearly one-quarter of a million dollars.

4) The 1989 Loma Prieta earthquake (magnitude 6.7) resulted in more than 300 natural gas leaks and over 300 hazardous materials releases. Fifty of these involved hazardous gases other than natural gas. One incident involved the rupture of a 2-inch anhydrous ammonia line at a food-processing plant, resulting in the release of between 5,000 and 20,000 pounds of ammonia.

5) The 1994 Northridge earthquake (magnitude 6.8) resulted in more than 15,000 natural gas leaks linked to 3 street fires, 51 structure fires, and 172 mobile home fires. The earthquake induced at least 130 other hazardous materials releases. One of these was an oil pipeline rupture which released 173,000 gallons of product and ultimately cost $30 million to remedy. Another was a railcar release of 2,000 gallons of sulfuric acid. The authors indicate that hazardous materials releases occurred at 10 percent of the industrial facilities and 5

percent of the commercial facilities in the zone of greatest impact.

What is most striking about this listing of EIHRs is the number of hazardous materials incidents that are reported to be associated with earthquakes. Addressing the 130 IHRs reported during the 1994 Northridge Earthquake could take weeks or months to accomplish. The effort required to resolve the 300 nearly simultaneous IHRs documented during the 1989 Loma Prieta Earthquake is mind-boggling.

In contrast to Showalter and Myers (1994), Lindell and Perry (1996) find little direct correlation between earthquake magnitude and the number of EIHRs, due to other effects including soil conditions, mitigation measures employed in the area, and the specific location and concentration of hazardous materials sources. They conclude, however, that a thorough postevent investigation will reveal the presence of EIHRs in almost all cases of damaging earthquakes. They also indicate that the actual numbers of EIHRs probably are significantly under-reported (Lindell and Perry 1997) due to the general confusion that reigns following a significant earthquake, the independent actions of facility personnel who clean up releases without reporting them, and those, perhaps, ignored and not reported by the responsible parties.

Some of the sequences of events that can be documented associated with EIHRs are quite improbable (Lindell and Perry 1996). One example comes from an unidentified locality during the 1964 Alaskan earthquake (but probably the city of Seward). The earthquake generated a tsunami that resulted in the rupture of some oil storage tanks and in a break in the hose connecting a tank vessel loading diesel fuel in the harbor. The spilled fuel ignited. A second tsunami drove the burning fuels inland, igniting the oil in several railroad tank cars. The tank cars exploded sequentially in a chain reaction which ultimately resulted in the ignition of a bulk fuel storage yard many blocks away. If anything can go wrong, it will.

The pattern of the impacts of EIHRs is unique and has relevance to the planning process. An earthquake may induce widespread and nearly simultaneous releases of hazardous materials. It is common for multiple hazardous materials incidents to require response at the same time. Most hazardous materials response planning

assumes that hazardous materials events are nearly random and statistically independent events (Noll, *et al.* 1988). The capabilities of any community's hazardous materials response programs will be seriously taxed in the event of a widespread disaster of this type.

Beyond the pure numbers that indicate the magnitude of the EIHR problem, it is instructive to examine the specific hazardous materials issues that may be involved in the management of the response to and recovery from such a disaster. The two examples that follow demonstrate the types of demands that may be placed on emergency managers confronted with an EIHR event.

In 1987, the Whittier Narrows earthquake in southern California resulted in the rupture of a chlorine storage tank in the city of Santa Fe Springs (Seligson, *et al.* 1996). The ruptured tank released approximately 240 gallons of chlorine gas which drifted as a plume toward the city of Whittier prompting the evacuation of some areas. People living in southern California experience magnitude 5.9 earthquakes on a relatively frequent basis. Hough and Jones (1997) report that there have been 74 magnitude 5.5 and larger events in Southern California since 1932, so it is probable that a magnitude 5.9 occurs at least once every few years. It was the co-location of the earthquake epicenter near the chlorine storage facility in Santa Fe Springs, not just the magnitude of the earthquake, that resulted in this release.

Just how much of a risk does chlorine storage pose to residents in the Los Angeles area? One study (Seligson, *et al.* 1996) has modeled the potential impacts of a large earthquake and concluded that nearly 7,000 people could have been exposed to this release. While this earthquake would not be strong enough to cause major damage, it clearly could have a significant impact on the population through secondary release of hazardous materials. Thus, the hazardous materials issue becomes the dominant source of harm in this scenario.

The simulations analyzed by Seligson and coworkers also included a far worse case event, that of a magnitude 7.0 earthquake along the Newport-Inglewood Fault which cuts through the Los Angeles Basin. After identifying 22 sources of chlorine and ammonia in the area and assuming that the storage vessels were all compromised, the model suggests that as many as 133,000 people— or 2 percent of the population of Los Angeles

County—would be exposed to harmful concentrations of these two chemicals released during the earthquake. This scenario would produce a public health emergency that probably could not be handled effectively by a medical infrastructure already damaged by an event of this magnitude. Protective actions involving 130,000 people would stretch the capabilities of any emergency services organization under more routine circumstances, let alone following a destructive earthquake.

A second example of the impacts of EIHR comes from the earthquake that impacted Japan in the vicinity of the City of Kobe in January, 1995. In addition to the hazardous materials releases caused directly by the Kobe earthquake, Japan's environmental agency reported that the collapsed buildings resulted in a significant increase in the concentration of asbestos fibers in the ambient air (Hadfield 1995). Japanese construction commonly utilized asbestos until 1965 for fireproofing and soundproofing, even in residential buildings. Many of the structures destroyed in the event had been constructed prior to 1965. For days following the earthquake it was reported that a "haze of asbestos dust hung over the city . . ." and that the areas where demolition crews were working had especially high levels of airborne asbestos (Hadfield 1995).

The 1993 national average concentration for ambient asbestos samples in Japan was reported to be 0.43 fibers per liter of air. Measured concentrations in Kobe and a nearby town in February following the earthquake averaged nearly twice this (0.8 fibers per liter of air), and in the area where building demolition was ongoing the average level was 11.2 fibers per liter. This value exceeds the maximum concentration of 10 fibers per liter allowed under Japan's Air Pollution Control Law that governs asbestos removal actions (Hadfield 1995). Buildings undergoing demolition in Japan are usually sprayed with water to avoid raising clouds of asbestos dust. Following the earthquake, however, water pipes and roof tanks were damaged to the point that water was not available during demolition.

In this example, the actions of cleanup crews involved in the recovery from the earthquake were coupled with the direct impacts of the disaster to compound an already bad situation. The risks to public health from the airborne asbestos could, theoretically, result in many more deaths than the 5,000 resulting directly from the earthquake.

It seems prudent to assume that any building involved in a major earthquake is likely to be a source of IHRs until proven otherwise. For the case of collapsed buildings, the probability that hazardous materials are involved is near certainty.

As can be seen, the IHR problems associated with earthquakes are impressive. Generally speaking, the most severe public safety impacts would be expected to come from releases of toxic or poisonous gases and long-term impacts from the exposure to asbestos. Other localized impacts may result from spills and releases of other hazardous materials classes, especially flammable liquids. Earthquakes result in the most widespread and immediate IHR impacts of the natural phenomena studied to date.

An interesting additional problem—that of the preparedness of the population living in the vicinity of potential IHRs—has been studied by Steinberg, *et al.* (2002). Their study surveyed a random sampling of residents living within 5.6 kilometers of a petroleum refinery in southern California. The study demonstrated that there is little readiness on the part of individuals when confronting an EIHR, even in this area where there has been substantial community outreach regarding the dangers of earthquakes. Local emergency response officials as well as plant health and safety officials indicated that such a scenario had been anticipated and they were prepared to respond to an EIHR. Without an understanding and appreciation on the part of the local citizenry, however, EIHR response actions could be compromised.

Hurricanes

The second most important sources of IHRs are hurricanes. Impacting wide areas of coastal communities where they strike, hurricanes result in wind damage, flooding, and the destruction of buildings that may release hazardous materials. Direct impacts could include the destruction of storage tanks, the flooding of warehouses and docks, and the destruction of storage areas containing hazardous materials. Cruz, *et al.* (2001), for example, examined the potential impacts of hurricanes on a petroleum refinery and identified several IHR release scenarios due to equipment damage, pipe and connection damage, power failures, punctured tanks and vessels, and structural damage. The primary concern where hurricanes make landfall, however, is the accumulation, staging, and disposal of tremendous volumes of debris, some of it hazardous.

One example that illustrates some of the risks of debris is from southern Florida in 1992. Hurricane Andrew has been described as one of the costliest natural disasters in United States' history. Several examples of localized hazardous materials impacts were identified among the devastation. As in Kobe, asbestos was again a prominent hazard.

The sheer volume of the hurricane-derived debris was staggering. In all of south Florida the hurricane resulted in 40 million cubic yards of debris. This is equivalent to one football field stacked *five miles* high (National Park Service 1994)! On September 21, 1992, at the peak of the cleanup activity, the effort involved more than 4,000 personnel, 2,158 trucks, and 720 loaders. Contractors moved 290,000 cubic yards of debris on that day alone (Emergency Management Institute).

Approximately 23 percent of the storm-generated debris was composed of building materials, including a significant amount of asbestos (National Park Service 1994). Other hazardous materials were also released by the destruction of storage sheds and buildings. Household hazardous and toxic wastes (HHW) are a major concern in residential areas. HHW can include common household chemicals, propane tanks, oxygen bottles, batteries, and other chemicals such as pesticides and paints (Emergency Management Institute undated). HHW and other hazardous wastes must be separated from the waste stream and staged for appropriate removal by trained contractors.

One significant obstacle to the cleanup following a hurricane is that there is often no way to tell where the hazardous materials are present until debris removal begins. Crews involved in debris clearance must be aware of the potential for IHRs and must be able to notify appropriate authorities if IHRs are encountered.

Most of the asbestos encountered by the National Park Service within the National Parks of south Florida resulted from roofing shingles and siding stripped from buildings by the hurricane's winds. Some damage was caused by the direct impact of storm surge and waves on asbestos-containing structures. Much of the asbestos was blown and washed into adjacent water bodies. The National Park Service addressed the asbestos problem by contracting for the removal and disposal of asbestos debris, as well as the other hazardous materials released during the storm (National Park Service 1994).

The woody and other organic debris generated by hurricanes and staged during the cleanup will, in time, decompose and emit toxic or volatile vapors (Emergency Management Institute). Debris-burning activities will also produce some adverse air quality impacts. All debris storage and disposal areas require active air monitoring to ensure that workers and the general public are not exposed to hazardous air pollutants.

A similar set of problems was encountered by the United States Army Corps of Engineers in the cleanup following Hurricane Marilyn in the Virgin Islands (Anonymous 1995). The hurricane generated more than 300,000 cubic yards of debris in September, 1995 that required disposal. The landfills on the islands of St. Croix and St. Thomas were full, so the Corps opted to burn or bury the waste. Hazardous waste was reported to be barreled and transported to the United States mainland. The lack of a disposal facility on the islands resulted in the suggestion that the debris be moved to the mainland. The Corps estimated that the shipping would cost $31 million.

Catallo, Theberge, and Bender (1989) discuss the problems associated with waste disposal in coastal areas. They suggest that a direct result of human preferences for living in areas subject to coastal storms and hurricanes is the disposal of wastes, including hazardous wastes, in these same areas. They estimate that half of the nation's Superfund sites occur in or near estuarine, riparian, or coastal lowland settings. This fact, coupled with the demonstrable eustatic rise in sea level observed in long-term tidal records, suggests that future impacts of coastal storms and hurricanes on waste disposal areas could result in an increased likelihood of IHRs through time.

Dealing with the debris resulting from a major hurricane shows the interplay of hazardous materials management and solid waste disposal. While not a large proportion of the debris and waste disposal stream, the sheer magnitude of the volume of debris involved raises the hazardous and asbestos-laden waste to the level of more than merely a trivial problem.

Floods

Floods represent the most common natural hazard in the United States (FEMA 1994). The power of flowing water in storm-swollen streams is immense. Structures containing hazardous materials, disposal sites, hazardous materials storage areas in the flood plains, and—as we saw in the example of the San Jacinto River—utility crossings of flooding streams are significant potential sources of secondary releases to the environment. Despite zoning and siting criteria, there are large quantities of hazardous materials in areas inundated by flood waters.

Denning (1992) has investigated the types of hazardous materials problems that may be associated with a flood. Based upon the experience of an unnamed southern state in the spring of 1991, Denning's instructive study classified the specific hazardous materials–related problems experienced during this flood as follows:

1) *The displacement of underground storage tanks and their contents by flood waters.* Some tanks floated out of the ground while others filled with water and discharged their inventories, becoming both an environmental problem and a fire hazard.

2) *The flooding of reserve pits, tanks, and wells within oil fields.* We could add the flooding and displacement of all pits and lagoons located in the flood plain whether they were oil field–related or not, as well as drum and container storage areas inundated by the flood waters.

3) *The interruption of ongoing hazardous materials site cleanup.* Flooding can redistribute contaminants and impact previously uncontaminated areas, and certainly can interfere with critical construction timetables.

4) *Wind-induced damages, such as at an airport where a hangar collapsed on aircraft and resulted in a release of aviation fuel.* Aircraft (and vehicles) are a source of both toxic and flammable fluids.

5) *The inundation of landfills by the flooding.* Landfills can be damaged, submerged, or washed out by periodic flooding. Floods can remove daily cover from putrefying waste and, under some conditions, result in compromising the structural integrity of the landfill. The release of municipal waste to the environment can result in a widespread public health emergency. Wright, Inyang, and Myers (1993) discuss ways to reduce the risk of landfill releases due to floods and other natural hazards through the planning process.

6) *The inundation of sewage systems and wastewater treatment plants.* In addition to the interruption of sewage service, the plants themselves handle hazardous materials and can be a source of hazardous materials releases.

7) *The contamination of wells by flood waters.* This is an acute problem in rural areas, but also in urban areas where the municipal well fields are impacted. Floodwaters contaminate aquifers by directly entering the wellbore and recharging the ground water with bacteria and chemical-laden flood waters.

8) *The inundation of automobile junkyards.* Junkyards, even the best managed of them, are sources of petroleum, coolant, and debris. Those located in the flood plain are clear sources of IHR.

9) *The release of transformer fluids into flood waters.*

10) *Barge accidents on waterways releasing cargoes and fuels.* Flooded streams are always hazardous to navigate, and moored barges and vessels, exposed to great stress from the flow, may be cast adrift during the flood.

11) *Trucking accidents in bad weather and the release of diesel fuel and hazardous materials cargoes.*

12) *And, as a last example from this study, a fire and explosion at a chemical plant manufacturing anhydrous ammonia and other hazardous chemicals.* The explosion killed 8 and injured 100 employees, required the evacuation of 1,500 residents including the local hospital and its 20 patients. (It was noted by Denning that the chemical plant explosion was not caused by the floods; but its timing coincident with the flooding demonstrates the types of incidents that can happen when communities are already responding to emergency situations. Again, if anything can go wrong, it will.) The explosion and chemical release would be difficult enough to deal with by the community. During the flooding, the additional requirements of responding to the explosion nearly stretched local responders ". . . to their limits" (Denning 1992).

Denning's (1992) list is long. It points out several specific types of impacts any jurisdiction might expect in a disastrous flood, but even it is not all-inclusive. To it we could undoubtedly add many more potential hazardous materials impacts, including, perhaps, the flooding of facilities at nuclear weapons plants (Anonymous 1996). All of the impacts listed above are secondary to the primary disaster of the flood. Local resources, already committed to life-saving missions along compromised transportation systems, using overloaded communications systems, and without electrical power, are hard pressed to deal effectively with public safety issues caused by hazardous materials releases. Most of the hazardous materials releases involved in this flood were small and easily dealt with during the recovery period (Denning 1992), but there is no reason to believe that this must be the case.

Some of the released materials will, with luck, be diluted or dispersed by the flood waters, and in that way, public safety impacts are minimized. Alternatively, some flood processes may act to concentrate the occurrence of hazardous materials, such as the trapping of drums and containers on the upstream side of bridges and culverts. Some of these hazardous materials incidents will require significant resources to resolve. Secondary hazards caused by hazardous materials releases were real concerns to responders in this study.

Another example of flooding causing IHR incidents comes from the experience of Virginia following two flooding disasters in 1996 (Virginia Department of Emergency Services 1996). In January, snow melt and a warm rain resulted in significant flooding, primarily to the west of the Blue Ridge in the Shenandoah Valley but also involving several communities on the eastern side of the Appalachians. That September, widespread flooding impacted the same areas as Tropical Storm Fran moved into Virginia after coming ashore as Hurricane Fran in North Carolina.

These flooding events resulted in a significant number of containers being swept downstream throughout much of the Commonwealth. The drainages involved included the Dan, James, Maury, Rapidan, Roanoke, and Shenandoah Rivers—approximately one-third of the land area of the state. The location, recovery, and identification of the contents of these containers involved a significant effort. The field activities following the January flooding had not been completed before Tropical Storm Fran hit, adding to the number of containers involved and requiring that all areas investigated during the January floods be surveyed again. In all, 2,838 containers of varying sizes ranging from gasoline cans to propane and petroleum storage tanks were recovered from the streams and the flood plains, characterized, and disposed of properly. This example is not at all unique. The Virginia Department of Emergency Management collected more than 600 containers from the City of Franklin following the flooding of Hurricane Floyd in 1999. In the spring of 2003 floods along the Holston River in southwest Virginia resulted in the recovery of more than 3,000 containers. The flooding associated with Hurricane Isabel (September, 2003) in the Tidewater areas of Virginia added another several hundred containers. Floods displace hazardous materials and make the investigation of these materials a major public safety undertaking.

The cost of the 1996 collection effort was approximately one quarter of a million dollars, or an average cost of nearly $100 per container recovered, which is a standard that has been exceeded in recent years. This estimate does not include the costs of locating the containers, primarily by National Guard helicopter overflights. Understandably, most of the containers were empty at the time of the flooding, but a significant number of them—perhaps 20 percent—contained hazardous materials or residues. Notwithstanding the actual number of containers that carried hazardous materials downstream, a significant effort was undertaken to find those that were actually a hazard. Public safety considerations demand that all of the containers be found and investigated.

These examples serve to demonstrate the magnitude of IHRs in flooding events and the difficulty of dealing with these hazardous materials incidents. The costs of these incidents fall primarily on government, as the releases are the result of an *Act of God* and exempted from much regulatory authority, including cost recovery.

The Federal Government Response Organization

There is a high probability that some IHRs will accompany any significant disaster. The systematic approach taken by the Federal government

Table 1. Emergency Support Functions and the Lead Federal Agencies under the Federal Response Plan

Emergency Support Function	
ESF	**Topic**
1	Transportation
2	Telecommunications and Information Technology
3	Public Works and Engineering
4	Firefighting
5	Emergency Management
6	Mass Care, Housing, and Human Services
7	Resource Support and Logistics Management
8	Public Health and Medical Services
9	Urban Search and Rescue
10	Oil and Hazardous Materials
11	Agriculture
12	Energy
13	Public Safety and Security
14	Economic Stabilization, Community Recovery, and Mitigation
15	Emergency Public Information and External Communication

to respond to all disasters is has been described in the *Federal Response Plan* (FRP). The FRP, prepared by FEMA and adopted by 27 Federal departments and agencies, is designed to facilitate the delivery of all types of Federal response assistance to states to help them deal with the consequences of large-scale disasters. As mentioned above, FEMA and DHS intend to revise the FRP with the NRP which becomes effective in early 2005. These documents detail the support that the Federal government gives *to the states*. The states, in turn, provide both their own support and the Federal support to the localities. The system is designed so that localities remain in charge of disaster response in their own communities and that State and Federal assistance is provided to augment local response capabilities as the conditions warrant. While support is given primarily to public sector organizations and agencies (fire, police, emergency medical services,

etc.) the Federal-State-local partnership also assists private organizations and, indeed, integrates public support to the community with support from private organizations.

The FRP was organized around twelve Emergency Support Functions (ESFs) and the NRP modifies and expands the number of ESFs to fifteen. Each of these EFSs under the FRP had a single Federal agency or department which leads the Federal response under that ESF. At the time of this writing, the NRP has not identified the primary agency responsible for all ESFs but it is expected that each ESF will, again, have primary agencies assigned. The ESFs identified by the draft NRP are identified in Table 1.

The Corps of Engineers' operations in the Virgin Islands following Hurricane Marilyn, for example, were the result of the Corps being the lead Federal agency for ESF #3–Public Works and Engineering and responsible for debris clearance and disposal in this disaster under the FRP that was in effect at that time. The system allows these Federal agencies and departments to plan their own response strategies, and these individual agency plans are incorporated into the plan by reference. It is expected that the NRP will be organized in a similar way. It is DHS' and FEMA's responsibility to ensure that all of the plans mesh.

Recognition of the reality of hazardous materials disasters is underlined by the existence of ESF #10 –Oil and Hazardous Materials. While developing the plans, FEMA understood that there is a need to prepare for the direct response to man-caused disasters (such as the Bhopal and the Chernobyl Incidents) as well as a secondary hazardous materials response in any disaster situation. The Lead Federal Agency under ESF #10 will, presumably, be the Environmental Protection Agency (EPA).

EPA's concept of operations under ESF #10 is described in the FRP and will be described in an Annex to the NRP. The purpose of ESF #10 is to provide Federal support to State and local governments in response to an actual or potential discharge of hazardous materials following a catastrophic earthquake or other catastrophic disaster. As such it is intended primarily to address IHRs. EPA has provided for a coordinated response by placing the response mechanisms of the National Contingency Plan (NCP) within the NRP coordination structure. This means that the response to all oil and hazardous substance releases associated with a natural or man-caused disaster will be in accordance with the NCP. EPA, the United States Coast Guard, Department of Energy, or Department of Defense On-Scene Coordinators (OSCs) will be assigned to each release or to the multiple releases, and the OSC will be responsible for implementing the appropriate remedy.

The FRP provided that the EPA Co-Chair of the Regional Response Team (RRT) would be assigned to the FEMA Disaster Field Office (DFO) working directly under the FEMA Federal Coordinating Officer (FCO) to coordinate all activities of the OSCs. All DFO personnel working in support of ESF #10 were to be, to the extent possible, members of the RRT. Among the planning assumptions under ESF #10 are that emergency exemptions for the disposal of contaminated material will be required. At the national level, the support structure is intended to be implemented by the EPA Director of the Chemical Emergency Preparedness and Prevention Office (CEPPO) in the Office of Solid Waste and Emergency Response (OSWER). When the NRP Annex for ESF #10 is finalized it may result in some modifications to this scheme.

The presence of ESF #10 in the DFO allows incoming information regarding hazardous materials releases to be acted upon in a coordinated fashion. Response priorities are established at the regional level with input from EPA Headquarters and State, and local representatives.

[Note: The NRP has changed the concept of the DFO by creating a Joint Federal Office (JFO) in the Federal response to any large scale disaster. The JFO is the operational office for all Federal activities during the disaster—including, for instance, the FBI Joint Operations Center (JOC). The JFO is overseen by a new postion, that of the Principal Federal Official (PFO). The PFO is the designated representative of the Secretary of Homeland Security at any disaster. Despite these modifications to the disaster response system there should be little difference in the delivery of services to states and local governments during disaster operations.]

When EPA becomes involved in a disaster response, it has the authority to involve other Federal agencies in support of ESF #10. For example, EPA can enlist the assistance of the

Occupational Safety and Health Administration (OSHA) to ensure that site-specific health and safety plans are reviewed in a timely manner, and the Department of Agriculture to assist in the development of natural resources damage assessments. Disposal of wastes and discharge of treated wastewater can go forward under existing EPA authority without the need for obtaining permits, thus streamlining the response effort.

Much of this coordination will be transparent to the local government and to private industry response organizations. What is significant is that a process for coordinating the response to hazardous materials releases exists within the overall disaster response structure. The upshot of this is that allocation of resources and priority of response assets will take place in a coordinated fashion.

Federal and State Support to Local Government

As we saw with the San Jacinto River incident, there is a formal process by which the governors of the states can request assistance from the Federal government to respond to and recover from major disasters. The flooding in Southeast Texas was of sufficient magnitude that the Governor declared a State of Emergency and requested a Federal Disaster Declaration. In declaring a State of Emergency, the Governor is invoking a range of state laws that allow for assistance to be given to local governments (among other provisions) in their response to a disaster. The range and scope of these laws vary from state to state; however, they generally allow for augmentation of local capabilities using State assets such as the National Guard. They also, in general, provide for an alternative funding mechanism and procurement system so that assistance can be provided in a timely manner.

State law also may provide for the ability of local government to declare a State of Emergency. In Virginia, for example, a local declaration allows the local Director of Emergency Management to expedite contracts and to control the sale and distribution of food (including alcohol), fuel, and other commodities. If the local jurisdiction requests additional assistance, the Governor may declare a State of Emergency. This declaration would then implement several additional powers at the State level, including the ability of the Governor to control access and egress from areas of the Commonwealth.

FEMA's support to localities is always channeled through the states. FEMA support, through the Stafford Act, is initiated when the Governor requests the President to provide Federal assistance. The request requires considerable documentation of the severity of the disaster to support a Federal declaration, and requires a clear statement on the part of the Governor that State capabilities are or will be overwhelmed. The most common Federal assistance will be in the form of recovery assistance, although FEMA does have formidable response assets as well.

Other Federal agencies have the ability to support local governments and the states directly under existing authorities and do not require a presidential declaration before implementation. Two of the most important are the assistance provided by EPA and the Military Aid to Civil Authorities provided by the Department of Defense.

EPA can respond to the release of oil and hazardous substances at any time under its existing Comprehensive Environmental Response, Compensation, and Liability Act (CERCLA) and the Oil Pollution Act (OPA) authorities, including during disasters. An EPA or Coast Guard OSC has the capability to address hazardous materials releases without a presidential declaration. In addition, any Department of Defense base commander can respond to a request for assistance from local government in order to protect property or to alleviate human suffering under his or her own authority. These capabilities are frequently exercised when a quick response involving a large number of personnel is needed; such as during floods or when an impending levee break is imminent. Some Defense Department bases have a hazardous materials response capability that could be utilized.

The overall system of Emergency Management revolves around local government and private response capabilities. As this brief discussion implies, the problem of responding to hazardous materials emergencies, even in conjunction with a disaster, is fundamentally a local problem, and includes a mechanism by which additional assets can be obtained in a graduated and measured way if the local capabilities are overwhelmed.

Local governments and industries are responsible for doing all they can to address any IHR issues. Capabilities vary from locality to locality across the nation. If they are overwhelmed, local government can request mutual aid from adjacent jurisdictions, assistance from any Department of Defense installations nearby, or from EPA, but the most probable next step is to contact the State Emergency Management agency. The state's job is to coordinate the mobilization of State-level assets (including the National Guard) and to prioritize the requests for assistance they receive from local government. In large-scale disasters, the state will also coordinate the request for Federal assistance and coordinate the application of Federal assistance to localities, to businesses, and to private citizens impacted by the disaster, including when IHRs are involved.

Local Government and Private Sector Roles and Responsibilities

The bottom line with IHRs, and with all emergency management for that matter, is that local government and industry are ultimately responsible for effective hazardous materials response during a disaster. This may occur under extremely adverse conditions of weather and infrastructure damage, and will need to be prioritized along with all other demands of the moment. Some issues can be addressed by effective planning; for instance, by industry not relying exclusively on government capabilities in responding to hazardous materials releases.

The protection of public safety is an ethical issue for both government and industry. While no activity is risk-free and while many necessary industrial activities involve hazardous materials that may be released, the goal of all response and hazardous materials professionals must be to minimize the potential for releases and to optimize our capabilities in responding to those releases that do occur. As we have seen, IHRs may occur at the most difficult times and under the most bizarre of circumstances. It is incumbent upon local government and industry to operate safely and in a manner protective of public safety.

Industry has a vested interest in minimizing the impacts of IHRs. All hazardous materials releases must eventually be remediated and, as we have seen through many years of regulatory action, it is usually cheaper in the long run to prevent or minimize releases facility-wide than to remediate even one. It is foolish and unethical to view IHRs as a cost of doing business. In addition, local impacts can be severe, and the proximity of industry to any release suggests that the facilities themselves and their personnel may be the recipients of the greatest impacts. Ultimately, of course, industry owns the hazardous materials involved and is ultimately responsible for the safe and effective custody of those materials. Industry has the greatest knowledge of the hazards associated with any release of these materials and the greatest expertise in the response to and cleanup of spills and releases. Industries in hazardous areas—especially those prone to earthquakes, hurricanes, and floods—must prepare for the potential for IHRs.

Government also has a vested interest in ensuring that the impacts of IHRs are minimized. Response to hazardous materials releases anywhere outside of facility operational areas usually falls to public sector responders. IHRs occur at times when other issues may be more pressing, or the IHR itself may be overwhelming. In either case, local capabilities are limited, so it makes sense to attempt to minimize the number and severity of IHRs through effective planning. Government may also be impacted by IHRs through the ownership of infrastructure. Transportation routes are owned by the public and are impacted during releases. Publicly-owned water utilities and sewage treatment plants can be severely impacted by IHRs. Let us not forget, also, that government owns a lot of hazardous materials as well.

The studies of IHR suggest that the planning process can be used to predict vulnerabilities to IHR and that mitigation efforts can be put in place to minimize their impacts. CHMMs and other managers and planners should serve as those individuals responsible for considering these impacts as part of local government and industry *all hazards* planning.

Summary

IHRs usually are secondary events that occur coincident with and as a direct result of a larger natural or man-caused disaster. In many instances the IHRs add to and complicate an already difficult situation. In other instances, the IHR may predominate over the initial disaster event in terms of potential harm and resources required to respond effectively. The IHR may result in more local damage than the original event and, due to the number and severity of the IHRs that occur, may be a significant challenge to public safety in the long term. The co-location of a natural or man-caused disaster and hazardous materials is required for an IHR to occur, and the severity of the IHR is related to the proximity to population centers as well as the properties of the materials involved. The response to IHRs is labor- and time-intensive, but these resources must be applied to the remediation of IHRs if the public safety is to be protected. The ability of local governments to respond to IHRs varies across the nation.

A small but significant number of IHRs occur each year. Current research concludes that IHRs are associated with every type of disaster that has been studied, and some studies suggest that, all other things equal, larger events give rise to more numerous or more severe IHRs. Three phenomena—earthquakes, hurricanes, and floods—give rise to approximately 90 percent of all reported IHRs, with earthquakes accounting for nearly three-fourths of the documented incidents. It follows that industries, companies, and government agencies (and the surrounding communities) that use hazardous materials located in earthquake-, hurricane-, or flood-prone areas are at risk for the occurrence of IHRs.

The emergency management system in place in the United States is adaptable to the response to hazardous materials emergencies as well as other types of natural or man-caused disasters. The Federal response structure includes the potential occurrence of IHRs in the *National Response Plan* under ESF #10–Hazardous Materials, with the EPA as the lead Federal agency. Probably, the Federal response structure will follow the National Contingency Plan in addressing IHRs. The *National Response Plan* is also sufficiently robust to allow for a coordinated Federal response even if the disaster is itself a hazardous materials release, such as occurred at Bhopal and Chernobyl. In addition, many Federal agencies and departments can assist local governments through existing authorities in responding to IHRs. These include the EPA and the Department of Defense.

State response and recovery structures vary from state to state, but in general all allow for the coordination of State-level assets (including the National Guard) to support the efforts of local government and industry at the local level. Legal options exist in each state whereby the Governor can invoke a Declaration of Emergency in support of local efforts.

Ultimately, however, the response to and recovery from any disaster—whether it involves IHR or not—is a local responsibility. Government has well-defined roles in the protection of public safety, the providing of human services, and the protecting of infrastructure. Industry has important roles that are both appropriate and that positively impact on the company's profitability. Local response to disasters is a true public–private partnership. After all, both government and industry are part of the impacted community.

Proper planning and mitigation efforts will help reduce the occurrence and the severity of the impacts of IHRs. Strengthening and hardening hazardous materials against disasters that are likely to occur within a community is a prudent mitigation step. In many cases, hazardous materials have been released when there has been little or no structural damage to the building, suggesting that hazardous materials storage systems are less robust than they should be. Realistic hazardous materials response systems should be adopted, such that industries do not rely exclusively on local government response teams in the event of an IHR. While specific IHR incidents may become a high priority in any disaster response, governmental resources will not be available to deal with every release associated with a disaster.

Finally, the hazardous materials planning performed under Title III of the Superfund Amendments and Reauthorization Act (SARA) should be used to include IHRs in a possible response scenario. For industries located in those communities prone to IHRs, a reasonable and expected worst-case release should include loss of power, unavailable governmental response assets, and a damaged transportation and communications infrastructure as part of their planning assumptions. Anything that can go wrong really will.

Disclaimer

The opinions expressed in this chapter are solely those of the author and may not be representative of the position of the Virginia Department of Emergency Management or the Commonwealth of Virginia.

Bibliography

Anonymous. "Corps of Engineers Looking for New Ways to Dispose of Hurricane Marilyn Debris, Waste." *HAZMAT News*, Vol. (6): p. 7, 20 November 1995.

Anonymous. "Report Says Most Nuclear Weapons Plants at Risk from Natural Disasters." *HAZMAT News*. Vol. (7): pp. 1-2, 29 July 1996.

Catallo, W. J., N. B. Theberge and M. E. Bender. *Sea Level Rise and Hazardous Wastes in the Coastal Zone: An Ecological Perspective*, in Coastal Zone '89, Proceedings of the Sixth Symposium on Coastal and Ocean Management. O. T. Magoon, Ed. Charleston, SC: ASCE, 1989.

Cruz, A. M., Steinberg, J., and Luna, R., "Identifying Hurricane Induced Hazardous Materials Release Scenarios in a Petroleum Refinery." *Natural Hazards Review,* Vol (2), No. (4): pp. 203–210, November 2001.

Denning, E. J. *Hazardous Materials as Secondary Results of Flooding: A Case Study of Planning and Response*. Quick Response Report #49. Boulder, Co: University of Colorado Natural Hazards Center, 1992.

Emergency Management Institute. *Debris Management Course Participant Manual*. Emmitsburg, MD: Emergency Management Institute.

Fedarko, K. "Flood, Flames, and Fear." *Time*. Vol (148): 31 October 1994.

FEMA. "The Emergency Program Manager." Emergency Management Institute Home Study Course IS-1. Emmitsburg, MD: FEMA, 1993.

FEMA. "Emergency Preparedness U.S.A." Emergency Management Institute Home Study Course HS-2, Emmitsburg, MD: FEMA, 1994.

Hadfield, P. "Asbestos Shock in Kobe Cleanup." *New Scientist.* p. 6, 4 March 1995.

Hough, S. E., and L. M. Jones. "Aftershocks: Are They Earthquakes or Afterthoughts?" *EOS*, Vol (78), No (45). pp. 505–508, 11 November 1997.

Lindell, M. K., and R. W. Perry. "Addressing Gaps in Environmental Emergency Planning: Hazardous Materials Releases during Earthquakes." *Journal of Environmental Planning and Management.* Vol (39), No (4), pp. 529–543, 1996.

Lindell, M. K., and R. W. Perry. "Hazardous Materials Releases in the Northridge Earthquake: Implication for Seismic Risk Analysis." *Risk Analysis.* Vol (17), No (2), pp. 147–156, 1997.

National Park Service. *Hurricane Andrew, 1992: The National Park Service Response in South Florida.* Washington, DC: US Department of the Interior, 1994.

National Response Team. *Information Exchange— Lessons Learned from Exercises and Incidents.* Vol (3), No (1), 1997.

Noll, G., M. Hildebrand, and J. Yborra. *Hazardous Materials: Managing the Incident.* Stillwater, OK: Oklahoma State University Fire Protection Publications, 1988.

Seligson, H. A., R. T. Eguchi, K. J. Tierney, and K. Richmond. *Chemical Hazards, Mitigation and Preparedness in Areas of High Seismic Risk: A Methodology for Estimating the Risk of Post-Earthquake Hazardous Materials Release.* Technical Report NCEER–96–0013. Buffalo, NY: National Center for Earthquake Engineer-ing Research, 1996.

Showalter, P. S. and M. F. Myers. "Natural Disasters in the United States as Release Agents of Oil, Chemicals, or Radiological Materials between 1980–1989: Analysis and Recommendations." *Risk Analysis.* Vol (14): pp. 169–182, 1994.

Steinberg, L. J., Basolo, B., Burby, R., Levine, J., and Cruz, A. M., *Earthquake-Induced Technological Disasters: A Case Study of Possible Effects and Emergency Response in the Urban Environment.* In Proceedings of the National Conference in Earthquake Engineering. Boston, MA: Earthquake Engineering Research Institute, July 2002.

Virginia Department of Emergency Services. *Annual Report.* Richmond, VA: Technological Hazards Division, Virginia Department of Emergency Services, 1996.

Wright, F. G., H. I. Inyang, and V. B. Myers. "Risk Reduction through Regulatory Control of Waste Disposal Facility Siting." *Journal of Environmental Systems.* Vol (22), No (1): pp. 27–35, 1993.

Brett A. Burdick *is the Director of the Technological Hazards Division with the Virginia Department of Emergency Management (VDEM) in Richmond, Virginia, where his primary responsibility is directing the hazardous materials planning, training, and response system in the Commonwealth of Virginia. He also serves as the Primary Manager overseeing the Commonwealth's Terrorism Consequence Management Preparedness Program. Prior to coming to VDEM, Mr. Burdick served as Director of the Office of Environmental Response and Remediation in the Waste Division of the Virginia Department of Environmental Quality, and as the Ground Water Services Manager overseeing the Underground Storage Tank Program in the Northern Regional Office of the State Water Control Board. He holds a BA in Geology and recently completed his Master of Science from the Virginia Commonwealth University. He is a Registered Professional Geologist in two states and is a Certified Hazardous Materials Manager at the Master's Level. Over the last 20 years, Mr. Burdick has published several technical papers and presented research findings in the fields of geology, hydrogeology, oceanography, hazardous materials management, and terrorism consequence management.*

CHAPTER 33

Clandestine Methamphetamine Labs: A Hazardous Materials Disaster

John A. Valicenti, PhD, CHMM
Michael A. Kay, ScD, CHMM

Introduction

Methamphetamine (commonly known as *meth*) is the most rapidly emerging threat in rural America. The level of methamphetamine production as well as the associated abuse and violence has increased dramatically in recent years throughout the United States. This chapter covers these aspects associated with clandestine meth labs: hazardous chemicals and their environmental and health effects, chemical and equipment availability, drug syntheses, as well as the contribution of environmental observations and local intelligence to the identification and cleanup of the illicit labs. The Kentucky State Police (KSP) have adopted a written program called Guidelines and Procedures for the Seizure of Clandestine Drug Laboratories that addresses illicit lab entry, the identification of hazardous materials, handling and removal, officer training and protection, local officer and community involvement, media communication as well as compliance with Occupational Safety and Health Administration (OSHA) and Environmental Protection Administration (EPA) regulations in order to cope with this immediate threat to officer and community health and safety.

Clandestine Lab History

Since 1962, the United States has experienced over 100,000 illegal drug manufacturing sites, known as clandestine laboratories (Bucklin 2004). In the 1960s, clandestine labs produced D-Lysergic Acid Diethylamide (LSD), Ecstasy (MDMA) and Phencyclidine (PCP), which all flourished during the *Love Generation* period. The marijuana crop fields of motorcycle gangs were easily detected by the law. The gangs needed a better stimulant that was easy to make. The synthetic drug, methamphetamine (MAP), became their calling card. Gangs flaunted their swastikas before TV cameras and referred to their favorite means of production of meth as the *Nazi* method. Ironically, this same drug, which was discovered in 1932, was used by kamikaze pilots toward the end of World War II and by the suicidal invading Chinese during the Korean War. Ninety-eight percent of the clandestine labs in the United States produce methamphetamine. Amphetamine derivatives are used by modern army soldiers and air force pilots to keep themselves awake. They are also used in the licit pharmaceutical industry as *over the counter* (OTC) nasal decongestants and diet aids. Amphetamine and its derivatives are Schedule 2 controlled pharmaceuticals and used in the treatment of medical conditions such as hyperactivity and attention deficit disorder.

Kentucky Statistics

Methamphetamine (also called *MAP*, *meth*, *speed*, *crank*, *crystal* or *ice*) is a potent central nervous system stimulant that can be smoked, snorted, injected or ingested. The Kentucky State Police consider this addictive drug as an emerging threat to Kentucky, particularly in the rural areas of the state (Kentucky State Police 2004). The level of production, distribution, and violence attributable to MAP has increased dramatically since 1999. Clandestine lab seizures in Kentucky have increased from ten in 1999 to nearly five hundred in 2003. This level has been already been reached in the first half of 2004. Sophisticated police identification techniques have contributed to this huge increase. The lab seizure rise was accompanied by a 42% increase in user treatment from 1998 to 2000 (Kentucky Drug Assessment Report). The KSP believe that the actual user numbers have increased more than just lab discoveries. Formerly, large Mexican cartels and California crime mobs supplied most of the meth to Kentucky, but now, locally produced meth has eclipsed the amount of out-of-state production. Small-scale production has been further stimulated by the availability of cheap, simple chemicals and equipment, and shorter, simplified syntheses (or recipes). These recipes are freely available on the Internet.

Small quantities of methamphetamine produced locally are not sold at wholesale in Kentucky. Meth sells for about $100 per gram on the street (Kentucky State Police 2004). The value escalates with increased *whiteness* (purity of the drug) and the increase in the level of *high* (stimulation) obtained. The largest meth grab in Kentucky to date has been two pounds, which had an estimated street value of $100,000. Initially, a 1-milligram dose of meth stimulates the user to a huge high. Addicted users (tweakers) require escalating drug amounts in order to obtain the same stimulation. This drastic, intense craving for the drug has led to the proliferation of small clandestine labs. Meth can be synthesized in less than 24 hours in order to quickly satisfy tweaker needs. Single doses of 10 to 50 milligrams can result in coma and/or death. When the tweaker craves more meth, the craving results in more frustration and restlessness, contributing to increased anxiety and restlessness. Tweaker case histories indicate that tweakers can become violent without provocation. This mental state has been labeled **meth psychosis**. Tweakers experiencing meth psychosis are very dangerous. Some are antagonized at the mere sight of a police uniform.

What's That Smell?

A Kentucky State Police (KSP) officer stopped a car that was weaving back and forth on an interstate highway. Upon exiting his cruiser, the officer smelled ammonia coming from the suspect car, probably the trunk. The officer asked for help and a team of four officers were soon at the scene. After a 45 minute struggle (two officers at a time taking turns), the tweaker was finally handcuffed. The trunk was full of meth production supplies.

— abuser of stimulants

Meth history lessons have helped Kentucky prepare an effective program in order to respond to clandestine labs that produce illicit drugs. This program sets guidelines that are designed to protect law enforcement officers and communities from severe health and environmental hazards.

Chemicals, Physical and Health Hazards and Effects

The chemicals used by *cooks* (drug makers) to manufacture methamphetamine are well known and easily obtained. A wide variety of corrosives (*e.g.*, lye, muriatic acid), solvents (*e.g.*, naphtha, ether) and respiratory irritants (*e.g.*, ammonia, iodine) are commonly present in meth labs. The cooks know little about the dangers that these hazardous materials present and lack the scientific knowledge to make proper risk assessments. Frequently, misinformation is contained in their recipes. Dangerous chemicals that the cook thinks necessary are mistakenly used. One example is the use of bleach and peroxide to clean up clandestine labs. These disinfectants and stain removers have explosive and flammable properties that have destroyed many labs.

Corrosives such as hydrochloric, sulfuric, phosphoric and hydroiodic acids and the alkaline compound, sodium hydroxide, kill living cells. The occupants of clandestine meth labs seldom wear proper personal protective equipment (PPE) or have adequate ventilation, such as with a chemical fume hood. As a result, they frequently experience symptoms such as eye damage, burns, inflammation, gastrointestinal disturbances, thirst, dizziness, convulsions and respiratory irritation.

Health and physical hazards arise from volatile solvents such as ether, toluene, methanol, naphtha and benzene. These compounds attack target organs in the body, such as the liver and kidneys, cause eye, nose and throat irritation, dizziness and nausea; they are potential carcinogens. All are extremely flammable.

Anhydrous ammonia, a necessary chemical used in a *Nazi* meth-manufacturing recipe, is a caustic, noxious gas that is hydrophilic and attacks eye and mucous membranes. Ammonia is used as fertilizer by farmers and is frequently stolen from farm field tanks. Pumps are used to transfer the gas into gas cylinders, such as propane tanks. Beware of blue brass valves on ammonia tanks. This is an indication of corrosion and thus, instability. Corroded ammonia cylinders behave like rockets when they explode.

Tincture of iodine solution is a common disinfectant in very dilute solutions. Meth labs use pure iodine crystals to generate hydroiodic acid, a necessary ingredient in one type of meth synthesis. Fumes of sublimed iodine are a typical lab atmospheric contaminant. The iodine crystals are mixed with corrosive hydrochloric and sulfuric acids to produce the hydroiodic acid. The final result is a corrosive atmosphere that causes skin irritation and damage to mucous membranes and lung tissue.

Pyrophoric red phosphorus is used in the *Red, White and Blue Method* of meth preparation. This solid bursts into flames in air at slightly higher than room temperatures, causing burn injuries and havoc.

Lithium metal is used along with ammonia in the *Nazi* meth production method. The metal is easily removed from small batteries. Lithium liberates flammable hydrogen when dropped into water causing fire and explosion. Hazard responders should not use water fire-hoses to put out fires in meth labs.

In the 1970s, cooks used radioactive thorium oxide as a catalyst to make phenyl-2-propanone (P2P), a precursor of meth. Few cooks were aware of the radioactivity of the metal salt. The chemical waste cleanups of these radioactive confined spaces were some of the most dangerous ever confronted by response teams in the United States.

The most dangerous chemical in the meth lab to a responder may be the drug itself. The white salt of the drug has no smell to indicate its presence. Symptoms of overexposure include the dilation of pupils, sweating, dry mouth, flushed skin and tremors. The long-term cumulative health effects attributed to methamphetamine include cardiac and neurological damage. Meth users exhibit aggressive and psychotic behavior, irritability, anxiety, paranoia, and auditory hallucinations. Meth is popular because the stimulation lasts longer than other more expensive drugs such as cocaine. Waste removers, cleanup teams, and responders must wash their hands, hair and clothes before they exit meth labs. Most injuries to suspects and officers result from the inhalation of toxic gases, direct contact with contaminated victims and suspects, on and off the site, and self-contamination during meth site cleanup.

All classes of Department of Transportation (DOT) hazardous materials may be found in clandestine meth labs. First responders and site cleanup workers need to use appropriate PPE (personal protective equipment) and follow established safety procedures. Because of the safety requirements for clandestine lab cleanup, several states license firms allowed to perform drug lab decontamination and cleanup.

Chemical Availability

The availability of these hazardous chemicals at grocery stores and pharmacies astounds police investigators and has led to the proliferation of small labs. Nonprescription, pseudoephedrine capsules (pharmacies), ammonia and ammonium nitrate (farm fertilizers), lithium metal (small batteries), red phosphorus (matches), denatured alcohol (antibacterial agent), iodine (antibacterial agent), lye (drain and oven cleaners), sodium chloride (table salt), isopropanol (rubbing alcohol), flammable solvents (Coleman® fuel, patio grill accelerants) and sulfuric acid (liquid fire) are used in meth production. Muriatic acid (also known as hydrochloric acid) is available at plumbing and welding supply companies. Other chemicals not found in local pharmacy and grocery stores such as methylamine can be purchased from major chemical supply houses.

Please the Customers

KSP found an aisle of products at a super mall retailer that was beyond comprehension. The shelf in one aisle row contained bags of ammonium nitrate fertilizer, patio grill fluid, table salt, bottles of popular anti-allergy tablets, tincture of iodine medication, and small batteries. It looked like a warehouse for meth cooks. Across the aisle, electric frying pans, Pyrex dishware, wine glasses and coffee filters were stacked. Officers said it looked like a meth lab equipment storeroom! When asked by KSP about the situation, the store manager said, "We had a lot of requests for these things so we were just trying to please the customers". A quick call to the chain corporate head-quarters solved the problem.

Those who encounter the most serious over-exposures are not the trained responders but untrained local officers who enter labs without knowledge of the hazardous substances and people present. The KSP is ensuring that all local enforcement officers in Kentucky know what to do when they hear about a meth lab. Local officers are told to call the KSP and stay away from lab locations. Interference by local law enforcement officers remains a problem particularly during election years.

You Never Know!

Some Western Kentucky University geology students were mapping unknown sections of Mammoth Cave near Bowling Green, Kentucky. Several hundred feet below ground, behind several crawl tubes and spaces, they came upon a meth lab. Fortunately, it was not occupied. The KSP said that was the toughest hazardous waste site cleanup ever!

Environmental Effects and Observations

The meth cooks leave approximately six pounds of hazardous toxic waste for each pound of methamphetamine produced. Leftover chemicals are often poured down household drains, wells, storm drains or directly onto the ground. Discarded chemicals have been discovered in national forests, public parks, near schools, on vacant lots, and in commercial trash receptacles. These chemical wastes present explosion, fire and health risks, and environmental hazards that may persist for decades. Solvents such as acetone, ether, naphtha, toluene and benzene used in the meth manufacturing process pose long-term hazards because they remain in the soil and groundwater for years. Rural water supplies are at particular risk because rural areas frequently have no system in place to monitor water supplies for contamination. Farmers may use contaminated water to irrigate crops and water livestock. Cleanup costs are extremely high because contaminated soil, buildings and other materials must be removed and incinerated.

Kitchen and bathroom sinks as well as bathroom tubs, copper tubing and nonflammable carpet present expensive and special problems regarding decontamination and/or destruction.

Environmental observations are especially important in the identification and detection of clandestine labs in hotels, motels and trailer parks. Observers may note chemical odors in hotel guest rooms or the strong scent of an aerosol air freshener used to mask the odor of a meth lab. Anyone who cleans guest rooms should be suspicious of stains on a carpet or the drain area of a tub, toilet or sink. Waste baskets that contain discarded coffee filters or cloth with an unknown stain or sludge residue and other containers containing residue left for disposal are typical meth lab remnants.

Landlords and householders should report to local authorities suspicious activity, such as guests declining housekeeping services as well as nervous, paranoid guests and neighbors. A large group of people smoking outside of their home or trailer is a possible clue to a meth lab presence. Get to know your hotel guests and neighbors! Call law enforcement or the local health department first!

materials—including their properties, exposure symptoms and effects; and be certified as an Emergency Medical Technician (EMT). All the training requirements are found in applicable OSHA regulations.

OSHA Regulations Applicable to Clandestine Drug Laboratories

29 CFR 1910.120 Hazardous Waste Operations and Emergency Response

29 CFR 1910, Subpart I Personal Protective Equipment

29 CFR 1910.146 Permit-Required Confined Spaces

29 CFR 1910.147 The Control of Hazardous Energy (Lockout/Tagout)

29 CFR 910.1030 Bloodborne Pathogens

29 CFR1910.1200 Hazard Communication

The Clandestine Lab Emergency Responders

Emergency responders who are exposed to hazardous chemicals require training in the identification, handling, packaging and transportation of hazardous chemicals and wastes. In Kentucky, the team approach is effective in providing on-the-job experience. This experience increases the hazard awareness that is needed before one moves in on a meth lab.

Clandestine Lab Officers (CLO) must have at least three years of experience as a KSP officer. They are trained to use, maintain and test a self-contained breathing apparatus (SCBA). Respirator use also requires an annual physical examination. The CLO must be able to identify, enter and work in confined spaces; know applicable lockout-tagout procedures; work in hazardous areas that may result in an exposure to bloodborne pathogens; be able to assess the risks of working with hazardous

Some of the officers wear guns and several take part in undercover operations. Four officers (two in-two out) make up a team that approaches the clandestine lab. A trailer that is outfitted with PPE, shower, and cleaning facilities as well as waste cleanup storage boxes, bags and equipment is brought to each site.

A Hazard Clandestine Lab Officer (HCLO) may be called in depending upon the intelligence and information available about the facility. The HCLO is trained to defuse explosive devices, including bombs as well as chemical and biological release systems. Booby traps such as explosives, chemicals and gas release systems connected to trip wires, digital timers and laser beam igniters, can hinder and discourage officer intervention. Vicious animals, poisonous snakes, and fish hooks hung at face level on almost transparent fishing line have all been encountered in clandestine drug labs. Cooks and tweakers in a meth lab are usually very well armed (automatic and semi-automatic assault weapons and automatic and semi-automatic shotguns) and must be considered extremely dangerous.

Social workers are called in to the clandestine lab location to negotiate with the suspects regarding hostage release. There is a common and nagging presence of children around these locations. In Kentucky, upon the release of hostage children, the Cabinet for Health and Family Services (CHFS) helps with child protection services.

The Incident Commander (IC) has the ultimate responsibility to authorize lab entry by officers. The IC may be on- or off-site and uses special satellite communication as necessary. A site risk assessment is done that includes identification of the types and amounts of chemicals as well as the number of suspects and hostages present. Entry by an officer is not attempted before this assessment is done.

Supervision of waste cleanup, including contractor notification and public communication to the media are responsibilities of the IC. A waste remover exemption is maintained by the KSP (who do not store more than 220 pounds of hazardous waste in the KSP facility for one week). The KSP have reduced waste removal costs significantly by doing it themselves rather than outsourcing waste removal to private contractors or Federal agencies. Federal grants provide money for officer training, the trailers and PPE.

Methamphetamine Syntheses

The cleverness, ingenuity, innovation and creativity of illicit methamphetamine makers and suppliers should not be underestimated. Other than beakers and occasional mechanical or digital balances, the KSP seldom come upon any sophisticated lab glassware or equipment in illicit labs. Scientific glassware and equipment are expensive and difficult to steal. Wine glasses, canning bottles, Pyrex kitchenware and common plastic containers are typical meth reaction vessels. Microwave ovens, electric skillets, hairdryers, toasters and area heaters serve as heat sources. Coffee filters are used. Copper tubing and propane tanks serve as gas transporters and storage containers. None of this equipment is safety-certified (electric grounding wires, safety glass, *etc.*) and explosions are frequent. Some cooks trap the toxic off-gases

with carbon grill cubes (charcoal briquettes), dry water-wet ammonia with appropriate agents, and pump ammonia into their reaction vessels with fire extinguishers and baffles. Never underestimate the creativity of greedy criminals or desperate addicts.

In other areas of the country, sophisticated clandestine drug labs have been found using scientific labware stolen from colleges and universities, or purchased from laboratory supply houses by appropriating the names of legitimate customers and changing the delivery address. Security of labware and chemicals is very important.

Laboratory Smorgasbord

A small college decided to paint and renovate its organic chemistry laboratories during Spring Break. Students were used to box and remove all glassware and equipment from the laboratories. The few college personnel involved thought that the students belonged to one of the other faculty. When everything was removed and the boxes lining the hallway, one of the "students" taped open the latch on an outside door. That night a truck pulled up to the loading dock, and the boxes were quickly transferred to the truck. The next morning the theft was noticed and reported to the police. Labware from that college was still being found years later in clandestine drug lab raids in the northwest.

Early meth lab syntheses used P2P as a starting material to generate meth. Several chemical reactions that used chemicals such as ammonium nitrate and methylamine were required. Impure drug product and lengthy reaction times were problems. Pseudoephedrine is the starting point for the *Red, White and Blue Method* for meth preparation. Pyrophoric red phosphorus and hydroiodic acid remove an oxygen atom from the common anti-allergy medicine to produce meth. The hydroiodic acid is generated from the reaction of iodine with hydrochloric (muriatic) or sulfuric acid. The *Birch* or *Nazi Method* uses aluminum foil, lithium and ammonia to do the same job. Hazardous by-products contaminate the synthetic drug. The meth is rarely greater than 80% pure. Free metals, including aluminum, copper, brass and iron and various water soluble salts, are common impurities.

The purest meth is obtained from meth-user urine. Forty percent of meth passes unused through the body into the urine. The compound is extracted from the urine by cooks and precipitated as a chloride salt (KSP 2004).

The chemical structure pseudoephedrine, found in of some common nonprescription decongestants and allergy medicines, is similar to meth itself. These medicines control serotonin flow in the body and thereby reduce allergy symptoms. The Federal Drug Administration (FDA) has cleared such drugs for nonprescription sale. However, knowledge of the long-term effects of such drugs upon the body, and data about their chronic effects is limited, especially in children and the elderly. Consult your physician before using these tablets. Remember that pseudoephedrine is only one oxygen atom and one chemical step away from methamphetamine an addictive, life-threatening, Controlled Substance Act (CSA) Schedule II restricted drug. Also, remember that the body is an amazing chemical breakdown machine.

Pseudoephedrine derivatives and antihistamines (not generally related to pseudoephedrine or ephedrine) do not have the cardiovascular changes that can be generated by the decongestants. For example, chlorphenarimine maleate (Chlortrimeton®) has been extensively tested and is regarded as safe even for pregnant women after the first trimester.

Summary of Common Sense Guidelines and Recommendations

"Laboratory takedown operations should be the last step after intelligence gathering and surveillance" (Ferris 2004). Intelligence-gathering about the nature of the meth lab, including chemicals present and people in and around the area, should be emphasized. All available information about lab locations should be evaluated before any entry is attempted. In some cases, building plans will be on file with local jurisdictions. Foreknowledge may even prevent the future setup of labs. Injuries that occur during initial entry into the labs can be

avoided. Since fire and explosions in meth labs before and after law enforcement entry are common; it is critical to know the number of occupants, the physical lab layout, and the type and amount of chemicals present. All efforts should be made to remove suspects and/or hostages from the lab before entry. A trained hostage negotiator should be used as necessary. Plans for psychological and physical aid to children, whose presence around meth labs alarms and frightens law enforcement officers, should be made beforehand. In such situations, entry teams may also need access to medical and psychological help close to the site.

Illicit lab entry guidelines must address immediate danger to life and health (IDLH) atmosphere concerns. Murphy's Law prevails; that is, if it can happen, it will. Assume the worst-case scenario! Laboratory waste cleanup and removal as well as respiratory programs must be in regulatory compliance with OSHA standards. Bombs and hazardous materials booby traps present an added danger. Local police who come upon active or inactive labs and the communities where labs are operating must be made aware of dangers of possible booby traps and hazardous materials exposures. For those who happen to come upon a meth lab or suspect meth lab production, call the local police or public health department immediately. KSP have received more information about active meth labs from local neighbors than from their undercover agents.

The Agency for Toxic Substances and Disease Registry (ATSDR) recommends that proper perimeter control be established to prevent entry. Meth lab cleanup teams should consider airing-out the property for several days before entry (ATSDR). Any absorbent material surfaces such as carpet and dry wall should be inspected because of porosity issues. Air monitoring should be done according to OSHA standards. Ventilation systems tend to collect fumes and dust that may be redistributed throughout the location. Re-painting and sealing surfaces can be helpful. The best cleanup solution to the illicit lab contamination problem is the total removal of all carpet, walls and furniture followed by a thorough cleaning of the ventilation system. In some cases, interior insulation may also have to be removed.

Because of the danger to casual passersby, meth lab materials discovered in open, accessible places, such as vacant lots, parks, or near popular trails or roads in State or National forests, need to be removed as soon as possible.

The clandestine drug lab problem seems to be expanding at present. Drug lab awareness training (how to recognize clandestine drug laboratories and who to report them to) should be given to such workers as utility meter readers, utility workers (gas, electric, phone, cable, and water), park employees, building inspectors, real estate agents, and any other workers whose jobs frequently bring them in contact with differing locations. Already major pharmacy chains and *big box* stores have repackaged pseudoephedrine products in smaller quantities and limit the total quantity that can be purchased. Although this is a start, many more steps are needed before this problem will be brought under control.

Bibliography

Bucklin, J. "Environmental, Health & Safety Cleanup Issues Surrounding Clandestine Laboratories." Presented at the *National ACHMM Conference*. August, 2004. Las Vegas, NV.

Ferris, J. "National OSHA Administrative Office, Health & Safety Regulatory Update." Presented at the *National ACHMM Conference*. August, 2004. Las Vegas, NV.

Kentucky State Police. "Clandestine Laboratories." Presented at the *Governors Health and Safety Conference*. May, 2004. Louisville, KY.

National Drug Intelligence Center. *Kentucky Drug Threat Assessment*. Johnston, PA: U S Department of Justice. July, 2002.

Publishers Group, LLC. "Methamphetamine Labs; Neighborhood Resource Guide." Plymouth, MN 2005.

Other Resources

Agency for Toxic Substances and Disease Registry (ATSDR) information center toll-free at 1-888-422-8737; ATSDRIC@cdc.gov.

Kentucky State Police, Captain M.Bailey, Bowling Green, KY.

John A. Valicenti has worked for 24 years in the hazardous materials management field as an adjunct chemistry professor, hazardous materials manager, chemistry laboratory supervisor, and, most recently, as a Senior Industrial Hygiene Consultant for the Commonwealth of Kentucky. His areas of expertise include laboratory safety and health, hazardous materials management, and indoor air quality. Dr. Valicenti has given publications at six national ACHMM conferences. He is the author of a 1997 paper, "Air Quality Monitoring During Construction and Initial Occupation of a New Building," published in the Journal of the Air and Waste Management Association.

Dr. Michael A. Kay has held in positions in government, GOCO (Government-Owned-Contractor Operated), academic, industrial, and private practice during his 36-year career. He has experience in hazardous materials management, occupational safety and health, and environmental compliance. Dr. Kay's expertise is in the fields of radioactive materials management programs, (health physics, and licensing), forensic sciences, data validity in court, oil pollution analysis, and clandestine drug laboratories. Dr. Kay was a Technical Advisor for the Media Resources, Inc. (formerly of Vancouver, Washington) training videos, Clandestine Drug Labs I–Awareness, Clandestine Drug Labs II–Takedown, Lockout-Tagout for Affected Employees, *and* Lockout-Tagout for Authorized Employees. *Dr. Kay has trained police, fire, National Park Service, and industrial employees on clandestine drug labs, occupational safety, and hazardous waste and emergency operations—awareness level. Dr. Kay is also a recertification peer reviewer for the Institute of Hazardous Materials Management, and has presented papers on "Navigating the Recertification Maze" at national and local chapter ACHMM meetings.*

Part VII

Air Quality

CHAPTER 34

The Clean Air Act

Adriane P. Borgias, MSEM, CHMM
Daniel L. Todd, QEP, CHMM

The purpose of this chapter is to provide the hazardous materials manager with an overview of the Clean Air Act and other significant Federal requirements. The Clean Air Act governs a broad range of activities from manufacturing and processing, to transportation and management of hazardous chemicals. This overview covers the topics that will be of particular interest to the hazardous materials manager. These include: important terms and concepts used in the Act, a brief summary of the provisions of each Title, and a brief guide to the implementing regulations. The more subtle nuances of the Clean Air Act, such as special requirements relating to research programs, energy emergencies, Federal facilities, sewage treatment, and other special-interest measures, will not be covered in depth this chapter. For more information on these topics, the reader is urged to refer to the Act and implementing regulations. Reference tables to the Act and implementing regulations can be found at the end of the chapter.

A Brief History of the Clean Air Act

The Clean Air Act (CAA) was originally signed into law in 1955. Prior to 1970, only minor changes were made to the original law. In 1970, the basic principles that form the backbone of the Act as it exists today were developed. The 1970 Clean Air Act was written to address the air pollution that was occurring due to increasing urban growth and industrialization. Major amendments were again made to the Act in 1990. The most significant aspects of these amendments were the inclusion of an operating permit program (a program *intended* to simplify the complex permitting requirements that were currently in place) and a major revision of the way in which hazardous air pollutants (HAPs) are regulated. The new amendments gave EPA specific direction and a schedule for implementation of HAP regulations.

Air quality in the United States has improved significantly since the 1970 version of the Clean Air Act. According to the Environmental Protection Agency (EPA), the combined ambient concentrations of the six major air pollutants have dropped by about a third in the past 30 years. The 1990 amendments and subsequent regulations focus on continued improvement in air quality. In particular, this includes the control of hazardous air pollutants, acid rain precursors, ozone, particulates, and visibility.

The Clean Air Act, As Amended in 1990

Today's Clean Air Act, as amended in 1990, consists of 11 Titles that regulate a wide variety of activities associated with the control of air pollutants. The first six Titles are of the most importance to the hazardous materials manager. These Titles regulate air pollution prevention and control, emissions standards, acid rain, permits, and protection of the stratospheric ozone.

The Clean Air Act addresses the complex set of pollutants that are created as a result of our growing reliance on industries, particularly industries in urban areas. These pollutants threaten not only our health but our environment and economic infrastructure as well (agriculture, property, air, and ground transportation). Consequently, the primary stated goal of the Clean Air Act is to improve air quality by preventing these pollutants from being generated and emitted

to the air. This important goal is often lost in the day-to-day efforts needed to assure compliance with the complex requirements of the Act.

The framework for protecting and enhancing the quality of the nation's air resources includes (1) establishing a national air pollution prevention and control research program, (2) providing technical and financial assistance to State and local governments, and (3) developing regional programs where needed.

Of the 11 Titles, the first six are summarized below.

Title I: Air Pollution Prevention and Control. Title I focuses on the control of pollution in urban areas. This Title describes air quality criteria, control regions, and implementation plans for the improvement and maintenance of healthy air. A significant amendment to this Title is the direction provided to EPA to set, by the year 2000, emissions standards for what is now 188 Hazardous Air Pollutants.

Title II: Emissions Standards for Moving Sources. Title II regulates motor vehicle and aircraft emissions. The 1990 amendments refined the requirements of this Title in response to the substantial increase in vehicle miles driven and in pollutants from these sources. The regulation of fuels, including the clean fuels program, fleets, and clean-fuel vehicles is included here.

Title III: General. Title III contains general provisions and procedures relating to the Act. Included in this Title are sections on citizen suits, employment effects, and employee (whistleblower) protection.

Title IV: Acid Deposition Control. This Title regulates the acid emissions from electric generation sources. The control of acid emissions from power plants was first legislated in 1980 as the Acid Precipitation Act. Actual controls of acid rain emissions, however, were delayed until 1990 when expanded requirements were folded in. These new requirements consist of a program that provides market-based incentives for sulfur dioxide and nitrogen oxides reduction.

Title V: Permits. Added with the 1990 amendments, Title V requires operators of major sources of air pollution to obtain permits prior to construction and operation. Title V outlines the basic requirements of the operating permit program.

The Title V program has a number of significant purposes. First, it is intended to strengthen the ability of the urban areas to come into compliance with the air quality standards by including previously excluded major sources in the permitting arena. Second, the program is intended to *standardize* the permitting process by implementing a nationwide program similar to the existing National Pollutant Discharge Elimination System (NPDES) under the Clean Water Act. Third, it creates a self-funded permit program by assessing the emitting sources fees on a per-ton-of emissions basis.

Title VI: Stratospheric Ozone Protection. Originally included in Part B of Title I of the Act, the 1990 amendments created a new Title VI that regulates the use and phase-out of ozone-depleting substances. It provides for proper handling, recycling, and disposal of these substances as well as a mechanism for introducing ozone-safe alternatives.

The new Title VI strengthens the requirements of the original law by creating a structured program to identify, evaluate, manage, and phase out these substances. National recycling and emissions reduction programs are established. Economic incentives are provided via an allowance trading program.

Titles VII–XI. The remaining five Titles of the Act are not covered in detail in this chapter. Their topics include

- *Title VII.* Provisions Relating to Enforcement
- *Title VIII.* Miscellaneous Provisions
- *Title IX.* Clean Air Research
- *Title X.* Disadvantaged Business Concerns
- *Title XI.* Clean Air Employment Transition Assistance

Important Concepts and Terms Used throughout the Act

There are several key concepts and terms used throughout the Act that are important to know.

Most of these concepts are introduced in Title I and are used in the other Titles as well. These concepts are described below.

Responsibility for Air Pollution Prevention and Control

Congress determined that the states, tribes, and local governments are primarily responsible for air pollution prevention and control. As a result, EPA was given the authority to delegate to the states and tribes many provisions of the Act. The most significant of these are the development of State or Tribal plans for achieving and maintaining healthy air; the issuance of construction and operating permits; as well as motor vehicle inspection and maintenance programs.

Congress also believed that Federal leadership and financial assistance are crucial to the success of the clean air program. Cooperative State and local programs are encouraged through research and development programs, training grants, program development funds, and, when approved by Congress, the partial funding of interstate commissions.

Not all provisions of the Act can be delegated to states or tribes. Programs such as the marketing and trading of emissions allowances under the acid deposition and ozone NO_x budget programs, new motor vehicle emissions standards, and stratospheric ozone protection have retained EPA oversight.

National Ambient Air Quality Standards

A key component of the Act is the development and use of the *National Ambient Air Quality Standards* (NAAQS). NAAQS are established for air pollutants that threaten public health and welfare, whether from diverse mobile or stationary sources. The criteria for setting NAAQS include variable factors such as atmospheric conditions, types of pollutants present and their interactions, as well as the potential adverse effects on public health and welfare.

Primary NAAQS are developed for a particular pollutant to protect public health with an *adequate* margin of safety. Sensitive populations, such as children and the elderly, are used as the basis for calculation of the safety margin. Secondary NAAQS are intended to protect public welfare. This includes the effects of air pollution on vegetation, materials, structures, and visibility.

The EPA develops the NAAQS using all available peer-reviewed scientific data. The data for each pollutant is compiled into a *Criteria Document* and the pollutants that are addressed are commonly referred to as **criteria pollutants**. The standards are reviewed extensively by the scientific community, public interest groups, and the general public. The group which has the most credibility in the review process is the Clean Air Scientific Advisory Committee (CASAC), a Congressionally mandated group of independent scientists and technical experts. The CAA requires that the NAAQS be reviewed/revised once every five years.

Note that the cost-benefit of controlling a criteria pollutant is not one of the factors considered when a NAAQS is promulgated. However, concurrent with issuing a NAAQS, EPA is required to issue data relating to the cost of controlling the pollutant, the benefits and environmental impact of control, as well as alternative methods for its control (such as alternative fuels, processes, and operating methods).

To date, NAAQS have been issued for the six criteria pollutants: ozone (O_3), carbon monoxide (CO), particulate matter (PM_{10}–*respirable* particulates and $PM_{2.5}$–*fine* particulates of less than 10 and 2.5 microns, respectively), lead, nitrogen dioxide (NO_2), and sulfur oxides (SO_x). Their standards are summarized in Table 1.

These criteria pollutants are generally associated with urban areas because of both the number of people impacted by their presence (an estimated 170 million in 2000) and the concentration of sources in these areas. More than sixty percent of the large urban areas in the United States and some regions exceed the NAAQS for ozone. Ambient CO, $PM_{10,}$ and $PM_{2.5}$ also exceed the NAAQS in many urban areas. The remaining three pollutants (lead, SO_x, and NO_2) rarely exceed the NAAQS.

Attainment, Nonattainment, and Unclassified Areas

When EPA issues a NAAQS, states are required to monitor and evaluate the quality of the ambient air in their jurisdiction. Areas in which the air quality is cleaner than the NAAQS (*i.e.*, the concentrations of criteria pollutants in the ambient air are below the standard) are considered by EPA to be in **attainment**. Areas in which the air quality

Table I. National Ambient Air Quality Standards for Criteria Pollutants

Criteria Pollutant	Primary Standard		Secondary Standard	
Carbon Monoxide	9 ppm (10 mg/ m^3)	[Note 1]	None	
	35 ppm (40 mg/ m^3)	[Note 2]		
Lead	1.5 µg/m^3	[Note 3]	1.5 µg/m^3	[Note 3]
Nitrogen dioxide	0.053 ppm (100 µg/m^3)	[Note 4]	0.053 ppm (100 µg/m^3)	[Note 4]
Ozone	0.12 ppm	[Note 5]	0.12 ppm	[Note 5]
	0.08 ppm	[Note 6]	0.08 ppm	[Note 6]
PM_{10}	50 µg/m^3	[Note 4]	50 µg/m^3	[Note 4]
	150 µg/m^3	[Note 7]		
$PM_{2.5}$	15 µg/m^3	[Note 4]	15 µg/m^3	[Note 4]
	65 µg/m^3	[Note 7]		
Sulfur oxides	0.030 ppm	[Note 4]	0.05 ppm	[Note 8]
	0.14 ppm	[Note 7]		

Notes

1) Maximum 8-hour average; not to be exceeded more than once per year

2) Maximum 1-hour average; not to be exceeded more than once per year

3) Maximum arithmetic mean averaged over a calendar quarter

4) Annual arithmetic mean concentration

5) Maximum 1-hour average; not to be exceeded more than 1 day per calendar year

6) Daily maximum 8-hour average

7) 24-hour average; not to be exceeded more than once per year

8) 3-hour average

is poorer than the NAAQS are considered by EPA to be in **nonattainment** and, depending on the pollutant, are further classified as basic, marginal, moderate, serious, severe, or extreme. Some parts of the country, primarily rural areas, are considered to be **unclassified** because there is insufficient available air quality data to make a determination.

These designations are important because they are used throughout the Clean Air Act to define the requirements for states as well as operators of air pollution sources. Note that the concept of attainment is pollutant-specific. An area can be in *attainment* for one criteria pollutant but in *nonattainment* for another; thus the area is in both attainment and nonattainment at the same time.

The implementation of this program is very important. Designation as a *nonattainment area* has significant economic implications. It can substantially limit industrial growth, either construction of new sources or expansion of existing facilities. A more detailed discussion follows in the Title 1 section of this chapter.

Class I, II, and III Areas

In order to protect existing air quality in attainment and unclassified areas, the Act further designates areas on the basis of land use. The intent of these classifications is threefold:

1) To ensure economic growth

2) The prevention of significant deterioration (PSD) of the existing air quality

3) To ensure public participation in the decision making process (*i.e.*, air permitting)

The class designations affect operators of new or modified major sources wishing to obtain a permit in an attainment area. As discussed later, the PSD procedures require explicit consideration of the impacts a source may have on these areas. The resulting permit limitations are based on the class of the impacted areas.

Class I areas have the highest degree of protection and allow for very little deterioration of air quality. Congress specified that certain areas as *mandatory Class I areas* that cannot be reclassified. They include:

- International parks, national wilderness areas and memorial parks larger than 5000 acres

- National parks exceeding 6000 acres in size. States have the ability to designate similar areas if the size of the area exceeds 10,000 acres. In addition, tribes can designate lands within the boundaries of their reservations as Class I areas.

All other areas in the United States are **Class II areas.** Class II areas allow for moderate deterioration of air quality and include some Federal lands, such as

- National monuments, primitive areas, recreational areas, wildlife refuges, wild and scenic areas, lakeshores and seashores greater than 10,000 acres

- Newly established national parks

The Act did not designate any **Class III areas**, the least restrictive class. But it does contain provisions for redesignating Class II areas to Class III. There are currently no Class III areas in the United States.

State and Tribal Implementation Plans

The states and tribes create detailed descriptions regarding how they will fulfill their responsibilities towards achieving and maintaining clean air. The **State Implementation Plan**, also known as a **SIP**, and the **Tribal Implementation Plan**, or **TIP**, are essentially collections of the regulations the state or tribe uses to control pollutants.

The Clean Air Act lays out the requirements for these plans. An implementation plan is a publicly available document that describes in detail the state's or tribe's strategy for implementation, maintenance, and enforcement of the primary and secondary national air quality standards. The plan also identifies, or designates, areas of attainment and nonattainment. EPA has the final approval authority for these area designations as well as the implementation plans. EPA publishes its approval of the plans in the Federal Register for subsequent inclusion into the Code of Federal Regulations. In the event a state or tribe is unable to complete its implementation plan, then the EPA has the ability to issue a Federal Implementation Plan for the area.

In order to obtain EPA approval, an implementation plan, must be developed in consultation with the local political subdivisions affected by the plan and include certain requirements:

1) Enforceable emissions limitations and other control measures with schedules for compliance. These control measures can include economic incentives such as fees, marketable permits, and auctions of emissions rights.

2) Systems to monitor, compile, and analyze data on ambient air quality for any pollutant with a NAAQS. This data must be made available to EPA upon request.

3) An enforcement program aimed at ensuring NAAQS is achieved and includes the regulation and permitting of new or modified sources.

4) Prohibitions on activities that contribute to nonattainment in another state or interfere with the measures another state is taking to protect the significant deterioration of air quality or protect visibility.

5) Assurances that there are adequate personnel, funding and authority to carry out the plan provisions.

6) The EPA may also require that stationary sources conduct emissions monitoring, report, and correlate the results with any applicable emissions limitations or standards.

7) Provide the authority and ability to take action should a source present an imminent and substantial endangerment to public health or welfare, or the environment.

8) A periodic review and revision of the plan, as necessary.

9) For nonattainment areas the plan must include the requirements that are specific to the area. These requirements vary by pollutant and severity of the pollutant's impact.

10) Provides for adequate consultation with Federal land managers or local governments impacted by the requirements of the implementation plan, a public air quality advisory and awareness program, and a process in place that will prevent sources from contributing to a significant deterioration of air quality. This last provision is related to the concepts of *New Source Review* and *Prevention of Significant Deterioration* and will be discussed more thoroughly in a later section.

11) Requires that permit fees from stationary sources cover the costs of processing the permit application as well as implementing and enforcing the terms of the permit.

An implementation plan can have a direct effect on existing stationary (nonvehicular) sources of air pollution. For example, the plan can require the installation, maintenance and replacement of equipment in order to bring an area into compliance with the NAAQS, as well as the monitoring and reporting of emissions from the sources. An indirect source review program can also be included in the plan. *Indirect sources* are sources that do not produce pollution but have the ability to attract vehicles, or other mobile sources of pollution. Examples of indirect sources include buildings, parking lots and garages, roads, and highways.

Enforcement of an Implementation Plan

Federal enforcement of an implementation plan is the responsibility of the EPA. The EPA can enforce on a person (owner/operator of a source) or a state that has violated or failed to enforce the plan.

Enforcement on an individual can result in the issuance of a compliance order, an administrative penalty, or a civil action. Civil penalties of up to $25,000 per day for each violation (to a maximum of $200,000) are allowed by law. The penalties cited in this chapter are periodically adjusted for inflation. For example, in 2004 these penalties were adjusted to $27,500 and $200,000, respectively. Higher penalties can be assessed if the EPA and Attorney General determine that it is appropriate. This determination is not subject to judicial review.

A Federal enforcement action against a state can be initiated if the state is not adequately managing its implementation plan. When the EPA notices enforcement trends indicating that the state's implementation plan is not adequate, then the EPA notifies the state. Once this happens, EPA retains its authority to enforce against individuals until it is satisfied that the state is adequately managing its plan.

The EPA can impose sanctions against states that fail to:

1) Submit an implementation plan

2) Meet plan requirements

3) Submit required information to EPA

4) Gain EPA approval of the required submittals

5) Implement the plan

The sanctions that EPA can impose on states with nonattainment areas include the prohibition of new transportation projects and stricter emissions-offset requirements for new sources.

Exempted from the sanctions are transportation projects which can be demonstrated to result in a safety improvement, public transit projects, high-occupancy vehicle roads and parking, work trip reduction programs, traffic flow improvements which achieve net emissions reductions, as well as accident and information programs to reduce congestion.

Sources: Mobile, Stationary, Major, Synthetic Minor, Area, New, Modified, and Existing

Sources are emitters of air pollutants. The air pollutants include the criteria pollutants, for which NAAQS have been issued, as well as the hazardous air pollutants (HAPs). (HAPs are discussed in more detail in the next section.)

The Clean Air Act broadly regulates sources as mobile or stationary. *Mobile sources* include vehicles, airplanes, and other forms of transportation. On an individual basis, these sources are relatively small emitters of criteria pollutants and HAPs. Therefore, regional air pollution caused by mobile sources can generally be thought of as being caused by an aggregation of individual activities. This creates the need for a different regulatory framework than is in place for stationary sources and is discussed in more detail in a later section.

Stationary sources are sources of air pollution which don't move, such as a building, structure, facility, or other installation. Stationary sources can also include *portable sources*, such as concrete batch plants or a portable diesel generator that, when placed at a particular location becomes a stationary source. For the purposes of construction and operating permits, a stationary source is considered to be a *major source* if it emits or has the potential to emit a significant quantity of one or more air pollutants. The significant quantity varies with the type of pollutant and is illustrated in Table 2.

A *synthetic minor source* has the theoretical capacity to operate as a major source but the owner/operator has voluntarily accepted an enforceable limitation in order to keep its emissions below the levels listed in Table 2. Some states refer to this as a *Federally Enforceable State Operating Permit* (FESOP).

Area sources are stationary or nonroad sources that are too small and/or too numerous to be included in a stationary source inventory.

Table 2. Categories of Major Sources Based on Potential to Emit

Type of Pollutant	Type of Source	Single Air Pollutant	Combination of Air Pollutants
Criteria Pollutant	Specifically listed in §169 (1) of the CAA	≥ 100 T/yr	Not applicable
Criteria Pollutant	Any other source not listed in §169 (1) of the CAA	≥ 250 T/yr	Not applicable
Hazardous Air Pollutant	Any stationary source or group of stationary sources within a contiguous area and under common control	≥ 10 T/yr	≥ 25 T/yr

Examples of area sources include: water heaters, gas furnaces, fireplaces, and wood stoves.

As will be discussed in more detail in a later section, air pollution from stationary sources is generally controlled through the state or local permitting programs. These programs distinguish between new, modified, and existing sources. A **new source** is one that has not started construction prior to the *affected date,* as defined in the relevant regulation. A source has been **modified** when it has been physically changed or is operated in a manner that increases the emissions of existing or new pollutants. A major modification is any physical change or change in the method of operation of a stationary source that would relate to a significant net emissions increase of any regulated pollutant. The definition of *significant* is specifically provided in the form of various pollutant emissions rates. An **existing source** is any source other than a new source.

New Source Review and Prevention of Significant Deterioration

New Source Review. The Clean Air Act requires that State Implementation Plans include a process for review of the construction and operation of new and modified stationary sources . This process is called **new source review** (NSR). The term is also used in nonattainment areas to refer to the evaluation and scoping of a proposed project, including emissions limitations, and public involvement. The NSR program is intended to *make reasonable further progress* toward achieving attainment of the NAAQS. Therefore, sources being permitted through the NSR process are required to install the Lowest Achievable Emission Rate (LAER) When an area becomes designated as nonattainment, there is less flexibility in the permitting process. Emissions thresholds are lowered, increasing the possibility that LAER will be required, regardless of cost considerations and feasibility. New or modified sources in these areas must also obtain **emissions offsets** as part of their permitting requirements. Emissions offsets are surplus emissions reductions that may be obtained through changes in the plant process or purchased from other facilities. The offsets are intended to compensate for the sources' impact on air quality. The offsets concept provides a source with an opportunity to find the most cost-effective way to reduce emissions.

Prevention of Significant Deterioration. The term *prevention of significant deterioration* (PSD) applies to permitting of stationary sources of criteria pollutants in attainment areas. The PSD program is intended to *preserve* the air quality of an area. PSD only applies to the criteria pollutants and does not apply to the regulation of HAPs. In attainment areas, *major sources* are required to evaluate their impact on the ambient air quality prior to starting construction. It is important to note that the permitting trigger for a PSD-major source is significantly higher than the permitting trigger for construction or operating permits.

The purpose of the PSD program is to further the goal of the Clean Air Act through the implementation of the following objectives:

1) Protect public health and welfare

2) Preserve, protect, and enhance air quality in our scenic and wild areas

3) Prevent the significant deterioration of air quality

4) Have informed public participation in the decision-making process

Since the Prevention of Significant Deterioration program is required to be part of the SIP, the EPA can regulate for PSD if an implementation plan is not in place. Although a state may be authorized by EPA to implement a PSD permitting program, the EPA retains its authority to make the final permit determination and to stop construction of a source at any time.

An owner wishing to construct a new source or modify an existing source in an attainment area must first provide the permitting agency with enough information for the agency to define the permit conditions. With the information provided, the agency must ensure that the new source will not violate the state's control strategy or interfere with the attainment of a NAAQS in the local area and region. Therefore, the permit application must be sufficiently detailed so that the permitting agency understands the source (nature and amounts of emissions as well as location, design, construction, and operation of the source).

Air quality modeling will be required in virtually every permit determination. Most PSD applications involve several iterations of modeling, and can cost tens of thousands of dollars. In some cases, one year of pre-construction ambient air monitoring may also be required. Additionally, Federal land managers of nearby Class I areas (note that the practical definition of *nearby* is continually expanding) must be contacted and provided an opportunity to comment on the potential air quality impacts–including visibility. Nearby states and tribes must also be afforded an opportunity to comment on the permit.

Obtaining a permit under the PSD rules is a public process. Any information submitted by the owner as well as any determinations made by the agency are public information. In addition, public participation is invited via a notice and comment period. In some cases a public hearing is also required.

In an attainment area, the emissions from a new source are not allowed to cause violations of the NAAQS. In issuing a PSD permit, the State or Federal agency must determine the **Maximum Allowable Increase** (MAI) of pollutants that will be emitted from the source as well as any other applicable standard. The MAI represents a ceiling concentration for the pollutant and is also referred to in the regulations as an *ambient air increment*. The Maximum Allowable Increase is calculated as a function of location or class of the source and can also be incorporated as a requirement of the SIP. The resulting permitted emissions levels result in *consumption* of the increment, which must be considered when permitting sources in the future.

The resulting PSD permit provides the owner or operator with specific allowable emissions that are below the MAI. **Allowable emissions**, under the rules, are the more stringent of the applicable New Source Performance Standards (see discussion at the end of this section), SIP limitations, or Federally enforceable permit conditions (including the use of the Best Available Control Technology, or BACT—a concept that is discussed in more detail in a later section).

National Emissions Standards for Hazardous Air Pollutants

Sources that emit hazardous air pollutants must conform to the National Emissions Standards for Hazardous Air Pollutants (NESHAPS). EPA develops NESHAPS for a wide variety of source categories and subcategories. The NESHAPS

require the maximum degree of reduction in HAP emissions. If feasible, this maximum degree of reduction may be accomplished by prohibiting the emission of a particular substance.

The factors EPA must use when setting NESHAPS include cost, non-air quality environmental and health impacts, and energy requirements. The resulting standards can require a variety of methods to achieve emissions reduction including process changes; material substitutions; closed systems; collection, capture, or treatment of pollutants; as well as design, equipment, work practice, or operational standards (including operator certification and training).

The Alphabet Soup of Control Technologies: NSPS, BACT, LAER, MACT, RACT, BART, GACT, RACM, and BACM

The Clean Air Act specifies the use of a variety of control technologies to minimize the emissions of air pollutants and ensure reasonable progress toward the attainment of NAAQS. This alphabet soup of control technologies is used throughout the different Titles of the Clean Air Act. The specific terms are defined below.

New source performance standards (NSPS) are source-specific emissions-control limitations and requirements intended to promote the *best* technological system of continuous emission reduction. The NSPS take into account factors such as cost, as well as non-air health and environmental impacts, and energy requirements. The Clean Air Act requires that NSPS be reviewed once every eight years. The emissions control requirements for new or modified sources must be stricter than the NSPS.

BACT or **Best Available Control Technology** is required for new or modified sources being permitted in an attainment area under the Prevention of Significant Deterioration rules, and may also be used in nonattainment areas under the New Source Review rules. Sources implementing BACT are using the most effective control technology that is available. The statutory definition of BACT is

> An emission limitation based on the maximum degree of reduction of each pollutant

subject to regulation . . . taking into account energy, environmental, and economic impacts and other costs . . . is achievable for the facility through the application of production processes, and available methods, systems, and techniques . . .

BACT determinations are made by the permitting agency on a case-by-case basis and must ensure that the resulting source emissions level is in compliance with the NSPS for that source. Practically speaking, the permittee must determine BACT prior to filing the permit application. The BACT determination is not a trivial process and requires a reivew of all similar BACT determinations (state-by-state, as well as international), then working down the list from the *top down* in order to choose the control technology that is technically and economically feasible. This evaluation includes site-specific factors unique to the source and must meet EPA's guidelines on the acceptable per ton cost for controlling the pollutant(s).

LAER, or **Lowest Achievable Emissions Rate**, is used by major sources in nonattainment areas, as part of the New Source Review process. The statutory definition of LAER is the more stringent of the following conditions:

1) The most stringent emission limitation [for that class or category of source] which is contained in the implementation plan of any state . . . unless the owner or operator . . . demonstrates that such limitations are not achievable.

2) The most stringent emission limitation which is achieved by practice [for that class or category of source]

Like BACT, LAER determinations are made on a case-by-case basis and are limited by the emissions levels set in the NSPS.

LAER does not take into direct consideration economic factors. BACT and LAER determinations are State-specific and the determination of what is BACT or LAER can differ between states. In some cases, after subsequent agency interpretation, can be little real difference between BACT and LAER.

The EPA, in cooperation with the states, maintains a BACT/LAER Clearinghouse database of sources. The clearinghouse can be accessed through the Technology Transfer Network: Clean Air Technology Center on the Internet–

<http://cfpub.epa.gov/rblc/htm/bl02.cfm>

and the query page can be found at

<http://cfpub.epa.gov/rblc/cfm/basicsearch.cfm>

MACT, or **Maximum Achievable Control Technology**, is a concept used in the permitting of hazardous air pollutants. The MACT concept was introduced as part of the 1990 CAA Amendments. Initially 174 different source categories were targeted. This initial listing of source categories (promulgated on July 16, 1992) has been updated several times with both additions of new source categories and deletions. The control technology for new and existing sources is determined by establishing the *MACT floor* or baseline. For existing sources, the MACT floor must equal

the average emission limitation achieved by the best performing 12% of the existing sources . . .

Or, if there are fewer than 30 sources in the category:

the average emission limitation achieved by the best performing 5 sources.

The MACT floor for new sources is

emission control that is achieved in practice by the best controlled similar source.

The intent of the MACT standards is to provide a performance-based method for reducing the emissions of Hazardous Air Pollutants (HAPs). Facilities with good emissions controls have an economic advantage when the standards are developed. The real challenge in determining MACT for a particular source is the definition and refinement of the source category and the subsequent *best performers*.

The 1990 amendments mandated EPA to develop MACT standards for an initial list of 189 HAPs by the year 2000. Subsequent revisions to the law have resulted in a current list of 188 HAPs. HAP requirements are discussed more thoroughly in a later section.

RACT, or **Reasonably Achievable Emissions Control Technology**, is incorporated by a state into its SIP in order to achieve compliance with the

NAAQS in nonattainment areas. RACT is defined as

> Devices, systems, process modifications, or other apparatus or techniques that are reasonably available and take into account:
>
> 1) The necessity of imposing such controls, and
>
> 2) The social, environmental, and economic impact of such controls

BART, or ***Best Available Retrofit Technology***, can be required on existing major sources in areas affected by the regional haze rule. EPA has only recently addressed visibility protection nationwide. BART, which would be applicable to 26 industrial source categories in 34 states, takes into account availability of the control technology, cost of compliance, current pollution control equipment used by the source, the remaining useful life of the source, and the expected improvement in visibility.

GACT, or ***Generally Achievable Control Technology***, is an alternative standard which, at the EPA's discretion, may be applied to HAP area sources in order to enable control the emissions of the most significant HAPs.

BACM and RACM are what EPA considers the ***Best Available*** and ***Reasonably Available Control Measures*** for the management of particulate matter less than 10 microns (PM_{10}). EPA has issued guidance on BACM and RACM for emissions from fugitive dust, residential wood combustion, and prescribed burning.

Title I—Air Pollution Prevention and Control

Title I of the Clean Air Act, as amended in 1990, consists of three parts: air quality and emissions limitations, prevention of significant deterioration of air quality, and plan requirements for nonattainment areas. Some of the significant features of Title I not discussed in the previous section are covered below.

Air Quality and Emissions Limitations

Title I of the Act is an overview of Congress' philosophy and intent. In Title I, air pollution is identified as being primarily an urban problem associated with increasing industrialization and urban growth. Pollutants threaten not only public health but also the public infrastructure such as agriculture, property, and transportation. In fact, at the time of the Clean Air Act Amendments, over 100 cities were in nonattainment for ozone.

One of the fundamental tenets of the Clean Air Act is that states and local governments are primarily responsible for air pollution prevention and control. The Federal government is responsible for providing cooperative oversight, financial assistance, and leadership. This philosophy can be seen throughout the Act in the State and Tribal Implementation Plan requirements, permitting programs, research programs, and grants.

Because air pollution doesn't necessarily stop at the State line, cooperation between states, and formation of regional pacts and commissions, are encouraged. Regional pacts, however, require congressional approval.

Title I also gives the states the primary responsibility and requirements for designating attainment and nonattainment areas as well as developing and implementing the State Implementation Plans.

After considering recommendations from the states and tribes, EPA promulgates the air quality designations, and can approve redesignation of an area to attainment status if it meets the following conditions:

1) The air quality meets the NAAQS

2) The SIP has been approved

3) The improvement in air quality has been due to permanent and enforceable reductions in emissions resulting from implementation of the SIP, Federal rules, and other permanent and enforceable reductions

4) A maintenance plan has been approved

5) The state meets all the requirements for implementation plans and plan requirements for nonattainment areas

Title I establishes the development by EPA of primary and secondary NAAQS as well as a transportation air quality planning process.

Title I also introduces the concept of New Source Performance Standards and specifies that any permit issued to a new or modified stationary source must comply with the standards of performance applicable to that source. This requires the source to employ a *technological system of continuous emissions reduction*. In addition, the construction and operation of a new or modified source must be in compliance with all other requirements of the Act.

Clean Air Mercury Rule. A recent example of the application of NSPS to control air pollution is the Clean Air Mercury Rule, which was finalized on March 15, 2005. The rule is intended to reduce emissions of mercury from coal-fired power plants. It is estimated that these plants emit approximately 48 tons of mercury a year. Once implemented, the rule will result in a 70% reduction in the mercury emissions from these facilities, to an estimated 15 tons per year. Mercury is a concern because it is a toxic persistent pollutant that accumulates in the environment and the food chain.

The mercury reductions will be accomplished by establishing new standards of performance for new and existing coal-fired power plants. In addition, a cap-and-trade approach will be implemented in two phases. The first phase will be accomplished as a result of the Clean Air Interstate Program (which is discussed at the end of this section) and will take advantage of any co-benefit reductions that can be realized through the control of SO_2 and NO_x emissions. Any remaining reduction in mercury emissions will be accomplished in the second phase, which is intended to be fully implemented by 2018.

Hazardous Air Pollutants

Hazardous Air Pollutants (HAPs) have been part of the Clean Air Act since 1970. However, because of the way the 1970 law was written, over the next 20 years EPA was only able to set regulatory standards for seven HAPs. The 1990 amendments increased the number of regulated HAPs to 189 and established a 10-year schedule for developing performance-based compliance standards. Congress required that EPA promulgate certain specific standards within two years; 25 percent of the standards within four years; an additional 25 percent within seven years; and the remaining 50 percent within 10 years, or by the year 2000. EPA has not been able to meet the statutory deadlines for issuing MACT standards. The current schedule for issuing these standards extends through 2007.

HAPs are pollutants that are known to have an adverse effect on human health. HAPs may be carcinogenic, mutagenic, teratogenic, neurotoxic, chronically toxic, bioaccummulative, or cause reproductive dysfunction. Examples of HAPs include benzene (found in gasoline), perchloroethylene (a common dry-cleaning solvent), and methylene chloride (used as a paint stripper). Asbestos and metals such as mercury, lead, chromium, and cadmium are also condsidered to be HAPs. The initial list of 189 HAPs that was included in the Act is periodically reviewed and revised, and one compound has been delisted since its promulgation in 1990.

In addition to defining HAPs, Title I also regulates HAP sources. EPA is required to maintain a list of HAP sources, both stationary and area. MACT and GACT are used to control emissions of HAPs from these sources. EPA has completed promulgating MACT standards for its mandated 2-, 4- and 7-year schedules. Since 1990, MACT rules have been promulgated for 45 industries including petroleum refining, dry cleaners, and cleaning machines that use halogenated solvents.

Because new MACT standards continue to be developed, it is critically important for the operator of a source to scrutinize the proposed and final MACT standards regularly. This will enable the operator to be aware of potential rules and to avoid inadvertent noncompliance. It is important also to recognize that a single facility can be subject to more than one MACT standard.

Incorporated into the Act is the incentive for sources to reduce HAPs prior to a regulatory mandate. If a source can achieve a 90 percent reduction in HAPs (or, for particulate HAPs, a 95 percent reduction) before a MACT standard has been issued, then the source can continue to operate at the reduced level for up to six years from the compliance date of the applicable standard. This 6-year window allows the source to continue operation under the Title V Operating Permit program until the next renewal period. Operating Permits, as will be discussed in the next section, are on a 5-year renewal cycle.

An increase in awareness to community needs resulted in the inclusion in the 1990 amendments of the accidental release provisions for 77 HAPs. Stationary sources that produce, process, handle, or store certain substances are required to implement an accidental release prevention program. This program is commonly known as the Section 112(r) requirements, referring to that section of the Clean Air Act Amendments. It is also known as the Risk Management Plan (RM Plan), or Risk Management Program (RMP).

An RMP is required if any of the 77 regulated substances (which have the potential to cause death, injury, or serious adverse effects to human health or the environment) are stored in quantities exceeding a threshold amount. The accidental release prevention program includes hazard assessment techniques, safe design and maintenance of the facility, as well as the means to minimize the consequences of a release.

Owners and operators affected by the RMP rules were required to comply by June 21, 1999 and revisions to the reporting requirements were issued in 2004. Refer to the Risk Management Progam chapter in this book for more information.

Federal Enforcement of the Clean Air Act

Like many of the other environmental statutes, Federal enforcement of the Clean Air Act is particularly onerous. Title I outlines the enforcement procedures for states as well as corporations and individuals that fail to meet the provisions of the Act.

EPA has the responsibility for Federal enforcement that can result in a number of actions, including

- Issuance of an administrative penalty order
- Issuance of a compliance order
- A civil action
- A criminal action

The type of enforcement action taken depends on the type of violation, its seriousness, and the good-faith actions taken by the violator to comply with the requirements.

Civil penalties can be assessed up to $25,000/day with a $200,000 maximum. These amounts are periodically adjusted upward to compensate for inflation. Criminal penalties can apply to knowing violations of the Act. Conviction of a criminal violation can result in a fine and/or imprisonment. In determining the amount of penalty to be assessed, the following factors are taken into account:

- The size of the business
- The economic impact of the penalty on the business
- The compliance history
- Good-faith efforts towards compliance
- Duration of the violation
- Previous penalties for the same violation
- The economic benefit of noncompliance

The Clean Air Act Amendments of 1990 also introduced a field citation program and bounty hunter provisions for citizens reporting. The purpose of the field citation program is to allow an EPA inspector to address minor violations. Civil penalties of less than $5000 can be issued to a facility immediately by an EPA inspector.

Under the bounty hunter provisions, EPA can pay an award of up to $10,000 to anyone who provides information that ultimately leads to a criminal conviction or civil penalty.

Visibility Protection

Title I includes in the PSD program a national goal to protect the visual resources of the United States. The Act protects visibility in Class I Federal areas (in particular, wilderness areas and national parks) by remedying existing and preventing any future impairment of visibility in these areas.

Visibility impairment is caused by a number of factors. Particulates such as dust and wood smoke have a direct impact on visibility. Gaseous pollutants, such as SO_2 and NO_x, are precursors to sulfates and nitrates—particulates that contribute to regional haze. Because the pollutants that can contribute to visibility impairment are capable of migrating long distances from their sources, Congress authorized the establishment of visibility transport regions and commissions. The commissions recommend measures to improve visibility, develop clean air corridors, alternative siting measures, and long-range strategies. The Grand Canyon Visibility Transport Commission, for example, was formed under the authority of the CAA to improve visibility in the 16 national parks and wilderness areas located on the Colorado Plateau. This transport commission is networked with other government and collaborative efforts, such as the National Park Service Visibility Program and the Western Regional Air Partnership.

Guidelines relating to visibility protection were first proposed in 1980, with proposed amendments published in 1997. In 1999 Regional Haze Regulations were issued that called for states to establish visibility goals for Class I areas and establish strategies to reduce emissions of air pollutants that cause visibility impairment. States were required to set reasonable progress goals in order to achieve an ultimate goal of natural background conditions in 60 years. Some of these strategies included enforceable measures such as the reduction of manmade emissions that contribute to impairment.

The 1999 rule was challenged in court, vacated in part and sustained in part. In 2001, prior to the court's decision, EPA published proposed guidelines intended to clarify one of the key elements of the rule, the installation of Best Available Retrofit Technology, or BART.

On July 7, 2005, EPA published a final regional haze rule (effective September 6, 2005) and guidelines for states to use in determining which facilities must install BART controls and the types of controls the facilities must use. The rule affects facilities that were built between 1962 and 1977 and that have the potential to emit greater than 250 tons per year of visibility-impairing pollution. Particulate matter (in particular, $PM_{2.5}$), SO_2, NO_x and, under some conditions, ammonia and VOCs are pollutants that affect visibility.

States will identify in their SIPs the facilities that will be required to install BART, using the following factors when making their determinations:

- The cost of the controls

- The impact of controls on energy useage or any non-air quality environmental impacts

- The remaining useful life of the equipment to be controlled

- Any existing pollution controls already in place

- Visibility improvement that would result from controlling the emissions

States participating in the Clean Air Interstate Rule (CAIR) cap-and-trade program for NO_x and SO_2, can apply CAIR controls as a substitute for controls under BART.

Clean Air Interstate Rule

The Clean Air Interstate Rule (CAIR), finalized on March 10, 2005, is based on Section 110(a)(2)(D) of the CAA that obligates a state to address the interstate transport of pollutants. The rule establishes a cap-and-trade system for SO_2 and NO_x emissions in 28 eastern states and the District of Columbia. These two pollutants are suspected of contributing to fine particulate pollution and ground level ozone and may causes exceedences of the NAAQS hundreds or thousands of miles from the source. The CAIR requires the affected states to update their implementation plans by 2006. The cap-and-trade reductions, applicable to power generating facilities, are then introduced in three phases, with the third phase scheduled to be implemented in 2015.

General Requirements for Nonattainment Areas

Title I creates the overall program for achieving the goals of the Clean Air Act. In addition to establishing air quality limitations, it establishes a state planning program intended to achieve *reasonable progress* toward attainment of NAAQS.

Once a nonattainment area is identified, EPA publishes a notice in the *Federal Register*. Subsequent to identification, a state must ensure that its SIP contains a plan to implement the following:

1)   The implementation of reasonably available control technology (RACT) on existing sources

2)   Reasonable further progress (RFP) toward attaining NAAQS

3)   An inventory that identifies and quantifies current emissions levels

4)   Construction and operating permits for new and modified sources

5)   Emissions limits and other control measures (including economic incentives such as fees, marketable permits, and auctions of emissions limits)

6)   Measures to be taken if an area fails to make RFP

A state's schedule for attainment of NAAQS is set out in the SIP. In general, for a primary NAAQS, the attainment date must occur within five years of its promulgation, with extensions possible of no more than 10 years. A secondary NAAQS does not have a statutory deadline for attainment but must be achieved as expeditiously as possible.

Any source in a nonattainment area is potentially under more stringent permitting and operating conditions than if it were located in an attainment area. States and local agencies may impose additional requirements in these areas that exceed the Federal standards. An operator wishing to construct or modify a source must demonstrate that the source will be beneficial when weighed against the environmental and social costs. The operator of the source must obtain a permit from the regulating agency prior to starting construction or modification. The source is under strict emissions limitations. The source emissions characteristics must meet NSPS, LAER must be installed, and the source must find offsetting emissions reductions from existing sources in the region.

As discussed earlier, the use of offsets is a market-based approach toward reducing air pollution and achieving attainment. The offsetting emissions reduction obtained from the existing sources must exceed the proposed increase. Offsets can be obtained from a different stack on the same source, the same facility, or other facilities within the nonattainment area. Trading of offsets is allowed.

One of the requirements for new projects in a nonattainment area is that these projects (which are generally transportation related) must conform to the SIP. SIP conformity means that the project promotes the SIP's overall purpose in eliminating or reducing the severity and number of NAAQS exceedances.

Once an area has passed its scheduled attainment date, EPA evaluates the area's air quality and publishes the results. If an area fails to attain NAAQS, the state must submit a revised SIP to EPA for approval. The attainment clock for the failed area starts over from the date of the published notice. The state has a statutory deadline of five to 10 years to come into attainment with the primary NAAQS.

Should a state fail to attain NAAQS, EPA has the authority to impose sanctions. As discussed previously, the EPA can take sanctions against a state for failure to prepare an adequate plan as well as failure to implement a plan. The sanctions include limiting funding for transportation projects, as well as increasing the offset ratio of emissions reductions to emissions increases.

These general provisions for nonattainment areas apply to all of the criteria pollutants, including sulfur oxides, nitrogen dioxide, and lead. Some of the criteria pollutants—ozone, carbon monoxide, and particulate matter—have additional requirements. These are summarized in the following sections.

Ozone Nonattainment Areas

Ground-level ozone is the primary constituent of smog. Ozone at ground level causes a number of deleterious health effects including respiratory infection, lung inflammation, and an aggravation of pre-existing respiratory diseases such as asthma.

Like carbon monoxide, ambient ozone concentrations have decreased substantially over the years. However, recent changes in the ozone NAAQS will impact the regulation of sources that emit VOCs and NO_x.

In 1997, EPA revised the NAAQS for ozone, changing the standard from 0.12 ppm, averaged over a 1-hour period, to 0.08 ppm, averaged over an 8-hour period. The new standard withstood a challenge in the courts, and is still in effect. EPA listed the nation's 1-hour ozone nonattainment areas in the spring of 2004 and a complete listing can be found on the EPA website.

Smog forms when ozone, unburned volatile organic compounds (VOCs), and NO_x combine in the atmosphere. The smog-forming chemical reaction requires heat, sunlight, and time. Thus, depending on the meteorological conditions, smog can form many miles away from the emitting sources. It is because of the fact that ozone is formed in the atmosphere rather than emitted directly from a source, that control of ozone pollution is achieved through the regulation of VOCs and NO_x.

A minimum of three years of ambient ozone concentration is needed to designate an area as attainment or nonattainment. Ozone nonattainment areas are classified as marginal, moderate, serious, severe, extreme, and other. Each of the classifications has prescribed actions and schedules for attainment. It is possible for areas that have been previously unclassified to subsequently become designated as nonattainment. An area can become reclassified to a higher (more restrictive) classification should it fail to attain NAAQS within six months of its scheduled attainment date. In addition, states can voluntarily reclassify to a more restrictive standard.

Rural transport areas are rural nonattainment areas associated with a larger metropolitan area. These areas are handled as marginal for ozone nonattainment.

Single ozone nonattainment areas that cover more than one state are called ***multi-state ozone non-attainment areas***. Multi-state nonattainment areas are required to coordinate their implementation plans. A state in such an area may petition EPA, and, through modeling or other methods, demonstrate its ability to be in attainment if it weren't for the failure of other states to achieve attainment.

In order to manage ozone, the CAA specifies both Federal and State actions. At the Federal level, the Clean Air Act requires that EPA issue guidelines for cost-effective control of VOCs and NO_x.

The EPA also has the ability to establish interstate regions and commissions in order to control interstate ozone. The findings of these commissions can result in recommendations for SIP revisions and other actions, which need to be taken in order to bring the area under control.

In the 1990s there were several initiatives addressing the problem of high ambient ozone levels in the eastern half of the United States,

specifically in the northeastern states. Ozone was recognized as a regional transport issue, and states east of the Mississippi River were required to revise their SIPs to deal with this. The resulting NO_X *SIP Call* required an additional 60% reduction in NO_X emissions at existing sources, which is well beyond what was required by NSPS or by the acid deposition program (Title IV of the Act). A cap-and-trade program, modeled after the program in Title IV, has subsequently been implemented. As a result, additional emissions monitoring systems are now required. For the majority of the affected sources the first regulated ozone season was in 2004 (see related discussion in the section of the Clean Air Rules of 2004 at the end of the chapter.)

For severe and extreme ozone nonattainment, failure to attain NAAQS can result in fees to major sources of $5000/ton of VOC.

Carbon Monoxide Nonattainment Areas

Carbon monoxide (CO) is a colorless, odorless gas that is formed during incomplete combustion of fuels. Carbon monoxide is poisonous at high concentrations, replacing oxygen in the blood and consequently reducing the amount of oxygen available to the body's organs and tissues. Ambient carbon monoxide concentrations in the United States have decreased by 37 percent between 1987 and 1996, despite a 26 percent increase in the number of vehicle-miles traveled during this same period.

Carbon monoxide nonattainment areas are classified as moderate or serious. Like the provisions for ozone nonattainment, an unclassified carbon monoxide area can be designated as nonattainment. Moderate areas that fail to achieve attainment in a timely manner can be reclassified as serious. Also, states which are part of multistate nonattainment areas must coordinate actions taken under their SIPs.

For carbon monoxide, both the moderate and serious classifications have prescribed actions and schedule for attainment. The types of actions required to control carbon monoxide become more stringent with poorer air quality. Depending on the attainment classification, measures such as a vehicle-miles inventory, use of oxygenated gasoline, and increased regulation of stationary sources may be required.

If a serious area fails to achieve attainment, then the state must revise its SIP, committing to an annual 5% decrease until NAAQS is achieved.

Particulate Matter Nonattainment Areas

Particulate matter (PM) is a general term for a mixture of solid and liquid particles in air. The particles originate from manmade sources (such as power plants, motor vehicles, and wood stoves) and natural sources (such as wind-blown dust).

PM contributes to a series of health effects including increased respiratory disease, decreased lung function, and death. Particulate matter also contributes to regional haze, and therefore is a component of the visibility requirements under the Act.

The ambient concentrations of *particulate matter less than 10 microns* (PM_{10}) decreased by approximately 25% between 1988 and 1996. In 1997, EPA revised the particulate matter NAAQS to include particles less than 2.5 microns in diameter ($PM_{2.5}$). Since 1999, the EPA and its state and tribal partners have operated a $PM_{2.5}$ monitoring network. Data from this network shows that the average concentration of $PM_{2.5}$ has decreased by about 8% from 1999–2002. EPA designated the nation's $PM_{2.5}$ nonattainment areas in the summer of 2004 . These designations became effective on April 5, 2005 and a complete listing can be found on the EPA Internet site. These 39 areas in 208 counties across the country are now subject to new source review and the transportation conformity requirements and have an ultimate goal of achieving the NAAQS by 2010.

Title II—Emission Standards for Moving Sources

EPA defines moving or ***mobile sources*** to include highway vehicles such as automobiles, trucks and motorcycles and nonroad vehicles such as trains, airplanes, agricultural equipment, industrial equipment, construction vehicles, off-road motorcycles, and marine vessels. Mobile sources represent a special regulatory challenge. Emissions from mobile sources originate from a multitude of individual sources, and it is the aggregated emissions from these sources that create regional air quality problems. For example, motor vehicles produce up to half of the smog-forming VOCs and nitrogen oxides, release greater than 50% of the HAPs and 90% of the CO in urban air. Although today's cars produce 60–80% fewer pollutants than the cars of the 1960s, and although people are using more mass transit today than they did then, the levels of pollutants from mobile sources have not substantially decreased. The reasons for this are that

- Americans drove more (1 trillion-vehicle miles in 1970 *vs.* an estimated 4 trillion in 2000)

- People live far from work and/or may not have access to mass transit

- Reformulated unleaded gasoline can release more smog-forming gases (VOCs) to the atmosphere

Motor Vehicle Emissions Standards

Congress decided to approach the regulation of moving sources from several directions. In ozone and CO nonattainment areas, where air quality problems are significant, vehicle maintenance and inspection programs are required.

Congress also mandated the control of air pollution from new motor vehicles such as automobiles, heavy-duty trucks, and motorcycles. Not only are emissions standards required, but fueling and onboard vapor recovery standards are prescribed, as well as special requirements for high-altitude vehicles.

Manufacturers fund the motor vehicle program. New vehicles must have a certificate of conformity with these standards as well as an emissions system warrantee. Manufacturers are required to maintain records of the performance tests.

As an example, the purchase of a new car today includes under-the-hood systems and dashboard warning lights for the emissions-control system. These devices must be operable for 100,000 miles.

Unlike other portions of the CAA, the regulation of vehicle emissions standards cannot be delegated to the states. Other than California, states cannot set independent standards for new motor vehicles. Only California can receive EPA authorization to

Table 3. Fuel Standards

Additive or Characteristic	Condition or Limitation
Any fuel or additive	Must be substantially similar to the fuel or additive used to certify vehicles after 1974
	Must not cause or contribute to the failure of an emissions control device or fuel system
Manganese	0.0625 g/gallon fuel
Leaded gasoline	Prohibited from use entirely after 12/31/95. Prior to 12/31/95, prohibited in a vehicle which is labeled "Unleaded Gasoline Only"
Sulfur	0.05% by weight in diesel
	0.10% by weight for heavy-duty diesel vehicles and engines

adopt and enforce other standards. Once California standards have been adopted by EPA, other states can follow suit.

Fuel Standards

Another approach used to control air pollution from moving sources is the regulation of fuel and fuel additives. For example, the use of tetraethyl lead in gasoline has been phased out and sulfur, which contributes to acid rain and smog, is required to be removed from diesel fuel.

EPA can register new fuels and fuel additives (including lead substitutes) only after the manufacturer demonstrates that the product and its emissions will not endanger public health and welfare. Lead substitutes must also be shown to be effective in reducing valve seat wear while avoiding other engine side effects. Like the new vehicle standards, the introduction of new fuels and fuel additives cannot be delegated to the states.

Certain additives are expressly forbidden from inclusion and/or use in fuels. The prohibitions are summarized in Table 3.

In the United States, nine of the major metropolitan ozone nonattainment areas are required to use reformulated gasoline as a means of controlling emissions of volatile organics. The purpose of the reformulation is to decrease benzene, a carcinogen, and other smog-forming chemicals. In order to recertify reformulated gasoline, it must meet certain criteria, summarized in Table 4.

The use of reformulated gasoline in nonattainment areas is controlled by a series of options, economic incentives, and other requirements. For example, states can petition EPA to voluntarily opt in to the reformulated fuels program. Manufacturers of reformulated gasoline can generate credits by creating formulas that exceed the minimum standards, and those credits can be transferred for use within the same nonattainment area. Also, manufacturers of reformulated gasoline are required to ensure that their average per-gallon emissions of VOCs, oxides of nitrogen, carbon monoxide, and toxic air pollutants are less than the 1990 baseline year.

In carbon monoxide nonattainment areas (39 urban areas in the United States), oxygenated fuels of not less than 2.7% O_2 by weight are required. The requirement is typically in effect during the winter months only. The added oxygenated compounds make the fuel burn more efficiently, resulting in a reduction of CO emissions.

Retailers of oxygenated gasoline are required to label the fuel dispensers, indicating that the fuel is oxygenated and will reduce CO emissions from the vehicle. Marketable credits for oxygenated gasoline are available for use within the nonattainment area, similar to the reformulated gasoline credits.

The control of emissions from urban buses built since 1994 is affected through the use of low-polluting fuels. The goal is to obtain a 50% reduction in PM emissions. Urban buses in metropolitan areas that had a 1980 population exceeding 750,000 are required to retrofit engines replaced or rebuilt after January 1, 1995.

In order to qualify as a *clean alternative fuel*, the fuel must meet certain standards and be useable by a certified clean-fuel vehicle. Examples of clean alternate fuels include methanol, ethanol or other alcohols, gasohol mixtures greater than 85% alcohol by volume, reformulated gasoline or diesel, natural gas, liquefied petroleum gas, hydrogen, or an alternate power source such as electricity.

Nonroad Engines

Nonroad engines include a wide variety of internal combustion engines from small lawn mower type engines to heavy-duty construction equipment. Locomotives, marine engines, and aviation equipment are also in this category. Historically, emissions control from these engines has not been considered in their design. Therefore they emit relatively higher levels of hydrocarbons, particulate matter, NO_x, CO, and CO_2 than other types of moving sources.

Emissions standards have been set for many of these engines. Depending on the engine, these standards are being phased in through the year 2008. Engine manufacturers are required to ensure that their engines meet the standards. For example, in May, 2004 EPA issued a comprehensive rule to limit emissions from nonroad diesel engines. This rule sets new engine standards that are intended to reduce particulate matter (PM) and NO_x from these sources by 90 percent. Emissions reductions from sources are achieved in a manner similar to mobile sources. The rules complement similar regulations for diesel highway trucks and buses. Emission-control standards are established for new engines to control PM and NO_x. The amount of sulfur in diesel fuel is limited to control sulfur emissions.

Aircraft emissions are controlled through the adoption of the International Civil Aviation Organization standards. These standards are enforced by the Federal Aviation Administration.

Clean Fuel Vehicles

The Clean Fuel Vehicle program, which is mandated in ozone nonattainment areas, is a special program intended to encourage the use of both low-emission vehicles and clean alternative fuels.

The Clean Fuel program was initiated and tested in California as a means to control air pollution in ozone nonattainment areas. Included as part of

Table 4. Reformulated Gasoline Criteria

Criteria	Specification
NO_x emissions	Less than the levels of NO_x emitted by baseline vehicles using baseline gasoline
Oxygen content	Greater than or equal to 2% by weight (could be waived if this condition prevents or interferes with attainment of a NAAQS)
Benzene content	Less than 1% by volume
Heavy metals (lead and manganese)	None allowed
Aromatics	Less than 25% by volume
Detergents	Sufficient to prevent the accumulation of deposits in engines and/or fuel supply systems
VOC emissions	15% less than vehicles using baseline gasoline before 2000. 25% less after 2000, measured on a mass basis
Toxic air pollutants	15% less than vehicles using baseline gasoline before 2000, 25% less after 2000, measured on a mass basis

the State Implementation Plan are requirements that clean fuels be made available, with sufficient facilities for refueling. The state has the ability to provide economic incentives toward the use of clean fuel vehicles by issuing emissions credits.

Clean fuel vehicle requirements apply only to vehicles of up to 8500 pounds gross vehicle weight rating. The requirements include specifications for on-board diagnostics, evaporative emissions, as well as emissions standards for Non-Methane Organic Gas (NMOG), CO, and NO_x.

Fleets of greater than 10 vehicles owned by a single entity (including the government) and operated in populated ozone and CO nonattainment areas are required to phase in the purchase of clean fuel vehicles. After the year 1999, 50% of the new fleet vehicles are required to have clean fuel capabilities.

The phase-in of the Clean Fuel program is required to be written into the SIP. Other requirements to be included in the SIP are

- The availability of clean alternative fuels at central fueling areas
- The issuance of credits to the fleet operator for exceeding the minimum requirements of the program. The credits may be held, traded, sold, or banked for later use

States can voluntarily opt in early to the clean fuel program for any ozone nonattainment areas.

Inspection and Maintenance Programs

The inspection and maintenance (I/M) programs are a third mechanism used to control emissions from moving sources. I/M programs, run at State and local levels, ensure that vehicles and their emissions systems are adequately maintained. Approximately 110 cities and states have or are required to have programs in place to check motor vehicle tailpipe emissions.

Title III—General

Title III of the Clean Air Act contains general administrative requirements. This section describes the procedures that the EPA must use to delegate air programs to the state. The procedures are intended to

- Ensure regional fairness and uniformity in criteria, procedures, and policy
- Ensure auditability of each states' performance, compliance with, and enforcement of the Act
- Provide a mechanism for the identification and standardization of inconsistent or varying criteria, procedures, and policies

With the exception of appropriations under the CAA, tribes are treated the same as states. Although a tribe is not eligible for the same amount of money as a state (up to 0.5% of the annual appropriations for the program), a tribe is eligible for grant and contract assistance to carry out the Act. Furthermore, tribes with governing bodies capable of administering the Act, can be delegated certain responsibilities and programs. For example, tribes can prepare their own Implementation Plans and permitting programs.

EPA's Duties and Authorities

Title III outlines EPA's duties and authorities as well as other procedures and standards. For example, EPA has the right to immediately restrain the operation of any source that is presenting an *imminent and substantial endangerment to public health and welfare*. EPA has the ability to issue other orders necessary for the protection of public health, welfare, or the environment. EPA can also issue subpoenas for the purpose of obtaining information about any investigation, monitoring, reporting requirement, entry, compliance inspection, or administrative enforcement proceeding under the Act.

Title III contains the procedural requirements for petitioning EPA for review of a NAAQS, the rulemaking process, and judicial review, as well as congressional appropriations.

Another important aspect of Title III is that it gives EPA the authority to review legislation, regulations, and projects for their potential environmental impact on air quality.

Civil Suits

The provisions for civil suits are found in Title III. Any citizen can take civil action against a source or the EPA for

1) An alleged violation of an emission standard, limitation, or order

2) EPA's failure to comply with the Act

3) Failure to obtain a permit prior to modification or construction, or an alleged violation of a permit condition

For the purposes of a civil action, the term *emission standard or limitation* refers to State or Federal requirements relating to the quantity or rate of emissions. Note that the term is, in fact, defined quite broadly, and includes

1) A schedule or timetable of compliance, and emission limitation, standard of performance, or emissions standard

2) A control or prohibition of a motor vehicle fuel or fuel additive

3) A permit condition or requirement relating to attainment and nonattainment areas

4) Any State implementation plan requirement relating to transportation control measures, air quality maintenance plans, vehicle inspection and maintenance programs, vapor recovery, visibility, and ozone protection

5) A standard, limitation, or schedule issued under the Title V program

Civil penalties under the citizen's suits provisions can, at the discretion of the court, be deposited in a penalty fund or used to fund beneficial mitigation projects. The maximum penalty in a citizen's action is $100,000.

Economic Impact

The Clean Air Act Amendments monitor the cost effectiveness of air pollution control. Under the Act, EPA is required to submit various reports to Congress regarding the economic impact of its air quality programs. These reports include:

- A biennial economic impact analysis for the criteria air pollutants as well as hazardous air pollutants, mobile sources, in addition to SO_2 and NO_x substitutes

- The costs and effects for the New Source Review, New Source Performance Standards, and the regulations controlling ozone, Prevention of Significant Deterioration, emissions standards, fuels, and aircraft

One important aspect of the economic picture is the potential change in employment resulting from the Act. This change includes threatened and actual plant closures, layoffs, and other adverse employment affects. EPA has the ability to conduct full investigations of these matters upon request. The request can come from an employee or employees' representatives.

Employees who believe they may have been discharged because of participation against an employer in an enforcement proceeding are provided with *whistleblower* protection under the Act. Employees in this situation may file a written complaint with the Secretary of Labor and an investigation of the incident will be conducted. If the employee prevails in the complaint, then the employer is liable for all costs and expenses, as well as compensatory damages to the employee.

Air Quality Monitoring

Title III authorizes the EPA to establish an air quality monitoring network. The primary purpose of the monitoring network is to track air quality throughout the United States using uniform monitoring methodology and criteria.

The states and local agencies implement the program, which has been set up by EPA. It consists of four categories of monitoring stations.

SLAMS, or *State and Local Air Monitoring Stations*, is a network of 4000 monitoring stations that measure criteria pollutants, as determined by the needs of the state or local agency. SLAMS are generally located in urban areas.

NAMS, or *National Air Monitoring Stations*, are 1080 key sites within the SLAMS network. They are also located in urban areas, focusing on areas of maximum pollutant concentrations and high population density.

SPMS, or *Special Purpose Monitoring Stations*, are used to supplement the SLAMS. They are not permanent stations but are installed by the State and local agencies as needed in order to support their air programs.

PAMS is a network of about 75 *Photochemical Assessment Monitoring Stations* in 25 urban areas. PAMS measure VOCs and NO_x, which are the precursors to the formation of regional ozone.

PAMS are required in any ozone area that is designated as serious, severe, or extreme.

The $PM_{2.5}$ monitoring network uses Federal Reference Methods, chemical speciation techniques, and other research methods to determine $PM_{2.5}$ concentrations and identify the chemical nature of the particulate matter.

CASTNET is the Clean Air Status Trends Network and consists of approximately 70 sites, mostly in the northeast, that measure sulfate and nitrate ions, which are the precursors of acid precipitation.

The Air Toxics Monitoring network consists of almost 250 sites operated by states and local entities. In the past, these sites have operated independently of Federal funding since the Clean Air Act does not mandate air toxics monitoring. This trend is changing, however, as EPA has focused its program on air toxics and some Federal grants have been awarded for the purpose of air toxics monitoring.

Title IV—Acid Deposition Control

Acid deposition or *acid rain* is believed to be caused by sources that emit two of the by-products of combustion: SO_2 and NO_x. Acid rain affects forest ecosystems, damages structures, impairs visibility, and impacts public health. Fossil fuel-fired electrical generators have been identified as significant sources (in particular, the coal-burning power plants of the Midwest). SO_2 and NO_x emitted from these facilities travels toward the east coast of the United States and Canada where it falls to the earth as rain, gases, or dust. As a result, fossil fuel-fired power plants are regulated as a means to control acid rain. Sources in the 38 eastern states are the most affected by the Title IV requirements.

In the Clean Air Act Amendments of 1990, Congress set as a goal the control of acid rain through the reduction of SO_2 by 10 million tons and NO_x by 2 million tons from the 1980 levels. Congress dictated that energy conservation and renewable, clean alternatives are to be taken into consideration when calculating emissions reductions.

The most significant aspect of the acid rain law was the control of acid rain emissions through *economic incentives* as opposed to *command and control* emissions limits.

Sulfur Dioxide

The economic incentives used by the acid rain program consist of annual SO_2 emissions allowances which are allocated to the operator of the source. An ***allowance*** is defined as authorization for an affected unit to emit one ton of SO_2 during a calendar year. Every January 1, an affected utility unit is allocated allowances. The allowances have economic value and can be sold and traded by the sources. Since 1980, the number of allowances that are issued to an affected source have signficantly decreased in an effort to lower the amount of SO_2 that is emitted to the atmosphere. These allowances are assignable by the owner/operator to other units under the owner/operator's control. The owner/operator must request reassignment in the permit application.

In simple terms, for each ton of SO_2 emitted, one allowance is consumed (*i.e.,* turned over to EPA). If there are allowances left over at the end of the year, they can be transferred within the utility system or sold to another facility for future use. If, on the other hand, the source does not hold enough allowances to cover the emissions, it must procure them from someone (buy or trade), or be in noncompliance.

(The NO_x Budget program discussed in the section on Ozone Nonattainment Areas, also uses an allowance consumption program. Allocations are defined each calendar year for the *Ozone Season*, which is defined as May 1 through September 30 of each year.)

In the acid rain program, assigning bonus allowances for avoided emissions encourages energy conservation and renewable energy. Avoided emissions can result from such activities as the installation of clean coal technology, use of solar or wind power, and implementation of customer energy conservation programs. Utilities are eligible for these allowances if they do all of the following:

1) Directly fund the qualified energy conservation and renewable energy measures.

2) Quantify the avoided SO_2 emissions.

3) Adopt and implement a State-approved plan for least-cost energy conservation and power by evaluating new power supplies, energy conservation, and renewable energy resources.

4) Certify their rates and charges by the Department of Energy, and ensure that they do not negatively impact the utility's net income.

Allowances for energy conservation and renewable energy are allocated from the Conservation and Renewable Emissions Fund. A total of 300,000 allowances are in the fund, which is reduced on an annual basis from the year 2000 to 2009. Allowances remaining after 2010 are allocated as part of the Phase II program.

Phase II implementation of the acid rain program began on January 1, 2000. Phase II affects approximately 2000 electric generation units. Included in Phase II are units with an output capacity exceeding 25 megawatts and all new units. In addition to tightening the restrictions on Phase I plants, Phase II sets new restrictions on smaller units.

Nitrogen Oxides

Nitrogen oxides (NO_x) are also regulated under the acid rain program. Unlike the SO_2 program, NO_x emissions are not tradable or capped. NO_x emission rates are established for utility boilers. The rates are based on low NO_x burner technology and the degree of reduction achievable through retrofit technology. Source operators have the option of complying with an individual emission rate for the boiler or averaging emissions over two or more boilers.

The NO_x reduction program was fully implemented in January 2000. It is focused on coal-fired boilers and has resulted in an emissions decline of more than 50% since 1995.

Permitting

Acid rain sources are regulated through what are commonly referred to as Title IV permits. The permit program, which is enforced as part of the Title V operating program, can be delegated to the states. Refer to the next section for a discussion of Title V permits.

The acid rain provisions prohibit annual emissions of sulfur in excess of the number of allowances, exceedance of applicable emissions rates, and the use of any allowance prior to its allocated year. Certain sources not normally covered by the acid rain provisions can voluntarily opt into the program and be eligible for allowances.

Each permit is accompanied by a compliance plan that describes how the source will meet the prescribed SO_2 and NO_x emissions limitations. Each acid rain source must have a permit and operate in accordance with its terms and the terms of the compliance plan. The CAA specifies that acid rain sources install and operate continuous emissions monitoring systems (CEMS). The purpose of the CEMS is to ensure that data is available for SO_2, NO_x, opacity, and the volumetric flow rate of each unit.

Although operations of an electric utility cannot be terminated for not having a permit or compliance plan, the strict enforcement provisions and penalties described below still apply.

The penalties for exceeding emissions limitations are \$2000/ton excess NO_x emitted or \$2000/SO_2 allowance held by the source. The SO_2 owner/operator is also liable for offsetting the excess emissions through additional emissions reductions the following year. For enforcement purposes, each ton of SO_2 emitted over the allowance amount is considered to be a separate violation.

Title V—Permits

The Title V Operating Permit program was added with the 1990 amendments. The Title V program is modeled after the Federal National Pollutant Discharge Elimination System (NPDES), a permitting program that is currently used to control point source water pollution.

Prior to 1990, the permitting of sources in the United States varied greatly depending on the location and type of industry. Under the Federal rules, major sources were only required to obtain a Permit to Construct (PTC). Although the PTC usually carried with it operating restrictions, Operating Permits were generally not required. Facilities that had multiple activities occurring at the same location could be regulated under multiple complicated and sometimes conflicting permits.

The 1990 amendments established a Federal operating permit program. The purpose of the program, which is administered by EPA, is to *simplify* permitting of a source by bringing all requirements into a single document. The Title V program affects major sources; that is, any source with a *potential to emit* pollutants in excess of the quantities listed in Table 2 is required to get a Title V permit. It is important to note that certain assumptions are made in calculating the potential to emit. The source is assumed to be at maximum production for 24 hours-per-day and 365 days-year.

A source that is covered under the operating permit program is required to submit a timely application to the EPA or regulating agency. The agency is under an obligation to review and issue a permit in a timely manner. The 1990 Amendments provide specific guidelines to achieve this.

The Operating Permit program can be delegated by EPA to the states. State permit programs can be more stringent than the EPA's. Once a state has an operating permit program in place, then covered sources are required to pursue a permit with that state.

The permit process begins with the submission of an application. The application summarizes the processes occurring at the facility, the terms and conditions of existing permits, and the compliance status of the facility, not only with permits but with all applicable sections of the Clean Air Act. If the facility is out of compliance, then a compliance plan must be submitted with the application. If the facility is in compliance, then a *responsible official* (generally an officer of the company) certifies compliance. The source's responsible official must also certify, under penalty of perjury, that all data and information included in the application is true and accurate. The application, which is a public document, must be timely, and complete.

Once submitted, the applicant may receive a **permit shield.** When granted a permit shield, the applicant is deemed by the permitting agency to be in compliance with all other aspects of the Clean Air Act. It does not extend to noncompliance

with a permit condition, applicable requirements that have not been covered in the application, or new requirements promulgated after the issuance of a Title V permit. Prior to issuance, EPA must review the permit. If other states may be impacted by the source's operations, then EPA ensures that these states are notified.

The agency, in issuing a permit, must include enforceable emissions limitations and standards, as well as schedules for compliance and compliance monitoring.

EPA has the option of developing a general permit for numerous similar sources. Title V also contains provisions for temporary sources.

The Title V permit program also addresses *continuous compliance*, and has a requirement for the certification (at least annually, by the responsible official) of the compliance status. As such, any instances of noncompliance are to be identified and reported to the regulatory agency on a regular basis. Further, as Title V permits are being renewed, EPA is requiring extensive Compliance Assurance Monitoring Plans.

Title VI—Stratospheric Ozone Protection

Scientists have been monitoring the stratospheric ozone layer since the late 1970s. The stratospheric ozone layer, which is 9–31 miles above the earth, shields the earth from harmful ultraviolet rays. Ultraviolet radiation can cause eye cataracts and skin cancer as well as possible harm to agriculture (plants) and plant life in the Antarctic seas. Scientific studies have led to the discovery that certain manmade chemicals, (in particular, certain organic chemicals containing halogens), were responsible for drastic deterioration of the earth's ozone layer. These chemicals have the effect of catalyzing and thus enhancing a chemical reaction that destroys stratospheric ozone.

The Montreal protocol, originally signed by nations around the world in 1987, is an international agreement to limit the worldwide production and use of certain halogenated hydrocarbons. Because of the long atmospheric lifetime of these substances, stratospheric ozone depletion is expected to continue well into the next century. Even with the controls on these substances that are stipulated in the Montreal Protocol, it will not be until the year 2045 that the ozone losses which have already occurred are predicted to recover.

Title VI of the CAA prescribes the process the United States will use to meet the terms of the protocol. Ozone-depleting substances are divided into two classes based on their ozone-depleting potential. Class I substances have the highest ozone-depleting potential and contribute significantly to harmful effect on the stratospheric ozone layer. Class I substances include certain chlorofluorocarbons, halons, carbon tetrachloride, and methyl chloroform. Class II substances are chemicals which are *known to* or *may reasonably be anticipated to* have harmful effects on the ozone layer. Class II substances include certain hydrochlorofluorocarbons.

The Clean Air Act requires EPA to prepare a list of Class I and Class II substances. New substances can be added to the list and Class II substances can be recategorized as Class I substances. Class I substances, however, cannot be removed. In addition, EPA is required to publish the chlorine and bromine loading potential, the atmospheric lifetime, and global warming potential of each listed substance.

Producers, importers, and exporters of Class I and II substances are required to report to EPA. The EPA uses this information to prepare its report to Congress on the production, use, and consumption of these substances. This report is prepared every three years. Every six years, the EPA reports to Congress on the environmental and economic effects of any atmospheric ozone depletion.

Note that phaseout of both Class I and II substances can be accelerated for a particular substance if

Table 5. The Implementing Regulations of the Clean Air Act

Clean Air Act Topic	CFR Reference
Tribal Clean Air Act Authority	40 CFR 49
National Ambient Air Quality Standards	40 CFR 50
State Implementation Plans and Prevention of Significant Deterioration	40 CFR 51–52, 62, 96, 97
Ambient Air Quality and Monitoring, and Planning	40 CFR 53, 58, 81
Citizen Suits	40 CFR 54
New Source Performance Standards	40 CFR 60
National Emission Standards for Hazardous Air Pollutants	40 CFR 61, 63
Compliance Assurance Monitoring	40 CFR 64
Enforcement	40 CFR 65-67
Risk Management Plans	40 CFR 68
State Operating Permits	40 CFR 70
Federal Operating Permits	40 CFR 71
Acid Rain	40 CFR 72–78
Fuel Additives	40 CFR 79–80
Designation of Air Quality Planning Areas	40 CFR 81
Stratospheric Ozone Protection	40 CFR 82
Motor Vehicle Controls	40 CFR 85–88
Control of Emissions from Other Engines	40 CFR 89-94
Federal NO_x Budget Trading Program	40 CFR 96-97

1)   There is scientific evidence that a more stringent schedule is necessary in order to protect the environment

2)   Substitutes and/or other technology is available that makes it possible to achieve a more stringent schedule

3)   The Montreal Protocol phaseout schedule is modified

In fact, EPA's current regulations on stratospheric ozone protection, require an accelerated phaseout of Class I and Class II substances. The production and consumption of most of the Class I substances were completely phased out by 1995. Methyl bromide was phased out in 2004. (There are, however, limited exceptions for essential uses of certain substances for the purposes of aviation safety, medical devices, export to developing countries that are parties to the Montreal Protocol, national security, and fire suppression.)

Class II substances are scheduled for phaseout beginning in the year 2003. At that time, certain Class II substances introduced into commerce will have production, import and use restrictions. The production phaseout of all Class II substances must be completed by the year 2030. There are exceptions to this schedule for medical devices and developing countries.

Nonessential products, such as plastic party streamers, cleaning fluids, and other consumer products that contain chlorofluorocarbons, were phased out from 1992 through 1994.

As part of the phaseout program, a trading scheme has been devised which encourages greater reductions in the use of Class I and Class II substances. Transfers between pollutants based on their ozone-depleting potential are allowed, as well as trade of consumption allowances between persons under certain circumstances. Production allowances may also be transferred between other parties to the Montreal Protocol under certain conditions.

The EPA regulates the use, labeling, and consumption of Class I and II substances. It is important to provide proper labeling of containers of Class I and Class II substances. Those who handle these substances must maintain appropriate record-keeping, and meet the Federal reporting requirements. Specific regulations regarding the use and disposal of these substances during service,

repair, and disposal of appliances have been issued. For example, Class I and II substances must be recycled whenever possible. Anyone servicing a motor vehicle air conditioner must be properly trained and certified to do so. In addition, the equipment used to service these air conditioners must also be certified. Release of Class I and Class II substances to the atmosphere is specifically prohibited.

In order to encourage the replacement of Class I and Class II chemicals with environmentally acceptable alternatives, the EPA has created the Significant New Alternatives Policy Program (SNAP). The purpose of this program is to identify alternative refrigerants, solvents, and fire retardants that decrease the environmental risk. EPA maintains a clearinghouse of alternative chemicals, product substitutes, and alternative manufacturing processes. EPA also publishes by specific use a list of the prohibited substitutes as well as safe alternatives. Substances can be added to the list by petition. Health and safety studies are required from any person producing a Class I chemical substitute, prior to introducing that chemical substitute into commerce.

Implementing Regulations

The Clean Air Act, as amended in 1990, is administered and enforced by EPA. The Act has become, upon implementation, complex and difficult to interpret. The application of its requirements to a particular facility requires a good understanding of the law, the Federal, State, and, in some cases, local regulations. As a place to start, the Federal implementing regulations for the Clean Air Act are found in 40 CFR 49–95. Table 5 is a guide to locating in the regulations specific topics covered by the Clean Air Act.

Internet Resources

<http://www.epa.gov/air/data/aqsdb.html> (Environmental Protection Agency. Air Data: About the AQS Database)

<http://www.epa.gov/airmarkets/acidrain> (Environmental Protection Agency. Clean Air

Markets–Environmental Issues. Acid Rain Program)

<http://www.epa.gov/ttn/catc/> (Environmental Protection Agency. Technology Transfer Network. Clean Air Technology Center)

<http://www.epa.gov/ozone/> (Environmental Protection Agency. Ozone Depletion)

<http://www.epa.gov/ttn/atw> (Environmental Protection Agency. Technology Transfer Network. Air Toxics Website)

<http://www.epa.gov/airtrends/econ-emissions. html> (Environmental Protection Agency. Air Emissions Trends: Continued Progress through 2004)

<http://www.epa.gov/airtrends/factbook.html> (Environmental Protection Agency. Air Trends. Fact Book and Related Information)

<http://www.epa.gov/oar/oaqps/> (Environmental Protection Agency. Air and Radiation. Air Quality Planning and Standards)

<http://www.epa.gov/air/transport/> (Environmental Protection Agency. Air and Radiation. Transportation and Fuels)

<http://www.epa.gov/oar/oaqps/peg_caa/pegcaain. html> (Environmental Protection Agency. *The Plain English Guide to the Clean Air Act.* EPA 400–K–93–101, 4/93)

<http://www.epa.gov/air/toxicair/index. html>(Environmental Protection Agency. Air and Radiation. Toxic Air Pollutants)

<http://www.epa.gov/oar/oaqps/takingtoxics/> (Environmental Protection Agency. *Taking Toxics Out of the Air: Progress in Setting 'Maximum Achievable Control Technology Standards under the CAA'.* EPA/451/K–98–001, 2/98)

<http://www.epa.gov/ttn/naaqs/ozone/rto/rto.html> (Environmental Protection Agency. Technology Transfer Network. Ozone Implementation. Regional Transport of Ozone)

<http://www.unep.org/ozone/Treaties_ and_Ratification/2B_montreal_protocol.asp> (United Nations Environmental Programme. Ozone Secretariat. Montreal Protocol)

<http://www.epa.gov/airtrends/sixpoll.html> Environmental Protection Agency. Air Trends. Six Principal Pollutants)

<http://www.epa.gov/docs/epacfr40/chapt-I.info> (Environmental Protection Agency. Laws and Regulations. Chapter I Environmental Protection Agency)

<http://www.epa.gov/ttn/atw/socatlst/socatpg. html> (Environmental Protection Agency. Technology Transfer Network. Air Toxics Website. Source Category List and Promulgation Schedule)

<http://www.epa.gov/ttn/atw/mactfnl.html> (Environmental Protection Agency. Air Toxics Website. Table of Final MACT Rules)

<http://www.epa.gov/ttn/naaqs/ozone/rto/126/ links.html> (Environmental Protection Agency. Technology Transfer Network. Ambient Air Quality Standards. Links for 126 Petitions)

Adriane P. Borgias is the owner of fusion environment&energy, LLC, an environmental consulting firm that specializes in environmental management systems and collaborative decision-making. Ms. Borgias has a BS in Chemistry from the University of California, Berkeley, and an MS in Environmental Management from the University of San Francisco. She has over 25 years of experience in the energy industry in research, corporate, and operating departments, as well as an independent consultant. For the past 6 years, Ms. Borgias has worked with Indian Tribes in the Pacific Northwest, in the areas of air and water quality. Ms. Borgias is a former licensed nuclear reactor operator and has been a Certified Hazardous Materials Manager since 1986. She has served the Academy at the local and national level and is a past national president. In 1990, Ms. Borgias received the President's Award for Outstanding Service to the Academy. She was also the 1996 recipient of the Academy's Founder's Award. Ms. Borgias has contributed chapters to Women in Chemistry and Physics, a Biobibliographic Sourcebook *and is profiled in* Northwest Women in Science: Women Making a Difference. *Ms Borgias dedicates this chapter to her father Dr. Frank C. Pennington, PhD, who's pursuit of science and passion for chemistry was her inspiration.*

Daniel L. Todd *is the Vice President and General Manager of Air Quality Services, LLC of Evansville, Indiana. He has been involved with advancing the field of air quality management since 1974, serving as a regulator, as a researcher, as the principal air specialist for an electric utility, and is currently managing a multi-faceted air related service provider. Mr. Todd has directed projects pertaining to ambient air monitoring, continuous emissions/opacity monitoring, source emissions testing, consulting, permitting, and regulatory development. He holds a BS (Environmental Science) from the University of Evansville and a MS in Environmental Science from Indiana University. Mr. Todd has been a Qualified Environmental Professional since 1995 and a Certified Hazardous Materials Manager since 1998. He is active in both the Indiana and national Air & Waste Management Association, serving on several committees. He also is involved with numerous industry organizations, and has provided air-related presentations at regional and national meetings.*

The authors would like to acknowledge in particular the invaluable assistance of their peer reviewer: Ann W. McIver.

CHAPTER 35

A Step-by-Step Guide to Risk Management Planning

Dale M. Petroff, NRRPT

Introduction

The purpose of this chapter is to provide a step-by-step guide for the Certified Hazardous Materials Manager (CHMM) assigned to develop and implement a Risk Management Plan (RMP). Because the RMP addresses hazards to the public, the use of the one plan concept is discussed for the integration of the RMP with the other spill control, emergency response, and hazardous materials contingency plans required under other regulations.

This chapter will guide the user through the RMP development process. The EPA's general guidance document, *General Guidance on Risk Management Programs for Chemical Accident Prevention (40 CFR Part 68), (General Guidance)*, forms the basis for this chapter and is the best source of information for the RMP process. The sections of this chapter follow those of the guidance document with a few exceptions.

On June 20, 1996, The Environmental Protection Agency (EPA) published the final rule for Section 112(r) of the Clean Air Act (CAA), otherwise called the Risk Management Program (RMP) Rule (40 CFR 68). All facilities meeting the criteria of the rule were to have completed their RMP by June of 1999.

In April, 2004 the EPA revised the reporting requirements for the rule. The revisions

- Require that information on reportable chemical accidents be added to the RMP within six months of the date of the accident

- Require that changes to the emergency contact information be reported within one month

- Remove the requirement to include a brief description of the Off-Site Consequence Analysis in the RMP summary. This revision was made because EPA and Federal law enforcement agencies became concerned that this information may result in a security risk.

- Add three additional data elements to the RMP:

    - Emergency contact email address (if it exists)

    - Purpose and type of any submission that revises or otherwise affects previously filed RMPs

    - Name, address, and telephone number of the contractor/consultant who prepared the RMP (if any)

The objective of the RMP Rule is to identify and reduce risks to the public from hazardous substances. The information developed by the facility is intended to assist local fire, police, and emergency response personnel to prepare for and respond to chemical accidents. Additionally, it is intended to provide local residents with an understanding of the chemical hazards in communities. The EPA anticipated that publically available RMPs would stimulate communication between industry and the public and consequently improve accident prevention and emergency response practices at the local level.

Background

The RMP requirement was established in response to the increased threat from chemical releases to the public. After the Bhopal incident in 1984, the general population in the United States became aware of the potential risks posed by various industrial sites in their communities.

Facilities are subject to the RMP Rule based on the quantity of regulated substances they have on-site. These facilities are required to implement a Risk Management Program and submit a summary of the program (called the Risk Management Plan) to a central location specified by EPA by June 20, 1999.

Public awareness of the potential danger from accidental releases of hazardous chemicals has increased over the years as serious chemical accidents have occurred around the world (*e.g.*, the 1974 explosion in Flixborough, England, and the 1976 release of dioxin in Seveso, Italy). Public concern intensified following the 1984 release of methyl isocyanate in Bhopal, India, that killed more than 2,000 people living near the facility. A subsequent release from a chemical facility in Institute, West Virginia sent more than 100 people to the hospital and made Americans aware that such incidents can and do happen in the United States. The Risk Management Program is the EPA's response to that concern.

A Certified Hazardous Materials Manager (CHMM) may be called to develop and implement an RMP for a facility. In preparing for that task, there are some key elements to remember.

First, if an RMP is required for a facility, then it is probably necessary to implement the Occupational Safety and Health Administration's (OSHA) Process Safety Management (PSM) Standard (29 CFR 1910.119) since the regulated chemicals and quantities are similar. The Clean Air Act Amendments (CAAA) of 1990 places responsibility for the prevention of accidental chemical releases on both OSHA and EPA. OSHA has responsibility for the protection of workers from accidental chemical releases under Section 304 of the Amendments and has promulgated the PSM Standard (29 CFR 1910.119) to satisfy this requirement. EPA has responsibility for protection of the general public and the environment from accidental chemical releases under Section 112(r) of the Amendments. EPA promulgated the Risk Management Program rule (40 CFR 68) to satisfy this requirement.

The EPA believes that one chemical accident prevention program can serve to protect workers, the public, and the environment, and has incorporated the OSHA PSM Standard as the chemical accident prevention program for certain facilities subject to both rules. If a facility is not required to have a PSM program but it is required to have an RMP it makes sense to evaluate impact on facility workers as well as the public when assessing consequences of an accidental release.

Therefore, if required, a PSM program should be developed prior to developing an RMP. The PSM analysis will provide key information on the development of accident information used to determine off-site impact.

Always remember that the results of the Off-Site Consequence Analysis (OCA) may become an issue with the local emergency management agency and/ or members of the public. All Consequence Analysis results should be kept confidential until they have been thoroughly reviewed and validated. Since the 9-11 attacks there has been concern that terrorists may use RMP information to plan attacks. The release of any information developed under the RMP should be coordinated with the State agency responsible for homeland security issues. The State point-of-contact can be found on the Department of Homeland Security website at <http://www.ready.gov/useful_state.html>. There is a fact sheet regarding some of the security requirements that can be downloaded from the EPA Chemical Emergency Preparedness and Prevention page for RMP information (<http:// yosemite.epa.gov/oswer/CeppoWeb.nsf/content/ RMPoverview.htm>). Always check with the State level Homeland Security Office before releasing any information, as they should be up-to-date on this issue.

The successful implementation of a combined RMP-PSM program will require the development of an emergency response plan that addresses both on-site worker safety and potential off-site impacts. The public and local authorities will want notification even if the Worst-Case Release Scenario has no off-site impact. Facilities need to demonstrate that they are good neighbors, or they may be forced out of the area.

The RMP must be made available to the public. How the release of the information is addressed is key to ensuring that concerns of stakeholders are addressed. The involvement of the local emergency management agency and local government through the Local Emergency Planning Committee (LEPC) or the Chemical Accident Emergency Response (CAER) group is critical in gaining that acceptance.

The RMP is seen as a continuation of the chemical safety work begun under the Emergency Planning and Community Right-to-Know Act (EPCRA) (also known as the Superfund Amendments and Reauthorization Act [SARA] Title III), and the PSM regulations of OSHA.

EPCRA is intended to help local communities prepare for chemical accidents. It requires communities to develop emergency response plans, based on information from industry concerning hazardous chemicals.

The PSM program, as discussed in this chapter, requires the analysis of the processes, procedures, and operations that may cause a chemical accident at a facility. The objective of this hazard analysis is to determine how the accident scenarios may be avoided. The PSM rules are based on the assumption that the listed chemicals, if released, will result in significant chemical concentrations within the boundaries of the facility. Again, the focus of this regulation is worker safety.

Risk management planning, as part of an integrated safety management program, will relate to local emergency preparedness and response, to pollution prevention, and to worker safety. The RMP is an element of an integrated approach to hazardous material management and safety.

The prevention of accidental releases of hazardous chemicals is the shared responsibility of industry, government, and the public. The first steps toward accident prevention are identifying the hazards and assessing the risks. Once information about chemicals is shared, industry, government, and the community can work together toward reducing the risk to workers, public health, and the environment.

Preparation

The first step in any project is preparation. The EPA has published an excellent guide for the RMP process entitled *General Guidance on Risk Management Programs for Chemical Accident Prevention (40 CFR Part 68)*. This guide is the basis for discussion in this chapter. The guide, which is approximately 100 pages in length, is a good resource for anyone contemplating the development of an RMP.

The guide can be found at EPA's Chemical Emergency Preparedness and Prevention Office website. The reference is:

<http://yosemite.epa.gov/oswer/CeppoWeb.nsf/content/EPAguidance.htm> (Environmental Protection Agency. *General Guidance on Risk Management Programs for Chemical Accident Prevention (40 CFR Part 68)*. RMP Series. EPA 550–B–04–001. April, 2004.)

The document is maintained as an Adobe-formatted document and the EPA provides a link where a free copy of Adobe Acrobat reader program may be obtained. The document is broken into several parts and 2.39 megabytes of disk space is required to download the entire document. The guide is organized into eleven chapters with six appendices.

Careful study of the guide should answer most questions about the development and implementation of the RMP. Once you are familiar with the contents of the guide, the process of determining applicability and data collection can begin.

Applicability

The first step in developing an RMP is to determine the applicability of the regulations to the facility. While there is a great deal of overlap with the PSM Program, the PSM requirements do not completely cover the RMP requirements.

In 40 CFR 68.10, *applicability* is defined as follows:

An owner or operator of a stationary source that has more than a threshold quantity of a regulated substance in a process, as determined under 40 CFR 68.115, shall comply with the requirements of this part no later than the latest of the following dates:

(1) June 21, 1999;

(2) Three years after the date on which a regulated substance is first listed under 40 CFR 68.130; or

(3) The date on which a regulated substance is first present above a threshold quantity in a process.

The table in 40 CFR 68.130 that lists regulated toxic substances and their threshold quantities is not reproduced here, as it is subject to change. Check in the *Federal Register* for the latest revision prior to making an initial determination. After the initial determination has been made, it should be reviewed whenever a change to the process is being evaluated and on a regular basis. The most current regulations can be found on the internet at <http://www.gpoaccess.gov/nara/cfr>.

During the determination process, two definitions in the regulation are critical. These are *stationary source* and *threshold quantity*.

Stationary source means any buildings, structures, equipment, installations, or substance emitting stationary activities which belong to the same industrial group, which are located on one or more contiguous properties, which are under the control of the same person (or persons under common control), and from which an accidental release may occur.

A stationary source includes transportation containers that are no longer under active shipping papers and transportation containers that are connected to equipment at the stationary source for the purposes of temporary storage, loading, or unloading. The term *stationary source* does not apply to transportation, including the storage incident to transportation, of any regulated substance or any other extremely hazardous substance under the provisions of this part, provided that such transportation is regulated under 49 CFR 192, 193, or 195. Properties shall not be considered contiguous solely because of a railroad or gas pipeline right-of-way.

Threshold quantity means the quantity specified for regulated substances pursuant to Section 112(r)(5) of the Clean Air Act as amended listed in 40 CFR 68.130 and determined to be present at a stationary source as specified in 40 CFR 68.115 of this part.

Again, if the process or the products at the facility change, then the facility must prepare an RMP at the time a regulated substance is first present in a process and is above a threshold quantity.

In the determination process, if it is determined that storage of feed materials, intermediate products, or finished products requires the development of an RMP, then a review of the necessary quantities should be made. If the facility can operate with amounts below the threshold quantities, then a change to the amounts that are stored should be considered. Also, the replacement of the material with a less toxic product should be considered.

When determining the threshold quantity, it is important to make a separate evaluation for each different material. The RMP guide is very clear on this point:

A toxic substance is never aggregated with a different toxic substance to determine whether a threshold quantity is present. If your process consists of co-located vessels with different toxic substances, then you must determine whether each substance exceeds its threshold quantity.

Remember the RMP is not done once during the lifetime of the facility. The RMP must be maintained, and facility managers are responsible for evaluating the applicability of any changes in the regulations.

Program Eligibility

The EPA has established three tiers of requirements to reduce the level of effort for facilities with lower risk of off-site impacts. These tiers are referred to as Programs 1, 2, and 3. A facility may not be able to determine final eligibility until the consequence analysis has been completed. A facility will first have to complete several Hazard Assessment tasks prior to determining which program is applicable.

Program 1, for *no impact* facilities, has the fewest requirements, while Program 3 has the most. The program tier that the facility falls under defines the level of effort needed to establish and maintain the RMP; it also defines the information that must be certified in the final report.

The various program eligibility requirements are listed below, but these should be verified by consulting a current revision of the regulation before proceeding.

Program 1 Eligibility Requirements

A covered process is eligible for Program 1 requirements as provided in 40 CFR 68.12(b) if it meets all of the following requirements:

1) There are no public receptors within the distance to an endpoint from a worst-case release

2) The process has had no release of a regulated substance in the past five years where exposure to the substance, its reaction

products, overpressures generated by explosion involving the substance, or radiant heat from a fire involving the substance resulted in one or more offsite deaths, injuries, or response or restoration activities for exposure of an environmental receptor

and

3) Emergency response activities have been coordinated with the local responders. (This requirement applies to any covered process, regardless of program level.)

Program 2 Eligibility Requirements

Processes not eligible for Program 1 or subject to Program 3 are placed in Program 2, which imposes streamlined prevention program requirements, as well as additional hazard assessment, management, and emergency response requirements.

Program 3 Eligibility Requirements

Processes not eligible for Program 1 and either subject to OSHA's PSM standard under Federal or State OSHA programs or classified in one of ten specified North American Industry Classification System (NAICS) codes are placed in Program 3. Program 3 imposes OSHA's PSM standard as the prevention program as well as additional hazard assessment, management, and emergency response requirements.

Chapter 2 of the guidance document covers this in depth.

If at any time a covered process no longer meets the eligibility criteria of its program level, the owner or operator shall comply with the requirements of the new program level that applies to the process and update the RMP.

Once applicability and a program determination have been made, then the Consequence Analysis should be conducted.

Consequence Analysis

The Consequence Analysis is the keystone to the RMP. The results of the Consequence Analysis

define which program the facility falls under and determine the level of emergency planning that must be done.

The Consequence Analysis can be conducted by the facility or a contractor can be hired to accomplish this. The EPA has published guidance documents that provide detailed information on conducting the Consequence Analysis that can be used by facility personnel who do not have previous experience.

The guidance documents are intended for facilities that plan to do their own air dispersion modeling. The EPA has prepared a guidance document, *Risk Management Program Guidance for Off-Site Consequence Analysis,* that is available at the same website as the *General Guide* and can be downloaded as an Adobe formatted file. This file will require 1.029 megabytes of space to download.

The *RMP Guidance for Off-Site Consequence Analysis* provides simple methods and reference tables for determining distance to an end point for Worst-Case and Alternative Release Scenarios. This method will tend to be very conservative and overestimate off-site impacts. If by using this method no off-site impacts are identified, then the analysis can be concluded and documented.

If the use of the reference table methodology shows that there are off-site impacts, then a more advanced Consequence Analysis should be performed using one of the many computer software programs available.

In conjunction with the National Oceanic and Atmospheric Administration (NOAA), the EPA has developed a software program, RMP*Comp™, that performs the calculations described in the *RMP Guidance for Off-Site Consequence Analysis.* The current version is RMP*Comp™ 1.07. This is a new version, posted on the web on October 29, 2001. It corrects bugs found in previous versions and modifies some functionality. In particular, it:

1) Allows Boiling Liquid Expanding Vapor Explosions (BLEVEs) for gases and liquified (by pressure) gases.

2) Changes the way Worst-Case Scenarios of flammable liquids and gases liquified by refrigeration are treated.

what about meteorological data?

Approach	Examples	Advantages	Disadvantages
Simple guidance	EPA's *Off-Site Consequence Analysis Guidance*	• Free • No computer requirements • Simple to use • Provides all data needed • Provides tables of distances • Ensures compliance with rule	• Conservative results • Few site-specific factors considered • Little flexibility in scenario development
Simple computer models	EPA models such as RMP*Comp™	• No/low cost • May be simple to use • Can consider some site-specific factors	• Some may not be simple to use • Likely to give conservative results • May not accept all of EPA's required assumptions • May not include chemical-specific data • May not address all consequences
Complex computer models	Commercially available models	• May address a variety of scenarios • May consider many site-specific factors	• May be costly • May require high level of expertise
Calculation methods	"Yellow Book" (Netherlands TNO)	• Low cost • No computer requirements	• May require expertise to apply methods • May required development of a variety of data

From: *General Guidance on Risk Management Programs for Chemical Accident Prevention (40 CFR Part 68)*. RMP Series. EPA 550–B–04–001. April, 2004.)

Figure 1. Considerations for Choosing a Modeling Method

The software can be found and downloaded at:

<http://yosemite.epa.gov/oswer/CeppoWeb.nsf/content/rmp-comp.htm>

NH_3

In addition, EPA has prepared industry guidance for several industries covered by 40 CFR 68. In these documents, EPA provides chemical-specific modeling for the covered industries. All of the information provided in Chapter 4 of the *General Guidance* is also included in EPA's *RMP Guidance for Off-Site Consequence Analysis* and the industry-specific guidance documents available from EPA.

If the cited guidance documents are used to carry out the Off-Site Consequence Analysis, Chapter 4 of the *General Guide* may be skipped. For modeling, Chapter 4 will provide the information needed to comply with the rule requirements; it does not, however, provide methodologies.

Whether the analysis at the facility is conducted by facility personnel or contractors, the analysis must be acceptable to the EPA. As discussed earlier, EPA's *RMP Guidance for Off-Site Consequence Analysis* may be used. The results that are obtained using the methods in EPA's guidance are expected to be conservative. The conservative assumptions were introduced to compensate for high levels of uncertainty. The use of the EPA guide is optional, and other air dispersion models, fire or explosion models, or computation methods can be used, provided that

- They are publicly or commercially available or are proprietary models that the facility is willing to share with the implementing agency

- They are recognized by industry as applicable to current practices

- They are appropriate for the chemicals and conditions being modeled

- The applicable definitions of Worst-Case Release Scenarios are used

- The applicable parameters specified in the rule are used

Figure 1, "Considerations for Choosing a Modeling Method" has been excerpted from the *General Guide*. This chart has been designed to provide additional suggestions on making the decision of whether to use a complex model or the simpler methodology in the EPA guidance document.

When conducting an Off-Site Consequence Analysis, it is a good practice to have all the analyses independently developed and reviewed by two different individuals. This approach is more costly and time-consuming, but the impact caused by overestimation during the results analysis may be even more costly in terms of resources devoted to emergency preparedness, pubic relations, source reduction, and additional equipment.

The Off-Site Consequence Analysis consists of two elements: a Worst-Case Release Scenario and an

Alternative Release Scenario. The development of these scenarios is discussed in detail in the *General Guide*. An overview follows.

A *Worst-Case Release Scenario Analysis* is applicable to all covered processes, regardless of program level. In order to determine whether a process is eligible for Program 1, the Worst-Case Release Scenarios for each toxic and flammable substance in the process that is above the threshold quantity must be evaluated. The process is eligible for Program 1 if there are no public receptors within the distance to an end point for all of the worst-case scenarios analyzed for the process. (The other Program 1 criteria must also be met—see Chapter 2 of the *General Guide*). For every Program 1 process, the Worst-Case Release Scenario with the greatest distance to an end point must be reported.

If the site has Program 2 or Program 3 processes (processes that are not eligible for Program 1— see Chapter 2 of the *General Guide*), then the following must be reported:

- One worst-case analysis representing all toxic regulated substances present above the threshold quantity and

- One worst-case analysis representing all flammable regulated substances present above the threshold quantity

An additional worst-case analysis may need to be submitted if a worst-case release from elsewhere at the source would potentially affect public receptors different from those affected by the initial worst-case scenario(s).

An *Alternative Release Scenario Analysis* is applicable to all Program 2 and Program 3 processes. Alternative Release Scenarios should be those that may result in concentrations, over-pressures, or radiant heat levels that reach the end points specified for these effects beyond the fenceline of the facility.

Information on one Alternative Release Scenario Analysis must be presented

- For each regulated toxic substance held above the threshold quantity, including the substance considered in the worst-case analysis

- To represent all flammable substances held above the threshold quantity

If the distance to the end point for the worst-case release just reaches the facility fenceline, there may not be an alternative release scenario with a distance to an end point that goes beyond the fenceline. However, an alternative release scenario must still be reported. It may be important to explain in the RMP Executive Summary why the distance does not extend beyond the fenceline.

In developing the Consequence Analysis, the complex models that can account for many site-specific factors may give less conservative estimates of off-site consequences than the simplified methods in EPA's guidance. This is particularly true for alternative scenarios, for which EPA has not specified many assumptions.

However, complex models may be expensive and require considerable expertise to use. These may be beyond the ability of a facility to utilize. The EPA's optional guidance is designed to be simple and straightforward. The trade-off in deciding how to carry out the required consequence analyses will need to be considered.

Whether EPA's guidance or another modeling method is used, it should be noted that the results obtained from modeling the Worst-Case or Alternative Release Scenarios should not be used to predict the likely results of an accidental release. The worst-case assumptions are very conservative and, regardless of the model used, can generate very conservative results. Although the results from modeling alternative scenarios will be less conservative, conservative end points must still be used.

In addition, results of an actual release will depend on many site-specific conditions (*e.g.*, wind speed and other weather conditions) and factors related to the release (*e.g.*, when and how the release occurs, how long it takes to stop it). It is important to make reasonable assumptions regarding such factors in developing the alternative scenarios, but the circumstances surrounding an actual release may be different.

Different models will likely provide different results, even with the same assumptions, and most models have not been verified with experimental data. Therefore, results of even sophisticated modeling have a high degree of uncertainty and should be viewed as providing a basis for discussion, rather than as predictions. Modeling results should be considered particularly uncertain over long distances (*i.e.*, 10 kilometers or more).

The *General Guide* does identify possible sources of assistance for the conduct of modeling the various scenarios required. Chapter 4 of the *General Guide* discusses the parameters of developing the scenarios and conducting the analysis of Worst-Case and Alternative Release Scenarios. Prior to choosing an approach, this chapter should be studied carefully.

As part of the Consequence Analysis, receptor end points must be determined. The rule requires that residential populations within the circle defined by the end point for the Worst-Case and Alternative Release Scenarios (*i.e.*, the center of the circle is the point of release and the radius is the distance to the end point) be estimated in the RMP.

In addition, whether certain types of public receptors and environmental receptors are within the circles must be report in the Plan. These end points determine the potential impact of the facility and which program is applicable to the facility. Chapter 4 in the *General Guide* provides excellent information on how to determine the receptors and the sources of information needed to make the determination.

When the Consequence Analysis has been completed, then the facility must determine the applicable program. At this point, the facility processes should be reviewed to determine if the reduction of source terms is more cost-effective than implementing the applicable program.

Administrative controls will probably not be acceptable to the EPA or the State agency regulating this program, as they are too easily overcome by human error. Positive controls, such as a lockout or alarm system to control levels, with a double contingency to prevent the accumulation of the larger source terms, may be acceptable.

Once the program applicability has been determined, the prevention program and Risk Management Plan itself must be developed.

Management System

The management system provision in 40 CFR 68.15 requires any facility that has at least one Program 2 or Program 3 process (see Chapter 2 of the *General Guide* for information on determining the program levels of processes) to

- Develop a management system to oversee the implementation of the risk management program elements

- Designate a qualified person or position with the overall responsibility for the development, implementation, and integration of the risk management program elements

- Document the names of people or positions and define the lines of authority through an organizational chart or other similar document (if the responsibility for implementing individual requirements of the risk management program is assigned to people or positions other than the person or position with overall responsibility for the risk management program)

The Management System Provision

Management commitment to process safety is a critical element of a facility's risk management program. Management commitment should not end when the last word of the risk management plan is composed. For process safety to be a constant priority, the facility must remain committed to every element of the risk management program.

The rule takes an integrated approach to managing risks. Each element must be implemented on an ongoing, daily basis, becoming an integral part of the facility operations. Therefore, commitment and oversight must be continuous. When the requirements of the management system provision are satisfied there is insurance that:

- The risk management program elements are integrated and implemented on an ongoing basis

- All groups within a facility and/or process understand the lines of responsibility and communication

How to Meet the Management System Requirements

The sources covered by the rule are diverse. The EPA has recognized the need to maximize flexibility in complying with this program. Facility personnel are usually the best resource to use in deciding the appropriate methods for implementation and incorporation of the risk management program elements.

A key element in the performance of any program is that responsibility is assigned and the authority is granted to carry out that responsibility. A small facility may name an individual in the risk management plan as being responsible for the program. A medium or large facility may have more managerial turnover than smaller sites. For this reason, it is recommended in Chapter 5 of the *General Guide* that the facility identify a position, rather than the name of the specific person, with overall responsibility for the risk management program elements. Remember, the only element of the management system that must be reported in the RMP is the name of the qualified person or position with overall responsibility. *Note that changes to this data element in the RMP do not require the RMP to be updated.*

All of the positions identified in the RMP documentation must report their progress to the person/position with overall responsibility for the program. However, nothing in the risk management program rule prohibits a facility from satisfying the management provision by assigning process safety committees with management responsibility—provided that an organizational chart or similar document identifies the names or positions and lines of authority.

Defining the lines of authority and roles and responsibilities of staff that oversee the risk management program elements will help to

- Ensure effective communication about process changes between divisions

- Clarify the roles and responsibilities related to process safety issues at the facility

- Avoid problems or conflicts among the various people responsible for implementing elements of the risk management program

- Avoid confusion, and allow those responsible for implementation to work together as a team

- Ensure that the program elements are integrated into an ongoing approach to identifying hazards and managing risks

Management's commitment to the Risk Management Program is crucial to its success. Only with the commitment of the management will the RMP be prevented from being just another stack of paper written up to meet a regulatory requirement.

The RMP with the PSM are part of an integrated safety management system that can prevent severe losses due to accident or the failure to mitigate that accident when it happens. In most cases, if there is a loss of life, medium to small companies will not be able to withstand the losses. Therefore, remember the facility generally only gets one mistake; the *3-Strike Rule* is not in effect.

In addition to financial losses, the loss of the goodwill of the community may result in the facility becoming a focal point for State and local regulators. For example, during an incident in the southeast United States, a processing facility had two releases in two days and some off-site injury which resulted in a stop-work order from the EPA as well as the regulatory focus of two states and several counties. So—learn from the mistakes of others and use the ounce of prevention, as a pound of cure may not be enough.

The CHMM standard of ethics requires the Certified Hazardous Materials Manager to be committed to the safety of facility personnel, the general public, and the environment.

Prevention Program

The best accident to have is the one that has been prevented. In addition to determining off-site impacts, a major goal of the RMP is the development of an accident prevention program. The required prevention programs are keyed to the Program levels 2 or 3 determined earlier in the process.

The details for developing and implementing a Program 2 prevention program are contained in Chapter 6 of the *General Guide*. The requirements for a Program 3 prevention program are detailed in Chapter 7 of the *General Guide*.

Most Program 2 processes are likely to be relatively simple and may be located at small businesses. The EPA has developed the Program 2 prevention program by identifying the basic elements that are the foundation of sound prevention practices—safety information, hazard review, operating procedures, training, maintenance, compliance audits, and accident investigation.

By meeting other Federal regulations, State laws, industry codes and standards, as well as good engineering practices, a Program 2 facility has probably met most of the Program 2 prevention element requirements.

Many Program 3 facilities will need to do little that is new to comply with the Program 3 prevention program, because they should already have the OSHA PSM program in place.

Keep in mind that EPA and OSHA have different legal authority for a Program 3 facility, whether the program builds upon the PSM standard or is newly created:

- EPA has authority for off-site consequences
- OSHA has authority for on-site consequences

If the facility already complies with the PSM standard, the Process Hazard Analysis (PHA) team may have to assess new hazards that could affect the public or the environment offsite. Protection measures that are suitable for workers (*e.g.*, venting releases to the outdoors) may be the very kind of thing that imperils the public.

To integrate the elements of the prevention program, the facility manager must ensure that a change in any single element of the program leads to a review of other elements in order to identify any effect caused by the change.

Most importantly, accident prevention should become an institution at the site. Like the entire risk management program, a prevention program is more than a collection of written documents. It is a way to make safe operations and accident prevention the way business is done everyday.

Emergency Response

One of the most effective ways to mitigate an accident is to develop a comprehensive emergency response program. Chapter 8 of the *General Guide* covers how to develop and implement an emergency response program as well as how to

determine if a facility can opt out of an employee response program. If there is at least one Program 2 or Program 3 process at the facility, then 40 CFR 68 may require that an emergency response program (consisting of an emergency response plan, emergency response equipment procedures, employee training, and procedures to ensure the program is up-to-date) is implemented. This requirement applies if facility employees will respond to some releases involving regulated substances.

Nonresponding Facilities

The EPA recognizes that, in some cases (particularly for retailers and other small operations with few employees), it may not be appropriate for employees to conduct response operations for releases of regulated substances.

For example, it would be inappropriate, and probably unsafe, for an ammonia retailer with only one full-time employee to expect that a tank fire could be handled without the help of the local fire department or other emergency responder. The EPA does not intend to force such facilities to develop emergency response capabilities. At the same time, facility personnel are responsible for ensuring effective emergency response to any releases at the facility.

If the local public responders are not capable of providing such response, then steps must be taken to ensure that an effective response is available (*e.g.*, by hiring response contractors or providing support to the local government in order to enable them to respond).

The EPA has issued guidance for responding and nonresponding facilities. EPA has also adopted a policy for nonresponding facilities similar to that adopted by OSHA in its Hazardous Waste Operations and Emergency Response (HAZWOPER) Standard (29 CFR 1910.120), which allows certain facilities to develop an emergency action plan to ensure employee safety, rather than a full-fledged emergency response plan. If the facility's employees will not respond to accidental releases of regulated substances, then the facility needs to be in compliance with the emergency action plan and program requirements. However, the facility must ensure that some sort of response will be provided.

If employees are not required to respond to regulated substance releases at the facility, then the facility is required to coordinate with local response agencies to ensure that they will be prepared to respond to facility emergency. This will help to ensure that the community has a strategy for responding to and mitigating the threat posed by a release of a regulated substance from the facility. To do so, the facility must ensure that it has a way to notify emergency responders when there is need for a response. Coordination with local responders also entails the following steps:

- If the facility has a covered process with a regulated toxic, then the facility should work with the local emergency planning entity to ensure that it is included in the community emergency response plan, prepared under EPCRA, a response to a potential release.

- If the facility has a covered process with a regulated flammable, the facility should work with the local fire department regarding a response to a potential release.

Although these activities in do not need to be described in the risk management plan, it is important to document and keep a record of

- The emergency contact (*i.e.*, name or organization and number) that will be called in the event of a toxic or flammable release

- The organization that the facility worked with on response procedures

Again, a facility located in an area such Houston, Texas, or Mobile, Alabama, where there are a large number of facilities having regulated substances and local emergency response organizations that are trained and equipped to respond, the non-response option is normally very acceptable.

If the facility is in a rural county without a hazardous material response capability, then the nonresponse option would be acceptable only with limitations in the quantity of hazardous material on-site, if the facility has a small staff on-site and a very low population in the receptor zones.

What is a Local Emergency Planning Committee?

Local emergency planning committees (LEPCs) were formed under the Emergency Planning and Community Right-to-Know Act (EPCRA) of 1986. The committees are designed to serve as a community forum for issues relating to preparedness for emergencies involving releases of hazardous substances in their jurisdictions. They consist of representatives from local government (including law enforcement and fire fighting), local industry, transportation groups, health and medical organizations, community groups, and the media. LEPCs

- Collect information from facilities on hazardous substances that pose a risk to the community

- Develop a contingency plan for the community based on this information

- Make information on hazardous substances available to the general public

Contact the mayor's office or the county emergency management office for more information on your LEPC.

From: *General Guidance on Risk Management Programs for Chemical Accident Prevention (40 CFR Part 68). RMP Series.* EPA 550–B–04–001. April, 2004.)

Figure 2. The Concept of a Local Emergency Planning Committee

Responding Facilities

If the facility employees will respond to releases of regulated substances from the facility, then the emergency response program must contain an emergency response plan (maintained at the facility) that includes

- Procedures for informing the public and emergency response agencies about releases

- Documentation of proper first aid and emergency medical treatment necessary to treat human exposures

- Procedures and measures for emergency response

- Procedures for using, inspecting, testing, and maintaining the emergency response equipment

- Training for all employees in relevant procedures (personnel must be qualified in accordance with the HAZWOPER standard)

- Procedures to review and update, as appropriate, the emergency response plan to reflect changes at the facility and ensure that employees are informed of changes

Finally, the plan must be coordinated with the community plan developed under the Emergency Planning and Community Right-to-Know Act (EPCRA). In addition, at the request of local emergency planning or response officials, any information necessary for developing and implementing the community plan must be provided.

In Chapter 8 of the *General Guide,* the *concept* of a Local Emergency Planning Committee (LEPC) is explained. This has been reproduced in Figure 2. If the facility's county or city does not have an LEPC then the facility manager may want to join with other regulated companies to organize one or to develop a Chemical Accident Emergency Response (CAER) group using the guidance developed by the Chemical Manufacturers Association.

Although EPA's required elements are essential to any emergency response program, they are not comprehensive guidelines for creating an adequate response capability. Rather than establish another set of Federal requirements for an emergency response program, EPA has accepted the concept

of an Integrated Contingency Plan (ICP), which is explained in detail in a later section of this chapter.

If the facility has a regulated substance on-site, then it is already subject to at least one emergency response rule: OSHA's emergency action plan requirements (29 CFR 1910.38). Under OSHA HAZWOPER, any facility that handles *hazardous substances* (a broad term that includes all of the CAA regulated substances and thus applies to all facilities with covered processes) must comply with either 29 CFR 1910.38(a) or 1910.119(q). If the facility has a HAZMAT team, then it is subject to the 29 CFR 1910.119(q) requirements.

Various Federal regulations requiring emergency response plans have been reproduced from Chapter 8 of the *General Guide* and are shown in Figure 3. If the facility determines that its existing emergency response programs that have been developed to comply with these other rules satisfy the elements listed at the beginning of this section, then no additional actions are needed to comply with these elements. Additional guidance on making this decision is provided in Chapter 8 of the *General Guide.*

Be careful not to confuse writing a set of *emergency response procedures* in a plan with developing an *emergency response program.* An emergency response plan is only one element of the integrated effort that makes an emergency response program. Although the plan outlines the actions and equipment necessary to respond effectively, other aspects of the program such as training, program evaluation, equipment maintenance, and coordination with local agencies must occur regularly if the plan is to be useful in an emergency.

Again, it will take management commitment to ensure that an emergency response program is established and capable of responding to an emergency. An emergency response program that integrates emergency operating procedures and alarm response can become the most effective means of preventing damage, injury, or loss of life. The goal of the program is to enable facility personnel to respond quickly and effectively to any emergency.

Figure 4 contains useful references listed in the *General Guide.* They will be helpful in developing specific elements of a response program.

Hazardous Materials Emergency Planning Guide (NRT–1), National Response Team, 2001. Although designed to assist communities in planning for HAZMAT incidents, this guide provides useful information on developing a response plan, including planning teams, plan review, and ongoing planning efforts.

Criteria for Review of Hazardous Materials Emergency Plans (NRT–1A), National Response Team, May 1988. This guide provides criteria for evaluating response plans.

Integrated Contingency Plan, National Response Team, (61 FR 28642, June 5, 1996). This provides guidance on how to consolidate multiple plans developed to comply with various Federal regulations into a single, functional emergency response plan.

Emergency Response Guidebook, US Department of Transportation, 2000. This guidebook was developed jointly by the US Department of Transportation, Transport Canada, and the Secretariat of Communications and Transportation of Mexico (SCT) for use by firefighters, police, and other emergency services personnel who may be the first to arrive at the scene of a transportation incident involving a hazardous material. It is primarily a guide to aid first responders in (1) quickly indentifying the specific or generic classification of the material(s) involved in the incident, and (2) protecting themselves and the general public during this initial response phase of the incident. The ERG is updated every three to four years to accommodate new products and technology. Copies are made free of charge to public emergency responders through State emergency response coordinators.

Response Information Data Sheets (RIDS), US EPA and National Oceanic and Atmospheric Administration. Developed for use with the Computer-Aided Management of Emergency Operations (CAMEO) software, these documents outline the properties, hazards, and basic safety and response practices for thousands of hazardous chemicals.

From: *General Guidance on Risk Management Programs for Chemical Accident Prevention (40 CFR Part 68).* RMP Series. EPA 550–B–04–001. April, 2004.)

Figure 3. Federal Guidance on Emergency Planning and Response

Risk Management Plan

As stated previously, any facility that falls under the provisions of the Risk Management Program must submit a Risk Management Plan to EPA.

Elements of the Risk Management Plan

The length and content of the RMP will vary depending on the number and program level of the covered processes at the facility. Any facility with one or more covered processes must include in its RMP

- An executive summary (40 CFR 68.155)

- The registration for the facility (40 CFR 68.160)

- The certification statement (40 CFR 68.185)

- A worst-case scenario for each Program 1 process; at least one worst-case scenario to cover all Program 2 and 3 processes involving regulated toxic substances; at least one worst-case scenario to cover all Program 2 and 3 processes involving regulated flammables, 40 CFR 68.165(a)

- The five-year accident history for each process (40 CFR 68.168)

- A summary of the emergency response program for the facility (40 CFR 68.180)

The following is a list of some of the Federal emergency planning regulations:

- EPA's Oil Pollution Prevention Regulation (SPCC and Facility Response Plan Requirements): 40 CFR 112.7(d) and 112.20–112.21

- MMS's Facility Response Plan Regulation: 30 CFR 254

- RSPA's Pipeline Response Plan Regulation: 49 CFR 194

- USCG's Facility Response Plan Regulation: 33 CFR 154, Subpart F

- EPA's Risk Management Programs Regulation: 40 CFR 68

- OSHA's Emergency Action Plan Regulation: 29 CFR 1910.38(a)

- OSHA's Process Safety Standard: 29 CFR 1910.119

- OSHA's HAZWOPER Regulation: 29 CFR 1910.120

- OSHA's Fire Brigade Regulation: 29 CFR 1910.156

- EPA's Resource Conservation and Recovery Act Contingency Planning Requirements: 40 CFR 264, Subpart D; 40 CFR 265, Subpart D; and 40 CFR 279.52

- EPA's Emergency Planning and Community Right-to-Know Act Requirements: 40 CFR 355. (These planning requirements apply to communities, rather than facilities, but will be relevant when facilities are coordinating with local planning and response entities.)

- EPA's Storm Water Regulations: 40 CFR 122.26

Facilities may also be subject to State and local planning requirements

From: *General Guidance on Risk Management Programs for Chemical Accident Prevention (40 CFR Part 68)*. RMP Series. EPA 550–B–04–001. April, 2004.)

Figure 4. Federal Emergency Planning Regulations

Any facility with at least one covered process in Program 2 or 3 must also include in its RMP

- At least one Alternative Release Scenario for each regulated toxic substance in Program 2 or 3 processes, and at least one Alternative Release scenario to cover all regulated flammables in Program 2 or 3 processes, 40 CFR 68.165(b)

- A summary of the prevention program for each Program 2 process (40 CFR 68.170) and RMP

- A summary of the prevention program for each Program 3 process (40 CFR 68.175)

Subpart G of 40 CFR 68 (see Appendix A of the *General Guide*) provides more detail on the data required for each of the elements. The actual RMP form, however, will contain more detailed guidance to make it possible to limit the number of text entries. For example, the rule requires that the major hazards identified during a Process Hazard Assessment (PHA) or hazard review and on public receptors affected by Worst-Case and Alternative Release Scenarios be reported.

EPA has made RMP*Submit 2004 available for completion and filing of the Risk Management Plan. RMP*Submit™ is free software that can be used for electronic submission of the Risk Management Plan. RMP*Submit 2004 is based on the RMP requirments found in 40 CFR 68 and includes the amendments that were published April 9, 2004. The software and its instructions for use are available on EPA's web site:

<http://yosemite.epa.gov/oswer/ceppoweb.nsf/content/ap-rmsb.htm>

The instructions for RMP* Submit 2004 cover each of the data elements to be reported in the RMP. The instructions explain each data element and help the plan writer to understand what acceptable data are for each. Copies of the RMP rule, Frequently Asked Questions, and other information can also be downloaded from the EPA website.

RMP*Submit 2004 provides a list of options that can be selected for various elements. Except for the executive summary, the resulting RMP consists primarily of yes/no answers, numerical information (*e.g.*, dates, quantities, distances), and a few text answers (*e.g.*, names, addresses, chemical identity).

Where possible, RMP*Submit 2004 will provide *pick lists* to help in completion of the form. For example, RMP*Submit 2004 will provide a list of regulated substances and automatically fill in the CAS numbers when a substance is selected.

Information and instructions on trade secrets and confidentiality are covered in the *General Guide,* Chapter 9.

When Does the Off-Site Consequence Analysis (OCA) Need to Be Revised? The OCA needs to be revised whenever a change at the facility results in the distance to an end point from a worst-case release rising or falling by at least a factor of two. For example, if the inventory at the facility increases substantially or if passive mitigation is installed to limit the potential release rate, then the distance to an end point should be reestimated. If the distance is at least doubled or halved, then revise the RMP must be revised. For most substances, the quantity that would be released would have to increase by more than a factor of five to double the distance to an end point.

Can a Facility File Predictively? Predictive filing is an option that allows a facility to submit an RMP that includes regulated substances that may not be held at the facility at the time of submission. This option is intended to assist facilities such as chemical warehouses, chemical distributors, and batch processors whose operations involve highly variable types and quantities of regulated substances, but who are able to forecast their inventory with some degree of accuracy. Under 40 CFR 68.190, the RMP is required to be updated and resubmited no later than the date on which a new regulated substance is first present in a covered process above a threshold quantity.

By using predictive filing, a facility will not be required to update and resubmit its RMP when a new regulated substance is received, if that substance was included in the latest RMP submission (as long it is received in a quantity that does not trigger a revised Off-Site Consequence Analysis as provided in 40 CFR 68.36).

If predictive filing is used, then the facility's Risk Management Program must be implemented and the RMP prepared exactly as if the facility actually held all of the substances included in the RMP. This means that all rule requirements must be met for each regulated substance that is filed, whether or not that substance is actually held on-site at the time that the RMP is submitted. Depending on the substances that are filed, this may require that additional Worst-Case and Alternative Release Scenarios be performed and additional prevention program elements be implemented. If this option is used, then the facility must still update and resubmit its RMP if it receives a regulated substance that was not included in its latest RMP. The facility must also continue to comply with the other update requirements stated in 40 CFR 68.190.

How Is a Facility De-Registered? If the facility is no longer covered by this rule, then a letter must be submitted to the RMP Record Center within six months indicating that the stationary source is no longer covered.

Implementation

The implementing agency is the Federal, State, or local agency that is taking the lead for implementation and enforcement of 40 CFR 68. The implementing agency will review RMPs, select some plans for audits, and conduct on-site inspections. The implementing agency should be the primary contact for information and assistance.

Under the CAA, EPA will serve as the implementing agency until a State or local agency seeks and is granted delegation under CAA Section 112(l) and 40 CFR 63, Subpart E. Check with the

EPA Regional Office to determine if the state where the facility is located has been granted delegation or is in the process of seeking delegation. The Regional Office will be able to provide contact names at the State or local level. Appendix C of the *General Guide* has addresses and contact information for EPA Regions and State implementing agencies.

Delegated Programs

If the program is delegated, what does that mean to the facility? To gain delegation, a State or local agency must demonstrate that it has the authority and resources to implement and enforce 40 CFR 68 for all covered processes in the State or local area. Some states may, however, elect to seek delegation to implement and enforce the rule only for sources covered by an operating permit program under Title V of the CAA.

When EPA determines that a State or local agency has the required authority and resources, EPA may delegate the program. If the state's rules differ from 40 CFR 68 (a state's rules are allowed to differ in certain specified respects, as discussed below), EPA will adopt, through rulemaking, the State program as a substitute for 40 CFR 68 in the state, making the State program Federally enforceable.

In most cases the state will take the lead in implementation and enforcement, but EPA maintains the ability to enforce 40 CFR 68 in delegated states. Should EPA decide that it is necessary to take an enforcement action in the state, the action would be based on the State rule that EPA has adopted as a substitute for 40 CFR 68. Similarly, citizen actions under the CAA would be based on the State rules that EPA has adopted.

Under 40 CFR 63.90, EPA will not delegate the authority to add or delete substances from 40 CFR 68.130. EPA also plans to propose, in revisions to 40 CFR 63, that authority to revise Subpart G (relating to RMPs) will not be delegated. With respect to RMPs, a facility would continue to be required to file the 40 CFR 68 RMP, in the form and manner specified by EPA, to the central location EPA designates.

Check with the state to determine whether additional data for state use is needed or if amended copies of the plan should be submitted to the state in order to cover State elements or substances. If the state has been granted delegation, it is important contact the state in order to determine if the state has requirements in addition to those in 40 CFR 68. State rules may be more stringent than 40 CFR 68. The EPA guidance documents do not cover State requirements.

Reviews/Audits/Inspections

Reviews. The implementing agency is required under 40 CFR 68 to review and conduct audits of RMPs. *Reviews* are relatively quick checks of the plans in order to determine whether they are complete and whether they contain any information that is clearly problematic. For example, if an RMP for a process containing flammables fails to list fire and explosion as a hazard in the prevention program, then the implementing agency may flag that as a problem. The RMP data system will perform some of the reviews automatically by flagging RMPs that have been submitted without the necessary data elements completed.

Audits and Their Conduct. Facilities may be selected for audits based on any of the following criteria, set out in 40 CFR 68.220:

- Accident history of the facility

- Accident history of other facilities in the same industry

- Quantity of regulated substances handled at the site

- Location of the facility and its proximity to public and environmental receptors

- The presence of specific regulated substances

- The hazards identified in the RMP

- A plan providing for random, neutral oversight

Under the CAA and 40 CFR 68, audits are conducted on the RMP. *Audits* will generally include an evaluation of the RMP for its adequacy and may result in RMP revisions in order to ensure compliance with 40 CFR 68. Audits are used to identify whether the underlying risk management program is being implemented properly. The implementing agency will look for any inconsistencies in the dates reported for compliance with prevention program elements. For example, if the facility reports that the date of its last revision of operating procedures was in June, 2004 but its training program was last reviewed or revised in December, 2000, the implementing agency will ask why the training program was not reviewed to reflect new operating procedures.

The agency will also look at other items that may indicate problems with implementation. For example, if the facility reports on a distillation column at a refinery, but used a checklist as its PHA technique, or fails to list an appropriate set of process hazards for the process chemicals, the agency may seek further explanations as to why the facility reported in the way it did. The implementing agency may compare facility data with that of other facilities in the same industrial sector using the same chemicals to identify differences that may indicate compliance problems. If audits indicate potential problems, they may lead to requests for more information or to on-site inspections.

The number of audits conducted will vary from state to state and from year to year. Implementing agencies will set their own goals, based on their resources and particular concerns.

Inspections. *Inspections* are site visits to check on the accuracy of the RMP data and on the implementation of all 40 CFR 68 elements. During inspections, the implementing agency will probably review the documentation for rule elements, such as the PHA reports, operating procedures, maintenance schedules, process safety information, and training.

Unlike audits, which focus on the RMP but may lead to determinations concerning needed improvements to the risk management program, inspections will focus on the underlying risk management program itself. Implementing agencies will determine how many inspections they need to conduct.

Audits may lead to inspections or inspections may be done separately. Depending on the focus of the inspection (all covered processes, a single process, or particular part of the risk management program) and the size of the facility, inspections may take several hours to several weeks.

Relationship with the Title V Permit Programs

40 CFR 68 is an applicable requirement under the CAA Title V permit program and must be listed in a Title V air permit. A facility does not need a Title V air permit solely because it is subject to 40 CFR 68. However, if the facility is required to apply for a Title V permit because it is subject to requirements under some other part of the CAA, then the facility must

- List 40 CFR 68 as an applicable requirement in its permit

- Include conditions that require the facility to either submit a compliance schedule for meeting the requirements of 40 CFR 68 by the applicable deadlines or

- Include compliance with 40 CFR 68 as part of its compliance certification statement

The facility must also provide the permitting agency with any other relevant information the agency requests.

The RMP and supporting documentation are not part of the permit and should not be submitted to the permitting authority. The permitting authority is only required to ensure that the RMP has been submitted to EPA and that the plan is complete. The permitting authority may delegate the review of the plan to other agencies.

If a facility has a Title V permit and it does not address the 40 CFR 68 requirement, then the permitting authority should be contacted in order to determine if the permit needs to be amended.

Penalties for Noncompliance

Penalties for violating the requirements or prohibitions of 40 CFR 68 are set forth in CAA Section 113. This section provides for both civil and criminal penalties. EPA may assess civil penalties of not more than $27,500 per day per violation.

Anyone convicted of knowingly violating 40 CFR 68 may also be punished by a fine pursuant to Title 18 of the *United States Code* or by imprisonment for no more than five years, or both. Anyone convicted of knowingly filing false information may be punished by a fine pursuant to Title 18 or by imprisonment for no more than two years.

One Plan

A facility subject to the Risk Management Program of the Clean Air Act is usually subject to a number of other regulations in regard to hazardous materials. In the past, this has meant separate plans and documents for each of these regulations. The One Plan (also known as the Integrated Compliance Plan, or ICP) concept has been developed to allow the combination of these requirements.

The National Response Team (NRT) announced the *One Plan* guidance (*ICP Guidance*) for integrated contingency planning in June 1996. This guidance provides the method to consolidate multiple plans that a facility may have prepared in order to comply with various regulations into one functional emergency response plan.

The *ICP Guidance* was developed to

- Provide a mechanism for consolidating multiple facility response plans into one plan that can be used during an emergency

- Improve coordination of planning and response activities within the facility and with public and commercial responders

- Minimize duplication and simplify planning

The *ICP Guidance* resulted from recommendations in the December 1993 NRT Report to Congress: *A Review of Federal Authorities for Hazardous Materials Accident Safety*. The NRT received input from representatives from State and local agencies, industry, and environmental groups prior to developing the guidance. Five agencies signed the one-plan guidance: the Environmental Protection Agency (EPA), the United States Coast Guard (USCG), the Occupational Safety and Health Administration (OSHA), the Office of Pipeline Safety of the Department of Transportation (DOT), and the Minerals Management Service (MMS) in the Department of the Interior. The NRT and the agencies responsible for reviewing and approving compliance with hazardous materials regulations agree that integrated response plans prepared in accordance with this guidance will be acceptable and will be the Federally preferred method of response planning.

The *ICP Guidance* gives facilities a common-sense option for meeting multiple emergency requirements under nine different regulations. The *ICP Guidance* is the outgrowth of the 1994 presidential review of Federal authorities related to hazardous materials accident prevention, mitigation, and response. That review identified multiple and overlapping facility emergency response plans as a problem area. Within the guidance document is a core facility response plan for releases of oil and hazardous substances. Plans prepared by facilities in accordance with the guidance will satisfy requirements of the five participating agencies and will be the Federal preferred method of such planning.

Regulations Covered by the ICP Guidance

Rather than a regulatory initiative, the ICP document is guidance. It presents a sample contingency plan outline that addresses requirements of the following Federal regulations:

- The Clean Water Act (CWA) (as amended by the Oil Pollution Act [OPA]) Facility Response Plan Regulations (EPA, Coast Guard, DOT, MMS)

- EPA's Risk Management Program Regulation, Oil Pollution Prevention Regulation, and the Resource Conservation and Recovery Act (RCRA) Contingency Planning Requirements

- OSHA's Emergency Action Plan Regulation, Process Safety Management Standards, and the Hazardous Waste Operations and Emergency Response (HAZWOPER) Regulation

Format of the ICP

A facility may use the ICP sample format or use an alternate format. The ICP sample format includes the following three sections:

1) Plan introduction

2) A core plan that serves as the primary response tool

3) A series of annexes that provide more detailed supporting information and regulatory compliance documentation

The ICP sample format is based on the Incident Command System (ICS). By organizing an integrated contingency plan according to the structure of the ICS, a facility will allow the plan to dovetail with established response management practices. This should promote its usefulness in an emergency.

Cross-References

The *ICP Guidance* supports the use of linkages (*i.e.*, references) to facilitate coordination with other facility plans and with external plans such as Local Emergency Planning Committee (LEPC) plans and Area Contingency Plans. When a facility submits a plan for Federal agency review, it must provide a table indicating where the regulatory required elements can be found in the one-plan format. The *ICP Guidance* includes tables that cross-reference the requirements of individual regulations with the ICP sample format.

The NRT intends to continue promoting the use of the *ICP Guidance* by regulated industries, and encourages Federal and State agencies to rely on the *ICP Guidance* when developing future regulations. The *ICP Guidance* was published in the *Federal Register* on June 5, 1996 (61 FR 28642).

For copies and more information, call the

RCRA, RCRA Contingency Planning Require-ment, Superfund, and EPCRA HOTLINE: (800) 424–9346 (TDD: [800] 553–7672)

In the Washington, DC area, call the HOTLINE at (703) 412–9810.

The ICP Guidance is also available on EPA's Chemical Emergency Preparedness and Pre-vention Office website at

<http://yosemite.epa.gov/oswer/ceppoweb.nsf/ content/sta-loc.htm#OnePlan>

The one-plan approach will minimize duplication of effort and unnecessary paperwork burdens. The consolidation of the various plans will allow for the development of an integrated emergency plan and training of facility personnel.

Communication with the Public

Possibly the most important part of the RMP process is communicating results of the RMP to the public. It is important to avoid the *Not In My Backyard* response when communicating to the public. Once the RMP has been prepared and submitted, EPA will make it available to the public. Public availability of the RMP is a requirement under Section 114(c) of the Clean Air Act (the Act provides for protection of trade secrets, and EPA will accordingly protect any portion of the RMP that contains Confidential Business Information).

Therefore, a facility manager can expect that the local community will discuss the hazards and risks associated with the facility as indicated in the RMP. The facility manager will necessarily be part of such discussions. The public and the press are likely to ask questions, because only the facility personnel can provide specific answers about the facility and its accident prevention program.

This dialogue is a most important step in preventing chemical accidents and should be encouraged. Facility managers should respond to these questions honestly and candidly. Refusing to answer, reacting defensively, or attacking the regulation as unnecessary are likely to make people suspicious and willing to assume the worst.

If the people and business residents in the vicinity of the facility believe that its operations threaten their health and safety, they will take action. They will contact their elected officials and demand that steps be taken. Local governments can regulate a facility out of business if a threat is perceived and there is no confidence that the facility is committed to prevention of and effective response to incidents.

A basic fact of risk communication is that trust, once lost, is very hard to regain. This has been a problem for the Nuclear Power Industry since the Three Mile Island incident. The industry did not inform the public of risks prior to the accident, and during the event failed to effectively communicate what was happening and was perceived as not telling the truth. One example of good risk communication is found in the airline industry. When fatal crashes have occurred, those airlines with an effective public communications/relations plan have fared better than those without.

Communication with the community about these issues should begin as early as possible. This includes discussions with Local Emergency Planning Committees (LEPCs), State Emergency Response Commissions (SERCs), other local and State officials, and other interested parties. Communication with the public can be an opportunity to develop a good relationship with the community and build a level of trust between the facility, its neighbors, and the community at large.

It is important to ensure that the public understands that by complying with the RMP Rule, the facility management is taking a number of steps to prevent accidents and protect the community. These steps are the individual elements of a risk management program. A well-designed and properly implemented risk management program will set the stage for informative and productive dialogue.

Some industries have developed guidance and other materials to assist in this process—contact the appropriate trade association for more information.

Risk communication means establishing and maintaining a dialogue with the public about the hazards at an operation, and discussing the steps that have been or can be taken to reduce the risk posed by these hazards. Of particular concern under this rule are the hazards related to the chemicals that are used and what would happen if there is an accidental release. Chapter 11 of the *General Guide* covers the subject in depth and offers excellent suggestions for developing a risk communications program. This area is one where expert assistance should be seriously considered.

Conclusion

The RMP is a demanding task. It requires expertise in a number of specialties, and is one of the few programs that require the off-site impacts of a facility to be analyzed and provided to the public.

The key points in the implementation of the RMP are:

- Identify the regulating agency
- Understand that audits and inspections will occur on some basis and may not be the result of actions or incidents at the facility
- Include the RMP in Title V Permit documents
- There are penalties for noncompliance

The person most likely to bear the responsibility for the facilities RMP should keep in mind that the implementation and maintenance of the plan are as critical as any other aspect. Having an analysis on a bookshelf or in a computer file does not mean that that the job is done and no more work is required.

The Worst-Case Release Scenarios are usually well beyond the probabilities considered in the design and construction of the facility. However, the potential is there, and one accident resulting in serious injury or death to members of the general public or workers can mean the termination of the facility and possibly the financial ruin of the company.

Bhopal was the result of inattention to the consequences of accumulating an intermediate product that was an extremely hazardous material. Controls in process and inventory, can result in substantial long-term savings. The RMP is a challenge, but when added to the rest of the regulations it fills in the last piece of the puzzle. The completed picture is an integrated safety management program that safeguards facility workers and the general public.

***Dale M. Petroff** is currently a Senior Program Analyst with Science Applications International Corporation (SAIC) in Washington, DC specializing in continuity of operations, emergency preparedness, and security. He is a graduate of the United States Military Academy. Mr. Petroff has over twenty-five years of experience at Department of Energy sites, military installations, and waste processing, nuclear power, and fossil fuel facilities. Over the last twenty-two years, Mr. Petroff has developed and conducted* *incident response training for fixed facilities and transportation accidents. He has been a member of an emergency response organization and has been involved in the development of emergency response programs at chemical facilities, coal fired power plants, nuclear reactors and DOE facilities. He is currently a supporting Continuity of Operations Planning (COOP) for several organizations in the Capitol Complex. During his military service, he was a Nuclear Biological Chemical Warfare Defense Officer, a Battalion Intelligence Officer, Weapons Company Commander, and a Reserve Military Police Company Commander. Mr. Petroff's publications include: "Terrorism and Risk Communications," Dale M. Petroff, coauthor with Scott Lonchar, in* The Military Engineer; *"Responding to Dirty Bombs," and "Security of Hazardous Materials," in* Occupational Health & Safety; *as well as numerous technical reports on decontamination and hazards assessment for emergency planning.*

CHAPTER 36

Indoor Air Quality: A General Overview

Valentino P. DeRocili, PhD, CHMM

Indoor Air Quality: A General Overview

Introduction

Maintaining adequate indoor air quality is crucial to providing a safe environment at work and in the home. Every day, millions of people are exposed to a number of safety and health hazards relating to poor indoor air quality. These hazards are sometimes capable of producing serious diseases and injuries and, in some cases, may be fatal. These hazards are usually preventable if the conditions of poor indoor air quality are recognized and controlled at an early stage. Poor ventilation and inadequate source control (*e.g.*, uncontrolled moisture, carbon monoxide emission, environmental tobacco smoke exposure, and chemical contact) in buildings, as well as inadequate knowledge of hazards, can all be linked to a number of safety and health problems. Building deficiencies and their associated indoor air quality hazards are also important, including human exposure to allergens, mold, bacteria, insects, and rodents. This chapter will explore the spectrum of building-associated safety and health hazards as a result of poor indoor air quality, the conditions that typically create the hazard, and a response to these conditions. The contents of this chapter should not be construed as advice and are intended for general information purposes only. It is important to seek the recommendations of a qualified indoor air quality expert or consultant concerning any specific situation or issue.

Indoor Air Quality

Indoor air quality refers to the quality of the air inside a building including the concentrations of pollutants and thermal conditions (temperature and relative humidity) that affect the health, comfort, and performance of occupants. According to the United States Environmental Protection Agency (EPA), "an increasing amount of scientific evidence has indicated that the air within homes and other buildings can be more seriously polluted than the outdoor air in even the largest and most industrialized cities" (EPA 1995). Further research has indicated that people spend approximately ninety percent of their time indoors and the risks to health for many people may be greater due to exposure to air pollution indoors than outdoors. Accordingly, those most susceptible to the effects of indoor air pollution are those groups of people who may be exposed to indoor air pollutants for the longest periods of time including the young, the elderly, and the chronically ill, especially those suffering from respiratory or cardiovascular disease, or immune disorders.

The indoor environment in any building is a result of the interaction between the site, the climate, the building's structure and mechanical systems, the indoor and outdoor contaminant sources, and building's occupants. Indoor air quality problems have been on the increase as use of chemical products has increased and ventilation has been reduced in order to save energy, resulting in tighter building envelopes. A healthy indoor environment requires good indoor air quality, which includes the introduction and distribution of adequate ventilation air, control of airborne contaminants, and the maintenance of acceptable temperatures and relative humidity. Good indoor air quality also enhances occupant health, comfort, and productivity in the workplace.

The primary cause of indoor air quality problems is indoor pollution sources that release gases, vapors, or particles into the air. Inadequate ventilation can increase indoor pollutant levels when not enough outdoor air is introduced to dilute emissions from indoor sources. This inadequate distribution of ventilation air will prevent indoor air pollutants from being sufficiently transported out of the building. Furthermore, high temperature and humidity levels can increase the concentrations of some indoor pollutants. Accordingly, the principal factors involved in the development of indoor air quality problems are contaminant (pollution) source; heating ventilation and air-conditioning (HVAC) system (ventilation); pollutant pathways; and the activities of building occupants.

Indoor Air Quality Regulations

EPA has been at the forefront regarding indoor air quality regulations, using their expertise related to air quality, general authority to conduct research, and develop public policy. However, EPA along with a variety of Federal agencies including National Institute for Occupational Safety and Health (NIOSH), Department of Housing and Urban Development (HUD), Occupational Safety and Health Administration (OSHA), and Consumer Product Safety Commission (CPSC) have limited authority under current legislation. Considering that indoor air quality is generally not in the public realm and naturally lends itself to voluntary participation, EPA has emphasized voluntary efforts in controlling indoor air pollution. Consequently, EPA is working towards a public education program that would provide individuals with information so they can make educated choices about the quality of the indoor air that they breathe.

Whereas the Federal government has yet to mandate general indoor air quality regulations, the individual states are crucial in the development of policies dedicated towards this effort. Recently, there has been considerable activity in State legislatures on the subject of indoor air quality and State policies have begun to address a variety of individual pollutants, practices, and building types.

Ventilation and Indoor Air Quality

Natural and mechanical ventilation can be used either to exhaust pollutants from a fixed source, or to dilute pollutants from all sources within a space with outdoor air. When there is little ventilation, the rate at which outdoor air replaces indoor air is low and pollutant levels can increase. Outdoor air enters and leaves a building by the following processes:

Infiltration

Outdoor air flows into the building through gaps in the exterior construction. Moisture, cold drafts, and unwanted noise can lead to occupant discomfort and allow the entry of dust and airborne pollutants. Furthermore, EPA estimates that twenty-five to forty percent of the energy used for heating and cooling in a typical residence can be due to infiltration.

Natural Ventilation

Outdoor air flows into the building through open windows and doors.

Mechanical Ventilation

Indoor air is continuously removed, and filtered; conditioned outdoor air is distributed throughout the building by devices such as HVAC systems that include fans and duct work.

Many of the building components, its furnishings and equipment, as well as its occupants and their activities produce pollution. In a well-functioning building, some of these pollutants will be directly exhausted to the outdoors and removed as outdoor air enters the building and replaces the inside air. This air exchange is brought about by infiltration, natural ventilation, and mechanical ventilation. However, the outside air may also contain contaminants that will be brought inside the building during these processes.

A properly designed and functioning HVAC system provides thermal comfort, distributes adequate amounts of outdoor air to meet ventilation needs of all building occupants, as well as isolates and removes odors and contaminants through pressure control, filtration, and exhaust fans. The majority of HVAC systems distributes a blend of outdoor air and recirculated indoor air that has been filtered, heated or cooled, and sometimes humidified or dehumidified. A high or low relative humidity can produce thermal discomfort while a high relative humidity can promote microbial growth. Furthermore, the thermal environment (temperature, relative humidity and airflow) are important to indoor air quality. Numerous complaints of poor indoor air quality may be resolved by simply modifying the temperature or relative humidity. Occupants who are thermally uncomfortable usually have a lower tolerance to other building discomforts. Higher building temperatures also correlate to a higher rate at which chemicals are released from building materials. The American Society of Heating, Refrigerating, and Air-Conditioning Engineers (ASHRAE) describes the temperature and humidity ranges that fall within the comfort zone for most individuals dressed in typical indoor clothing and involved in mostly sedentary activities. According to ASHRAE, the recommended indoor range of humidity levels is thirty to sixty percent and should be maintained year round.

Building Factors Affecting Indoor Air Pollution

The following factors bring about poor indoor air quality:

- The presence of indoor and outdoor air pollution sources
- Poorly designed, maintained, or operated ventilation systems
- Uses of the building that were unanticipated or poorly planned for when the building was designed or renovated

Pollutant Sources

The most important factor influencing indoor air quality is the presence of pollutant sources. The relative importance of any single source depends on the quantity and the emission rate of a given pollutant and hazardous nature of those emissions. Common pollutants or pollutant classes of concern in buildings include:

- Environmental tobacco smoke
- Combustion products

- Biological contaminants
- Volatile organic compounds
- Formaldehyde
- Soil gases
- Pesticides
- Particles and fibers

Indoor sources of contaminants commonly found in buildings include:

- Housekeeping and maintenance
- Occupant-related sources
- Building uses
- Building-related sources
- HVAC system
- Moisture
- Vehicles in an attached garage

Common sources of contaminants that are introduced from outside of the buildings include:

- Ambient outdoor air
- Vehicular sources
- Commercial/manufacturing sources
- Utilities/public works
- Agriculture
- Construction/demolition
- Building exhaust
- Water sources
- Birds and rodents
- Building operations and maintenance
- Ground sources

Specific indoor air pollutants include:

- Radon
- Environmental tobacco smoke
- Biological contaminants including
  - Bacteria
  - Molds
  - Mildew
  - Viruses
  - Animal dander
  - House dust mites
  - Cockroaches
  - Pollen
- Carbon monoxide, nitrogen dioxide, and respirable particles from combustion sources such as
  - Unvented kerosene and gas space heaters
  - Woodstoves, fireplaces, and gas stoves
- Asbestos from
  - Deteriorating, damaged, or disturbed insulation
  - Fireproofing
  - Acoustical materials
  - Floor tiles
- Lead from
  - Lead-based paint
  - Contaminated soil and dust
- Formaldehyde from pressed wood products
- Pesticides from pest management practices
- Organic gases from
  - Building materials and furnishings
  - Carpet
  - Cleaning materials
  - Air fresheners
  - Paints, paint strippers and other solvents
  - Adhesives
  - Copying machines
  - Photography and print shops
- Contaminated outdoor air
  - Emissions from nearby sources
  - Soil gas from underground storage tanks and sewer gas
- Moisture or standing water that promotes excess microbial growth

A number of these aforementioned indoor air contaminants (radon, environmental tobacco smoke, combustion gases and particles, household chemicals, formaldehyde, pesticides, and asbestos) are suspected of causing, or are known to cause, cancer in humans.

All building occupants are exposed on a daily basis and without evident harm to some indoor air contaminants, including mold and mold spores. However, adverse health effects can occur if an individual receives an intolerable dose of the contaminant. This dose is related to the specific contaminant concentration, duration of exposure, and frequency of exposure. Because of the uniqueness of individuals, the dose required for adverse health effects can vary greatly between individuals.

Contaminants can enter the body by

- Inhalation

- Ingestion

- Skin contact

Contaminants follow various pathways when migrating from the source to reach occupant-breathing zones. These pathways may lead from an indoor source to an indoor location or from an outdoor source to an indoor location. Common airflow pathways for pollutants include:

- Stairwells

- Elevator shafts

- Electrical or plumbing chases, receptacles and outlets, ducts or plenums

- Flue leakage

- Room spaces

- Indoor air intake

- Windows, doors, cracks and crevices

- Substructure and slab penetrations

Typically, contaminants travel with the flow of air as air moves from areas of high pressure to areas of low pressure. Therefore, controlling building air pressure is an essential component of controlling indoor air pollution. Air should move from the occupants' air space, toward a source, and then out of the building; the direction of air motion being controlled by pressure. Driving forces such as winds, stack effect, HVAC/fans, flues and exhaust, and elevators change pressure relationships and, ultimately, airflow.

Ventilation Systems

If mechanical ventilation systems are poorly designed, operated, or maintained, they can contribute to indoor air quality problems. Inadequate ventilation occurs if ventilation systems are turned off in an effort to save energy or air supply and return vents within rooms are obstructed so that outdoor air does not reach the breathing zone of building occupants. Additionally, improperly located outdoor air-intake vents can also bring in outside air that is contaminated with automobile and truck exhaust, boiler emissions, fumes from dumpsters, or air vented from restrooms. Furthermore, ventilation systems can spread biological contaminants that have multiplied in cooling towers, humidifiers, dehumidifiers, air conditioners, or the inside surfaces of ventilation duct work. Legionnaire's disease and hypersensitivity pneumonitis are possible outcomes.

Building Uses

Indoor air pollutants can circulate from portions of the building used for specialized purposes such as print shops and dry-cleaning stores, into other portions of the same building, including office spaces. Additionally, carbon monoxide and other components of automobile exhaust can be drawn from underground parking garages through stairwells and elevator shafts into other portions of the same building including office spaces. Gasoline vapor emissions, including benzene, can also intrude from attached garages.

The Big Four

As previously discussed, indoor air in residential settings can be contaminated with hundreds, if not thousands, of contaminants in the form of gases, vapors, dusts, smoke, fumes, and fibers—including various aerosol combinations of these. Of these, four are outstanding because of their legacy of death and disease: carbon monoxide, radon, environmental tobacco smoke, as well as particles of dead dust mites and their fecal excrement.

Carbon Monoxide

Carbon monoxide is called the *Silent Killer* for good reason: its complete lack of warning properties. Thousands of people die every year from asphyxiation due to carbon monoxide, many in their residences and often while sleeping. The most common cause of this is faulty and inadequately ventilated fossil fuel heating appliances (furnaces, fireplaces, gas-fired water heaters). Consequently, a qualified professional should inspect these types of devices at least annually for

- Breaches and corrosion of the exhaust system that could leak carbon monoxide
- Improper combustion conditions
- Back drafting and improper ventilation

In addition, the Centers for Disease Control and Prevention (CDC) recommends that all residences be equipped with smoke detectors and carbon monoxide alarms and any communities require the installation of these devices.

Radon

In the United States, the inhalation of radon is the second leading cause of lung cancer, preceded only by environmental tobacco smoke. The most common source of indoor radon is uranium in the soil or rock underlying a home or building. When radon becomes trapped in buildings and concentrations accumulate indoors, exposure to radon becomes a concern. The EPA recommends that homes be tested for intrusions of radon gas and remediated as necessary.

Environmental Tobacco Smoke

Environmental tobacco smoke is the mixture of smoke that originates from the burning end of a cigarette, pipe, or cigar, and smoke that is exhaled by a smoker. It is a mixture of over 4,000 compounds, more than forty of which are known to cause cancer in humans, and many of which are strong irritants (EPA 1995). Passive inhalation of environmental tobacco smoke causes lung cancer. According to the CDC, infants and children are especially vulnerable because of their higher metabolic and respiratory rates and longer latency for deoxyribonucleic acid (DNA) damage that is manifested as pulmonary malignancies later in life.

Accordingly, the CDC recommends that smokers refrain from smoking indoors, especially when children are present.

Dust Mites

Dust mites are significant source of airborne allergens. The EPA and CDC regard dust mites as the leading cause of bronchial asthma. According to EPA,

> "exposures to house dust mites, animal-related allergens (*e.g.*, cat saliva, pet dander), and mold are estimated to cause 200,000 or more emergency room visits a year by asthma patients."

Moisture

Moisture is the key component in the growth processes of all molds. Without moisture, mold cannot live. With adequate moisture, molds can germinate and colonize quickly, causing destruction of its host substrate in a few hours. According to the CPSC, thirty to fifty percent of the buildings and homes in the United States and Canada have damp conditions that may encourage microbial (mold) growth. Recent studies have also suggested that over fifty percent of all homes and buildings in the United States and Canada have potential moisture problems. Accordingly, the control of moisture within buildings is critical in controlling microbial (mold) growth and therefore, maintaining good indoor air quality. The control of moisture is the only action that can prevent mold growth in buildings.

There are three categories of moisture sources in buildings: infiltration, generation, and accumulation.

Infitration. Exterior and/or interior conditions control the entry of moisture into interior spaces. These conditions include

- Moisture-laden air leakage by door openings and through cracks and crevices
- Diffusion through doors, walls, and partitions
- Entry of liquid water through cracks and then evaporation

- Leakage around electrical plugs and cracks in walls.

The penetration of storm water from the exterior and entry of water from piping systems into building spaces are common infiltration mechanisms. Leakage is most likely to occur when the surface of two building components is penetrated. Examples include roof and vent penetrations, chimneys, roof to wall interfaces and valleys, windows, and doors. The infiltration of moisture through building materials needs only a very small gap (3 microns or 3×10^{-6} meters wide in size) to occur. This can be the same size as some molds.

Generation. Moisture can be added to the building interior air during usage of the building and/or occupant habits such as showers, laundering, and cooking.

Accumulation. Moisture-laden air can build up or accumulate within a building.

Moisture can be solid (ice), liquid (puddles), or vapor (condensation). Mold cannot grow on ice; however, melting ice will wet porous substrates where mold can grow. Consequently, the saturation of building materials provides a *livable* substrate for mold. Further, liquid can evaporate at room temperatures to support mold growth on surfaces.

Mold needs water vapor (condensation) to support metabolism. Research suggests that mold activity can begin to thrive at 70 degrees Fahrenheit and 60 percent relative humidity. *Relative humidity* is the amount of water vapor air can hold at a certain temperature. Relative humidity changes with temperature; the higher the temperature, the more water vapor it can hold. A better indicator of how much water vapor is in the air is referred to as *dew point temperature*, the temperature at which air is saturated and produces dew. When the surface temperature of an object drops below the dew point temperature, dew (condensation) will form on the surface of the object.

To maintain a mold-free indoor environment, moisture must be controlled within buildings. However, moisture control may require more than exhaust ventilation or the HVAC system. Without moisture control in the indoor environment, microbial growth can produce conditions of reduced indoor air quality and may exacerbate human symptoms of irritation and allergenic reactions. In the most severe cases, infection and toxic shock have been attributed to mold exposure.

Health Effects

Occupants exposed to indoor air pollutants may experience health effects soon after exposure (*acute exposure*) or years later (*chronic exposure*). Immediate reactions to indoor air pollutants depends on factors such as age, pre-existing medical conditions, and the chemical sensitivity of the individual.

Individuals who may be susceptible to effects of indoor air contaminants include those who are allergic or asthmatic, have respiratory disease, or whose immune system is compromised. Common immediate effects are often nonspecific symptoms and may include:

- Headache
- Fatigue
- Shortness of breath
- Sinus congestion
- Cough
- Sneezing
- Eye, nose, and throat irritation
- Skin irritation
- Dizziness
- Nausea

These symptoms are similar to those attributed to other factors, such as colds and other viral illnesses, and it is often difficult to ascertain whether the symptoms have emerged as a result of exposure to air quality deficiencies, including the presence of indoor air contaminants. Additionally, environmental stressors, such as improper lighting, noise, vibration, overcrowding, ergonomic stressors, and job stress, can produce symptoms that are similar to those associated with poor indoor air quality. When the air temperature is too warm for the activity level, most of the building occupants may complain about physical sensations of discomfort, whereas a sensitive individual may also experience nonspecific symptoms such as fatigue, stuffiness, and headaches. Likewise, building occupants may perceive poor indoor air quality when there is the presence of odors, even though the odors may or may not be the cause of the reported symptoms.

Due to varying sensitivity between occupants, a certain individual may react to an indoor air quality deficiency while surrounding occupants display no adverse effects. Also, different reactions in different individuals can emerge as a result of the diverse patterns of contaminant distribution that can be produced by air movement in the building.

Building Associated Illnesses

Because indoor air quality problems and associated occupant complaints related to health and comfort have come to the forefront, certain terms have emerged that describe illnesses or effects specifically attributed to or associated with buildings. These include *Sick Building Syndrome*, *Building Related Illness*, and *Multiple Chemical Sensitivity*.

Sick Building Syndrome (SBS). This is catch-all term that is used to describe a series of nonspecific, acute symptoms experienced by building occupants for which no specific illness or cause can be identified. For the affected occupants, the symptoms appear to correlate with the time they spend in the building; that is, the symptoms are apparent when the occupants are present inside the building and disappear when the occupants leave. Common symptoms of SBS are often accompanied by nonspecific complaints such as stuffy or stale air and include

- Irritation of the eyes, nose, and throat

- Headache

- Stuffy nose

- Mental fatigue

- Lethargy

- Skin irritation

In most cases, a single causative agent is not identified and the complaints are often resolved when building operation problems and/or occupant activities are modified and/or corrected.

Building Related Illness (BRI). This term refers to a defined illness where a causative agent resulting from exposure to the indoor air has been identified for the associated health complaint. The causative agent can be chemical, however it is often biological. Specific symptoms may be apparent or those that are consistent with symptoms commonly associated with the flu can occur. Legionnaire's disease and hypersensitivity pneumonitis are common examples of BRI that can have serious, and even life-threatening, consequences.

Multiple Chemical Sensitivity (MCS). This term refers to a condition in which an occupant may be sensitive (have a reaction) to a broad range of chemicals in the indoor air, each of which may occur at a very low concentration. The affected occupant can be sensitive to particular contaminants at concentrations that do not have observable effects in other occupants. It has been reported that occupants who have MCS have difficulty being in most buildings. Accordingly, the medical profession is in disagreement as to whether MCS actually exists and what are the potential causative factors. However, medical professionals all agree that further research regarding MCS is required.

Identifying Indoor Air Quality Problems

Reported health effects and/or human activities that can be significant sources of indoor air pollution can be some useful indicators of an indoor air quality problem. Additionally, signs indicating that a building may be suffering from inadequate ventilation include moisture condensation on windows or outside walls, stuffy air, dirty HVAC equipment, areas where items or substrates contain microbial growth, and noticeable odors.

When occupant complaints progress to a level that sufficiently warrants an investigation into indoor air quality problems, an indoor air investigation can be performed to diagnose the causative agents. Local, State, or Federal public or occupational health agencies, or private consultants with indoor air experience can perform the investigation.

The primary objective of an indoor air quality investigation is to identify and solve the complaint in a manner that prevents it from recurring and that does not create other problems. The EPA and NIOSH have developed a building investigation protocol for investigating health and comfort complaints in public access buildings with respect to indoor air quality. The protocol is characterized by systematic information gathering and hypothesis testing. Generally, an indoor air quality investigation includes:

- An initial walk-through to help determine an explanation for the complaint consisting of a visual inspection

- An interview with occupants

- The collection of information regarding
  - Building occupants
  - The HVAC system
  - Pollutant pathways
  - Pollutant sources

- The collection of additional information if the walk-through was not successful in recognizing the cause of the reported problem

- The development of one or more hypotheses to explain the problem

- The testing of the hypotheses by
  - Manipulating building conditions or exposure
  - By performing appropriate tests which could include air sampling

If test results support the hypotheses, a control strategy is developed, follow-up validation is performed, and necessary modifications are implemented so that the problem will not recur.

Despite the fact that air sampling can appear to be the reasonable response to an indoor air quality problem, it is given limited attention by the EPA/NIOSH protocol. However, it is misleading to assume that no testing is needed to solve the problem. Commonly, air quality testing is used to determine temperature, humidity, ventilation adequacy, and air movement. Specific air samples should be collected only after other investigative activities have been used to collect considerable information. Furthermore, prior to the collection of air samples, investigators should develop a sampling strategy that is based on an understanding of how the building operates, the nature of the complaints, and a plan for interpreting the sampling results. For pollutants other than radon, measurements may be most appropriate when there are either health symptoms or signs of poor ventilation and specific sources or pollutants have been identified as possible causes of indoor air quality problems.

Controlling Indoor Air Problems

In order to prevent or control indoor air contaminant problems, the relationships between the factors that influence indoor air quality must be modified. Common strategies used to do this include *source control, ventilation improvements, air cleaning,* and *exposure control.* To mitigate successfully indoor air problems, a combination of these strategies is often employed.

Source Control

Source control is the removal or reduction of the indoor air contaminant (source), and is generally the most effective way to improve indoor air quality. Source control is often a more cost-effective approach to protecting indoor air quality than increasing ventilation since an increase in ventilation can increase energy costs. In some cases, modification of the environment is necessary for effective prevention or control of the indoor air contaminant problem. For example, if the causative agent of the indoor air problem is microbial growth, the disinfection of the affected area may not eliminate the problem. Growth of the biological contaminant could recur unless all sources of moisture are eliminated. Moreover, remnants of dead microorganisms remain allergenic.

Ventilation Improvements

Modifying the building's ventilation operations can decrease the concentrations of indoor air pollutants. Improving the ventilation can dilute the contaminants with an increased flow of outdoor air, or isolate/remove contaminants through the control of air pressure relationships with techniques that range from the adjustment of dampers to the installation of local exhaust. This approach is often effective when buildings are not adequately ventilated or a specific contaminant source cannot be identified.

Air Cleaners

Air-cleaning equipment is used to improve indoor air quality for occupants and therefore, must be properly selected and designed for the specific contaminants of interest. To ensure good long-term performance, air-cleaning equipment requires regular maintenance in accordance with the manufacturer's recommendations or else it could become a major pollutant source in itself. Air-cleaning equipment is most effective when used in conjunction with either source control or ventilation.

Generally, the technologies used to remove contaminants from the air include particulate filtration, electrostatic precipitation, negative ion generation, and gas sorption. The first three technologies are designed to remove airborne particulate, while the fourth is designed to remove gases. The overall effectiveness of air-cleaning equipment depends on its ability to collect pollutants (its efficiency) from indoor air, the amount of air it draws through the cleaning or filtering element, and the strength of the pollutant source.

Currently, EPA does not recommend using ozone-generating devices for removing contaminants from the indoor air. Further, EPA does not recommend the use of air cleaners to reduce the levels of radon and its decay products. The effectiveness of air cleaners for radon removal is uncertain because the devices only partially remove the radon decay products and do not decrease the amount of radon entering the building.

Exposure Control

Exposure control is an administrative approach for the removal or reduction of indoor air contaminants that includes the

- Scheduling of contaminant-producing activities to occur during unoccupied periods

- Notification of susceptible individuals about upcoming events (*e.g.*, roofing, pesticide application) so contact with the contaminants can be avoided

- Relocation of susceptible occupants away from the area where symptoms may be experienced

The best approach to the limiting complaints about contaminant-producing activities may be scheduling these activities during a time when the building is unoccupied. Activities such as roofing or demolition, for example, unavoidably produce odors or dust. The relocation of susceptible occupants is often considered the least desirable strategy and should be used only when all other approaches are ineffective in resolving occupant complaints.

Bibliography

Blackburn, C. "Factors That Contribute to Mold Growth Indoors After Water Damage." Burlington, WA: Dri-Eaz Products, Inc, 1997.

Godish, Thad. *Air Quality*. 3rd ed. New York, NY: Lewis Publishers, 1997.

Lstiburek, J. "Investigating Diagnosing Moisture Problems." *ASHRAE Journal*. 44(12): 36–41, 2002.

Nielsen, A. "Use of FMEA-Failure Modes Effects Analysis on Moisture Problems in Buildings." In *6th Symposium on Building Physics in the Nordic Countries*. Trondheim, Norway: 2002.

Marshall, R. R. *2001 Building Failures Study*. Ottawa, Ontario: CMHC Technical Series, 01–140, 2001.

Internet Resources

<http://www.aerias.org/kview.asp?DocId=51& spaceid=1&subid=6> (Aerias, LLC. Moisture and Humidity and the Negative Implications on Your Indoor Air.)

<http://www.aerias.org/kview.asp?DocId=52& spaceid=3&subid=29> (Aerias, LLC. Mold and Fungi, the Poisons Within.)

<http://www.cal-iaq.org/MIMH_2004-06.pdf> (California Department of Health Services. Indoor Air Quality Info Sheet, Mold in My Home: What Do I Do?)

<http://www.cdc.gov/niosh/topics/indoorenv/>
(Centers for Disease Control and Prevention.
National Institute for Occupational Safety and
Health. Indoor Environmental Quality.)

<http://www.epa.gov/iaq/ia-intro.html> (United
States Environmental Protection Agency. Indoor
Air Quality. Basic Information About Indoor Air
Quality.)

<http://www.epa.gov/iaq/largebldgs/baqtoc.html>
(United States Environmental Protection
Agency. Indoor Air Quality in Large Buildings
"Building Air Quality: A Guide for Building
Owners and Facility Managers, 1991.")

<http://www.epa.gov/iaq/largebldgs/i-beam_html/
ch1-fund.htm> (United States Environmental
Protection Agency. Indoor Air Quality in Large
Buildings: I-Beam Text Modules: Fundamentals
of IAQ in Buildings.)

<http://www.epa.gov/iaq/pubs/insidest.html>
(United States Environmental Protection
Agency. Indoor Air–Publications. "The Inside
Story: A Guide to Indoor Air Quality, 1995.")

<http://www.epa.gov/iaq/schools/tfs/guideh.html>
(United States Environmental Protection
Agency. Indoor Air–IAQ Tools for Schools. IAQ
Tools for Schools Kit–IAQ Coordinator's Guide.
Appendix H: Mold and Moisture.)

<http://www.mold-survivor.com/harriet
ammann.htm> (Harriett M. Ammann, PhD,
DABT. Is Indoor Mold Contamination a Threat
to Health?)

<http://www.osha.gov/SLTC/indoorairquality/
index.html> (United States Department of
Labor. Occupational Safety and Health Administration. Safety and Health Topics: Indoor
Air Quality.)

<http://www2.eli.org/research/iaqdatabases2004>
(Environmental Law Institute. The Indoor
Environment. Database of State Indoor Air
Quality Laws.)

Valentino P. De Rocili is the President of Compliance Environmental, Inc., an environmental health
and safety consulting firm located in Dover, Delaware. He has managed over $60 million of environmental
and safety-related projects in more than 24 years of hands on work experience in areas including indoor
air quality, mold investigation and remediation, hazard and risk assessment, PCBs, lead-based paint
inspection and abatement, waste management, underground storage tanks, wastewater and water
treatment, solid waste landfills, and compliance requirements. He is currently an Assistant Professor at
the University of Delaware, and the co-founder of the Delaware Chapter of Hazardous Materials Managers.
He serves on several technical committees including the Environmental Technical Review Committee for
the United States Air Force at Dover Air Force Base, and the Lead Advisory Group for the State of
Delaware Department of Health and Social Services. In 1996, he received the Champion of Excellence
Award from the National Academy of Certified Hazardous Materials Managers.*

Part VIII

Water Quality

CHAPTER 37

Clean Water Act

Adriane P. Borgias, MSEM, CHMM

Introduction

Overview of Chapter

The purpose of this chapter is to provide the hazardous materials manager with a general understanding of the Clean Water Act. The chapter provides a historical perspective of the Act and describes how regulatory and voluntary measures are used to achieve its goals. For the hazardous materials manager who needs to know more details about the specific requirements of the Act, a list of Internet resources is provided at the end of the chapter. The Environmental Protection Agency, in particular the regional office of the Agency, is a good starting point for gaining a better understanding of specific requirements. Although the Clean Water Act is Federal legislation, many provisions of the Act are delegable to the States. Therefore, when working towards compliance with the Act, it is also important for the hazardous materials manager to understand the delegations of authority and requirements that are in place at the State level. Many of the State agencies have information available over the Internet and staff that can answer activity- or industry- specific questions.

Historical Perspective

As early as 1899, the American people recognized the importance of clean water to their health and vitality. The Rivers and Harbors Act was passed in order to control the discharge of refuse into navigable waters. Section 13 of the Act established a permit system that was administered by the Army Corps of Engineers. This system was subsequently modified in 1972 as part of the Federal Water Pollution Control Act and is now known as the National Pollutant Discharge Elimination System (NPDES).

During the 1960s, the American public witnessed dramatic environmental changes and events that led to changes in the way the quality of our waters are protected. Rachel Carson's publication of *Silent Spring* in 1962 and other popular writings of the time, educated the public about the basic concepts of ecology and the impact of man's activities on the environment. Many of the major rivers in the United States were too polluted for swimming or fishing. Lake Erie, the warmest and shallowest of the Great Lakes, became the victim of excess nutrients. Algal blooms created anoxic conditions and in the 1960s the lake was declared to be *dead*. The most dramatic environmental event occurred on June 22, 1969, when an oil slick on the Cuyahoga River in Ohio caught on fire. As these events unfolded, the 70s became known as the *decade of the environment* and almost all of the major environmental legislation that is in place today was enacted during that time. The Federal Water Pollution Control Act was passed in 1972, and amended in 1977, to become the Clean Water Act as we know it today. The Clean Water Act uses a two-pronged approach by establishing water quality goals and marrying those goals with the plans and permits needed to achieve them.

The Clean Water Act continues to protect the health of our nation's waters and accommodates over 100 million more people than were in the United States in the 1970s. The *2000 National Water Quality Inventory* shows that water quality standards are being met in 61% of the nation's rivers and streams, 54% of the lakes, and 49% of the estuaries. Approximately 85% of the nation's rivers and lakes support their use as a drinking water supply. Progress can still be made in achieving clean water, however, and the report notes that the primary impairments are due to siltation, introduction of nutrients, bacteria, metals (primarily mercury), and oxygen depleting substances. In addition, pollution from urban and agricultural runoff also contributes to exceedances of the water quality standards. These findings have led to EPA's changing focus from end-of-pipe regulation to watershed-based activities and programs.

The Clean Water Act has evolved over time. Several amendments to the Act have been promulgated, providing assistance to municipal water treatment systems and a focus on water quality issues in the Great Lakes. However, the basic structure and mechanisms used to achieve the Act's intent has not changed significantly since 1977. The timeline for clean water legislation is shown in Figure 1.

Clean Water Act Timeline

1899 Rivers and Harbors Act

1972 Federal Water Pollution Control Act

1972 Great Lakes Water Quality Agreement

1977 FWPCA Amended to become the Clean Water Act

1981 Streamlined Municipal Construction Grants

1987 Clean Water State Revolving Fund

1990 Great Lakes Critical Programs Act

2002 Great Lakes Legacy Act

Figure 1. Clean Water Legislation

Objective and Goal of the Clean Water Act

The objective of the Clean Water Act is to *restore and maintain the chemical, physical, and biological integrity of the Nation's waters.* This objective is to be achieved by:

- Eliminating the discharge of pollutants and prohibiting the discharge of toxic pollutants into navigable waters

- Achieving water quality conditions that protect fish, shellfish, and wildlife and also provide for recreation

- Providing financial assistance for constructing publicly owned waste treatment facilities

- Assisting states and tribes in the planning, management, and control of pollution sources (point and nonpoint) within watersheds

- Supporting further progress in achieving the Act's goals through a major technology research and demonstration program

- Putting the primary responsibility and authority for implementation of the program on the states (and tribes that have applied for and received *Treatment As State* status)

While related in scope to the Safe Drinking Water Act, the Clean Water Act has broader coverage. The ability to use water for drinking is one of the beneficial uses that are recognized in the Act, but the Act does not regulate drinking water *per se.* In fact, the stated intent of Clean Water Act is to ensure that all surface waters of the United States are *fishable* and *swimmable.*

Key Provisions of the Clean Water Act

This chapter will cover the basic provisions of the Act that are of most interest to the hazardous materials manager. Table 1 identifies the significant implementing regulations corresponding to these provisions (most of which are contained within Title 40 of the *Code of Federal Regulations.*)

The Clean Water Act uses a two-pronged approach to achieve its goal: 1) water quality standards and criteria, and 2) permitting and certifications. How the hazardous materials manager uses these concepts will be discussed in more detail later in this chapter. The key provisions of the Act are contained in six Titles that are summarized below. The Environmental Protection Agency (EPA) is the key administrator for the Act although other agencies, such as the Army Corps of Engineers, play a key role in its implementation. As the administrator, EPA is tasked with cooperating with other Federal agencies, State and Tribal water pollution control agencies, interstate agencies, municipalities, and industries in order to adopt and implement comprehensive water pollution control programs. In addition to preventing, reducing, or eliminating pollution in the waters of the United States these programs are also required to consider and protect the many uses that these waters sustain such as:

- Propagation of fish, aquatic life, and wildlife
- Recreation
- Drinking water supply
- Agricultural uses
- Industrial use

(Note that *waste disposal* is not considered an allowable use under the Clean Water Act and the agency is authorized to make joint investigations with other agencies regarding discharges of sewage, industrial wastes or any other substance that may adversely affect the waters.)

The term **waters of the United States** has very specific meaning under the Clean Water Act and includes navigable waters, ground waters, surface waters, as well as underground waters. It is more specifically defined in Title 40 Code of Federal Regulations (CFR) 232.2(q).

Title I. Research and Related Programs

- Sets forth the goals and policies of the Act
- Establishes the areas of research and grant programs
- Gives EPA the authority to establish programs in cooperation with other Federal, State, and local agencies

Table 1. Significant Implementing Regulations of the Clean Water Act

CFR Citation	Topic
40 CFR 25	Public Participation Requirements under the CWA
40 CFR 104	Public hearings on effluent standards for toxic pollutants
40 CFR 110–113	Oil pollution prevention, discharge of oil, and contingency plans(for more information, refer to the chapter in this book titled "Oil Pollution Act")
40 CFR 116	Designation of Hazardous Substances
40 CFR 117	Determination of reportable quantities for hazardous substances(for more information, refer to the chapter in this book titled "Release Reporting and Emergency Notification")
40 CFR 121	State certification of activities requiring a Federal license or permit
40 CFR 122–125	The national pollutant discharge elimination system
40 CFR 129	Toxic pollutant effluent standards
40 CFR 130–132	Water quality planning, management and standards
40 CFR 133	Secondary treatment regulation
40 CFR 135	Prior notice of citizen suits
40 CFR 136	Guidelines establishing test procedures for the analysis of pollutants
40 CFR 140	Marine sanitation device standard
40 CFR 220–224, 227, 228	Ocean Dumping Permits
33 CFR 320–331, 40 CFR 230–233	Section 404 Dredge and Fill Activities and Nationwide Permits
40 CFR 300–302	National Oil and Hazardous Substances Pollution Contingency Plan (for more information, refer to the chapter in this book titled "Oil Pollution Act")
40 CFR 402–699	Effluent limitations guidelines for existing sources, standards of performance for new sources and pretreatment standards for new and existing sources

Title II. Grants for Construction of Treatment Works

- Provides funding to help states and other local governments construct sewage and waste-water treatment facilities so they may meet the effluent limitations that were required to be achieved by 1977

- Allows for the control of nonpoint source pollution through area wide planning as well as the installation and use of best management practices for agriculture, forestry, and other sources of runoff

Title III. Standards and Enforcement

- Prohibits the discharge of any unauthorized pollutant into waters of the United States (radiological, chemical, and biological warfare agents are specifically prohibited as well as high-level radioactive and medical waste)

- Requires point sources to comply with treatment technologies and effluent limitations in order to achieve applicable water quality standards

- Establishes an ongoing planning process for states and other local governments to:

  - Identify and prioritize waters that do not meet water quality standards, published as the *303(d) list*

  - Establish a Total Maximum Daily Load (TMDL) for each pollutant that causes an exceedance

- Requires states to inventory and revise biennially all navigable waters within the State This inventory is known as the *305(b) list* and is frequently combined with the *303(d)list*

- Requires EPA and the states to establish water quality criteria

- Establishes criminal and civil penalties for violations of the Clean Water Act

- Covers the discharge of oil and hazardous substances from ships and on- or offshore facilities by establishing response requirements and the National Contingency Plan

- Requires states to assess watersheds and prepare management plans that

  - Identify the best management practices that can be used to reduce pollutant loadings

  - Identify programs (such as enforcement, technical or financial assistance, education, training, technology transfer, and demonstration projects) that can be used to implement the best management practices

  - Identify and schedule annual milestones for implementing the programs and best management practices

  - Certify that the state has the authority to implement the programs

  - Identify sources of financial assistance

Title IV. Permits and Licenses

- Requires certification by the state for any Federal project in order to ensure that the project meets applicable effluent limitations, water quality standards, the national standards of performance for a new source, and the pretreatment standards

- Prohibits the discharge of pollutants into navigable waters and establishes the National Pollutant Discharge Elimination System (NPDES) for

  - Point source (end-of-pipe) discharges

  - Stormwater runoff from industrial facilities and construction activities

- Allows qualified States to administer their own NPDES

- Establishes a permit program (Section 404) for the discharge of dredge or fill material into navigable waters

Title V. General Provisions

- Contains general administrative provisions for the Clean Water Act

- Establishes a Water Quality Advisory Board

- Gives EPA emergency powers to respond to a situation that presents an imminent and substantial endangerment to the health or welfare of a person or persons

- Provides for citizen lawsuits and whistleblower protection

- Allows Indian Tribes to apply for *Treatment as State* status

Title VI. State Water Pollution Control Funds

- Establishes a water pollution control revolving fund for the purposes of

  - Constructing publicly owned treatment works

  - Implementing a management program under Section 319 of the Act

  - Developing and implementing an estuary conservation and management plan

Water Quality Standards and Criteria

Water quality standards and criteria are one of the important tools that the Clean Water Act uses to achieve its goal of *fishable and swimmable* waters. The water quality standards that are established by EPA or the states apply to **waters of the United States.** This generally refers to surface waters but the Clean Water Act also allows the inclusion of interstate, intrastate, territorial waters used in commerce, as well as territorial seas and wetlands. In adopting their own water quality standards, states, territories, and tribes can also include groundwater within the regulatory framework.

A **water quality standard** describes the desired condition of a water body and is used for determining if the water quality is impaired, setting NPDES limits, and determining the Total Maximum Daily Load for a pollutant. A water quality standard consists of three components:

- A **designated use**, such as recreation, aquatic habitat, industrial water supply, and drinking water supply. (Note: waste transport is not considered to be a designated use.) When assigning a designated use, the following factors are considered:

  - Current and potential uses of the water body

  - Value of the water body as a public water supply

  - Fish and shellfish habitat

  - Recreational, agricultural, and industrial uses

  - Physical and chemical characteristics of the water body

  - The socioeconomic and cultural characteristics

- **Water quality criteria**, which are levels of quality that protect the designated use. These include conditions such as pollutant concentrations, temperature, pH, turbidity, toxicity, or other. Water quality criteria are usually numerical values but they can also be narrative. Water quality criteria reflect the latest scientific knowledge relating to the impact of pollution on health and welfare, dispersal of pollutants in the ecosystem, and the overall impact of pollutant on the biological community, its diversity, stability, productivity, *etc.* Economic impacts are not considered when determining water quality criteria.

- **Antidegradation policy**, or a set of rules that should be followed when addressing activities that could lower the quality of high quality waters. The antidegradation policy includes:

  - *Tier 1: Protection of existing uses.* Consideration of the current use of the water as well as any use that occurred since November 28, 1975.

  - *Tier 2: Protection of fishable/swimmable waters.* Provides for a review process to ensure that lowering water quality does not impair existing uses.

  - *Tier 3: Protection of Outstanding National Resource Waters.* The Clean Water Act describes **Outstanding National Resource Waters** (ONRWs) as "high quality waters [that] constitute an outstanding National Resource, such as waters of National and State parks and wildlife refuges and waters of exceptional recreational or ecological significance." States are primarily responsible for designating these waters of exceptional ecological significance, which require special protection.

By adopting water quality criteria, states and tribes are setting the parameters needed to protect the designated uses for a particular water body. States and Tribes may adopt EPA's criteria, or they may adopt site-specific criteria in order to account for factors such as resident aquatic species. Section 307(a) of the Clean Water Act contains a list of 65 chemicals and chemical families that have since been interpreted to include the 126 **priority toxic pollutants** that must be considered in setting water quality criteria. The priority toxic pollutants were identified in the Clean Water Act because of their prevalence in wastewaters. They include heavy metals such as arsenic, cadmium, chromium, mercury, lead, and zinc; pesticides; polycyclic aromatic hydrocarbons, and polychlorinated biphenyls. Subsequent amendments of the Act established pretreatment standards for these substances in what are now 34 major industrial categories (40 CFR 122, Appendix A).

Total Maximum Daily Load

The Clean Water Act contains monitoring provisions to ensure that waters are meet the water quality standards and criteria. For waters that meet an applicable water quality standard, an anti-degradation policy is established and monitoring continues. For waters that don't meet the water quality standard, pollutant-specific load allocations (Total Maximum Daily Loads) and implementation plans are developed. The five-step process of TMDL development is shown in Figure 2.

A *Total Maximum Daily Load* (TMDL) represents the maximum amount of a particular pollutant that a water body can hold and still meet the established water quality standard. The first step in the calculation of the TMDL is the assessment of the water body. The pollutant loadings from point (end-of-pipe) and nonpoint (water runoff) sources are calculated. Natural background conditions are included in the calculation. Then the pollutant loadings are allocated between the sources, taking into account seasonal variations and including a *margin of safety*.

Point sources are discrete sources such as pipes, ditches, tunnels, wells or boats. Pollutant allocations from point sources are managed through the National Pollutant Discharge Elimination System. *Nonpoint sources* are not defined by discrete points. Areas such as agriculture, surface mining, construction, and timber harvest are examples of these types of sources. Load allocations from these sources are managed through the implementation of *best management practices* (BMPs). Best management practices are common-sense actions that are industry-specific and are used to protect water

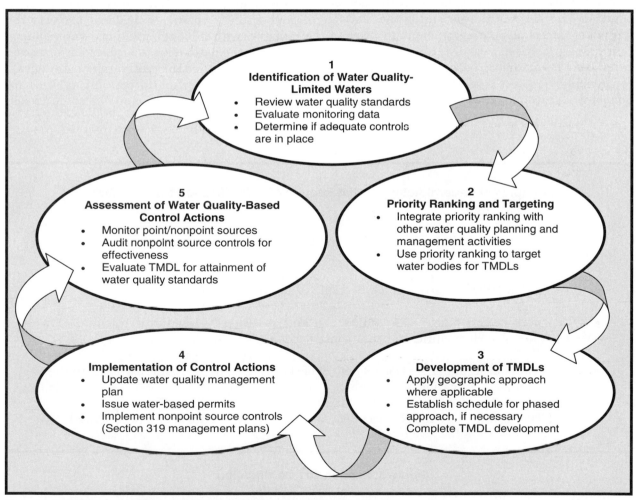

Source: <http://www.epa.gov/owow/tmdl/decisions/dec2.html>

Figure 2. Total Maximum Daily Load Process

quality. Although BMPs may be required by State law, the Clean Water Act does not have regulatory authority over these practices and relies upon coordination with State and local programs as well as voluntary compliance measures for implementation.

Once the TMDL is allocated, a *TMDL Implementation Plan* is developed. This important document establishes the controls and actions needed to bring the water body into compliance with its water quality standard(s). Because it is essential that pollution from both point and nonpoint sources is controlled, stakeholder involvement in the allocations and subsequent plan development is an important factor in a successful outcome.

It is important to note, that TMDL implementation is a process of continuous improvement. The monitoring and reporting provisions of the Clean Water Act require an independent evaluation of whether the actions taken under the TMDL implementation plan are sufficient to provide continuing protection of the water quality. EPA considers monitoring to be a high priority component of a State's permitting program and nonpoint source management plan.

Certifications and Permitting

The water quality certification requirements and permitting program are one of the other important tools that are used to achieve the goals of the Clean Water Act. These requirements are of particular interest to the hazardous materials manager because they are commonly associated with the regulated community. Compliance with these requirements is particularly important as the Clean Water Act has stiff penalties for non-compliance.

Section 401 Certification

Section 401 of the Clean Water Act requires that states review Federal permit applications and certify that the permitted activities will meet the water quality standards. In establishing this requirement, Congress ensured that states have an opportunity to review Federal projects for compliance with effluent limitations, water quality standards, the national standards of performance for a new source, and the pretreatment standards. A state may specify limitations as well as monitoring requirements and, in some cases,

---

Examples of Federal Activities that Require 401 Certification from the State

- Dredge and fill permits issued by the US Army Corps of Engineers under Section 404 of the Clean Water Act

- Federal NPDES permit under Section 402 of the Clean Water Act

- Licenses and permits issued by the Federal Energy Regulatory Commission (hydroelectric facilities, pipeline construction)

- Permits used under Sections 9 and 10 of the Rivers and Harbors Act (for activities that affect navigation)

- Licenses issued by the Nuclear Regulatory Commission (nuclear power plants)

Figure 3. Section 401 Certification

Table 2. Summary of NPDES Programs by Industry Sector

Agriculture

- Combined Animal Feeding Operations (CAFO)

Industrial and Commercial

- Water quality-based and technology-based permits
- Stormwater discharges (facilities)
- Stormwater discharges (construction activities)
- Pretreatment for discharges to municipal sewers
- Oil and gas discharges on the outer continental shelf
- Mining
- Cooling water intake structures

Municipalities and Wastewater Treatment Plants

- Secondary treatment standards for Publicly Owned Treatment Works
- Water Quality Based Permitting
- Combined Sewer Overflows
- Sanitary Sewer Overflows
- Municipal Separate Storm Sewer Systems (MS4s)
- National Pretreatment Program
- Biosolid disposal

conditions may be imposed on the license or permit in order to receive the certification. Examples of Federal permits that require 401 certification are shown in Figure 3.

National Pollutant Discharge Elimination System

The Clean Water Act specifically prohibits the unauthorized discharge of any pollutant to navigable waterways. Only pollutants that are included in a permit issued under the National Pollutant Discharge Elimination System can be discharged. The NPDES system covers two major categories of discharges. Point source discharges, or pollutants that are emitted from a discrete source such as a pipe, and stormwater discharges, or pollutants that result from the runoff of precipitation from natural and/or constructed stormwater systems. Stormwater is characterized as surface flow but it also generally includes channeled flow into a pipe or ditch that eventually leads to navigable waters. The NPDES is of particular interest to hazardous materials managers in that industrial, municipal, and other facilities are required to have an NPDES permit if their discharges go directly to surface waters. The

implementation of the NPDES has been the primary reason that water quality in the United States has improved significantly since the Clean Water Act was first passed in 1972.

Table 2 shows examples of NPDES programs by industry type.

Point Source Discharges. Prior to 1972, wastewaters from industrial facilities frequently contained toxic pollutants. The Clean Water Act established effluent limitations for these facilities that are based on the technology that is available to control pollutants and the water quality standards for the receiving waters. Industrial facilities that discharge to navigable waters are required to apply for an NPDES permit from either the state (if authorized by EPA to issue permits) or the EPA.

When issuing permits, permit writers take into account the following factors:

- Water quality standards for the receiving water body

- Nature and types of pollutants to be discharged by the facility

- An analysis of whether the proposed discharge causes or has the *reasonable potential* to cause an excursion of any water quality criteria

- The applicability of technology-based permit limits *versus* water quality-based effluent limits (including consideration of the facility's **waste load allocation**, which is the fraction of the TMDL for the water body that is assigned to the source).

- Ability of the effluent to rapidly and completely mix with the receiving water. This is determined by making a **mixing zone assessment** and assumes that there is an allocated zone within the receiving water where exceedance of the chronic water quality criteria is allowed, provided the designated use of the water is not impaired. Various types of models are used to make this assessment.

Stormwater Discharges. The control of pollutants in stormwater runoff is another important aspect of the NPDES. The stormwater permit program includes:

- Industrial activities from eleven categories of facilities, as identified by their Standard Industrial Classification (SIC)

- Construction activities that disturb one or more acres of land

- Municipalities with storm sewer systems that are not combined with the sanitary sewer system

Industrial activity stormwater discharges are permitted through a general permit system called the Multi-Sector General Permit (MSGP) or through an individual permit. The MSGP, if applicable, is the most convenient type of permit in that it specifies basic requirements that are available to facility operators. Some of the requirements pertain to all industry sectors. These include notification, the development of Storm Water Pollution Prevention Plans (SWPPP), as well as monitoring and reporting. Other requirements are associated with specific industry sectors such as the chemical, mining, oil and gas, hazardous waste management, landfill, air transportation, treatment works, and rubber manufacturing industries. Individual permits are used when the facility does not qualify for the MSGP.

Construction activity discharges can affect any industry sector and are covered under EPA's General Construction Permit. Like the MSGP, the General Construction Permit contains notification requirements, the development of a SWPPP, an endangered species assessment, and the implementation of best management practices.

To obtain coverage under a General Construction permit, an operator submits an electronic Notice of Intent (NOI) and discharges are allowed seven days after submittal of the NOI, only if the application is complete and accurate. The NOI contains site-specific information about the construction project including an evaluation of the waters into which the site discharges and the potential impact to Federally listed threatened or endangered species. A certification that the information provided was prepared by qualified personnel and is true, accurate and complete is also required.

The discharge of stormwater that is associated with the construction activity and related support activities is allowed under the permit provided appropriate controls and measures are outlined in an SWPPP. Other types of non-stormwater discharges are also allowed provided they do not contain toxic materials or detergents. Examples of these include discharges from fire-fighting activities, fire hydrant flushings, vehicle and external building wash waters, dust control water, potable water, pavement wash waters, air conditioning or compressor condensate, groundwater, spring water, foundation or footing drains, excavation dewatering, and landscape irrigation. No discharge from the construction site can violate an established TMDL for a receiving water nor can it impact threatened or endangered species or historic properties.

The SWPPP must be prepared prior to submitting the NOI and contain:

- A list of all potential sources of pollution which may reasonably be expected to affect the quality of stormwater discharges from the construction site

- The practices to be used to reduce pollutants in storm water discharges from the construction site

- An assurance of compliance with the terms and conditions of the permit

The basic elements of a SWPPP are described in Figure 4.

Figure 4. Elements of a Stormwater Pollution Prevention Plan for Construction Activities

Site and Activity Description

- Identification of all operators, their areas of control, and the nature of the project activity
- A general location and a legible site map

Controls to Reduce Pollutants

- Pollution control measures (*i.e.*, Best Management Practices)
- Stabilization and structural practices
- Post-construction storm water management measures that will be installed
- Measures to prevent the discharge of solid materials to waters of the United States
- Control of off-site vehicle tracking of sediments onto paved surfaces and the generation of dust
- Management of construction waste and hazardous materials, including spill prevention and response practices
- Pollutant sources from areas other than construction

Non-Storm Water Discharge Management

- An identification of all allowable sources of non-stormwater discharges and the appropriate pollution prevention measures

Documentation of Permit Eligibility Related to Endangered Species

- Documentation supporting a determination of permit eligibility with regard to federally listed threatened or endangered species and the impact of the project on critical habitat

Copy of Permit Requirements

- Copies of this permit and of the signed and certified NOI form that was submitted to EPA as well as the letter of completeness from EPA

Inspections

- Specification of the SWPPP inspections schedule and procedures throughout the project
- A record of each inspection and of any actions taken in accordance must be retained as part of the SWPPP for at least three years from the date that permit coverage expires or is terminated

Maintaining an Updated Plan

- Amendments to the plan due to a significant change in design, construction, operation, or maintenance at the construction site or a failure of the plan to prevent pollution

Signature, Plan Review and Making Plans Available

- A copy of the SWPPP (including a copy of the permit), NOI, and acknowledgement letter from EPA must be available at the construction site
- A sign or other notice containing the NOI must be posted conspicuously near the main entrance of the construction site

Documentation of Permit Eligibility Related to Total Maximum Daily Loads

- Documentation supporting a determination of permit eligibility with regard to waters that have an EPA-established or approved TMDL

Municipalities are issued individual stormwater permits based on their specific stormwater management program. In developing the program, municipalities must include measures to identify major outfalls and pollutant loadings, detect and eliminate nonstormwater discharges to the system, reduce pollutants in runoff, and control stormwater from new development/redevelopment areas. Note that the municipal program overlaps with the construction program. Development activities in some urban areas will need to be coordinated with the local jurisdiction.

Nationwide Permits

Under Section 404 of the Clean Water Act, the Army Corps of Engineers regulates the disposal of dredge and fill materials. 40 CFR 230 contains the guidelines for issuing permits for this activity. Like other aspects of the Clean Water Act, any activity that causes an exceedance of the water quality standard, violates an effluent limitation, jeopardizes a threatened or endangered species or is in violation of the Marine Protection and Sanctuaries Act of 1972 is prohibited. The guidelines describe the types of aquatic habitats and potential impacts as well as actions that can be taken to minimize impact.

The purpose of the Nationwide Permit (NWP) program is to streamline the evaluation and approval of certain types of activities that are expected to have only a minimal impact on water quality. The program consists of forty-three permits that authorize specific activities on a nationwide basis. Thirty-five of these permits are authorized under Section 404 (See Table 3). The permits, which are reviewed, modified, and reissued or revoked every five years, contain general conditions for

- Navigation (no adverse effect)
- Proper Maintenance (to ensure public safety)
- Soil Erosion and Sediment Controls (to be maintained in effective operating condition)
- Aquatic Life Movements (cannot disrupt the necessary life-cycle movements of indigenous aquatic species)
- Equipment (place on mats or take other measures to minimize soil disturbance)
- Regional and Case-by-Case (as determined by the Corps, state or tribe)
- Wild and Scenic Rivers (activity is prohibited unless there is no adverse effect)

- Tribal Rights (cannot impair reserved Tribal rights, such as hunting and fishing rights)
- Water Quality (ensure no more than minimal degradation)
- Coastal Zone Management (consistent with State program)
- Endangered Species (cannot jeopardize a Federally listed threatened or endangered species)
- Historic Properties (must meet the requirements of the National Historic Preservation Act)
- Notification (preconstruction notification requirements that vary by permit)
- Compliance Certification (that work was done in compliance with the terms of the NWP)
- Use of Multiple Nationwide Permits (cannot use multiple permits to increase project size)
- Water Supply Intakes (work in the vicinity of a public water supply intake is prohibited unless the work is for the purpose of repair of the intake and adjacent bank structures)
- Shellfish Beds (work in shellfish beds is prohibited unless for the purpose of harvesting)
- Suitable Material (fill material can't consist of trash and must be free of toxic substances)
- Mitigation (to compensate for environmental loss; determined on a case-by-case basis)
- Spawning Areas (must be protected; work in spawning areas is prohibited)
- Management of Water Flows (water flows must be maintained during the project)
- Adverse Effects from Impoundments (minimize)
- Waterfowl Breeding Areas (to be avoided)
- Removal of Temporary Fills (must be removed)
- Designated Critical Resource Waters (less than minimal impacts)
- Fills Within 100-year Floodplains (prohibited and must comply with FEMA floodplain management requirements)
- Construction Period (sets limitations based on permit dates)

In addition, there are terms and conditions that are specific to the individual permit and other terms may be imposed on a geographic, category, or activity-specific basis.

Table 3. The 35 Nationwide Permits Authorized under Section 404 of the Clean Water Act

Permit Number/Title

3. Maintenance

    (i)   repair, rehabilitation, and replacement of previously authorized, currently serviceable structures or fill (only minor deviations allowed)

    (ii)   discharges associated with removal of accumulated sediments and debris in the vicinity of existing structures (200 feet from structure)

    (iii)   discharges associated with restoration of upland areas damaged by a storm, flood, or other discrete event (restore to original high water mark; dredge less than 50 yds^3)

4. Fish and Wildlife Harvesting, Enhancement, and Attraction Devices and Activities

5. Scientific Measurement Devices (less than 25 yds^3 for weir and flumes)

6. Survey Activities

7. Outfall Structures and Maintenance

    (i)   Construction of outfall structures and associated intake structures

    (ii)   Maintenance excavation and dredging to remove accumulated sediments (to original capacity)

12. Utility Line Activities

    (i)   Utility lines (less than ½ acre)

    (ii)   Utility line substations (less than ½ acre)

    (iii)   Foundations for overhead utility line towers, poles, and anchors (minimum necessary)

    (iv)   Access roads (less than ½ acre)

13. Bank Stabilization (minimum necessary)

14. Linear Transportation Projects (less than ½ acre in non-tidal; $^1/_3$ acre in tidal)

15. U.S. Coast Guard Approved Bridges

16. Return Water From Upland Contained Disposal Areas

17. Hydropower Projects

18. Minor Discharges (less than 25 yds^3, 1/10 acre of special aquatic sites)

19. Minor Dredging (less than 25 yds^3)

20. Oil Spill Cleanup

21. Surface Coal Mining Activities

22. Removal of Vessels

23. Approved Categorical Exclusions

24. State Administered Section 404 Programs

25. Structural Discharges

27. Stream and Wetland Restoration Activities

29. Single-family Housing (less than ¼ acre)

30. Moist Soil Management for Wildlife

31. Maintenance of Existing Flood Control Facilities (as approved by District Engineer)

32. Completed Enforcement Actions (less than 5 acres non-tidal or 1 acre tidal wetlands)

33. Temporary Construction, Access and Dewatering

34. Cranberry Production Activities (less than 10 acres; no net loss of wetlands)

36. Boat Ramps (less than 50 yds^3 fill; 20 ft width for boat ramp)

37. Emergency Watershed Protection and Rehabilitation

38. Cleanup of Hazardous and Toxic Waste

39. Residential, Commercial, and Institutional Developments (less than ½ acre for new construction; 300 lineal feet of streambed)

40. Agricultural Activities (less than ½ acre for new construction; 300 lineal feet of streambed)

41. Reshaping Existing Drainage Ditches

42. Recreational Facilities

43. Stormwater Management Facilities (less than ½ acre for new construction; 300 lineal feet of streambed)

44. Mining Activities (less than 1/2 acre)

The Watershed Approach

In the thirty years since the enactment of the Clean Water Act, significant improvements have been made in the quality of the nation's waters. For the most part, these improvements have been the result of a rigorous permitting and enforcement program, targeting and controlling end-of-pipe discharges through NPDES permits.

As we move into the 21st century, the EPA programs that protect our waters are now using the *watershed approach* to achieve success. In order to improve water quality on a watershed basis, EPA has set specific objectives, using both pollution prevention and restoration approaches to improve water quality and/or achieve water quality standards. In implementing these approaches, EPA will integrate the suite of tools already provided by the Clean Water Act (water quality standards, monitoring, TMDLs, NPDES permits, and grants) on a watershed basis, engaging the diverse community of stakeholders to find solutions to water quality problems. Watershed planning is an important element of the Clean Water Act. EPA believes that a comprehensive watershed approach should be the guiding principle behind clean water programs. The Great Lakes Initiative is an example of this approach at a large regional and international level. More than 30 million people live within this watershed, which includes the five Great Lakes: Superior, Michigan, Huron, Erie, and Ontario and is the largest surface freshwater system on the earth. Environmental restoration in this area is funded by more than 140 different Federal programs with input from Canada, eight states, almost 40 tribal governments, and numerous metropolitan areas, county, and local governments.

Other major watershed programs that are supported by EPA include the National Estuary Program, Chesapeake Bay Program, and the Gulf of Mexico Program. More detailed information about these and the Great Lakes Initiatives can be found through links on EPA's Office of Water website.

At a more local level, the EPA also supports the development of watershed plans and TMDLs in specific geographic areas. EPA's Targeted Watersheds Grant program supports creative socioeconomic approaches to water restoration and protection. The watersheds that receive EPA funding under this program are striving to achieve measurable environmental results while engaging their local communities in the process. Innovative ideas such as water quality trading are being considered as a means to deliver cost effective water pollution control.

Internet Resources

<http://assembler.law.cornell.edu/uscode/html/uscode33/usc_sup_01_33_10_26.html> (Legal Information Institute. U. S. Code Collection. Title 33, Chapter 26, US Code, Water Pollution Prevention and Control)

<http://cfpub.epa.gov/npdes/> (Environmental Protection Agency. National Pollutant Discharge Elimination System)

<http://cfpub.epa.gov/npdes/home.cfm?program_id=6> (Environmental Protection Agency. National Pollutant Discharge Elimination System Stormwater Program)

<http://www.asiwpca.org/publications/publications.htm> (Association of State and Interstate Water Pollution Control Administra-tors. *Clean Water Act Thirty-Year Retrospective: History and Documents Related to the Federal Statute*)

<http://www.epa.gov/305b/2000report/> Environmental Protection Agency. Monitoring and Assessing Water Quality. (2000 National Water Quality Inventory)

<http://www.epa.gov/ebtpages/water.html> (Environmental Protection Agency. Browse EPA Topics. Water)

<http://www.epa.gov/glnpo/index.html> (Environmental Protection Agency. Great Lakes)

<http://www.epa.gov/ow/> (Environmental Protection Agency. Water Homepage)

<http://www.epa.gov/owow/tmdl/intro.html> (Environmental Protection Agency. Total Maximum Daily Load. Introduction to TMDLs)

<http://www.epa.gov/owow/watershed/initiative/> (Environmental Protection Agency. Targeted Watershed Grants Program)

<http://www.epa.gov/water/waterplan/> (Environmental Protection Agency. Water. National Water Program Strategic Plan 2004–2008 and National Program Guidance for 2005)

<http://www.gpoaccess.gov/> (Government Printing Office. GPO Access-A Service of the Government Printing Office)

<http://www.usace.army.mil/inet/functions/cw/cecwo/reg/33cfr330.htm> (Army Corps of Engineers. Nationwide Permit Program)

<http://www.usace.army.mil/inet/functions/cw/cecwo/reg/nationwide_permits.htm> (Army Corps of Engineers. Nationwide Permit Information)

<http://www.usace.army.mil/inet/functions/cw/cecwo/reg/sec404.htm> (Army Corps of Engineers. Section 404 of the Clean Water Act)

<http://www.usace.army.mil/inet/functions/cw/cecwo/reg/Summary_table.pdf> (Army Corps of Engineers. Summary of 2002 Nationwide Permits)

Adriane P. Borgias *is the owner of fusion environment&energy, LLC, an environmental consulting firm that specializes in environmental management systems and collaborative decision-making. Ms. Borgias has a BS in Chemistry from the University of California, Berkeley, and an MS in Environmental Management from the University of San Francisco. She has over 25 years of experience in the energy industry in research, corporate, and operating departments, and she is an independent consultant. She has over 20 years of experience in environmental and hazardous materials management, with particular experience in agency collaboration, regulatory review and development; environmental management systems, auditing and continuous improvement; hazardous materials and waste compliance activities; permitting; pipeline construction and inspection; as well as site assessment, investigation, and remediation. For the past 5 years, Ms. Borgias has worked with Indian Tribes in the Pacific Northwest, in the areas of air and water quality. Ms. Borgias is a former licensed nuclear reactor operator and has been a Certified Hazardous Materials Manager since 1986. She has served the Academy at the local and national level. In addition to being co-founder of the Northern California Chapter of ACHMM, Ms. Borgias has served as a National Committee Chair, Board Member, Treasurer, and President. In 1990, Ms. Borgias received the President's Award for Outstanding Service to the Academy. She was also the 1996 recipient of the Academy's* Founder's Award. *Ms. Borgias has contributed chapters to* Women in Chemistry and Physics, a Biobibliographic Sourcebook *and is profiled in* Northwest Women in Science: Women Making a Difference. *She would like to acknowledge in particular John M. Higgins, PhD, PE, CHMM the author of this chapter in the previous edition of the* Desk Reference.

CHAPTER 38

Oil Pollution Act

Mark L. Bricker, PE, CHMM

Introduction

The Oil Pollution Act (OPA) was signed into law in August of 1990. The OPA was the initial congressional response to the *Exxon Valdez* oil spill of March 1989. The *Valdez* spill, which has been called the "Pearl Harbor" of the United States environmental movement, galvanized public support behind legislation to ensure that future oil spills are minimized, that effective responses are made to those that do occur, and that those responsible pay for the damages and are subject to severe penalties.

It would be a mistake to view the OPA as a response only to the *Valdez* spill and other tanker incidents that occurred in 1989 and 1990 (*e.g.*, the *Mega Borg* fire and explosion in the Gulf of Mexico in 1990, the *American Trader* oil spill near the southern California coast in 1990, and a rash of incidents in later June, 1989). Congress had been working for almost 15 years to consolidate and rationalize oil spill response mechanisms under various Federal laws, including Section 311 of the Federal Water Pollution Control Act, (Clean Water Act [CWA]), the Deepwater Port Act of 1974, the Trans-Alaska Pipeline Authorization Act of 1973 (TAPAA), and the Outer Continental Shelf Lands Act Amendments of 1978 (OCSLA). Congress was also trying to harmonize these various oil spill laws with State laws, international conventions, and other Federal environmental laws, especially the Comprehensive Environmental Response,

Compensation, and Liability Act of 1980 (CERCLA or Superfund).

The main elements of the OPA are as follows:

1) A comprehensive Federal liability scheme, addressing all discharges of oil to navigable waters, the exclusive economic zone (a zone contiguous to the territorial sea extending 200 miles from shore), and shorelines.

2) A single, unified Federal fund, called the Oil Spill Liability Trust Fund, to pay for the cleanup and other costs of federal oil spill response. The Fund was authorized at $1 billion per spill incident.

3) Stronger Federal authority to order removal action or to conduct the removal action itself.

4) Drastically revised Spill Prevention, Control, and Countermeasure Plan requirements for onshore facilities, offshore facilities, and vessels.

5) Tougher criminal penalties.

6) Higher civil penalties for spills of oil and for spills of hazardous substances.

7) Tighter standards and reviews for licensing tank vessel personnel, and for equipment and operations of tank vessels, including requiring the use of double hulls.

8) No pre-emption of State laws, and an endorsement of the United States' participation in an international oil spill liability and compensation scheme.

9) Several provisions pertinent to Prince William Sound, to Alaska, and to other provisions of the United States.

The OPA improved the nation's ability to prevent and respond to oil spills by: (1) establishing provisions that expand the Federal government's ability and (2) providing the money and people necessary to respond to oil spills. Under the OPA, the United States Coast Guard (USCG) is the designated Federal response authority. Rule-making authority for onshore facilities was delegated to the Coast Guard and the Environmental Protection Agency (EPA).

The Oil Pollution Act Law

Far more comprehensive and stringent than any previous United States (US) or international oil pollution liability and prevention law, the OPA comprises nine titles.

Title I–Oil Pollution Liability and Compensation. Title I contains the definitions used in the OPA, establishes the liability scheme for oil spills, provides the mechanisms for recovery from the Oil Spill Liability Trust Fund and from responsible parties, and establishes financial responsibility requirements.

Title II–Conforming Amendments. Title II makes conforming changes in the Intervention on the High Seas Act, the CWA, the Deepwater Port Act, and the OCSLA.

Title III–International Oil Pollution Prevention and Removal. Title III outlines participation in international oil spill prevention and removal regimes and directs the Secretary of State to review international agreements and treaties and to negotiate agreements with Canada regarding oil spills on the Great Lakes, Lake Champlain, and Puget Sound.

Title IV–Prevention and Removal. Title IV has three subtitles:

- *Subtitle A–Prevention* provides for the review of information contained in the National Driver Register for issuing licenses, certificates of registry, and merchant marines' documents; provides for the suspension and revocation of those documents for alcohol and drug abuse incidents; and establishes prevention measures.

- *Subtitle B–Removal* provides Federal removal authority and requirements for the national planning and response system.

- *Subtitle C–Penalties and Miscellaneous* strengthens the civil and criminal penalties available to the government.

Title V–Prince William Sound Provisions. Title V contains several provisions designed specifically to avoid future spills in Prince William Sound.

Title VI–Miscellaneous. Title VI contains miscellaneous provisions such as the continuation of regulations replaced by OPA until repealed, suspended, or amended, and the Outer Banks Protection Act.

Title VII–Oil Pollution Research and Development Program. Title VII provides for an oil pollution research and development program.

Title VIII–Trans-Alaska Pipeline Provisions. Title VIII contains provisions dealing with the Trans-Alaska Pipeline System and oil spills in the Arctic Ocean.

Title IX–Amendments to Oil Spill Liability Trust Fund. Transfers funds from the several pre-existing Federal oil spill funds into the Oil Spill Liability Trust Fund.

Key Terms of the Oil Pollution Act

Section 1001 of the OPA contains 37 definitions used throughout the Act. The OPA restates verbatim many of the definitions of the CWA. Definitions of a few of the key terms in the OPA are described below.

Navigable waters—Navigable waters are broadly defined to include all waters that are used in interstate or foreign commerce, all interstate waters including wetlands, and all intrastate waters, such as lakes, rivers, streams, wetlands, sloughs, prairie potholes, wet meadows, playa lakes, or natural ponds. The interpretation of this definition varies by EPA region.

Vessel—Vessel is defined to include every description of watercraft or other artificial contrivance used, or capable of being used, as a means of transportation on water, other than a public vessel. Public vessels are noncommercial government vessels.

Tank vessels—These are vessels constructed, adapted to carry, or that carry oil or hazardous materials in bulk as cargo or cargo residue and that are US documented vessels, operate in US waters, or transfer oil or hazardous material in a place subject to the jurisdiction of the US.

Facility—Facility is any structure, group of structures, equipment, or device (other than a vessel) which is used for exploring, drilling, producing, storing, handling, transferring, processing, or transporting oil. The term also includes any motor vehicle, rolling stock, or pipeline used for these purposes. Facilities are further subdivided into onshore and offshore facilities. The boundaries of a facility may depend on several site-specific factors, such as the ownership or operation of buildings, structures, and equipment on the same site and the types of activity at the site.

Nontransportation-related facilities—Nontransportation-related facilities refer to all fixed facilities, including support equipment (but excluding certain pipelines) railroad tank cars en route, transport trucks en route, and equipment associated with the transfer of bulk oil to or from water transportation vessels. The term also includes mobile or portable facilities such as drilling or workover rigs, production facilities, and portable fueling facilities while in a fixed, operating mode.

Key Provisions of the Oil Pollution Act

A summary of key provisions in the OPA is provided below.

§1002(a). Provides that the responsible party for a vessel or facility from which oil is discharged, or which poses a substantial threat of a discharge, is liable for: (1) certain specified damages resulting from the discharged oil and (2) removal costs incurred in a manner consistent with the National Contingency Plan (NCP).

§1002(c). Exceptions to the OPA liability provisions include: (1) discharges of oil authorized by a permit under Federal, State, or local law, (2) discharges of oil from a public vessel, or (3) discharges of oil from onshore facilities covered by the liability provisions of the Trans-Alaska Pipeline Authorization Act.

§1002(d). Provides that if a responsible party can establish that the removal costs and damages resulting from an incident were caused solely by an act or omission by a third party, the third party will be held liable for such costs and damages.

§1004. The liability for tank vessels larger than 3,000 gross tons is increased to $1,200 per gross ton or $10 million, whichever is greater. Responsible parties at onshore facilities and deepwater ports are liable for up to $350 million per spill; holders of leases or permits for offshore facilities, except deepwater ports, are liable for up to $75 million per spill, plus removal costs. The federal government has the authority to adjust, by regulation, the $350 million liability limit established for onshore facilities.

§1016. Offshore facilities are required to maintain evidence of financial responsibility of $150 million, and vessels and deepwater ports must provide evidence of financial responsibility up to the maximum applicable liability amount. Claims for removal costs and damages may be asserted directly against the guarantor providing evidence of financial responsibility.

§1018(a). The OPA does not pre-empt state law. States may impose additional liability (including unlimited liability), funding mechanisms, requirements for removal actions, and fines and penalties for responsible parties.

§1019. States have the authority to enforce, on the navigable waters of the state, the OPA requirements for evidence of financial responsibility. States are also given access to Federal funds (up to $250,000 per incident) for immediate removal, mitigation, or prevention of a discharge, and may be reimbursed by the Trust Fund for removal and monitoring costs incurred during oil spill response and cleanup efforts that are consistent with the NCP.

§4202. Strengthens planning and prevention activities by: (1) providing for the establishment of spill contingency plans for all areas of the US, (2) mandating the development of response plans for individual tank vessels and certain facilities for responding to a worst-case discharge or a substantial threat of such a discharge, and (3) providing requirements for spill removal equipment and periodic inspections.

§9001(a). Amends the Internal Revenue Act of 1986 to consolidate funds established under other statutes and to increase permitted levels of expenditures. Penalties and funds established

under several laws are consolidated, and the Trust Fund borrowing limit is increased from $500 million to $1 billion.

Planning and Response System

The OPA addresses development of a National Planning and Response System. Under the current US national emergency response infrastructure for oil spills, planning occurs on four basic levels:

- National
- Area
- Local
- Facility

In the event of an oil spill, the facility response plan is immediately activated. Depending on the nature of the spill, local, area, or Federal plans may also be put into motion.

National Response

The National Oil and Hazardous Substances Pollution Contingency Plan, more commonly called the National Contingency Plan (NCP), is the Federal government's blueprint for responding to both oil spills and hazardous substance releases. The NCP is the result of our country's efforts to develop a national response capability and promote overall coordination among the hierarchy of responders and contingency plans. The NCP differs somewhat from the other types of contingency plans in that it provides the framework for our National Response System, and it serves as a guide for the way in which the different levels of responding organizations coordinate their efforts. The first NCP was developed and published in 1968, in response to a massive oil spill from an oil tanker off the coast of England the year before. The NCP was revised in 1994 to reflect the oil spill provisions of the OPA.

Area Response

Area response plans are often brought into action when facilities are unable to handle spills on their own. Under the OPA, EPA initially established 13

Areas covering the US and convened Area Committees composed of Federal, State, and local government agencies to prepare contingency plans for the designated Areas. The Area Contingency Plans include detailed information about resources (such as equipment and trained response personnel) available from the government agencies in the Area. They also describe the roles and responsibilities of each responding agency during a spill incident, and how the agencies will respond if they are called upon in an emergency. These plans also describe how two or more Areas might interact, such as when a spill occurs in a river that flows between Areas, to ensure that a spill is controlled and cleaned up in a timely and safe manner.

Local and Facility Response

When a release or spill occurs, the party responsible for the release, its response contractors, the local fire and police departments, and the local emergency response personnel provide the first line of defense. If needed, a variety of State agencies stand ready to support, assist, or take over response operations if an incident is beyond local capabilities.

Facility Oil Pollution Prevention Regulations

EPA first promulgated oil pollution prevention regulations in 1973 in the *Code of Federal Regulations* (40 CFR 112). The oil pollution prevention regulations establish requirements for facilities to prevent oil spills from reaching the navigable waters of the US or adjoining shorelines. The regulations apply to owners or operators of certain facilities that drill, produce, gather, store, process, refine, transfer, distribute, or consume oil. The regulations contain two major types of requirements: (1) prevention requirements known as Spill Prevention, Control, and Countermeasure Plans (SPCC Plans), and (2) Facility Response Plan (FRP) requirements.

On July 17th, 2002, EPA issued a final rule amending the Oil Pollution Prevention regulation.

This rule addresses requirements for SPCC Plans and some provisions that affect FRPs. On April 17, 2003, EPA extended the deadline for incorporating changes into existing SPCC Plans to August 17, 2004. For facilities in operation on or before August 16, 2002, EPA extended the deadline for implementing changes to February 18, 2005.

These regulations form the basis of EPA's Spill Prevention, Control, and Countermeasure (SPCC) program, which seeks to prevent oil spills from certain above-ground storage tanks (ASTs) and underground storage tanks (USTs). An owner or operator of a nontransportation-related facility is required to prepare an SPCC Plan if the following conditions occur:

- The facility has an aggregate above-ground storage capacity of more than 1,320 gallons, or a total underground storage of 42,000 gallons; or

- The facility could be expected to discharge oil in harmful quantities into navigable waters of the US

In 1990, Congress enacted the OPA which, among other things, required certain oil storage facilities to prepare FRPs. In response, EPA proposed revisions to the oil pollution prevention regulations in two phases. EPA proposed its first set of revisions to the regulation on October 22, 1991. These proposed revisions, in addition to strengthening and clarifying previous regulatory language, outline the additional requirements for regulated oil storage and handling facilities. On July 1, 1994, EPA issued the Phase II SPCC revisions, which increase the preparedness and response capabilities of onshore facilities through an expanded regulatory framework. The revisions incorporate the new requirements added by the OPA that direct facility owners or operators to prepare, and in some cases submit to the Federal government, plans for responding to a worst-case discharge of oil.

Facility owners or operators that are SPCC-regulated facilities must determine whether they could *substantially* harm the environment in the event of an oil spill. Owners or operators of *substantial harm facilities* are required to prepare and submit a Facility Response Plan to EPA. A Facility Response Plan is a separate document

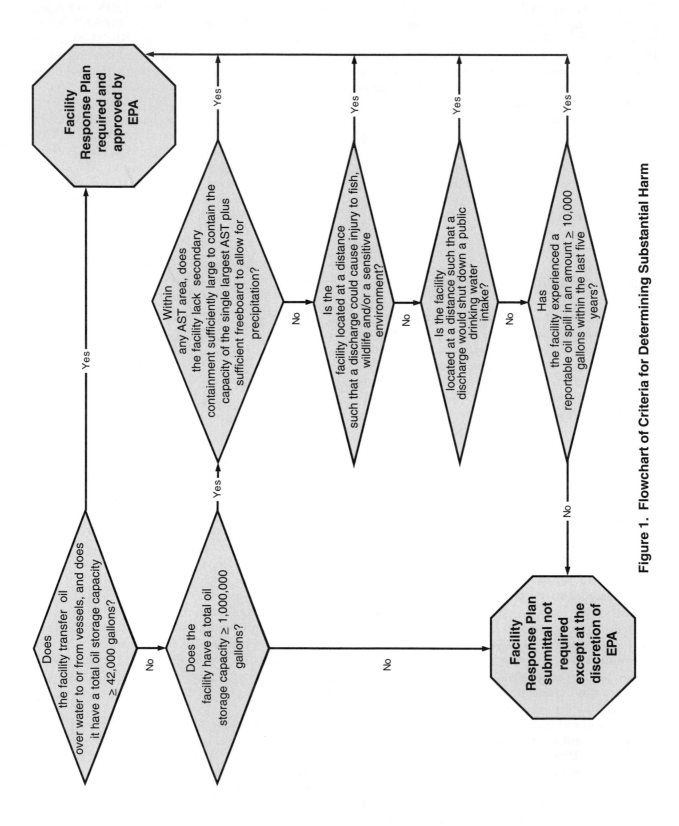

Figure 1. Flowchart of Criteria for Determining Substantial Harm

from a SPCC Plan. A facility is defined as a *substantial harm facility* if it meets the following criteria (see also Figure 1):

- The facility transfers oil over water to or from vessels, and has a total oil storage capacity of at least 42,000 gallons; or

- The total oil storage capacity at the facility is at least 1 million gallons and at least one of the following criteria is met:

    - The facility's secondary containment for each AST area will not hold the volume of the largest single AST plus sufficient freeboard for precipitation.

    - A discharge could injure fish, wildlife, or sensitive environments.

    - A discharge would shut down operations at a public drinking water intake.

    - The facility has had a reportable spill of at least 10,000 gallons within the last five years.

The sections below describe a SPCC Plan and a Facility Response Plan.

SPCC Plans

The oil pollution prevention regulations require each owner or operator of a regulated facility to have a fully prepared and implemented SPCC Plan. A SPCC Plan is a detailed, facility-specific, written description of how a facility's operations comply with the prevention guidelines in the oil pollution prevention regulation. These guidelines include such measures as secondary containment, facility drainage, dikes or barriers, sump and collection systems, retention ponds, curbing, tank corrosion protection systems, and liquid level devices.

The 2002 changes to the rule clarify applicability to owners or operators that use or store oil. A registered professional engineer must certify the SPCC Plan. Facilities must implement the SPCC Plan, including carrying out the spill prevention and control measures established for the type of facility or operations, such as measures for containing a spill (*e.g.*, berms). In the event that a facility cannot implement containment measures, the facility must develop and incorporate a strong spill contingency plan into the SPCC Plan. In addition, facility owners or operators must conduct

employee training on the contents of the SPCC Plan. Facilities must prepare an SPCC Plan within six months of the date they commence operations, and they must implement the plan within one year of the date operations begin. As indicated above, facilities in operation on or before August 16, 2002, must amend the SPCC Plan for the facility by August 17, 2004, and implement the plan by February 18, 2005.

The effect of the 2002 SPCC rule is expected to be positive. According to EPA, the changes will reduce the number of facilities regulated by about 55,000 and reduce the overall regulatory burden. Highlights of nine key changes in the 2002 SPCC rule are as follows:

- Exempts completely buried storage tanks that are subject to the technical requirements of the UST regulations in 40 CFR 280 or 281

- Exempts portions of certain facilities or any facility used exclusively for wastewater treatment or associated with oil production. This exemption does not apply to production, recycling, or recovery of oil

- Establishes a *de minimis* container size of 55 gallons or less

- Establishes an aggregate above-ground storage capacity threshold of greater than 1,320 gallons and removes the 660-gallon-in-one-container threshold

- Revises the trigger for submitting information on spills at SPCC-regulated facilities to EPA. Facilities are now required to submit SPCC plans after having two discharges (more than 42 gallons each) in any 12-month period

- Allows deviations from most rule provisions (with the exception of secondary containment requirements) when equivalent environmental protection is provided

- Provides for a flexible plan format, but requires a cross-reference showing that all regulatory requirements are met

- Clarifies rule applicability to the storage and operational use of oil

- Increases the review frequency to five years from three years

There is no rigid format for a SPCC Plan. Each SPCC Plan is unique. The regulations in 40 CFR 112.7 require certain elements to be included in the plan. If an alternative format is used, it must be an equivalent plan that meets all of the applicable requirements. In addition, a section must be included that cross-references the location of requirements listed in 40 CFR 112.7 with the equivalent requirements in the equivalent plan.

Three areas that must be addressed in the SPCC Plan are: (1) operating procedures implemented by the facility to prevent oil spills, (2) control measures installed to prevent oil from entering navigable waters or adjoining shorelines, and (3) countermeasures to contain, clean up, and mitigate the effects of an oil spill that has an impact on navigable waters or adjoining shorelines. Other important elements of an SPCC Plan include, but are not limited to, the following:

Management Approval. A signed statement of an individual with the authority to commit management and the financial resources necessary to implement the plan. This individual is typically the facility manager.

Professional Engineer Certification. A signed and certified statement of a registered professional engineer. The certifying engineer does not have to be registered in the state in which the facility is located, unless required by specific State law. The registered professional engineer must be familiar with the provisions of the oil pollution prevention regulations, and must have examined the facility. The engineer's name, registration number, and state of registration must be included as part of the SPCC Plan. In addition, the engineer's seal must be affixed to the SPCC Plan as part of the certification.

Oil Spills. A facility that has experienced one or more spill events within 12 months prior to the effective date of 40 CFR 112.7(a) should include a written description of each such spill, corrective action taken, and plans for preventing reoccurrence.

Description of Physical Layout and Facility Diagram. A detailed description of the physical layout of the facility that should include a facility diagram showing the location and contents of each container, completely buried tanks, and transfer stations and connecting pipes. The description also must include the following: (1) the type of oil in each container and the storage capacity; (2) the

discharge prevention measures; (3) discharge or drainage controls; (4) countermeasures for discharge discovery, response, and cleanup; (5) methods of disposal or recovered materials; and (6) a contact list and phone numbers for the facility response coordinator, the National Response Center, contracted cleanup contractors, and other Federal, State, and local agencies who must be contacted if a discharge occurs.

Oil Spill Predictions. Predictions of the direction, rate of flow, and total quantity of oil that could be discharged where experience indicates a potential for equipment failure.

Facility Inspections. A record of inspections signed by the appropriate supervisor or inspector and kept for a period of three years.

Personnel and Training. Designation of a person who is accountable for discharge prevention and who reports to facility management. At a minimum, oil-handling personnel must be trained in the operation and maintenance of equipment to prevent discharges; discharge procedure protocols; applicable pollution control laws, rules, and regulations; general facility operations; and the contents of the SPCC Plan. Discharge prevention briefings for oil-handling personnel should be conducted at least once a year.

Security Measures. Identification of measures for protecting the facility from trespassers who potentially could cause a release or spill.

Five-year SPCC Plan Review. Some changes can be made without the review and approval of a registered professional engineer (*e.g.*, name changes of facility personnel), but other changes require the review and approval of a registered professional engineer (*e.g.*, new spill control devices, changes in processes).

Appropriate Secondary Containment or Diversionary Structures. A description of containment and/or diversionary structures or equipment to prevent discharged oil from reaching navigable waters. (For on-shore facilities, one of the following should be used at a minimum: dikes, berms, or retaining walls; curbing; culverting, gutters, or other drainage systems; weirs, booms, or other barriers; spill diversion ponds; retention ponds; or sorbent materials.)

Facility Response Plans

A *Facility Response Plan* (FRP) is required by facilities that meet the definition of substantial harm. The FRP addresses how a facility will respond to a worst-case oil discharge and a substantial threat of such a discharge. A worst-case oil discharge is the largest foreseeable discharge in adverse weather conditions, as determined using worksheets supplied in the regulations (40 CFR 112, Appendix E). The facilities that must prepare and submit an FRP are a small, high-risk subset of the SPCC regulated community. An FRP includes

- An Emergency Response Action Plan (ERAP)

- Facility information

- Emergency response information such as a list of authorities to notify, response equipment list, schedule of response equipment testing and deployment, list of personnel, evacuation plans, and description of each individual's duties

- A hazard evaluation, including hazard identification, vulnerability analysis, analysis of oil spill potential, and reportable oil spill history

- A small, medium, and worst-case discharge scenario

- A description of discharge detection systems

- A description of plan implementation

- A schedule and description of self-inspection, drills, exercises, and response training

- Diagrams of the facility, including storage tanks, transfer areas, containment systems, and hazardous material storage areas

- A description of security measures, including automatic and manual measures

An *Emergency Response Action Plan* is the heart of an FRP. The ERAP contains all of the information that is needed to combat a spill, organized for easy reference. The following information should be included in the ERAP:

- Information on the individual who certified the plan

- Emergency notification phone list

- Spill response notification form

- List of response equipment and its location

- Schedule of response equipment testing and deployment drills

- List of response team members

- Evacuation plan

- Description of the response resources for small, medium, and worst-case discharges

- Facility diagram

The worst-case discharge volume is an essential element of an FRP. It is calculated on a facility's oil storage capacity, not a facility's inventory. The calculation method typically uses the oil storage capacity of the largest tank or a permanently manifolded group of tanks within a secondary containment area. Facilities without secondary containment must use the capacity of all storage tanks.

Besides planning for a worst-case scenario, facility owners and operators must plan for small and medium spills. A small spill is one whose volume is 2,100 gallons or less, provided the amount is less than the worst-case discharge. A medium spill is greater than 2,100 gallons and less than or equal to 36,000 gallons or 10 percent of the largest tank's capacity, whichever is less. Addressing the medium-spill scenario is necessary only if the medium-spill volume is less than the worst-case discharge.

In certain cases, the information required in an FRP is similar to that contained in a SPCC Plan. In such cases, owners or operators may photocopy the information for the FRP. The FRP does not need to be certified by a registered professional engineer, but the facility owner or operator must certify that the information in the plan is accurate.

Facility owners or operators must demonstrate access to the required response personnel and equipment to respond effectively to identified spill scenarios. If the FRP relies on facility-owned equipment, an inventory must be provided. Facilities that rely on other arrangements must include evidence of contracts.

The 2002 SPCC rule change affects whether or not a facility needs to prepare and maintain an FRP and how the worst-case discharge planning levels are calculated. Certain facilities may no longer meet the storage capacity thresholds for the substantial harm criteria, while other facilities might have to develop an FRP. According to the new rule, the regulation no longer applies to the following:

- Completely buried tanks that are subject to UST technical requirements in 40 CFR 280 and 281

- Containers with a storage capacity of less than 55 gallons

- Portions of certain facilities or any facility used exclusively for wastewater treatment

Vessel and Offshore Oil Pollution Prevention Regulations

Owners and operators of tank vessels and offshore facilities are required to prepare and submit for approval response plans similar in content to an FRP. The tank vessel and offshore FRPs must be consistent with the NCP and Area Contingency Plans. Tank vessel and offshore FRPs must identify the qualified personnel having full authority to implement removal actions, and the plans must require immediate communications between Federal officials and private removal contractors.

The tank vessel and offshore facility must identify and ensure by contract or other approved means the availability of private personnel and equipment necessary to remove to the maximum extent practical a worst-case discharge and to mitigate or prevent a substantial threat of such a discharge. A worst-case discharge for a vessel is a discharge of its entire cargo in adverse weather conditions. For an offshore facility, the worst-case discharge is the largest foreseeable discharge in adverse weather conditions.

The response plans must also describe training, equipment testing, periodic unannounced drills, and response actions of vessel and offshore facility personnel to mitigate or prevent the discharge. The plans must be updated periodically and be resubmitted for approval for each significant change.

The OPA requires licensing and drug and alcohol testing for new applicants, renewal applicants, and current holders of merchant marine pilots licenses. Holders of licenses are tested for drugs and alcohol on a random, periodic, reasonable cause, and post-accident basis. The terms of merchant marine pilot licenses were changed to five years. The OPA also added additional grounds for suspensions and revocations of licenses. For instance, the individual in charge of a vessel may be relieved of command if found to be under the influence of alcohol or drugs and incapable of commanding the vessel.

Tank vessels are required to have a double hull. This requirement for new vessels went into effect immediately after OPA was adopted. A phaseout schedule for existing vessels began in 1995 and runs until 2015. Older and larger vessels are retired first.

Oil Spill Liability Trust Fund

Under the Oil Pollution Act of 1990, the owner or operator of a facility from which oil is discharged (also known as the *responsible party*) is liable for the costs associated with the cleanup of the spill and any damages resulting from the spill. The EPA's first priority is that the responsible parties clean up their own oil releases. However, when the responsible party is unknown or refuses to pay, funds from the Oil Spill Liability Trust Fund (Fund) can be used to cover removal costs and/or damages resulting from discharges of oil. The Fund is administered by the USCG's National Pollution Funds Center (NPFC).

The Fund can provide up to $1 billion for any one oil pollution incident, including up to $500 million for the initiation of natural resource damage assessments and claims in connection with any single incident. The main uses of Fund expenditures are:

- State access for removal actions

- Payments to Federal, State, and Indian tribe trustees to carry out natural resource damage assessments and restorations

- Payment of claims for uncompensated removal costs and damages

- Research and development and other specific appropriations

Penalties

Under the Clean Water Act, as amended by the OPA, EPA has greater authority to pursue administrative, judicial, and criminal penalties for violations of the regulations and for discharges of oil and hazardous substances. Under the new penalty system, three different courses of action are available to EPA in the event of a spill: (1) an administrative penalty may be assessed against the facility, (2) a judicial penalty may be assessed against the facility in the Federal court system, or (3) a criminal action may be sought against the facility in the Federal court system.

EPA may assess administrative penalties against oil or hazardous substance dischargers as well as facility owners or operators who fail to comply with oil pollution prevention regulation. The administrative penalty amounts that violators must pay have increased under the OPA, and a new system of administrative penalties was created based on two classes of violations. Class I violations may be assessed an administrative penalty up to $10,000 per violation, but no more than $25,000 total. The more serious Class II violations may be assessed up to $10,000 per day, but no more than $125,000 total. However, a facility that has been assessed a Class II administrative penalty cannot be subject to a civil judicial action for the same violation.

Judicial penalties may be assessed against facility owners or operators who discharge oil or hazardous substances, who fail to properly carry out a cleanup ordered by EPA, or who fail to comply with the oil pollution prevention regulation. Courts may assess judicial penalties for discharges as high as $25,000 per day or up to $1,000 per barrel of oil spilled (or $1,000 per reportable quantity of hazardous substance discharged). For those discharges that result from gross negligence or willful misconduct, the penalties increase to no less than $100,000 and up to $3,000 per barrel of oil spilled (or per unit of reportable quantity of hazardous substance discharged). Owners and operators of facilities that fail to comply with an EPA removal order may be subject to civil judicial penalties up to $25,000 per day, or three times the cost incurred by the Oil Spill Liability Trust Fund, as a result of their failure to comply. Finally, if the facility fails to comply with its EPA-approved SPCC plan, the civil judicial penalty may reach $25,000 per day of violation.

EPA may pursue criminal penalties against facility owners or operators who fail to notify the appropriate Federal agency of a discharge of oil. Specifically, under the Clean Water Act, the Federal government can impose a penalty up to a maximum of $250,000 for an individual or $500,000 for a corporation, and a maximum prison sentence of five years.

Conclusion

The OPA sets out general requirements for the progressive oil pollution prevention, and a liability and compensation regime. The OPA took well over a decade to develop and enact, and will take years to implement fully. With the OPA's emphasis on planning, preparedness, and prevention, the need to respond to worst-case incidents and those posing substantial threats to public health and the environment should be reduced. The OPA's true effectiveness will be measured over time by the absence of oil spill catastrophes and near-misses, and by the reduction in the thousands of smaller spills that occur each year.

Bibliography

Bergeson, Lynn L. "EPA Issues New Spill Prevention Control and Countermeasure Rule." *Pollution Engineering*. 34 (10): October, 2002.

Gokare, Manjunath A. and J. Ronald Lawson. "Preparing for Disaster." *Industrial Wastewater*. p. 21, November/December 1994.

"Oil Pollution Prevention and Response; Non-Transportation-Related Onshore and Offshore Facilities." *Federal Register*. 67 (17 July 2002): 47042–47152.

Olney, Austin. *Environmental Law Handbook,* 14th ed. Rockville, MD: Government Institutes, Inc., 1997.

Openchowski, Charles. "Federal Implementation of the Oil Pollution Act of 1990." *Environmental Law Reporter*. Vol. (21): p. 10605, October 1991.

Rogers, William H., Jr. *Environmental Law,* 2nd ed. St. Paul, MN: West Publishing Co., 1994.

Russell, Randle V. "The Oil Pollution Act of 1990: Its Provisions, Intent, and Effects." *Environmental Law Reporter*. Vol. (21): p. 10119, March 1991.

"SPCC Deadlines Extended." *The Environmental Manager's Compliance Advisor*. Issue Number 591: May 19, 2003. p 1.

Internet Resources

<http://www.epa.gov/superfund/programs/er/index.htm> (Environmental Protection Agency. Emergency Response Program. Homepage)

<http://www.epa.gov/oilspill/spccrule.htm> (Environmental Protection Agency. Oil Program. Revised Spill Prevention, Control and Countermeasure Rule)

Mark L. Bricker *is a Senior Environmental Engineer at CH2M HILL's Bellevue, Washington, office where he helps private industry clients meet regulatory requirements while achieving their operational needs and objectives. Mr. Bricker has more than 26 years of environmental and engineering experience with a former Fortune 500 company and as a consultant. Mr. Bricker has been involved with hazardous materials management for 14 years. He directed corporate oversight of an environmental management program for operations in five states, and has worked closely with State and Federal regulatory agencies to negotiate permit and regulatory compliance issues. Mr. Bricker has conducted several environmental due diligence investigations for major merger and acquisition transactions. He also has extensive negotiation experience in a regulatory and business setting. He has conducted environmental assessment and compliance audits at client-owned sites and third-party disposal facilities nationwide.*

CHAPTER 39

Ground Water

Michael R. Matthews, PE, PG, CHMM[*]

Ground Water

For many hazardous materials managers, ground water is the medium of most interest and concern. This resource is used as a source of drinking water for humans and livestock, for irrigation, and for numerous industrial applications throughout the country. Therefore, the degradation of ground water has the potential of impacting the health and well-being of people, but plants and animals can also be affected.

The degradation of ground water can last for centuries, and contaminants can move many miles from the original source of release. The potential impact of ground water contamination can be devastating. It behooves any environmental manager to understand the basic concepts of ground water occurrences, movement, and quality.

Source of Ground Water

It is difficult to determine the beginning or the end of the *hydrologic cycle*, the constant movement of water by precipitation, overland runoff, and evaporation. For our discussion on ground water we must focus on precipitation (rain, snow, or hail). Rainwater that percolates into the soil is the

---

[*] This chapter, originally published in the first edition of the *Desk Reference* was revised for this edition by Adriane P. Borgias, CHMM.

ultimate primary source of ground water. Rainfall varies with the seasons, and in the United States most ground water percolation occurs during the winter months. Any particular rainfall droplet may suffer a variety of fates. It may: 1) run off of the soil surface and coalesce with other runoff to form streams or rivers, 2) run directly into lakes or reservoirs, 3) evaporate directly into the atmosphere, 4) infiltrate into the soil and become part of soil moisture, 5) be absorbed by plants, or 6) percolate into the ground, through soil, and become part of a ground water aquifer. Higher evaporation rates, water storage, and plant uptake and transpiration processes use a major portion of spring, summer, and fall rainfall.

Rainfall that has entered the earth is stored in aquifers. An **aquifer** is any geologic formation capable of holding water in sufficient quantities to produce *free water*. **Free water** is water not incorporated into the soil as moisture. Aquifers can be unconsolidated soil or rock formations. The area where rainfall infiltrates through the soil and percolates down into the aquifer is known as a *recharge area*. Recharge areas are very difficult to map, even though the concept is relatively simple. Man can contribute to and influence the recharge process by influencing recharge conditions (*e.g.*, land use activities) and by contributing to ground water contamination.

Just as water can enter the ground and become stored in aquifers, it can also leave the subsurface and discharge at points or areas where the aquifer contacts the surface terrain. In the eastern United States, nearly all streams and rivers normally are discharge points for ground water. This discharge is what keeps rivers flowing during summer drought conditions. Springs and artesian wells are also discharges of ground water to the surface. In some regions streams can be recharge as well as discharge areas (*e.g.*, carbonate bedrock areas).

Aquifer Characteristics

An aquifer is any geologic formation that contains water. An aquifer is not the water itself! Aquifers can be sand, soil, gravel, or porous stone. Beneath any one land surface location there can exist multiple aquifers, each with different characteristics. Impervious layers called *aquitards* separate these aquifers. The first aquifer that is usually encountered consists of unconsolidated materials. These unconsolidated materials include both surface and subsurface soil. Surbsurface soil includes silt, sand, and gravel—typical aquifer materials. Beneath the soil is bedrock. Going deeper into the earth one finds changes in geology. Each geologic change can define a different aquifer with different characteristics.

The United States Geological Survey classifies aquifers as excellent (water exists in quantities for large users), good (water is sufficient for domestic use), or poor (the water that is present is not capable of being pumped or yields less than 5 gallons per minute, dries up, *etc.*). Figure 1 illustrates a multiaquifer system.

Saturated and Unsaturated Zones

Directly beneath the soil surface lies an area in which the soil particles are surrounded in varying degrees by air and water. This area is called the **unsaturated zone** (or sometimes the **vadose zone**). Beneath this unsaturated zone is an area where soil particles are completely surrounded by water and no air is present. This is called the **saturated zone** and makes up the aquifer itself. The boundary between the unsaturated and saturated zones, called the **potentiometric surface,** is the area where the pressure exerted by the surface of the water table is equal to the atmospheric pressure at that depth.

Unconsolidated Aquifers

Unconsolidated material (soil) can be stream-deposited material (alluvium), wind deposits (sand dunes), glacial outwash, or deeply weathered bedrock. Water is present in and around the particles of soil and rock in the aquifer.

Consolidated Aquifers

Unconsolidated materials become rocks through a process called *lithification* (compaction and cementation). Sedimentary aquifers are divided into carbonate (limestone or dolomite) and non-carbonate (*e.g.*, sandstone or shale) aquifers.

In carbonate aquifers, water is present in the enlarged solution cavities. These cavities vary

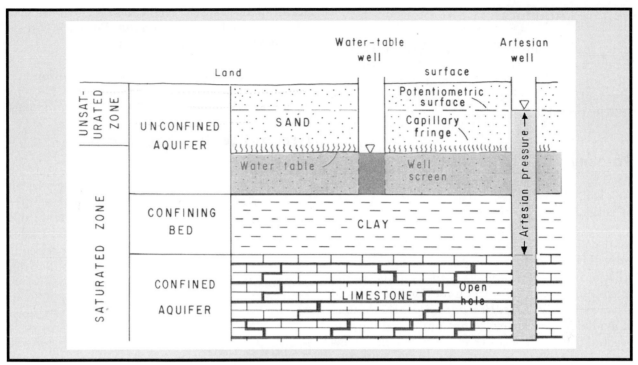

Source: Heath 1998

Figure 1. Aquifers and Confining Beds

greatly in size and length. Different types of carbonates dissolve differently. Some are very large and form huge cave systems.

Consolidated noncarbonate aquifers hold water in the spaces around the soil and rock particles. How much water the aquifer can hold depends on the degree of cementation and fracturing that is present in the aquifer and the size of the particles in the rock.

Sedimentary rocks such as sandstone hold water around the sand grains. Igneous and metamorphic rocks generally do not contain much water unless they are fractured from folding or faulting activities. When folding or faulting occurs, rocks fracture. Water can accumulate in the fractures and flow along the fracture zone. Lava can have coarse-grained material deposited between flows and these flows can be interconnected by cooling fractures into a very complex water storage pattern.

Unconfined Aquifers

Unconfined aquifers are also called **water table aquifers**. Water table aquifers are usually in unconsolidated material. The water table rises and

falls seasonally. Water tables tend to rise in winter when more rainfall infiltrates and tend to fall in summer due to less rainfall infiltration.

Movement of water is by gravity. Water is going to flow downhill. The water table surface can respond to changes in atmospheric pressure, since the void spaces above the water table are directly exposed to the atmosphere through interconnected spaces and pores in the soil. Water table aquifers are usually nearest the land surface and are most often monitored for contamination.

Confined (Artesian) Aquifers

The defining feature of these aquifers is a confining bed that overlies the water-bearing formation. The water beneath this confining layer is under pressure and tends toward equilibrium with atmospheric pressure and recharge potential. The imaginary point where this balance occurs is called the *potentiometric* or *piezometric surface*. This is where the term *piezometer* comes from. A piezometer is installed primarily for the measurement of water table elevations, whereas a monitoring well is intended for sampling. Both are essentially the same with minor construction differences.

Perched Aquifers

In a perched aquifer, percolating water is held up locally by some type of confining bed (hard pan, clay layer, *etc*.). This can be a permanent or seasonal situation and can be confused with the true water table.

Porosity

Any soil, sand, gravel, or fractured rock consists of solid particles and empty spaces (voids) in between the particles. The ratio of voids to the total volume of a soil or rock is called its **total porosity**. Porosity is expressed as a decimal fraction or a percentage. Porosity tells us the maximum amount of water a rock or soil can hold if it is saturated. **Effective porosity** is the volume of available pore space in the aquifer, taking into account the void spaces that are too small to pass water or unavailable for fluid flow. The effective porosity of an aquifer is always less the total porosity. Typical values of porosity are presented in the following table:

Material	Porosity (percent)
Unconsolidated Deposits	
Gravel	25-40
Sand	25-50
Silt	35-50
Clay	40-70
Rocks	
Fractured basalt	5-50
Karst limestone	5-50
Sandstone	5-30
Limestone, dolomite	0-20
Shale	0-10
Fractured crystalline rock	0-10
Dense crystalline rock	0-5

(Freeze and Cherry 1979)

Related characteristics of aquifers are the terms specific yield and specific retention. **Specific yield** is the volume of water that will drain by gravity from a specific volume of rock or soil. **Specific retention** is the volume of water that is retained as a coating on soil or rock particles after gravity draining. Both specific yield and specific retention are expressed as percentages. Porosity can be described by the following equation.

Porosity = Specific Yield + Specific Retention

Ground Water Movement

The flow of water through an aquifer is governed by several physical characteristics of the aquifer matrix. These include porosity, permeability, transmissivity, and hydraulic conductivity. Under ideal conditions (unconsolidated, homogeneous matrices such as sand or gravel soils) the flow can be estimated by Darcy's Law.

Darcy's Law

The utility of Darcy's Law is that is can be used to calculate the velocity and travel times of pollutants in ground water. The general formula is usually expressed as

$$Q = KA \, (H_1 - H_2) \, / \, L \tag{1}$$

Where:

Q = discharge (gallons or cubic feet/unit of time)

K = the hydraulic conductivity (a measure of the aquifer's ability to transmit water)

A = cross sectional area (the area the water moves through horizontally)

$(H_1 - H_2)/L$ = a dimensionless friction or head pressure loss term. $(H_1 - H_2)$ is the difference in head (elevation), usually expressed in feet. L is the lineal distance between the H_1 and H_2 locations.

Hydraulic conductivity (K) is a measure of how quickly a fluid will pass through the aquifer. Hydraulic conductivity takes into account the properties of the fluid (density, viscosity) as well as the aquifer materials and is expressed in units of length/unit time.

If the effective porosity is known and the hydraulic conductivity can be determined, then the average ground water velocity can be calculated using the equation:

$$\overline{V} = Q/n_e A = (K/n_e)(H_1 - H_2)/L \qquad (2)$$

Where n_e = the effective porosity.

The most important K value to remember is 10^{-7} cm/sec (clay). This value has typically been selected for protection of the ground water resource in many regulations because it represents relatively impermeable conditions. The finer the material, the smaller the K value.

Permeability is another measure of how easily a fluid will move through the aquifer. Unlike hydraulic conductivity, which accounts for the properties of both the fluid and the aquifer materials, permeability is only a function of the aquifer materials. While the two terms are very similar and often confused, permeability is a laboratory-derived value and hydraulic conductivity is a field-derived parameter. Vertical permeability is usually less than horizontal permeability, and it is important to recognize this when assessing ground water movement.

Transmissivity

The ***transmissivity*** of an aquifer is a measure of its capacity to deliver water. Transmissivity is the product of the hydraulic conductivity and the aquifer thickness.

Example

Compute ground water velocity through a sandy soil matrix that is between a well and a nearby stream. Water level in a well 400' (L) from stream is 1480' MSL (H_1). Water level in the stream is 1475' (H_2). Soil in the area is sand (K = 100 ft/day). Effective porosity of the soil is 40%.

$$\text{Flow rate} = \overline{V} = Q/n_e A$$
$$Q/n_e A = K(H_1 - H_2)/n_e L$$
$$= 100 \text{ ft/day}(1480-1475)/(400 \times 0.40)$$
$$= 3.1 \text{ ft/day}$$

$$T = Kb \qquad (3)$$

Where:

T = Transmissivity

K = Hydraulic Conductivity

b = Aquifer Thickness (variable thickness)

Typical K Values		
	cm/sec	ft/day
Gravel	100–0.1	3×10^5–300
Sand	1–10^{-5}	3000–0.03
Clay	10^{-5}–10^{-10}	0.03–3×10^{-7}

Transmissivity in a particular aquifer varies in time and space. In an unconfined aquifer, the transmissivity is almost always seasonally variable throughout the aquifer. In a confined aquifer, transmissivity is constant at a particular point in the aquifer as long as both layers are confining, but varies from place to place within the aquifer.

Unconsolidated Aquifers

Water flows by gravity downhill. In unconsolidated aquifers, this movement is in and around the rock and soil particles. This movement can be estimated using Darcy's Law. Darcy's Law is usually valid in unconsolidated materials (water table aquifers), but is not valid where aquifer characteristics are not uniform (carbonate aquifers or water movement in rock fractures).

Consolidated Aquifers

Consolidated aquifers are much more difficult to measure and estimate flow. Movement in certain formations that may have relatively uniform thickness can sometimes be assessed in a manner similar to unconsolidated aquifers (*e.g.*, sandstone aquifers). However, ground water movement is more often in the fractures or solution cavities of these rocks. The fractures are not uniform. The fractures vary in width and length. Fractures and solution cavities are not necessarily continuous and can somewhat randomly change directions.

In monitoring ground water movement in consolidated aquifers, the location of fractures, the size of openings, length of the fracture or cavity, and the pattern of the fractures or cavities are of vital importance in determining where ground water will move and how fast it will move.

Water movement in fractures and solution cavities is also governed by gravity. Water will move fairly quickly as it flows through the fracture or void, much like water flows in a pipe or river. Water movement in fractures and solution cavities can move great distances in relatively short periods of time.

Sinkholes

The formation of sinkholes is a process that takes a long time. Carbonate rocks with cracks or fissures provide openings for rainfall to enter. In general, rainwater is naturally slightly acidic. The acidic water dissolves the calcium carbonate and forms a *solution cavity*. With time this cavity becomes bigger (similar to cave formations). Once the cavity is big enough it can no longer support the soil above it and the soil collapses (sometimes catastrophically–a common occurrence in Florida).

Water enters from openings at the surface and is directly recharged (injected) into the aquifer without the benefit of filtration. People with wells connected to these water sources can see nearly instant changes to water quality during storm events as sediment is washed into their drinking water. Pollutants and other debris can enter just as easily.

Characteristics of Aquifer Ground Water Flow

Hydraulic conductivity measurements in the laboratory (usually taken from field samples) do not always equal actual field conditions. Natural conditions are subject to varying conditions that are not easy to define.

In addition there are many different types of flow. One-dimensional flow obeys Darcy's Law. This flow can be steady but more typically varies with time

and is considered unsteady (*e.g.*, water tables rise and fall seasonally). Water movement can also be radial. This is best understood by imagining movement toward a large pumping ground water well. This movement can also be steady or unsteady depending on how much water is pumped and when it is pumped. Large ground water withdrawals by industry or agriculture can influence ground water movement and must be considered when assessing ground water flow patterns.

The boundaries between different types of aquifers impact ground water movement in different ways. All aquifers have boundaries and are interconnected. Water percolates down through unconsolidated aquifers until it reaches bedrock. What it does next depends on the type of bedrock it encounters.

If shale or slate is encountered, the water may not infiltrate and may move along the soil and bedrock interface until it discharges at a seep or seepage. If limestone is encountered, the water will move along the rock surface until a solution cavity is encountered where it will enter and follow the cavities until discharged.

In consolidated rocks that have been folded or faulted, the infiltrating water could flow along the bedrock surface until a subsurface structure (*e.g.*, fault) causes the water to follow it preferentially down a path of less resistance.

Boundary conditions between aquifers can and do modify flow. Sometimes these boundaries act as recharge points to lower aquifers and discharge points from aquifers located above the lower aquifers.

When geology changes occur, so do aquifer characteristics. Geologic features also are frequently hydraulically connected with streams. Streams that act as discharge points for ground water are called **gaining streams**. Sometimes (particularly in carbonate areas) streams can actually help recharge the ground water. These are called **losing streams**.

Effects of the Water Table

Depth to ground water is measured from the ground surface and is correlated to a set elevation scheme (mean sea level). Management of the water

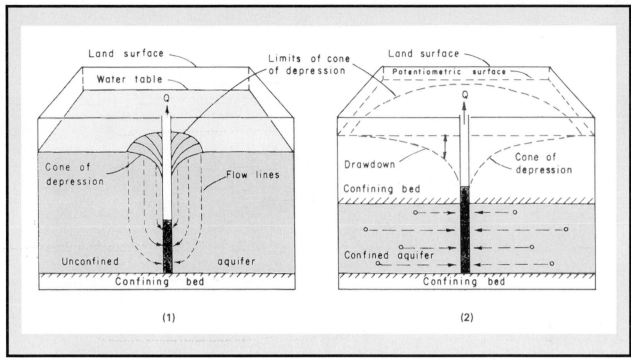

Source: Heath 1998

Figure 2. Cone of Depression

table is useful in controlling ground water contamination. When ground water is removed from an unconfined aquifer by a pumping well (*e.g.*, irrigation), the water withdrawal depresses the water table around the well. This water table depression is referred to as a ***cone of depression*** See Figure 2-(1). for the geometric shape it assumes around the well.

If the water is being pumped from a confined aquifer, then the potentiometric surface of the aquifer would be depressed even though there would be no noticeable depression in the water table. This is illustrated in Figure 2-(2).

Since water flows downhill due to gravity, a cone of depression can be used to artificially control ground water movement toward a pumping well. This is particularly useful in the management of contaminants that tend to float on the surface of the water table due to being less dense than water. If contaminants move toward the pumping well they can be easily recovered and removed from the aquifer.

The cone of depression of large well fields can be very large, and impact the movement of ground water for miles in all directions from the wellhead if the removal of water is steady and of great quantity. This condition exists around the city of Memphis, Tennessee, which utilizes ground water for its drinking water. The area of ground water in an aquifer that is influenced by the removal of ground water is referred to as the *zone of influence* for a specific well.

Visual images of the top of water tables can be depicted in ***potentiometric maps*** (Figure 3). These maps are a visual image of the water table. Flow direction is determined by first mapping the elevation of the water at numerous locations. Contour lines called ***isopleths*** are drawn between points of equal ground water elevations. The flow direction is determined by a perpendicular line drawn from the isopleth with the highest elevation, so that the line intersects the next highest isopleth perpendicularly. This process is repeated from isopleth to isopleth until the flow direction is determined.

Ground Water Quality

The primary origin of ground water is rainfall. Therefore, the original quality of ground water is essentially equal to the quality of the rain as it

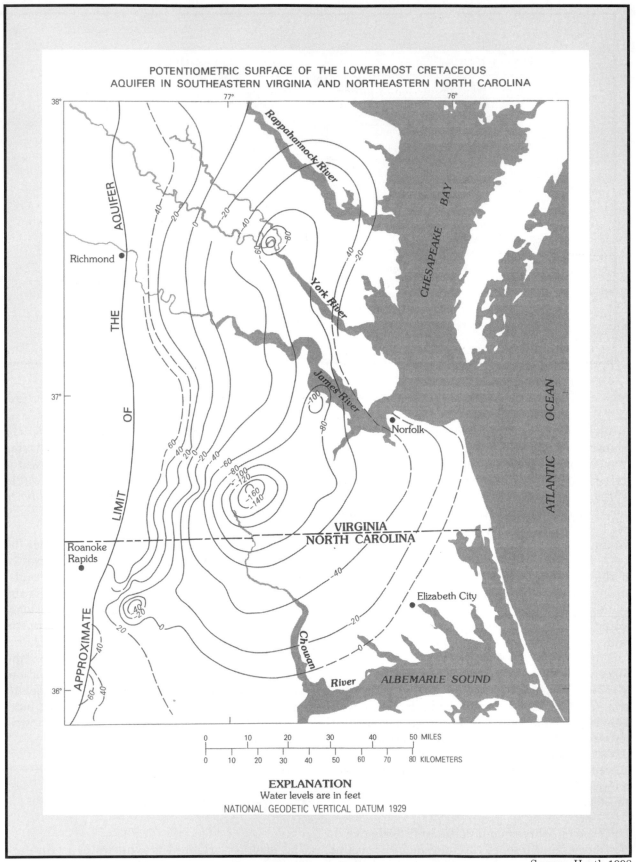

Source: Heath 1998

Figure 3. Potentiometric Map

enters an aquifer. Characteristics of rainfall generally are that: 1) it will act as a solvent because it is slightly acidic; 2) its density is about 1.0; 3) it has a quality that is determined primarily by the dissolved gases (CO_2, SO_2, N_2, O_2) and particulates (dust, minerals, dichlorodiphenyltrichloroethane [DDT], *etc.*) picked up as the rain falls through the atmosphere.

Rainfall, with a pH of about 5.7, is naturally slightly acidic. Acid rainfall has a pH much less than natural rainfall (often 4.0–5.0). Because of its acidic nature, rainfall can dissolve rock (primarily carbonate rocks). As the rock dissolves away, the minerals in the rock are released to the ground water and impact its quality. The release of carbonates into ground water acts to buffer ground water and raise its pH to above 7.0. Ground water that has not been in the subsurface for a long time will have a density of around 1.0 (fresh water). The longer ground water is underground the more chance it has to pick up dissolved minerals. The more minerals in the ground water, the more dense it becomes.

Denser liquids tend to sink below lighter liquids. Therefore, fresh water that has few minerals will float on salt water (full of minerals). As a general rule, ground water becomes more saline with depth.

The nature of geologic formations can impart quality changes to ground water. Carbonate formations can release many minerals such as calcium and magnesium to the water. The concentration of calcium and magnesium will determine whether or not ground water is hard or soft. Inert sand and gravel does not tend to dissolve in ground water so these kinds of formations do not have as much of an impact on water quality.

Contaminants in the Subsurface

Vadose (Unsaturated) Zone. In the vadose zone, inorganics are removed from ground water by the cation exchange capacity of the soil. Generally soils have a net negative charge, and this charge attracts and holds metals but it is not necessarily a permanent removal mechanism. Once the charges are matched, further removal ceases.

The net negative charge of soil repels negatively charged inorganics like chlorides, sulfides, cyanides, arsenates, *etc.* These inorganics move quickly and easily through soil. Also, plants take up nutrients in the soil and effectively remove them from the vadose zone.

Biodegradation is the primary means of attenuation for organics in the vadose zone. Movement depends on solubility of the organic in question. Organics tend to leave residues in soil that leach into ground water over long periods of time.

Ground Water. Both organic and inorganic contaminants can be present in ground water. Inorganics are not easily removed from ground water. Ground water is a preservation medium (usually acidic, little oxygen, and cool). These are the very conditions that are used to preserve metals for laboratory analysis. Cations are attenuated sooner than anions, and dilution occurs with dispersion. Hence, the concentration of contaminants typically is reduced with distance from the source.

Processes/Reactions Affecting Pollutants. Nature is dynamic, and numerous factors can change contaminants once introduced into the environment. Geochemical reactions can occur such as: precipitation, acid-base reactions (*e.g.*, limestone-dissolving and releasing minerals), adsorption/desorption, and complexation. There are biochemical processes than can also affect pollutants: organic decomposition, cell synthesis, transpiration (plant use), and respiration (bacteria use). The mechanism of natural attenuation can be used to decrease the concentrations of organic compounds in ground water. This mechanism relies on the biodegradation of organic pollutants by bacteria, converting the organic pollutants in-place to nontoxic products.

Physical processes move and remove pollutants by transporting contaminants to other locations, mixing contaminants and water together, dispersing (scattering) pollutants in the subsurface, filtering out solids, evaporating liquids, and removing pollutants by gas movement. Dilution is usually slow, however, unless ground water is in a large solution cavity where rapid mixing can occur, particularly after a storm event. It has been observed that organic phases can flow at rates greater than or slower than water flow. Pathogens can be transported, filtered, and reproduced in certain situations in a series of biophysical processes.

Plume Migration. Contaminant plume shape and migration can be affected by additional factors that must be considered. Density factors of the pollutants will determine whether the contaminant will settle to the bottom of the aquifer, like DNAPL—dense non-aqueous phase liquids (*e.g.*, polychlorinated biphenyls [PCBs]). Conversely, LNAPL—light non-aqueous phase liquids (*e.g.*, many organics), tend to float on the water table surface, or mix throughout the aquifer.

How the contaminant is released (continuous, spill, or intermittent) will determine the shape of the contaminant plume. Continuous releases over long periods of time become long, tear-shaped plumes as dispersion and mixing spreads the contaminants out with distance. Plumes from spills will move with the ground water in a mass, but leaving a smear of contaminants on soil and rock that it moves through. With time and distance the plume may effectively disappear, due to the various processes noted above and since additional material is not added. Intermittent releases result in plumes where the concentrations of contaminants rise and fall as the mass of the various releases moves past a measuring location.

Regulations

Safe Drinking Water Act

The Safe Drinking Water Act primarily addresses ground water through the underground injection control (UIC) program (40 CFR 144). Injection activities that could allow contaminants to enter underground sources of drinking water are strictly regulated. Injection wells fall into five primary categories. Classes I–IV are wells used for injection of hazardous wastes, solution mining, and oil or gas production and storage. Class V wells include those wells not specifically addressed in Classes I–IV: sinkholes, leach pits, cesspools, and septic systems. Individual and single-family septic systems (serves fewer than 20 persons per day) used solely for sanitary wastes are exempt. This act also provides for protection of sole-source aquifers and wellhead protection.

Resource Conservation and Recovery Act

The Resource Conservation and Recovery Act (RCRA) is extremely comprehensive and includes solid wastes, hazardous wastes, and underground storage tanks. Ground water is addressed in this act in three ways. First, RCRA includes ground water protection requirements that delineate how facilities must be constructed or operated to protect ground water. Second, RCRA mandates resource assessment and characterization of ground water (the collection of ground water movement and quality data). Finally, RCRA requires monitoring of the ground water resources in order to assess compliance with or the effects of waste management activities on ground water.

Comprehensive Environmental Response, Compensation, and Liability Act

The Comprehensive Environmental Response, Compensation, and Liability Act (CERCLA) addresses accidental spills and abandoned hazardous waste sites. CERCLA has many steps that must be performed: 1) Preliminary Assessment/Site Investigation, 2) Remedial Investigation/Feasibility Study, 3) Remedial Design, 4) Remedial Action and 5) Operation and Maintenance.

This act manages ground water primarily through resource assessment/characterization (gather ground water movement and quality data in the early assessment phases) and monitoring of the ground water resources (to assess compliance with Record of Decision or Consent Agreement).

Bibliography

Freeze, R. A., and J. A. Cherry. *Groundwater.* Englewood Cliffs, NJ: Prentice-Hall, Inc. 1979.

Heath, Ralph C. *Basic Ground Water Hydrology.* US Geological Survey Water-Supply Paper 2220. Washington, DC: USGS, 1998.

Michael R. Matthews has spent nearly 25 years working in the environmental field, primarily in solid waste, hazardous waste, and ground water management. His early career (eight years) focused on the design and management of solid waste transportation and disposal systems. For four years he was responsible for Tennessee Valley Authority's ground water quality program (in seven states), and implemented ground water protection programs at the local level. Mr. Matthews has worked in the field of hazardous materials management since 1985. He has been responsible for the management and remediation of numerous hazardous waste sites. He has also performed ground water assessments, remedial investigations/feasibility studies, and risk assessment. Mr. Matthews has experience in Phase I and II site assessments, UST removal and corrective actions, air pollution permitting, RCRA Part B permitting, and other similar work.

The editor would like to acknowledge the contributions of the peer reviewers, Bruce Reiter, Bruce Bowers, Laura Splichal, and Brandan Borgias for their valuable contributions in the revision of the chapter for this edition of the Desk Reference.

CHAPTER 40

Safe Drinking Water Act

A. Thomas Merski, MPH, MBA
John P. Englert, MS, JD

Introduction

Water is among the most basic and important needs to life. A safe source of clean drinking water is vital to any community's ability to live and grow. In the United States, the public has a presumption that our drinking water is safe and potable no matter where we travel. In 1974, the United States Congress passed Public Law 93–523, commonly known as the Safe Drinking Water Act (SDWA), as a means of assuring the public assumption of clean drinking water.

The law has incurred a series of amendments in 1986, 1988 (Lead Contamination Control Act) and 1996 and requires water purveyors to take actions to protect drinking water provided from *public water systems* and their sources: rivers, lakes, reservoirs, springs, and ground water wells. (Note: the SDWA does not regulate private residence wells or systems that serve fewer than twenty-five people). The SDWA applies to every public water system in the United States. The United States Environmental Protection Agency (EPA) estimates that there are currently more than 167,000 public water systems providing water to almost all Americans (EPA, Public Drinking Water Systems Programs).

In comparison to other environmental legislation of this era, the SDWA was designed specifically as a means to protect public health by regulating the nation's public drinking water supply under a set of national standard rules. As such, this law was focused upon water purveyors rather than the industrial community. As a result of the legislative intent, the SDWA is not a law that the average Certified Hazardous Materials Manager (CHMM) will deal with frequently in his or her daily routine (unless the CHMM is working for a water supply system or a company that, due to its facility location, serves as one). Nonetheless, every CHMM needs to be aware of the SDWA; a law that has ancillary regulatory impacts stemming from its basic goal of protection of human health. For example, the SDWA's maximum contaminant levels (MCLs) are frequently used in environmental remediation programs as standards for determining whether ground or surface water requires remediation and as a basis for clean-up standards. Additionally, the SDWA's source protection programs may result in restrictions and controls on activities that are potential causes of contamination in water supply source areas.

Historical Perspective–Why the Protection of Drinking Water?

The history of drinking water protection goes back to ancient times. Ancient peoples understood that good quality drinking water could make the difference between health and illness. The ancient peoples could see, smell and taste the difference in water quality; they just did not understand why one water was different from another. For example, the ancient Romans not only designed and built aqueducts to transport clean water from the mountains into their cities, but they would also store and preserve the quality of drinking water by using silver vessels (an inadvertent bacteriastatic method) (AWWA, Brief History of Drinking Water). This cause and effect logic occurred nearly 2,000 years before 19th century science linked microbes and illness.

Progress in the water purity field was slow even after Louis Pasteur and Robert Koch established the connection of microbes and disease (Barzilay, et al. 1999). States and local governments began establishing public health programs to protect water supplies as a reaction to the large number of typhoid and other disease outbreaks in the early 20th century. These first public health activities took the form of water pollution control programs. The intent was to keep surface water supplies safe

by identifying and limiting sources of sewage contamination. Early water pollution control programs concentrated on keeping raw sewage out of surface waters that were used as drinking water.

Such cause-and-effect relationships were documented in instances such as Dr. John Snow's 1854 investigation into a cholera outbreak in London. Snow was able to link a popular water well located in a poor section of London to an outbreak of cholera because of one woman's preference for water from this particular well. Using elementary tools of epidemiology, he concluded that the woman got sick since she insisted on drinking water from the well in spite of the fact that the well was in a neighborhood across town. Snow used logic to connect the cholera outbreak to the well with to the rich woman's drinking water preference (she had grown up drinking water from that well) and ultimately to the fact that the well was contaminated with sewage. Snow ended the cholera outbreak by simply removing the handle from the well's pump (McMahon and Pugh 1970).

The first drinking water protection programs in the United States were aimed at providing both a sufficient and a safe source of water to a community. Initially, these programs were included in water pollution control activities since they focused both on identifying and maintaining safe sources of drinking water. Poorly treated sewage was the predominant cause of most water-borne disease outbreaks in this timeframe.

The physical treatment of drinking water also began in the late 1800s to the early 1900s. Generally, this occurred in cities with above-average numbers of diarrheal disease outbreaks. The city of Lawrence, Massachusetts is credited with being among the earliest to provide drinking water with sand filtration. The earliest city to use disinfection as a treatment method was Jersey City, New Jersey in 1909 (Barzilay, et al. 1999). By the 1930s, the use of filtration and chlorination had virtually eliminated from the American landscape outbreaks of major waterborne diarrheal diseases such as typhoid and cholera.

Federal regulation and standardization of drinking water quality began in 1914 when the United States Public Health Service (USPHS) set standards for the bacteriological quality of drinking water. Initially, these standards only applied to water systems that provided drinking water for interstate carriers like ships and trains, and only applied to contaminants capable of causing contagious disease. The Public Health Service revised and expanded these standards in 1925, 1946, and 1962. In 1942, the USPHS adopted a set of drinking water requirements that included bacteriological sampling in the distribution system and maximum permissible concentrations for lead, fluoride, arsenic, and selenium. The 1962 USPHS standards regulated twenty-eight substances. Most of the fifty states adopted the Public Health Service standards either as regulations or as guidelines for all of the public water systems within their respective jurisdictions (EPA 2000).

It is notable that the United States drinking water standards were non-enforceable guidelines until the Federal Safe Drinking Water Act of 1974. The only exception to this was the coliform standard, due to its perceived impact on interstate commerce. The SDWA came about in large part because of concerns about organic contaminants, and the law set forth the process that the Environmental Protection Agency would use to set health-based maximum contaminant levels (MCLs) and the aesthetic-related (*i.e.*, taste and appearance) secondary MCLs.

SDWA Terms, Definitions and Implementation

Scope and Objectives of the SDWA

In 1974, Congress established its intent for the SDWA upon making the determination that the country needed a national law to standardize drinking water quality. The purpose of the SDWA is to:

- Ensure the safety of the public drinking water supplies

- Protect groundwater from contamination by controlling activities that could endanger drinking water sources

- Authorize EPA to establish primary and secondary national drinking water standards (*Maximum Contaminant Levels*–MCLs) to be implemented in a collaborative effort with the states and *Maximum Contaminant Level Goals* (MCLGs), that are less than the

MCL and are set at a level where there are no known or anticipated adverse health effects. MCLGs are public health goals and are not enforceable limits.

The SDWA standards of compliance apply to drinking water *at the tap* as delivered by *public water supply systems*. A public water system (PWS) is defined in SDWA §401(4)(a), 42 USC §300f(4)(a) and 40 CFR 141.2 as

. . . a system for the provision to the public of water for human consumption through pipes or other constructed conveyances, if such system has at least fifteen service connections, or regularly serves at least twenty-five individuals.

Thus, individuals with water systems that serve fewer than fifteen connections or less than twenty-five people do not fall under the Federal regulations. States with primacy may of course regulate public water system with fewer connections or which serve fewer individuals. (Note: CHMMs who have responsibility for drinking water facilities at their locations should make it a point to learn about the State drinking water program where the facilities are located. Some states have requirements that are more stringent than the Federal requirements.)

The SDWA divides the term Public Water Systems (PWS) into two distinct subdivisions: *Community Water Systems* (CWSs) and *Non-Community Water Systems* (NCWSs).

- CWSs include any PWS that serves more than twenty-five people or greater than fifteen connections year-round. (For example, a CWS can be either a municipal water system, or water systems that serve a mobile home park or a rural apartment house).

- NCWSs are PWSs that do not serve a permanent resident population. This latter category is further defined, and includes two water system types.

  - The first, *Non-Transient, Non-Community Water Systems* (NTNCWSs) includes systems serving at least twenty-five people (the same people all the time) at least six months of the year, such as some churches, schools, and factories. (Note: CHMMs may be impacted by this PWS definition)

–   The second, *Transient Non-Community Water Systems* (TNCWSs), includes facilities such as roadside stops, commercial campgrounds, hotels, and restaurants that have their own water supplies and serve a transient population for at least sixty days per year (40 CFR 141.2).

History of the SDWA Amendments

From 1974 to 1986 when the SDWA was amended, State regulations varied in many respects. For example, states differed in requirements for ground water disinfection, mandated filtration, monitoring of organic chemicals, and operator certification requirements. The SDWA provided the basis to raise the standards among all states and made drinking water programs consistent nationwide.

Under the 1986 amendments, Congress became more prescriptive and required EPA to regulate eighty-three contaminants within three years after enactment. The Amendments declared the interim standards promulgated in 1975 (which adopted the prior USPHS drinking water standards) to be final and required EPA to require disinfection of all public water supplies as well as filtration for surface water systems. Further, Congress required EPA to regulate an additional twenty-five contaminants (which were to be specified by EPA) every three years and to designate the best available treatment technology for each regulated contaminant. States with primacy were required to adopt regulations and begin enforcing them within eighteen months after EPA's regulations were promulgated. The 1986 SDWA Amendments also required states to establish Well-Head Protection areas to protect ground water sources of drinking water and placed a ban on future use of lead-containing pipes and solder.

Subsequent to the 1986 Amendments was the Lead Contamination Act of 1988. This Act prohibited lead in new water coolers, provided a recall of all water coolers with lead-lined tanks and provided grants to schools to change out the plumbing in water fountains. As a follow-on to this Act, EPA promulgated the Lead and Copper Rule in 1991, which abolished MCLs for lead and copper while establishing an action level for lead at 0.015 ppm (40 CFR 141, Subpart I). This rule requires the sampling of the distribution system to determine the levels of lead and copper. Should a PWS exceed

the MCLG source treatment, further testing and public notification is required.

In 1996 the SDWA was amended again, primarily to deal with concerns about the existence of an overly burdensome regulatory structure brought about by the 1986 Amendments and to impose science-based requirements for the regulation of public water systems. Congress eliminated the 1986 requirement that EPA must regulate an additional twenty-five contaminants every three years. Instead, EPA was allowed to establish a process for selecting contaminants to regulate based on scientific merit. The 1996 Amendments recognized the trade-off between adding chlorine to drinking water to control the impact of acute water-borne microbial concerns and managing the concomitant creation of chlorinated by-products in the disinfection process, some of which are suspected to be cancer-causing agents.

The 1996 Amendments also established several new elements. These provisions included the requirement for states to establish and implement a Source Water Assessment Program for all PWS, requirements for a PWS to provide annual Consumer Confidence Reports and a requirement for Operator Certification. These Amendments also required EPA to: include a cost-benefit analysis when selecting new contaminants for regulation; establish an updated microbial contaminants and disinfection by-products standard; provide public information and consultation; and make minor revisions to the Lead and Copper Rule.

State and Federal Roles in Implementation

The division of labor between EPA and the states is actually a complex alliance under the SDWA. Congress has authorized funds that are provided to the states for implementing the SDWA within their respective borders. This funding is supplementary to funds that a state currently expends in its oversight effort. States must apply to EPA for primary enforcement authority or *primacy*. The term primacy refers to the authority granted to a state to implement SDWA within its jurisdiction.

Primacy is awarded when a state demonstrates that it has the ability and authority to implement SDWA standards that are at least as stringent as

EPA's. (Note: A state may establish drinking water standards that are more stringent than EPA's to reflect water quality conditions within its jurisdiction.) Generally, the agency with primacy has the responsibility is to assure that every PWS within its jurisdiction is testing for contaminants with the required frequency, review plans for water system improvements, conduct on-site inspections and sanitary surveys, provide training and technical assistance, and take enforcement action against water systems not meeting the standard. To date, EPA reports that all states and territories, with the exception of Wyoming and the District of Columbia, have received primacy. EPA also indicates that no Indian tribe has yet applied for and received primacy (EPA, Public Drinking Water Systems Programs).

Under the SDWA, EPA has a great deal of oversight responsibility. First, EPA is charged to oversee those State drinking water programs to which primary enforcement responsibility has been awarded (for both the drinking water and the Underground Injection Contorl programs). EPA is also charged to provide guidance, assistance, and public information about drinking water. The Agency must also collect and assess drinking water data, to assist with future rule making on newly identified problems in the nation's water supplies. Finally, EPA is required to implement any portion of the SDWA (*i.e.*, both the drinking water and certain source protection programs) when a state has not been awarded primacy for any portion of the SDWA.

Provisions Protecting Public Water Systems

Under the SDWA the ultimate programmatic goal is to protect public health. To ensure that drinking water is safe, the SDWA imposes requirements for the operation of public water supply systems and for protecting the sources of water used by those systems to reduce the likelihood that chemical or biological contaminants will appear in harmful levels in either sources of supply or at the tap provided for human consumption.

Public Water Supply System Requirements

The SDWA imposes requirements on public water suppliers throughout the treatment and distri-

bution process. First, water must be tested and treated to meet the MCLs. The results of these analyses are reported to the respective state (or EPA) that is implementing SDWA program primacy. Should a PWS fail to either monitor or to meet an MCL, it is the water supplier's responsibility to notify its customers of the deficiency in either monitoring or in meeting the standard. Many water suppliers are also required to prepare annual reports for their customers. Informing the public of deficiencies is a major part of the SDWA. (Note: a CHMM in charge of such a PWS must understand and comply with these monitoring and notification criteria.) The SDWA also mandates that states have programs to certify water system operators and make sure that new water systems have the technical, financial, and managerial capacity to provide safe drinking water. The following sections describe the key features of the drinking water standards and the public information and notification requirements that are relevant to most CHMMs.

National Drinking Water Standards. As part of its responsibilities under the SDWA, EPA establishes national standards for tap water that help ensure consistent quality in our nation's water supply (SDWA §1412, 42USC §300g–1). To identify threats to public health, EPA prioritizes contaminants for potential regulation based on risk and the frequency of their occurrence in water supply systems. To establish health impacts, EPA sets a health goal based on risk that considers subgroups in a typical population. This would include risks to the most sensitive people, *e.g.*, infants, children, pregnant women, the elderly, and persons with compromised immune systems. Upon compilation and analysis of these data, EPA will either set a legal limit for the contaminant in drinking water, or establish a required treatment technique to reduce the amount of that particular constituent in water (e.g., nitrate that occurs naturally in some groundwater and may require removal prior to distribution). This limit or treatment technique is set to be as close to the health goal as feasible. As part of the regulatory process, EPA must also conduct a cost-benefit analysis of the new standard and must consider input from interested parties when establishing standards.

The SDWA requires EPA to establish National Primary Drinking Water Regulations (NPDWRs) for contaminants that may cause adverse public health effects. The regulations include both mandatory levels, MCLs, and non-enforceable health goals, MCLGs, for each included contaminant. MCLs and MCLGs are particularly significant since they can be and are often used under Superfund as Applicable or Relevant and Appropriate Requirements (ARARs) in environmental clean-ups. The use of these standards for clean-up standards is established in Section 121 of the Comprehensive Environmental Response, Compensation, and Liability Act (CERCLA or Superfund), 42 USC §9261(d). (Note: All CHMMs should note the inter-program relationship among these various environmental laws.)

When EPA establishes primary drinking water standards the Agency uses a three-step process:

1) EPA identifies contaminants that may adversely affect public health and occur in drinking water with a frequency and at levels that pose a threat to public health. The Agency identifies these contaminants for further study, and determines the potentially regulated contaminants.

2) Upon determining which contaminants to regulate, EPA establishes an MCLG. This goal is the level of a contaminant in drinking water below which there is no expected risk to health. These goals allow for a margin of safety usually for a specific target population.

3) Finally, EPA specifies an MCL. This number is the maximum permissible level of a contaminant present in drinking water when delivered to any user of a PWS. The MCLs are enforceable standards, and are set as close to the health-based goals as is feasible (taking into account the economic impact). The Agency solicits and considers public comment on any action that it proposes.

The SDWA defines a feasible MCL as the level that may be achieved with the use of the best technology, treatment techniques, and other means that EPA finds (after examination for efficiency under field conditions) are available and taking cost into consideration. When it is not economically or technically feasible to set an MCL, or when there is no reliable or economic method to detect contaminants in the water, EPA will set a required Treatment Technique that specifies a way to treat the water to remove or reduce the contaminant to an acceptable level. See SDWA §1412(b), 42 USC §300g-1(b).

National Primary Drinking Water Regulations Development. The amendments to the SDWA have specified that review and adoption of new standards is part of EPA's mission. In turn, EPA has established priorities for the development of regulation over the coming years. EPA has noted its intent to strengthen control of the promulgated standards and to establish new standards to ensure the future quality of the nation's drinking water.

To accomplish this goal, the SDWA requires EPA to publish a list of contaminants known as the drinking water *Contaminant Candidate List*, known commonly as the CCL. This is a list of contaminants that are known to occur in public water systems and which (if justified by data) may require regulation under the SWDA. The CCL was initially published in March 1998 and is divided into several categories. These categories included contaminants

- To be placed on the CCL (for future regulatory determinations)

- Requiring further toxicological research

- Recommended for monitoring

- Needing health advisory development or other guidance

- For which no action was required

The 1996 Amendments required the first CCL by February 1998, with follow-up lists every five years thereafter. Every six years, the EPA is also required to re-evaluate the existing regulations to determine if modifications are necessary (EPA, Drinking Water Contaminant Candidate List).

In addition, the EPA will select up to 30 unregulated contaminants from the CCL to evaluate and prioritize for future monitoring. These contaminants are regulated under EPA's Unregulated Contaminant Monitoring Rule (UCMR). This rule enables EPA to break down the selected contaminants into three lists:

- *List 1–Assessment Monitoring* for contaminants for which analytical methods exist

- *List 2–Screening Surveys* for contaminants with newly developed analytical methods and for which less occurrence data is available

- *List 3–Pre-Screen Testing* for recently emerged drinking water concerns and for which analytical methods have not been developed

Public Information and Notification. Along with the standard setting process, the SDWA also mandates the frequency for monitoring. Frequency will vary with the type of PWS (*i.e.,* community/ non-community) and the size of the system based on the number of persons served or the number of service connections.

When a serious problem with water quality arises, any impacted PWS must quickly notify its consumers. Additionally, a PWS that provides water to the same population year-round must provide annual consumer confidence reports on the source and quality of their tap water. Primacy states and/or EPA must prepare annual summary reports of water system compliance with drinking water standards and make these reports available to the public. The SDWA requires that the public have a chance to be involved in developing source water assessment programs, State plans to use drinking water State revolving loan funds, State capacity development plans, and State operator certification programs.

Source Protection

In addition to the controls imposed on public water supply systems, the SDWA also created programs to protect the sources of drinking water supplies. There are four source area programs that a CHMM should have some knowledge of, as these may impact operations under his or her purview in one way or another. These programs are:

1) Source Assessment

2) Underground Injection Control (UIC)

3) Sole Source Aquifer (SSA)

4) Wellhead-Protection

Each program is described briefly in the following sections.

Source Area Assessment. The Source Area Assessment program was added to the SDWA in the 1996 Amendments, and requires states to develop and implement by 1999 a program that analyzes existing and potential threats to the quality of public drinking water. The states must delineate source water protection areas, develop a contaminant source inventory, determine the susceptibility of the water supply to contamination from the inventoried sources, and report the results

of these assessments to the public (EPA, Source Water Protection). Contaminant sources may include industrial operations that use significant quantities of hazardous materials, and other activities where there is a potential to impact water quality. A CHMM involved in any of these activities has to be prepared for the public scrutiny that ensues with being identified in a contaminant source inventory.

Underground Injection Control. The Underground Injection Control Program is another major provision of the SDWA intended to prevent underground injection of contaminated fluids from contaminating underground sources of drinking water. This program applies to potential sources of drinking water as well as current sources. As with the PWS portion of the SDWA, the UIC program is designed for State implementation (or by EPA in lieu of State primacy).

(Note to CHMMs: the UIC program is also tied into EPA's hazardous waste statutes. Prohibitions mandated by the Hazardous and Solid Waste Amendments (HSWA) to the Resource Conservation and Recovery Act (RCRA) on the underground injection of hazardous wastes were promulgated on July 26, 1988 (53 FR 28118). This rule amended existing Underground Injection Control (UIC) regulations as they pertained to hazardous waste injection. These restrictions are also codified in 40 CFR 148 and the applicable sections of 40 CFR 268, which are part of EPA's regulatory framework for implementing the land disposal restrictions.)

Elements of the UIC program include:

- *Permits*–requires well identification numbers, submittal of well record forms, construction and operating permits, application package, and notification of closure

- *Definition of terms*–defines *underground source of drinking water, well, fluid* and *well injection*

- *Wells*–defines five classes of injection wells

- *Penalties*–defines civil and criminal penalties stipulated for UIC violations

- *Commitments*–Defines criteria for commitments in application package

The following are the key terms and the regulatory definitions that shape the scope of the UIC Program (40 CFR 146.3):

Underground Source of Drinking Water (USDW)–means an aquifer or its portion that supplies any public water system or that contains a sufficient quantity of ground water to supply a public water system, and currently supplies drinking water for human consumption or contains fewer than 10,000 mg/L of total dissolved solids.

Well–means a bored, drilled, or driven shaft whose depth is greater than the largest surface dimension, or a dug hole whose depth is greater than the largest surface dimension, or an improved sinkhole, or a subsurface fluid distribution system.

Fluid–means a material or substance that flows or moves whether in a semi-solid, liquid, sludge, gas, or any other form or state.

Well injection–means the subsurface emplacement of fluids through a well.

Although the UIC Program is commonly understood to apply to injection wells, the broad definitions of well and fluid have expanded the scope of the program to some unusual activities. For example, the disposal of high-level radioactive waste and spent nuclear fuel in a deep geologic repository is considered to be underground injection. See *Natural Resources Defense Council v. EPA,* 824 F. 2d 1258 (1st Cir. 1987). Similarly, injection of fluids to enhance the production of oil and gas wells, a process called hydraulic fracturing or **hydrofracing** has been found to be underground injection and subject to the UIC requirements. See *Legal Environmental Assistance Fund v. EPA* 118 F. 3d 1467 (11th Cir. 1997). In light of these cases, the CHMM should be mindful that any subsurface placement of material in a drilled or dug depression that is deeper than it is wide could be subject to UIC requirements.

Classes of UIC Wells. EPA and the States regulate injection wells according to the type of waste the wells inject and how deep the waste is injected. EPA has defined the following five classes of underground injection wells:

- *Class I Wells*–applies to industrial, municipal, and other injection wells for disposal of fluids into subsurface or groundwater and includes industrial, municipal, or privately owned disposal wells for disposal of industrial waste, domestic sewage, or other waste not hazardous or radioactive. (Class I wells are *prohibited* in many states.)

- *Class II Wells*–pertains to oil or gas production and storage. It should be noted that UIC was mandated to *not* interfere with oil and gas production, but courts have construed this narrowly. This is discussed more fully in *Legal Environmental Assistance Fund v. EPA* 118 F. 3d 1467 (11th Cir. 1997) and *Arco Oil and Gas Co. v. EPA*, 14 F. 3d 1431 (10th Cir. 1993), where fluids from a carbon dioxide well, although similar to fluids from natural gas wells, are subject to the UIC program. The SDWA allows a state to obtain primacy from EPA for oil and gas related injection wells without being required to adopt the complete set of applicable Federal UIC regulations.

- *Class III Wells*–pertains to injected fluids for extraction of minerals.

- *Class IV Wells*–pertains to injected hazardous wastes or radioactive contaminants into or above the formation containing an USDW (widely prohibited). The 1986 Amendments included a set of stringent requirements for deep injection wells designed to dispose of hazardous wastes.

  - Although these wells are generally prohibited in most cases, EPA can approve Class IV wells to inject *partially treated* ground water in remediation projects under CERCLA or RCRA.

  - Ground water pump and treat projects could qualify as a Class IV when listed wastes are contained in the ground water, and listed constituents remain in the ground water that is injected into the subsurface after treatment.

- *Class V Wells*–all other injection wells (corrective action wells associated with aquifer restoration). Note to CHMMs: a major impact from the UIC program comes from the Class V well program. Frequently in rural situations, where conventional wastewater treatment is not available, co-mingled hazardous waste can find its way into septic systems. This is a site-by-site issue that the CHMM needs to keep in mind.

Violation of any requirement of applicable UIC program or order requiring compliance is subject to criminal and civil penalties. This includes fines of up to $27,500 per day for each day of criminal violation, and up to $11,000 per day for civil violation, with up to 2 years imprisonment for criminal violations, in addition to any fine that is levied.

Sole Source Aquifer Program. The Sole Source Aquifer (SSA) Program was established under Section 1424(e) of the SDWA, 42 USCA §300h-3(e). It authorizes the EPA Administrator to determine that an aquifer is the sole or principal source of drinking water for an area. Once an area is designated as a sole source aquifer, no commitment of Federal financial assistance can be made for any project that the Administrator determines may contaminate the aquifer. Designating an area as an SSA may also limit other activities in the area that have a potential for creating ground water contamination, such as solid waste landfilling and on-site containment and disposal options at remedial action sites.

The EPA Administrator, either on his or her own initiative or by petition designates sole Source Aquifers. See 42 USCA §300h-3(e). Any individual, corporation, company, association, partnership, State or Federal agency is qualified to petition for an SSA designation. To be designated as an SSA, the Administrator must find that the aquifer is needed to supply fifty percent or more of the drinking water for a given aquifer service area (*i.e.,* the area where the entire population served by the aquifer lives), and for which there are no reasonably available alternative drinking water sources should the aquifer become contaminated. If the Administrator makes this finding, the area designated as an SSA includes the area above the aquifer, and the ***recharge area*** where surface water or precipitation replenishes the aquifer by infiltration. See EPA, Region 2 Water, Petitioners Guidance Internet site and 40 CFR 149.2(c).

Once an area is designated as an SSA, all projects within the project review area that receive Federal financial assistance and that have the potential to contaminate the SSA are subject to EPA review. Note that EPA review is not required if there is no Federal funding involved in the proposed project. The project review area may be larger than the SSA designated area, as it may include *stream flow source areas*, which are upstream headwater areas of losing streams (*i.e.,* a stream that loses water to the ground) that flow into the recharge area (EPA, Region 2 Water, Petitioners Guidance). The range of Federally funded projects is expansive, and examples of projects that have been reviewed by

EPA under the SSA program include:

- Highway improvements and new road construction

- Public water supply wells

- Transmission lines

- Wastewater treatment facilities

- Construction projects that involve disposal of storm water

- Agricultural projects that involve management of animal waste

- Projects funded through Community Development Block Grants.

If EPA's review identifies concerns for ground water impacts, EPA can make specific recommendations and impose pollution prevention requirements as a condition of the Federal funding (EPA, Source Water Protection).

The designation of an area as an SSA may also impact activities that do not involve Federal funding. For example, the SSA designation may be considered in the identification and evaluation of remedial alternatives at sites undergoing remedial action under CERCLA, 42 USCA § 9601 *et seq.,* or under similar State programs. In such cases, the SSA designation could be considered as either an ***Applicable or Relevant and Appropriate Requirement*** (ARAR), or as a requirement *To Be Considered* in the identification of clean-up standards and selection of a remedial alternative, which could favor actions that remove contaminated materials to a location outside of the SSA designated area over on-site containment and disposal options (EPA 1988).

The SSA program has also served as a basis for State and local laws concerning the types of activities that can be conducted in SSA designated areas. One such law is New York's Long Island Landfill Law, which imposes significant restrictions on the siting of new landfills and expansion of existing landfills in Nassau and Suffolk Counties, designated by EPA as an SSA (ECL §27–0704). This law has also been interpreted by the New York State Department of Environmental Conservation to prohibit the on-site disposal of contaminated soils. See *In the Matter of the Petition of Coltec Industries, Inc. for a Declaratory Ruling.* NYSDEC Declaratory Ruling 27–32, February 28, 2001.

Wellhead Protection Program. Another source water protection program is the Wellhead Protection (WHP) Program. The WHP is a pollution prevention and management program used to protect underground-based sources of drinking water. The Safe Drinking Water Act's Amendments of 1986 established the national WHP Program. A *wellhead protection area* is the area surrounding a drinking water well or *well field* (an area containing one or more drinking water wells that produce a usable amount of water) and is protected to prevent contamination of the wells. This area includes the *recharge zone*, which is the land area that replenishes the aquifer. The law specifies that certain program activities, such as delineation of wellhead protection areas, contaminant source inventory, and source management, be incorporated into State Wellhead Protection Programs, which are approved by EPA prior to implementation. While Section 1428 of the SDWA applies only to states, a number of tribes are implementing the program as well. All states except Virginia have EPA-approved State WHP programs (EPA, Drinking Water State Revolving Fund).

The WHP is an institutional response to maintaining the integrity of a drinking water source. The source water protection program is non-regulatory at the Federal level. State and local governments may, but SDWA does not require them to, implement regulatory or non-regulatory protection programs based on their source water assessments.

State WHP programs vary greatly. For example, some *require* community water systems to develop management plans, while others rely on education and technical assistance to encourage voluntary action. WHP programs are the foundation for many of the State Source Water Assessment Programs required under the 1996 SDWA amendments.

Since the program's inception in 1986 EPA has approved fifty Wellhead Protection programs in the United States, including the territories of Guam and Puerto Rico.

Emergency Powers

The Emergency Powers section of the SDWA empowers EPA to respond to imminent and substantial endangerment to health and to impose penalties on persons who tamper with public water systems. Additionally, community water systems are directed to conduct assessments of the vulnerability of their systems to terrorist attacks and to prepare or revise existing emergency response plans to incorporate the results of the vulnerability assessments (SDWA §1431, 42 USC §300i).

When the EPA Administrator has information that a contaminant is present in, or likely to enter, a public water system or underground source of drinking water, or that there is a threatened or potential terrorist attack that may present an imminent and substantial endangerment to the health of persons, he or she may act as deemed necessary to protect the health of such persons. Such actions may include issuing orders as may be necessary to protect health and commencing a civil action for appropriate relief, including a restraining order or temporary or permanent injunction. See SDWA §1431(a), 42 USC §300i. The statute authorizes EPA to act even where there is no evidence that anyone is actually drinking contaminated water, only the risk of harm must be imminent, not the harm itself. See, *Trinity American Corp. v. EPA*, 150 F. 3d 389 (4th Cir. 1998). Failure to comply with such an order can result in a civil penalty of up to $15,000 per day.

Tampering with a public water supply is a criminal offense. Tampering includes the introduction of a contaminant into a public water system or otherwise interfering with its operations with the intent of harming persons. A person tampering or threatening to tamper with a public water supply may be imprisoned for up to ten years and penalized up to $1,000,000 for such tampering or $100,000 for threatening to tamper with a public water supply (SDWA §1432, 42 USC §300i-1).

Summary

The SDWA is comprised of several programs intended to protect the public by protecting drinking water that is provided *via* Public Water Systems. These programs are intended for State implementation with EPA oversight and include:

- *Source Water Protection*—protection of the entire water supply source, either groundwater or surface source waters, from contamination.

- *Underground Injection Control*–protection of the potential sources of groundwater from the subsurface injection of fluids

- *Ground Water Protection*–protection of sole source aquifers used for a PWS and includes the Wellhead Protection Program

- *Public Water System Supervision*–requires EPA to develop standards, monitoring, enforcement, technical assistance, and provide financial assistance.

Together these programs ensure that public water suppliers provide safe drinking water to the public and notify the public when the systems fail to meet the monitoring or MCL standards. The Underground Injection Control, Ground Water, and Source Water Protection programs protect source water, thereby enhancing the capacity of public water supplies to achieve their public health objectives.

The importance of the SDWA to the CHMM is:

- When a company water system that provides drinking water to its work force meets the definition of a public water supply, then the SDWA becomes part of the company's compliance program and it must be understood for its compliance criteria.

- The SDWA's drinking water standards are the basis of many cleanup levels that may need to be achieved to remediate releases that impact soil and groundwater.

- Source area protection program requirements can restrict or otherwise impact the types of activities that can be performed in an area designated for drinking water protection.

- The UIC program can dictate what types of fluids and materials can be injected into the subsurface and where such injections can take place.

Internet Resources

<http://www.awwa.org/> (American Water Works Association.Homepage)

<http://www.awwa.org/Advocacy/learn/info/HistoryofDrinkingWater.cfm> (American Water Works Association. Brief History of Drinking Water)

<http://www.epa.gov./region02/water/aquifer/petition> (Environmental Protection Agency. Region 2 Water. Petitioner's Guidance)

<http://www.epa.gov/safewater/>(Environmental Protection Agency. Ground Water and Drinking Water Program)

<http://www.epa.gov/safewater/ccl/index.html> (Environmental Protection Agency. Drinking Water Contaminant Candidate List)

<http://www.epa.gov/safewater/dwsrf/index.html> (Environmental Protection Agency. Drinking Water State Revolving Fund)

<http://www.epa.gov/safewater/pws/pwss.html> (Environmental Protection Agency. Public Drinking Water Systems Programs)

<http://www.epa.gov./safewater/swp/ssa.html> (Environmental Protection Agency. Source Water Protection. Sole Source Aquifer Protection Program Overview)

<http://www.epa.gov/superfund/action/guidance/remedy/arars/overview.htm> (Environmental Protection Agency. Superfund. An Overview of ARARS. "CERCLA Compliance With Other Laws Manuals")

Bibliography

Barzilay, J., *et al.*, *The Water We Drink*. New Brunswick, NJ: Rutgers University Press, 1999.

McMahon, B. and T. Pugh. *Epidemiology–Principles and Method*. Boston, MA: Little, Brown and Company, 1970.

Environmental Protection Agency. *CERCLA Compliance With Other Laws Manual: Interim Final*. EPA/540G-89/006. Washington DC: EPA, August 1988.

Environmental Protection Agency. *The History of Drinking Water Treatment*. EPA–816–F–00–006. Washington DC: EPA. February 2000.

A. Thomas Merski is a Senior Environmental Scientist for URS Corporation's Pittsburgh, Pennsylvania office, where he provides both clients and URS staff with a broad array of technical and support capabilities. With over 30 years of experience dealing with a wide variety technical and policy issues, he has led efforts that include the evaluation of public health impacts, regulatory compliance, program and policy analysis of water and waste programs, including oversight of spill response activities, and the comparative evaluation of environmental technologies. Mr. Merski assists URS staff and clients to identify and deploy innovative environmental technologies for specific site remediation efforts. These technologies are generally alternative remedial methods for ameliorating surface and subsurface releases of petroleum and other hazardous materials. Mr. Merski worked for over 17 years with environmental regulatory agencies primarily at the United States Environmental Protection Agency's Region III office in Philadelphia, where he worked with the implementation of the Safe Drinking Water Act and the development of Wellhead Protection Program. He has over 16 years experience in providing consulting services the field of environmental technology evaluation, deployment and commercialization assistance. Mr. Merski received a BS from Kent State University, a Master of Public Health degree from the University of Pittsburgh, and an MBA from Waynesburg College. He has written a number of articles on the assessment and deployment of environmental technologies and their commercialization.

John Englert is a partner in the Pittsburgh office of the law firm Kirkpatrick & Lockhart Nicholson Graham LLP, where he maintains a practice focusing on environmental, health and safety compliance, especially those matters involving hazardous substances, radioactive materials and wastes. Mr. Englert has over 24 years of environmental safety and health experience, with particular experience in the regulation and management of hazardous and radioactive wastes and other hazardous substances. Mr. Englert joined K&LNG in 1994 and represents clients in environmental and nuclear regulatory compliance issues involving use and disposal of hazardous and radioactive materials, site assessment and remediation, facility decontamination and decommissioning, general environmental compliance, hazardous materials transportation, and nuclear and radiological safety. Mr. Englert has considerable experience with federal and state environmental and safety regulatory programs, as well as DOE, NRC and Agreement State nuclear regulatory programs. Mr. Englert received a BA and MS from the University of Buffalo in 1977 and 1980 respectively and his JD magna cum laude, also from the University of Buffalo in 1993. He has published numerous articles on environmental compliance and waste management issues.

Part IX

Management of Wastes

CHAPTER **41**

RCRA Overview: A Generator Perspective

Gregory C. DeCamp, MS, CHMM

Introduction

Purpose, Scope, and Approach

Compliance with the Resource Conservation and Recovery Act (RCRA) hazardous waste management requirements is a serious challenge faced by most hazardous material managers at one time or another. This chapter is intended to help the hazardous material manager successfully meet this challenge. An overview is provided of most major elements of the RCRA regulations. However, emphasis is placed on hazardous waste determination, accumulation, storage, and related waste generator issues that often must be solved by managers themselves with little specialized assistance. Key regulatory requirements are presented and practical approaches to compliance are noted. Sources of additional information on topics of potential interest are listed in the bibliography at the end of the chapter.

Regulatory compliance is addressed in this chapter in terms of the Federal RCRA hazardous waste management program in Subtitle C of the RCRA statute and implementing regulations codified by the Environmental Protection Agency (EPA) at 40

627

Code of Federal Regulations (CFR) 260–266, 268, 270, 271, and 273. (See 40 CFR 240–282 for the full spectrum of RCRA rules, including those related to nonhazardous waste and the underground storage tank program.) Although Congress and EPA designed the RCRA program to be implemented by the states (including the District of Columbia as well as specified United States territories and protectorates listed in 40 CFR 260.10), no significant attempt is made in this chapter to address State or local hazardous waste requirements.

It is helpful to know that State hazardous waste programs must be consistent with and at least as stringent as the Federal RCRA program in order to obtain EPA authorization (RCRA §3006, 40 CFR 271) and that many states adopt major portions of the regulations verbatim or with only minor changes. State requirements nonetheless often differ from those of the Federal program, for example, by designating a larger universe of wastes as hazardous or requiring more frequent or detailed reporting. Differences also occur when a state that is authorized by EPA for a particular part of the RCRA program (*e.g.*, base program, land disposal restrictions, corrective action) has not yet *caught up* with the Federal program by revising its program to accommodate recently promulgated Federal rules applicable to that part and obtaining

Table 1. The Federal Hazardous Waste Management Regulations

40 CFR Part	Title	Description
260	Hazardous Waste Management System–General	Generally applicable information, including RCRA overview, procedures for change petitions, generally applicable definitions
261	Identification and Listing of Hazardous Waste	Solid and hazardous waste definitions/criteria
262	Standards Applicable to Generators of Hazardous Waste	Rules for Hazardous waste determination, on-site accumulation and treatment, preparation for transport, import/export
263	Standards Applicable to Transporters of Hazardous Waste	Rules for transporters of hazardous waste
264	Standards for Owners and Operators of Hazardous Waste Treatment, Storage, and Disposal Facilities (TSDFs)	Rules governing virtually all aspects of permitted TSDFs
265	Interim Status Standards for Owners and Operators of Hazardous Waste TSDFs	Rules for TSDFs conditionally allowed to operate under *interim status authorization* until a RCRA permit is obtained. Similar to, but less stringent than, 40 CFR 264 rules.
266	Standards for the Management of Specific Hazardous Waste and Specific Types of Hazardous Waste Management Facilities	Rules for management of certain hazardous wastes that are recycled, boilers and industrial furnaces (BIFs), and military munitions
268	Land Disposal Restrictions (LDRs)	LDR provisions, including treatment standards
270	The Hazardous Waste Permit Program	RCRA permit requirements, including permit application contents and procedures
271	Requirements for Authorization of State Hazardous Waste Programs	Protocols for states to obtain authority to implement parts of the Federal RCRA program[1]
272	Approved State Hazardous Waste Management Programs	List useful for determining the extent to which a state is authorized to implement the Federal RCRA program[1]
273	Standards for Universal Waste Management	Standards that may be used for specified common hazardous wastes as a more lenient alternative to the standard RCRA hazardous waste rules[1]
279	Standards for the Management of Used Oil	Standards that may be used to manage most used oil that is recycled, including that exhibiting one or more characteristics of hazardous waste.

[1] This topic not substantially addressed in this chapter.

EPA approval, an annual requirement. Further, EPA may directly administer some parts of the RCRA program in states not yet authorized for those parts. In any event, it is essential for hazardous materials managers to remain abreast of regulatory developments on both the Federal and State level. EPA tracks the status of State authorizations for specific parts of the program in its State Authorization Tracking System (StATS), accessible online.

In a similar vein, some hazardous wastes are regulated under both RCRA Subtitle C rules and other Federal laws and regulations. Examples include polychlorinated biphenyl (PCB) contaminated hazardous waste, which is also regulated under the Toxic Substances Control Act (TSCA) and radioactive hazardous waste which is also subject to Atomic Energy Act (AEA) rules. These *mixed wastes* present special management problems that generally are too detailed for this chapter. However, it is important to understand these additional regulations and how they are accommodated while also complying with RCRA Rules. For examples of conditional exemptions and/or alternate management standards EPA has developed to relieve the burden of redundant regulation for these wastes, see 40 CFR 261.8 and 40 CFR 266, Subpart N.

Hazardous waste generation and storage topics are addressed in this chapter roughly in the order they are addressed in EPA's hazardous waste regulations. This approach is generally logical and promotes familiarity with the regulations, a necessity for practicing hazardous materials managers. Table 1 lists those parts of the RCRA regulations normally associated with the RCRA Subtitle C program.

Historical Background

This chapter is not intended to provide a history of RCRA, detailed accounts of which are readily available from EPA and others. However, a basic understanding of its origin and intent is helpful as a part of a framework for understanding material that is presented later.

RCRA (42 United States Code [USC] §6901, *et seq.*) had its beginnings in the Solid Waste Disposal Act (SWDA) of 1965, which generally addressed solid waste problems and gave states the responsibility for solid waste management plans. The Resource Recovery Act of 1970 amended SWDA to include EPA funding for resource recovery provisions, but had little practical effect on waste management practices in the United States. The modern-day RCRA came into being with passage of the Resource Conservation and Recovery Act of 1976, which amended and replaced SWDA entirely. This comprehensive legislation was the first to address hazardous waste in a meaningful manner (in Subtitle C), and also to address nonhazardous solid waste (in Subtitle D) as well as resource recovery. EPA's implementing regulations for this legislation, which initiated the *basic RCRA program*, were issued in May 1980 and were effective on November 19, 1980. The basic law has been amended several times. However, the Hazardous and Solid Waste Amendments (HSWA) of 1984 are by far the most notable amendments to date. HSWA was promulgated primarily to counter continued threats to human health and the environment posed by soil and ground water contamination (*e.g.*, by continued landfilling of hazardous waste) that were not effectively addressed by the basic RCRA program, and significantly expanded RCRA to include highly prescriptive requirements, listed below.

Land Disposal Restrictions (LDRs). Standards hazardous waste must meet to ensure threats to human health and the environment are minimized prior to placement in or on the land.

Minimum Technological Requirements. Requirements for double liners, leachate collection systems, as well as ground water monitoring for so-called *land-based units, (i.e.*, hazardous waste surface impoundments, landfills, and waste piles), which pose the greatest risk of ground water contamination.

Corrective Action Program. Requirements to remediate past releases of hazardous constituents from solid waste management units at facilities that have or are seeking a RCRA permit.

Underground Storage Tank (UST) Program. Comprehensive requirements in RCRA Subtitle I for underground tanks that store hazardous substances as defined under the Comprehensive Environmental Response, Compensation, and Liability Act (CERCLA), except RCRA hazardous waste (hazardous waste tanks are addressed under RCRA Subtitle C; *e.g.*, see 40 CFR 264 and 265, Subpart J).

Other notable amendments to RCRA include the Federal Facility Compliance Act, enacted in 1992, which strengthened authority to enforce RCRA at Federal facilites, and the Land Disposal Program Flexibility Act of 1996, which provided for regulatory flexibility for the land disposal of certain wastes.

Compliance Strategy

The ideal strategy for compliant management of hazardous waste is developed and implemented in the context of a well-organized environmental management system. A system that adheres to the basic principles of International Organization for Standardization's ISO 14001 standard, or an equivalent system, helps ensure that activities are planned and carried out safely with minimal potential for noncompliance. The hazardous waste management strategy should also reflect consistency with EPA's Pollution Prevention Hierarchy, Pollution Prevention Act, §6602(b), which calls for environmentally responsible source reduction and recycling (*i.e.*, waste minimization) as the first and second priorities in dealing with pollution, including hazardous waste. Avoiding or minimizing generation of hazardous waste in the first place and recycling of waste unavoidably generated should always be investigated as potentially cost-effective initial steps in any hazardous waste management strategy. Stringent RCRA regulations can also be partly or entirely avoided by legitimately recycling the waste. Where waste generation is unavoidable, the Pollution Prevention Hierarchy calls for environmentally safe treatment whenever feasible, and disposal only as a last resort. The following sequence of activities is suggested as part of an orderly approach to RCRA compliance:

- Become familiar with RCRA hazardous waste regulations and determine requirements potentially applicable to your operation.

- Obtain the support of your management to ensure that you have the resources necessary to implement an effective program.

- Evaluate pollution prevention/waste minimization opportunities and incorporate feasible and cost-effective options into projects beginning in the early planning and design phases. With passage of HSWA, EPA requires that generators certify (*e.g.*, on hazardous waste manifests) that they have a waste minimization program in place, and has issued acceptability criteria for such a program and guidance for establishing and implementing it (see Bibliography).

- Plan for management of any waste well before it is generated, if possible, particularly if special management requirements are likely to apply (*e.g.*, RCRA requirements for hazardous waste).

- Determine if the waste meets the RCRA definition of solid waste and, if so, whether it is considered RCRA hazardous waste.

- Determine hazards to human health and the environment posed by the waste, and measures necessary to address these hazards, including measures specifically required by RCRA.

- Implement measures determined to be necessary to address hazards and achieve or maintain RCRA compliance.

- Evaluate effectiveness and make improvements where necessary.

The RCRA Hazardous Waste Regulations—General Considerations

There seems to be no easy way to develop a working knowledge of the maze of RCRA regulations, even if one's interest is limited to that of the waste generator, as is the case for most hazardous materials managers. Even persons who have specialized in hazardous waste management for many years can be easily stumped. The moral: overviews of the sort presented in this chapter or in typical introductory or review courses are a good place to start, but are no substitute for careful study of current regulations and guidance documents and consultation with experts when one is attempting to address real compliance issues. In this context, it is helpful to know that RCRA regulations are codified in the *Code of Federal Regulations* (CFR) only once per year (each July 1), so full knowledge of current regulations requires familiarity with not only those codified in the CFR but also those published in the *Federal Register* (FR) since the last codification. Fortunately, real-time updates of the regulations are now available online. Review of the preambles to proposed and final rules provided in the FR is also very often helpful for regulatory interpretation and an abundance of guidance is available online. Finally, direct consultation with EPA or the applicable State RCRA regulatory authority is usually very helpful, and may be essential in cases where compliance determinations remain unclear or where regulatory discretion can be exercised. To get an idea of the current status of EPA's regulatory efforts and agency plans for regulatory changes, essential for compliance planning, consult EPA's "Semiannual Regulatory Agenda," published spring and fall in the FR. (See the Bibliography for useful weblinks to laws, regulations, and guidance.)

Waste Management Planning

Good planning is the most effective way to ensure that hazardous wastes are managed safely and in accordance with RCRA requirements. RCRA provides no *grace period* for compliance; regulatory requirements apply at the time and place the waste is generated (*i.e.*, at the *point of generation of the waste*). This implies that adequate resources necessary to comply with RCRA requirements must be in place at the time of generation. Depending on the specific RCRA requirements that apply, needed resources may include the following:

- Containment facilities and supplies (*e.g.*, containers, tank systems, containment buildings) adequate to safely accumulate and store the waste when generated and facilitate subsequent management (*e.g.*, analysis, storage, treatment, disposal)

- Security to prevent contact of the waste by unauthorized persons (*e.g.*, locks, fences, signs)

- Release prevention and response provisions (*e.g.*, communication system, fire and spill control equipment, contingency plan)

- Waste sampling and analysis provisions (*e.g.*, facilities, equipment, contract with qualified laboratory)

- Provisions for waste inventory, inspections, and monitoring

- Provisions for recordkeeping and reporting

- Personnel training

- Provisions for subsequent management (*e.g.*, transportation, treatment, disposal facilities or vendor contracts)

Planning for generation and storage of hazardous waste should address all hazardous wastes that could reasonably be expected to occur at a facility, not only those which are normal or routine. Examples of potential nonroutine wastes for which contingent hazardous waste management plans should be developed include

- Commercial chemical products upon discard

- Residue from spills of commercial chemical products, process intermediates

- Abandoned or *orphaned* waste containers

- Waste from nonroutine activities (*e.g.*, remodeling, maintenance, changes in process)

Upon generation of a waste, a generator must notify EPA of that activity and obtain an EPA Identification (ID) Number or amend their previous notification to reflect the new activity, as discussed later in this chapter.

RCRA Introductory Regulations

The introductory part of the RCRA regulations (40 CFR 260) includes information that is useful to persons engaged in virtually any aspect of hazardous waste management.

Confidentiality of Information

Normally, any information provided to EPA under the RCRA regulations is available to the public under the Freedom of Information Act. However, some protection from disclosure of proprietary information can be obtained by asserting a claim of business confidentiality as described in this section (40 CFR 260.2).

Definitions

Many of the terms used in the RCRA regulations, even seemingly common words, have special meanings which must be understood to interpret the regulations correctly. This section (40 CFR 260.10) defines terms used throughout the regulations. Additional definitions are provided in individual parts of the regulations.

Rulemaking Petitions

Virtually any provision in the RCRA regulations can be changed using processes described in 40 CFR 260.20–260.41. Therefore, if requirements are clearly inappropriate and potential advantages outweigh the substantial time and money typically required, petitioning for a regulatory change may be a good idea. A firm technical and legal basis for any petition is essential for success. Petitions most likely to be considered by generators or storers of hazardous waste are *delisting petitions* to remove a waste at a particular facility from the hazardous wastes listed by EPA in 40 CFR 261, Subpart D, and petitions to exclude certain wastes that are recycled.

Overview of Hazardous Waste Management Regulations

EPA provides an overview of the RCRA regulations in about two pages of text and four flowcharts in 40 CFR 260, Appendix I. This information merits a quick read for a general overview of RCRA solid waste and hazardous waste definitions and regulations that apply to hazardous wastes. However, it was last updated April 1, 1983, and much of the detail is no longer correct. As a result, it no longer entirely fulfills EPA's intent to help those unfamiliar with the program determine the RCRA regulations that apply to them.

Waste Determinations

Determining whether a material is a hazardous waste is the generator's first hurdle in complying with RCRA's hazardous waste (Subtitle C) rules. Under RCRA, hazardous waste is a subset of solid waste, and each term has a very specialized meaning. Therefore, the waste determination process first involves the application of criteria, including specific attributes and exceptions, to determine if a material qualifies as a RCRA solid waste. If the material is a RCRA solid waste, additional criteria must then be applied to determine if the solid waste qualifies as hazardous waste.

The determination process must be undertaken carefully in view of the risk of noncompliance resulting from an incorrect determination. Each waste determination should involve a careful, stepwise consideration of each element of the solid and hazardous waste definitions in 40 CFR 261 with close attention to the definitions in 40 CFR 260.10 and 261.1. Computer-based and hard copy guidance specifically designed to assist in negotiating this maze is available; the RCRA Hotline at (800) 424–9346 and documented regulatory interpretations involving a wide variety of wastes from EPA's Office of Solid Waste are particularly helpful (see Bibiliography).

Highlights of the solid and hazardous waste definitions and determination process are described below.

Solid Waste Determination

The RCRA statute basically defines *solid waste* as any garbage, refuse, sludge, and other discarded material, including solids, semisolids, liquids, and contained gases. Note that the focus of the statute is on discarded material and that the definition of solid waste does not restrict it to solid-phase material. Note also that uncontained gases, which generally are regulated under the Clean Air Act, are not RCRA solid wastes. This statutory definition includes specific exceptions for several wastes, chiefly on the basis that they are regulated under other statutes. In practice, one must refer to the regulatory definitions and associated criteria at 40 CFR 261 to determine if a material is a solid waste and, if so, whether it is a hazardous waste. The following paragraphs summarize this waste determination process as well as pertinent defitions and criteria; however, the regulations are substantially more detailed and subtle, so this summary should not be considered definitive for actual waste determinations.

In determining whether a material is a solid waste, one must determine if it is a discarded material that is not specifically excluded from the solid waste definition. In practice, one can tentatively assume that the material meets the arduous definition of *discarded* material, and first determine if it is excluded. A material may be excluded by either (1) a variance granted in response to a petition under 40 CFR 260.30 or .31 or, (2) by being a material specifically described in 40 CFR 261.4(a). The former case is rare and

Table 2. Major RCRA Solid Waste Exclusions
See 40 CFR 262.4(a) for a complete list

- Domestic sewage and any mixture of domestic sewage and other waste that passes through a sewer system to a publicly owned treatment works (POTW), or under certain circumstances, Federally owned treatment works (FOTWs), for treatment

- Point source industrial wastewater discharges regulated under Clean Water Act, Section 402 (*i.e.*, National Pollutant Discharge Elimination System [NPDES]), not including wastewater prior to discharge or sludge from treatment

- Irrigation return flows

- Source, special nuclear, or by-product material as defined under the Atomic Energy Act

- Materials subjected to *in situ* mining techniques that are not removed from the ground during extraction process

- *Excluded scrap metal* being recycled (processed scrap metal from all sources; unprocessed, as-generated scrap metal from steel mills, foundries, refineries, and metal working/fabrication industries)

- Certain shredded circuit boards being recycled

- Various conditionally exempted materials generated in industrial processes that are being recycled, often by being used/reused in the process, including the following: pulping liquors, spent sulfuric acid, secondary materials maintained in a closed-loop system, wood-preserving solutions and wastewater, recovered oil, certain materials generated in the coking, steelmaking, chemical, petroleum refining, and zinc fertilizer industries

readily determined by simple inquiry to the owner of the waste or the regulator. 40 CFR 262.4(a) currently lists over twenty materials that are excluded from being solid waste, as summarized in Table 2. If a material is excluded from being a solid waste, it cannot be a hazardous waste.

If a material is not specifically excluded in 40 CFR 262.4(a), then one must decide if it is *discarded*. To summarize 40 CFR 261.2, a material is generally considered to be discarded, and thus a solid waste, if it is subject to one or more of the following four actions:

1) *Abandoned*—Disposed of, burned or incinerated, or accumulated, stored, or treated (but not recycled) before or in lieu of being disposed of, burned or incinerated.

2) *Recycled*, or accumulated, stored, or treated before recycling—by being

a) *Used in a "manner constituting disposal"*—Placed on the land directly or as an ingredient in a product (except commercial chemical products ordinarily applied to the land).

b) *Burned for energy recovery or used to produce a fuel* (except commercial chemical products that are already fuels).

c) *Reclaimed*—Regenerated or processed to recover a usable product (except sludges and by-products that exhibit a characteristic of hazardous waste but which are not listed as a hazardous waste [concepts discussed later],commercial chemical products, and certain mineral processing wastes).

d) *Accumulated speculatively*—(Except commercial chemical products). This provision is specifically intended to discourage *sham recycling*. In general, if a person can demonstrate that a material is potentially recyclable, a feasible means of recycling is available, and at least 75 percent of the material present on January 1 of a calendar year is recycled or transferred to another site for recycling within that year, then the material is not considered to be speculatively accumulated. See 40 CFR 261.1(c)(8).

3) *Inherently waste-like*—(*i.e.*, Specific dioxin and furan-containing wastes and other materials that are ordinarily managed as waste or which pose a substantial hazard when recycled).

4) *A military munition specifically identified as a solid waste* in 40 CFR 266.202.

Materials that do not otherwise qualify as discarded by meeting one or more of the four criteria listed above are not RCRA solid wastes. In particular, materials that can be shown to be recycled in any of the following ways are not RCRA solid wastes:

- Materials used or reused as ingredients in an industrial process to make a product, if not first reclaimed

- Materials used or reused as effective substitutes for commercial products

- Materials returned to the original process from which they are generated if not first reclaimed or land-disposed (*i.e.*, placed virtually anywhere except in a tank, container, containment building, or drip pad as defined in RCRA)

As a result of this complex definition, determining whether a material is a solid waste is often much more difficult than determining whether a solid waste is hazardous waste, as discussed below.

Hazardous Waste Determination

The RCRA statute broadly defines *hazardous waste* as solid waste that, because of quantity, concentration, or physical, chemical, or infectious characteristics: (a) causes or significantly increases mortality or serious irreversible or incapacitating reversible illness, or (b) poses a substantial present or potential hazard to human health or the environment when improperly managed. EPA

thus has Subtitle C jurisdiction over a correspondingly broad range of wastes. In attempting to establish a practical way to implement this definition, EPA has focused on potentially harmful physical or chemical characteristics of wastes and on the toxicity of specific chemicals in the waste (*e.g.*, poisons, carcinogens, teratogens, mutagens), and has established two ways of designating wastes as hazardous: (1) listings, and (2) characteristics. Each listed waste and each hazardous waste characteristic is denoted by a specific Hazardous Waste Number or *Code* assigned by EPA. Some states define more wastes as hazardous than are acknowledged in the Federal regulations; examples include used oil, PCB-contaminated waste, and other toxics.

It is not sufficient to merely determine if a waste is hazardous. One must determine all Hazardous Waste Numbers that apply to a waste in order to enable compliance with RCRA rules. EPA sets forth the gerenal approach to be used for hazardous waste determination at 40 CFR 262.11, which directs that a generator of a RCRA solid waste must accurately determine if that waste is hazardous by

1) Determining if the waste is excluded from regulation in 40 CFR 261.4.

2) Determining if the waste is listed as a hazardous waste in 40 CFR 261, Subpart D.

3) Determining if the waste exhibits a characteristic of hazardous waste as defined in 40 CFR 261, Subpart C using either analytical methods or by applying knowledge of the hazardous characteristic in light of the materials or process used. EPA's approved analytical methods are documented in *Test Methods for Evaluating Solid Waste, Physical/Chemical Methods*, EPA Publication SW–846.

4) If the waste is determined to be hazardous, the generator must refer to 40 CFR 261, 264, 265, 266, 268, and 273 to determine any further exclusions or restrictions pertaining to management of a specific waste.

The key steps in this process are discussed below.

Exclusions from the Hazardous Waste Definition. In a similar manner to that described previously for solid waste determinations, a solid waste may be excluded from the hazardous waste definition by petition (granted under 40 CFR 260.20 and

Table 3. RCRA Hazardous Waste Exclusions[1]

- Household waste, including any solid waste derived from residences, hotels, campgrounds, *etc.*

- Agricultural crop and animal waste returned to the soil as fertilizers

- Mining overburden returned to the mine site

- Fly ash, bottom ash, slag, and flue gas emission control wastes derived primarily from fossil fuel combustion (except as specified in 40 CFR 266.112 from hazardous waste combustion)

- Drilling fluids and other wastes from exploration, development, or production of crude oil, natural gas, or geothermal energy

- Certain chromium-containing waste, mostly from the leather tanning industry, where it can be assured the chromium is not or would not be converted to a toxic (hexavalent) form

- Solid waste from extraction, beneficiation, and specifically listed processing of ores and minerals

- Cement kiln dust waste

- Discarded arsenical treated wood or wood products that fail the Toxicity Characteristic Leaching Procedure (TCLP) test (discussed later in this chapter) for Hazardous Waste Codes D004 through D017 but which are not otherwise hazardous waste, if discarded by persons who use the treated wood and wood product for their intended use

- Petroleum-contaminated media and debris that fail the TCLP for D018 through D043 only and are subject to RCRA Underground Storage Tank (UST) corrective action provisions

- Used chlorofluorocarbon refrigerants from totally enclosed heat transfer equipment that are reclaimed for further use

- Non-terne plated used oil filters that have been gravity hot-drained

- Used oil re-refining distillation bottoms used as feedstock for asphalt products

- Dredged material subject to requirements of a Clean Water Act, Section 404 permit[2]

[1] See 40 CFR 261.4(b) for a complete description and exceptions.
[2] See 40 CFR 261.4(g).

260.22) or by specific exclusion. The former exclusions are listed by EPA in 40 CFR 261; Appendix IX. The latter, listed in 40 CFR 261.4(b) and (g), are solid wastes that are excluded from being hazardous wastes due to practicalities of enforcement, economics, relatively low hazard potential, resource recovery potential, or other reasons. Most of these latter exclusions are summarized in Table 3 of this chapter; however, one must consult the regulations for an actual determination.

As discussed later in this chapter, EPA provides conditional exemptions from many or all RCRA regulations for some solid wastes that are determined to be hazardous. It is useful to know at this stage of the determination process that solid waste samples collected for the purposes of testing to determine waste characteristics or composition (*e.g.*, for hazardous waste determination) or treatability are conditionally exempt from regulation. See 40 CFR 261.4(d)–(e).

Listed Hazardous Waste. EPA lists a waste on the basis that it may exhibit hazardous characteristic(s) (*i.e.*, ignitability [I], corrosivity [C], reactivity [R], and toxicity [E] as described below for characteristic waste) or otherwise may be toxic

(T) or acutely hazardous (H). These *listed hazardous wastes* and their cause(s) for listing are tabulated in 40 CFR 261, Subpart D under four series of hazardous waste codes (F-, K-, P-, and U-series), as described below.

F-Listed Wastes. These are generic wastes from nonspecific sources that are produced by a variety of industries. Common examples include F006 sludges from treatment of wastewater from electroplating operations, F039 leachate resulting from land disposal of two or more listed hazardous wastes, and the F001–F005 spent solvents summarized below with the basis for listing in parentheses:

- F001–specified spent halogenated solvent/ solvent mixtures from degreasing operations (T)

- F002–specified spent halogenated solvent/ solvent mixtures *not* from degreasing (T)

- F003–specified spent nonhalogenated solvent/ solvent mixtures (I)

- F004–specified spent nonhalogenated solvent/ solvent mixtures (T)

- F005–specified spent nonhalogenated solvent/ solvent mixtures (I, T)

Hazardous waste determinations for spent solvents require very close attention to the listing descriptions in 40 CFR 261.31. The F001–F005 listings apply only to chemicals/mixtures that contain, before use, constituents and constituent amounts specified in the listing description, are used for their solvent properties (*e.g.*, degreaser, extractant), and are spent (*i.e.*, no longer usable without being reclaimed). A given spent solvent waste may qualify for more than one of these five spent solvent codes.

Of nearly thirty F-listed wastes designated to date, only six are listed on the basis of acute toxicity (H): F020–F023, F026, and F027, which are primarily pesticide manufacturing wastes containing dioxins. The hazardous constituents prompting the assigned basis codes for each F-listed waste are provided in 40 CFR 261, Appendix VII.

K-Listed Wastes. These are hazardous wastes from specific industrial processes. K-listed wastes are grouped by industry category, including the following: wood preservation, inorganic pigment, organic chemical, inorganic chemical, pesticides,

explosives, petroleum refining, metal production (various), veterinary pharmaceuticals, ink formulation, and coking. Typical wastes include wastewater treatment sludges and distillation bottoms from specified manufacturing operations. Some examples are

- K011–bottom stream from the wastewater stripper in the production of acrylonitrile (R,T)

- K088–spent potliners from primary aluminum production (T)

- K099–untreated wastewater from production of 2, 4–D (T)

None of the K-listed wastes to date has been designated on the basis of acute toxicity (H). The hazardous constituents prompting the assigned basis codes for each K-listed waste are provided in 40 CFR 261, Appendix VII.

P-Listed Wastes (Acutely Hazardous) and U-Listed Wastes. Both P-listed and U-listed wastes consist of the following:

- Specified commercial chemical products or manufacturing chemical intermediates (including those which are off-specification) that are discarded unused

- Residues thereof in containers or container liners (unless *RCRA empty*)

- Residue or contaminated media or debris resulting from cleanup of spills of such chemical products or intermediates

These listings consist of commercially pure and technical grades of these chemicals, and products in which the listed chemical is the sole active ingredient. Products in which a listed chemical is not the sole active ingredient do not qualify as P- or U-listed wastes.

The difference between the P- and U-listed chemicals is that the P-list are those considered to be acutely hazardous (coded *H*) by EPA. Acutely hazardous wastes are subject to special controls as discussed later in this chapter.

Exclusion for ICR Listed Waste. It is important to know that wastes listed as hazardous in Subpart D solely on the basis of ignitability, corrosivity, or reactivity (*i.e.*, coded *I, C*, and/or *R* only, as described above) are regulated differently than other listed wastes. This condition is currently applicable to about thirty listed wastes, including F003 spent solvents (listed for ignitability only), which are generated in many operations. In particular, if a waste otherwise meets the definition for such listing, but does not actually exhibit the listing characteristics upon its generation (at the point of generation), then it is not a hazardous waste nor is it subject to RCRA on the basis of that listing. On the other hand, if the ICR-listed waste is decharacterized (*i.e.*, if the listing characteristic is removed by treatment or other means) subsequent to its generation, then it is no longer a hazardous waste on the basis of that listing, but it is still subject to associated RCRA land disposal restrictions (LDRs) set forth in 40 CFR 268. See 40 CFR 261.3(g) and 66 FR 27269, May 16, 2001.

Characteristic Hazardous Waste. The determination of hazardous waste listings as described above most often requires knowledge of the waste's origin, and a given listed waste code generally applies to a narrow category of wastes. In contrast, determining if a waste is a characteristic hazardous waste requires evaluation of specific physical and chemical properties of the waste and applies to a broad spectrum of solid wastes regardless of origin. EPA has established characteristic hazardous waste on the basis of four properties and has assigned D–series waste codes, as follows: ignitability, D001; corrosivity, D002; reactivity, D003; and toxicity (Code *E*, not to be confused with toxicity Code *T* as a basis for listing), D004–D043.

Table 4 contains the specific criteria for the first three types of characteristic waste (the so-called *ICR wastes*), analytical methods prescribed for their determination, and common examples of such wastes. Because the potential ill effects of these wastes is immediate (*e.g.*, fire, explosion, chemical burns), they are given special consideration in the RCRA regulations (*e.g.*, see general precautions for their storage at 40 CFR 264/265.17 and the requirement for minimum setback of fifty feet from property lines for container storage of *I* and *R* wastes at 40 CFR 264/265.176).

The characteristic of **toxicity** is based on the toxic properties of (to date) 8 metals and 32 organic compounds, as listed in Table 5. The hazard of greatest concern with regard to such toxins is contamination of ground water and exposure via ingestion of contaminated ground water, so (except for manfactured gas plant wastes) EPA requires use of a standard test protocol, the Toxicity Characteristic Leaching Procedure (TCLP), to

simulate leaching of these constituents from waste that has been land-disposed (*e.g.* in a landfill) from percolation of water through the waste. The regulatory level of each constituent, also shown in Table 5, is expressed as a risk-based concentration in the TCLP extract, a simulated leachate. The **TCLP test procedure**, detailed in SW 846, is different for liquid and solid phase waste. For liquid wastes (those containing < 5% dry solids), the waste after filtration is defined as the **TCLP extract**. For solid phase wastes, the procedure involves prescribed preparation of a representative sample of the waste (including size reduction, if necessary) followed by simulated leaching of the waste sample in mildly acidic aqueous buffer solution for 16–20 hours, followed by analysis of potential toxic constituents in the extract. A minimum sample size of 100 grams is recommended for both liquid and solid phase samples. For the latter, an amount of extraction fluid equal to 20 times the weight of the sample is specified. This aspect of the test procedure is occasionally useful in process knowledge waste determinations, in that if the total concentration of a constituent in a solid phase waste is less than twenty times the TCLP regulatory standard (the dilution factor in the TCLP), then the waste cannot exhibit the toxicity characteristic for that constituent.

The wastes shown in Tables 4 and 5 are commonly referred to as **characteristic hazardous waste** and bear all D–series codes that apply. Waste that exhibits any one or more of the first three of these characteristics, also known as **Ignitable, Corrosive, Reactive (ICR) wastes** (Table 4), have chemical properties that can be immediately dangerous if improperly managed and thus merit special protective measures in the regulations.

The Mixture and Derived-from Rules and Related Criteria. EPA has expanded the hazardous waste universe beyond that established by the criteria described above, to include two additional classes of listed waste. The final step in the hazardous waste determination process is to ascertain whether the solid waste meets the criteria for either or both of these classes of waste. This involves evaluation with respect to EPA's so-called *mixture rule* and *derived-from rule*.

The **mixture rule** in 40 CFR 261.3(a)(2)(iii–iv) applies to listed hazardous waste mixed with solid waste, and can be generally stated as follows:

really?

A mixture of listed hazardous waste (in any amount) and a nonhazardous solid waste is also a listed waste and bears the same listed waste codes as the listed portion of the mixture, unless that portion was listed on the basis of hazardous characteristic(s) only (*i.e., basis code I, C, R, E as described above*) and the mixture exhibits none of the characteristics.

EPA provides exceptions to this rule that can be of critical importance to the hazardous waste manager. These include mixtures of wastewater regulated under the Clean Water Act with certain listed hazardous wastes in *de mimimus* amounts and under specified conditions, including toxic chemicals from laboratory operations and certain listed solvents in amounts resulting in very small concentrations at the headworks of the wastewater

Table 4. Characteristic Hazardous Waste Summary: Ignitable-Corrosive-Reactive Wastes

EPA Hazardous Waste Number	Characteristic	Description and Specified Analytical Methods
D001	Ignitability	• Liquids (other than <24 vol% aqueous alcohol solution) with flash point <140°F (60°C), using specified ASTM standard closed cup methods • Nonliquids capable, under standard temperature and pressure, of causing fire through friction, absorption of moisture, or spontaneous chemical changes and, when ignited, burn vigorously enough to create a hazard • Ignitable compressed gas (as defined by DOT in 49 CFR 173.300) (Note: The ignitability characteristic is different than the various classifications of flammable material under the International Classification System for hazardous materials used by DOT.) • Oxidizers (as defined in by DOT in 49 CFR 173.151) *Examples*: nonhalogenated organic solvents, pressurized acetylene cylinders, propane tank, concentrated nitric acid
D002	Corrosivity	Liquids that • Are aqueous and exhibit a pH $\leq$ 2 or pH $\geq$ 12.5, or • Corrode steel (SAE 1020) at a rate of 6.35 mm/yr (0.25 in/yr) at 130°F (55°C) as determined using specified methods from SW–846 *Examples*: strong acids and bases, including nitric acid, sulfuric acid, hydrochloric acid, sodium hydroxide (caustic), potassium hydroxide, *etc.*
D003	Reactivity	Solid waste with any of the following properties: • Normally unstable and undergoes violent change without detonating • Reacts violently with water • Forms potentially explosive mixtures with water • Generates toxic gases, vapors, or fumes in sufficient quantity to pose a threat to human health or the environment when mixed with water or (cyanide- or sulfide-bearing waste only) when exposed to pH conditions between 2 and 12.5[1] • Capable of detonation or explosive reaction if subjected to strong initiating source or if heated under confinement • Readily capable of detonation or explosive decomposition at standard temperature and pressure • Forbidden, Class A, or Class B explosive as defined in 49 CFR 173 *Examples*: peroxides formed from outdated ether, elemental sodium, elemental phosphorus, magnesium powder, hydrazine, picric acid, and possibly pressurized aerosol cans.

[1] Toxic quantities are not specified, but 250 mg HCN or 500 mg H_2S per kg of solid waste is noted as a common reference threshold in Department of Energy RCRA Information Brief EH–231–007/1291 available online; see Bibliography.

treatment facility, as well as *de minimis* losses of U- and P-listed wastes from manufacturing operations, such as minor spills or leaks from well-maintained equipment and rinsate from empty containers or containers rendered empty by that rinsing. See 40 CFR 261.3(a)(2)(iv)(A)–(G). An exception is also made for certain mixtures of listed and characteristic wastes from certain mining and mineral processing wastes.

Additional considerations regarding mixtures that are pertinent to mention at this point include the following:

Rebuttable Presumption for Used Oil. With certain limited exceptions, used oil that contains more than 1000 ppm of total halogens is presumed to be a hazardous waste due to mixing with listed halogenated hazardous waste (*e.g.*, spent solvents). This presumption is rebuttable by demonstrating that such hazardous waste is not present. See 40 CFR 261.3(a)(2)(iv).

Impermissible Dilution. Mixtures of characteristically hazardous waste (but not listed waste, except solely ICR-listed wastes as described above) and nonhazardous solid waste are hazardous only

Table 5. Characteristic Hazardous Waste Summary: Toxicity Characteristic Wastes

EPA HW No.	Constituent Name	Regulatory Level (mg/l)[1]	EPA HW No.	Constituent Name	Regulatory Level (mg/l)[1]
Metals (8)					
D004	Arsenic	5.0	D008	Lead	5.0
D005	Barium	100.0	D009	Mercury	0.2
D006	Cadmium	1.0	D010	Selenium	1.0
D007	Chromium	5.0	D011	Silver	5.0
Organics (32)					
D012	Endrin	0.02	D028	1,2–Dichloroethane	0.5
D013	Lindane	0.4	D029	1,1–Dichloroethylene	0.7
D014	Methoxychlor	10.0	D030	2,4–Dinitrotoluene[2]	0.13
D015	Toxaphene	0.5	D031	Heptachlor (and its epoxide)	0.008
D016	2,4–D	10.0	D032	Hexachlorobenzene[2]	0.13
D017	2,4,5–TP (Silvex)	1.0	D033	Hexachlorobutadiene	0.5
D018	Benzene	0.5	D034	Hexachloroethane	3.0
D019	Carbon tetrachloride	0.5	D035	Methyl ethyl ketone	200.0
D020	Chlordane	0.03	D036	Nitrobenzene	2.0
D021	Chlorobenzene	100.0	D037	Pentachlorophenol	100.0
D022	Chloroform	6.0	D038	Pyridine[2]	5.0
D023	o–Cresol[3]	200.0	D039	Tetrachloroethylene	0.7
D024	m–Cresol[3]	200.0	D040	Trichloroethylene	0.5
D025	p–Cresol[3]	200.0	D041	2,4,5–Trichlorophenol	400.0
D026	Cresol[3]	200.0	D042	2,4,6–Trichlorophenol	2.0
D027	1,4–Dichlorobenzene	7.5	D043	Vinyl chloride	0.2

[1] Based on Toxicity Characteristic Leaching Procedure (TCLP), SW–846 Method 1311.
[2] Quantitation limit is > calculated regulatory level and therefore becomes the regulatory level.
[3] If *o*–, *m*–, and *p*–cresol concentrations cannot be differentiated, total cresol (D026) regulatory level is used.

if the mixture exhibits one or more characteristics and is not otherwise excepted. This is not meant to suggest that mixing nonhazardous solid waste with a characteristic hazardous waste is in all cases allowable. Mixing these wastes for purposes of avoiding legitimate treatment would constitute impermissible dilution (40 CFR 268.3). In addition, although these mixtures no longer are considered hazardous waste, they nonetheless may be subject to applicable LDR rules at 40 CFR 268, discussed later in this chapter. See 40 CFR 261.3(d).

Contained-In Policy. The mixture rule only addresses mixtures of hazardous waste and solid waste. In cases where the material mixed with the hazardous waste is not a solid waste—commonly environmental media like soil, ground water, sediment, or debris (which includes manufactured items and certain naturally-occurring materials like cobbles, such as that defined at 40 CFR 268.3), EPA's so-called **contained-in policy** governs. Under this policy, if the non-waste contains or is contaminated by a listed hazardous waste or if the mixture exhibits a characteristic of hazardous waste, then it must be managed *as if the entire mixture was hazardous waste* unless or until the hazardous waste is determined to no longer be present (*e.g.*, via a *contained-in determination* from the regulator), at which time the nonsolid waste material escapes Subtitle C regulation, with the possible exception of LDR requirements under limited circumstances. In the meanwhile, all applicable hazardous waste codes, including listed waste codes, apply to the entire mixture.

The **derived-from rule** in 40 CFR 261.3(c)(2)) can be practically stated as follows:

> Any solid waste generated from the treatment, storage, or disposal of a listed hazardous waste (*i.e.*, a derived-from waste) is also a listed waste and bears the same listed waste codes as the original waste, unless the hazardous waste was listed only for exhibiting the characteristics of ignitability, corrosivity, and/or reactivity and the mixture does not exhibit a hazardous waste characteristic. Any solid waste generated from the treatment, storage, or disposal of a waste that is hazardous by characteristic only, is hazardous only if it exhibits one or more hazardous characteristic.

Sludge derived from treatment of a toxic hazardous waste at a wastewater treatment plant, and ash derived from incineration of listed toxic waste, are examples of so-called *derived-from* waste. Notable exemptions from the derived-from rule are materials reclaimed from hazardous waste that are used beneficially (except if burned for energy recovery or used in a manner constistuting disposal) and residues from certain treatment processes, as specified at 40 CFR 261(c)(2).

As one can imagine from the above discussion, the introduction of hazardous waste, particularly listed waste, into an operation can result in compliance problems that are difficult and expensive to solve, so it's important to understand these rules and their implications.

Determining Regulations Applicable to a Hazardous Waste

Once it has been established that a waste is a hazardous waste and all hazardous waste codes applicable to that waste have been identified, the next challenge is to determine the specific regulations that apply. As with the waste determination process, determining the extent to which a hazardous waste is regulated requires methodical review of numerous conditions, the most commonly encountered of which are summarized in this section. As a general rule, a hazardous waste is subject to *full Subtitle C regulation* (*i.e.*, 40 CFR 262–266, 268, 270), unless it is entirely or partly exempted or subject to alternative management standards as briefly described below.

Nonrecycled but Exempted Hazardous Waste

The following hazardous wastes are conditionally exempt from virtually all RCRA Subtitle C regulations. Further, except as noted for treatability study samples, persons whose only hazardous waste activity is generation of these wastes are not required to notify EPA or obtain an EPA Identification Number.

In-Process **Wastes**. Hazardous wastes generated in product or raw material tanks, transport vehicles or vessels, pipelines, manufacturing process units (except surface impoundments), until removed or until 90 days after the process (*i.e.*, manufacturing, product or raw material storage or transport) ceases. See 40 CFR 261.4(c).

Characterization Samples. Samples collected to determine characteristics or composition during collection, transport to the laboratory and back to the generator, analysis, and associated legitimate storage. Conditions include compliance with Department of Transportation (DOT), United States Postal Service (USPS), or other applicable packaging and transport requirements. See 40 CFR 261.4(d).

Treatability Study Samples. Samples collected for purposes of conducting a treatability study during collection and transport and associated preparation and storage. Conditions include amount restrictions (*e.g.*, 1,000 kg nonacute hazardous waste, 1 kg acute hazardous waste; larger amounts for contaminated media waste) and compliance with DOT, USPS, or other applicable packaging and transport requirements. Samples undergoing treatability studies and the associated laboratory or testing facility are similarly exempt. Conditions include notification, obtaining EPA Identification Number, timing and amount restrictions, recordkeeping, and reporting. See 40 CFR 261.4(e), (f).

Conditionally Exempt Small Quantity Generator (CESQG, or "sea-squeegee") Waste. Hazardous waste generated by a CESQG, up to specified quantities (40 CFR 261.5).

Residues of Hazardous Waste in Empty Containers. Hazardous waste that remains in an empty container or an inner liner removed from an empty container. The term *empty container* is highly specific as described below (40 CFR 261.7).

Recyclable Materials

Hazardous wastes that are legitimately recycled, termed ***recyclable materials***, are generally subject to less than full Subtitle C regulation in view of RCRA's mandate to encourage recycling. In general, they fall into one of the categories specified in 40 CFR 261.6.

Totally Exempted Recyclable Materials. Certain hazardous wastes that are being legitimately recycled, including industrial ethyl alcohol and scrap metal not qualifying as excluded scrap metal under 40 CFR 261.4(a), and several petroleum industry wastes. See 40 CFR 261.6(a)(3).

Recyclable Materials Subject to Special Standards of 40 CFR 266. Recyclable materials used in a manner constituting disposal, hazardous waste burned in boilers and industrial furnaces (BIFs), recyclable materials from which precious metals are reclaimed, and spent lead acid batteries being reclaimed. See 40 CFR 261.6(a)(2). The 40 CFR 266 regulations are discussed in more detail in a separate section below.

Other Recyclable Materials. For most other recyclable materials, the recycling operation itself is subject to little or no RCRA regulation, while associated storage and transport are fully regulated. See 40 CFR 261.6 (b), (c). For example, generators and transporters of such recyclable materials are required to submit notification to EPA of their hazardous waste activities and comply with applicable standards for generators (40 CFR 262) or transporters (40 CFR 263). Owners and operators of facilities that store recyclable materials before they are recycled are likewise required to submit notification to EPA and comply with 40 CFR 264, 265, 268, and other applicable standards. In contrast, RCRA regulation of the recycling operation itself is limited to EPA notification, pertinent hazardous waste manifest requirements for receipt or return of such materials and reporting of discrepancies, and, if the recycling operation occurs at a facility that is otherwise subject to RCRA permitting requirements, the RCRA air emission standards at 40 CFR 264, 265; Subparts AA and BB.

Alternate Management Standards for Universal Waste and Used Oil

As a means of encouraging responsible management, EPA has developed management standards at 40 CFR 273 and 279 for the following two classes of commonly occurring hazardous waste that may be used in place of management under 40 CFR 260–270. Both of these sets of standards are less stringent than the predecessor Federal programs, so authorized states are not obligated to adopt them.

Universal Wastes. Certain hazardous wastes that are generated in large quantity by a variety of generators, so-called *universal wastes*, may be managed in accordance with EPA's Standards for Management of Universal Waste at 40 CFR 273 to the extent they are adopted by authorized states. EPA has so far designated four types of hazardous waste as universal wastes, each of which is specifically defined at 40 CFR 273.9: batteries; pesticide stocks that have been recalled or which are being collected and managed under a waste pesticide collection program; mercury-containing thermostats; and lamps, which include fluorescent lamps as well as a wide variety of other lamp types in common used which have a high potential to fail the TCLP—particularly for mercury and/or lead. These regulations provide alternative standards for universal waste management from generation through accumulation and transport to destination facilities for treatment, recycle, or disposal. Treatment, recycling, and disposal of universal wastes remain subject to RCRA rules that would otherwise apply.

The Universal Waste Regulations also include procedures for petitioning EPA to add other wastes to the universal waste management system and criteria for inclusion. Common wastes that have been suggested as universal wastes are solvent-contaminated wipers, aerosol cans, cathode ray tubes, and mercury-containing equipment. EPA has formally proposed a rule to add cathode ray tubes and mercury-containing equpement to the list of universal wastes (67 FR 40508, June 12, 2002), but intends to propose a conditional exemption for solvent-contaminated wipers at 40 CFR 261.4 rather than add them to the universal waste system (see 68 FR 65586, November 20, 2003 and 69 FR 8353, February 24, 2004). Some states have issued management standards for these types of waste independent of the universal waste rules.

Recycled Used Oil. Recycled used oil that exhibits a hazardous characteristic but which is not a listed hazardous waste (*e.g.*, by mixing with listed waste) may be managed in accordance with EPA's Used Oil Management Standards at 40 CFR 279 to the extent adopted by authorized states. Subject to certain exceptions and conditions, some recycled mixtures of used oil and other materials (*e.g.*, fuel) may also be managed as used oil under these regulations (see applicability criteria at 40 CFR 279.10).

Empty Containers and Tanks

Under RCRA rules, *containers* are portable devices ranging up to and including transport vehicles, and *tanks* are stationary devices made primarily of nonearthen materials (40 CFR 260.10; 59 FR 62917). Since hazardous waste remaining in an empty container or an inner liner removed from an empty container is not subject to hazardous waste rules, it is important to know EPA's definition of empty container at 40 CFR 261.7, essential elements of which are as described below.

Compressed Gas Containers (Including Aerosol Cans). Containers of compressed gases (*e.g.*, acetylene and propane cylinders, aerosol cans) are considered empty with respect to the compressed gas when pressure in the container approaches atmospheric pressure. Of course, if these containers also contain other materials, they may not be empty with respect to those materials (see additional criteria below).

Containers/Inner Liners That Contained Acute Hazardous Waste. These containers are considered empty when triple-rinsed with solvent capable of removing the waste, or cleaned by another method demonstrated in the scientific literature or generator testing to achieve equivalent removal, or (containers with liners only) when the intact liner is removed.

Other Containers. All other containers are considered empty when all waste is removed that can be removed using practices commonly employed for that container type, *and*

- < 2.5 cm (1 in.) of residue remains in the bottom of the container or inner liner, *or*

- For containers < 110 gallons, < 3 % (by weight) of the total capacity remains, *or*

- For containers > 110 gallons, < 0.3% (by weight) of the total capacity remains

EPA has not included in the regulations a specific definition of empty with respect to hazardous waste tanks, so consultation with the regulator may be advisable. The management of aerosol cans that are still pressurized and/or contain product but are unusable or contemplated for discard present another common but potentially complex RCRA management problem that can involve the *RCRA empty* criteria. First, disregarding chemical properties, discarded pressurized cans could be viewed by a regulator as reactive hazardous waste, particularly if they are not protectively managed, and puncturing them, which would render them empty with respect to the compressed gas, could also be viewed by a regulator as treatment by *decharacterization* (in this case, removal of the reactivity characteristic) that must be effected in a RCRA-permitted or interim status facility or 90-day accumulation tank or container (discussed later). If the container is not RCRA empty with respect to its contents (*e.g.*, solvent, paint) and if they meet hazardous waste criteria, then the cans with contents must be managed as hazardous waste upon discard. This situation demands a practical approach to compliance by all parties. From a RCRA compliance perspective, it can be advantageous to maintain the aerosol cans in the *commercial chemical products* realm, to the extent practical. For example, cans that remain operable can be depressurized prior to discard, and it may be practical to evaluate potential for and to effect reconditioning of inoperable containers (replacement of spray buttons) and/or puncturing cans for purposes of emptying—collecting contents for continued use (*e.g.*, in nonaerosol form or use in other sprayers that can be pressurized) or discard, and isolating the containers for discard. Recycling may be a discard option for both the containers and contents. Discarded materials from the process can be more readily and practically managed in accordance with RCRA rules. Of course, all steps of the process must be undertaken in a manner protective of human health and the environment and in compliance with applicable regulations (*e.g.*, OSHA). Devices are available to process aerosol cans as described, including collecting liquid contents and (if required) gases and crushing the containers. Obtaining concurrence of the regulator on management practices may be a good idea.

Determining Generator Category

As a practical matter, EPA imposes less stringent rules on generators of relatively small quantities of hazardous waste. Three generator categories are recognized on the basis of type and amount of hazardous waste generated and accumulated on-site in any given calendar month: conditionally exempt small quantity generator (CESQG), small quantity generator (SQG), and large quantity generator (LQG). The generator categories, category criteria, and extent of regulation for each are summarized in Table 6. A more detailed comparison of regulatory differences is presented later.

Not all hazardous wastes are counted in the determination of generator category. Wastes that are excluded are specifically listed in 40 CFR 261.5(c) and (d). Examples include certain wastes exempted from RCRA (*e.g.*, some recyclable materials), universal wastes managed under 40 CFR 273, and wastes managed immediately on-site in elementary neutralization units or wastewater treatment plants. The status determination can be quite complicated for generators whose

Table 6. Hazardous Waste Generator Categories and Summary of Key Regulatory Differences

Regulatory Aspect	CESQG 40 CFR 261.5	SQG 40 CFR 62.34 (d) and (f)	LQG 40 CFR 262.34(a–c)
Generation Limits (kg/month):			
Acute Hazardous Waste	≤ 1	≤ 1	> 1
Acute Hazardous Waste Spill Residue	≤ 100	—	—
Total Hazardous Waste	≤ 100	100–1000	> 1000
Maximum Storage Limit (kg):			
Acute Hazardous Waste	1	1	> 1
Acute Hazardous Waste Spill Residue	100	100	> 100
Total Hazardous Waste	1000	6000	> 6000
General Extent of Regulation	Exempt from Subtitle C except 40 CFR 262.11 (hazardous waste determination)	Reduced generator accumulation requirements	Full Subtitle C regulation

waste generation is subject to large fluctuations, because EPA has taken the position that a generator can be subject to different standards at different times, depending on generator status with respect to a waste in a given calendar month. Similarly, the Biennial Report (described later) of a generator whose status fluctuates in a year would cover only activities for those months the generator has LQG status (51 FR 10146). The bottom line: it is advisable for all three categories of generators to accurately track, by waste types, both the amount generated and the amount accumulated/stored on-site so that they can determine their generator category and the applicable RCRA rules for any calendar month, and to have documentation on-hand that substantiates their category determination and also enable any required reporting, as discussed later in the chapter.

Standards for Generators, Importers, and Exporters of Hazardous Waste

RCRA regulations at 40 CFR 262, the so-called *generator standards*, initiate RCRA's *cradle-to-grave* management scheme for most hazardous wastes. In this respect, the rules are designed to ensure that waste generators recognize hazardous waste as such and manage it under RCRA Subtitle C from the moment it is generated through its initial accumulation, storage, and preparation (*e.g.*, packaging) for subsequent transport, storage, treatment, or disposal as required. These standards also set forth rules for importers and exporters of hazardous waste.

The Cradle: Hazardous Waste Determination, Notification of Hazardous Waste Activity, and Obtaining an EPA ID Number

As described earlier in this chapter, EPA requires (40 CFR 262.11) that generators of solid waste determine if their waste is hazardous waste by methodically determining if it is excluded, listed as a hazardous waste, or (by testing or process knowledge) exhibits any of the characteristics of hazardous waste. Upon positive determination, 40 CFR 262.11 directs that the generator review

the remainder of the regulations to determine the extent to which that waste is regulated. These requirements apply to all generators, regardless of category.

EPA further ensures through standards in 40 CFR 262.13 that hazardous waste is promptly brought under RCRA management standards by requiring virtually all hazardous waste generators, except those qualifying as CESQGs per criteria in 40 CFR 261.5 (see Table 6), to notify EPA or the authorized State regulator of their hazardous waste generation activities. The notification is made on EPA Form 8700–12 to EPA (or on a corresponding State-specific form to State authorities) and EPA (or the authorized state) issues a unique identification number (*i.e.*, the EPA ID Number) which is included on virtually all subsequent regulatory submittals. Persons engaged in any other hazardous waste activity (including transport, storage, treatment, recycling, and disposal) must also provide regulatory notification of that activity and obtain an EPA ID Number. The EPA forms that are established for the RCRA program, including EPA Form 8700–12, are available online, through the EPA RCRA Call Center at (800)424–9346; and from the EPA RCRA Information Center at 401 M Street, SW (5305W), Washington, DC 20460; email: rcra-docket@epamail.epa.gov; and fax at (703) 603–9234.

Land Disposal Restriction Determination

Upon determining that their waste qualifies as hazardous waste, generators (except CESQGs) must also make a Land Disposal Restriction (LDR) determination. A waste that is an ***LDR restricted waste*** has a promulgated treatment standard that must be met before it can be land-disposed. If the waste is restricted, it is then also important to know if the waste is a ***prohibited waste***, or actually prohibited from land disposal. Generally, a restricted waste is a prohibited waste upon the effective date of the treatment standard if the waste does not meet the applicable treatment standard and no other variances are applicable (see detailed discussion of LDR, 40 CFR 268, later).

The LDR standards apply at the point of generation of the waste, and are generally designated for each applicable Hazardous Waste Number (*i.e.*, Hazardous Waste Code) by type of waste (*e.g.*, wastewater, nonwastewater) and treatment subcategory. Therefore, an accurate determination of applicable treatment standard(s) requires knowledge of the waste when it is generated. This information is needed to plan and carry out any required treatment, whether on-site or off-site. The determination as to whether a waste meets a treatment standard can be made by either testing or knowledge of the waste.

Assuming that a waste is a hazardous waste and not subject to any variances from the LDR treatment standards (*e.g.*, treatability variance, national capacity variance, no migration variance), the following basic items of information are needed at the point of generation of a hazardous waste to determine what, if any, treatment standards apply:

- All Hazardous Waste Codes that apply to the waste

- Type of waste (*i.e.*, debris, wastewater, non-wastewater as specifically defined in 40 CFR 268.2)

- Treatment/regulatory subcategory (as listed in Table 268.40) for each Hazardous Waste Code

- All physical/chemical parameters for which the waste may require analysis to confirm that treatment is necessary and/or demonstrate that it meets applicable treatment standards, including:

    - parameters/constituents contributing to its Hazardous Waste characteristic(s) or listing(s) (see 40 CFR 261, Subparts C and D, and Appendix VII)

    - any underlying hazardous constituents (as defined in 40 CFR 268.2) reasonably expected to be present

    - any specified technologies required for treatment of the waste, from Table 268.40

This information can then be used to look up all treatment standards applicable to the waste and to plan for any analyses that may be necessary to determine what treatment is required and/or demonstrate compliance with applicable treatment standards. The standards are variously expressed as total constituent concentrations or constituent concentrations in TCLP waste extract (using methods specified in SW–846), or as a requirement to apply a specified technology. See Tables 268.40 and 268.42(a). Alternative standards are available for certain waste forms including hazardous debris

(certain solid phase wastes with predominant particle size > 60 mm), contaminated soil, and lab packs. Additional information is provided below in the discussion of LDR regulations.

Considerations for Sampling, Analysis, and Characterization

As previously indicated, generators must characterize their waste sufficiently to enable them to manage that waste in full compliance with RCRA. Required information includes that needed to determine if the waste is hazardous waste, all hazardous waste codes that apply, and compliance status of the waste with respect to applicable LDR treatment standards. Of primary importance, however, is the need to be thoroughly familiar with all potential hazards posed by the waste and measures that must be taken to address these hazards, regardless of whether or not the hazard is RCRA-regulated. For example, the predominant risk posed by *mixed waste* (hazardous waste that is also radioactive) may be posed by radiation, which becomes a controlling factor in most aspects of its management.

A thorough knowledge of the chemical compatibility of the waste with containment provisions of associated management units (*e.g.*, tanks, containers, secondary containments) and other wastes or materials with which it may be mixed or otherwise come in contact with (intentionally or unintentionally) is important for the safe management of virtually all hazardous wastes. Once the physical and chemical properties of a waste are known, compatibility charts are available to identify potentially incompatible materials (see 40 CFR 264/265, Appendix V and the Bibliography for this chapter). Examples of commonly encountered problems are use of incompatible replacement fittings in tank systems containing corrosives and container storage areas with incompatibles in common containment (*e.g.*, organics such as used oil with oxidizers like concentrated nitric acid, or strong acids with strong bases).

Waste characterization must be conducted using a representative sample of the waste. Approved sampling and analysis procedures are described in SW–846. Other EPA-approved methods (*e.g.*, American Society for Testing and Materials [ASTM] methods) are also acceptable. Methods

Table 7. Key Requirements for Satellite Accumulation Areas

Regulatory Topic	Key Requirements
Maximum Allowable Accumulation Volumes	• Each satellite area is limited to the following cumulative volume, regardless of the number of containers of waste accumulated at that satellite area: ≤ 55 gallons of nonacutely hazardous waste or ≤ 1 quart of acutely hazardous waste[1].
Allowable Type, Number, and Condition of Accumulation Units	• Only containers are allowed (*i.e.*, portable devices per 40 CFR 260.10). Accumulation in any other allowable accumulation device (*e.g.*, tanks) must meet 40 CFR 262.34 requirements for 90–day (LQGs) or 180–day (SQGs) accumulation areas[2]. • There is no limit on the number of containers at a satellite area. • Containers must be in good condition and compatible with wastes they contain per 40 CFR 265.171, 172.
Location Restriction and Control	• The satellite area must be located at or near the point of generation of the waste[3] and must be under the control of the operator of the process generating the waste[4].
Labeling	• All containers must be marked with the words *Hazardous Waste* or other words that identify the content of the containers.
Container Management	• All containers must be kept closed except when adding or removing waste (40 CFR 265.173[a])[5]. If a container begins to leak, the waste must be transferred to a compliant container or otherwise managed in compliance with RCRA (40 CFR 265.171).
Limit on Number of Satellite Areas, Total Volume Accumulated, and Duration of Accumulation	• EPA has not limited the number of satellite areas at a generator's site or the cumulative total volume of waste that may be accumulated in satellite areas, but considers establishment of multiple satellite areas for purposes of circumventing regulatory responsibilities to be noncompliance (49 FR 49569, 12/20/84). • EPA has not set specific limits on the length of time hazardous waste is left in a satellite accumulation area • The basic definition of satellite accumulation area at 40 CFR 262.34(c) requires the existence of a process generating the accumulated waste. Therefore, when a process is permanently discontinued, waste being accumulated at its satellite area(s) must be placed in 90-day (180-day if SQG) storage or a permitted or interim status hazardous waste management unit (HWMU). It may be advisable to consult with the regulator in the case of extended temporary process shutdowns. • Storage of hazardous wastes restricted from land disposal, including that in satellite areas, is prohibited except to accumulate sufficient quantity to facilitate proper recovery, treatment, or disposal (40 CFR 268.50).
Training Requirements	• EPA has specified no particular training requirements for personnel working in or near satellite accumulation areas. However, as a condition for 90-day (LQGs) or 180-day (SQG) storage of hazardous waste without a permit or interim status, LQG employees must be trained in accordance with 40 CFR 264.15 or 265.15, and SQG employees must be familiar with waste-handling and emergency procedures relevant to their responsibilities (40 CFR 262.34[d][5]).
Transfer of Excess Hazardous Waste	• In the event the volume accumulated in a satellite area exceeds 55 gallons of nonacutely hazardous waste or 1 quart of acutely hazardous waste, that excess amount must be moved within 3 days to temporary storage allowable under 40 CFR 262.34 or a permitted or interim status hazardous waste management facility, and the container(s) holding that excess amount must be marked with the date the excess accumulation began (40 CFR 262.34[c][2]), thereby providing evidence of compliance with the transfer and/or storage time limits.
Other Transfer Restrictions	• Hazardous waste from a satellite accumulation area may not be transferred to another satellite accumulation area. It must be moved to either a 90-day (LQG) or 180-day (SQG) accumulation area or to a permitted or interim status hazardous waste management facility.

[1] Individual states may interpret these limitations differently.

[2] See Table 8.

[3] The meaning of *at or near* is subject to interpretation, so it may be advisable to consult with the regulator in cases where the desired location is not proximate to the point of generation. Achieving substantial risk reduction (*e.g.*, reduced fire hazard by placing a satellite area at somewhat greater distance) without incurring substantial loss of control by the operator can be a factor in obtaining regulatory concurrence on the location.

[4] What constitutes adequate control is subject to interpretation, so it may be advisable to consult with the regulator in cases where adequate control is questionable. The extent of security provisions in place at the process location can be a factor in obtaining regulatory concurrence. Locking satellite area containers, cabinets, or enclosures in cases where the operator is not always present in the immediate area is a control measure that can be a factor in obtaining regulatory concurrence.

[5] The term *closed* is subject to interpretation. However, a good conservative rule of thumb in most circumstances is to ensure that little or no container contents could escape even if the container were upset. Therefore, firm connection and closure devices should be provided on filler funnel devices, all screw-type lids and bungs should be at least hand tight, drum locking rings should be firmly secured, *etc.*

for obtaining representative samples of various waste forms are described in 40 CFR 261, Appendix I and other documents referenced therein, including SW–846, several ASTM standards, and guidance documents from EPA's Office of Solid Waste.

As is the case for all hazardous waste management activities, the safety of personnel performing sampling and analysis is a first-order concern. Such activities should be undertaken only after thorough identification and analysis of the hazards involved (*e.g.*, physical, chemical, radiological, biological), development of a plan to address those hazards, and training on that plan. Depending on the situation, pre-eminent hazards may be associated with the hazardous properties of the waste itself (particularly for ICR, incompatible, and acutely toxic wastes) or other factors (*e.g.*, drowning hazard at impoundments, injury from operating machinery). Use of appropriate personal protective equipment (PPE) and other safety-related facilities and equipment and safety-conscious procedures are key.

Hazardous Waste Accumulation, Storage, and Treatment by Generators

EPA allows conditional generation and storage of hazardous waste on-site without a RCRA permit or interim status authorization. The applicable conditions, detailed at 40 CFR 262.34, provide for accumulating small amounts of hazardous waste close to points of waste generation, and for accumulating or consolidating larger amounts of hazardous waste (*e.g.*, for shipment off-site) for limited time periods, typically 90 days for LQGs, 180 days for SQGs. (LQG's that generate F006 wastewater sludge from electroplating operations intended for recycling for metals recovery may also qualify for 180-day storage and other accumulation requiremnts that are specific to that waste, as set forth at 40 CFR 262.34 (g) through (i); however, these special requirements are not further addressed in this chapter, and LQG accumulation areas are uniformly referred to as 90-day accumulation areas for simplicity.) In addition, generators may also treat their wastes without a permit or interim status provided that the 40 CFR 262.34 provisions and certain other requirements are met, as discussed below.

Satellite Accumulation. EPA's initial regulations promulgated on November 19, 1980, were substantially modified five years later to provide

practical rules for generators to accumulate small quantities of hazardous waste at so-called *satellite accumulation* areas at or near the point of generation and under the control of the operator (49 FR 49568). Table 7 lists key requirements for satellite accumulation areas, which are applicable to both SQGs and LQGs. CESQGs are exempt from these and other Subtitle C requirements. See 40 CFR 292.34(c). As indicated in Table 7, and accompanying footnotes, some of the regulatory language related to satellite accumulation is not precise, so discretion is advised.

90-Day and 180/270-Day Accumulation Areas.
Many hazardous waste generators ship their wastes off-site for treatment or disposal. Therefore, EPA conditionally allows generators to temporarily accumulate or store hazardous wastes moved from satellite accumulation areas or accumulated directly from generator processes on-site without a RCRA permit or interim status authorization. The amount of hazardous waste that can be temporarily accumulated or stored in this manner is not specifically limited. However, as noted above for satellite areas, any storage of hazardous waste that is restricted from land disposal is prohibited except to accumulate sufficient quantity to facilitate proper recovery, treatment, or disposal (40 CFR 268.50). These accumulation areas are often established by generators to consolidate and package waste for shipment to an off-site Treatment, Storage, and Disposal Facility (TSDF).

Table 8 lists the main conditions under which this temporary accumulation/storage is allowed (40 CFR 262.34). As may be inferred from the footnotes to Table 8, differences in interpretation of applicable rules can easily result in compliance issues. For example, explicit language regarding removal of accumulated waste from 90-day and 180/270-day storage in tanks is not included in 40 CFR 262.34, particularly in comparison to that provided for containment buildings. Nonetheless, it is EPA's position that tanks used for 90-day or 180/270-day accumulation must be fully emptied at these prescribed intervals (47 FR 1248, January 11, 1982)—a consideration for both tank system design and management practices. In addition, states often have specific rules related to these accumulation areas that differ from Federal rules. For example, South Carolina requires secondary containment for container storage of hazardous waste liquids at 90-day accumulation areas, but EPA rules (40 CFR 265, Subpart I rules invoked by 40 CFR 262.34) do not. Similarly, Federal rules

Table 8. Key Requirements for Temporary On-site Accumulation/Storage without a Permit or Interim Status Outside of Satellite Accumulation Areas

Regulatory Aspect	Key Requirements	
	SQG 40 CFR 262.34(d) and (f)	LQG 40 CFR 262.34(a) and (b)[1]
Accumulation Time Limit (from time of introduction of first waste to the unit)	*180 days (270 days if transporting to TSDF > 200 miles away)*, extendable by 30 more days for unforeseen, temporary, and uncontrollable circumstances[2].	*90 days*, extendable by 30 more days for unforeseen, temporary, and uncontrollable circumstances.
Allowable Waste Accumulation/ Storage Units and Management Standards	*Containers* managed under Subpart I (except minimum requirements for setback from property line for ignitable and reactive waste). *Tanks* managed in accordance with relaxed SQG tank standards at 40 CFR 265.201). EPA indicates that tanks must be emptied completely at least every 90 days (records required)[3].	*Containers* managed under Subpart I *Tanks* managed under Subpart J (with minor exceptions). Tanks must be emptied completely every 90 days. *Drip Pads* managed under Subpart W (plus maintain procedures and records to demonstrate that wastes are removed at least every 90 days). *Containment Buildings* managed under Subpart DD (plus obtain PE certification that building complies with Subpart DD design standards, and maintain procedures and records to demonstrate that wastes are removed at least every 90 days).
Air Emission Standards (40 CFR 265; Subparts AA, BB, CC) Compliance	Not required (40 CFR 262.34[d]).	Required[4]
Labeling and Marking of Tanks and Containers (40 CFR 262.34[a][2,3])	Same as LQG.	*Containers*–accumulation start date must be clearly marked and visible. *Containers and Tanks*–clearly marked with the words, "Hazardous Waste" (additional labeling/marking required for off-site transport per DOT rules—see text).
Compliance with 40 CFR 265.16, Training Requirements	Not required, but generator must ensure all employees are familiar with waste-handling and emergency procedures (40 CFR 262.34[d][5]).	Required
Compliance with 40 CFR 265, Subpart C; Preparedness and Prevention	Same as LQG.	Required[4]
Compliance with 40 CFR 265, Subpart D; Contingency Plan and Emergency Procedures	Not required, but emergency response information must be posted. Emergency Coordinator must be on premises or on call, and must ensure proper response (*e.g.*, fire, spill response, notification) (40 CFR 262.34[d][5]).	Required[4]
Compliance with LDRs, 40 CFR 268	Same as LQG.	Required[5]
Allowable Disposition of Waste	RCRA Subtitle C, TSDF; legitimate reclaimer/recycler, or (for universal waste) a 40 CFR 273 regulated facility.	RCRA Subtitle C TSDF; legitimate reclaimer/ recycler, or (for universal waste) a 40 CFR 273 regulated facility.
Compliance with 40 CFR 265, Subpart G; Closure and Postclosure Care	Not required, but all hazardous waste must nonetheless be removed and properly disposed of at closure (40 CFR 265.201[d]).	Only 40 CFR 265.111 and 114 apply, requiring that applicable closure standard be met and that contaminants be removed and disposed of properly. Failure to *clean close* incurs postclosure care.

[1] LQGs that generate F006 wastewater treatment sludges from electroplating operations are conditionally afforded more lenient rules with respect to that waste.

[2] Some states do not allow the extra time for remoteness from a TSDF.

[3] See 47 FR 1248, January 11, 1982 and *RCRA Online* Faxback No. 11163, June 17, 1986.

[4] See discussion on key provisions under 40 CFR 264/265.

[5] See discussion on key provisions above and under 40 CFR 268.

require weekly inspections of 90-day container storage areas, and the term *weekly* is variously interpreted (*e.g.*, every 7 days, once per calendar week). In sum, generators accumulating hazardous waste on-site should be particularly sensitive of these differences and resolve ambiguities as needed to ensure compliance.

Treatment without a RCRA Permit. EPA allows generators to treat their hazardous wastes on-site without a RCRA permit or interim status authorization, provided that this treatment takes place in accumulation containers, tanks, or containment buildings (but not drip pads) managed in accordance with 40 CFR 262.34 and other management standards invoked therein as summarized in Tables 7 and 8 (51 FR 10168, 57 FR 37194). If this treatment is done for the purposes of meeting LDR treatment standards other than the alternate standard for debris at 40 CFR 268.45, then the generator must also develop and follow a written waste analysis plan that describes procedures to be used to comply with the treatment standards. See 40 CFR 268.7(a)(5). Some states (*e.g.*, Maryland) do not allow treatment in accumulation areas.

Preparing and Manifesting Hazardous Waste for Off-Site Transport

RCRA rules seek to ensure safeguarding and continuous accountability for hazardous waste being shipped off-site by requiring that generators

- Package, label, mark, and placard waste shipments in accordance with United States Department of Transportation regulations.

- Use only transporters and destination treatment, storage, and disposal facilities (TSDFs) that have an EPA ID Number (40 CFR 262.12).

- Track all such shipments using the prescribed hazardous waste manifest.

In addition, the designated TSDF is required to send written notification to the generator that the facility is permitted to receive the waste and will accept it (40 CFR 264/265.12), so it is important to make these advance arrangements. As a final caution, generators intending to ship their waste to another state should become familiar with and observe not only regulations applicable in the originating state, but also applicable rules of the destination state and all states through which the shipment passes.

Packaging, Labeling, Marking, and Placarding. RCRA basically defers to the Department of Transportation requirements for packaging, labeling, marking, and placarding hazardous waste shipments. The following points are pertinent to these activities:

- Packaging must be in accordance with DOT packaging regulations (49 CFR 173, 178, 179), which are designed to ensure the waste will be safely contained during transport.

- Each package must be labeled in accordance with DOT regulations at 49 CFR 172 (Subpart E) to ensure that persons handling them can quickly identify the waste and the potential hazards it poses. With certain exceptions, labels generally must be affixed to the surface of the container near the proper shipping name. If a container has a volume > 64 cubic feet (approximately 480 gallons), labels must be placed on at least two sides.

- Containers must also be marked in accordance with DOT marking requirements at 49 CFR 172 (Subpart D). Markings consist of detailed information (*e.g.*, shipping names, identification numbers) designed to facilitate proper handling. All markings must be durable, in English, affixed to the surface of the container or on a tag or sign, displayed on a background of contrasting color, and be unobscured. In addition, containers < 110 gallons must be marked with the words shown in Figure 1.

One special form of packaging problem commonly encountered by generators is that associated with numerous small containers of hazardous waste (*e.g.*, discarded chemicals). As described in 40 CFR 264/265.316, these wastes may be specially packaged as so-called *lab packs* in accordance with DOT standards (49 CFR 173, 178, 179) by overpacking in containers of no more than 416-liter (110-gallon) capacity, typically in fiber drums, and surrounded by compatible absorbent material sufficient to absorb all liquids. Incompatibles must be segregated and reactives must generally be rendered nonreactive (40 CFR 264/265.316). Vendors are often used to ensure compliance.

It is the generator's responsibility—not the transporter's—to either placard the transport vehicle or freight container, or offer the initial

> **HAZARDOUS WASTE – Federal Law Prohibits
> Improper Disposal.
> If found, contact the nearest police or public safety
> authority
> or the U.S. Environmental Protection Agency.
> Generator's Name and Address**
>
> _____
> _____
> _____
> _____
>
> **Manifest Document Number**
>
> _____

Figure 1. RCRA Label Information for Off-Site Transportation Containers ≤ 110 Gallons

transporter appropriate placards in accordance with DOT regulations at 49 CFR 172, Subpart F (40 CFR 262.33). Placarding is not required in a few instances; *e.g.*, where the vehicle or freight container holds <1001 pounds of hazardous materials (unless considered a poison inhalation hazard) or rail cars loaded with transport vehicles or freight containers (49 CFR 172.504, 172.505). In general, placards are specific to the waste being transported and are placed on the front, back, and both sides of the vehicle as specified, such that they will be readily visible.

Manifesting. Hazardous waste shipments generally must be tracked using the manifesting system prescribed in 40 CFR 262, Subpart B and DOT regulations at 49 CFR 172.205. The Federal Uniform Hazardous Waste Manifest (EPA Form 8700–22) or a corresponding State manifest must be used except for certain cases in which SQG waste is being reclaimed under a contractual agreement that specifies the type of waste and frequency of shipments, or cases where the off-site transport is essentially confined to public or private roadways through or bordering the site (40 CFR 262.20).

The following points are useful to consider when manifesting interstate shipments of hazardous waste:

- Use the Federal manifest (EPA Form 8700–22) in cases where neither the state of origin nor the destination state has its own hazardous waste manifest.

- Use the State manifest in cases where either the state of origin or the destination state, but not both, has its own hazardous waste manifest.

- In cases where both the state of origin and the destination state has its own hazardous waste manifest, the manifest of the originating state is generally used; however, check with both states to be sure.

The following key items of information must be included on the manifest:

- Document number

- Generator name, mailing address, telephone number, and EPA ID Number

- Name and EPA ID Number of each transporter to be used for the shipment

- Name, address, and EPA ID Number of the intended destination facility and, at the generator's option, an alternate facility

- Description of the waste as required by DOT regulations at 49 CFR 172.101, 202, and 203 (*e.g.*, proper shipping name)

- Total quantity of each hazardous waste by units of weight and type and number of containers

- Special handling instructions, if any

- Generator's certification (signature and date) that the information supplied on the manifest is complete and accurate, that packaging is in accordance with applicable national (DOT) and international regulations, and that the generator, if an LQG, has a waste minimization program in place or has made a good-faith effort to minimize waste generation and, if an SQG, that an appropriate waste management method has been selected

EPA Form 8700–22, its continuation sheet, and detailed instructions for completing it, are provided in an Appendix to 40 CFR 262. EPA is currently in the process of streamlining the manifesting process, including provision for transmitting and processing manifests electronically, a practice already allowed in some states (66 FR 28240, May 22, 2001).

The *hazardous waste manifest* basically provides a chain of custody for the waste during shipment. With certain exceptions for domestic United States shipments entirely by water or originating by rail, each party taking custody of the waste signs and dates the manifest and provides a signed copy to the party from whom the waste was received. In addition, upon acceptance of the waste the consignee (or TSDF) must send a signed and dated copy of the manifest back to the generator to confirm that the waste has arrived at its destination. Therefore, sufficient copies of the manifest must be prepared to allow one copy for the generator and each transporter and two copies for the designated TSDF, one of which must be returned to the generator upon acceptance of the waste (40 CFR 262.22, 262.23).

Exception Reporting. If an LQG does not receive a signed and dated copy of the manifest from the designated facility within 35 days of the date the waste was accepted by the initial transporter, the LQG must contact the transporter and/or TSDF to determine the status of the shipment. Further, LQGs must send to EPA a formal Exception Report, which includes a copy of the pertinent manifest and a cover letter explaining efforts to determine status of the shipment, if the signed manifest is not received within 45 days of initial transporter acceptance. Exception Reports are also required of SQGs, but are more lenient in that they need not be initiated until 60 days have elapsed and may merely consist of a copy of the pertinent manifest with notation that status of the shipment is unconfirmed (40 CFR 262.42).

LDR Notification. Shipments of hazardous waste must not only be manifested, as detailed above, but at a minimum, the initial shipment of a waste

must also be accompanied by a notification prepared by the shipper (*e.g.*, generator) that serves to inform the consignee and/or otherwise document the LDR treatment standards applicable to the waste and the status of the waste with respect to these standards. (Individual states may require notification with each shipment.) The notification requirements for generators, detailed in 40 CFR 268.7(a), must include the following items:

- Applicable Hazardous Waste Codes and Manifest Numbers

- Statement that the waste is not prohibited from land disposal, or statement that the waste is subject to the LDRs with a listing of constituents of concern (for F001–F005, F039) and underlying hazardous constituents (for characteristic wastes) that must be addressed by treatment

- Applicable treatment category, such as wastewater/nonwastewater per 40 CFR 268.2(d) and (f), treatment subcategory within a waste code, as identified in Table 268.40

- Available waste analysis data

- For an exempted waste not currently prohibited, the date it will become prohibited

- Date an exempted waste will again become prohibited

- For debris, contaminants intended to be treated under alternative standards for debris at 40 CFR 268.45

- For contaminated soil subject to LDRs, the constituents subject to treatment as described in 40 CFR 268.49(d) and statement indicating its status with respect to exhibiting a characteristic or containing listed hazardous waste, and status with respect to meeting LDR treatment standards

- Where applicable, certification that the waste meets the applicable treatment standards

- Where applicable, certification that a lab pack contains no chemicals excluded under 40 CFR 268, Appendix IV, and that it will be sent to a combustion facility in compliance with alternative treatment standards for lab packs at 40 CFR 268.42(c).

See additional discussion of LDR requirements later in this chapter.

Generator Recordkeeping and Reporting

Generators must keep prescribed records and submit prescribed reports pertinent to certain hazardous waste activities for which they are responsible. The following list includes recordkeeping and reporting requirements detailed in 40 CFR 262, Subpart D and selected additional requirements invoked by 40 CFR 262.34 for temporary on-site accumulation/storage of hazardous waste by LQGs and SQGs in 90/180-day accumulation areas. Additional notification and/or recordkeeping may be required for allowable treatemnt of waste in such accumulation areas (*e.g.*, analysis records, waste analysis plans for treatment to meet LDR standards). State requirements and forms often differ from those indicated here.

Reports and Notifications. *Notification of Hazardous Waste Activity.* All LQGs and SQG (CESQGs are exempt) must notify the EPA or the authorized State regulator of their hazardous waste activities or changes thereto, including wastes they generate and activities pertaining to that waste. The notification is made on EPA Form 8700–12 or the State-equivalen form.

Biennial Report. All LQGs (SQGs and CESQGs are exempt) must submit an account of their waste management activities, including types and amounts of hazardous waste generated, shipped, and otherwise managed, during the previous calendar year by March 1 of each even-numbered year using EPA Form 8700–13A or an approved equivalent (40 CFR 262.41). This is often included in annual reporting required by the Emergency Planning and Community Right-to-Know Act (EPCRA). Therefore, generators must have an effective system in place to inventory and track waste in order to ensure compliance. States may have more stringent reporting requirements; for example, South Carolina requires quarterly inventory and management activity reporting, which satisfies the Federal Biennial reporting requirement.

Exception Reports. Exception Reports must be submitted to EPA if the generator fails to receive a signed manifest from the designated consignee within the prescribed time from the date accepted by the initial transporter (45 days for LQGs, 60 days for SQGs)(40 CFR 262.42).

LDR Notifications. LQGs and SQGs must submit required LDR notifications with waste shipments See 40 CFR 268.7(a).

Records. Unless stated otherwise, the following records must be generated and kept for a minimum of three years or until any related enforcement actions are resolved, whichever is longer. A longer retention period may be advisable in view of potential liability issues.

Waste Determination Records. LQGs and SQGs must retain records of test results, waste analyses, or other determinations made in accordance with 40 CFR 262.11. Although not explicitly required, CESQGs should also maintain such records to support their status. See 40 CFR 262.40(c).

Biennial Reports and Exception Reports. LQGs are required to maintain copies of these reports as records. See 40 CFR 262.40(b).

Original Manifest. LQGs and SQGs must retain until receipt of signed manifest from designated facility. See 40 CFR 262.4(a).

Signed Manifest from Designated Facility. Required of both LQGs and SQGs. See 40 CFR 262.40(a).

LDR Notifications. LQGs and SQGs must retain as records LDR notifications, including certifications, waste analysis data, and related documentation. See 40 CFR 268.7(a).

Contingency Plan. LQGs accumulating waste in 90-day accumulation areas must maintain a contingency plan until closure (40 CFR 265; Subpart D).

Training Records. LQGs accumulating waste in 90-day accumulation areas must maintain training records for former employees for three years from their last date of employment and for current employees until closure (40 CFR 265.16).

Refusals of Emergency Response Arrangements. LQGs and SQGs accumulating waste in 90/180 day accumulation areas must document in the facility's operating record refusals by response organizations to enter into emergency response arrangements under 40 CFR 265, Subpart C (40 CFR 265.37).

Inspection Checklist and Records. LQGs and SQGs accumulating waste in 90/180-day accumulation areas must maintain written inspection checklists and maintain records of inspections and corrective actions (40 CFR 265.15).

Keeping records not specifically required of generators in RCRA rules can be helpful to demonstrate compliance. Examples include waste generation and storage records by CESQGs to substantiate their generator category status, records to substantiate emptying of 90-day and 180/270-day accumulation tanks, and training records at SQG facilties to help demonstrate that personnel managing hazardous waste at their 180/270-day accumulation units are familiar with proper waste handling and emergency procedures per 40 CFR 262.34(d)(5)(iii).

Requirements for Importers and Exporters of Hazardous Waste

Any person who imports hazardous waste must also comply with the generator standards in 40 CFR 262; Subparts E, and/or F, and H. The importer basically assumes the role of the generator for purposes of manifesting the waste, providing the name, address, and EPA ID Number, signed certification, *etc.* (40 CFR 262.60).

The basic requirements for exporters of hazardous waste at 40 CFR 262, Subpart E include the following:

- Written notification to EPA describing the intended activity

- Issuance of an EPA Acknowledgement of Consent to the exporter, a copy of which must accompany the shipment

- Written consent of the receiving country

- Special manifest requirements

- Conformance of the shipment to the terms of the receiving country's written consent

- The transporter must comply with the applicable requirements of 40 CFR 263

The special requirements detailed in 40 CFR 262, Subpart H apply to the export or import of hazardous waste subject to the manifest requirements of 40 CFR 262 or the universal waste management standards of 40 CFR 273 to or from designated member countries of the Organisation for Economic Cooperation and Development (currently the United States, Japan, Australia, New Zealand, and most European countries) for purposes of recovery (*i.e.*, resource recovery, reclamation, recycling, reuse, *etc.*).

Special Rules for Pesticide Waste Disposed of by Farmers

Farmers disposing of waste pesticides from their own use which qualify as hazardous wastes are not subject to any RCRA regulations for those wastes, provided each emptied pesticide container is triple-rinsed per 40 CFR 261.7 requirements and the residues are disposed on their own farm in a manner consistent with disposal instructions on the pesticide label (40 CFR 262, Subpart G).

Standards for Transporters

General Scope and Applicability

The RCRA requirements for hazardous waste transport (40 CFR 263) basically defer to DOT's hazardous materials transportation regulations at 49 CFR 171–179, and consist of relatively few additional requirements. A review of the definition of *on-site* at 40 CFR 260.10 and rules for manifesting shipments at 40 CFR 262.20(e) and (f) are instructive in determining the applicability of these RCRA transporter regulations. In summary:

- The RCRA transporter standards apply to persons engaged in off-site transport of hazardous wastes, regardless of the mode of transport, unless the shipment does not require a hazardous waste manifest.

- 40 CFR 263 does not apply to shipments within the generator or TSDF site, *i.e.*, on-site shipments. This basically means any transport across contiguous site property, even if dissected by roads or other public or private rights-of-way, provided that the transport is across rather than along such rights-of-way. Transport between noncontiguous generator or TSDF properties within a right-of-way between them that is under their control and from which the public is excluded is also considered on-site.

- Transport of hazardous waste along public or private rights-of-way within or along the border of a generator's contiguous site is considered off-site transport. However, a manifest is not required for such transport, and the only RCRA transporter regulations that apply are 40 CFR 263.30 and 263.31, which establish transporter responsibilities in the event of a hazardous waste discharge.

Summary of Transporter Requirements

A summary of the key RCRA hazardous waste transporter requirements is presented below.

EPA Identification Number. As with SQGs and LQGs, transporters of hazardous waste must notify EPA of their activities and obtain an EPA ID Number (40 CFR 263.10).

Temporary Storage in Transfer Facilities. Transporters may store manifested waste they are transporting in containers that meet DOT packaging standards (49 CFR 173, 178, 179) (per 40 CFR 262.30) at transfer facilities for up to 10 days without a RCRA permit (40 CFR 263.12).

Manifest System and Associated Recordkeeping.

Transporters

- May not accept hazardous waste without a manifest from a generator or exporter.

- Must sign and date the manifest upon receipt of the waste and provide a copy to the generator.

- Must comply with specific manifesting and tracking requirements related to exports, rail, and waterborne shipments as detailed in 40 CFR 263.20.

- Must deliver all of the waste accepted from the generator or intermediate transporter to the designated facility (or if precluded from doing so due to an emergency, the alternate designated facility) listed on the manifest, to the next transporter, or (for exports) to the designated destination facility outside the United States. (If the transporter is unable to deliver the waste as specified, he/she must contact the generator for further directions and modify the manifest as directed by the generator.)

- Are generally required to keep copies of manifests and other shipping papers for a minimum of 3 years.

(See 40 CFR 263.20–22.)

Hazardous Waste Discharges. Response to releases of hazardous waste in transit is the transporter's responsibility. Response actions include appropriate immediate action to protect human health and the environment, and cleanup of the discharge, including notification and containment.

Notification and Containment. The transporter must take appropriate immediate action to protect human health and the environment. Such actions must include notification of appropriate authorities and emergency responders (*e.g.*, Fire Department, Hazmat Team) and may include other appropriate action to contain the discharge. The National Response Center ([800] 424–8802) must be notified if the discharge results in death, hospitalization, property damage > $50,000, potential releases or exposure to radiation/radioactive materials or etiologic agents, life-threatening conditions, and releases of reportable quantities of a CERCLA hazardous substance. See 40 CFR 302.6(a).

Cleanup. The transporter must clean up the discharge or take such action as may be required or approved by Federal, State, or local officials so that there is no longer a threat to human health or the environment (40 CFR 263.30, 31).

Requirements for Treatment, Storage, and Disposal Facilities

RCRA regulations applicable to TSDFs are contained in 40 CFR 264/265. The 40 CFR 264 *Permitted Facility Standards* are applicable to TSDFs that have received approval of their Part B permit application and have received a RCRA permit. The 40 CFR 265 *Interim Status Standards* are mostly identical to, but in some respects more lenient than, the Part 264 standards. These latter standards apply to TSDF facilities or activities that are brought under RCRA Subtitle C by changes in the RCRA regulations, and govern continued operations, closure, and/or postclosure care activities pertinent to that facility, as applicable, unless or until a RCRA permit is issued. Finally, as noted previously (see Table 8), certain 40 CFR 265 standards must be met by generators accumulating waste on-site in accordance with 40 CFR 262.34. A summary of the 40 CFR 264/265 regulations, with particular note of those requirements pertinent to generators, follows.

General Provisions

Applicability. Subpart A of 40 CFR 264/265 explains the applicability of these regulations and RCRA's imminent hazard action provisions.

With some important exceptions, the 40 CFR 264/265 standards apply to facilities that treat, store, or dispose of hazardous waste (*i.e.*, TSDFs) through their operating life, closure, and, if applicable, postclosure-care period. Each of these terms has special meanings within RCRA that are essential to know for full interpretation (40 CFR 260.10). Simplistically, however:

- *Treatment*—Virtually any action that changes a hazardous waste to neutralize it, recover material or energy from it, or make it less hazardous, safer, or easier to manage.

- *Storage*—Holding waste temporarily, pending future management.

- *Disposal*—Virtually any action that introduces waste or waste constituents into the environment (*i.e.*, on/into air, water or land). Includes placement in waste piles outside of a RCRA-compliant containment building.

- *Closure/*postclosure—Prescribed activities that place TSDFs in an environmentally safe condition with minimum maintenance requirements. If hazardous waste or constituents above allowable risk levels remain after closure (*e.g.*, waste or waste residuals, contaminated soil, ground water) then prescribed postclosure care is required (40 CFR 264/265, Subpart G).

Several hazardous waste management activities are regulated primarily under other statutes and are not generally subject to 40 CFR 264/265 standards, including: ocean disposal regulated under the Marine Protection, Research, and Sanctuaries Act; underground injection of hazardous waste regulated under the Safe Drinking Water Act underground injection control (UIC) regulations; publicly owned treatment works (POTWs) and other wastewater treatment facilities as defined in the Clean Water Act (40 CFR 260.10).

Several other treatment, storage, and disposal activities are not subject to 40 CFR 264/265 standards (40 CFR 264/265.1). Of potential interest to generators are

- Treatment, storage, or disposal activities of generators accumulating waste on-site, except for the 40 CFR 265 requirements invoked by 40 CFR 262.34

- Operation of elementary treatment units; *i.e.*, containers, tank systems, transport vessels, *etc.* used for neutralizing wastes that are hazardous only because they are corrosive (*i.e.*, D002 characteristic waste, listed wastes with listing basis of *C* only)

- Addition of absorbent material to hazardous waste (or *vice versa*) in a container, provided it is done when waste is first placed in the container and containers are in good condition and compatible with these materials

Imminent Hazard Action. In Subpart A of 40 CFR 264/265, EPA reminds us of Section 7003 of the RCRA statute which states that, regardless of any other RCRA provision, EPA can bring enforcement action for any past or present management of solid or hazardous waste that poses imminent and substantial endangerment to human health or the environment.

General Facility Standards

The General Facility Standards in 40 CFR 264/265, Subpart B (applicable to virtually all TSDFs) consist of the basic requirements listed below. Of these, the training requirements of 40 CFR 265.16 are also applicable to LQGs who accumulate waste in 90-day accumulation areas (Table 8).

EPA ID Number. TSDFs must apply for and obtain from EPA an EPA ID Number in a similar manner to that previously discussed for SQGs and LQGs. EPA notification procedures are discussed in 45 FR 12746 (40 CFR 264/265.11).

Notifications. TSDFs must provide the following written notifications:

- Notice to generators intending to send hazardous waste to the TSDF, informing them that the facility has the appropriate permit(s) for, and will accept, that waste

- Notice to EPA of plans to receive waste from a foreign source at least four weeks in advance of expected arrival of the initial shipment of that waste

- Notice to EPA of change in ownership

(40 CFR 264/265.12)

General Waste Analysis. Before treating, storing, or disposing of a hazardous waste, a TSDF must obtain a detailed chemical and physical analysis of a representative sample of that waste in accordance with its written waste analysis plan. The analysis must contain all information necessary to perform the intended waste management activities in accordance with applicable RCRA requirements. The TSDF may request the generator to supply waste determination and characterization data for this purpose. In addition to physical and chemical data, generator-supplied information would typically include a description of the process generating the waste as necessary to confirm any listed waste codes that may apply and, for containerized liquid wastes sent to landfills, evidence that the sorbents used are not biodegradable (40 CFR 264/265.13).

[handwritten margin note: What about Gen. knowledge]

Security. In general, a TSDF must prevent unknowing entry and minimize the possibility of unauthorized entry to active areas of the facility by personnel and livestock through use of 24-hour surveillance or barriers (*e.g.*, fence) and controlled entry, with warning signs in English and the predominant local language stating *Danger– Unauthorized Personnel Keep Out* or equivalent wording at all entrances and approaches (40 CFR 264/265.14).

General Inspection Requirements. All TSDFs must inspect their facilities for conditions that are causing or may lead to release of hazardous waste constituents to the environment or threats to human health in accordance with a written inspection checklist. This includes such items as operating and structural equipment; safety, security, and emergency equipment; and monitoring equipment; areas prone to spills; *etc.* The inspections must be conducted often enough to preclude significant problems and minimally at frequencies specified elsewhere in 40 CFR 264/265

for specific types of facilities. Repairs or other deficiencies must be promptly effected or corrected. Inspections, deficiencies, repairs, and other corrective actions must be documented and records must be maintained (40 CFR 264/265.15). Don't be surprised if your friendly RCRA compliance inspector requests the facility inspection records for July 4 or December 25, if the rules require inspections on those days—Happy Holiday!

Personnel Training. Facility (*i.e.*, TSDF and LQG 90-day accumulation area) personnel must complete a program of classroom or on-the-job instruction that includes the following elements (40 CFR 264/265.16):

- The program must be a written program. Job titles, job descriptions, required qualifications, and training to be provided for each job position must be documented.

- The objectives and scope of the training program must be to enable personnel to perform the duties of their job positions in a way that ensures compliance with RCRA requirements, including their responsibilities under the facility contingency plan (see discussion related to 40 CFR 264/265, Subpart D, below). At a minimum, the training program must be designed to ensure that personnel are able to effectively respond to emergencies.

- Training must be conducted by a person trained in hazardous waste management.

- Personnel must be trained within 6 months of assuming a job position, and may not work unsupervised until they are trained.

- Annual refresher training is required.

- Records documenting that required training was provided to facility personnel are required. Therefore, in addition to documentation noted in the first bullet above, be sure to document personnel attending and dates of training (*e.g.*, by signature and date on attendance rosters) and dates persons begin and end work in a job position. The records must be kept for 3 years from the date an employee last worked at a facility. An individual's training records may accompany them if the employee is transferred within the same company. Inspectors can be expected to request access to any required record within a reasonable time, so it's a good idea to keep copies of such records at the facility.

The regulations are not specific about which facility personnel are subject to this required RCRA training program, so practical judgement is required. Clearly, some element of training is appropriate for personnel directly involved in hazardous waste management operations or other substantive compliance-related activities at a TSDF or 90-day accumulation area. The need for formal RCRA training for personnel whose duties are not directly related to compliance can be less clear. Similarly, differences of opinion are possible with regard to the 6-month and one-year requirements. If in doubt about such things, check with your regulator.

General Requirements for Ignitable, Reactive, and Incompatible Wastes. Ignitable, reactive, and incompatible wastes pose special hazards. The following two precautions must be taken by TSDFs, and are undoubtedly advisable for generators at hazardous waste accumulation areas:

1) Ignitable and reactive waste must be separated and protected from sources of ignition or reaction, including open flames, smoking, cutting and welding, sources of sparking (static, electrical, mechanical), hot surfaces, frictional heat, spontaneous ignition, radiant heat, *etc*. Such wastes generally should be kept remote from electrical devices (*e.g.*, outlets, thermostats, motors, instruments), and non-sparking tools should be used.

2) *No Smoking* signs must be conspicuously placed wherever there is a hazard from ignitable or reactive waste.

The following requirement is invoked by many of the specific management standards in 40 CFR 264/265, including standards for containers and tank systems (Subparts I and J, respectively), and in such cases are applicable to TSDFs and generators accumulating waste on-site in accordance with 40 CFR 262.34:

3) Where ignitable or reactive waste is treated, stored, or disposed, or where mixing of incompatible waste occurs, precautions must be taken to prevent hazardous reactions, including those which generate extreme heat or pressure; fire or explosions; toxic or flammable gas, vapor, mist, or dusts; *etc*.

For permitted TSDFs only, the effectiveness of all of the above precautions must be substantiated with supporting documentation; for example, from the published technical literature, results of trial tests or waste analysis (40 CFR 264/265.17).

Location Standards. Permitted TSDFs may not place noncontainerized or bulk liquid hazardous waste in a salt dome or salt bed, underground mine, or cave; interim status TSDFs may not place any hazardous wastes in such places. Permitted TSDFs are also prohibited from locating within the 100-year floodplain (unless special conditions are met) or within 200 feet of an active geologic fault. Some states have imposed additional standards, some of which are very strict (40 CFR 264/265.18).

Construction Quality Assurance Program. Land disposal units (*i.e.*, surface impoundments, waste piles, and landfills) subject to the design and operating requirements of 40 CFR 264 or 265 must develop and implement a construction quality assurance (CQA) program developed under the direction of a registered professional engineer to ensure the effectiveness of containment and related provisions of the facility (40 CFR 264/265.19).

Preparedness and Prevention

40 CFR 264/265, Subpart C sets forth basic general requirements, applicable to all TSDFs, LQGs, and SQGs, for preventing fire, explosion, or unplanned release of hazardous waste or hazardous waste constituents, and for preparing to respond to such events if they occur. A summary of these requirements follows.

Design and Operation. Facilities must be designed, constructed, maintained, and operated to minimize the possibility of fires, explosions, or unplanned releases.

Required Equipment. Facilities must be equipped with the following specified equipment, unless EPA is convinced that it is not needed in a particular situation.

- *Internal communications or alarm system* that can provide immediate emergency instructions to facility personnel (must be available to all involved personnel when hazardous waste is being moved or otherwise handled)

- *External communications device* that is immediately available and capable of summoning emergency assistance from local police/ fire departments, local/State emergency response teams (if only one employee is at an operating facility, this device must be immediately accessible to them)

- *Fire extinguishers* and other appropriate fire control equipment

- *Spill control and decontamination equipment* appropriate to the waste being managed

- *Fire water* at adequate volume and pressure for fire-fighting equipment (*e.g.*, hoses, sprinklers)

Note that communications systems must be immediately accessible, so portable devices (*e.g.*, radio or cell phone) may be needed at remotely located accumulation areas or remote parts of TSDFs. Also, location of all such equipment should be reasonably nearby, but not so close as to be rendered inaccessible or inoperable by a fire, explosion, or release!

Maintenance and Testing. Communications, fire control, spill control, and decontamination equipment must be maintained and tested as necessary to ensure it is operational in an emergency.

Aisle Space. Adequate aisle space must be maintained at a facility to allow the unobstructed movement of personnel and fire protection, spill control, and decontamination equipment to any area of facility operations unless it is demonstrated to EPA that aisle space is not needed for these purposes, which includes inspection and mitigation. The meaning of *adequate* here is subjective, and thus a potential source of disagreement with the regulator. A practical example is storing palletized drums more than one pallet wide between aisles, rendering interior drums more difficult to view during an inspection or access to stop or contain a leak.

Arrangements with Local Authorities. To the extent appropriate to the waste and potential need for their services, an attempt must be made to make prior arrangements with emergency response organizations, including

- Familiarization of fire and police departments, spill response teams, *etc.* with pertinent aspects of the facility (*e.g.*, types and amounts of waste, hazards posed, worker locations, ingress/egress routes)

- Establishment of primary response authority where more than one organization may respond

- Agreements with State emergency response teams, contractors, and equipment suppliers

- Familiarization of local hospitals with hazardous wastes managed at the facilities and the types of injuries that could result from a facility emergency

Refusals by response organizations to enter into such arrangements must be documented in the facility's operating record. Arrangements that are made must be documented in the facility's contingency plan.

Contingency Plans and Emergency Procedures

40 CFR 264/265, Subpart D requires that owners/ operators of all TSDFs and LQGs operating 90-day accumulation areas under 40 CFR 262.34 develop and implement a contingency plan, assign an Emergency Coordinator, and implement specific procedures to minimize hazards to human health or the environment from fires, explosions, or unplanned release of hazardous waste or hazardous constituents from their facilities to air, surface water, or soil.

Contingency Plan. A contingency plan designed to minimize hazards, as described above, must be in place for all TSDFs and 90-day accumulation areas operated by LQGs. In practice, the plan may be integrated with spill prevention, control, and countermeasure (SPCC) plans or other facility emergency plans. The plan must be implemented immediately whenever there is a fire, explosion, or release of hazardous waste/constituents at the facility which could threaten human health or the environment (40 CFR 264/265.51). A copy of the contingency plan and all revisions to the plan must be maintained at the facility and provided to all emergency responders that may be called upon to provide emergency services.

The following five items are required in a RCRA contingency plan (40 CFR 264/265.52):

1) *Emergency Response Actions.* Response actions facility personnel must take to minimize threat to human health and the environment, including actions to implement emergency

procedures specifically required in 40 CFR 264/265.56 (summarized below).

2) *Emergency Responder Arrangements.* As developed in accordance with Subpart C requirements, discussed above.

3) *Emergency Coordinators.* Names, addresses, telephone numbers (work and home) for primary and alternates in the order they will assume responsibility.

4) *Emergency Equipment.* A list of emergency equipment maintained at the facility in compliance with Subpart C requirements, with location, brief physical description, and outline of capabilities for each item on the list.

5) *Evacuation Plan.* Where evacuation may be necessary, a plan must be provided which describes signals to be used to initiate the evacuation, as well as primary and (where needed) alternate evacuation routes.

The contingency plan must be reviewed and revised, if necessary, if any one of the following five conditions occurs (40 CFR 264/265.54):

1) The permit is revised (TSDF only).

2) The plan fails in an emergency.

3) The facility changes in a way that increases potential hazard or ability to respond.

4) Emergency Coordinators change, or

5) Emergency equipment changes.

Emergency Coordinator and Emergency Procedures.

An employee designated as Emergency Coordinator must be on-site or on-call (*i.e.*, able to reach the facility in a short time in response to emergencies) at all times (40 CFR 264/265.55, 265.56). The Emergency Coordinator must be

- Responsible for coordinating all emergency response measures.

- Thoroughly familiar with the contingency plan, the facility, and its operations, including hazardous waste management operations.

- Authorized to commit resources necessary to implement the contingency plan.

In the event of an emergency, the actions specified in 40 CFR 264/265.56 and specifically described in the contingency plan must be carried out by the Emergency Coordinator or owner/operator, as indicated in Figure 2.

Simple, easy-to-follow contingency plans and emergency procedures that anticipate and provide for credible accident scenarios are absolutely essential to safe facility operation.

Manifest System, Recordkeeping, and Reporting

Requirements applicable to generators for manifesting of waste shipments, recordkeeping, and reporting were discussed previously. TSDFs have many of the same requirements as generators. Some additional requirements uniquely applicable to TSDFs are discussed below (40 CFR 264/265, Subpart E).

Manifest Discrepancies. TSDFs must note significant manifest discrepancies (*i.e.*, differences >10% in weight for bulk shipments or any variation in piece count) and attempt to reconcile them with the generator or transporter(s), as appropriate. The TSDF must report to EPA discrepancies not reconciled within 15 days of receiving the waste shipment.

Unmanifested Waste Reports. TSDFs must report to EPA waste shipments received without required shipping papers (*e.g.*, manifest).

Operating Record. TSDFs are required to keep a written operating record at the facility that documents substantive facility operations and activities, including types and amounts of waste managed, management effected, location of waste inventories, waste analysis and determination records, inspection and monitoring records, notices, certifications, and other information as described in Subpart E.

Ground Water Protection and Monitoring

Protection of ground water is EPA's primary goal in its strategy for hazardous waste disposal. This strategy seeks to use liquids management as a primary means to minimize the potential for hazardous waste or hazardous waste constituents to migrate from so-called *land disposal* units (*i.e.*, surface impoundments, landfills and land treatment units) to ground water. Elements of this liquids management approach include limitations on disposal of liquids, requiring the use of double liners and leachate collection systems, stormwater run-on and run-off controls, and impervious covering of wastes left in place at closure. The ground water monitoring programs specified in 40 CFR 264/265, Subpart F are designed to detect ground water contamination from land disposal units if the liquids management strategy is not fully implemented or otherwise fails. It is possible to obtain a waiver from the Subpart F ground water monitoring requirements in specified cases where it can be demonstrated to EPA that there is little or no potential for contamination of potential drinking water supplies or surface waters (40 CFR 264/265.90).

General Program Elements. Requirements for development and installation of ground water monitoring systems are similar for interim status

---

Emergency Coordinator Actions

1) **Notify all facility personnel** (Designee may perform if Emergency Coordinator is on call)
   - Internal alarm/communication
   - Initiate evacuation plan, if appropriate (off-site evacuation addressed below)

2) **Notify appropriate emergency responders** (Designee may perform if Emergency Coordinator is on call)
   - Fire department
   - Police/ambulance
   - Spill response/HazMat team
   - Other

3) **Determine nature and extent of releases** (for fires, explosions, releases) using
   - Observations
   - Records (*e.g.*, inventories, manifests)
   - Monitoring, sampling and analysis

4) **Assess potential hazards to human health and the environment**
   - Direct hazards (*e.g.*, from gases, vapors, direct releases to surface water)
   - Indirect hazards (*e.g.*, run-off of contaminated fire water to surface water)

5) **Initiate notifications for off-site releases**
   - If local evacuation may be required, first notify local authorities and assist in evacuation decision.
   - Notify Regional On-Scene Coordinator (if assigned) or the National Response Center [(800) 424–8802].

6) **Keep fire, explosions and releases in check** during emergency by taking all reasonable measures to
   - Stop processes and operations
   - Collect and contain released waste
   - Remove containers of waste

7) **Monitor for incipient hazards in shutdown processes and operations**
   - Leaks, pressure buildup, gas generation, and ruptures

8) **Provide for treatment, storage, and disposal of contamination post-emergency**
   - Waste, contaminated soil, surface water, *etc.*

9) **Prevent management of wastes at the facility that may be incompatible with released materials** until cleanup is completed.

10) **Ensure repair, replacement of all emergency equipment** required in the contingency plan prior to resumption of operations.

Facility Owner/Operator Post-Emergency Actions

1) **Issue restart notification** to EPA and appropriate State and local authorities, indicating that cleanup is complete and emergency equipment is in place prior to resuming operations at affected areas of the facility.

2) **Document all incidents for which contingency plan is implemented** in the operating record, including time, date, and details.

3) **Submit a written report to EPA within 15 days after the incident** which includes information specified in 40 CFR 264/265.56(j)

Figure 2. RCRA Emergency Emergency Response Procedures for TSDFs and LQG 90-day Storage Facilities

and permitted facilities. However, some basic program differences exist, and requirements in the regulations for interim status facilities (*i.e.*, 40 CFR 265) are in some instances more specific because corresponding requirements for permitted facilities are specified in the approved permits. Key program elements are discussed below.

Monitoring Well Design and Location. Both interim status and permitted facilities must have properly constructed monitoring wells in sufficient number and at locations that reasonably ensure detection of ground water contamination resulting from escape of hazardous waste or constituents from the land-based units of interest. The interim status standards at 40 CFR 265.91 specify that monitoring wells must be cased and appropriately screened, annular space must be sealed, and identification plates and locking caps or security devices must be provided.

Wells must be placed both upgradient to enable evaluation of background ground water quality and downgradient to enable detection of any releases from the unit. At interim status facilities, a minimum of one upgradient and three down-gradient wells is required, and the downgradient wells generally must be located at the edge of the waste management area unless (for existing units only) precluded by interfering structures and EPA is convinced an alternate location(s) would be effective. At permitted facilities, the design, number, and location of wells is specified in the permit, and downgradient wells are located at the **point of compliance** (POC), (the vertical surface located at the hydraulically downgradient edge of the area where waste will be placed, and extending down to the uppermost aquifer) (40 CFR 264.95).

Background Water Quality. Background water quality must be established at interim status facilities by monitoring the upgradient (background) wells quarterly for one year (40 CFR 265.92). Parameters to be monitored, specified in 40 CFR 265.92, consist of approximately 20 Interim Primary Drinking Water Standards parameters listed in 40 CFR 265, Appendix III to determine suitability as drinking water, six specified parameters to establish general quality of the ground water, and four parameters serving as indicators of ground water contamination. Background water quality for permitted facilities may be established on the basis of extensive data supplied in the Part B permit application and monitoring initially conducted under the permit.

Detection Monitoring. The initial phase of ground water monitoring, generally referred to as *detection monitoring*, has the objective of detecting statistically significant increases in contaminants at the downgradient (detection) wells as compared to upgradient (background) wells. At interim status facilities, approximately 30 parameters, including the four contamination indicator parameters, are monitored at least semiannually. The detection monitoring program at permitted facilities is specified in the permit, is developed to specifically address existing ground water quality and hazardous waste managed at the unit, and is likely to be considerably more extensive than at interim status units. Detection monitoring continues during the active life of a unit and during the postclosure care period, unless and until statistically significant contamination attributable to releases from the monitored unit is detected (*i.e.*, significant increase in contaminant indicators [or pH decrease] at detection wells as compared to background wells).

Assessment and Compliance Monitoring. The detection of statistically significant ground water contamination as a result of releases from the unit triggers a requirement for an assessment monitoring program at interim status facilities (40 CFR 265.93) or a compliance monitoring program at permitted facilities (40 CFR 264.99). The assessment monitoring program is based on a plan specific to the facility and designed to determine the nature, extent, and movement characteristics of the contamination. Assessment sampling on a quarterly basis is required until the facility undergoes final closure or until the program is replaced by monitoring conducted under a permit and/or corrective action requirements.

The compliance monitoring program at permitted facilities is designed to determine whether the ground water protection standard (GWPS) for the facility has been exceeded at the established POC. The GWPS, established in the permit for a facility when contamination is detected, specifies concentrations at the POC of selected hazardous constituents that are allowable during the compliance period. These are constituents that have been detected in the uppermost aquifer in detection wells and which are reasonably expected to be in or derived from waste in the unit. The corresponding concentration limits for these GWPS constituents are set at background levels or, if established under the Safe Drinking Water Act (SDWA), maximum contaminant levels (MCLs) for drinking water, unless EPA is convinced through a demonstration that an alternate concentration level (ACL) is appropriate (40 CFR 264.92). The compliance period begins when a compliance monitoring program is initiated and extends until closure is complete for the unit or, if a corrective action program is ongoing at a facility, until it is demonstrated that the GWPS has not been exceeded for three consecutive years (40 CFR 264.96). Constituent levels detected at POC wells must be statistically compared to GWPS levels at least semiannually, using prescribed statistical methods . See 40 CFR 264.97(h) and 264.99(f).

Corrective Action Program. RCRA Sections 3004(u), 3004(v), and 3008(h), (added by the HSWA) gave EPA the authority to require TSDFs that have or are seeking a RCRA permit to clean up releases from any solid waste management unit (SWMU) at their facilities, regardless of when such release occurred. The basic provisions of these powerful RCRA statutory provisions are codified in Subpart F at 40 CFR 264.100–101 and in 264, Subpart S, which currently consist of requirements for special management units that can be established to expedite cleanup (*e.g.*, by avoiding LDR treatment requirements that may otherwise become applicable to contaminated media and associated remediation waste, and thus present a disincentive to remediation). Much of the corrective action program is now carried out on the basis of EPA and/or State guidance and compliance agreements. For purposes of this chapter, it is sufficient to note that assessment monitoring program results for an interim status TSDF provide the basis for a regulatory determination to require corrective action at that facility. Similarly, corrective action is required when the GWPS is exceeded at a permitted facility, and the owner/operator must attempt to remove the hazardous constituents or treat them in place. See 40 CFR 264.100(b) and (c). A ground water monitoring program is required as part of the corrective action program to assess its effectiveness. See 40 CFR 264.100(d).

Closure and Postclosure

Applicability. Upon completion of operations, permitted and interim status hazardous waste management units (HWMUs) at TSDFs must be taken out of service, or closed, in accordance with requirements 40 CFR 264/265, Subpart G and the

closure performance standard at 40 CFR 264/265.111. LQG 90-day hazardous waste accumulation areas are also subject to the basic closure performance standard established in 40 CFR 265.111, and requirements to properly decontaminate or dispose of contaminated equipment, structures, and soil as described in 40 CFR 265.14. See 40 CFR 262.34(a). Two main types of closure are commonly recognized, as described below.

Clean Closure. Closure in which all hazardous waste and liners are removed, and contaminated equipment, structures, and soils associated with a unit are removed or decontaminated of hazardous waste and constituents to the extent necessary to protect human health and the environment. This type of closure typically is applicable to nonland-based units (*e.g.*, container, tank, and containment building storage and treatment units, incinerators). Cases in which some contaminants remain in place but are below protective levels are termed **risk-based clean closure**. Allowable residual contamination is determined in the context of closure plan approval by the regulator.

Closure with Waste in Place. **Dirty closure** applies to all closures that are not clean closures. This type of closure may involve partial removal or decontamination, waste stabilization measures and, usually, installation of low permeability cover or *cap* with run-on/run-off controls to minimize infiltration by precipitation. This type of closure is typical for land disposal units (*e.g.*, landfills) and nonland-based units from which all waste or contamination above allowable risk levels cannot be removed.

The difference between these two forms of closure is far-reaching, in that closures with waste in place incur the potentially costly long-term requirements for postclosure care at 40 CFR 264/265.116–120, while clean closures do not.

Closure Performance Standard. The performance standard for closure of HWMUs states that the owner/operator must close the facility in a manner that

- Minimizes the need for further maintenance

- Controls, minimizes, or eliminates, to the extent necessary to protect human health and the environment, postclosure escape of hazardous waste, hazardous constituents, leachate, contaminated run-off, or hazardous waste decomposition products to the ground, or surface water, or to the atmosphere

- Complies with Subpart G and closure requirements specified in the Subpart specifically applicable to the unit (*e.g.*, Subpart I or J closure requirements applicable to use and management of containers and tank systems, respectively)

(40 CFR 264/265.111)

In carrying out the closure, all contaminated equipment, structures, and soil must be properly disposed of or decontaminated, and in accordance with specific instructions in the Subpart applicable to the unit (40 CFR 264/265.114). A written certification signed by the owner/operator and a registered professional engineer attesting that the unit has been closed in accordance with its closure plan, must be sent to EPA within 60 days after closure.

Closure Plan. TSDFs must have in place a written closure plan that includes the following key elements:

- Description of the facility and hydrogeologic conditions

- Estimates of the maximum number, size, and capacity of operational units, and maximum hazardous waste inventory

- Detailed description of closure methods, including disposition of hazardous waste and contaminants, decontamination, ground water monitoring, and unit-specific closure operations such as capping

- Closure schedules

- Expected date of closure (for interim status facilities without EPA-approved plans)

Closure plans for new facilities must be submitted as part of their Part B permit applications. In general, closure plans for interim status facilities must be maintained at the facility and either submitted with their Part B permit application or, if the facility is to close under interim status, within 180 days of closure for land disposal units or within 45 days for other units (40 CFR 265.112).

Postclosure Care. A survey plat indicating the location and dimensions of waste left in place for *dirty closures* must be filed with local authorities

(*e.g.*, county government) and EPA upon closure, at which time postclosure care begins (40 CFR 264/265.116). Postclosure care is conducted in accordance with a written postclosure plan that is submitted to EPA with the Part B permit application for new facilities and at least 180 days prior to closure for interim status facilities. Postclosure care minimally consists of ground water monitoring and reporting, as well as monitoring and maintenance of containment systems (*e.g.*, cap and run-on/run-off control systems) and associated reporting. The postclosure care period continues for 30 years after closure, but may be shortened or lengthened by EPA as deemed necessary to protect human health and the environment (40 CFR 264/265.117–118).

Financial Requirements

RCRA does not allow interim status or permitted TSDFs to operate unless there is assurance that adequate financial resources will be available to pay for closure, postclosure care, and potential liability for incidents or accidents associated with their facilities. Therefore, EPA has established (at 40 CFR 264/265, Subpart H) detailed financial assurance requirements applicable to all TSDFs except those owned by the Federal or State governments. There are few differences in financial requirements between interim status and permitted facilities. Financial assurances for postclosure apply only to facilities required to undergo postclosure (*i.e.*, disposal units, waste piles, surface impoundments, tank systems and containment systems that would be *dirty closed*). The main provisions of these regulations are summarized below.

Closure and Postclosure Cost Estimates. Written cost estimates for a third party to close and, if appropriate, perform postclosure care in accordance with the facility's closure or postclosure plan must be prepared and maintained at the facility. The estimates must be updated annually and whenever a modification to the closure or postclosure plan is approved.

Closure and Postclosure Financial Assurance. Financial assurance, commensurate with the closure and postclosure cost estimates for the facility, must be maintained by the owner/operator. This assurance generally may be in the form of one or more of the following instruments:

- Trust fund
- Surety bond
- Letter of credit
- Insurance
- Financial test and corporate guarantee

Liability. TSDFs must demonstrate financial responsibility for bodily injury and property damage to third parties for accidental occurrences as listed below. The types of financial instruments noted above for closure and postclosure are also acceptable for this purpose:

Sudden Accidental Occurrences–$1 million per occurrence, $2 million annual aggregate (applicable to all TSDFs)

Nonsudden Accidental Occurrences–$3 million per occurrence, $6 million annual aggregate (applicable to hazardous waste landfills, surface impoundments, and land treatment facilities only)

The above coverage amounts are exclusive of legal defense costs.

Specific Standards for Management in Containers, Tank Systems, and Containment Buildings

Hazardous waste is most commonly managed in containers, tank systems, and containment buildings. Of particular importance to the objective of this chapter, all generators (except wood-preserving operations authorized to use drip pads [see Subpart W]) are restricted to these three types of units for managing their hazardous waste under the 90-day (LQG) or 180/270-day (SQG) storage provisions of 40 CFR 262.34. The following sections highlight the main requirements specific to these management units (40 CFR 264/265; Subparts I, J, and DD), with particular note of Part 265 requirements applicable to generators.

Use and Management of Containers

The container management standards of 40 CFR 264/265, Subpart I consist of relatively few straightforward design and operating requirements. With few exceptions as noted, the 40 CFR 265 requirements apply to interim status container storage TSDFs and to 90-day and 180/270-day waste accumulation areas operated by LQGs and SQGs (see Table 8). These requirements are summarized below.

Container Condition. Containers must be maintained in good condition. Practical but conservative judgement is required here. For example, minor surficial scratches or rust on a metal container are generally acceptable. However, pitting, corroded seams, bulging, or other indications of actual or potential compromised integrity should be remedied as soon as possible. Hazardous waste must be transferred from containers that are not in good condition or are leaking, or otherwise managed to ensure compliance.

Safety is the pre-eminent concern in any action to transfer waste or move waste in potentially compromised containers. Container integrity and other hazards should be evaluated prior to opening or moving containers. For example, severely corroded drums may be unsuitable for transporting by conventional means (*e.g.*, forklift with drum handling attachment) or vapor pressure in bulging drums containing spent solvents may need to be reduced (*e.g.*, by packing in ice) prior to venting. Careful overpacking of the containers may be an appropriate option, particularly where minimal handling is desired in view of safety concerns; however, consideration of future management plans for the waste is also important (40 CFR 264/265.171).

Container/Waste Compatibility. Containers must be compatible with the wastes they contain. For example, metal containers should not be used for corrosive acids, and some plastics and solvents are incompatible (40 CFR 264/265.172).

Container Management. Containers must always be closed except when adding and removing waste. The term *closed* is subject to interpretation. However, containers should be firmly closed in a way that would prevent escape of waste even if the container is upset. All screw-type lids and bungs should be kept tight, drum locking rings should be firmly secured, *etc.* (also see Subpart CC, air emission requirements). In addition, containers must not be handled in a way that may compromise them, as may occur from improper hoisting/rigging or forklift transfer techniques (40 CFR 264/265.173).

Container Marking and Labeling. Subpart I does not include requirements for marking and labeling containers. However, such requirements are nonetheless imposed by 40 CFR 262.34 on generators accumulating waste on-site without permit or interim status. (see Table 8). Specific requirements for container marking and labeling also may be imposed on container storage TSDFs by states (*e.g.*, South Carolina).

Secondary Containment. Permitted container storage facilities that store hazardous wastes containing free liquids (as determined by the paint filter test, Method 9095 in SW–846) or certain acutely toxic F-listed wastes must be provided with a secondary containment system designed and operated in accordance with specified requirements, including:

- Sufficiently impervious and sloped or otherwise designed to collect waste and precipitation and prevent its pooling around containers until it can be removed

- Capacity to contain the larger of 10% of total volume of containers or volume of the largest container (as computed from containers containing free liquid only)

- Run-on prevention or additional capacity to accommodate any run-on

- Prompt removal of leaked waste and precipitation

Permitted container storage facilities that do not store free liquids must merely be sloped or otherwise designed to keep precipitation from prolonged contact with the waste containers (40 CFR 264.175). As noted above, the secondary containment for free liquids must be *sufficiently impervious*—even uncoated or improperly coated concrete can and has been interpreted by regulators to be insufficient in cases that seem not to make sense, so it may be a good idea to check. The Federal regulations do not impose these secondary containment requirements on interim status units or generators accumulating waste on-site in accordance with 40 CFR 262.34(a). However, some states (*e.g.*, South Carolina) do.

Ignitable and Reactive Waste. Containers of ignitable and reactive waste must be located at least 15 meters (50 feet) from the facility property line. This provision is applicable to LQGs also, but not to SQGs accumulating waste on-site in accordance with 40 CFR 262.34 (see Table 8) (40 CFR 264/265.176).

Incompatible Waste. Incompatible wastes or waste and material may not be mixed together, and waste may not be added to a container that previously held a waste or material that is incompatible with it unless special precautions specified in 40 CFR 264/265.17(b) are complied with. Further, containers of hazardous wastes at a TSDF or LQG or SQG accumulation area must be isolated from nearby incompatible wastes or materials by means of dikes, berms, walls, or other appropriate devices. Examples of incompatibles are provided in Appendix V to 40 CFR 265 (40 CFR 264/265.177).

Inspections. Container storage facilities must be inspected at least weekly, and must address leaks and container deterioration in addition to items generally subject to inspection as required by General Facility Standards (40 CFR 264/265.15), discussed above (40 CFR 264/265.174). Again, the term *weekly* can mean different things in different states; *e.g.*, in South Carolina, it may mean every seven days; in Tennessee, they may expect days of inspection in that interval to be varied.

Air Emission Standards. The air emission standards of 40 CFR 264/265, Subpart CC apply to container management of certain organic hazardous waste as described separately below (see Table 9)(40 CFR 264/265.178).

Tank Systems

The management standards of Subpart J apply to TSDFs that store or treat hazardous waste in tanks or tank systems (see definitions in 40 CFR 260.10). With some minor exceptions, the 40 CFR 265, Subpart J standards also apply to LQGs and SQGs operating 90-day or 180/270-day accumulation tanks, but requirements for the latter are limited to relaxed tank standards at 40 CFR 265.201 (see Table 8). However, if tanks are used for 90-day or 180/270-day accumulation, it is EPA's position that they must be fully emptied at these prescribed intervals (47 FR 1248, January 11, 1982) even though this provision is not explicit in the regulations. Tank systems that are part of totally enclosed treatment units, wastewater treatment systems regulated under the Clean Water Act (CWA), or elementary neutralization units (*i.e.*, units used to neutralize waste that is hazardous only as a result of its corrosivity) are exempt from Subpart J requirements. The main provisions of Subpart J (40 CFR 264/265, Subpart J) are summarized below.

Containment and Detection of Releases.
Tank systems that are used to store or treat hazardous waste, except those that contain no free liquids, (per the paint filter liquids test; see SW–846) and are located inside a building with an impermeable floor, are required to have secondary containment and leak detetion systems in accordance with 40 CFR 264/265.193. New tanks cannot be placed in service without meeting the secondary containment provisions of 40 CFR 264.193, and existing tanks generally must meet essentially equivalent requirements within two years of becoming regulated or before 15 years of age, whichever comes later (40 CFR 264/265.193). Required elements of the secondary containment are listed below.

General Requirement. The system must detect and collect waste and accumulated liquids and prevent them from entering the environment.

Minimum Features. The system must be designed to be compatible with the waste, structurally sound and durable, capable of detecting leaks within 24 hours, and enable removal of accumulated wastes and liquids promptly (within 24 hours, if possible).

Design Options. The system must include one or more of the following: external liner, vault, double-walled tank, or equivalent device approved by EPA.

Specific Design Option Requirements. Specifics for external liners and vaults include prevention of run-on/infiltration or provision of capacity to accommodate 25-year, 24-hour storm event, and capacity to accommodate 100% of the largest tank volume.

Ancillary Equipment. Ancillary piping must be provided with full secondary containment (*e.g.*, trench, jacketing, double-wall piping) except for specific reliable components (*e.g.*, piping, welded fittings) that are subject to visual inspection on a daily basis.

A variance from the requirement for secondary containment is available if EPA can be convinced that human health or the environment would be protected. See 40 CFR 264/265.193(g) and (h).

Integrity Assessment for Existing Tank Systems.
Existing tank systems without secondary containment as described above must be assessed by a qualified registered professional engineer to determine if the tank is leaking or unfit for use. If the assessment indicates that the tank is fit and not leaking, it may be used for the interim time allowable under 40 CFR 264/265.193 until it is retrofitted with secondary containment, provided it passes annual leak tests or inspections. See 40 CFR 264/265.193(i). Otherwise, the tank system must be closed (40 CFR 264/265.191).

Design and Installation Requirements for New Tank Systems or Components.
New tank systems must be designed and installed in accordance with rigorous standards for containment, structural integrity, corrosion protection, *etc.* as set forth in this section. Certification (*e.g.*, by a qualified registered professional engineer) that the design and installation meets standards is also required (40 CFR 264/265.192).

General Operating Requirements.
The addition of hazardous waste and reagents to the tank system that could cause leaks or other failures is prohibited. Similarly, appropriate spill and overfill protective devices and practices, including maintenance of adequate freeboard in uncovered tanks, must be employed. Assurance that safe conditions will be maintained is provided by the requirement for general waste analysis (40 CFR 264/265.13) discussed previously under the General Facilities Standards (Subpart B), and by additional waste analysis and trial treatment or storage tests (*e.g.*, bench scale or pilot scale) or documentation of tests (40 CFR 264/265.200) on similar wastes (40 CFR 264/265.194).

Requirements for Ignitable, Reactive, and Incompatible Wastes.
The following special requirements apply to these wastes:

- Except in emergencies, ignitable and reactive wastes must be decharacterized before introduction to the tank system, or managed in the system so that ignition or reaction is precluded. Setbacks from public approaches and property lines prescribed by National Fire Protection Association (NFPA) *Flammable and Combustible Liquids Code* must be observed

- Incompatible wastes or waste and material may not be mixed together in a tank, and waste may not be added to a tank that previously held a material or waste that is incompatible with it unless special precautions specified in 40 CFR 264/265.17(b) are followed

(40 CFR 264/265.198–200)

Inspections. Inspections must be conducted once each operating day (*i.e.*, every day when hazardous waste is in the tank system), and must address spill/overfill control equipment, all aboveground portions of the system (for corrosion, leaks), monitoring and leak detection equipment data, materials of construction, secondary containment, and immediate surroundings to ensure continued integrity and detect any releases, in addition to items generally subject to inspection as required by General Facility Standards (40 CFR 264/265.15) discussed above. If the tank system includes a cathodic protection system, it must be checked within six months of installation and annually thereafter. All sources of impressed current for cathodic protection must be inspected or tested, as appropriate, bimonthly (40 CFR 264/265.195).

Response to Leaks and Spills; Disposition of Unfit Tanks. A tank system or secondary containment system from which there has been a leak or spill and is unfit for use must be removed from service immediately. Measures must be taken to stop and contain the leak or spill and assess its cause (*e.g.*, by inspection). Any release to the environment, except for those less than one pound that are immediately cleaned up, must be reported to EPA within 24 hours followed by a written report within 30 days. If the leak to the environment was a result of compromise or lack of secondary containment, such containment must be repaired or provided (unless, as for new systems, it can be readily inspected, *etc.*) before returning the system to service. Unfit tanks must be closed in accordance with 40 CFR 264/265.197 (40 CFR 264/265.196).

Closure and Postclosure Care. Tank systems can normally be closed in accordance with the closure standard of 40 CFR 264/265.111 (*i.e.*, achieve clean closure) as described above. Those which cannot must be closed as landfills and are subject to postclosure care (Subpart G), ground water monitoring (Subpart F) and postclosure financial assurance requirements (Subpart H). Tank systems without secondary containment must have in place a contingent plan for *dirty* closure and postclosure as well as a *clean closure* plan (40 CFR 264/265.197).

Air Emission Standards. The air emission standards of 40 CFR 264/265, Subparts AA, BB, CC apply to management of certain organic hazardous wastes in tank systems as described separately below (see Table 9)(40 CFR 264.201, 265.202).

Alternate Tank Standards for SQGs. The specific tank system requirements applicable to SQGs managing waste on-site in 180/270-day accumulation units are a relaxed version of Subpart J requirements described above and do not include requirements for secondary containment (40 CFR 265.201). Requirements that do apply include the following:

- General operating requirements (as described above, except that additional testing is not required).

- Requirements for ignitable, reactive, and incompatible wastes (as described above).

- Inspections (as described above, except that less critical system components and surroundings can be inspected weekly instead of daily).

- Compliance with closure performance standard (40 CFR 264/265.111) is not required, but all hazardous waste must nonetheless be removed and properly disposed of at closure.

Containment Buildings

The standards of 40 CFR 264/265, Subpart DD provide additional hazardous waste management flexibility to TSDFs and LQGs in the form of *containment buildings*. Units that meet containment building standards in this subpart are authorized for a variety of operations that cannot be readily performed with containerized waste or bulk waste in tanks. These include storage and manipulation of otherwise unconfined bulk waste (*i.e.*, waste piles) and/or performance of complex treatment processes without the need to otherwise confine the waste to RCRA-compliant tanks or containers. The containment building standards are comprised of relatively straightforward requirements related to design, operation, and closure.

Design Standards. Containment buildings must be designed with specific features, as described below.

Enclosure. The building must be a complete enclosed structure with floor, walls, and roof.

Structural Soundness and Durability. The building must be structurally sound and durable, with respect to stresses imposed by activities in the unit and environmental factors (lightweight doors are allowable if they do not contact waste and are effective barriers to fugitive dust emissions).

Primary Containment. Buildings to be used for management of only solid phase waste and reagents must be provided with a primary barrier appropriate to physical and chemical characteristics of the waste and durable with respect to stresses imposed by activities in the unit.

Secondary Containment. Buildings for management of hazardous waste containing free liquids or treated with free liquids must be provided with primary and secondary containment barriers impervious to the waste with liquid collection/removal system to remove liquids from the top of the primary barrier and a leak detection system to detect leaks of the primary barrier, which are durable with respect to stresses imposed by activities in the unit. A waiver from this requirement is potentially available if EPA is convinced that containment can be ensured without secondary containment.

Certification by a qualified registered professional engineer that the unit meets design requirements must be obtained and maintained in the operating record of the facility (40 CFR 264/265.1101).

Operating Standards. Containment buildings must be operated in accordance with specific requirements, including those listed below.

Incompatible Waste and Reagents. Incompatible hazardous wastes and treatment reagents that may compromise the containment building must not be introduced to the unit.

Containment Practices. Controls and practices must ensure containment of hazardous waste within the unit, including maintenance of primary barrier, controlling level of waste within the containment walls, prevent tracking of waste from the unit, and control of fugitive dust emissions. In containment buildings that include both areas with and without secondary containment, special written procedures are required to ensure that liquids or wet materials are not introduced to areas without secondary containment.

Prompt Repairs and Reporting. Conditions that have caused or may cause a release of hazardous waste must be repaired promptly. Releases must be documented, affected areas must be immediately removed from service and leakage must be removed, a written plan for repairs must be prepared and executed, and EPA must be notified of the release. Repairs must be certified by a qualified registered professional engineer and EPA must be notified of repair completion.

Inspections and Monitoring. Monitoring and leak detection equipment and associated data, the containment building, and the surrounding area must be inspected at least once every seven days.

Records. The operating record, including inspection and repair records, must be maintained for three years.

(40 CFR 264/265.1102)

Closure and Postclosure Care. Containment buildings can normally be closed in accordance with the closure standard of 40 CFR 264/265.111 (*i.e.*, achieve clean closure) as described above. Those which cannot must be closed as landfills and are subject to postclosure care (Subpart G), ground water monitoring (Subpart F) and postclosure financial assurance requirements (Subpart H).

Land-Based Units: Surface Impoundments, Waste Piles, Land Treatment Units, and Landfills

Surface impoundments, waste piles, land treatment units, and landfills, so-called *land-based units*, pose relatively high risk of contaminating ground water. Such units thus have in common special provisions for ground water protection including requirements for ground water monitoring (40 CFR 264/265, Subpart F) and financial assurance requirements for postclosure care (40 CFR 264/265, Subpart H). Additional special requirements for these units are set forth in 40 CFR 264/265; Subparts K, L, M, and N, respectively. Impoundments, waste piles, and landfills have very similar requirements, the key elements of which are summarized below.

Containment Provisions. With minor exceptions, new units and expansions of existing units must be designed to be consistent with RCRA minimum technological requirements (*i.e.*, double liners, leachate collection system—not applicable to impoundments—and leak detection/collection systems). Related containment measures are also required, including dike integrity and overtopping controls for impoundments and run-on/run-off controls for waste piles and landfills. Containment requirements for existing units are less stringent, but are accompanied by more prescriptive management and operating requirements (which are established in permits for new facilities). Interim status impoundments must meet liner requirements for new facilities within 48 months of becoming regulated.

Action Leakage Rates. A maximum allowable flow rate for removal of leakage through the primary liner by the leak detection system is established as a trigger for initiation of response actions.

Response Action. Facilities are required to develop and obtain regulator approval of a response action plan that describes actions to be taken if the action leakage rate is exceeded. Typically required elements of the plan include notification to EPA within seven days, written preliminary assessment and short-term action plan to EPA within 14 days, report to EPA of results of remedial actions taken and planned within 30 days and at 30-day intervals thereafter.

Inspections and Monitoring. Inspection of the containment system (*i.e.*, liner, *etc.*) is required during its installation for new systems. During operation, inspection of containment provisions is typically required weekly and after storms. Leakage removal volumes must typically be recorded weekly during operation and at a lower frequency dependent on leakage rate during postclosure.

Requirements for Special Wastes. Ignitables and reactives are either prohibited in these units or are allowable under narrowly defined conditions. Similarly, introduction of incompatible wastes and materials combinations are prohibited without observing the special precautions of 40 CFR 264.17(b). The acutely toxic dioxin-containing wastes F020, through F023, F026 and F027 are also prohibited without special management controls. Disposal of small containers in over-packed drums (lab packs) may be placed in landfills only if special requirements of 40 CFR 264/265.316 related to waste incompatibility, packaging, use of sorbents for free liquids, and related items are met. As discussed later, if these wastes are LDR prohibited wastes, they must meet applicable treatment standards.

Closure and Postclosure Care. These units must either close by removal (*i.e.*, clean close), or close by eliminating free liquids and stabilizing waste and waste residues in place where required and by installing a low permeability final cover meeting the technical requirements of 40 CFR 264/265.310 (*i.e.*, a RCRA-style cap) which includes appropriate run-on/run-off controls and erosion control measures. Postclosure care is required for units that are not clean-closed.

Other Requirements. The air emission standards of 40 CFR 264/265, Subparts BB and CC, apply to surface impoundments.

In contrast to the land-based units described above, operation of land treatment facilities involves intentional placement of hazardous waste onto the soil surface or incorporating it into the soil for purposes of treatment typically by immobilization or destruction (*e.g.*, by microbial action). Therefore, the protective requirements for land treatment units, provided in 40 CFR 264/265, Subpart M are substantially different than for the land-based units described above. These requirements are focused on ensuring that wastes are effectively treated in the unit and that hazardous constituents do not escape beyond the unit (*e.g.*, by infiltration beyond the soil column established as the treatment zone, erosion by wind or water, or incorporation into food chain crops).

Incinerators and Thermal Treatment Units

Thermal treatment of hazardous waste may be accomplished in hazardous waste incinerators, boilers and industrial furnaces (BIFs), and other thermal treatment units, as distinguished by definitions provided at 40 CFR 260.10 and applicability sections of the RCRA regulations that apply to these units. Basically, both incinerators and BIFs as addressed here are enclosed devices that employ controlled flame combustion to destroy hazardous waste. BIFs are distinguished from incinerators primarily by the fact that they are designed to use the thermal energy from the combustion process, typically in industrial processes. Other thermal treatment units as denoted here consist of devices other than incinerators and BIFs that are used for thermal treatment of hazarous waste (*e.g.*, calcining). RCRA requirements for hazardous waste incinerators are set forth at 40 CFR 264/265, Subpart O; requirements for BIFs are provided at 40 CFR 266, Subpart H; and requiremnst for other thermal treatment units are found at 40 CFR 265, Subpart P.

The following discussion is focused on the 40 CFR 264/265, Subpart O requirements for incinerators, which are similar to those at 40 CFR 266, Subpart H for two types of BIFs, hazardous-waste-burning cement kilns and lightweight aggregate kilns (LWAKs). This similarity stems from the fact that all of these types of units, collectively termed *hazardous waste combustors,* are ultimately subject to the maximum achievable control technology (MACT) standards for hazardous waste combustion, which embody most of their unit-specific requirements. Requirements for cement kilns and LWAKs are further addressed in the context of 40 CFR 266 requirements for BIFs presented later in the chapter. The requirements of 40 CFR 265, Subpart P for other thermal treatment units are briefly addressed at the end of this section.

The unit-specific TSDF requirements outlined here are in addition to requirements at 40 CFR 264/265, Subparts A–H (general standards for TSDFs), discussed previously, and air emission standards not related to the combustion process (*e.g.*, from equipment leaks, tanks, and containers) set forth in 40 CFR 264/265, Subparts BB and CC, discussed later in this chapter, all of which generally apply to hazardous waste combustion units as denoted above. However, incinerators that treat only certain ICR wastes (in particular, wastes that are hazardous only by virtue of ignitability, corrosivity, or reactivity) and that contain insignificant quantities of hazardous constituents listed in 40 CFR 261, Appendix VIII, are conditionally exempt from virtually all of the Subpart O requirements related to operation as discussed below, including the emission standards (see specific conditions at 40 CFR 264/265.340).

Integration of MACT Standards

The requirements of 40 CFR 264/265, Subpart O for incinerators (and those of 40 CFR 266 for cement kilns and LWAKs) were integrated with the MACT standards for hazardous waste combustion, set forth as part of the Clean Air Act (CAA)

National Emission Standards for Hazardous Air Pollutants (NESHAPs) at 40 CFR 63, Subpart EEE, in 1999 (see 64 FR 52827, September 30, 1999 and subsequent revisions). In general, this integration is represented by the provision at 40 CFR 264/265.340(b) that most of the Subpart O rules, with the notable exception of closure requirements at 40 CFR 364/365.351, are supplanted by the MACT standards requirements when compliance with the MACT standards is demonstrated by a comprehensive performance test and notification of compliance is sent to EPA. The RCRA Subpart O performance standards, operating requirements, as well as monitoring and inspection rules apply until that time. Permit conditions for RCRA-permitted incinerators based on these Subpart O rules also remian in force until their permits are modified to eliminate the duplicative requirements. The following discussion hightlights the Subpart O rules with notation of those replaced by the MACT standards, and some of the key MACT requirements.

Waste Analysis. Beyond the waste analysis normally required by 40 CFR 265.13, discussed previously, the RCRA rules at Subpart O provide that any new waste treated in interim status incinerators must be analyzed to ensure efficient operation of the incinerator and determine emissions that would result. It must minimally include heating value, halogen and sulfur content, and concentration of lead and mercury (unless the operator has data documenting their absence). Waste analysis requirements for permitted facilities are established in the permitting process. Sufficient waste analysis must be carried out throughout normal operation to verify that waste feed to the incinerator is within permitted limits (40 CFR 264/265.341). These waste analysis requirements do not apply once MACT standards become applicable and, where appropriate, associated permit requirements are deleted.

Performance Standards. Until supplanted by MACT standards, permitted incinerators must be designed, constructed, and maintained to achieve the specific performance standards established in Subpart O for organics, hydrogen chloride (HCl), and particulates, as follows (40 CFR 264.343):

- *Organics*—Performance standards for organics are stated in terms of destruction and removal efficiency (DRE) of the unit with respect to the principal organic hazardous constituents (POHCs), selected generally on the basis of destructibility and prevalence in the waste stream. A DRE of 99.99% is normally required for POHCs assigned for each waste feed specified in the permit application. A DRE of 99.9999% is required for facilities that incinerate acutely toxic F020–F023, F026, and F027 wastes (interim status units must obtain special certification for these wastes).

- *HCl*—Incinerators producing more than 1.8 kg/hr of HCl in stack emissions must reduce emissions to the greater of 1.8 kg/hr or that achieved by 99% removal.

- *Particulates*—Particulate emissions are limited to 180 mg per dry standard cubic meter (dscm), corrected for oxygen in the stack gas.

The ability to achieve these Subpart O standards is demonstrated in a formal trial burn.

The above RCRA standards are supplanted by the following emission limits in the recently promulgated MACT standards for hazardous waste combustors at 40 CFR 1203, when compliance with MACT standards is demonstrated on the basis of a comprehensive performance test and EPA is notified:

- *Organics*—Units must demonstrate a DRE of 99.99% for each POHC in the waste stream, or 99.9999% for F020–F023, F026, and F027 wastes as cited in the RCRA emsission standards noted above, plus more stringent, risk-based limits for dioxins and furans expressed as toxicity equivalents in nanograms per dry standard cubic meter (TEQ/dscm), as low as 0.2 ng TEQ/dscm corrected to 7 percent oxygen for new incinerators.

- *Hydrocarbons and Carbon Monoxide (CO)*—Hydrocarbons are further limited by direct limits or limits on carbon monoxide as a surrogate. For new incinerators, the limits are: either 10 parts per million by volume (ppmv) for hydrocarbons or 100 ppm by volume carbon monoxide (hourly rolling average, monitored continuously with a continuous emission monitoring system [CEMS]). If the latter, 10 ppm by volume hydrocarbons must be demonstrated during DRE test runs or equivalent tests.

- *Total Chlorine*—The HCl emission standards under RCRA stated above are supplanted by an emission limit that accounts for both HCl and chlorine gas. The total chlorine emission limit for new incinerators is 20 ppmv.

- *Particulates*—More stringent particulate matter limits than the RCRA limits cited above to help limit emission of metals, which may attach to emitted particles. The standard for new incinerators is 34 mg/dscm corrected to 7 percent oxygen.

- *Metals*—Specific metals emission limits are established for selected toxic metals. For new incinerators, emissions must not exceed the following (as micrograms/dscm, corrected to 7 percent oxygen): mercury, 130; lead and cadmium combined, 240; arsenic, beryllium, and chromium combined, 97.

Operating Requirements. The RCRA standards in Subpart O generally prohibit hazardous waste from being fed to either a permitted or interim status incinerator during startup or shutdown unless the incinerator is within normal operating conditions. Permitted incinerators must operate in accordance with conditions established in the permit application and observe specific requirements for waste feed, fugitive emissions control, waste feed cutoff, *etc.* as described in this section (40 CFR 264/265.345). These RCRA requirements are replaced by the MACT standards once they are made applicable to the unit. Under the MACT standards, the units must be operated within limits for parameters such as temperature, pressure, and waste feed that are established on the basis of the comprehensive performance test, and critical parameters are continuously monitored. The facility may also choose to use CEMS to monitor emissions in place of associated operating parameter monitoring.

Monitoring and Inspections. Until the MACT standards become applicable, RCRA Subpart O rules for interim status units provide that combustion and emission control instruments be monitored at least every 15 minutes and the incinerator and associated equipment must be inspected at least daily. The following Subpart O requirements for monitoring and inspection (40 CFR 264/265.347) apply to permitted facilities until they are supplanted by the MACT standards and associated permit modifications are effected:

- Continuous monitoring of combustion temperature, waste feed rate, combustion gas velocity indicator, carbon monoxide downstream of combustion zone and prior to release

- Upon request of EPA, sampling and analysis of waste and exhaust emissions

- At least daily inspection of the incinerator and associated equipment

- At least weekly testing of emergency waste feed cutoff system and associated alarms

The requirements for thermal treatment units other than those which qualify as incinerators or BIFs, per definitions in 40 CFR 260.10, are set forth at 40 CFR 265, Subpart P. The MACT standards as described above for combustion units are not applicable to Subpart P thermal treatment units. Only interim status standards have been promulgated at Subpart P, to accommodate existing units that are treating hazardous wastes that are newly designated. Such existing units and new units may be permitted under 40 CFR 264, Subpart X, as described later. The Subpart P requirements generally are similar to the RCRA requirements at 40 CFR 265, Subpart O, as described above for interim status incinerators. One notable exception is the provision of simplified standards for open burning or detonation of waste explosives, consisting of a prohibition on open burning of hazardous waste except for open burning and detonation of waste explosives, minimum distance setbacks from open burning or detonation sites to adjacent property, and a requirement to carry out the operation in a way that does not threaten human health or the environment.

Other Units

EPA has thus far established specific standards for four additional categories of units not previously discussed, none of which is common or applicable to a broad spectrum of facilities. Except for Subpart W, which applies only to the wood-preserving industry, these standards are not applicable to generators of hazardous waste. The standards are described in 40 CFR 264/265; Subparts Q, W, X, and EE.

Chemical, Physical, and Biological Treatment. 40 CFR 265, Subpart Q applies to TSDFs that treat hazardous waste by chemical, physical, or biological means in units other than tanks, surface impoundments, and land treatment facilities regulated under Subparts J, K, and M, respectively. The standards are similar to those established for interim status treatment in tanks or incinerators, and include waste analysis and

trial test requirements, operating requirements (restrictions on introduction of certain wastes, waste feed control), and inspection requirements.

Drip Pads. Drip pads are units established at wood-preserving operations to convey drips from the wood treatment process, precipitation, and/or surface water run-off to an associated collection system. The standards include specific design and operating requirements to effectively prevent leakage of waste to underlying soil and convey the waste to the collection system. Also included are requirements to inspect liners and cover systems during construction and the installed facility during operation weekly and after storms (40 CFR 264/265, Subpart W).

Miscellaneous Units EPA has established very general standards at Subpart X to accommodate the permitting of hazardous waste management units not appropriately addressed by other unit-specific standards of 40 CFR 264. The standard provides that miscellaneous units must be located, designed, constructed, operated, and closed in a manner that will ensure protection of human health and the environment. The standard further directs that permit terms and conditions shall include those requirements of other 40 CFR 264 Subparts that are appropriate for the miscellaneous unit. The absence of specific standards and well-established precedents makes it especially important to establish effective communications with the regulator when attempting to permit a unit under Subpart X. Examples of units that have been permitted under Subpart X include facilities for open burning/detonation of munitions and the United States Department of Energy (DOE) Waste Isolation Pilot Plant (WIPP), a geologic repository in New Mexico for transuranic radioactive wastes, some of which are also hazardous (40 CFR 264, Subpart X).

Hazardous Waste Munitions and Explosives Storage. The standards established for hazardous waste munitions and explosives include basic requirements for protective storage only (*i.e.*, the standards do not address treatment or disposal). Included are design and operating standards for minimizing potential for detonation or other means of release, requirements for monitoring, and standard provisions for closure and postclosure care. The standards apply only to military munitions (40 CFR 264/265, Subpart EE).

RCRA Overview: A Generator Perspective

Air Emission Standards

In response to a HSWA mandate at RCRA Section 3004(n), EPA established regulations in 40 CFR 264 and 265 for monitoring and control of organic air emissions from various categories of TSDFs, as follows:

- Subparts AA address emissions from certain HWMUs that treat hazardous waste exhibiting organic concentrations > 10 ppm by weight.

- Subparts BB address leaks from equipment managing hazardous waste with organics > 10% by weight.

- Subparts CC address emissions from containers, tanks, and surface impoundments containing hazardous waste with volatile organic (VO) concentrations > 500 ppm by weight.

The provisions of 40 CFR 264 and 265 do not differ substantially. However, 40 CFR 265, Subparts AA, BB, and CC (except for impoundments), apply not only to interim status TSDFs but also to LQGs managing hazardous waste in 90-day accumulation areas in accordance with 40 CFR 262.34(a). Satellite accumulation containers and SQG 180/ 270-day accumulation units are exempt from the air emission standards.

Table 9 summarizes the main requirements of the air emission requirements pertinent to generators. As shown, storage of hazardous waste in containers < 0.1 m³ (26.4 gallons) is not subject to the standards. Virtually the only standard for storage in containers > 0.1 m³ (26.4 gallons) and < 0.46 m³ (122 gallons), including 55-gallon drums, is conformance to DOT packaging requirements and provision of a cover/closure device or vapor barrier, which in any case is advisable if not required for off-site shipment of the waste. More stringent requirements apply to containers in which waste is treated by stabilization and containers > 0.46 m³ (122 gallons) storing *light liquid* organics, *i.e.*, hazardous waste in which the vapor pressure of one or more organic constituents is > 0.3 kPa at 20°C and the total concentration of such constituents is > 20% (wt). The air emission standards of Subpart AA for process vents, Subpart BB for equipment leaks, and Subpart CC for tanks, can be much more complex, requiring substantial allocation of resources to ensure compliance.

Specific Hazardous Wastes and Management Facilities

With the exception of rules at Subpart M for management of waste military munitions, current 40 CFR 266 requirements address a variety of resource recovery facilities and activities. As discussed previously under generator standards, management of certain hazardous wastes that are recycled (*i.e.*, recyclable materials) in accordance with the 40 CFR 266 management standards exempts them from other more stringent RCRA regulations. The 40 CFR 266 management standards are summarized below.

Recyclable Materials Used in a Manner Constituting Disposal. Subpart C applies to recyclable materials that are applied to or placed on the land (*e.g.*, for use as roadbed, fertilizer, *etc*). The standards basically indicate that, with few exceptions, such activities are subject to full Subtitle C regulation unless they are contained in products produced for use by the general public, have undergone a chemical reaction that makes them inseparable from the product, and meet the LDR treatment standards (or applicable prohibition levels if no treatment standards are yet established) for the hazardous waste they contain (40 CFR 266 Subpart C).

Recyclable Materials Utilized for Precious Metal Recovery. Subpart F applies to recyclable materials that are reclaimed to recover economically significant amounts of gold, silver, platinum, palladium, iridium, osmium, rhodium, ruthenium, or any combination thereof. Recovery of silver from spent photographic solutions is an example. Applicable requirements include notification to EPA of the activity, observance of manifesting and import/export requirements, and recordkeeping to demonstrate that the material is not being speculatively accumulated. Material that is speculatively accumulated is subject to full Subtitle C regulation (40 CFR 266, Subpart F).

Spent Lead-Acid Batteries Being Reclaimed. Subpart G pertains to spent lead-acid batteries being reclaimed (*i.e.*, that are recyclable materials). The standard basically specifies that persons who generate, transport, collect, or regenerate such batteries, or who store but do not reclaim them (other than those to be regenerated), are not subject to RCRA rules. However, the standard requires that facilities which store such batteries before reclaiming them (other than those to be regenerated) notify EPA of their activity and adhere to most applicable provisions of 40 CFR 264 with regard to that storage (40 CFR 266, Subpart G).

Hazardous Waste Burned in Boilers and Industrial Furnaces. Subpart H applies to hazardous waste burned or processed in BIFs for the purpose of energy or materials recovery. Two types of BIFs that burn hazardous wastes, cement kilns, and LWAKs, are regulated in a similar manner to hazardous waste incinerators, as noted in the previous discussion of 40 CFR 264/265, Subpart O requirements for incinerators. In particular, most of the 40 CFR 266, Subpart H requiremements for cement kilns and LWAKs are supplanted by CAA MACT standards at 40 CFR 63, Subpart EEE upon completion of a comprehensive performance test and notificaton of EPA. For RCRA-permitted units, permit conditions based on Subpart H also

Table 9. RCRA Air Emissions Standards (40 CFR 265; Subparts AA, BB, CC) Summary Requirements for Generators[1]

Regulatory Element	Subpart AA Process Vents	Subpart BB Equipment Leaks	Subpart CC Containers	Subpart CC Tanks
Applicable Units	Distillation, fractionation, thin film evaporation, solvent extraction, air/steam stripping units managing hazardous waste with organic concentration ≥ 10 ppm wt that are • Subject to RCRA permitting, or • Exempt from permitting under 40 CFR 262.34(a) but located at a facility subject to RCRA permitting (including recycling units), or • LQG 90–day accumulation units managed under 40 CFR 262.34	Equipment that contains or contacts hazardous waste with organics ≥ 10 wt % that is • Subject to RCRA permitting, or • Exempt from permitting under 40 CFR 262.34(a) but located at facility subject to RCRA permitting (including recycling units), or • LQG 90–day accumulation units managed under 40 CFR 262.34 Each piece of equipment subject to Subpart BB must be so marked	Containers with volume > 0.1 m³ (> 26.4 gallons) that received hazardous waste after 12/06/96 with volatile organic (VO) concentration ≥ 500 ppm wt at the generator's point of generation and • Subject to RCRA permitting, or • LQG 90–day accumulation units managed under 40 CFR 262.34(a)	Operating tanks that received Hazardous Waste after 12/06/96 with VO ≥ 500 ppm wt at the generator's point of generation and are • Subject to RCRA permitting, or • LQG 90–day accumulation units managed under 40 CFR 262.34(a)
Exceptions	Units already regulated under the Clean Air Act (40 CFR 60, 61, 63)	Units already regulated under CAA (40 CFR 60, 61, 63). Equipment in vacuum service or contacting hazardous waste with organics >10 wt % for <300 hours/year are partly exempted	• Units already regulated under CAA (40 CFR 60, 61, 63) • Remediation or mixed waste management units • Certain wastes in which VO levels have been reduced by specified amounts (e.g., ≥ 95% or to at least < 100 ppm wt) by treatment after point of origination and before entry to unit	
Major Controls	• Reduce emissions to <3 lbs/hr and 3.1 tons/year or by ≥ 95% (wt) • Closed vent systems (if used) must operate with no detectable emissions or operate at below atmospheric pressure • Control devices (if used) must comply with specific standards; e.g., >95% efficiency for vapor recovery, combustion systems; no visible emissions for flares	Specific standards for equipment categories, including pumps, valves, compressors, pressure relief devices, sample connection systems, open-ended valves and lines, closed vent systems/control devices, etc. Standards also may vary by type of service (e.g., gas or vapor service, light (i.e., high vapor pressure) material service²	• Containers >0.1 m³ (26.4 gal) and <0.46 m³ (122 gal), or >0.46 m³ and not in light material service²: Level 1 Controls • Containers >0.46 m³ in light material service²: Level 2 Controls • Containers >0.1 m³ treating hazardous waste by stabilization: Level 3 Controls • Level 1–meet DOT regulations(49 CFR 173, 178–180); cover/ closure device or vapor barrier • Level 2–meet DOT regulations(49 CFR 173, 178–180); emissions non-detectable or pass vapor tightness test • Level 3–vent through closed vent system/control device (directly or from enclosure)	• Tanks w/ maximum organic vapor pressure (MOVP) < specified limits not used for stabilization: Level 1 or 2 Controls • All Other Tanks: Level 2 Controls • Level 1–fixed roof with continuous barrier • Level 2–variable fixed and/or floating roof designs with stringent controls • Hard-piped hazardous waste transfers
Inspection/ Monitoring; Repairs	• Inspections (typically annual); monitoring (e.g. with portable instrument) as specified to determine leaks, etc. • Repair typically must be tried within 5 days and complete within 15 days	• Visual inspections, monitoring (e.g. with portable instrument) as specified by equipment/service category to detect leaks, etc. • Repair typically must be tried within 5 days and complete within 15 days	• Levels 1 & 2–initial and annual visual inspection; no monitoring • Level 3–Same as Subpart AA vents • Repairs typically must be attempted within 24 hrs and complete within 5 days	• Visual inspections, initial and typically annually, as specified by control level and tank design • Monitoring of Level 2 vents • Repairs typically must be tried within 5 days and complete within 45 days (except for tanks under negative pressure)
Recordkeeping	Operations, waste characterization, inspection/monitoring methods, results; other compliance documentation as specified	Equipment identification/characterization; waste characterization; inspection/ monitoring methods, results; other compliance documentation as specified	Inspection/monitoring plan, records; waste characterization data for Level 1 containers not in light material service to substantiate waste is not light material²; design, maintenance documentation; etc.	Inspection/monitoring plan, records; waste characterization data (e.g., MOVP determination); design, maintenance documentation; etc.

[1] Subpart CC air emission standards for impoundments are omitted from this table since they are not applicable to generators managing hazardous waste in 90-day accumulation areas per 40 CFR 262.34(a)

[2] *In light material service*, is defined for specific applications at 40 CFR 264.1031 and 265.1081; basically denotes liquids organics in which the vapor pressure of one or more organic constituents is >0.3 kPa at 20°C and the total concentration of such constituents is > 20% by weight.

apply until the permit is modified to eliminate redundancies. RCRA rules that continue to apply to these units after they become subject to the MACT standards include requirements generally applicable to TSDFs at 40 CFR 264/265, Subparts A–H; air emission standards not related to the combustion process (*e.g.*, from equipment leaks, tanks, and containers) set forth in 40 CFR 264/265, Subparts BB and CC; and specific 40 CFR 266 Subpart H rules related to unit closure, direct transfer of hazardous waste from transport vehicles to the unit; and management of residues from the treatment process. See 40 CFR 266.100 (b)(2). The MACT standards are as generally described previously for incinerators.

Some hazardous wastes and facilities are entirely exempt from 40 CFR 266, Subpart H requirements, the most notable of which include used oil burned for energy that is hazardous solely because it exhibits a hazardous waste characteristic, hazardous waste exempted at 40 CFR 261.4, and hazardous waste generated by CESQGs. Some BIFs, particularly smelting, melting, and refining furnaces that process waste solely for metal recovery, are conditionally exempt from most of the Subpart H requirements (40 CFR 266.100). In addition, BIFs that burn small quantities of certain hazardous wastes on-site and that meet other special conditions as specified at 40 CFR 266.108 are exempted from virtually all Subpart H requirements.

The Subpart H requirements at 40 CFR 266.101 basically indicate that most waste burned at BIFs is subject to other applicable RCRA requirements (*e.g.*, Part 262, 263, 264/265, and 270 standards) prior to being burned. Requirements related to the burning process itself are set forth at 40 CFR 266.102 and .103 for BIFs that have a RCRA permit and those that do not yet have a RCRA permit (*i.e.*, interim status facilities), respectively. The requirements for interim status and permitted facilities are similar. Major provisions include the following:

General TSDF Requirements—RCRA requirements generally applicable to TSDFs at 40 CFR 264/265, Subparts BB and CC apply to these units.

Waste Analysis Requirements—In general, facilities must perform an analysis of the hazardous waste with respect to hazardous constituents present. Limits on hazardous wastes burned are established in the permit for permitted BIFs and

in certifications to EPA for interim status BIFs. Interim status BIFs. may not burn dioxin-listed wastes (*i.e.*, F020–023, F026–027).

Operating Requirements—Operating requirements include limits on operating parameters such as waste feed rate and combustion temperature to ensure compliance with performance standards, including emission standards; provisions for control of fugitive emissions; and provisions for automatic waste feed cutoff when prescribed operating conditions are not met. These requirements are established in the permit for permitted facilities, generally on the basis of a formal trial burn. For interim status facilities, these requirements are developed by the owner/operator, demonstrated by compliance testing, and documented in compliance certifications to EPA.

Performance Standards—The RCRA performance standards for BIFs at 40 CFR 266, Subpart H are similar to the 40 CFR 264/265, Subpart O and MACT standards for incinerators, previously described, except for HCl, chlorine gas, and metals. For these constituents, owners and operators of boilers and most industrial furnaces have a choice of three approaches, or tiers, to ensure that emissions are below EPA's acceptable exposure levels. Under Tier I, control and monitoring is focused on waste feed, and it is assumed that 100 percent of these pollutants will enter the environment. Under Tier II, monitoring (*e.g.*, of stack emissions) is also implemented as needed to demonstrate that pollutant emissions are adequately controlled. Under Tier III, both monitoring and dispersion modeling are employed to demonstrate that pollutant exposure does not pose a threat to human health and the environment. A generalized and simplified summary of the Subpart H Emission standards for various constituents follows (see 40 CFR 266.104–107 for details):

- *Organics*—99.99% DRE for established POHCs (99.9999% for dioxin-listed hazardous wastes)

- *Hydrocarbons and CO*—With specified exceptions, 100 ppmv for CO or 10 ppmv for hydrocarbons, hourly rolling average basis. Continuous monitoring is required.

- *Particulates*—100 mg/dscm, corrected to 7 percent oxygen.

- *Metals*—Specified limits for noncarcinogenic metals (antimony, barium, lead, mercury, thallium, and silver) and carcinogenic metals (arsenic, cadmium, beryllium, chromium) established on the basis of waste feed rate screening (Tier I), emission rate screening (Tier II), site-specific risk assessment (Tier III), and variations thereof.

- *Total chlorine*—Specified limits for HCl and chlorine gas established on the basis of waste feed rate screening (Tier I), emission rate screening (Tier II), site-specific risk assessment (Tier III), and variations thereof.

Monitoring and Inspections—Requirements for BIFs are similar to those discussed previously for incinerators, and minimally include monitoring of feed rates and composition of hazardous waste, other fuels, and feed stocks; feed rates of ash, metals, chlorine and chloride; carbon monoxide, hydrocarbons, and oxygen downstream of the combustion zone and prior to release while hazardous wastes are being burned. The BIF and associated equipment must be visually inspected daily, automatic waste feed cutoff system and associated alarms normally must be tested weekly.

Standards for Direct Transfer—Special requirements apply to the direct transfer of hazardous waste from transport vehicle to a BIF without the use of a storage unit, including special containment and operating requirements (40 CFR 266.111).

Regulation of Residues—Residue from the combustion of hazardous waste may also be hazardous, *e.g.*, if it exhibits a characteristic of hazardous waste or it is derived from treatment of a listed hazardous waste. Regulations at 40 CFR 266.112 specify criteria that residue derived from the burning or processing of hazardous waste in a BIF must meet to be excluded from the definiton of hazardous waste under 40 CFR 281.4(b)(4), (7), or (8), which pertain to ash and flue gas emission control waste resulting primarily from combustion of fossil fuel (so-called Bevill wastes), ore and mineral processing wastes, as well as cement kiln dust waste.

Military Munitions. Subpart M provides criteria for determining when military munitions become a solid waste and provides management standards for solid waste military munitions that qualify as hazardous waste. The standards are narrowly focused in response to peculiar problems faced by the military with regard to the management of military munitions and are of no practical importance to most generators (40 CFR 266, Subpart M).

Land Disposal Restrictions

The land disposal restrictions (LDRs) prohibit land disposal of hazardous waste unless the waste meets treatment standards established by EPA. Mandated by Congress with passage of HSWA, the LDRs are intended primarily to protect ground water, and with related HSWA provisions (minimum technology requirements, corrective action) provide a powerful economic incentive for waste minimization. EPA has codified the LDR implementing regulations for disposal of hazardous waste in two places in its regulations based on the mode of land disposal. Disposal of hazardous waste by deep well injection into formations that are not drinking water sources (Class I wells) is addressed by Safe Drinking Water Act (SDWA) regulations at 40 CFR 148. All other forms of land disposal are addressed in RCRA regulations at 40 CFR 268. Only the latter regulations are addressed in any detail here.

The term *land disposal* is very broadly defined in 40 CFR 268.2 to include virtually any temporary or permanent placement in or on the land outside of so-called *corrective action management units* (CAMUs) established for temporary storage of remediation waste as described in 40 CFR 264, Subpart S. Placement of hazardous waste in a RCRA land-based unit (*i.e.*, surface impoundment, waste pile, landfill, land treatment facility) is also considered land disposal. Storage in RCRA tanks, containers, or other nonland-based units is not considered to be land disposal.

Unless exempted, a waste is deemed to be an *LDR restricted waste* upon promulgation of a treatment standard for that waste. A restricted waste is prohibited from land disposal (*i.e.*, is a *prohibited waste*) after the effective date of the treatment standard if it does not meet the applicable treatment standard and no other variances are applicable. The LDR effective dates for various wastes are listed in Appendices VII and VIII of 40 CFR 268.

The LDR treatment standards applicable to a waste *attach* at the point of generation of the waste. Therefore, even if a waste is rendered nonhazardous after it is generated, it is possible that the waste does not meet the treatment standard. In such cases the waste remains prohibited. Consequently, it is important to determine LDR requirements that apply to the waste concurrent with the waste determination process, ideally prior to waste generation. The initial step in this process is to establish whether the waste is subject to any exemptions, extensions, or variances from the standards.

Exemptions, Extensions, and Variances

The hazardous wastes described in this section are important to generators because the wastes are not prohibited from land disposal (40 CFR 268.1).

Newly Identified or Listed Wastes Without LDR Standards. EPA is obligated, but not always successful, in establishing treatment standards for newly identified and listed wastes within six months of their identification or listing. In the meantime, this hazardous waste may be land-disposed in an authorized RCRA Subtitle C facility (40 CFR 268.13).

Restricted Waste Prior to Effective Date of Prohibition. The effective date of the prohibition on land disposal may be set well after the standard is established, and the waste may be land-disposed in an authorized RCRA Subtitle C facility in the interim. For example, EPA may unilaterally delay the effective date for a waste on a national basis for up to two years if insufficient capacity exists to treat the waste. EPA may also grant case-by-case extensions of an effective date for up to two years if a generator or TSDF can justify the extension per 40 CFR 268.5 (40 CFR 268.5, 268.30–37).

Wastes Granted a No Migration Variance. EPA allows for an exemption from the land disposal prohibition upon demonstration that there will be no migration of hazardous constituents from the disposal unit for as long as the wastes remain hazardous (10,000 years typically is required as an assumption for associated modeling studies). However, such variances have been granted in only a few instances of deep well injection (40 CFR 268.6).

Decharacterized Wastes Disposed in SDWA Class I Injection Wells. Wastes which are hazardous only because they exhibit a characteristic and from which the characteristic has been removed may be disposed in an injection well meeting the definition of 40 CFR 146.6(a); *i.e.*, a SDWA Class I injection well. See 40 CFR 268.1(c)(3).

Decharacterized Wastes Managed in CWA or CWA-Equivalent Systems. Wastes which are hazardous only because they exhibit a characteristic (except D003 reactive cyanides) and which are not subject to an LDR treatment standard that is a specified technology other than deactivation (DEACT) may be land-disposed if the characteristic is first removed by at least one of the following:

- Management in a treatment system with an NPDES permitted discharge

- Treatment to meet CWA Section 307 pre-treatment requirements

- Management in a CWA-equivalent zero-discharge system

This is an important exemption for generators of characteristic waste who operate their own wastewater treatment facilities or who discharge to a publicly owned treatment works (POTW). However, it is important to know that the systems in which such decharacterization occurs must not qualify as land-based units. For example, decharacterization in an impoundment that is not a RCRA permitted or interim status unit is prohibited except under the special conditions noted at the end of this section. See 40 CFR 268.1(c)(4).

De Minimis Losses* of Characteristic Waste.** *De minimis* losses of wastes that are hazardous as a result of characteristic only that are discharged to CWA regulated wastewater facilities are not subject to LDR. ***De minimis losses, specifically defined in this section, includes minor leaks and spills, sample purgings, relief device discharges, rinsate from empty containers or containers that are rendered empty by that rinsing, and minor laboratory waste contributions to the wastewater facility (*e.g.*, <1% or 1 ppm at the facility headworks). Therefore, this can be an especially important exemption for generators who operate production and process facilities and facilities with laboratories. See 40 CFR 268.1(e)(4).

CESQG Hazardous Waste, Waste Pesticide Disposed by Farmers in Accordance with 40 CFR 262.70, and Universal Waste Managed under 40 CFR 273. As previously discussed, these wastes are not subject to any LDR requirements.

An otherwise prohibited waste may be *land-disposed* to a treatment impoundment or series of treatment impoundments under limited conditions

(40 CFR 268.4). The impoundments must meet minimum technological requirements, treatment residues must be analyzed in accordance with an EPA-approved Waste Analysis Plan (WAP) to demonstrate that LDR standards are achieved, and residues not meeting standards must be removed annually.

Treatment Standards

The LDR treatment standards developed by EPA are technology based. The standards presented in 40 CFR 268.40 may be applied to any waste, but have proven to be impractical for some waste forms. EPA has developed alternative standards that may be used for qualifying waste forms, including hazardous debris, hazardous contaminated soil, and lab packs. Highlights of LDR standards development and main provisions of the standards are summarized below.

LDR Standards Development. Section 3004 (m) of RCRA requires that EPA promulgate treatment standards which substantially diminish the toxicity or mobility of the hazardous waste such that short- and long-term threats to human health and the environment are minimized. EPA has attempted to comply with this mandate by developing standards based on performance of the best demonstrated available technology (BDAT) for treating various hazardous wastes. Examples of BDAT include:

- 99.99% DRE incineration for most organics

- Biological destruction of dilute organics in wastewater treatment facilities (WWTFs)

- Chemical precipitation of toxic metal ions in wastewater

- High temperature metal recovery (HTMR) for metallic nonwastewaters

- Slag vitrification for arsenic nonwastewaters

- Roasting or retorting for mercury nonwastewaters

- Alkaline dechlorination for cyanides

When standards are published in the *Federal Register*, EPA also indicates how to obtain the associated *Background Document* which documents the basis as BDAT, including treatment technologies considered, types of waste tested, methods, and test data.

The LDR treatment standards are expressed in one of three forms.

Total Concentration of Hazardous Constituents in the Waste. Used mostly for liquid phase wastes.

Concentration of Hazardous Constituent in TCLP Extract. Used mostly for hazardous metals in solid phase waste.

Specific Technologies. Used mostly for wastes which are difficult to treat or analyze to determine treatment effectiveness, or to promote recovery of metal in high-metal-content waste (*e.g.*, roasting/ retorting for high mercury content waste, HTMR for K061 emission control dust sludge from the primary production of steel in electric furnaces).

Concentration standards are generally preferred by EPA because of the treatment flexibility they afford. However, specified technologies are often the only practical way to achieve the *minimize threat mandate*.

Primary LDR Treatment Standards. The LDR Treatment standards presented in 40 CFR 268.40 are applicable to any prohibited hazardous waste. Table 268.40 lists these primary treatment standards. In this table, the treatment standards are assigned to wastes on the basis of hazardous waste code and treatment/regulatory subcategory (if any); and for each waste thus defined, wastewater and nonwastewater forms.

Hazardous Waste Code. For example, D, F, K, U, and P codes.

Treatment/Regulatory Subcategory. Subcategories may be established for a hazardous waste code on the basis of its origin (*e.g.*, D007 chromium-radioactive high-level wastes from reprocessing of fuel rods), subsequent management concentration of regulated hazardous constituent (*e.g.*, D009 mercury < 260 mg/kg), or waste form (*e.g.*, D008 lead-lead acid batteries).

Wastewater and Nonwastewater. Wastewater and *nonwastewater* forms are recognized for each of the categories/subcategories defined above. **Wastewaters** are defined as wastes with <1 % by weight total organic carbon (TOC) and <1% by weight total suspended solids. All other wastes are considered to be **nonwastewaters**.

For each hazardous waste thus defined in Table 268.40, the treatment standard is expressed as either application of a specified technology (described in 40 CFR 268.42; Table 1), or as maximum allowable concentration(s) of regulated hazardous constituent(s) in the waste or in TCLP extract. In addition, for all characteristic wastes with standards expressed as concentrations, the treatment standards also specify that underlying hazardous constituents (UHCs) in the waste must be at or below *universal treatment standard* (UTS) concentrations. Applicable UHCs and corresponding UTS concentrations are listed in 40 CFR 268.48, "Table UTS." In practice, EPA allows one to address only those UHCs *reasonably expected to be present in the waste*, not the entire universe of UHCs in the table. Table 10 provides summary examples of specified technologies for treating some common wastes, and the standard five-letter technology code assigned to the technology.

Alternate Standards for Hazardous Debris. Impracticalities in treating and demonstrating compliance with the 40 CFR 268.40 standards for relatively large, solid phase hazardous wastes prompted EPA to establish alternative standards (40 CFR 268.45). To qualify for the alternative standards, this waste must meet the 40 CFR 268.2 definition of *debris*, summarized as follows:

> Solid material > 60 mm (2.5 in) particle size that is intended for disposal and is a manufactured object, plant or animal matter, or geologic material, except for

– Materials for which a specified technology treatment standard is already established (*e.g.*, D008 lead-acid batteries in Table 268.40)

– Process residuals (*e.g.*, smelter slag, waste treatment residues)

– Intact containers of hazardous waste that retain at least 75 % of their original volume

Mixtures of untreated debris and other material are considered debris if they are comprised of debris by visual inspection. Debris that is hazardous waste is called *hazardous debris*.

The alternative treatment standards for debris that is hazardous (*hazardous debris*) is provided in 40 CFR 268.45, Table 1. They consist exclusively of the treatment technology types described below.

Extraction Technologies.

- Physical (*e.g.*, abrasive blasting, grinding, spalling, high-pressure spraying)

- Chemical (*e.g.*, water washing, liquid and vapor phase solvent extraction)

- Thermal (high-temperature metals recovery, thermal desorption)

Destruction Technologies.

- Biological (*e.g.*, biodegradation)

Table 10. Examples of Common LDR Treatment Technologies Specified in 40 CFR 268.40

Technology Name	Technology Code	Description	Waste Treated
Biodegradation	BIODG	Chemical breakdown of organics, nonmetallic inorganics by microbes	Many dilute organics; phosphorus, nitrogen, or sulfur-containing inorganics.
Chemical Oxidation	CHOXD	Oxidation with hypochlorite, chlorine, peroxide, ozone, or other oxidizer	Many organics, alternate specified technology for many organic wastewaters and some non-wastewaters
Combustion	CMBST	Treatment in 40 CFR 264/265, Subpart O incinerators and 40 CFR 266, Subpart H BIFs	Many dilute and concentrated organics; specified technology for many nonwastewater organics
Deactivation	DEACT	Removal of the hazardous characteristics, usually by chemical means (*e.g.*, neutralization, open burning, detonation)	ICR wastes; specified technology for D002, D003 except cyanides
Stabilization	STABL	Immobilization of metals or inorganics in Portland cement, lime/pozzolans, or similar matrices.	RCRA metals, inorganics (*e.g.*, metal containing sludge from industrial WWTF; incinerator ash

- Chemical (chemical oxidation, chemical reduction)

- Thermal (incineration in Subpart O, incinerator, and 40 CFR 266, Subpart H; BIF)

Immobilization Technologies.

- Macro-encapsulation (*e.g.*, surface coating or jacket of inert materials)

- Micro-encapsulation (*e.g.*, stabilization with lime/pozzolans, Portland cement)

- Sealing (*e.g.*, epoxy, silicone coating)

Associated performance and/or design and operating standards, and restrictions on contaminant or debris types are also specified in 40 CFR 268.45, Table 1. For example, physical extraction must be applied to achieve a *clean surface* for nonporous debris, but for porous debris at least 0.6 cm (0.5 in) of surface must also be removed.

Hazardous debris must be treated using one or more of the above technologies to address the following, as applicable to the waste:

- Ignitability, corrosivity, and reactivity (for debris that qualifies as D001, D002, or D003)

- Constituents for which the waste exhibits the toxicity characteristic (for debris that is characteristically hazardous)

- Constituents for which treatment standards are established in Table 268.40 (for debris contaminated with listed waste)

- Cyanide (for debris that is reactive for cyanide)

Mixtures of debris types or contaminant types must be treated to achieve treatment standards applicable to all types represented in the waste. If an immobilization technology is used in a series of treatments (*i.e.*, **treatment train**), it must be applied last. Hazardous debris that is also a waste polychlorinated biphenyl (PCB) must be treated to either the above standards or TSCA standards at 40 CFR 761, whichever are more stringent. Residues from the treatment of hazardous debris may also require treatment. See 40 CFR 268.45(d).

Alternate Standards for Contaminated Soil. The LDRs have proven to be a substantial economic disincentive to remediation of contaminated sites where the required cleanup involves excavation of contaminated soil that exhibits one or more hazardous waste characteristics or contains a listed hazardous waste. When such soil exits the remediation unit, associated CAMU or temporary unit (TUs) (40 CFR 264, Subpart S), it becomes waste and, if prohibited, must meet LDR treatment standards before it can be replaced, disposed of in a landfill, or otherwise land-disposed. EPA has developed the alternate standards in consideration of the technical difficulties of treating this waste form, and the fact that remediation processes are regulated in a way that controls risks posed by these soils (40 CFR 268.49).

Applicability. Hazardous soils that exhibit one or more characteristic or which did so when it was generated (*e.g.*, excavated and managed outside of an allowed corrective action unit) must meet LDR treatment standards. Hazardous soils that are deemed by EPA to contain a listed waste upon generation, and where that listed waste is prohibited, must also meet LDR standards.

Constituents Subject to Treatment. With minor exceptions, the alternate treatment standards must address all constituents listed in 40 CFR 268.48, "Table UTS," that are reasonably expected to be present in the soil and present in concentrations greater than 10 times the UTS.

Standards for All Soils. For all soils, constituents subject to treatment may be reduced to below UTS levels and satisfy the standard. Alternatively, these constituents must be reduced by at least 90% as measured by total constituent concentration for nonmetals and metals for which a metal removal technology is applied, and TCLP for all other metals; treatment to below 10 times UTS is not required.

Additional Standards for ICR Soils. ICR wastes must also be decharacterized prior to land disposal.

Additional Standards for Soils with Constituents that Are Not Analyzable. Soils containing constituents subject to treatment that cannot be analyzed must also be treated using appropriate specified technologies listed in Table 268.42.

Treatment Residues. Residues from the treatment of hazardous debris may also require treatment. See 40 CFR 268.49(e).

Alternate Standards for Lab Packs. EPA has provided alternate LDR treatment standard for *lab packs*, a form of packaging often used for small containers of waste chemicals described earlier in this chapter in the discussion of packaging requirements for generators. See 40 CFR 268.42(c). The alternative standard is treatment in an incinerator in accordance with 40 CFR 264/265, Subpart O standards as described earlier, and is available under the following conditions:

- The lab packs must be packaged in accordance with 40 CFR 264/265.316 as previously described for disposal (*e.g.*, with absorbent in accordance with DOT standards, segregated incompatibles, deactivated reactives, *etc.*).

- The lab packs must not contain any wastes listed in Appendix IV of 40 CFR 268, which consists of D009 mercury, chromium pigment K-listed wastes, arsenic containing P-listed wastes, and a few others.

- Incinerator residues from lab packs containing characteristic metal wastes are treated to meet applicable standards in 40 CFR 268.40.

Alternative Standards by Petition. EPA has made provisions for establishing an alternative LDR treatment standard for a waste in the form of treatability variances and equivalency demonstrations (40 CFR 268.42, 268.44). Under treatability variance procedures, generators or treaters can obtain approval of an alternative LDR standard (alternative concentration limit or application of alternative technology) by successfully demonstrating that their waste is fundamentally different than that evaluated by EPA in establishing the existing standard. Any person may seek an alternative standard through an equivalency demonstration, which seeks to convince EPA that the proposed alternative offers protection equivalent to the existing standard.

Other LDR Provisions

The following provisions are also important to full understanding of LDR requirements.

Dilution Prohibition and Storage Prohibition. EPA has imposed the prohibitions on dilution and storage to discourage efforts to circumvent the LDR treatment standards.

Dilution. Dilution is prohibited as a substitute for proper treatment. However, as reflected in the previous discussion, dilution as part of legitimate treatment in CWA regulated systems, except for cyanides, is generally permissible (40 CFR 268.3).

Storage. Storage of LDR restricted wastes is only permissible to accumulate sufficient quantities to facilitate proper recovery, treatment, or disposal (40 CFR 268.50).

Disposal of LDR-Compliant Waste. The following hazardous wastes are rendered nonhazardous by LDR treatment and may be disposed of in a non-hazardous RCRA Subtitle D landfill:

- Waste that is hazardous by characteristic only, after LDR-compliant treatment has removed the characteristic(s)

- Listed hazardous debris after LDR-compliant treatment using extraction or destruction technologies has been applied

All other LDR treated wastes remain hazardous wastes and must be subsequently managed in RCRA Subtitle C (hazardous waste) TSDFs.

Waste Analysis, Recordkeeping, and Notifications. Waste analysis, recordkeeping, and notification requirements for TSDFs are comparable to those previously described for generators (40 CFR 268.7). The following points are pertinent:

- Both generators and TSDFs applying LDR treatment must analyze the wastes in accordance with a written WAP. Testing or process knowledge may be used by generators to determine if a treatment standard is met. Testing must be done in accordance with SW–846 methods. The appropriate sampling methods (composite or grab) are specified in the regulations.

- LDR notification/certification must accompany at least the initial shipment of untreated and treated hazardous wastes to TSDFs. A one-time notification/certification to EPA is also required for treated waste that is shipped to a Subtitle D facility.

- Copies of waste analysis information and LDR notifications must be retained for at least three years.

For detailed requirements, see 40 CFR 268.7.

Hazardous Waste Permits

SQGs and LQGs managing hazardous waste on-site in accordance with 40 CFR 262.34, and CESQGs, are not required to obtain RCRA permits. However, such generators often send their hazardous waste to TSDFs that are subject to RCRA permitting requirements. In addition, generators can be required to obtain a RCRA permit if the nonhazardous wastes they manage become subject to regulation as hazardous waste. It is therefore useful for generators to know the basics of the RCRA hazardous waste permit program. Main provisions of this program, set forth in 40 CFR 270, are summarized in this section. For information on the administrative process by which permit applications, modifications, *etc.* are processed and permits are issued, see 40 CFR 124.

Applicability

Unless specifically exempted, facilities that treat, store, or dispose of hazardous waste must be permitted for their entire active life, including closure. See 40 CFR 270.1(b). Land-based hazardous waste facilities (*e.g.*, landfills) that have not been *clean-closed* which received hazardous waste after July 26, 1982 or that were certified closed after January 26, 1983 must also be permitted for the postclosure care period. The detailed requirements for such facilities are set forth in their RCRA permits. However, certain qualifying hazardous waste management facilities that are permitted under other laws (injection wells permitted under SDWA, POTWs with NPDES permits, ocean disposal authorized under the Marine Protection, Research, and Sanctuaries Act) are deemed to have a RCRA *permit by rule* (no RCRA permit application required), and requirements are set forth in those other permits (40 CFR 270.60).

The following persons or activities are specifically exempted from the requirement to obtain a RCRA permit:

- CESQGs, LQGs, and SQGs managing waste on-site in accordance with 40 CFR 262.34.

- Farmers who dispose of hazardous waste pesticides from their own use as specified (40 CFR 262.70).

- Treatment, storage, or disposal of hazardous waste exempted from regulation under 40 CFR 261.4 or 261.5.

- Totally enclosed treatment units and elementary treatment units as defined in 40 CFR 260.10.

- Transporters operating in compliance with RCRA. (Some states permit transporters also.)

- Persons adding absorbant to waste in a container or waste to an absorbant in a container under specified conditions. See 40 CFR 270.1(c)(2)(vii).

- Treatment or containment activities taken in immediate response to actual or imminent and substantial threat of hazardous waste release. See 40 CFR 270.1(c)(3).

It is the facility operator's duty to obtain the RCRA permit; however, specifically authorized representatives of both the owner and operator must sign and certify the permit applications. See 40 CFR 270.10(a).

Interim Status Authorization (Existing Facilities)

Existing TSDFs may become subject to RCRA hazardous waste permit requirements as a result of a regulatory change (*e.g.*, new listing or other change to 40 CFR 261 that changes the status of waste they manage from nonhazardous to hazardous). As explained above in the introduction to 40 CFR 264/265 standards, these TSDFs may continue to operate under interim status until they receive a RCRA permit, provided they do so in compliance with the 40 CFR 265 standards. Existing facilities that cannot qualify for interim status must close. Existing TSDFs wishing to continue operations must take the following permitting actions.

Notification. No later than 90 days after becoming regulated, provide notification of the hazardous waste activity to EPA under RCRA Section 3010, as described above for generators and TSDFs.

RCRA Part A Permit Application. No later than six months after the date of publication of regulations that cause the change to regulated status or 30 days after the effective date of those regulations, whichever first occurs, submit Part A of the RCRA Permit Application to EPA. See 40 CFR 270.10(d).

RCRA Part B Permit Application. Submit Part B of the RCRA permit application (described below) to EPA by the due date established by EPA. EPA is required to provide at least six months notice.

Permitting New Facilities

New TSDFs cannot begin construction until a RCRA permit has been obtained. To initiate the permitting process, the owner/operator must submit both Part A and Part B of the RCRA permit application to EPA. The regulations at 40 CFR 270.10(f) indicate that the application must be submitted at least 180 days before construction is expected to begin. However, the actual length of time required to obtain the permit can be much longer, even several years. Actual time required depends on many factors, including available regulator resources, complexity of the facility or activity, quality of the submittal, and public acceptability. Therefore, development of a realistic schedule for the facility requires coordination with the permitting agency far in advance.

Part A Permit Application

The Part A Permit Application consists of Forms 1 and 3 of the Consolidated Permit Application (EPA Form 8700–23). Information to be supplied in the Part A application is relatively simple and straightforward, and includes the items listed below. See 40 CFR 270.1(b), 270.13.

Facility, Owner/Operator Identification Information. Includes EPA ID Number, name, location, address, point of contact.

General Facility Information. Provides the standard industrial classification (SIC) codes, existing environmental permits, and business description.

Hazardous Waste Management Facility Information. Includes hazardous waste descriptions; description of hazardous waste processes (using standard process codes) and design capacities; photographs and scaled drawing(s) showing the location of all past, present, and planned treatment, storage, and disposal facilities; topographic vicinity map showing the facility and salient environmental features, including potential receptors (*e.g.*, surface waters, wells).

Certification. Both the owner and operator must sign and certify to the completeness and accuracy of the application.

Part B Permit Application

The Part B Permit Application consists of detailed information about the hazardous waste, proposed hazardous waste management facilities and activities, and pertinent natural and cultural features of the facility environs in a manner that demonstrates how the proposed facility and activity will conform to the applicable management standards for the facility (*i.e.*, applicable 40 CFR 264 standards). Part B information required for virtually all types of facilities is detailed in 40 CFR 270.14, 270.15–270.28 describes information required for specific types of facilities. The information is not provided on any special form. However, Part B applications are often prepared to conform to the following format established by a *Regulatory Completeness Checklist* used by EPA and at least some State regulators to review the applications:

- Section A: "Part A" Permit Application

- Section B: Facility Description

- Section C: Waste Characteristics

- Section D: Process Information

- Section E: Ground Water Monitoring

- Section F: Procedures to Prevent Hazards

- Section G: Contingency Plan

- Section H: Personnel Training,

- Section I: Closure Plan and (for land-based units), Postclosure Plan, Financial Requirements

- Section J: Other Federal Laws

- Section K: Certification

- Section L: Information Requirements for Solid Waste Management Units

- Section M: Closure Equivalency Demonstration

The "Part B" permit application typically consists of one or more lengthy volumes of information, and can be very time-consuming and costly to prepare.

RCRA Permit Conditions

The RCRA permit requirements include generally applicable conditions as well as conditions specific to the permitted facility (40 CFR 270, Subpart C). Generally applicable conditions include the following list (40 CFR 270.30).

Duty to Comply. The permittee is required to comply with all conditions in the permit. This typically includes conformance with conditions in the approved permit application and applicable RCRA regulations.

Duty to Reapply. RCRA permits issued by EPA are effective for up to 10 years; durations of permits issued by states vary. TSDFs that wish to continue the permitted activity beyond the expiration date must reapply at least 180 days prior to permit expiration (40 CFR 270.50, 270.51).

Need to Halt or Reduce Activity. The need to halt or reduce the permitted activity to maintain compliance is disallowed as a defense in an enforcement action.

Minimize Releases and Impact. In the event of noncompliance, permittees are required to minimize releases and take reasonable measures to prevent significant adverse impact to human health or the environment.

Proper Operation and Maintenance. A permittee is required to operate and maintain the facility in a manner that ensures compliance with permit conditions.

Duty to Provide Information. The permittee must provide compliance-related information to EPA upon request within a reasonable time. What is reasonable depends on the circumstances, but it may be useful to establish an acceptable time with your regulator, particularly if records are difficult to access.

Inspection and Entry. The permittee must allow EPA or an authorized representative to enter the facility premises or record storage areas at reasonable times for inspection, sampling, or monitoring. Such access may be requested with little or no notice. Therefore, typically it is advisable for facilities with substantial access requirements for security or other purposes to avoid potential inconvenience and embarrassment (at least) or noncompliance (at worst) by developing mutually agreeable access protocols with the regulator well in advance.

Conditions specific to the facility may include applicable technical requirements from 40 CFR 264 and 266, compliance schedules (*e.g.*, for corrective action as described under Subparts F and S), ground water protection standard (GWPS) limits for ground water monitoring at land-based units, *etc.*

Changes to RCRA Permits

RCRA permits may be terminated by EPA upon satisfactory closure of a facility or during the term of a permit for cause (40 CFR 270.43). The major provisions for changing a permit are described in (40 CFR 270, Subpart D).

Revocation and Reissuance. EPA may revoke and reissue permits for specifically identified causes, particularly if cause exists to terminate a permit or the permittee has notified EPA that they propose to transfer the permit to another person. When a permit is revoked and reissued, the entire permit is reopened and subject to revision and the permit is reissued for a new term (40 CFR 270.41).

Modification. If EPA chooses, permits may be changed by modification for the same reasons cited above for revocation and reissuance. EPA may also modify a permit for the following reasons: substantial changes in the permitted facility or activity, previously unavailable information important to permit limits becomes available, new statutory requirements or regulations become applicable, compliance schedule modifications are justified, or (for land disposal facility permits only) change is needed to ensure RCRA compliance. When a permit is modified, only the conditions subject to modification are reopened (40 CFR 270.41, 270.42).

Permit Modification at the Request of the Permittee. Permittees seeking permit modifications must do so by formal written request. Three classes of modification are established as follows: Class 1 Modifications, applicable to minor changes that do not substantially alter permit conditions;

Class 2 Modifications, applicable to changes necessary to respond to common variations in waste, technological advances, or compliance with new regulations without substantially changing permitted design specifications or management practices; and Class 3 Modifications, applicable to changes that substantially alter the facility or its operation. Most Class 1 modifications may be put into effect without response from EPA; however, some changes must await a written response. The requirements for Class 2 and Class 3 modifications are increasingly more stringent, and include public notice, public comment period, and other substantial administrative provisions (40 CFR 270.42).

Special Forms of Permits

EPA issues special forms of permits to accommodate variations in the type of unit being permitted or the circumstances of permit issuance (40 CFR 270, Subpart F).

Permits by Rule. As previously discussed, these apply to injection wells permitted under SDWA (40 CFR 144, 145), POTWs with an NPDES permit, and ocean disposal authorized under the Marine Protection, Research, and Sanctuaries Act (40 CFR 220), provided they comply with RCRA regulations specified in this section (40 CFR 270.60).

Emergency Permits. A temporary permit vehicle for addressing a condition posing imminent and substantial endangerment of human health or the environment, which may be initially issued orally, on short notice. An example of an activity that has qualified for an emergency permit is neutralization of reactive peroxide crystals formed on ether or picric acid containers, in the likely event they are intended for discard, and thus hazardous waste, upon discovery. (40 CFR 270.61).

Hazardous Waste Incinerator Permits. Incinerators and similarly complex treatment facilities require a separate form of permit because the permit process is phased to separately allow construction (for new facilities), trial burn, and operation (40 CFR 270.62).

Land Treatment Demonstrations Using Field Test or Laboratory Analyses. A separate form of permit may be issued as a treatment or disposal permit for these facilities based on data from field tests or laboratory analyses, or the permit may be issued in two phases (*i.e.*, field testing/laboratory analyses followed by facility construction and operation) (40 CFR 270.63).

Research, Development, and Demonstration Permits. A temporary permit may be issued to allow the development and demonstration of innovative and experimental hazardous waste treatment technology for up to one year, renewable for three additional one-year periods (40 CFR 270.65).

Boilers and Industrial Furnaces. Like those for incinerators, BIF permits require a separate form of permit because the permit process is phased to separately allow construction (for new facilities), trial burn, and operation (40 CFR 270.66).

Bibliography

General References

Aspen Publishers. *RCRA Regulations and Keyword Index*. New York, NY: Aspen Publishers. (Annual publication that provides an overview of RCRA programs, text of currently codified regulations, EPA regulatory interpretations and references, and keyword indexing.)

Aspen Editorial Staff. *Hazardous Waste Consultant*. New York, NY: Aspen Publishers. (Bimonthly journal that includes in-depth articles on regulatory, technical, and legal developments of interest; compliance flowcharts, TSDF listings; and other information of interest to generators.)

McCoy and Associates. *RCRA Reference*. Golden, CO: McCoy and Associates. (Annual publication that provides full text of currently codified RCRA regulations and a comprehensive index, as well as points to section numbers in a companion McCoy reference, *RCRA Unraveled*.)

McCoy and Associates. *RCRA Unraveled*. Golden, CO: McCoy and Associates. (Annual comprehensive summary of EPA RCRA interpretations and guidance. Companion to McCoy's *RCRA Reference*.)

RCRA State Authorizations

<http//:www.epa.gov/epaoswer/hazwaste/state/index.htm> (Environmental Protection Agency. RCRA State Authorization) EPA's State Authorization Tracking System (StATS), which shows authorization status of states for various parts of the RCRA program.

RCRA and Related Statutes, Regulations

<http://www.epa.gov/epahome/rules.htm> (Environmental Protection Agency. Laws and Regulations. Major Environmental Laws) General EPA site that provides access to historical and current information about environmental laws and regulations, including direct links to EPA's Semiannual Regulatory Agenda, codified RCRA regulations, and current RCRA regulations.

<http://www.epa.gov/epaoswer/osw/laws-reg.htm> (Environmental Protection Agency. Wastes. Regulations and Standards) A very useful general site that provides access to RCRA law and current regulations, RCRA history, RCRA Online guidance site, RCRA training and orientation materials, and relevant documents and information by topic area.

<http://www.epa.gov/fedrgstr/> (Environmental Protection Agency. Federal Register Environmental Documents) EPA's searchable *Federal Register* compilation from October 1994 – present, with link to the official Electronic *Federal Register* from the Government Printing Office.

<http://www.myregs.com/dotrspa/> (U.S. Department of Transportation. Office of Hazardous Materials Safety. Hazmat Regulations and Interpretations) A Department of Transporation site that provides access to hazardous materials transportation regulations and interpretations.

RCRA Guidance

<http://www.eh.doe.gov/> (U.S. Department of Energy. Environmental, Safety, and Health. Home) General site sponsored by Department of Energy, Office of Environment, Safety, and Health, includes links to a comprehensive collection of environmental, safety, and health information and services.

<http://www.epa.gov/rcraonline/> (Environmental Protection Agency. RCRA Online. Welcome to RCRA Online) Very helpful searchable databases maintained by EPA's Office of Solid Waste, useful for locating all kinds of EPA documents dealing with RCRA topics and issues, including letters and memoranda providing regulatory interpretations relating to waste determinations, compliance issues, *etc.*

<http://tis-nt.eh.doe.gov/oepa> (U.S. Department of Energy. Environmental Policy and Guidance) Department of Energy, Office of Environmental Policy and Guidance homepage, includes links to laws, regulations; substantial compilation of DOE RCRA guidance documents; software and other tools to facilitate compliance.

Hazardous Waste Forms

<http://www.epa.gov/epaoswer/hazwaste/data/form8700/forms.htm> (Environmental Protection Agency. Wastes. Notification of Regulated Waste Activity [EPA Form 8700-12] and RCRA Hazardous Waste Part A Permit Application [EPA Form 8700-23]) Forms and instructions for notifying EPA of hazardous waste activity and to initiate obtaining a RCRA permit.

<http://www.epa.gov/epaoswer/hazwaste/gener/manifest/> (Environmental Protection Agency. Wastes. The Hazardous Waste Manifest System) Link to publications describing the hazardous waste manifest (EPA Form 8700-22) and proposed changes to the system, including electronic submittals. The form is currently available as an appendix to 40 CFR 262.

Hazardous Waste Treatment, Storage, and Disposal Facilities

<http://www.epa.gov/epaoswer/hazwaste/data> (Environmental Protection Agency. Hazardous Waste Data) Contains links to national databases containing information about RCRA Hazardous Waste Treatment, Storage and Disposal Facilities.

Waste Minimization

Anonymous. "Waste Minimization—What, Why, and How." In *The Hazardous Waste Consultant.* New York, NY: Elsevier Science Inc., September/ October 1995.

<http://es.epa.gov/> (Environmental Protection Agency. Enviroene Homepage) Provides pollution prevention information, including technical library, vendor information , tools (*e.g.,* solvent substitution data system), *etc.*

<http://www.epa.gov/minimize/> (Environmental Protection Agency. Waste Minimization. The National Waste Minimization Program) The EPA National Waste Minimization Plan Homepage highlights EPA partnership with industrial organizations, government agencies, and communities to find ways to help individual companies reduce the amount of waste they generate.

Solid and Hazardous Waste Determination and Characterization

<http://www.epa.gov/epaoswer/hazwaste/test/ index.htm> (Environmental Protection Agency. Test Methods. OSW Methods Team) EPA publications, guidance, and expert contacts regarding analytical chemistry and characteristic testing methods, sampling and monitoring, and quality assurance.

<http://www.epa.gov/SW-846/sw846.htm> (Environmental Protection Agency. Test Methods. SW–846 Manual) General EPA site for hazardous waste sampling and analysis methods with links to online versions of EPA's official compendium of analytical and sampling methods, EPA Publication SW–846 *Test Methods for the Evaluation of Solid Waste—Physical / Chemical Methods*, and related sampling and analysis guidance, and ordering information for hard copies of these publications.

Hazardous Waste Compatibility and Related Information

Hatayama, H. K., *et al. A Method for Determining the Compatibility of Hazardous Wastes.* EPA–600/2–80–076. (National Technical Information Service, PB80–221005). Cincinnati, OH: Environmental Protection Agency, Office of Research and Development, April 1980.

<http://www.msdssearch.com> (MSDS-Search) Links to numerous sources of material safety data sheets from participating manufacturers and organizations.

<http://www.eh.doe.gov/chem_safety//chem_ comp.html> (U.S. Department of Energy. Environment, Safety, and Health. Chemical Compatibility) General site with links to useful tools, documents, and information related to chemical safety, including chemical compatibility charts and bibliography, and material safety data sheets.

Gregory C. DeCamp is an environmental scientist with 31 years of consulting experience and a Charter Member of the Magnolia Chapter of ACHMM in South Carolina. Mr. DeCamp is currently a Senior Environmental Scientist with Constellation Energy, and provides environmental management and regulatory support services to Constellation Energy power plant operations and external clients. From 1988 to 2000, Mr. DeCamp's professional activities were focused on U.S. Department of Energy facilities and operations, with particular emphasis on hazardous and mixed waste management and RCRA compliance issues. He has managed or conducted numerous environmental projects for industry and government, including facility siting and routing studies, ecological baseline studies and monitoring, impact analyses, facility design and operations consultation, compliance program development, auditing, and facility closure and remediation plan development. Mr. DeCamp extends his gratitude to ACHMM Past President Alan Eckmyre for encouraging him to write this chapter; to Alison Dean and Lisa Matis for review of the original manuscript; to James Burckhalter, CHMM and Hal Morris for their expert technical review and practical compliance tips for this latest edition; to CEG for labor and logistical support; and to Karen, Alison, and Andy, for their support and encouragement through it all.

CHAPTER 42

Pollution Prevention

Patricia A. Kandziora, CHMM
K. Leigh Leonard, CHMM

Introduction

With increased regulatory scrutiny following the cascade of regulations in the 1970s and 1980s, environmental management through the early 1990s was essentially compliance-focused. In the 1990s, with higher public expectations for corporate environmental stewardship and increased demand for *green* (environmentally friendly) products and services, corporate leaders began taking a fresh look at their environmental management programs. Many have found that undertaking a serious pollution prevention effort is a successful business response because it reduces their regulatory burden, increases public confidence, reduces long term risk, and nearly always cuts costs. Pollution prevention is also being furthered as a natural outcome of Environmental Management Systems (EMS), a business-oriented approach which emerged and rapidly gained acceptance during the 1990s.

In the 1990s a new paradigm, referred to as **sustainable development**, emerged that can encompass pollution prevention. Although there has been a lack of consensus on what it means in practice, the concept warrants mention as an important trend that can influence the selection of pollution prevention strategies for institutions and businesses that have adopted sustainable development goals.

689

Unlike most areas of environmental management, pollution prevention is driven more by business interests than by the existing laws and regulations. Pollution prevention projects that show powerful and positive impacts on the bottom line demonstrate that environmental managers can add real business value and go beyond forestalling liabilities and costs through compliance and preparedness.

This chapter provides a thorough treatment of pollution prevention, including definitions of key terms used by the Environmental Protection Agency (EPA) and other regulatory agencies. After reviewing the chapter, the reader will have a working knowledge of the regulatory history of pollution prevention and will be able to identify the business impacts of pollution prevention projects. The reader will also understand how pollution prevention fits into the emerging sustainability paradigm.

Defining the Terms

Over time, EPA has drawn distinctions between the terms *waste minimization* and *pollution prevention*. These nuances can be important to the environmental managers who need to communicate their efforts to EPA or its State counterpart. The term *sustainable development* is more youthful and has yet to be strictly defined by EPA. However, sustainable development, as it is currently understood, possesses characteristics that set it apart from pollution prevention and waste minimization. The purpose of this section is to explain the nuances in definitions of these terms as a foundation for the rest of the chapter.

Waste minimization, as currently defined by EPA, pertains to wastes regulated under the Resource Conservation and Recovery Act (RCRA), particularly hazardous wastes, and includes *source reduction* and *environmentally sound recycling* (EPA 1994).

Source reduction is defined in Section 6605(5)(A) of the Pollution Prevention Act. It is any practice that

- Reduces the amount of any hazardous substance, pollutant, or contaminant entering any

waste stream or otherwise released into the environment (including fugitive emissions) prior to recycling, treatment, or disposal

- Reduces the hazards to public health and the environment associated with their release

Environmentally sound recycling in the context of the Resource Conservation and Recovery Act means activities defined under the hazardous waste regulations as *recycling;* 40 CFR 261.1(c)(4), (5), and (7). This includes materials that are used, reused, or reclaimed. A material is **used** or **reused** if it is employed as an ingredient in an industrial process to make a product, or if it is employed in a particular function or application as an effective substitute for a commercial product. A material is **reclaimed** if it is processed to recover a usable product, or if it is regenerated.

EPA also defines in the solid and hazardous waste regulations the term **by-product,** which means a material that is not one of the primary products of a production process and is not solely or separately produced by the production process, 40 CFR 262.1(c)(3).

Pollution prevention is defined in the Pollution Prevention Act and subsequent EPA publications (EPA 1994). Unlike waste minimization, the context of pollution prevention is not limited to solid and hazardous waste. Rather, it encompasses releases to all media: air emissions, wastewater and storm water discharges and spills, and releases to soil or ground water, as well as solid and hazardous waste generation. Pollution prevention means *source reduction* as defined above. In addition, it includes other practices that reduce or eliminate the creation of pollutants through

- Increased efficiency in the use of raw materials, energy, water, or any other resources, and

- Protection of natural resources by conservation

Strictly speaking, there are practices (like recycling) that are considered to be waste minimization, but are not pollution prevention. In addition there are pollution prevention measures that are not considered to be waste minimization because they impact on media other than solid and hazardous waste. Figure 1 provides a visual representation of the relationship between pollution prevention and waste minimization.

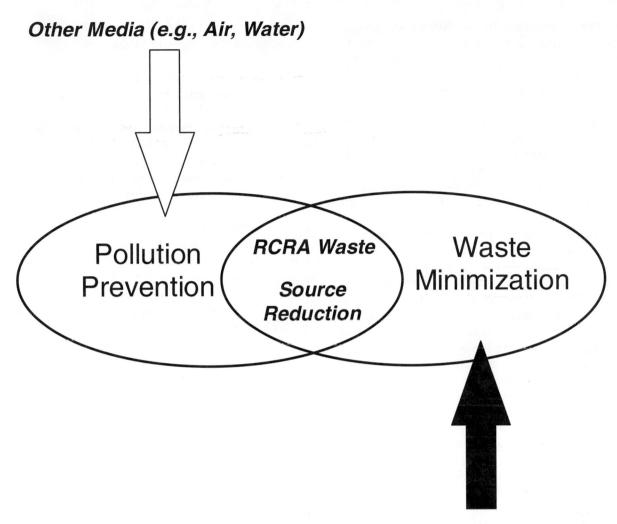

Other Media (e.g., Air, Water)

Pollution Prevention

RCRA Waste

Source Reduction

Waste Minimization

Environmentally Sound Recycling

**Figure 1. Relationship Between Pollution
Prevention and Waste Minimization**

This chapter is primarily about pollution prevention. As such, the authors will generally use the term *pollution prevention* or the abbreviation *P2* for the remainder of the chapter, unless referring to examples that accentuate waste minimization or sustainable development.

Environmental Management Systems. During the 1990s, the development and maturation of the *Environmental Management System* (EMS) framework accelerated pollution prevention outcomes. EMS became accepted as a viable business approach when the International Organization for Standardization (ISO) finalized its EMS standard, ISO 14001, in 1996. EMS is, in essence, strategic planning and quality improvement principles directed towards an organization's environmental matters. This *Plan-Do-Check-Act* approach to environmental management involves developing a comprehensive listing of the ways the organization affects the environment (called *environmental aspects*), applying criteria to determine which environmental aspects are most significant, then setting objectives and targets to focus efforts on selected significant aspects. Pollution prevention strategies often provide the drivers to achieve selected objectives and targets, so it goes hand-in-hand with EMS. On the flip side, the EMS framework provides top management support, which ensures that pollution prevention projects tied to the EMS are adequately supported and given the best opportunity to succeed. (See the chapter entitled "Introduction to Environmental Management," for a full discussion of EMS principles.)

For example, a company completes its inventory of environmental aspects and determines that generation of hazardous waste organic solvents is one of its most significant impacts. Company management adopts, through the EMS process, an objective of reducing hazardous waste solvent generation with a target for the coming fiscal year to achieve a twenty-five percent reduction per unit of product. The management focus on this target rapidly leads to the development of several ideas to substitute less hazardous solvents in some processes and to completely eliminate them in other processes through process modification. These specific pollution prevention actions become the means for achieving the EMS objective. Also, because the EMS process is based upon a broad awareness of the environmental objectives throughout the organization, the system promotes individual contribution at all organizational levels. The network of awareness encourages participation that leads to a greater likelihood that pollution prevention opportunities will be identified. Experience shows that when line staff are engaged in this manner they can become a significant and continuous source of pollution prevention ideas.

Sustainable development has been defined by the United Nations World Commission on Environment and Development as meeting the needs of the world's current population without making it impossible for the world's future citizens to meet their needs. The global nature of this definition often makes implementation challenging within business organizations. Those businesses that are ready to make sustainable development operational begin by transforming principles, behaviors, and practices involved in their basic internal workings. Those base principles and behaviors have to do with:

- Transparency in business objectives and practices

- Governance practices including business environmental ethics

- Social responsibility programs including community, workforce, and other involved stakeholders

- Environmental health and safety processes based on continuous improvement.

Sustainable development, like EMS, requires the development of indicators (leading or lagging), and metrics against them to measure and verify improvements in the categories mentioned. These measures go together with the concept of the *triple bottom line*, under which companies are evaluated by stakeholders not only on financial performance, but also on environmental and social performance. As an extension of this, many businesses now include environmental and social performance in their annual reporting to shareholders. Environmental aspects that readily lend themselves to the development of metrics include:

- Consideration of residuals (*e.g.*, air emissions, waste water, and solid and hazardous waste)

- Energy and material inputs and outputs associated with a process

- Life-cycle environmental costs of the product or service produced

Pollution prevention becomes the means of impacting these aspects in a measurable way. It forms an important element of environmental management, a piece of the integrated program encompassed by a sustainability business model.

What are the distinctions between P2 and sustainable development? The scope of change contemplated from a sustainable development perspective goes to the heart of the long-term goals and mission of the business or organization, while pollution prevention generally involves a project-related approach for one or more aspects of a specific business or manufacturing process. Also, the timeframe for pollution prevention is usually shorter. (Generally, pollution prevention project proposals with payback periods exceeding two years will be passed over.) Sustainable development forces organizations to look at their value to the communities in which they operate, their product value to the market, their integrated business efficiency, and their ethical processes and to share this self-analysis with shareholders and stakeholders both. This view applies to a business' quarterly financial profile as much it does to their business, social, and environmental profile for the next several decades.

Waste Minimization and Pollution Prevention at the Federal Level

As chronicled in this book, environmental laws initially focused on *end-of-pipe* pollution control, cleanup of contaminated sites, and putting in place national and local spill response plans. Beginning with the Hazardous and Solid Waste Amendments in 1984, a new trend started to emerge. EPA and State regulatory agencies started to shift their focus toward reducing the amount of waste generated and toxics emitted.

Regulations and policies concerning waste minimization and pollution prevention have evolved dramatically since the mid-1980s. EPA's initial approach was to incorporate pollution prevention into the existing hazardous waste regulatory requirements. In contrast, the present approach is multimedia and more policy-driven than regulatory in nature. Policies emphasize technical assistance, grants, partnerships and voluntary efforts. Regulations continue to be fine-tuned, however, in ways that support EPA's agency-wide emphasis on P2 and the concept has gradually become more integrated with EPA's mainstream media programs. EPA's most recent Strategic Plan (EPA 2003) extensively incorporates P2 into its five strategic goals. P2 is negotiated into permits and settlements, and incorporated into annual environmental reports required by regulation (*e.g.*, Hazardous Waste Activity reports and Toxic Release Inventory reports). Through its Performance Track program, EPA has started to offer regulatory relief to those organizations that demonstrate they have an EMS, with its inherent P2 achievements, in place. Regulatory relief currently under consideration includes extended hazardous waste generator accumulation time limits and accelerated processing of air permit modifications.

Table 1 shows the major milestones at the Federal level that have stimulated pollution prevention activities. (A complete list of Federal mandates for P2 may be found at <http://www.epa.gov/p2/p2policy/provisions.htm>.) Each of these milestones and its effects on pollution prevention are discussed in detail below.

Table 1. Milestones in Pollution Prevention

Year	Title of Act	Effect on P2
1984	Resource Conservation and Recovery Act	• Requires generator and Treatment, Storage, and Disposal (TSD) facilities to certify their waste minimization program • Requires biennial reporting on waste minimization
1986	Emergency Planning and Community Right-to-Know Act (Parts 311 – 313 of the Superfund Amendments and Reauthorization Act)	• Requires public disclosure of chemical inventories • Requires public disclosure of chemical releases • Requires reporting of pollution prevention efforts for chemicals reported on the Toxic Release Inventory
1990	Clean Air Act (as amended)	• Allows permit waivers for facilities that reduce their toxics emissions by 90–95% • Stimulates P2 because *prevention of significant deterioration* standards bring entities in nonattainment areas under increasingly stringent emissions limitations
1990	Pollution Prevention Act	• Mandates EPA to develop and implement a strategy to promote source reduction • Provides authority for grants to promote source reduction • Those required to file a toxic chemical release form must include information on reduction and recycling of toxics

Resource Conservation and Recovery Act

Waste minimization was incorporated into the Resource Conservation and Recovery Act as part of the 1984 Hazardous and Solid Waste Amendments (HSWA). This resulted in three minor regulatory provisions that stimulated the waste minimization efforts of hazardous waste generators and licensed treatment, storage and disposal (TSD) facilities.

§3002(a)(6). Codified as 40 CFR 262.41(a) and 40 CFR 262.87(a), requires generators to describe, as part of their biennial report, their efforts to reduce the volume or toxicity of hazardous waste they generate, and to describe the changes actually achieved during the present reporting year as compared with previous reporting years.

§3002(b). Codified as 40 CFR 262, Appendix to Part 262, "Uniform Hazardous Waste Manifest and Instructions" (EPA Forms 8700-22 and 8700-22A and their instructions), requires generators (except Conditionally Exempt Small Quantity generators) to certify on each hazardous waste manifest that they have a program in place to reduce the volume or quantity and toxicity of their waste to the degree determined by the generator to be economically practicable. (For more information, refer to the chapter in this book entitled, "RCRA Overview: A Generator Perspective.")

§3005(h). Codified as 40 CFR 264.74(b)(9), requires the owner/operator of any Treatment, Storage, and Disposal facility to sign the same certification at least annually, and to file the certification in the facility operating record.

To provide more substance to these reporting and certification requirements, in May 1993, EPA issued its *Guidance to Hazardous Waste Generators on the Elements of a Waste Minimization Program* (58 FR 31114). It lays out a model framework for waste minimization programs including these elements:

- Top management support

- Characterization of waste generation and waste management costs

- Periodic waste minimization assessments

- Appropriate cost allocation

- Encouragement of technology transfer

- Program implementation and evaluation

The purpose of the guidance is to describe EPA's idea of what it means to have a hazardous waste minimization program *in place*, as stated by the certification. EPA published the guidance as Interim Final guidance and, to date, has not finalized it.

In November 1994, EPA issued *The Waste Minimization National Plan* (EPA 1994) that established ongoing national goals for waste minimization. Details of the current National Waste Minimization Program can be found at: <http://www.epa.gov/epaoswer/hazwasteminimize/index.htm>. A current focus is the Waste Minimization Partnership Program, which has a goal of achieving by 2005, a fifty percent reduction by weight from 1991 levels for thirty Waste Minimization Priority Chemicals, as reported in the Toxic Release Inventory (TRI).

Emergency Planning and Community Right-to-Know Act

In keeping with a general movement toward public disclosure, Congress enacted in 1986, the Emergency Planning and Community Right-to-Know Act (EPCRA), Sections 311–313 of the Superfund Amendments and Reauthorization Act. This program requires certain companies to disclose, through mandatory reporting, the amounts and kinds of toxic materials they store and use (called the Tier II report) and the amount and kinds of toxic chemicals they release into the environment (called the TRI report). EPA and its State counterparts have facilitated public access to these annual reports by compiling the data and making summaries available on the World Wide Web and by request. Meeting compliance with EPCRA requirements served as a wake-up call to many plant managers as they became aware of the toxic chemicals their companies use and process. They and their company management grew more sensitive to public concerns about the plant's environmental impacts. Even prior to the Pollution Prevention Act, these reporting requirements provided incentive for facilities to make reductions in the storage, use, and release of chemicals regulated under EPCRA. Since the September 11, 2001 attack on the World Trade Center and the contamination of United States mail by anthrax, heightened concerns about security and potential terrorism threats have added new incentives for reducing the amounts of hazardous chemicals stored and used at a particular location.

Pollution Prevention Act

In 1990, Congress passed the Pollution Prevention Act. It set forth national policy regarding the preferred hierarchy of waste management options:

> The Congress hereby declares it to be the national policy of the United States that pollution should be prevented or reduced at the source whenever feasible; pollution that cannot be prevented should be recycled in an environmentally safe manner, whenever feasible; pollution that cannot be prevented or recycled should be treated in an environmentally safe manner whenever feasible; and disposal or other release into the environment should be employed only as a last resort and should be conducted in an environmentally safe manner; PL 101–58–Nov 5, 1990, Omnibus Budget Reconciliation Act of 1990 (Pollution Prevention Act of 1990), §6602(b).

Four of the policy provisions of the Pollution Prevention Act are as follows: (1) it requires EPA to establish an office to oversee and coordinate the agency's pollution prevention activities; (2) it provides for grants to states for technical assistance programs on source reduction; (3) it requires EPA to institute a Source Reduction Clearinghouse to facilitate information and technology transfer; and (4) it requires EPA to report to Congress on its progress on these initiatives biennially.

The Pollution Prevention Act also expands the requirements for Toxic Release Inventory (TRI) reports required under EPCRA. Under the expanded provisions, for each toxic chemical covered by TRI requirements, facility owner/operators are required to file a source reduction and recycling report. The report must include, for the current reporting year:

- The quantity of the chemical entering any wastestream (or otherwise released into the environment), the percentage change from the previous year, and the amount the owner/operator expects to report for the next two calendar years

- The amount of the chemical which is recycled, the percentage change from the previous year, and the amount the owner/operator expects to report for the next two calendar years

- Source reduction practices used with respect to that chemical during such year at the facility, and techniques the owner/operator used to identify source reduction opportunities

- A ratio of production in the reporting year to production in the previous year

- The amount of the chemical released into the environment due to a catastrophic event, remedial action, or other one-time event not associated with production

- The amount of the chemical treated and the percentage change from the previous year

The Pollution Prevention Act also resulted in specific EPA programs and initiatives. The Office of Prevention, Pesticides, and Toxic Substances was created to oversee EPA's fulfillment of its responsibilities under the Pollution Prevention Act. For example, it is responsible for EPA's Source Reduction Review Project (SRRP), initiated in 1992, which is charged with assessing proposed regulations for Pollution Prevention opportunities. Its results include pollution prevention considerations being incorporated into two new pesticide regulations (EPA 1997). EPA has also injected pollution prevention into its compliance activities, most directly through its Supplemental Environmental Projects (SEPs). These incorporate pollution prevention projects into enforcement settlements in exchange for reductions in fines or penalties for alleged violations.

In addition to coordinating the pollution prevention efforts of EPA's various branches, the Office of Prevention, Pesticides and Toxic Substances is directly responsible for EPA's Design for Environment (DfE) partnerships and its Pesticide Environmental Stewardship Program. The DfE program provides technical assistance to businesses to help them incorporate environmental considerations into product design, process change, and technical and management systems. Some sectors that EPA has partnered with through DfE include flexographic and screen printing, chemical formulation, computer display manufacture, and adhesives.

The Pesticide Environmental Stewardship Program (PESP) is a cooperative effort involving EPA, the US Department of Agriculture, and the Food and Drug Administration. The program strives for reduced pesticide use and risk and then provides for wide promotion of methods for success. The program seeks partners and supporter organizations to formally commit to the goals of the PESP and develop a long-term strategic approach to risk reduction that includes measurable activities to achieve pesticide risk reduction, usually combined with annual reporting requirements.

In the regulatory realm, EPA has been expanding the scope of the Toxic Release Inventory (TRI). In recent years, EPA has increased the number of industry sectors and toxic chemicals subject to the requirements. Also, in 1994, EPA nearly doubled the number of chemicals covered. EPA has also added 16 persistent, bioaccumulative, and toxic chemicals (PBTs) to the list of chemicals subject to TRI reporting. These PBTs generally have much lower thresholds for reporting than other TRI reportable chemicals.

A related EPA program is the 33/50 program, which challenged 1,300 companies, operating more than 6,000 facilities, to reduce releases of 17 high-priority TRI chemicals (EPA 1997). The goal was to reduce these releases by thirty-three percent by 1992 and by fifty percent by 1995. Due to cooperation of affected industries, this goal was achieved a year early.

Business Impacts of Waste Minimization and Pollution Prevention

Historically, waste minimization and pollution prevention projects have been detached from their corporation's or organization's larger purpose. P2 and waste minimization projects are often stand-alone efforts like paper and can recycling or a shift from a more to a less toxic raw material. The context of P2 and waste minimization has most often been that of compliance (enforcement mandate), liability (reduce exposure), or immediate cost reduction. Indeed, the widely cited American Chemical Society's publication, *Less is Better*, prepared in 1985 by EPA's Task Force on RCRA

heralds the value of waste minimization as a source of multiple benefits, including savings of fifty percent of the purchase price in a laboratory setting. The premise is that by keeping a small, practical chemical inventory in the laboratory, one avoids the pitfall of waste generation management costs outstripping the superficial savings of low dollar, large volume ordering. This is often true in an industrial setting as well.

Volume purchases usually require a primary cash outlay that may necessitate a loan at interest—which could prohibit another investment. Other secondary benefits of a utilitarian inventory include: reduced inventory management overhead (Occupational Safety and Health Act [OSH Act] requirements for grounding systems and fire cabinets, equipping staff with personal protective equipment [PPE]); reduced potential for injury, human suffering, and lost production time; potential decrease in worker's compensation premium modifier; simpler in-house and community emergency response preparation.

A good community image may result from promoting these initiatives. In his presentation to the Chemical Heritage Foundation in September 1998, Eastman Chemical's Chief Executive Officer, Earnest Deavenport, Jr. observes that the United State's chemical industry is doing well with a fifty percent reduction in releases of toxic chemicals to air, land, and water since 1988; and a fifty percent reduction in similar materials transferred off-site for disposal or treatment over the same period (Storcks 1998).

However, he points out that chemical companies must address societal issues important to communities, extend stewardship beyond merely counseling customers, and ensure that the industry is making health, safety, and environmental issues a priority. As people become more conscientious of the ethics and records of those with whom they do business, it is imperative for companies to examine ways to operate in a sustainable manner; one way to do that is through a commitment to P2.

Top management support is essential for P2 to thrive. To support a P2 program, top management must first understand how it fits the corporate mission. Customarily, capital investment in environmental programs has a limited appeal. Often viewed as a threshold expenditure, environmental compliance is simply one of the costs of doing business and nothing more. Unfortunately, this perception carries through for P2 when P2 is not marketed well internally or, more often, when the accounting system is not flexible enough to capture the benefits. But, it need not be true. Who has the responsibility to bring P2 opportunities into the boardroom, to present them as a way of doing business—from design to market? Traditionally the environmental manager's role has been to integrate environmental compliance with every affected aspect of the organization and to keep top management informed.

Anyone with doubt as to the business impacts of pollution prevention need only turn to any number of waste management companies' audited corporate annual reports. These reports have shown diminishing revenue for hazardous waste landfills in the 1990s, and an overcapacity for incinerators. Their employees have credited waste minimization by generators as one of the reasons for these

conditions. The waste source is drying up. Also, with the land ban regulations in place, specialty treatment business opportunities have evolved (*e.g.*, mercury retort, lead waste smelting, secondary fuels operations for cement kilns), further curtailing the amount of wastes available for traditional disposal/destruction technologies.

Feasibility requires that each P2 initiative be analyzed for a return on investment, as a key early step. The P2 model outlined for return on investment and profiled in Table 2 suggests parameters that cover all P2 project needs. The payback can be both explicit and indirect. The parameters create a balance sheet for the P2 investment opportunity and a more tangible depiction of the initiative.

Once these figures are weighed comprehensively, the P2 initiative can be presented to management

Table 2. Balance Sheet for P2 Investment

Investment	Debit $?	Credit $?
Process equipment (capital improvement, deconstruction)		
Construction material (utility infrastructure, HVAC)		
Research and development (to integrate the project with existing processes)		
O&M (labor, analyticals)		
Site preparation		
Input material: changes in source material		
Start-up		
Training: relative to the new P2 process		
Engineering		
Utility connections		
Process equipment		
Capital: new construction to accommodate the P2 process		
By-product recovery		
Inventory management costs: emergency response		
PPE		
Medical (surveillance)		
Long-term liability		
Environmental risk program overhead: auditing, insurance		
Waste management, packaging, transportation, treatment/disposal long-term liability for cradle-to-grave management of the waste, personnel exposure monitoring, emergency response costs		
Totals		
Net Cost		

as a business priority just like marketing, design, and manufacturing initiatives.

In Wisconsin, some agrichemical dealerships are reducing the environmental impact of their on-site operations and saving money in the long run. The owners of these facilities, where thousands of tons of pesticides and fertilizers are stored and handled every year, are implementing a P2 program called Environmental Partners©.

The program grew from an effort of an agrichemical industry advisory group that wanted to address problems with storage and handling of bulk fertilizers and pesticides at the facilities. The group realized that with reasonable preventive measures that exceed compliance, they could increase their financial position over time through savings or prospective new business. The group saw economic advantages in going beyond the rules if a facility could customize their efforts and gain valuable environmental and economic results that include waste minimization and avoiding clean-up costs. For their efforts, they also can receive public and wider industry recognition, which means valuable advertisement of their business.

An important aspect of the program is that Wisconsin Department of Agriculture, Trade and Consumer Protection (DATCP) assists facilities in choosing alternatives, disseminating methods, costs, and performance information to future participants, and broadcasting individual dealership successes to the wider industry and government.

What's to be gained? Participants understand that the extra care they take on a daily basis contributes to a cleaner environment. According to participants, these efforts help facilities avoid costly environmental cleanup that often results from cumulative contamination. They also benefit from increased credibility within the community, complimentary promotional materials for their facility which include an article in the local newspaper, web-posting of their achievements and an opportunity for peer group recognition through several corporate award programs.

What's involved? Facility employees assess problem areas and develop and implement a customized plan to improve performance in or eliminate selected problem areas.

Ideas that Work. Descriptions and illustrations of P2 ideas tried at agrichemical dealerships in Wisconsin are shared among the industry and through design and operation descriptions on DATCP's webpage. These to-the-point publications include cost, design and practical policy detail to get facilities started on their own adaptation:

- **Environmental Policy:** Creating and implementing a policy and procedures for over all environmental performance

- **Build a Pad Grate:** Reduces tracking of pesticides and fertilizers off of mixing and loading pads

- **Housekeeping Practices:** Eases and encourages prompt clean up of small spills

- **Containment Water Testing:** Ensures rainwater is clean before discharge from a containment system

- **Anhydrous Ammonia Loading:** Reduces the risk of contaminating soil with ammonia

- **Covered Load Out:** Eases clean up of spilled product and reduces fertilizer runoff from loading pad

- **Inexpensive Load-In Solutions:** Reduces fertilizer runoff at rail unloading area

- **Sludge Management:** Enables proper disposal of agrichemical sludge

- **Concrete Containment Structures–Maintenance and Repair:** Keeps control of stored inventories of agrichemicals

In the agrichemical industry, where a fraction of a dollar on the ton makes the difference in competition, the Wisconsin Environmental Partners© program is a bold and effective P2 partnership effort.

In summary, P2 can be an integral part of the corporation's focus. To approach pollution prevention and waste minimization in this manner infuses environmental management deeper into the mission of the corporation by honing market opportunities. Pursuing P2 opportunities with this type of motivation positions the environmental function as a top management consideration, and reconstitutes the environmental manager's role in the context of the corporate mission.

Bibliography

American Chemical Society. *Less is Better.* Washington, DC: ACS, 1985.

Environmental Protection Agency. *2003–2008 EPA Strategic Plan: Direction for the Future.* EPA–190–R–03–003. Washington, DC: EPA, September 2003.

Environmental Protection Agency. *Pollution Prevention 1991: Progress on Reducing Industrial Pollutants.* NTIS PB93–157725 (formerly EPA 21p–3003). Springfield, VA: National Technical Information Service, 1991.

Environmental Protection Agency. *Pollution Prevention 1997. A National Progress Report.* EPA/742/S–97/00. Washington DC: EPA, 1997.

Environmental Protection Agency. *Preventing Pollution through Regulations. The Source Reduction Review Project: An Assessment.* EPA–742–R–96–001. Washington, DC: EPA, 1996.

Environmental Protection Agency. *The Waste Minimization National Plan.* EPA 530–D–94–001. Washington DC: EPA, 1994.

Habicht, Henry F., II. "Memorandum of May 28, 1992". EPA/742/F–92/001. Washington, DC: EPA, 1992.

"Hazardous Waste Identification and Listing; Carbamate Production. Final Rule. (40 CFR 261, 271, and 302)." *Federal Register* 60 (9 February 1995): 7824.

"Identification and Listing of Hazardous Waste." *Code of Federal Regulations.* Title 40, Pt. 261.1, 1980.

"Pesticide Chemicals Category; Formulating, Packaging and Repackaging Effluent Limitations Guidelines (40 CFR 455)." *Federal Register* 61 (6 November 1996): 57518.

Petersen, John. L., Margaret Wheatley, and Myron Kellner-Rogers. "The Year 2000: Social Chaos or Social Transformation?" *The Futurist.* October 1998.

"Standards Applicable to Generators of Hazardous Waste." *Code of Federal Regulations.* Title 40, Pt. 262.1, 1980.

William Storcks. "Deavenport: Industry Will Survive 'Witch Trials.' " *Chemical and Engineering News.* Vol. (76), No. (26), 5 Oct 1998.

Internet Resource

<http://www.datcp.state.wi.us/arm/agriculture/pest-fert/poll_prev/> (Wisconsin Department of Trade, Agriculture, and Consumer Protection. Agrichemical Pollution Prevention.)

Patricia A. Kandziora is a chemist and environmental analyst with the Wisconsin Department of Agriculture, Trade and Consumer Protection. She has 25 years of experience in the environmental health and safety profession, as an EHS and risk management program director, field investigator, staff trainer, bench chemist, and she is an author and editor of various technical publications. She has also been a guest columnist on third-party liability in local and trade publications. Her professional specialties include chemical safety, pesticides, integrated pest management and environmental management.

K. Leigh Leonard is a consultant with PRIZIM Inc., and has over twenty years of experience working in the environmental health and safety field. Her background includes EMS development and compliance strategies for universities, top-level research organizations, and large civilian Federal agencies. She has performed audits, management reviews, and provided EMS assistance for numerous colleges and universities. Ms. Leonard has over fifteen years EHS management experience at a large university system, including strategic planning, policy and procedure oversight, and training program development. She has numerous publications, including Pollution Prevention and Waste Minimization in Laboratories *and is editor of the electronic information service* eLaboratory Safety and Environmental Management.

The authors would like to acknowledge these individuals for reviewing this chapter and providing valuable contributions, comments and suggestions: Tim Anderson, Environmental, Health, and Safety

Services Manager, Natural Resource Technology; Karen Delahaut, Senior Outreach Specialist, University of Wisconsin—Madison; Kevin Dressman, Acting Chief, Operations Branch—Safety, Health and Environmental Management Division; US Environmental Protection Agency.

CHAPTER 43

RCRA Corrective Action

Louis Martino, CHMM
David R. Green, MS

Introduction

The Resource Conservation and Recovery Act (RCRA), as amended, addresses the management of solid and hazardous waste generated at ongoing industrial operations, wastes referred to here as *as generated wastes*—that is, waste created by ongoing manufacturing operations. The program is designed to address the management of *as generated waste* is familiar to many professionals and is described elsewhere. RCRA also authorizes the United States Environmental Protection Agency (EPA) and authorized states to direct RCRA permit holders and permit applicants to investigate and, in some cases, remediate, releases of hazardous wastes from what is referred to as *solid waste management units* (SWMUs) at the operating hazardous waste management facilities. This program is referred to as ***RCRA corrective action*** or *corrective action*. Corrective action is currently underway at 3,700 of the 6,400 facilities subject to RCRA corrective action (EPA 2000a). Although less visible than the nation's other cleanup program, Superfund, the corrective action program includes a greater number of sites and has far greater impact on ongoing, viable industrial operations.

Prior to the passage of the Hazardous and Solid Waste Amendments (HSWA) of 1984, corrective action was limited to responding to releases to groundwater identified during groundwater monitoring at RCRA-regulated units, such as landfills and surface impoundments used to manage wastes from on-going hazardous waste operations (commonly referred to as *as generated* wastes) (63 Federal Register [FR] 65881). Before HSWA, the statutory authorities applicable to corrective action were:

- **Section 3004(a).** This section required the EPA to promulgate regulations establishing standards for hazardous waste treatment, storage, and disposal facilities (TSDFs), EPA promulgated regulations pursuant to this statutory authority that requires cleanup of certain releases from hazardous waste treatment, storage, and disposal units.

- **Section 7003.** This section authorizes EPA to order cleanups of situations that may present an imminent and substantial endangerment to human health and the environment.

HSWA established regulatory authorities to address releases to groundwater, surface water, soil, sediment and air originating from regulated units used to manage *as generated waste* **and** to address releases from waste handling units used to manage waste prior to the implementation of RCRA. With the expanded regulatory authorities established under HSWA came regulatory proposals that laid the groundwork for a program that would mirror Superfund. This was perhaps an inevitable outcome, given that Congress expanded corrective action authority to prevent RCRA-permitted and interim status facilities from becoming Superfund sites. After several years of trying unsuccessfully to follow the Superfund blueprint, Congress, the general public, EPA, and State agencies became dissatisfied with the slow pace of RCRA corrective action cleanups, forcing EPA to search for alternatives to the traditional *command and control* approach then being used in the corrective action program. The net effect of this search was that EPA became more willing to experiment with alternatives to the traditional approaches, such as the Superfund blueprint.

Chronology of Corrective Action Program Development

Codification of Statute

The expanded RCRA Corrective Action Program came into being with the Hazardous and Solid Waste Amendments of 1984 (HSWA). On July 15, 1985, EPA issued regulations codifying the statutory provisions of RCRA Section 3004(u) and (v) (50 FR 28702). HSWA Section 3004(u) requires treatment, storage, and disposal facility (TSDF) permits issued after November 8, 1984, to include the requirements for corrective action. RCRA Section 3004(u) also requires that the permits contain schedules of compliance when corrective action activities cannot be completed before the issuance of a final operating permit. Further, RCRA Section 3004(v) authorizes EPA to require owners and operators of permitted or interim status facilities to remediate releases that have migrated beyond the boundary of the facility. RCRA Section 3008(h) gives EPA the authority to issue administrative orders requiring corrective action at facilities operating under the interim status provisions of RCRA Section 3010. Frequently, corrective action at interim status facilities is required by compliance order issued under RCRA Section 3008(h).

Corrective action requirements are typically triggered by (1) applying for a RCRA permit to address *as generated waste*, (2) discovery of a release of hazardous waste or hazardous waste constituents from a solid waste management unit (SWMU) at a permitted or interim status TSDF, (3) discovery of additional SWMUs or releases at a facility already conducting corrective action, or (4) discovery of an imminent and substantial endangerment of human health and the environment at any type of RCRA facility (*i.e.*, generator, transporter, or TSDF). A *solid waste management unit* (SWMU) is any discernible unit in which solid wastes have been placed at any time, regardless of whether or not the unit was intended for the management of solid or hazardous wastes (68 FR 8757). Such units include any area at a facility where solid wastes have been routinely and systematically released. Regulated units (RU), which include surface impoundments; waste piles;

land treatment units and landfills that received hazardous waste after July 26, 1982 are also considered SWMUs. Corrective action for releases from RUs is regulated under 40 Code of Federal Regulations (CFR) 264, Subpart F. The remaining SWMUs, the more populous SWMU subset, are addressed by a combination of HSWA authorities and guidance as discussed below (68 FR 8757). In any case, when a release of hazardous waste or hazardous waste constituents is discovered at a TSDF, corrective action typically is required. Typically, regulators and the regulated entity facilitate implementation of corrective action via the RCRA Permit.

Soon after codification of the corrective action requirements in HSWA, EPA developed guidance for the investigation and remediation of SWMUs that tended to follow the Superfund blueprint. Procedures for site assessment, interim measures and site investigation were described in three guidance documents from the EPA Office of Solid Waste and Emergency Response (EPA 1986, EPA 1988, and EPA 1989).

Subpart S Proposal

In the 1990 Subpart S proposal, EPA proposed detailed technical regulations for implementing the RCRA Corrective Action Program (55 FR 30798). In many ways, the approach described in the Subpart S proposal followed a Superfund-like blueprint. The Subpart S proposed rule describes a multi-phase approach to investigating and responding to releases of hazardous wastes and hazardous waste constituents at RCRA facilities. These phases are the RCRA Facility Assessment (RFA), RCRA Facility Investigation (RFI), Corrective Measures Study (CMS), and Corrective Measures Implementation (CMI)—which are similar in scope and purpose to the Preliminary Assessment/Site Inspection, Remedial Investigation, Feasibility Study, and Remedy Implementation steps of the National Oil and Hazardous Substances Pollution Contingency Plan (NCP) (40 CFR 300).

It should also be noted that corrective action can include Interim Measures which are akin to the Interim Remediation Action activities in the NCP. Although, as discussed below, most of the Subpart S proposal was never finalized, and EPA is now focusing on a results-based approach in lieu of the process-oriented approach described in the Subpart

S Proposal, these corrective action phases (RFA, RFI, CMS, and CMI) continue to have a strong influence on corrective action activities at RCRA facilities. Each phase is briefly described.

The RCRA Facility Assessment. The RFA is the first phase of the traditional RCRA corrective action process. Usually EPA or a State regulatory agency will conduct the RFA; however, in some rare cases, the regulatory agency may direct the facility to conduct the RFA. The RFA consists of a review of existing information about a facility, a visit to the facility; and, if warranted, limited sampling of environmental media. The intent of the RFA is to identify SWMUs and to determine if there are actual or potential releases of hazardous wastes or hazardous waste constituents from the SWMUs (EPA 1986). RFAs have been completed at nearly all TSDFs.

Interim Measures. If there is an actual or potential imminent release of hazardous waste or hazardous waste constituents, EPA or the authorized state may require the facility to conduct interim measures. Interim measures may be conducted during any phase of the corrective action process, but are most often required following the RFA or the initial phases of the RFI. *Interim measures are actions used to mitigate any immediate threats* while a comprehensive corrective action strategy is developed and implemented. Interim measures range from simple actions, such as fencing an area to prevent access, to complex groundwater pump-and-treat operations to prevent further contaminant migration (EPA 1988). Interim measures have been used as a tool for implementing aspects of the stabilization intiative (see the following discussion).

The RCRA Facility Investigation. The RFI is the second phase of the traditional RCRA corrective action process. The RFI is a detailed investigation, conducted by the facility, to determine the nature, extent, direction, and migration rate of the release. An RFI is an investigation focused on characterizing a release from a specific SWMU; however, RFIs for large areas or multiple SWMUs are not uncommon (EPA 1989).

The Corrective Measures Study. The CMS is the third phase of the traditional RCRA corrective action process. A facility will be required to conduct a CMS if the RFI identifies a release that may pose a threat to human health or the environment. A CMS involves the identification and evaluation of alternatives for remediating the release, but may also include an evaluation confirming the need for corrective measures. Typically included in a CMS are a preliminary and detailed screening of alternatives (including a *no action* alternative), bench- and pilot-scale testing of one or more alternatives (if warranted), and the tentative selection of the alternative to be implemented at the SWMU.

Corrective Measures Implementation. Implementation of the corrective measure selected to address the release is the final phase of the traditional RCRA corrective action process. This phase includes all aspects of the design, construction, operation, monitoring, and demonstration of completion of the corrective measure. After the facility has successfully demonstrated its completion of the corrective measure, the facility's permit or the RCRA administrative order will be modified by EPA or the authorized state, bringing to an end the facility's obligation to conduct corrective action.

As previously noted, the Subpart S proposal was never adopted as regulation. Nonetheless, the process-oriented approach included in the Subpart S proposal became a reality at many RCRA facilities after the process was integrated into permit schedules of compliance, State regulations, as well as State and national administrative orders. It should be noted that two units first proposed in the Subpart S proposal were eventually described in a final rule. Based upon the Subpart S proposal, EPA promulgated a rule to regulate the units that can be used to manage remediation waste either temporarily (Temporary Unit [TU]) or in permanent disposal sites (Corrective Action Management Unit [CAMU]) (58 FR 8658). This rule defines a CAMU as an area within a facility that is designated to manage remediation waste generated from corrective action activities. As promulgated, this rule allows remediation waste to be placed into CAMUs without triggering land disposal restrictions or minimum technology requirements for the land disposal of hazardous waste. As noted below, this CAMU rule was modified in 2002. A *TU* is a tank or container storage unit used to treat and store remediation waste generated at the facility that would not be subject to minimum technology or procedural hazardous waste regulations.

The Stabilization Initiative and the Advanced Notice of Proposed Rulemaking

In 1996, EPA published an Advance Notice of Proposed Rulemaking (ANPR) (61 FR 19432) to introduce EPA's strategy for promulgating new corrective action regulations and to emphasize areas of flexibility within the current program as well as to describe program improvements under consideration. The ANPR had several purposes:

- Introducing EPA's strategy for improvement of the program

- Providing a status report on the program

- Highlight areas of flexibility within the existing program

To a large extent, the Stabilization Initiative and the ANPR contained the antecedents for the reforms of the corrective action program that we see today.

Deferral from Subpart S to the ANPR as Guidance.
EPA announced the partial withdrawal of the Subpart S rulemaking in 1999 (64 FR 54604). The proposed rule was withdrawn because EPA determined that regulations were not necessary to carry out the Agency's responsibilities under RCRA 3004(u) and 3004(v) and that promulgating a comprehensive set of RCRA regulations could disrupt the thirty-three State programs already authorized, or seeking authorization, to carry out the program in lieu of EPA. In trying to strike the appropriate balance between the use of guidance and policy documents and a formal regulatory approach for implementing RCRA corrective action, EPA elected to tip the balance away from a regulatory *command and control* and process-oriented program to a more *results-based* approach. In the Subpart S withdrawal notice, EPA stated that this decision hinged on the view that no single approach to corrective action is likely to be appropriate at all sites, given the diversity of corrective action facilities, the degree of investigation required, and the degree of corrective action required to protect human health and the environment. EPA also stated that the ANPR provided updated information as to the Agency's position on many issues discussed in the Subpart S proposal and should be considered the primary

implementation guidance for corrective action (64 FR 54604). Some of the more critical aspects of the ANPR are described below. Much of the guidance first outlined in the ANPR is still being promoted by EPA.

Use of Alternate Authorities Such As State Cleanup Programs. Independent State cleanup programs are usually modeled after the NCP, the implementing regulation for the Comprehensive Environmental Response, Compensation and Liability Act (CERCLA). Currently over half of the states have Superfund-like cleanup authorities. In many cases, EPA believes these authorities are substantively equivalent in scope and effect to both the CERCLA program and to the RCRA Corrective Action program. EPA has, therefore, considered the use of State Superfund-like cleanup programs to compel or conduct cleanups at RCRA facilities in lieu of RCRA corrective action. To date, there have been few instances where these authorities have been used for active hazardous waste management facilities. However, in the final rule describing standards applicable to owners and operators of closed and closing hazardous waste management facilities, EPA provides for the use of alternate authorities to cleanup SWMUs (63 FR 56710).

Consideration of Land Use. EPA has been criticized for frequently assuming that the future use of RCRA sites will be residential. Residential use is typically the least restrictive land use, and as such carries with it the greatest potential for exposures. It consequently demands the most conservative exposure assessments, which, in turn, lead to the most stringent cleanup standards (*i.e.*, lower concentrations of residual contamination). EPA is considering changes in the regulatory program that would help promote consideration of future land use in the corrective action context. In the document, *EPA Guidance on Land Use in the CERCLA Remedy Selection Process* (EPA 1995), EPA stated that

> Discussions with local use authorities and other locally affected parties to make assumptions about future land use are also appropriate in the RCRA context. EPA recognizes that RCRA facilities typically are industrial properties that are actively managed, rather than the abandoned sites that are often addressed under CERCLA.

Therefore, consideration of nonresidential uses is especially likely to be appropriate for RCRA facility cleanups.

EPA has reiterated the concept of realistic land use consideration in remedy selection more recently in *Reuse Assessments: A Tool to Implement the Superfund Land Use Directive* (EPA 2001b).

RCRA corrective action sites are sometimes Brownfield sites. As discussed below in the section on recent developments, successful corrective action cleanup of a Brownfield site can be significantly impacted by land use considerations.

Point of Compliance. For groundwater, the ANPR described the ***point of compliance*** (POC) as the area of contaminated groundwater or, when waste is left in place, at and beyond the boundary of the waste management area encompassing the original source(s) of groundwater contamination. This last approach is often referred to as the *throughout the plume/unit boundary* POC.

Since publication of the ANPR, EPA has recognized that the POC for groundwater can vary, depending on the particular goal that has been agreed upon by the facility management and regulator. A *throughout the plume/unit boundary* POC is one approach. However, as described below in RCRA Cleanup Reforms, consistent with what EPA refers to as the Environmental Indicator (EI) of *Migration of Contaminated Groundwater Under Control*, if the final groundwater cleanup objective is to contain the plume, the POC could be located beyond the boundary of the containment zone (EPA 2002b).

Self-Implementing Corrective Action. EPA is shifting more of the responsibility for conducting corrective actions to the regulated community and is examining a number of approaches to self-implementation. The EPA's intent is to (1) reduce the inefficiencies created by the current command-and-control review and approval process, (2) increase the number of facilities conducting corrective actions, and (3) speed up the cleanups. As discussed in the section on RCRA Cleanup Reforms, EPA is considering the use of tailored oversight to eliminate unnecessary administrative or technical steps in order to more quickly meet environmental objectives.

Standardized Lists of Action Levels and Media Cleanup Standards. While EPA provided a table of action levels for constituents in the 1990 Subpart S proposed rule, it does not maintain a list of nationally accepted action levels or media cleanup standards. Some individuals have opined that clearly defining these numbers will promote reduced transaction costs, national consistency, and voluntary actions. The EPA is concerned lest the use of standardized lists of action levels or media cleanup standards oversimplify risk management decisions and reduce the ability to address site-specific circumstances. Despite this concern, in many or most cases, standardized lists are being used. A 2002 study of the implementation of the RCRA Corrective Action Program revealed that action levels are derived from standardized lists, such as State action levels, EPA region-specific action levels, and 1990 Subpart S action levels (EPA 2002a).

Performance Standards. EPA is considering establishing performance standards for the corrective action program in lieu of a detailed review and approval of work plans and other documents. EPA believes that focusing the corrective action program on clear, measurable performance standards rather than prescriptive administrative processes will significantly increase the pace and quality of corrective action cleanups while simultaneously reducing transaction costs. As discussed in the section on RCRA cleanup reforms, EIs (Current Human Exposure under Control and Migration of Contaminated Groundwater under Control) are examples of performance standards.

Voluntary Corrective Action. The 1990 Subpart S proposal discussed voluntary corrective actions that could be conducted by site owner/operators who were not seeking RCRA permits, and voluntary actions that could be initiated by facility owner/operators who had not yet received permits. Site and facility owner/operators, on the other hand, are concerned that any action they may take voluntarily will be *second-guessed* by the regulator. EPA is considering ways of encouraging voluntary corrective action and of providing incentives to facility owner/operators who are willing to voluntarily initiate cleanup. In a study on the implementation of RCRA, it was reported that about half of the facilities studied conducted voluntary corrective actions (EPA 2002a). To some extent, EPA is trying to foster voluntary corrective

action cleanups through use of RCRA Prospective Purchaser-Agreements (PPAs) and RCRA comfort/status letters. The purpose of the PPA is to provide a buyer with a Federal covenant not to sue, thus giving the buyer an incentive to perform corrective action. A comfort/status letter would not contain such a Federal *no action* covenant. A comfort/status letter is meant to clearly state EPA's or the State regulator's understanding of and position regarding the regulatory and environmental status of the site as well as the potential future remedial actions at the site (EPA 2003a).

Consistency with the CERCLA Program. Many in the regulated community, especially Federal facilities, have long been concerned about the duplication of effort required by the various cleanup programs. At some facilities, both RCRA corrective action and Superfund are applicable to cleanup activities. EPA believes the coordination of cleanup activities at facilities with overlapping jurisdictions has generally not been a problem; however, the Agency is considering ways to improve coordination. In 1996, EPA addressed coordination between RCRA Corrective Action/Closure and CERCLA site activities by discussing issues related to

- Acceptance of decisions made by other remedial programs

- The concept of deferral from one program to another

- Coordination between programs to avoid duplication of effort

- The use of risk based levels when developing the "clean closure" of regulated units and for site wide remediation (EPA, 1996)

In addition, the EPA is weighing whether the use of the same terms for remedial activities, such as investigations or remedy selection, would improve coordination at sites with overlapping jurisdictions. As discussed below, EPA's One Cleanup Initiative is fostering a national dialogue to help create a one cleanup program mentality.

Less Focus on Solid Waste Management Units. EPA is concerned that the proposed definition of SWMU deters facilities from addressing contamination on a site-wide basis. In addition, EPA indicates that more than sixty corrective action permits have been appealed on the basis of the improper application of the definition of a SWMU (61 FR 19432). Numerous other permits and orders involve prolonged discussions of the SWMU definition and its site-specific application. The primary areas of discussion and appeals have been in response to whether releases were routine and systematic and whether units had any solid or hazardous waste management activities.

Public Participation and Environmental Justice. EPA intends for the final corrective action regulations to be consistent with the Agency's efforts to improve permitting and public participation while providing sufficient flexibility to meet site-specific goals. EPA is trying to improve public participation, especially the participation of communities which have not been effectively involved in the corrective action process to date. As discussed later, this need for improvement in public participation is one of the RCRA Cleanup Reforms.

When Permits Can Be Terminated. The 1990 Subpart S proposed rule contained a provision requiring owners and operators to obtain RCRA permits for the entire period needed to comply with the requirements of Subpart S, the proposed 40 CFR 270.1(c). EPA intended this to apply even where the hazardous waste management activities that originally triggered the permit requirement no longer apply. This provision sought to ensure that corrective action would be carried to its conclusion. EPA is considering whether extended permitting is the best approach to ensuring that corrective action is carried out over the long term, or whether other alternatives should be considered. As a general matter, the requirement to continue the effect of a permit after the regulated activity ends serves no other purpose, and is a contributing factor to the high transaction costs seen in the corrective action program. For example, one approach might be to terminate the permit when active hazard waste management ceased, but to continue the cleanup obligation through some other vehicle, such as a post-closure permit. As discussed in the Recent Developments section, EPA is trying to address the question of permit termination by rethinking the concept of completion of corrective action.

Definition of Facility for Corrective Action. EPA's definition of a facility for purposes of corrective action has been problematic in some situations. For the purposes of corrective action, a facility is considered to exist from fence-line to fence-line. As a result, the SWMUs and environmental media affected by SWMU releases existing within the fence-line of a facility are subject to corrective action. In some circumstances the concept of contiguity, as EPA currently interprets that term, could bring large tracts of land that are only incidentally involved with hazardous waste management under corrective action jurisdiction. In many cases, these large tracts of land could be addressed using another cleanup authority (*e.g.*, CERCLA or State cleanup programs). EPA has found that imposing this interpretation of contiguity in situations involving large areas of Federally owned land (*e.g.*, Department of Energy [DOE] facilities, Department of the Interior [DOI] lands) can lead to results that arguably were not what Congress anticipated when it enacted the corrective action requirements, forcing the Agency to address contamination that would otherwise be low priority. As discussed in the partial withdrawal of the Subpart S proposal, the Agency remains concerned regarding the definition of facility and seems to be open to altering the definition (56 FR 54604). EPA did modify the definition of facility so that facility-wide corrective action requirements would not apply at facilities that do not manage *as generated waste* but only manage remediation waste (63 FR 65937).

RCRA Cleanup Reforms

By the middle to late 1990s, stakeholders, the regulated community, and State regulators identified a number of factors that reduced the effectiveness the RCRA Corrective Action Program. In a 1997 report to Congress, the General Accounting Office (GAO 1997) highlighted the following impediments:

- Improper emphasis on process steps

- Lack of clarity in cleanup objectives

- Improper emphasis on minimum technology requirements meant for highly concentrated as generated waste

- The triggering of land disposal restrictions also meant for highly concentrated as generated waste

- Permitting requirements

In an effort to address these impediments, EPA embarked on what is referred to as *RCRA cleanup reforms*. Some of the reforms meant to streamline RCRA cleanups include:

- Results-based approaches meant to eliminate process steps, including setting cleanup goals, providing procedural flexibility in how goals are met, inviting innovative technical approaches, and allowing cleanup action with reduced oversight, where appropriate

- A focus on environmental indicators (EIs)— Current Human Exposure under Control and Migration of Contaminated Groundwater under Control—as the metrics to gauge progress in achieving risk reduction

- Prompt implementation of regulations to limit the applicability of some RCRA requirements meant for highly concentrated as generated waste (land disposal restrictions, minimum technology requirements, and permitting) in RCRA cleanup situations

- Foster maximum use of existing program flexibility through training and outreach in order to accelerate changes in culture

- Pilot innovative approaches

- Enhance community involvement and connect communities to cleanup

- Capitalize on redevelopment potential (EPA 1999b and EPA 2001a)

EPA has been moderately successful at reforming the corrective action program. EPA has stressed two near-term results-oriented goals based on the EI construct (EPA 1999a). These goals, which were developed in response to the Government Performance and Results Act of 1993 (GPRA), are that of some 1,714 RCRA facilities prioritized for cleanup, 95% will have *current human exposures under control* and 70% will have *migration of contaminated groundwater under control* by 2005 (EPA 2000a). In a report on the Superfund program released on September 2, 2003, GAO acknowledged that the *human exposure controlled* and *migration of contamination controlled* EIs have been useful in managing the cleanup programs, but urged EPA to focus on developing additional performance indicators to guide future program decisions in the Superfund program. In the context of the Superfund program, the GAO report states:

Given the program's limited funding, EPA could use performance indicators to help evaluate, prioritize, and serve as the basis for making funding decisions. If successfully implemented for the Superfund program, establishing these measures would also help EPA and the Congress make the difficult funding, policy, and program decisions that the current budget environment demands. In doing so, EPA will have an opportunity to make fundamental changes to improve the management of the Superfund program.

These same statements are fully applicable to the corrective action program. EPA has developed a number of results-based approaches and performance indicators for the corrective action program discussed further in the Recent Developments section.

In 1998, EPA promulgated a number of rules that significantly impacted the RCRA cleanup program. The examples below point to an important consideration: the corrective action program is often impacted by other regulations within the RCRA program. A practitioner in the RCRA Corrective Action Program also needs to maintain a keen understanding of the rest of the RCRA program. The Hazardous Waste Identification Rule for Contaminated Media (HWIR-Media) made it faster and easier to obtain permits for treating, storing, and disposing of remediation wastes that were also hazardous wastes, using a streamlined permit referred to as a Remedial Action Plan (RAP). The HWIR-Media rule expanded the applicability of the CAMU regulations, indicating that a CAMU can be designated at a remediation-only facility operating under a RAP (63 FR 65874).

The post-closure regulations promulgated by EPA in 1998 were another significant step forward, removing the requirement to obtain a permit for the post-closure care period. It provides for the use of alternative mechanisms to address post-closure needs. As a result, impediments encountered when one unit is subject to post-closure care and other units are subject to corrective action have been removed (63 FR 56710).

The land-disposal restriction regulations promulgated in 1998 established land-disposal restriction treatment standards that are more appropriate for contaminated soils (63 FR 28556).

EPA also published a useful guidance document in 1998 addressing the management of remediation waste. This guidance document consolidates existing statutes, regulations, policies, and guidance that can be used to judiciously apply RCRA hazardous waste requirements to remediation waste. Some examples of the approaches addressed in the guidance include areas of contamination, CAMUs, permit waivers, and exemptions for less than 90-day accumulations of remediation waste (EPA 1998).

Recent Developments

Some relatively recent developments that could have long term impact on the corrective action program include: EPA's expectations for final remedies, the interaction between corrective action and Brownfield investigation/cleanup, policies on corrective action completion and CAMUs, the One Cleanup Initiative, and various results based approaches.

Expectations for Final Corrective Action Remedies

The EPA has identified a number of expectations for final corrective action remedies:

- Treatment should be used to address principle threats (*i.e.*, contaminants that are highly toxic, highly mobile, cannot easily be contained, and represent a potential threat to human health and the environment) posed by the contamination whenever practicable and cost-effective.

- Contaminated ground water should be returned to their maximum beneficial uses wherever practicable and within a time-frame that is reasonable given site-specific conditions. In those instances where it is not practical to return contaminated groundwater to a beneficial use, EPA expects that the further migration of the plume and exposure to the contaminated groundwater will be prevented.

- Engineering controls, such as containment, for wastes and contaminated media that can be reliably contained, pose relatively low long-term threats, or for which treatment is impracticable.

- A combination of methods (*i.e.*, treatment, engineering and institutional controls), as appropriate, should be used to achieve protection of human health and the environment.

- Institutional controls, such as water and land use restrictions, should be used primarily to supplement engineering controls as appropriate for short- and long-term management to prevent or limit exposure to hazardous wastes and constituents. The EPA does not expect that institutional controls will often be the sole remedial action.

- Facilities should consider using innovative technology when such technology offers the potential for comparable or superior treatment performance or ability to implement, lessen adverse impact, or lower costs for acceptable levels of performance when compared with more traditional technologies.

- Contaminated soils should be remediated, as necessary, to prevent or limit direct exposure of human and environmental receptors, and to prevent the transfer of unacceptable concentrations of contaminants (*i.e.*, via leaching, runoff or air borne emissions) from soils, including subsurface soils, to other media (EPA 2000b).

The Relationship Between Brownfields and Corrective Action

One of EPA's cleanup reforms is to encourage the redevelopment potential of RCRA cleanup sites. EPA reports on the *launch* (its term) of four RCRA/Brownfield pilots to showcase the inherent flexibility in some of the concepts described in the July 1999 RCRA cleanup reforms (EPA 1999b). EPA reports on the launch of 4–6 additional RCRA Brownfield pilot projects in 2001 to continue showing the flexibility available to expedite cleanups under RCRA (EPA 2001a). More recently, at the 2002 National Corrective Action Conference, EPA Region VI reported on the status of a program called *Ready for Reuse*, a new measure of remedial progress in the corrective action process specifically meant to support Brownfields development.

Unless all RCRA cleanup sites are or become Brownfield candidates, the laudable drive to redevelop fallow industrial sites may have little impact on the corrective action program. However, if these Brownfield pilots succeed in showcasing the flexibility that EPA maintains is inherent in the program, the pilots may have some positive impact on the corrective action program as a whole.

Completions and Grandfathered CAMUs

In January 2002, newer restrictive definitions of CAMU and CAMU-eligible wastes were distilled out of the original CAMU/TU regulations. The CAMU amendments established as *Grandfathered CAMUs* those CAMUS that were approved before April 22, 2002, and clarified that Grandfathered CAMUs can continue to receive remediation waste unlike other CAMUs that can receive only the more restrictive CAMU-eligible waste (67 FR 2962). *CAMU-eligible waste* is waste that meets minimum treatment standards for its principal hazardous constituents. In addition, CAMUs established after April 22, 2002, must meet, not the usual minimum technology requirements, but minimum liner and cap requirements similar to the criteria for municipal solid waste landfills (EPA 2002a).

This more restrictive CAMU rule was somewhat offset by guidance on the completion of corrective action at RCRA facilities. In a February 2003 *Federal Register* announcement, EPA advocated two primary concepts related to completing corrective action. These concepts were developed in an effort to provide formal recognition of progress with benchmarks that can be achieved within a reasonable timeframe and for reasonable costs. EPA details two types of corrective action completion: (1) corrective action complete without controls, meaning that a full set of corrective measures is defined, the facility has completed construction and installation of all required remedial actions, and that site-specific media cleanup standards have been met; and (2) corrective action complete with controls, meaning that the criteria in the other construct have been met, except that required operations and maintenance and monitoring actions must continue to be performed. EPA also acknowledges that a completion determination can be implemented for less than an entire facility (68 FR 8757).

The *One Cleanup Program* Initiative

As stated previously, one of the challenges facing the regulated community is the overlap of the various environmental restoration statutes and regulatory programs. The goal of the One Cleanup Program (OCP) is to improve the coordination, speed, and effectiveness of cleanups. The OCP has three main thrust areas:

- More effective and consistent cleanups

- Clear and more useful information about cleanups

- Better cross-program performance measures

Under the first thrust area, *More Effective and Consistent Cleanups*, EPA has established the following action items:

- Area-wide pilot projects, in which EPA proposes to work with the regions, states, tribes, local governments, and other Federal agencies to select and conduct area-wide pilot projects. The pilot projects are to be selected to demonstrate cross-program coordination and consistency in cleaning up groups of co-located or similar contaminated sites.

- Cleanup Programs Council, which involves establishment of a standing council of directors from the nation's waste cleanup programs that will meet regularly to provide a coordinated, high-level perspective of critical waste cleanup issues.

- Cross-program task forces will be established to conduct more detailed analyses of critical cleanup issues and support new policy guidance. The list of task forces currently includes groundwater cleanup and long-term site stewardship. EPA is also considering the formation of work groups to address cross-media cleanup issues related to PCBs, lead, asbestos, and the cleanup of watersheds.

- The Federal facilities Executive Leadership Policy Steering Committee, comprised of Assistant Secretary/Assistant Administrator-level executives from Federal agencies involved in the cleanup of contaminated sites, to identify and coordinate cross-agency cleanup issues.

In the second thrust area, *Clear and Useful Information about Cleanups*, EPA intends to work with states, tribes, and local communities to develop an integrated network of systems that provides clear and useful information about the cleanup of contaminated sites. This network of systems will clearly identify the agencies involved, the strategy for cleanup, and those responsible for safeguarding institutional controls and providing long-term monitoring and maintenance at contaminated sites. EPA envisions three systems being developed:

- A *Sites in My Community* information network/linked system that includes information useful to the public (*e.g.*, current point of contact, information about involved Federal/State/Tribal/local agencies, and descriptions of multiple program coordination and cleanup approaches and long-term monitoring and maintenance requirements).

- An *Institutional Controls Tracking* network/linked system, in which EPA will lead a national effort to develop linkages between systems for tracking institutional controls—a critical component for ensuring the long-term protectiveness and safety of cleanups.

- A *Waste Sites Technologies* information system, in which EPA will build on existing systems and efforts to speed up and broaden the transfer of scientific and technological information about contaminated sites and cleanups.

In the last thrust area, *Better Measures of Progress*, EPA intends to evaluate and pilot the development of performance measures that demonstrate the overall effectiveness and benefit of the nation's combined cleanup efforts. Over the next year, EPA will collaborate with its partners to consider new cross-program measures in four sub-areas:

- Protection of human health through waste cleanup activities

- Protection of the environment and ecology through waste cleanup activities

- Amount of land made available through cleanup activities for productive uses

- Economic benefit of waste cleanup activities

It remains to be seen whether this initiative will result in a *one cleanup program*; however, EPA's steps in the area at least offer the opportunity to bring about the much-needed changes (EPA 2003b). Additional information on the One Cleanup Initiative is available online at

<http://www.epa.gov/swerrims/onecleanup program>

Results Based Approaches and Performance Measures

As part of its efforts to improve the corrective action program, EPA has developed guidance on results-based approaches that emphasizes the value of outcomes and that eliminates unnecessary procedural steps. In 2003, EPA identified five results-based approaches to corrective action including:

1) **Tailored Oversight.** The primary goal of tailored oversight is to minimize process steps and achieve goals

2) **Procedural Flexibility.** Procedural flexibility advocates moving away from process driven steps in order to achieve cleanup goals

3) **Performance Standards.** This approach involves regulator and facility teams that establish site-specific performance standards with which the facility must comply in order to complete corrective action

4) **Targeted (or Focused) Data Collection.** Which advocates using a number of expedited site characterization tools such as conceptual site model, data quality objectives

5) **Use of a Holistic Approach.** Which is described as a facility-wide view of human health risks (EPA 2003d)

Targeted or focused data collection offers the possibility of significantly improving the corrective action process. Over the course of the last 10 years EPA has worked to streamline the sampling, analysis, and data management activities that are conducted during site assessment, characterization, and cleanup. The most recent embodiment of this effort is a concept called the ***TRIAD Approach***. TRIAD relies on a three-pronged strategy to identify and manage the uncertainty associated with the information used to make decisions. Central to the TRIAD approach is development of a conceptual site model (CSM) as a tool to delineate distinct contaminant and receptor populations for which different characterization strategies are used, risk assessments or estimates prepared, and cleanup strategies evaluated and adopted. The main elements of the TRIAD approach include systematic project planning, use of a dynamic work strategy, and use of information management systems to communicate the results of real-time data generation and analysis.

Systematic Project Planning: wherein the end goals for a project are identified as early as possible during the course of the project. Once the end goals are defined to the maximum extent possible, systematic project planning involves charting the most resource-effective course to achieve those desired outcomes. For example, one of the most important factors in environmental restoration is determining the appropriate, or reasonably anticipated, future land-use for the site. Discussions with the internal stakeholder, the regulatory agency, local land-use planning authorities, local officials, and the public should be conducted as early as possible in the response process to determine the appropriate or reasonably anticipated future land-use(s). This decision should then be factored into efforts to characterize the site, conduct risk assessments, and select the appropriate response(s).

A Dynamic Work Strategy: often in the form of a regulatory agency-approved decision matrix or decision tree that is used by experienced staff who are empowered to make critical decisions in the field about how subsequent site activities will progress based on the decision logic developed during the planning stage. Obviously such real-time decision making requires sufficiently rapid turnaround of analytical data and close communication with the regulatory agency during implementation.

Real-Time Measurements: generated in the field or in a fixed laboratory, combined with on-site data management and display software to quickly and efficiently use and share data among interested parties, is also a key element. Again, it is during upfront planning that decisions are made about the types, rigor, and quantities of data needed to answer the questions raised by the CSM. Those decisions then guide the design of sampling plans that address the need for generating representative data upon which to base decisions.

Additional information on TRIAD is available online at

<http://www.triadcentral.org>

In EPA's 2003 Strategic Plan, the Section titled "Land Preservation and Restoration" establishes the following performance measures to document progress in achieving a number of corrective action goals:

- **Site Assessment.** Assess 100% of new baseline facilities

- **Human Exposures Under Control**. Control all identified unacceptable human exposures at or below health-based levels for current and/ or ground water use conditions at 95% of new baseline facilities

- **Groundwater Migration Under Control.** Control the migration of contamination ground water through engineered remedies or natural processes at 80% of the new RCRA baseline facilities

- **Remedy Selection.** Select final remedies at 30% of new RCRA baseline facilities

- **Construction Completion.** Complete construction of remedies at 20% of new RCRA baseline facilities. Construction completion is a benchmark used to show that all significant construction activity has been completed, even though cleanup goals may not have been met (EPA 2003c)

Conclusions

Although corrective action programs likely differ from state to state, and despite attempts to move away from process oriented approaches, the vestiges of the traditional approach (RFA, RFI, CMS and CMI) have already been performed at numerous facilities. EPA continues to try to change the process-oriented culture of regulators to a more results-oriented culture. Thus, the process-oriented approach is continually tinkered with by EPA and authorized states. In addition to the process-oriented approach, the corrective action program is shaped by an assemblage of regulations, policies, reforms, initiatives, and guidance, which has been published, withdrawn, amended, or reinterpreted at different times over almost a quarter of a century. EPA's continued attempts to accelerate the pace of corrective action cleanups is to be commended. Using the metrics of the EIs, the early indications are that the Agency is succeeding. Furthermore, corrective action cleanups may be expedited by establishing completion benchmarks and by crafting a subset of hazardous waste regulations for remediation wastes that differs from the regulations for as generated waste. Nevertheless, given the changes that have occurred over the history of the corrective action program, readers are urged to remain aware of future changes as the program evolves.

Bibliography

"Amendments to the Corrective Action Management Unit Rule." *Federal Register* 67 (20 January 2002):2962.

"Codification Rule." *Federal Register* 50 (15 July 1985): 28702.

"Corrective Action Management Units and Temporary Units; Corrective Action Provisions: Final Rule." *Federal Register* 58 (16 February 1993): 8658.

"Corrective Action for Releases from Solid Waste Management Units at Hazardous Waste Management Units; Advance Notice of Proposed Rulemaking." *Federal Register* 61 (1 May 1996): 19432.

"Corrective Action for Solid Waste Management Units (SWMUS) at Hazardous Waste Management Facilities, Proposed Subpart S Rule." *Federal Register* 55 (27 July 1990): 30798.

Environmental Protection Agency. *A Study of the Implementation of the RCRA Corrective Action Program.* Office of Solid Waste and Emergency Response. Washington, DC: EPA, April 2002a.

Environmental Protection Agency. *Coordination between RCRA Corrective Action and Closure and CERCLA Site Activities.* Office of Enforcement and Compliance Assurance. Washington, DC: EPA, 24 September 1996.

Environmental Protection Agency. *EPA Guidance on Land Use in the CERCLA Remedy Selection Process.* OSWER Directive No. 9355.7–04. Washington, DC: EPA, May 1995.

Environmental Protection Agency. *Fact Sheet #1. History of RCRA Corrective Action.* Office of Solid Waste and Emergency Response. Washington, DC: EPA, March 2000a.

Environmental Protection Agency. *Fact Sheet # 2. Expectations for Final Remedies at RCRA Corrective Action Facilities.* Office of Solid Waste and Emergency Response. Washington DC: EPA, March 2000b.

Environmental Protection Agency. *Handbook of Groundwater Protection and Cleanup Policies for RCRA Corrective Action.* EPA 530–R–01–15. Washington, DC: EPA, September 2002b.

Environmental Protection Agency. *Implementation of RCRA Facility Assessments.* OWSER Directive No. 9502.00–04. Washington DC: EPA, August 1986.

Environmental Protection Agency. *Interim Final Guidance for RCRA Corrective Action Environmental Indicators.* Office of Solid Waste. Washington, DC: EPA, 5 February 1999a.

Environmental Protection Agency. *Management of Remediation Waste under RCRA.* EPA–530–F–026. Office of Solid Waste and Emergency Response. Washington, DC: EPA, 14 October 1998.

Environmental Protection Agency. *Memorandum from Sylvia K. Lowrance, Director Office of Solid Waste and Bruce M. Diamond, Director Office of Waste Programs Enforcement to Regions I–X Waste Management Division Directors.* Washington, DC: EPA, 25 October 1991.

Environmental Protection Agency. *Memorandum Prospective Purchaser Agreement and Other Tools to Facilitate Cleanup and Reuse of RCRA Sites.* Washington, DC: EPA, 2003a.

Environmental Protection Agency. *One Cleanup Program: Fact Sheet.* 500–F–03–002. Office of Solid Waste and Emergency Response. Washington, DC: EPA, April 2003b.

Environmental Protection Agency. *RCRA Cleanup Reforms Faster, Focused, More Flexible Cleanups.* 530–F–99–018. Office of Solid Waste and Emergency Response. Washington, DC: EPA, July 1999b.

Environmental Protection Agency. *RCRA Cleanup Reforms II: Fostering Creative Solutions.* EPA 530–F–01–001. Office of Solid Waste and Emergency Response. Washington, DC: EPA, January 2001a.

Environmental Protection Agency. *RCRA Corrective Action Interim Measures Guidance (Interim Final)*. OSWER Directive 9902.4. Washington, DC: EPA, June 1988.

Environmental Protection Agency. *RCRA Corrective Action News: A Record of Success*. Office of Solid Waste. Washington, DC: EPA March 2003d.

Environmental Protection Agency. *RCRA Facility Investigation Guidance*. OSWER Directive 9502.00–6c, OSW: 530/SW–89–031.Washington DC: EPA, May 1989.

Environmental Protection Agency. *RCRA Orientation Manual*. EPA 530–R–02–016. Washington, DC: EPA, September 2002bc.

Environmental Protection Agency. *Results-Based Approaches and Tailored Oversight Guidance for Facilities Subject to Corrective Action Under Subtitle C of the Resource Conservation and Recovery Act (RCRA)*. EPA 530–R–03–012. Washington, DC: EPA September 2003d.

Environmental Protection Agency. *Reuse Assessments: A Tool to Implement the Superfund Land Use Directive*. Office of Solid Waste and Emergency Response. OSWER Directive 9355.7–06P. Washington, DC: EPA, June 2001b.

"Final Guidance on Completion of Corrective Action Activities at RCRA Facilities: Notice." *Federal Register* 68 (25 February 2003): 8757.

General Accounting Office. *Hazardous Waste Progress under the Corrective Action Program is Limited, but New Initiatives May Accelerate Cleanups: Report to the Ranking Minority Member, Committee on Commerce, House of Representatives*. GAO/RCED–98–3. Washington, DC: GAO, October 1997.

General Accounting Office. *Superfund Program: Current Status and Future Fiscal Challenges*. GAO–03–850. Washington, DC: GAO, Setember 2003.

Green D. R. "Integration of RCRA Corrective Action and CERCLA Remedial Actions," in *Proceedings of the 20th Environmental Symposium and Exhibition of the American Defense Preparedness Association* in San Antonio, Texas. Arlinton, VA: NDIA, 1994.

Green D. R., L. Corathers and J. Coalgate. "An Overview of the Corrective Action Management Unit and Temporary Unit Regulations," in *Proceedings of the Waste Management '95 Symposium* in Tucson, Arizona: 1995.

"Hazardous Waste Identification Rule for Contaminated Media: Final Rule." *Federal Register* 63(30 November 1998):65874.

"Land Disposal Restrictions Phase IV: Rule." *Federal Register* 63 (26 May 1998):28556.

"Post-Closure Regulations: Rule." *Federal Register* 63 (22 October 1998):56710.

"Subpart S Withdrawal Notice." *Federal Register* 64 (7 October 1999):54604.

Louis Martino is an Environmental Systems Engineer at Argonne National Laboratory in Washington, DC. Mr. Martino is a Certified Hazardous Material Manager with expertise in the following areas: RCRA rule development, project management, hazardous waste site investigation/remediation techniques, pollution prevention; property transfer and compliance auditing, as well as regulatory policy analysis. He has over 25 years of experience working in these disciplines. In the past, Mr. Martino worked for the State of Maryland implementing RCRA in the state. He also co-authored and co-taught a training course on RCRA corrective action for the US Department of Energy. Most recently, Mr. Martino has been involved in the investigation/remediation of US Army installations containing fuel release sites, chemical warfare agent testing/disposal sites, and OB/OD units. Responsibilities include project management, authoring project documents, and health and safety. Mr. Martino recently co-authored a paper documenting the results of the development of techniques to evaluate the efficacy of a phytoremediation remedy.

David Green is an Associate with Booz Allen Hamilton, in McLean, Virginia. Mr. Green has over 15 years experience in the environmental management field. His primary area of expertise includes management of waste munitions and energetics, unexploded ordnance (UXO) remediation, and military range management. For the last ten years, his primary focus of effort has been on improving the policies, procedures, and regulations applicable to the management of waste military munitions and the conduct of response actions to UXO. Specific efforts include contributions to the development of the EPA Munitions Rule and the proposed DOD Munitions Response Site Prioritization Protocol, and to a variety of related DOD policy efforts, development of strategic and implementation plans, and participation in various public outreach and partnering efforts. Mr. Green has been an author or co-author of several documents and articles on RCRA corrective action and CERCLA response actions for DOE, as well as one of the developers and instructors for DOE's RCRA Corrective Action Workshop and the US Army Training and Doctrine Command RCRA Corrective Action Workshop. He has served as compliance audit team member, addressing waste management and remediation for multimedia compliance audits at federal and private facilities.

CHAPTER 44

Treatment Technologies in Hazardous Waste Management

Gazl A. George, PhD, CHMM

Introduction

Proper treatment of hazardous wastes has become an art and/or a concern to all generators and Treatment, Storage, and Disposal facilities (TSDs). This is because of the enactment of the Resource Conservation and Recovery Act (RCRA) in 1976, and the subsequent passage of the "Superfund" Cleanup law in 1980, as well as a complex series of amendments to cover new hazardous wastes, methods of characterization, treatment standards, and specific treatment technologies.

Hazardous Waste Treatment facilities must address all of the following factors:

1) Health and safety of operators and neighbors

2) Process economics

3) Rate of success

4) Flexibility to include the treatment of numerous parameters, such as toxic metals and

organics covered by the Land Disposal Restrictions (LDRs)

5) Public exposure from air emissions, water discharges and land disposal as a result of facility operations

6) Impact of future regulations on the available process(es); can they be expanded?

7) Market support in providing volumes of hazardous wastes sufficient to justify continuity of business and associated research and development

Readers must familiarize themselves with the RCRA hazardous waste regulations presented in 40 CFR 260–272, in order to determine whether or not a waste is hazardous. This is achieved by referring to 40 CFR 261, which is confusing to "newcomers" due to terminology and foggy regulatory language. An overview of the RCRA requirements can be found in the RCRA chapter of this book.

Hazardous Waste

A waste will be subject to the hazardous waste regulations if it meets any of the following conditions.

1) **Characteristic Waste.** Waste exhibiting any of the four characteristics of a hazardous waste: ignitibility, corrosivity, reactivity, or toxicity.

The various categories of characteristic hazardous wastes are detailed below.

Characteristic of ignitability (D001)—A waste that exhibits any of the following properties:

- It is a liquid other than aqueous solution containing less than 24% alcohol by volume and has a flash point less than 140°F (60°C), as determined by a Pensky Martens closed cup tester (American Society for Testing and Materials [ASTM] Method D–93–79 or D–93–80) or Setaflash closed cup tester using method ASTM D–3278–78.

- It is not a liquid and is capable under standard temperature and pressure of causing a fire through friction, absorption of moisture, or spontaneous chemical changes; and when ignited burns so vigorously and persistently, that it creates a hazard.

- It is an ignitable compressed gas as defined in 49 CFR 173.300 and as determined by the test methods described in the above regulations or equivalent test methods approved under 40 CFR 260.20 and 260.21.

- It is an oxidizer as defined in 49 CFR 173.151.

Characteristic of corrosivity (D002)—A waste exhibits the characteristic of corrosivity if a representative sample of the waste has either of the following properties:

- It is aqueous and has a pH of less than or equal to 2, or greater than or equal to 12.5, as determined by a pH meter, using the Environmental Protection Agency (EPA) publication SW–846.

- It is a liquid and corrodes steel at a rate greater than 6.35 mm (0.25 inch) per year at a temperature of 55°C.

Characteristic of reactivity (D003)—A waste exhibits the characteristic of reactivity if a representative sample of the waste has any of the following properties:

- It normally is unstable and readily undergoes violent changes without detonating.

- It reacts violently with water.

- It forms a potentially explosive mixture with water.

- It generates toxic gases, vapors, or fumes when mixed with water.

- It is a cyanide, or a sulfide-bearing waste which, when exposed to pH conditions between 2–12.5, can generate toxic gases, vapors, or fumes.

- It is capable of detonation or causing an explosive reaction if subjected to heat or initiators.

- It is readily capable of explosive decomposition or reaction at standard temperature and pressure.

- It is a forbidden explosive defined in 49 CFR 173.51, 49 CFR 173.53, and 49 CFR 173.88.

**Table 1. TCLP Concentration Limits for
Characteristic Wastes**

Metals		mg/L	Base Neutral Extract		mg/L
D004	Arsenic	5.0	D027	1,4–Dichlorobenzene	7.5
D005	Barium	100.0	D030	2,4–Dinitrololuene	0.13
D006	Cadmium	1.0	D032	Hexachlorobenzene	0.13
D007	Chromium	5.0	D033	Hexachlorobutadiene	0.5
D008	Lead	5.0	D034	Hexachloroethane	3.0
D009	Mercury	0.2	D036	Nitrobenzene	2.0
D010	Selenium	1.0	D038	Pyridine	5.0
D011	Silver	5.0	D023	m–Cresol	200.0
			D024	o–Cresol	200.0
Organics		**mg/L**	D025	p–Cresol	200.0
D018	Benzene	0.5	D026	Total Cresol	200.0
D019	Carbon tetrachloride	0.5	D037	Pentachlorophenol	100.0
D021	Chlorobenzene	100.0	D041	2,4,5–Trichlorophenol	400.0
D022	Chloroform	6.0	D042	2,4,6–Trichlorophenol	2.0
D028	1,2–Dichloroethane	0.5			
D029	1,1–Dichloroethylene	0.7	**Pesticides**		**mg/L**
D035	Methyl ethyl ketone	200.0	D020	Chlordane	0.03
D039	Tetrachloroethylene	0.7	D012	Endrin	0.02
D040	Trichloroethylene	0.5	D031	Heptachlor and its epoxide	0.008
D043	Vinyl Chloride	0.2	D013	Lindane	0.4
			D014	Methoxychlor	10.0
			D015	Toxaphene	0.5
			Herbicides		**mg/L**
			D016	2,4–D	10.0
			D017	2,4,5–TP (Silvex)	1.0

Waste codes D004–D043—Characteristic codes and their relevant characteristic level (concentrations) as determined by the TCLP (Toxicity Characteristic Leaching Procedure) for concentration-based constituents in waste, as shown in Table 1.

2) **Listed Hazardous Waste.** Wastes specifically listed in Subpart D of the regulations:

- Non Specific Source (F-Listed)
- Specific Source (K-Listed)
- Acute Hazardous Waste (P-Listed)
- Toxic Hazardous Waste (U-Listed)

3) **Mixtures.** The waste is a mixture of a listed hazardous waste and a nonhazardous waste.

4) **Declared to be Hazardous.** The waste has been declared to be hazardous by the generator.

It is important that generators of hazardous wastes investigate, experiment with, and implement waste minimization techniques through recycling, such as reclaiming of usable products or regeneration; source reduction, such as product substitutions, or source control; and finally, treatment using approved technologies.

Treatment Technologies

Treatment of hazardous wastes to eliminate their toxicity and/or their hazardous characteristics can be achieved using a wide spectrum of technologies which revolve around two main pathways—namely chemical and mechanical (physical). ***Chemical treatment*** includes all forms of chemical reactions such as reduction, oxidation, thermal oxidation, precipitation, neutralization, electrochemical, photolytic, biological degradation, *etc.* ***Mechanical or physical treatment*** includes those procedures that modify the physical properties of waste materials; for example: filtration, phase separation, filter pressing of suspended materials, centrifugation, agitation, adsorption, *etc.*

Filtration of Suspended Materials

Filtration can be achieved using a porous medium subjected to a pressure gradient such as gravity or pumping. This technology is normally used as a final polishing step following treatment processes such as neutralization, chemical precipitation, biological treatment of organic wastes, and oily wastewater separation by emulsion breaking and dissolved air flotation.

Solid separation can be conducted using simple screening techniques such as in-line strainers, filters and screens. More efficient filtration can be achieved using deep bed filtration, such as specialized cartridge filters and gradient granular beds for slurries that need to be dewatered (typically 1–25% by weight solids). Centrifugal filters, vacuum filters, belt filters as well as plate and frame filter presses generate a filter *cake* reaching or exceeding 50% solids by weight.

Since filtration is a physical process, it has numerous limitations. These limitations include but are not limited to

- Inability to separate dissolved solids unless coupled with another process.

- Except for membrane filtration, this process is not chemically selective for various waste constituents.

- High solids, viscous liquids, such as tars, cannot be filtered.

In all filtration processes, the filtrate is tested for compliance with the relevant discharge permits and the solids can either be deposited in a licensed landfill or sent for further treatment, such as chemical fixation with lime or cement.

Simple Acid–Base Neutralization

This treatment involves mainly wastes carrying characteristic hazardous waste code D002 or similar listed codes such as K062, U123, U134, *etc.*

This treatment method utilizes the simple reaction between an acid and a base. An ***acid*** is any substance that dissociates in solution to produce a proton (H+) and a ***base*** is any substance that accepts a proton. Strong acids or bases are those completely dissociating in solution such as nitric acid or potassium hydroxide, respectively; whereas weak acids and bases only partially dissociate in solution, such as acetic acid and ammonium hydroxide, respectively.

$$HNO_3 + NaOH \rightarrow NaNO_3 + H_2O + heat \qquad (1)$$

Nitric Acid ⟶ Sodium Hydroxide ⟶ Salt ⟶ Water

Most neutralization reactions involve the adjustment of the acidic or alkaline waste stream with the relevant suitable reagent to obtain a final pH of 6–9 to meet the water discharge requirements established under the Clean Water Act (CWA).

To select an efficient neutralization system, the waste constituents must be properly identified. For example, while hydrochloric acid can be directly neutralized with sodium hydroxide, hydrofluoric acid must be neutralized with lime to yield calcium fluoride, which is insoluble. Furthermore, some acids must be pretreated. For example, chromic acid must be reduced from chromium (+6) to chromium (+3) at an acidic pH using sodium metabisulfite prior to introducing lime slurry. The lime slurry precipitates the chromium (+3) hydroxide as a greenish sludge which can be directed to the process clarifier.

Neutralization of acids or bases which contain high solids such as tank bottoms can be routinely performed using chemical fixation/stabilization with lime to achieve an acceptable residue for landfilling. However, initial laboratory scale determinations must be conducted to avoid excessive heat generation, which can be controlled through dilution and/or slow additions.

Chemical Precipitation

This is a widely used process that takes advantage of the solubility products of certain compounds of the hazardous constituent (solute) to obtain an insoluble form, either via chemical reaction or changes in the composition of the solvents. The precipitated portion (solids) can then be separated by settling and/or filtration.

Metals and certain anions are commonly removed using such reactions. However not all metals are directly amenable to precipitation. Examples include chromium (+6), salts, arsenic salts, and certain amphoteric ions.

Industries generating liquid wastes suitable for this process include metal plating, metal polishing, inorganic pigments, mining, steel and nonferrous metals, circuit board and wood treatment using chromated copper arsenates (CCA).

Chemical precipitation can be achieved using the reactions described below.

Hydroxide Precipitation. When the solubility product of a metal hydroxide is suitable for precipitation, the use of sodium hydroxide (caustic) or calcium hydroxide (lime slurry) results in a metal hydroxide residue:

$$M^{+2} + 2(OH^-) \rightarrow M(OH)_2 \downarrow \qquad (2)$$

The precipitation of chromium, however, requires that all hexavalent chrome-containing ions be reduced to the trivalent state, since hexavalent chromium cannot be removed directly by hydroxide introduction. Using sulfurous acid as a reducing agent:

$$3H_2SO_3 + H_2Cr_2O_7 \rightarrow Cr_2(SO_4)_3 + 4H_2O \qquad (3)$$

$$Cr_2(SO_4)_3 + 3Ca(OH)_2 \rightarrow 2Cr(OH)_3 \downarrow + 3CaSO_4 \qquad (4)$$
Green Precipitate

Chelated wastes, such as those containing ammonia, ethylenediaminetetraacetic acid (EDTA), citric acids, amines, and sulfamates, require pH adjustment into higher alkaline ranges to effectively precipitate the chelated metals. The use of flocculants and coagulants, such as aluminum sulfate, ferric chloride, ferrous sulfate, dithiocarbamate, cationic and anionic polymers, is essential in chelated metals treatment. Also, the choice between caustic versus lime is a function of the types of chelators present.

Sulfide Precipitation. The use of sulfides to precipitate metals is superior to the use of hydroxides since the metal sulfide precipitate has a much lower solubility than the hydroxide of the same metal. For example, lead hydroxide has a solubility of slightly less than 0.1 g/l compared to about 10^{-8} g/l for lead sulfide. Furthermore, the sulfide ligand is a reducing agent in addition to being a precipitating agent, which can be advantageous in treating chromium wastes as follows:

$$Cr_2O_7^{-2} + 2FeS + 7H_2O \rightarrow \qquad (5)$$

$$2Fe(OH)_3 + 2Cr(OH)_3 \downarrow + 2S + 2OH^-$$

Soluble mercury salts are best precipitated using sulfide addition to achieve solubilities of less than 10^{-45} g/l.

Again, as with hydroxide precipitation, certain metals do not respond to the introduction of sulfides. These metals include arsenic, which has to be co-precipitated with iron. When using sulfide as a precipitating agent, extreme care must be exercised to avoid hydrogen sulfide generation. This can be achieved by ensuring that the operating pH is greater than 8. In addition sulfide must be closely monitored in the effluents, since most precipitation reactions use excess reagents to ensure reaction completion.

Other Precipitation Processes. Certain metals such as cadmium (D006) and lead (D008) respond to carbonate precipitation comparably to hydroxide precipitation, with the advantage of a lower pH and a denser, easier-to-filter sludge at a pH of 8.

Soda ash is used as the source of carbonate in this treatment:

$$Cd(NO_3)_2 + Na_2CO_3 \rightarrow CdCO_3 \downarrow + 2NaNO_3 \qquad (6)$$

Phosphate precipitation is effective in selectively removing trivalent cations such as chromium, aluminum, and iron from wastes containing divalent or monovalent cations.

Sulfate precipitation is effective in the removal of barium (D005) as barium sulfate:

$$Ba^{+2} + SO_4^{-2} \rightarrow BaSO_4 \downarrow \qquad (7)$$
White Precipitate

Selenides can be removed by reaction with iron to form iron selenide, an insoluble compound, whereas other selenium salts can be treated with sulfur dioxide to precipitate elemental selenium.

Chemical Oxidation and Reduction (Redox Reactions)

This technology is used as a pretreatment step for numerous waste codes in liquid, sludge, or solid phases prior to other treatment trains such as chemical precipitation and/or chemical fixation.

Oxidation is the process of losing electrons whereas *reduction* is the process of gaining electrons. Therefore in each oxidation reaction there is a material that is oxidized and another that is consequently reduced.

The above processes are best suited for liquids. However, sludges and solids can be similarly treated via wetting, increasing contact time, and the introduction of surface tension modifiers such as surfactants.

Oxidation. The following examples of oxidative reactions demonstrate the effectiveness of this process in treating both inorganic and/or organic species to either render the waste nonhazardous or to create waste that passes the Land Disposal Restriction (LDR) requirements by meeting the relevant treatment standards.

Treatment of Cyanides. The major sources of cyanides can be attributed to metal finishing and the expanding circuit board industries. Cyanides are present as sodium cyanides, potassium cyanides, zinc cyanides, copper cyanides, silver cyanides, and gold cyanides.

Dilute waste streams have up to 1000 ppm reactive cyanides, while concentrated streams containing plating bath materials reach in excess of 200,000 ppm of both simple and/or complex cyanides. Other contributors to these wastes are the photographic industry, heat treating, mining and coking operations.

The most common chemical process utilized in the destruction of cyanides is alkaline chlorination or simply the use of household bleach (sodium hypochlorite):

$$2NaCN + 5NaOCl + H_2O \rightarrow \qquad (8)$$
$$N_2 + 2NaHCO_3 + 5NaCl$$

This reaction is carried out at a pH > 10 to avoid the liberation of the dangerous gas cyanogen chloride.

Another oxidation process utilizes hydrogen peroxide to convert the cyanide into cyanate as in the following equation:

$$NaCN + H_2O_2 \rightarrow NaCNO + H_2O \qquad (9)$$

Potassium permanganate has been used in cyanide treatment; however, due to the cost of permanganate and the incomplete destruction of the cyanide ligand, it has been rarely used in industrial applications:

$$NaCN + 2KMnO_4 + 2KOH \rightarrow \qquad (10)$$
$$2K_2MnO_4 + NaCNO + H_2O$$

Cyanide oxidation is instantaneous in simple cyanides such as sodium or potassium cyanides. However in complex cyanides, such as $Cu(CN)_2$, and $Ni(CN)_2$, an initial step is required in order to dissociate the complex and remove the complexing metal; converting the cyanide into a simple cyanide that is easily amenable to alkaline chlorination:

$$K[Cu(CN)_2] \rightarrow CuCN + KCNO \qquad (11)$$
Bleach   Insoluble   Cyanate
pH>12

$$CuCN + Na_2S \xrightarrow{[OH]^-} CuS \downarrow + NaCN + NaOH \qquad (12)$$
Sodium Remove Sludge Simple
Sulfide by Filtration Cyanide

$$2NaCN + 5NaOCl + H_2O \rightarrow \qquad (13)$$
$$N_2 \uparrow + 2CO_2 \uparrow + 2NaOH + 5NaCl$$

Equation (13) is derived from the simple alkaline chlorination sequence:

$$CN^- + H^+ + OCl^- \rightarrow CNCl + OH^- \tag{13a}$$

$$CNCl + 2OH^- \rightarrow CNO^- + Cl^- + H_2O \tag{13b}$$

$$2CNO^- + 3OCl^- + H_2O \rightarrow \tag{13c}$$
$$2CO_2\uparrow + N_2\uparrow + 3Cl^- + 2(OH^-)$$

The above reaction can be simplified if bleach is added under alkaline conditions with heat and pressure (reactor) to produce nitrogen and carbon dioxide gases.

Organic Compounds. Treatment of low concentrations of organics (<1% by weight to volume) can be achieved using commercially available oxidizers such as permanganates, bleaches, peroxides, ozone, chlorine gas, *etc.*

The following generalized reactions are examples of oxidation of certain organic species:

Phenols.

$$C_6H_5OH + 14H_2O_2 \xrightarrow{Fe^{+2}} 6CO_2 + 17H_2O \tag{14}$$
Phenol   Hydrogen Peroxide

Alcohols.

$$CH_3CH_2OH \rightarrow CH_3COOH \tag{15}$$
Ethanol   Acetic Acid
(Primary Alcohol)

$$R_2CH(OH) \rightarrow RCOR \tag{16}$$
Secondary Alcohol

Aldehydes.

$$RCHO \rightarrow RCOOH \tag{17}$$
Organic Acid

$$HCHO \rightarrow HCOOH \tag{18}$$
Formaldehyde   Formic Acid

Sulfur-bearing organics.

$$2RSH \rightarrow RSSR + H_2O \tag{19}$$

$$RSSR' \rightarrow RSO_3H + R'SO_3H \tag{20}$$

Organic Halides: R-X (Non Oxidative).

$$RCH_2X \xrightarrow[\text{HOH}]{} RCH_2OH + HX \tag{21}$$
Hydrolysis   Alcohol   Acid

X = F, Cl, Br, I

These reactions must be catalyzed by either hydroxyl or hydrogen ions, and are also a function of solubility in water.

Metals Precipitation. Certain metals require an oxidation step (higher valence) to be precipitated more efficiently and to achieve the least solubility.

For example:

$$Hg^{+1} \rightarrow Hg^{+2} + e^- \tag{22}$$

$$Hg^{+2} + S^{-2} \rightarrow HgS\downarrow \tag{23}$$
(solubility product close to 10^{-45} g/l)

Other metals, such as arsenic (+3), require oxidation to arsenic (+5) to avoid any possibilities of the formation of the deadly gas arsine, AsH_3, which occurs in a reducing medium in the presence of hydrogen.

Chemical Reduction. Chemical reduction has been used to treat both hazardous and nonhazardous waste. The most common reaction is that of chromium (+6) reduction to chromium (+3) prior to precipitation as the hydroxide.

$$4CrO_3 + 6NaHSO_3 + 3H_2SO_4 \rightarrow \tag{24}$$
Sodium Bisulfite
$$2Cr_2(SO_4)_3 + 3Na_2SO_4 + 6H_2O$$

Certain wastes such as halogenated organic compounds in concentrations less than 1% by weight can be reduced using iron:

$$Fe + 2H_2O + 2RX \rightarrow \tag{25}$$
$$2ROH + Fe^{+2} + 2X^- + H_2\uparrow$$

X = F, Cl, Br, I

Chemical reduction has been recently used to desensitize (deactivate) certain shock-sensitive nitro-compounds such as DNT (dinitrotoluene) at concentrations less than 5000 ppm using patented reducing mixtures. This reduction step converts the nitro groups into the respective amine groups hence rendering these residues harmless.

Wet Oxidation

The introduction of a rich source of oxygen such as air (about 20% oxygen) to a liquid waste containing organics or oxidizable species at temperatures ranging from 150°C to 350°C and a pressure ranging from 300–3000 psi results in oxidation. This process can be either batched or continuous flow, and is widely used compared to other technologies due to the relatively low associated cost.

This technology was also modified to be conducted in deep shafts (wells) instead of tanks. Because this process is a *plug-flow* process, where oxygen and liquid move together, it is a great deal more efficient than conventional wet air oxidation. Heat, pressure, reaction, cooling, and depressurizing all occur in one vertical subsurface shaft, thus ensuring safety.

Direct Chemical Oxidation

Nonthermal, aqueous and ambient pressure Direct Chemical Oxidation (DCO) has been widely used since the early 1990s for the oxidation of liquid/solid organic hazardous and mixed wastes. This technology has been successfully used to de-militarize, decommission, and destroy weaponized chemical and biological agents, (also known as Weapons of Mass Destruction, or WMD).

Such chemical technology can handle, with a high rate of success, a wide spectrum of organics such as halogenated solvents, explosives, oil, and grease in various physical consistencies such as solid, sludge, liquid, separated phases and even soils contaminated with organic compounds, such as those listed previously.

$$Na_2S_2O_8 + \text{(Organic Compound)} =$$
$$2NaHSO_4 + (CO_2 + H_2O + \text{Inorganic residue}) \quad (26)$$

Peroxydisulfate forms the basis for DCO; sodium or ammonium peroxydisulfates are the preferred salts.

The oxidation potential for the peroxydisulfate is very high. At +2.05 volts it is only lower than that of fluorine and ozone. This reaction occurs via the formation of a sulfate radical anion at about 70 to 100 degrees Celsius when activated with minor amount of ultraviolet (UV) light.

The advantages of DCO, as compared to other forms of aqueous/ambient treatments of organic compounds (in particular, water insoluble or layered compounds) are:

1) The peroxydisulfate ion is among the strongest oxidizers currently known, operating at a potential of $E = +2.05$ V (compared to the permanganate ion potential of $E = 1.70$ V)

2) The cost is approximately $0.75/lb

3) With some UV and thermal catalysis, peroxydisulfate will spontaneously form the sulfate free radical anion

4) When the sulfate free radical is introduced to layered organic compounds in water (such as halogenated solvents, oils, *etc.*) emulsification/solubilization takes place, hence aqueous oxidation is enhanced

5) DCO can be an advantage in remedial projects where soils are impacted by organic contaminants. The presence of catalyzing metal species such as Iron(II) and sunlight (UV) yield reaction efficiencies between 80 to 90%

Biological Treatment

Most municipal and domestic wastewaters, including some industrial effluents, are treated using biological processes to detoxify these wastes prior to final discharge. It is anticipated that by the early 21st century, most industrial wastewaters will be biologically treated due to changing regulations under the Clean Water Act.

Despite the fact that numerous forms of biological treatment exist, two main treatment trains are more frequently used by municipalities and Publicly Owned Treatment Works (POTWs):

- *Aerobic* (use of air or oxygen)

- *Anaerobic* (absence of air or oxygen)

The above two types can be used in series, parallel, or individually.

Aerobic systems. *Activated Sludge.* The basic design categories of activated sludge systems include conventional, complete mix, and step aeration. The addition of powdered activated carbon (PACT) to a biological process has been used with success in treating hazardous wastes such as wastewaters containing solvents.

Organic wastes and recycled sludge are introduced to a reactor where aerobic bacteria are maintained in suspension. The residence time in the bioreactor (hydraulic residence time) is obtained by dividing the reactor volume by the volumetric flow rate. Sludge then leaves the reactor for settling tanks, where it is separated from the waste stream. Most of the sludge is filter-pressed, the remainder being recycled to the reactor.

The recycled fraction volume is determined by the desired *food* to mass ratio (F/M) measured as BOD (biochemical oxygen demand) divided by the mixed liquor suspended solids (MLSS): kg BOD / kg MLSS.

Aerated Ponds and Lagoons. This method of treatment is similar to an extended aeration activated sludge process where a basin is used instead of a reactor. Air injection is performed through diffuse aerators and the biomass is kept in suspension. Modern lagoons recycle the biomass. Aerated lagoons are used for low- to medium- strength organic wastes and efficiency is linked to adequate mixing, annual air temperature over $5°C$, and a good inlet/outlet design.

Aerobic Digestion. Two versions exist, varying only in the oxygen supply: conventional, and pure oxygen. These systems can handle many types of wastes. Some examples are waste-activated or trickling filter sludge, mixtures of waste-activated or trickling filter sludge and primary sludge, or waste sludge from activated sludge treatment plants designed without primary settling.

Other common aerobic systems include

- *Trickling filters*
- *Rotating Biological Contactors*
- *Bioaugmentation*

Anaerobic Digestion. This treatment is one of the oldest processes used for sludge stabilization. It involves the oxidation of organic and inorganic matter with anaerobic and facultative organisms

in the absence of molecular oxygen carried out in sealed containers. The by-product of such activity is methane gas (55%), CO_2, N_2, and H_2S produced at the rate of 1 liter per gram of volatile acids consumed. Optimum conditions include a pH > 6.5 and a temperature of 85–90°F.

Thermal Treatment Processes

Incineration. *Incineration* can be defined as a unit of operation that utilizes thermal decomposition via oxidation to reduce carbonaceous matter. Principal products of such process are carbon dioxide, water, ash, and heat energy. Various by-products are also generated including sulfur, nitrogen compounds, halogens and their compounds.

These units are integrated systems comprised of the incinerator itself, a waste delivery system, gas scrubbing equipment, effluent management system, ash discharge system, and energy recovery operations.

In the field of hazardous waste incineration there are more liquid injection incinerators than all other types combined. Wastes are aspirated and burned directly in the flame or combustion zone. The injection nozzle location is determined primarily by the heating value (Btu) of acceptable wastes.

Incinerators operate at temperatures ranging from $1000°C$ to $1700°C$ ($1832°F$–$3092°F$), with a waste residence time in the *hot zone* from milliseconds to about 3 seconds.

In any incinerator design, the chemical, physical, and thermodynamic properties of the components must be considered. This includes storage tanks, pumps, mixers, valves, nozzles, refractory, heat recovery, quench systems, and all related pollution control equipment.

Since wastes in most cases are heterogeneous, the characteristics must be carefully defined before finalizing the design. The chemical and physical parameters to be considered include

- Corrosivity
- Ignitability
- Reactivity
- Toxicity
- Btu value (heating value)
- Moisture and volatile matter

Table 2. Waste/Incinerator Selection Criteria

Waste Type	Rotary Kiln	Multiple Hearth	Fluidized Bed	Liquid Incinerators	Catalytic Combustor	Multiple Chamber	Wet Air Oxidation	Molten Salt
Aqueous organic sludge		X	X				X	
Halogenated aromatics	X		X	X If pumpable				X
Organic liquids				X			X	
Granular	X	X	X					
Irregular–bulky	X					X		
Low melting point	X		X	X If pumpable				
Organics with fusible ash	X	X						X
Organics–vapor laden					X			
Toxic high organics				X	X		X	

- Viscosity and specific gravity
- Polymerization
- Solid content
- Ash content
- Explosiveness
- Nitrogen, halides, sulfur, and metals, *etc.*

Many factors must be considered in selecting an economical yet efficient system for waste disposal and volume reduction through combustion; these factors are

- Segregation
- Transportation

- Solid and liquid preparation
- Storage and equalization
- Handling and feeding
- Residue handling and disposal
- Environmental impact
- Regulatory requirements

There are many incinerator configurations used to burn nonhazardous and hazardous wastes in liquid, sludge, and solid forms; these include:

- Multiple hearth furnaces
- Fluidized bed incinerators

Table 3. Operating Parameters for Various Thermal Units

Process	Temperature Range (°F)	Residence Time
Pyrolysis	900 –500	12 – 15 minutes
Multiple-Hearth	1400 –1800	0.25 to 1.5 hours
Fluidized Bed	1400 –1800	A few seconds
Liquid Incinerators	1200 –3000	0.1 – 2 seconds
Direct Flame	1000 –1500	0.3 – 0.5 seconds
Catalytic Combustor	600 –1500	1 second
*Rotary Kiln (liquid)	1500 – 3000	2 seconds
*Rotary Kiln (solid)	1500 –3000	hours
Molten Salt	1500 – 1800	0.75 seconds
Multiple Chamber	1500 – 1800	secs. (gases), mins. (solids)
Wet Air Oxidation	300 – 550 (at 1500 psig)	10 – 30 minutes

*   Cement kiln data are similar to rotary kiln data.

- Liquid waste incinerators
- Waste gas flares
- Direct flame incinerators
- Catalytic combustion incinerators
- Rotary kilns
- Cement kilns
- Molten salt incinerators
- Multiple-chamber incinerators
- Oceanic (ship-mounted) incinerators
- Infectious waste incinerators
- Industrial boilers
- Pyrolysis units

A description of the most commonly applicable incinerators in the hazardous waste industry will be briefly discussed. Selection criteria and operating parameters are shown in Tables 2 and 3.

Multiple Hearth Incinerators. Incineration usually requires a minimum of six hearths while pyrolysis requires a greater number. Wastes enter the furnace by dropping through a port at the top of the furnace. A spiral shaft located centrally rotates the waste counterclockwise across the various hearths through the furnace, thus dropping the waste from hearth to hearth. Burners and combustion air ports are located in the walls of the furnace.

Air is cleaned by passing the hot gases from the furnace through a precooler, which sprays fine water spray droplets. The cool gas is then passed through a Venturi throat into which additional water is sprayed. At this time, gases are subcooled (120°F) and stripped of water prior to discharge.

Multiple-hearth furnaces operating in pyrolysis modes can handle feed material with a heat release potential greater than 25,000 Btu/lb of water and still maintain a temperature of about 1500°F.

Pyrolysis. Incineration requires high air input whereas **pyrolysis** is theoretically a zero air, indirect heat process (air starved incineration).

Waste organics are distilled or vaporized to form combustion gases, which can be used as fuel for an external combustion chamber. Pyrolysis is used when wastes have a high Btu (thermal) content greater than 3500 Btu/lb.

Fluidized Bed. This is a simple device consisting of a refractory lined vessel containing inert granular material. Gases are blown through this inert material at a rate to cause the bed to expand and act as a fluid. Gases are injected through nozzles, which restrict downflow. Hot gases leave the fluidized bed and enter heat-recovery or gas cleaning devices similar to the multiple-hearth incinerators.

Wastes enter the bed through nozzles located either above or within the bed. Excess air requirements for normal incineration are limited to about 40% above the stoichiometric combustion requirements of the waste.

These units experience problems caused by low ash fusion temperatures, which can be avoided by keeping temperatures below the ash fusion level or by adding chemicals that raise the fusion temperature.

Liquid Incinerators. These are the most flexible and economical (labor-free) units. The feed waste acts as a liquid at a viscosity below 10,000 Saybolt Second Units (SSU). Waste is atomized through a suspension burner, which is normally a rotary cup or a pressure atomizer. The burner nozzle is mounted at one end of the refractory lined chamber. Gases exit to the scrubbing equipment. These units are normally equipped with storage and blending tanks to ensure homogeneous flows.

Cement Kilns. A wide variety of hazardous wastes can be treated in cement kilns. Properly managed, they can accomplish what rotary kiln incinerators can without an increase in emissions or a negative environmental impact. Many of the candidate waste streams provide an alternative source of fuel resulting in resource recovery rather than simple waste destruction. Cement kilns can accommodate a variety of materials both as fuels and feed in the cementation process, however there are limitations on the use of hazardous waste materials, which can be divided into two categories:

1) Materials presenting process constraints such as high sodium and potassium

2) Materials unacceptable due to public opinion, such as polychlorinated biphenyl (PCB) and dioxin waste

Rotary Kilns. The rotary kiln is a cylindrical horizontal, refractory-lined shell that is mounted at an incline (about 5°). Rotation of the kiln causes mixing of the waste with combustion air. The ratio of length to diameter of the kiln ranges between 2:1 to 10:1 and it rotates at a speed ranging from 1 to 5 rpm. The combustion temperature ranges from 1500°F–3000°F, and generally samples have residence times ranging from seconds to hours depending on the waste introduced.

These units are effective when the size and nature of the waste precludes the use of other types of incinerators. A few examples of likely materials are debris, bottles, boxes, and pharmaceutical containers. Kilns can operate either in batch or continuous feeding modes.

Exhaust gases from the kiln pass through an afterburner chamber to ensure complete destruction of organic compounds, and then through a precooler, Venturi scrubber, and packed column prior to atmospheric release.

Molten Salt Incinerators. Molten salts baths comprised of 90% sodium carbonate and 10% sodium sulfate operate at temperatures ranging from 1500°F–1800°F. Sometimes lithium and potassium carbonates are used to improve encapsulation of heavy metals. Spent salts can be either recycled or landfilled.

Industrial Boilers. In **fire tube boilers**, heat is transferred from hot combustion products flowing inside tubes to the water surrounding them. Combustion takes place in a cylindrical furnace within the shell. Fire tubes run the length of the shell above and around the furnace. Gases from combustion travel forward through the tubes to the front of the boiler.

Water tube boilers circulate water throughout the combustion chamber through thousands of feet of steel tubing. Heat is transferred from the path of the flue gas into the adjacent water tubes.

Oceanic and Ship-Mounted Incinerators. Ship-mounted incinerators are used to dispose of organic or organometallic wastes that cannot be burned in conventional incinerators. A downside to these units is the stringent EPA scrutiny of their effluents.

Chemical Fixation and Solidification

Treatment of hazardous and nonhazardous wastes using chemical fixation/solidification (CFS) involves the use of raw materials such as fly ash, silica fume, slag, natural pozzolans, cement, cement kiln dust, and lime flue dusts.

The terms *fixation* and *stabilization,* abundantly used in this industry, refer to the reduction or elimination of the toxicity or the hazard potential of a certain waste stream by lowering the solubility and leachability of the toxic or hazardous components. Another term most commonly used is *solidification*, which references the formation of monoliths with considerable structural strength. The difference between solidification and fixation is that the former does not necessarily involve a chemical reaction between waste and raw material, but only encapsulatation of the waste particles to limit the surface area exposed to leaching.

Micro- and macro-encapsulation are used to define processes designed to minimize leachability. *Micro-encapsulation* yields a semi-homogeneous product resulting from the treatment of finely divided powders, sludges, or viscous liquids, whereas *macro-encapsulation* is the encapsulation of solid waste with an impervious layer to eliminate the exposure to leaching. In general, chemical fixation/stabilization/solidification act together to bind the active components of waste in numerous fashions as described below.

Sorption. This treatment involves the addition of a sponge-like solid (such as sodium silicate, gypsum, *etc.*) to absorb any free liquid that might be present in the waste. This process acts only in a physical fashion to merely acquire the liquid fraction onto the surfaces of the solid. The solid materials do not interact chemically with the waste nor do they reduce the leachability of the hazardous components.

pH Adjustment. In this process, the wetted calcium oxide portion of the reagent contributes to neutralization of the hydronium ion, raising the pH to over 10 and hence precipitating the vulnerable heavy metals as their respective hydroxides. The availability of carbonates, phosphates, and sulfates also enhances precipitation of metals such as cadmium, nickel, and barium, respectively.

Pozzolan Interaction. Fine, noncrystalline silica from fly ash or cement kiln dust (CKD), and calcium from lime products give rise to a weak cementation process, thus providing a primary containment to isolate waste from the outside environment.

In this process, the available soluble silicates react with the polyvalent metal ions resulting in highly insoluble nonstoichiometric metal silicates in an amorphous matrix.

A pozzolanic reaction has certain limitations that are a function of particular variables. These are:

1) At least 30% lime is required to give sufficient product strength.

2) Water and wetting for dry wastes is a must to initiate reactions.

3) Oil and grease can negatively impact the quality of the residue.

4) Borates, chromates/dichromates, and sugars interfere with the bonding in the silicate matrix.

5) Pretreatment is required in most cases to meet the relevant LDRs such as D007 wastes and most organic species.

6) When strong lime is used (high calcium oxide), high pH results in two adverse phenomena: the formation of gas and/or leachate and the possible dissolution of some amphoteric metals such as lead, zinc and arsenic.

It is well established that cement-based processes are more effective than lime-based processes in displaying chemical resistance and integral strength.

Chemical Fixation of Organic Compounds. For a short period of time, the EPA introduced treatment standards for organic constituents (D012–D043) measured by TCLP, which allowed numerous treatment facilities to be inventive in finding methods to "hide" the organics. Such methods were: sorption on the surface, dilution, adsorption onto powdered or granular carbon added to the fixation medium, and/or volatilization by introducing "hot" lime into the formulation.

Due to the fact that the above treatment patterns were not effective in reducing the long-term leaching of these organics, EPA published the new LDRs (Land Disposal Restrictions) as measured by total concentration—thus requiring a destructive step prior to solidification.

Pretreatment technologies include: hydrolysis, biodegradation, chemical oxidation, chemical reduction, salt formation, low-temperature de- composition, dehalogenation, and catalytic destruction.

In general, the most common organic wastes encountered in chemical fixation/solidification facilities are:

1) Aqueous wastes containing less than 1000 ppm of organic constituents that are considered hazardous

2) Aqueous wastes containing less than 1000 ppm of nonhazardous organic constituents

3) Solvent- and oil-based organic wastes that are considered RCRA wastes

4) Aqueous wastes containing large concentrations of emulsified organics (up to 25%) that are considered hazardous under RCRA

5) Same as (4) but nonhazardous

6) Solid wastes contaminated with <1% of hazardous organics to cover all the above categories of waste mixtures

7) Mixed inorganic wastes with low organic constituents above the LDR levels

Chemical Fixation of Inorganic Compounds. This discussion will be limited to metals and nonmetals (and their compounds), which are hazardous wastes as defined under RCRA in 40 CFR 261.

Arsenic. Due to the fact that arsenic is classified as a nonmetal, (*i.e.*, it combines with metals to form arsenides, arsenites, and arsenates) it is difficult to precipitate in regular hydroxide precipitation reactions. It has been found that the most effective pathway for treatment of arsenic is the co-precipitation with iron as the arsenate prior to fixation:

$$4As(ONa)_3 + 5FeSO_4 + 4Ca(OH)_2 + 5H_2SO_4 \rightarrow \quad (27)$$
$$FeAs_2O_4 + 2FeAsO_4 + 6Na_2SO_4 + 2Fe(OH)_3 +$$
$$4CaSO_4 + 6H_2O$$

Barium and Compounds. Barium is a widely used element in processes such as heat treating, brick manufacturing, chemical diagnostics, pigments, plastics, fire-extinguishing foams, and pyrotechnics. Barium can be easily treated using chemical fixation in the presence of sulfates and carbonates and silicates to yield a solubility of about 1–5 mg/l, well below the TCLP regulatory level of 100 mg/l.

Cadmium and Its Compounds. Cadmium associates itself with lead, zinc, and copper. It is widely used in electroplating, batteries, pigments, catalysts, phosphors, photography, electronics, and plastic stabilizers.

Lime fixation media are used to take the operating pH up to about 10, where solubility is at its minimum for cadmium hydroxide (0.1 mg/l). To improve precipitation, iron salts can render the leachable cadmium concentrations nondetectable. Carbonates present within the fixation medium will also improve cadmium fixation especially in low calcium oxide media.

Chromium and Its Compounds. Chromium compounds are widely used in plating/metal finishing, pigments, leather tanning, wood preservation (CCA), drilling muds, catalysts, coatings, *etc.*

The ideal chemical fixation medium is sulfide-rich pozzolan, which will cause chemical reduction of Cr (+6) to Cr (+3), and consequent precipitation as $Cr(OH)_3$, locked in a tight matrix. Alternatively, ferrous sulfate can be added as a reducing agent.

Lead and Its Compounds. Lead is widely used in numerous industries as the metal, lead oxides, halides, tellurides, nitrates, acetates, carbonates, sulfates, peroxides, silicates, *etc.* Lead is also used as an organometallic product, such as tetraethyl lead. Since lead is amphoteric, pH must be closely monitored to avoid solubilization. The addition of phosphates to divalent lead compounds renders them highly insoluble (0.1 mg/l). The presence of active silicates with phosphate precipitates leads to non-detectable concentrations.

Mercury and Its Compounds. Compounds of mercury can only be treated at total concentrations less than 250 ppm due to RCRA regulatory limitations. Despite their high cumulative toxicity, mercury compounds have been widely used in agriculture, catalysis, dental work, electrical equipment, chlorine production, magnets, paints, pigments, paper, and pharmaceuticals.

Mercury salts have been successfully treated at low and medium concentrations using chemical fixation technology coupled with a solubility modifier, such as sulfides, thiourea, and thiocarbamates. These reduce the soluble mercury to levels reaching 10^{-48} g/l. In many instances, activated carbon is introduced to adsorb mercury, specifically when organo-mercury compounds are present.

Selenium and Its Compounds. Selenium coexists in sulfur- and copper-bearing deposits and is widely used in ceramics, glass, pigments, rubber, lubricants, electronics, photocopying machines, and pharmaceuticals. Selenium treatment is based on chemical fixation with high-silicate, iron-rich matrices, which can be improved by the introduction of sulfide ions.

Silver and Its Compounds. Most silver-bearing wastes are associated with those bearing high concentrations of lead, gold, copper, and zinc.

Silver is used widely in jewelry, photographic processes, electronics, catalysis, solders, mirrors, and dental products.

Most silver wastes sent to TSDs are of low unrecoverable concentrations. Treatment can be relatively easy (except in cases of silver cyanides). Silver precipitates as silver chloride when high chlorides are present with a solubility product of 1.7×10^{-10}. Silver complexes are common in the photographic industry. Silver ammonia complexes are more difficult to treat and require an oxidation step such as alkaline chlorination to achieve precipitation. Chemical fixation agents showing high efficiency toward silver are those having high silicates with calcium chloride. These agents enhance both speed of cementation and, due to the common-ion effect, the precipitation of silver as $AgCl$.

Evaluation of *On-Site Impacted Soils* Treatment at Remedial Sites

Contaminated soils that are impacted by one or more waste codes under RCRA can be managed on-site in order to comply with the specified criteria and relevant RCRA standards. These standards require that the excavated wastes or soils be treated so that they are nonhazardous and do not leach hazardous constituents. Treatment can be performed in preparation for the following:

1) Off-site treatment/disposal, or

2) On-site disposal of chemically treated soils that meets Federal, State and local guidelines

On-site soils treatment must be determined and evaluated on a case-by-case basis. It is always recommended that a *standby* contingency plan be drawn in case problems are encountered during the treatment.

The evaluation factors for chemical treatment and remedial action include both site-specific physical and treatment-specific chemical factors.

Site-Specific Physical Considerations

- Access roads and weight limits
- Availability of utilities on site
- Percentage debris and size of debris
- Proximity to emergency response capabilities
- Proximity to landfills or Treatment, Storage, and Disposal Facilities (TSDFs)
- Site security measures
- Location of all waterways, sewer lines, manholes or National Pollution Discharge Elimination System (NPDES) out-falls, storm water plan and drainage patterns
- Available geological data

Chemical Treatment Considerations for On-Site Treatment

- Available site investigation and remedial plans
- Applicability of assigned waste codes and any Underlying Hazardous Constituent (UHC)
- Applicability of State and local rules with respect to various criteria that govern on-site remedial actions such as *in situ* placement of soils that might fall under a State restriction (for example, total lead must not exceed 400 ppm)
- The presence of any polychlorinated biphenyls (PCBs) or dioxins (as shown in laboratory reports). State and local guidelines for these two parameters must be evaluated.
- Is the groundwater impacted? If pumping of groundwater is required, remember that this can serve as the treatment reagent or dissolution water for soils treatment
- Evaluate the treatment process applicability, efficiency and the timetable for such treatment; always use sensible and flexible

contingency in time and cost estimates (allow about 10–15% flexibility in cost and time)

- Evaluate all sampling, testing and reporting procedures
- The most important determining factor for success in on-site remedial work is to conduct multiple treatability studies on *worst case samples* showing the highest levels of contamination with the parameter(s) of concern and satisfying the *worst interfering matrices,* such as oil and grease. These trials must be reproducible.

On-site remediation of impacted soils involves the following scenarios.

Treat and Haul the Residue to a Subtitle D Landfill. This method of contaminated site management involves wastes that initially failed the TCLP test and were deemed to be *characteristically hazardous,* and also have high concentrations of total contaminant(s) that exceed State guidelines or clean up criteria for industrial or residential land use. The treated residue will meet the TCLP requirements and becomes classified as non-hazardous waste but the other parameters necessitate removal of the residue to a subtitle D landfill.

Excavate Then Haul the Waste to a TSDF. This method of remediation is applicable to sites that are unsuitable for on-site chemical treatment because they have been characterized with RCRA waste codes requiring incineration or other treatments. This includes wastes containing PCB or dioxin concentrations that require removal, or residues that will eventually require the use of technology-based treatment standards. Some listed waste codes at remedial sites require (as described in the remedial investigation report) that the excavated wastes be hauled to a permitted TSDF or Subtitle C landfill.

Treatment Where the Waste is Excavated, Piled On-Site, Tested, Treated, Tested Again and Returned to the Site. This scenario involves a contaminated site where the wastes have failed the TCLP and been characterized as hazardous for one or more of the RCRA D codes. The total concentrations of all the parameters of concern must fall below the criteria for maximum total concentrations set by State or Federal guidelines. Successful treatment renders all excavated *wastes* non-hazardous and compliant with fill material requirements.

In Situ Treatment via Direct Chemical Application to a Pre-Tested Area Followed by Testing and Reporting. This type of remedial action is conducted when contamination levels are considered to be *low risk*, contamination is at a shallow depth (less than one foot) and the parameters of concern are not necessarily specified by RCRA regulations. Since no excavation is conducted, the contaminated soils are NOT wastes thus the UHC (underlying constituents) rules do not apply. Furthermore, the treated contaminated soils can be left *in situ* if testing of the leaching characteristics shows that toxic metals or organic contaminants will not represent a long-term hazard as a result of contact with rain, temperature fluctuations and future site use. *In situ* treatment and placement is the most economical and *generator/PRP friendly* remedial choice.

The *in situ* remedial options can use any portable means for chemical treatment, in single or multiple-stage applications. The hazardous materials manager on-site should understand that cost of remediation from most expensive to least expensive is generally in the following order:

- Excavation and disposal of the waste at a TSDF

- Excavation, testing, treatment, and testing, with wastes returned to site

- Treatment and disposal of the waste at a Subtitle D landfill

- *In situ* treatment with direct chemical application to a pre-tested area

Bibliography

Balazs, G., J. F. Cooper, P. R. Lewis, and M.G. Adamson. *Direct Chemical Oxidation: A Non-Thermal Technology for the Destruction of Organic Wastes.* Lawrence Livermore National Laboratory, California: Department of Energy, 1998.

Brunner, Calvin R. *Handbook of Incineration Systems.* Reston, VA: Incinerator Consultants, Inc., 1991.

Conner, Jesse R. *Chemical Fixation and Solidification of Hazardous Wastes.* New York, NY: Van Nostrand Reinhold, 1990.

Cheremisinoff, Paul. *Waste Incineration Pocket Handbook.* Northbrook, IL: Pudvan Publishing, 1991.

Environmental Protection Agency. *Test Methods for Evaluating Solid Waste, Physical/Chemical Methods, SW–846,* 4th ed. Washington, DC: EPA, 1996.

Freeman, H. M. *Standard Handbook of Hazardous Waste Treatment and Disposal,* 2nd ed. New York, NY: McGraw-Hill, 1997.

Malhotra, V. M., Ed. *Fly Ash, Silica Fume, Slag and Natural Pozzolans in Concrete.* Vols. 1 and 2. Proceedings, Third International Conference. Trondheim, Norway: American Concrete Institute, 1989.

Manahan, Stanley E. *Environmental Chemistry,* 5th ed. Chelsea, MI: Lewis Publishers, 1991.

Peyton, G. R. "The Free-Radical Chemistry of Persulfate-Based Total Organic Carbon Analyzers." *Marine Chemistry,* 41: 91–103, 1993.

Tropy, Michael F. *Anaerobic Treatment of Industrial Wastewaters.* Pollution Technology Review #154. Park Ridge, NJ: Noyes Data Corp., 1988.

Wilk, L., S. Palmer, and M. Brelon. *Corrosive Containing Waste Treatment Technology.* Pollution Technology Review #159. Park Ridge, NJ: Noyes Data Corp., 1988.

Gazi A. George is the President of GTSI, and serves as a Consultant to the Board of Directors, Titan International Inc. of Quincy, Illinois. He handles all Environmental, Health and Safety aspects at their multi-state facilities for the manufacturing of military, agricultural, construction and mining wheel and/tires (in Illinois, Mississippi, Texas, Virginia and Iowa). He is also the lead E H & S consultant for Soave Enterprises of Detroit, Michigan and handles numerous projects for the Automotive Services Group, scrap yards and site remediation. Dr. George obtained his Ph.D. in Chemistry in 1976 from the University of Lancaster, England. He spent five years as a Nuclear Scientist with the Iraqi Atomic Energy Commission and was the Director of Nuclear Waste Management and Radiation Protection Departments at the various nuclear facilities. He received extensive training from top nuclear institutes and facilities in Austria, Belgium, France, Germany, Holland, Russia and the United Kingdom. After his resignation and escape from Iraq in 1981, he was one of a few Iraqi scientists that was sentenced to death in absentia by Saddam Hussein's regime. He was then hired by a Division of Johnson & Johnson Pharmaceutical (DEVRO, Inc.) in Scotland, United Kingdom, where he was the Industrial Hygiene and Compliance Manager for two plants near Glasgow. Between 1985 and 1988, he moved to Detroit, Michigan where he was appointed as Technical Manager at CyanoKEM (American NUKEM) specializing in the chemical treatment of cyanides, toxic heavy metals and reactives. From 1988–1992 Dr. George worked as the Corporate Director then Vice President at Envotech (currently EQ) in Belleville, Michigan. He then joined City Management Corporation (A division of Soave Enterprises, Detroit, Michigan) in 1992, where he managed the Treatment Storage and Disposal Facilities (TSDFs) in Florida and Detroit. His duties expanded to cover treatment facilities in California, Arizona, Louisiana, and Florida, in addition to Michigan. Dr. George has published many scientific papers in numerous countries and has developed manuals for complex waste treatments such as cyanides, sulfides, toxic metals and radioactive isotopes.

Mixed Waste Management

Thomas Hillmer, CHMM

Chapter Overview

This chapter covers in detail the regulations that are applicable to the commercial nuclear industry regarding mixed waste. It reviews the regulatory history of mixed waste and what elements should be included in a mixed waste management program. It discusses the dilemma that facilities storing mixed waste once faced waste and recent Federal regulations that have made management of mixed waste a part of normal operations.

Introduction

Mixed waste is defined in 40 CFR 266.210 as any waste that contains both a RCRA hazardous waste component and is also low-level radioactive waste. Both the Environmental Protection Agency (EPA) and the Nuclear Regulatory Commission (NRC) regulate mixed waste. The NRC generally regulates commercial and non-Department of Energy (DOE) Federal facilities. DOE currently is self-regulating, and its orders apply to DOE sites and contractors. Using their authority, NRC and DOE regulate mixed waste with regard to radiation safety. Using its authority, EPA regulates mixed

735

waste with regard to hazardous waste safety. The NRC is authorized by the Atomic Energy Act (AEA) to issue licenses to commercial users of radioactive materials. The Resource Conservation and Recovery Act (RCRA) gives EPA the authority to control hazardous waste from *cradle-to-grave*. Once a waste is determined to be a mixed waste, the waste handlers must comply with both AEA and RCRA statutes and regulations. However, the provisions in Section 1006(a) of RCRA allow the AEA to take precedence in the event provisions of requirements of the two acts are found to be inconsistent.

When the United States Congress envisioned a country served by nuclear power facilities in the mid-1960s, they failed to envision that regulatory interpretations would create disposal problems for mixtures of nuclear and hazardous waste in the decade of the 1990s.

For a number of years every nuclear power facility relied on the weight of the EPA's notice of non-enforcement because there were no approved disposal facilities that were licensed to take all the various types and forms of mixed waste that have been generated (56 *Federal Register* (FR) 43730, *et seq.,* 63 FR 59989–92, and 63 FR 59991–2). Both the NRC and EPA were fully aware of this dilemma but continued to delay decisionmaking that would enable the generator to meet a single set of regulations.

EPA continued to consider as *relatively low priority* enforcement actions against individuals who store mixed waste when: (1) there is no "available treatment or disposal capacity" for the mixed wastes and (2) the wastes are stored according to "prudent waste management practices" in order to minimize risk to public health and the environment. The management of this extended policy included:

- Inventory and compliance assessment of storage areas, including recordkeeping, regular inspections, and voluntary corrective action in the event of noted deficiencies

- Identification of mixed wastes, including identification, sources, generation rate and volumes, and process information of the hazardous components of the waste

- Waste minimization plans, including active measures to avoid the generation of mixed wastes

- Good-faith efforts, including demonstration of ongoing good-faith efforts to locate and utilize mixed waste treatment technology and disposal capacity

The extended policy was limited in scope to only those categories of mixed waste for which there is no treatment or disposal capacity. EPA stated in the extended policy that it believed (1) treatment was currently available for most low-level mixed wastes (LLMW), but treatment continued to be unavailable for a few wastes, such as mixed wastes containing dioxins, PCBs, lead-based paint solids, and wastes with very high levels of radioactivity; and (2) where treatment technology was available, there was excess capacity at the commercial mixed waste treatment facilities.

EPA defines ***available treatment technology and disposal capacity*** to mean any facility that is

> commercially available to treat or dispose of a particular waste and has either (1) a RCRA permit or interim status, (2) a research, development, and demonstration permit under 40 CFR 270.65; or (3) a land treatment permit under 40 CFR 270.63.

Few management options existed for mixed waste generators who were at risk of being in non-compliance with the storage prohibition regulations. One problem created by the EPA position was that wastes which once could be disposed of as low-level radioactive waste would have to meet EPA land ban requirements. These requirements stipulated that waste be processed in a licensed treatment facility with a process that had been approved for the specific waste in question. Meanwhile, nuclear facilities had been designed with processing capabilities necessary to meet licensing requirements for radioactive waste and not EPA land ban requirements. A significant effort in both time and money would be necessary to develop a treatment method, obtain the needed NRC license, and retrofit that process and equipment into existing nuclear facilities. Another problem in complying with EPA regulations was the time necessary to obtain permits, which could vary depending on whether the generator was regulated directly by the EPA or by an authorized state. Other questions and concerns created by the EPA interpretation included:

- Which other environmental regulations that were not then applicable became applicable after a facility became RCRA-permitted?

- How would the closure of a permitted storage facility affect an operating nuclear facility and NRC's decommissioning of a facility?

All these issues, along with the severe and continuing shortage of off-site mixed waste treatment, storage, or disposal facilities available for the management of mixed waste, would force generators of even the smallest quantities of mixed waste to accumulate those wastes on-site for indefinite periods.

Applicable Regulations

Many diverse statutes or acts are applicable to mixed waste. The most important are the Atomic Energy Act (AEA, 1954), the Resource Conservation and Recovery Act (RCRA, 1976), the Clean Water Act (CWA, 1977), the Hazardous and Solid Waste Amendments (HSWA, 1984), the Superfund Amendments and Reauthorization Act (SARA, 1986), and the Pollution Prevention Act (PPA, 1990). Federal regulations such as the *Code of Federal Regulations*, Energy, Title 10 (10 CFR); the *Code of Federal Regulations*, Protection of the Environment, Title 40 (40 CFR); and the *Code of Federal Regulations*, Transportation, Title 49 (49 CFR) were derived from these and other acts.

Table 1 lists applicable NRC, EPA, Occupational Safety and Health Administration, (OSHA), and Department of Transportation (DOT) regulatory references that must be reviewed in order to develop a complete mixed waste management plan.

The Federal government may grant authority to the states to regulate in its place. When the NRC grants that authority to a state, the state is called an ***Agreement State***. When the EPA grants the state authority, the state is called an ***Authorized State***. A list of Agreement States is located in 57 FR 54932.

Regulatory History

Regulation of waste that contains both a radioactive component and also a RCRA hazardous component became effective on July 3, 1986 (Laswell and Doohan 1993). On that date, the EPA, in a *Federal Register* notice, stated that the EPA would regulate any waste that contained hazardous waste and that was also radioactive, regardless of whether or not another regulatory body already regulated the waste. In 1987 the NRC and EPA issued additional guidance on the definition and identification of mixed waste (EPA 1987).

Prior to the EPA determining that they had to regulate the hazardous waste portion of any nuclear waste generated, all radioactive waste was processed, usually on-site, and disposed of as radioactive waste. After the EPA made its determination it became necessary for any facility that processed or stored its radioactive waste, which also contained any hazardous waste, to obtain a treatment, storage, or disposal (TSD) permit. This also meant that any radioactive disposal site would also become a TSD facility if they accepted mixed waste. When the EPA made their determination, no facility was permitted by both the NRC and EPA to process or dispose of mixed waste. With no facility licensed to accept all types or forms of mixed waste, the generator had no option but to begin to store mixed waste on its own site.

Historically, the volume of commercial waste affected by the EPA decision was very small. During 1990 the NRC and EPA conducted a survey with the objective of compiling a national profile on the volumes, characteristics, and treatability of commercially generated low-level mixed waste (NRC 1992). The profile was divided into five major facility categories: academic, industrial, medical, NRC-Agreement State-licensed government facilities, and nuclear utilities. A breakdown of the annual generation of mixed waste by reporting facility grouping is shown in Table 2.

The study found that for 1990, an estimated 81,227 cubic feet of mixed waste was generated by reporting facilities across the United States. Using weighting factors, a statistically valid estimate of the national profile yielded a generation of approximately 140,000 cubic feet. Of this amount, approximately 71% were organic solvents such as chlorofluorocarbons (CFCs) and corrosive organics. Waste oil made up 18%, toxic metals made up 3%, and "Other" waste made up the remaining 8%. The study indicated that almost half the waste being generated was not being properly classified as mixed waste and that a significant amount of

Table 1.
Summary of Regulatory Requirements for the Management of Mixed Waste

NRC Regulations Regarding the Management of Mixed Waste	
10 CFR 20	Standards for protection against radiation
10 CFR 61	Licensing requirements for the land disposal of radioactive waste
10 CFR 71	Packaging and transportation of radioactive material
EPA Regulations Regarding the Management and Storage of Mixed Waste	
40 CFR 260	Hazardous waste management system: General
40 CFR 261	Identification and listing of hazardous waste
40 CFR 262	Standards applicable to generators of hazardous waste
40 CFR 264	Standards for owners and operators of hazardous waste treatment, storage, and disposal facilities
40 CFR 265	Interim status standards for owners and operators of hazardous waste treatment, storage, and disposal facilities
40 CFR 268	Land disposal restrictions
40 CFR 270	EPA administered permit programs: The Hazardous Waste Permit Program
40 CFR 272	Approved state hazardous waste management programs
DOT Regulations Regarding Mixed Waste Transportation	
49 CFR 171	General information, regulations, and definitions
49 CFR 172	Hazardous materials tables and hazardous materials communication regulations
OSHA Regulations Regarding Management of Mixed Waste	
29 CFR 1910.1200	Hazardous waste operations, emergency response
29 CFR 1910.120	Hazard communication and the training of workers

mixed waste was not being stored as mixed waste but being disposed of as non-mixed waste. The total volume of classified mixed waste in storage, at that time, was estimated at 75,000 cubic feet. These values did not include Federal Government facilities controlled by the Department of Defense (DoD) and Department of Energy (DOE).

Today, the generation of mixed waste has decreased in the commercial electric utility sector to nearly zero. This result is primarily due to pollution prevention programs, which have been very successful in finding nonhazardous chemicals to replace hazardous chemicals previously used. Commercial mixed waste volumes are very small (approximately 2%) compared to the total volume of mixed waste being generated or stored by DOE. To put the waste values in perspective, a comparison with the generation and storage of mixed waste at one DOE site is included. In November of 1995, the Idaho National Engineering Laboratory (INEL) estimated that it would generate an average of 20,000 cubic feet per year over the next 5 years. This value represents a significant reduction in the past generation rate. This new waste generation will be added to the 2,700,000 cubic feet already in storage at INEL. This represents about 12% of the total of all DOE mixed waste then in storage (INEL 1995). Recently, DOE has projected that it will generate and store, at 37 DOE sites in 22 states, an estimated 8,000,000 cubic feet of low-level mixed waste over the next 20 years.

Table 2.
Generation of Mixed Waste by Facility Type

Facility Type	Amount of Mixed Waste Generated (in Cubic Feet/Year)
Academic	20,421
Industrial	19,056
Governmental	18,324
Nuclear Utilities	13,275
Medical	10,151

DOE waste contains an additional subset of mixed waste. *Mixed transuranic waste (MTRU)* is waste that has a hazardous component and radioactive elements heavier than uranium. The radioactivity in the MTRU must be greater than 100 nCi/g and co-mingled with RCRA hazardous constituents. The principal hazard from MTRU is from alpha radiation through inhalation or ingestion. MTRU is primarily generated from nuclear weapons fabrication, plutonium-bearing reactor fuel fabrication, and spent-fuel reprocessing. Approximately 55% of DOE's transuranic (TRU) wastes are MTRU. MTRU currently is being treated and stored at six DOE sites.

DOE has developed Site Treatment Plans (mandated by the Federal Facilities Compliance Act [FFCAct]) to handle its mixed wastes under the review of EPA or its authorized states. These plans are being implemented by orders issued by EPA or the State regulatory authority. DOE is also developing a Waste Management Programmatic Environmental Impact Statement for managing treatment, storage, and disposal of radioactive and hazardous waste. This plan will provide environmental input for DOE's proposed action of identifying future configurations for selecting waste management facilities.

Dual Regulation

Is dual regulation necessary? That question has been asked since the inception of the EPA position that EPA must also regulate mixed waste. The NRC conducted an analysis of low-level radioactive waste and EPA hazardous regulations in view of the generation of mixed waste and found that, in general, there was no conflict in the regulations (NRC 1985). This point need clarification since dual regulation had, in fact, meant that some waste that could once have been shipped and disposed of at a low-level waste facility has had to be held in storage. This was because the waste did not meet the specific license and or permit requirements of the single commercial mixed waste burial facility.

A literature review was undertaken to determine if a detailed comparison between the NRC regulations and the EPA regulations, which cover mixed waste, existed and were part of the public record. The review found that the EPA had received a detailed comparison as part of submitted comments on the proposed Hazardous Waste Management Rule (Hillmer 1996).

The nuclear industry has shown that dual regulation provides no additional protection to the public and the environment. They argue that adequate regulations existed under the NRC regulatory framework by comparing the EPA regulations for storage of hazardous waste in tanks to the regulations governing the storage of low-level radioactive liquid (Envirosphere 1988). This study was presented to the NRC and EPA, but the EPA maintained that even though they believed the regulations were equivalent they were legally required to regulate the hazardous portion of low-level radioactive waste.

In lieu of a regulatory solution, the generator of mixed waste had to comply with dual regulations in the best way possible. In cases where mixed waste could not be processed or disposed, requirements for storage had to be met.

Mixed Waste Management

The *Mixed Waste Management Guidelines* (EPRI 1993) prepared by utility and industry experts, offers a complete overview of the development and management of mixed waste programs and provides guidance for developing or assessing the adequacy of mixed waste management programs. Major management issues include generator status, waste characterization, permit requirements, mixed waste transportation requirements, land disposal restrictions, and mixed waste source reduction. This information, along with 40 CFR 266, if followed, allows the generator to be in compliance with EPA regulations. The EPA has published a document that outlines how to conduct inspections of mixed waste facilities. This document can be a useful tool to ensure compliance by using it to perform self-auditing activities (EPA 1991). In 1994, Edison Electric Institute (EEI), while working with the Electric Power Research Institute (EPRI), issued a compliance manual for the nuclear industry (EEI 1994). More recently, the EPA and NRC issued additional guidance on storage of mixed waste (60 FR 40204) and the new 40 CFR 266 regulations allow for contingency management of most mixed waste.

One of the key elements of a comprehensive mixed waste management program is to properly characterize waste streams that have the potential to be a mixed waste. Accurate characterization of a potential mixed waste stream includes a determination of whether the waste is radioactive, a solid waste, and is a hazardous waste. In addition, the characterization process should consider how the waste would ultimately be managed so that appropriate information is available and documented relative to proper handling, treatment, storage, and/or disposal of the waste.

It is very important that a *due diligence review* be performed before using any treatment, storage, or disposal facility, in order to ensure that the waste will be handled in accordance with all applicable regulations. Currently, there are only a few facilities that are authorized to receive certain categories of mixed waste for treatment or storage. EPA identifies those facilities that it believes are capable of providing mixed waste treatment, storage, and disposal on the EPA mixed waste homepage:

<http://www.epa.gov/radiation/mixed-waste>

The technical record to this rulemaking provides overwhelming evidence that the radiation protection standards and engineering performance objectives of the AEA for on-site storage, the on-site treatment, the off-site transport and disposal of LLMW in a qualified Low Level Radioactive Waste Disposal Facility (LLRWDF) are protective of the hazardous waste constituents in LLMW. This protection eliminates the need for superimposing RCRA standards on these materials because human health and environmental protection from chemical risks would not be compromised when the EPA deferred to the NRC management practices of LLWM.

Mixed Waste Identification

In, *Nuclear Utility Mixed Waste Stream Characterization Study* (EPRI 1994), EPRI outlines the characterization process, summarizes industry experience relative to key characterization issues, and provides industry data (including more than 400 actual sample results) on the majority of plant processes identified as having the potential to generate mixed waste.

The regulatory guidance for identification (57 FR 11798, *et seq.*), for sampling (EPA 1986), and for testing (57 FR 10508) has been written and was used in identifying and evaluating the proper management of mixed waste. Additionally, the EPA and NRC supplied guidance in a jointly issued letter of October 4, 1989, which contained an attachment entitled "Definition and Identification of Commercial Low-Level Radioactive and Hazardous Waste."

Mixed Waste Determination

The key to the entire need for a storage permit is whether or not a mixed waste has been generated and then must be stored. In most nuclear facilities, the determination as to whether a waste is a mixed waste is made after the material in question has been identified as a waste material. Most facilities have a chemical control program or a pollution prevention program, which is the primary method of controlling the use of chemicals. These programs use Material Safety Data Sheets to determine how to handle any waste generated using the chemical. One of these program functions is to ensure that hazardous material, which could become a hazardous waste, does not enter a radiological controlled area (RCA) and is the main method of ensuring that mixed waste is not generated.

When hazardous materials are used in an RCA and have become a waste, the first determination that is made is whether the material has become radioactively contaminated. The methodology and references developed in this chapter comprise a program necessary to determine a mixed waste has been generated. The following questions are included as a guide to determine if an unknown material is a mixed waste. The questions are only guidelines to be used to initially characterize and classify the waste. A detailed review of the use of the material, a review of any chemical analysis, and a review of the State and Federal regulations should be made to ensure proper final characterization.

There are three conditions that the waste must meet in order for it to be classified as a mixed waste. These conditions can be determined by asking the following questions:

1) Is the waste radioactive?

2) Is the waste a solid waste or is it exempted?

3) Does the waste meet the requirements of a hazardous waste?

The legal definitions of these types of waste are the key to determining if your waste is *mixed waste*.

Proper characterization of potential mixed waste streams is the first step in appropriate management of mixed waste. After the waste stream has been characterized, it will become apparent if the waste must be processed to meet land ban restrictions, shipped off-site for processing or disposal within the required time frame, or stored in accordance with the new 40 CFR 266 rules.

Special Management Concerns

Mixed waste has other special management concerns that also must be considered. Of paramount concern for many NRC licensees, especially commercial nuclear power plants that were subject to intense regulatory scrutiny by regulators and the public, was the fact that, for certain LLMW, there were simply no treatment or disposal options available. This meant that some NRC licensees have no choice but to store LLMW on-site for indefinite periods of time in potential violation of RCRA's land disposal restriction (LDR) storage prohibition. See RCRA §3004(j).

Because of dual regulation mixed waste must be stored so as to be in compliance with NRC and EPA guidance on storage of the waste. EPRI has prepared a management guideline on the proper management and compliance with NRC storage regulations (EPRI 1992). The EPA regulations on storage are contained in 40 CFR 264 and 265 and the storage exclusion for contingency management is located in 40 CFR 266. Both the radiation and the chemical hazard associated with mixed waste must be considered. Basic radiation protection concerns and management practices associated with sampling and storage must be incorporated in operating procedures (Gollnick 1988). These procedures will need to be incorporated into a contingency plan. How the facility meets the EPA requirements for Pollution Prevention (PL 101–508) and the NRC policy on volume reduction must be included in station procedures (46 FR 51100–1).

When mixed waste is to be processed or shipped off-site, compliance with EPA, NRC, and DOT regulations must be met (49 CFR 171 and 172, 10 CFR 71 and 57 FR 14500, *et seq*.). DOE has developed Site Treatment Plans to handle its mixed wastes under the review of EPA or its authorized states.

Training requirements for personnel working with mixed waste are specified by the EPA, NRC, and OSHA (29 CFR 1910.1200). The training must also include specific training on DOT regulations associated with the shipment of hazardous waste (EPRI 1993).

State Regulations

Each state has its own set of regulations that are based on the Federal requirements. Individual State regulations must be reviewed in order to ensure that mixed waste is managed in accordance with both State and Federal regulations, since a state may add additional requirements to those hazardous waste aspects of the Federal requisites. It is important to note that not all states are authorized to manage RCRA programs. In those states the EPA will have authority. Also, not all states that are authorized to regulate RCRA have the right to regulate mixed waste. For specific information on a state's authorization status, see the EPA's State Authorization Homepage:

<www.epa.gov/epaoswer/hazwaste/state/>

Regulatory Outlook

In general, facilities that manage mixed waste are subject to the RCRA Subtitle C (Hazardous Waste) requirements for hazardous waste in 40 CFR 124 and 260–270 implemented by EPA, or to comparable regulations implemented by states or territories that are authorized to implement RCRA mixed waste authority. The RCRA Subtitle C program was developed primarily for implementation by the states with oversight by EPA. As mandated by the Federal Facilities Compliance Act, which was signed into law in October 6, 1992, DOE has developed Site Treatment Plans to handle its mixed wastes under the review of EPA or its authorized states.

The Federal government in 40 CFR 266 Subpart N responded to the dual regulation problem by reducing the unnecessary complications and burdens of LLMW (64 FR 63497–63501), as well as reducing the radiation exposures of workers managing mixed wastes (66 FR 27221). Given the applicability of NRC waste management controls, EPA concluded that imposition of RCRA Subtitle C hazardous waste regulation on LLMW, in addition to pre-existing NRC controls, was not necessary to protect human health and the environment. This regulatory relief resolved, for most mixed waste, the dual regulatory dilemma. Subpart N facilitates the final disposal of certain LLMW that historically have been stored on-site

under both the RCRA and NRC regulatory regimes.

40 CFR 266 Subpart N regulations streamline the regulation of LLMW by providing for a conditional exclusion from hazardous waste regulation for these materials provided certain conditions are met. Subpart N is comprised of two parts: (1) the storage and treatment conditional exemption, and (2) the transportation and disposal conditional exemption. The storage and treatment conditional exemption excludes from hazardous waste regulation the storage and qualified treatment of LLMW while managed at a NRC-licensed facility, provided certain key provisions are met and maintained. This includes ensuring that LLMW is managed in accordance with all applicable NRC requirements (40 CFR 266.230). The transportation and disposal conditional exemption excludes from hazardous waste regulation the off-site transportation and disposal of LLMW.

Subpart N also eliminates the compliance problem that mixed waste generators had been confronting concerning RCRA's land disposal restriction (LDR) storage prohibition under RCRA Section 3004(j). This provision prohibits the storage of hazardous wastes for prolonged periods of time, even when there is no treatment or disposal capacity for such wastes, as is the case for LLMW under the dual RCRA/NRC regulatory regime. To provide interim relief for LLMW generators confronting this compliance predicament, EPA had issued its RCRA LDR enforcement policy. Under this policy the Agency exercised enforcement discretion in not pursuing violations of the LDR storage prohibitions against NRC licensees who had no option but to store LLMW for prolonged periods of time. The 40 CFR 266 Subpart N eliminates this technical compliance problem and the need for EPA's enforcement policy because, under the rule, LLMW can be legally stored under applicable NRC requirements.

The rule also established a full exclusion for LLMW from hazardous waste regulation for the on-site storage or *in tanks or containers* treatment. The EPA rule required that waste be managed in accordance with applicable NRC or Agreement State license conditions for this exclusion to be used. The storage and treatment exclusion applies to LLMW that is generated under a single NRC or NRC Agreement State license.

The exclusion for off-site transportation and disposal of LLMW or eligible naturally occurring and/or accelerator-produced radioactive material (NARM) from RCRA hazardous waste controls requires that the waste is: (1) treated to meet applicable RCRA LDR treatment standards, and (2) is disposed of in a low-level waste disposal facility licensed by the NRC or an Agreement State in accordance with 10 CFR 61. Additional flexibility is provided for manifesting LLMW or eligible NARM.

Summary

EPA is providing increased flexibility to facilities for managing low-level mixed waste (LLMW) and naturally occurring and/or accelerator-produced radioactive material (NARM) containing hazardous waste. The Agency is exempting low-level mixed waste from RCRA Subtitle C requirements, including permitting, storage and treatment requirements as long as the waste is generated under a single NRC license, meets the conditions specified, and is stored and treated in a tank or container. In addition, LLMW and NARM, that meet applicable treatment standards, may be conditionally exempt from RCRA transportation and disposal requirements. This waste may be disposed of at low-level radioactive waste disposal facilities that are licensed by NRC. The rule also provides additional flexibility for manifesting these wastes when they are destined for disposal at such facilities. Although mixed waste meeting the applicable conditions is exempt from certain RCRA requirements, it must still be managed as radioactive waste according to NRC regulations. It also should be noted that DOE disposal facilities are not eligible to accept the exempt waste since they are not subject to NRC regulation.

The complexity and number of regulations involved in the management of mixed waste has been increasing since dual regulation of mixed waste began; thus it is imperative that mixed waste be managed properly and that all precautions be made to adequately identify and correctly characterize mixed waste. Historically, various organizations have attempted to assist in the management of mixed waste by publishing guidance documents. These documents should be reviewed along with the new rule when implementing a mixed waste management program.

Bibliography

"Approach to Reinventing Regulations on Storing Mixed Low-Level Radioactive Waste." *Federal Register* 64 (1 March 1999): 10064.

Edison Electric Institute. *Mixed Waste Storage and Treatment Regulatory/Compliance Manual.* EPRI TR–104223. Washington, DC: EPRI, 1994.

Electric Power Research Institute. *Guidelines for Interim Storage of Low-Level Waste.* Final Report, TR–101669, Research Project 3800. Palo Alto, CA: EPRI, 1992.

Electric Power Research Institute. *Mixed Waste Management Guidelines.* EPRI TR–103344. Palo Alto, CA: EPRI, 1993.

Electric Power Research Institute. *New DOT Training Requirements for Hazardous Material Employees and Implementation by Nuclear Utilities.* TR–102662, Project 2691–13. Palo Alto, CA: EPRI, 1993.

Electric Power Research Institute. *Nuclear Utility Mixed Waste Stream Characterization Study.* EPRI TR–104400. Washington DC: EPRI, 1994.

Environmental Protection Agency. "EPA Newswatch." *EH&S Developments Newsletter.* CPI Electronic Publishing. pp 5-6, 30 November 1995.

Environmental Protection Agency. *Test Methods for Evaluating Solid Waste, Physical/Chemical Methods.* SW–846. Washington DC: GPO, 1986.

Environmental Protection Agency, Office of Waste Programs Enforcement. *Conducting RCRA Inspections at Mixed Waste Facilities.* OSWER 9938.9. Washington DC: GPO, 1991.

Environmental Protection Agency and Nuclear Regulatory Commission. *Guidance on the Definition and Identification of Commercial Mixed Low-Level Radioactive and Hazardous Waste and Answers to Anticipated Questions.* Washington DC: EPA, 1/8/87.

Envirosphere Company. *Comparative Assessment of the Environmental Protection Agency's Regulations for Hazardous Waste Tank Systems (40 CFR 265, Subpart J) and Comparable Nuclear Regulatory Commission Requirements.* Washington, DC: Edison Electric Institute, 1988.

"Extension of the Policy on Enforcement of RCRA Section 3004(J) Storage Prohibition at Facilities Generating Mixed Radioactive/Hazardous Waste." Enforcement Policy." *Federal Register* 63 (6 November 1998): 59989–92.

Gollnick, D. *Basic Radiation Protection Technology*. ISBN 0-916339–04–1. Altadena, CA: Pacific Radiation Corporation, 1988.

"Guidance on the Storage of Mixed Radioactive and Hazardous Waste." *Federal Register* 60 (7 August 1995) : 40204, *et seq.*

"Hazardous Waste Management System; Identification and Listing of Hazardous Waste; Toxicity Characteristic Revisions; Final Rule." *Federal Register* 55, (29 March 1990): 11798, *et seq.*

Hillmer, T. P. *A Case Study on the Development of a RCRA Part B Permit for Storage of Mixed Waste at a Nuclear Facility*. Unpublished master degree practicum. Phoenix, AZ: Arizona State University, 1996.

Idaho National Engineering Laboratory. *Site Treatment Plan Summary*. Idaho Falls, ID: Department of Energy, Idaho Operations Office, 1995.

Laswell, D. and M. Doohan. "Mixed Waste Dilemma: A Mixed Regulatory Bag?" *Environmental Protection*, pp. 37–42, March 1993.

"Low-Level Waste Shipment Manifest Information and Reporting." *Federal Register* 57 (21 April 1992): 14500, *et seq.*

"Mixed Waste Enforcement Policy." *Federal Register* 56 (29 August 1991): 43730, *et seq.*

"NRC Volume Reduction Policy (Generic Letter No. 81-39)." *Federal Register.* 46 (16 October 1981): 51100–1.

Nuclear Regulatory Commission. *An Analysis of Low-Level Waste: Review of Hazardous Waste Regulations and Identification of Radioactive Mixed Waste.* NUREG–CR–4406. Washington, DC: GPO, 1985.

Nuclear Regulatory Commission. *National Profile on Commercially Generated Low-Level Radioactive Mixed Waste.* NUREG/CR–5938 ORNL–6731. Washington, DC: GPO, 1992.

"Pollution Prevention Act of 1990." (PL 101–508), *United States Statutes at Large*. 104 Stat. 1388.

"Proposed Guidance Document on the Testing of Mixed Radioactive and Hazardous Waste." *Federal Register* 57 (26 March 1992): 10508.

"State Authorization for Mixed Waste Programs." *Federal Register* 57 (23 November 1992): 54932, *et seq.*

Thomas Hillmer *is an Environmental Consultant for Arizona Public Service Company at the Palo Verde Nuclear Generating Station. He has received a Master of Technology degree in Industrial Technology with emphasis in hazardous materials management from Arizona State University, a MBA in Management from Western International University, Phoenix, Arizona (where he graduated with distinction), and a BS degree in Earth Science with major concentration in Environmental Studies from the University of Wisconsin-Parkside, Kenosha, Wisconsin. Mr. Hillmer has worked in the nuclear industry for more than 30 years, managing radioactive and hazardous waste. He has served on various technical advisory committees of the Electric Power Research Institute, Edison Electric Institute's Utility Nuclear Waste Management Group, and the Nuclear Management Resource Council, dealing with pending waste disposal regulations. Mr. Hillmer has published and presented nearly two dozen papers on environmental management, waste processing, volume reduction, decontamination, storage, and disposal of nuclear and mixed waste.*

Part X

Chemical Perspectives

CHAPTER 46

Introduction to the Chemistry of Hazardous Materials

Richard E. Hagen, PhD, CHMM

Introduction

Goals of this Chapter

This chapter discusses key chemical principles as applied to hazardous materials and chemistry. The science is placed in a regulatory setting with some discussion of good environmental practices and risks to avoid. This chapter is strictly an overview, therefore, the reader is urged to keep a chemistry reference book handy. See the Bibliography at the end of this chapter for useful references, especially the hazardous materials chemistry textbook by Meyer.

More specifically, the primary goal of this chapter is to provide a brief chemistry refresher integrated with regulatory requirements for hazardous materials managers who have responsibilities for

- A facility

- Hazardous materials manufacture, distribution, or handling

- Chemical emergency response
- Environmental field or remedial operations
- Hazardous materials consulting, environmental science, and related environmental responsibilities

This chapter will provide an introductory explanation of typical physical, chemical, and certain biological properties of materials and their significance. Since hazardous materials ultimately are either chemicals or are chemical mixtures, it is critically important that the hazardous materials manager have a firm grasp of chemical principles. Failure to understand these principles may put the hazardous materials manager, the facility, or the general public in a dangerous situation. Without some knowledge of chemical principles, the hazardous materials manager will be blindly following recipes or procedures prescribed by others.

Hazardous Chemicals Definitions and Lists

Before we get into the chemistry of hazardous materials, we need to look at the bewildering array of terms and definitions associated with the word *hazardous* In a sense, all chemical substances might be considered hazardous under certain conditions. Sugar or wheat flour in certain particle sizes can be hazardous. For example, the dust formed when grinding sugar in a food plant can cause respiratory problems for line workers. Flour dust in a flourmill is a potential explosion hazard even though the same dust, when collected, can be used to bake a loaf of bread.

Key References on Chemical Hazards

The hazardous materials manager is forewarned that wherever possible, he or she should not rely totally on memory when taking action in a hazardous materials incident or release. The National Institute of Occupational Safety and Health (NIOSH) has compiled an excellent handbook on the many chemical and hazard properties discussed below. The reader is urged to obtain and use this reference entitled *Pocket Guide to Chemical Hazards*. This guide, found on the Internet at

<http://www.cdc.gov/niosh/npg/npg.html>

presents critical information and data in abbreviated form over 600 chemicals and substance groupings found in the work environment.

The Department of Transportation's (DOT) *Emergency Response Guidebook* has a wealth of practical information for dealing with chemical emergency situations. It is available on the Internet for download at

<http://hazmat.dot.gov/pubs/erg/gydebook.htm>

Sax's *Dangerous Properties of Industrial Materials*, 11th edition by R. J. Lewis, is another essential reference. This three-volume set provides quick access to dangerous properties of over 3700 chemicals via DOT Guide Numbers, Chemical Abstracts Service (CAS) Numbers, and chemical synonyms.

The Internet has a number of excellent web sites useful to the hazardous materials manager. A few such sites are given in the discussions below. The hazardous materials manager is encouraged to use web search engines to find very useful technical/regulatory information. However, *when using the Internet, extreme care must be taken to assure that the information obtained is accurate.* Critical technical information found on the Internet (and from many other sources, as well) should be independently verified for accuracy before taking action.

Regulatory Definitions of *Hazardous*

Hazardous chemicals and their mixtures are highly regulated in much of the world; therefore, regulatory definitions often become critical when determining appropriate actions to meet safety and regulatory needs. The regulatory definitions used by United States (US) regulatory agencies are discussed below and will be used throughout this chapter.

Occupational Health and Safety Administration Definitions of Hazardous Chemicals

The US Occupational Safety and Health Administration (OSHA) has promulgated regulations that have the effect of defining or identifying hazardous chemicals, materials, substances, and wastes. The fine points of such regulations should be understood by the hazardous materials manager and will be summarized below.

Hazardous Chemical. OSHA (http://www.osha.gov), whose purview is worker safety, has perhaps the most comprehensive definition of hazardous chemicals as found in 29 CFR 1910.1200. For more information, also see

<http://www.osha-slc.gov/SLTC/
hazardoustoxicsubstances/>

Physical hazard—An OSHA *physical hazard* exists for a chemical when there is scientifically valid evidence that it is a combustible liquid, a compressed gas, an organic peroxide, an oxidizer, or is otherwise explosive, flammable, pyrophoric, unstable (reactive) or water reactive.

Health hazard—An OSHA *health hazard* exists for a chemical when there is statistically significant evidence based on at least one study conducted in accordance with established scientific principles that acute or chronic health effects may occur in exposed employees. The term health hazard includes chemicals that are carcinogens, toxic or highly toxic agents, reproductive toxins, irritants, corrosives, sensitizers, hepatotoxins, nephrotoxins, neurotoxins, agents which act on the hematopeoietic system, and agents which damage the lungs, skin, eyes, or mucous membranes.

Environmental Protection Agency Definitions and Lists of Hazardous Chemicals

The Environmental Protection Agency (EPA) at

<http://www.epa.gov>

has promulgated regulations that set forth much of the basic vocabulary used by persons engaged in the regulatory aspects of hazardous materials management. In the United States, key laws have directed EPA to write regulations listing and/or defining hazardous chemicals. These laws include the

- Resource Conservation and Recovery Act as amended (RCRA, 1976)

- Comprehensive Environmental Response, Compensation, and Liability Act as Amended (CERCLA or Superfund, 1980)

- Superfund Amendments and Reauthorization Act as Amended–Title III (also known as SARA Title III, 1987)

- Clean Air Act (CAA, especially as Amended 1990 to include regulation of Air Toxics)

- Federal Insecticide, Fungicide and Rodenticide Act, as Amended (FIFRA, 1947)

- Toxic Substances Control Act as Amended (TSCA, 1976)

Extremely Hazardous Substances. *Extremely hazardous substances* (EHS) are identified in a list published by EPA, pursuant to Section 302 of SARA Title III. In the United States, when a facility inventories an EHS in quantities equal to or greater than a trigger quantity, the facility is subject to emergency planning and notification requirements. These trigger quantities are termed *threshold planning quantities* pursuant to the *Community Right-to-Know* regulation. Chemicals appearing on the EPA EHS list are subject to EPA spill reporting requirements under Section 304 of SARA Title III.

Hazardous Chemicals. Sections 311 and 312 of SARA Title III list pure chemical substances (using chemical nomenclature) that must be reported annually by facilities when inventory quantities equal or exceed 10,000 lbs, or that exeed limits established by local jurisdictions. It is significant that when a Material Safety Data Sheet (MSDS) that is prepared according to OSHA regulations lists a hazard for a chemical, EPA also deems the chemical hazardous as a result of this regulation.

EPA's Tier II Community Right-to-Know report required under the SARA Title III, Sections 311 and 312 regulations (40 CFR 370.2), identifies the following hazard categories, as defined under 29 CFR 1910.1200 of the OSHA regulations

- *Immediate (acute) health hazard, including highly toxic, toxic, irritant, sensitizer, corrosive.* Has a short-term adverse effect to a target organ, and the effect is of short duration.

- *Delayed (chronic) health hazard, including carcinogens.* Has a long-term adverse effect to a chronic target organ, and the effect is of long duration.

- *Fire hazard including flammable, combustible liquid, pyrophoric, and oxidizer.*

- *Reactive, including unstable reactive, organic peroxide, and water-reactive.*

Toxic Chemicals. EPA, under authority of Section 313 of SARA Title II Community Right-to-Know legislation, has prepared a list of toxic chemicals. Generally, if a facility *uses* 10,000 pounds or *manufactures* 25,000 pounds of a chemical on the Section 313 list, the facility is subject to annual reporting of emissions and releases.

Hazardous Substances. *Hazardous substances* are listed in EPA regulation 40 CFR 302.4 under CERCLA in a table that specifies reportable quantities (RQs) for each substance. When the RQ is exceeded in a chemical release incident, a facility owner is required to report the release to the National Response Center as well as other State and local authorities.

EPA Consolidated List of Chemicals. EPA has published a consolidated list of chemicals subject to the Emergency Planning and Community Right-to-Know Act (EPCRA) and Section 112r of the Clean Air Act. See

<http://www.epa.gov/ceppo/pubs/title3.pdf>

This very helpful list cross-references individual chemicals with their regulatory requirements under these two Acts.

Hazardous Waste. EPA, pursuant to RCRA, establishes two broad categories of hazardous wastes in 40 CFR 261: *listed hazardous wastes* and *characteristic hazardous wastes*. These *categories* apply only to wastes, not useable products or virgin materials.

Listed Hazardous Wastes. EPA has published a series of lists identifying process wastes and discarded commercial chemical products that are *RCRA hazardous* by definition. Such itemized wastes are termed *listed hazardous wastes.*

Characteristic Hazardous Wastes. For all other waste chemical products, waste mixtures, or discarded materials, EPA specifies four hazard categories for the characterization of such wastes as hazardous or nonhazardous. Wastes are listed as *characteristic hazardous wastes* if they exhibit one or more of the following properties (as determined by standardized EPA testing methods):

1) Ignitability

2) Corrosivity

3) Reactivity

4) Toxicity

Other EPA Hazardous Chemical Lists. It should be noted that EPA has written other regulations that list hazardous substances and pollutants. Such regulations stem from the

- Clean Air Act (CAA), under which EPA has developed a list that currently contains 188 hazardous air pollutants, also called *air toxics* or *Hazardous Air Pollutants* (HAPs) See

<http://www.epa.gov/ttn/atw/188polls.html>

- Clean Water Act (CWA), under which Congress required EPA to develop a list of *toxic* pollutants, now known as a list of *priority pollutants* consisting of some 126 specific chemical substances. See

<http://www.epa.gov/waterscience/pc/revcom.pdf>

- Toxic Substances Control Act (TSCA), whereby EPA regulates certain chemicals posing unreasonable risks such as asbestos, lead in paint, polychlorinated biphenyls (PCBs), dioxin, and other chemicals

- Priority List of Hazardous Substances (CERCLA 1999). See

<http://www.atsdr.cdc.gov/99list.html>

Department of Transportation Definition of Hazardous Material

The United States Department of Transportation (DOT) and international transportation authorities have promulgated a set of definitions and categories for those materials deemed hazardous. See

<http://hazmat.dot.gov/>

Hazardous material—DOT, in 49 CFR 171.101, provides hazardous material descriptions and shipping names. The nine broad DOT hazard categories are

1) Explosives

2) Gases

3) Flammable Liquids

4) Flammable Solids

5) Spontaneous Combustibles, and Dangerous When Wet

6) Oxidizers and Organic Peroxides

7) Poisons and Infectious Substances

8) Corrosives

9) All other hazardous materials

With these regulatory definitions and chemical hazards in mind, we can now segue into the more basic chemical principles upon which the regulatory frameworks have been built.

Key Chemical Principles and the Periodic Table

Definition of Chemistry

Chemistry is the science of matter, energy, and their reactions. Matter is anything that occupies space and has mass. Some 112 types of matter, in their simplest forms, the chemical *elements,* have been identified; 90 of those elements are found naturally on the earth, while the remaining 22 elements are manmade. Chemists have found that in many instances, certain groups or families of elements have similar properties.

The *Periodic Table* provides very useful information to a hazardous materials manager by organizing the elements into *Groups* and *Periods* of similar chemical and physical properties. The reader is urged to reference the Periodic Table (see Figure 1) throughout the remainder of this chapter.

Atoms, Elements, Molecules, and Compounds. *Elements* are composed of extremely small, normally indivisible particles called *atoms*. Atoms of a particular element such as sodium have the same average mass, and other properties are the same. Atoms of different elements generally have different average masses (or *atomic weights*) and different properties.

A *molecule* is a group of atoms that are chemically bonded together. A chemically combined substance that is composed of more than one element is a *compound.* For example, aluminum (Al) and carbon (C) are sold in commerce in their *atomic* forms. But these two elements (atoms) can combine, to form the aluminum carbide (Al_4C_3), a molecule that, as a compound, exhibits its own unique physical characteristics and chemical properties.

Atoms of two or more elements may combine in more than one ratio to form compounds with very different hazard properties. In many instances, this is important from a hazard assessment standpoint. For example, carbon and oxygen can combine to form carbon monoxide (CO) or carbon dioxide (CO_2). CO is a poisonous gas that can be very harmful in small concentrations. CO_2 is a small component of the atmosphere and is necessary, in the correct concentration, for the human breathing cycle. CO_2 is also a greenhouse gas, which most scientists believe contributes to global climate change.

Key differences exist between elements that are pure or uncombined and those same elements that have combined with other elements to form molecules or compounds. Metallic sodium, as an example, is highly reactive and hazardous when immersed in water. Sodium chloride, a common compound known as *table salt*, is relatively harmless and nonreactive in water. *Knowing the exact chemical form of an element or a compound is absolutely critical in assessing its hazards, establishing methods to render it less hazardous, and defining conditions for its safe disposal!*

The Periodic Table of Elements. Chemists have used the Periodic Table (Figure 1) for over a century to categorize and simplify their understandings of the elements their chemical properties. Hazard properties align closely with chemical properties in many instances. In the Periodic Table, elements in a given vertical column are in the same *group* and those in a given horizontal row are in the same *period*.

The key goal of this discussion about the Periodic Table is to begin to rationlize the long list of elements and chemical compounds. The hazardous materials manager should attempt to relate common reactions involving salts, acids, and other compounds, when discussed below, to the Periodic

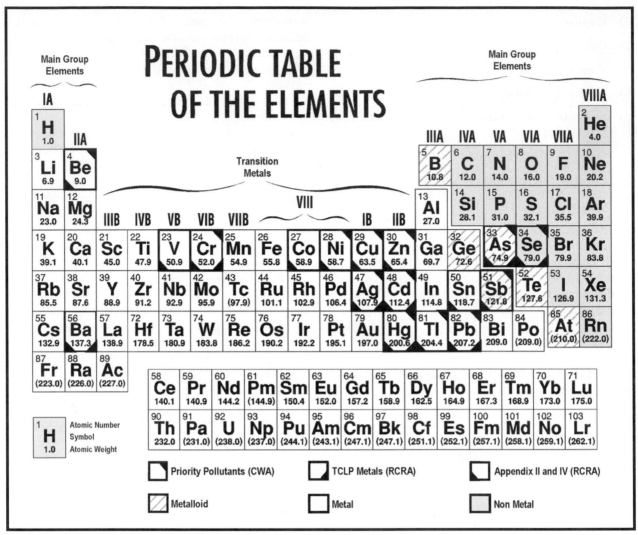

Reproduced with the permission of Columbia Analytical Services, Inc. Kelso, Washington (www.caslab.com).

Figure 1. The Periodic Table

Table. Compounds from a given group will have many similar properties such as solubility, electrical conductance, pH, *etc.*

In order to understand the Periodic Table better, we will first look at a few basics of subatomic structure. Atoms are composed of a ***nucleus*** plus ***electrons***. The nucleus resides in the center of an atom and contains all the positive charges (***protons***) of the atom as well as the atom's mass. Most atomic nuclei also contain ***neutrons***. Neutrons contribute mass or weight to the atom but do not have an electrical charge. Electrons, which surround the nucleus, are negatively charged and contribute an insignificant amount to atomic weight.

The number of protons in the nucleus defines the element's ***atomic number***. The total number of protons plus neutrons defines the ***mass number***. The number of protons in a nucleus of a given element is always the same. But the number of neutrons for that same element may vary. When this happens, atoms that have the same number of protons but different numbers of neutrons are called ***isotopes***. For example, the most common form of elemental carbon contains six protons and six neutrons. In this isotopic form the atomic weight of the element is twelve. But in nature, a certain proportion of carbon atoms contain eight neutrons such that this isotopic form of carbon has a mass of fourteen (six protons plus eight neutrons).

Certain isotopes are radioactive. Carbon-14 is weakly radioactive while carbon-12 is not radioactive. Note that certain other isotopes are radioactive, such as uranium-235, lithium-9, *etc.*

All elements with atomic numbers greater than bismuth (83) are radioactive. Radioactivity can be defined as the spontaneous emission of certain types of radiation (alpha, beta, and gamma) by unstable atomic nuclei. (Radiation safety principles are discussed in another chapter in the *Desk Reference*.) A number of hazardous substances are radioactive and can cause serious environmental problems.

The *atomic weight* is the average atomic mass of all naturally occurring isotopes of a given element and is shown in the Periodic Table along with the atomic number. In nature, the ratios of the carbon isotopes including carbon 13 are such that the average atomic weight of all forms of carbon is 12.0115, as shown in the Periodic Table. From a chemical reactivity standpoint, isotopic forms of an element generally undergo the same chemical reactions and form the same compounds.

Atoms are electrically neutral. They achieve this electrical balance through equal numbers of protons (+ or positive charges) and electrons (– or negative charges). The way the electrons organize themselves in regions of space or *orbitals* around the nucleus determines the chemistry, reactivity, and often the hazards of an element. In general, when an element's outermost orbitals, the *valence orbitals* contain the maximum allowable number of electrons for that region, the element or compound is stable and will resist chemical reactions. However, when an outer orbital is incomplete with regard to electron-holding capacity, the element is potentially reactive.

During chemical reactions, electrons are exchanged or shared between reacting elements until the valence orbital is filled to capacity, most commonly with eight electrons. The outer orbitals of *inert gases* contain eight electrons in their natural state. Thus they do not ordinarily undergo chemical reactions.

An ion is a charged particle that is produced when an atom or group of atoms gains or loses one or more electrons. Metals, nearly all of which have fewer than four valence electrons, tend to lose their valence electrons to form positive ions called cations. For example, elemental sodium (Na), when it loses a valence electron, becomes a cation and is represented as Na^{+1}.

Nonmetal atoms are those that tend to gain electrons to form negative ions called **anions**.

Anions readily gain an electron to fill an outer valence orbital completely with eight electrons (an octet or stable set of electrons). For example, the *halogens* shown in the Periodic Table Group VIIA (fluorine and below) have seven valence electrons. Elemental chlorine (Cl), when it gains an electron to become an anion, is shown as Cl^{-1}.

The Periodic Table helps organize chemical knowledge, since the physical and chemical properties of the elements are *periodic* (or repeating) functions of their atomic numbers. The Periodic Table represents each element with its official symbol and arranges the elements left to right by increasing atomic number. For example, H (hydrogen) has an atomic number of one while C (carbon) has an atomic number of six. Atomic numbers are shown above the symbol and the atomic weight (which is not used to determine periodicity) is shown below the element's symbol.

Some Key Facts Regarding the Periodic Table and Families of Elements.

- All the elements to the left of and below the staircase-like line-break on the Periodic Table are *metals*. Sodium (Na), aluminum (Al), iron (Fe), copper (Cu), tungsten (W), *etc.* are metals.

- Elements above and to the right of the line-break are *nonmetals* that in one form or another also form compounds with metals. Carbon (C), nitrogen (N), phosphorus (P), chlorine (Cl), and neon (Ne), are examples of nonmetals.

- *Metalloids* are found in the Periodic Table in the intermediate region between metals and nonmetals. Their properties are generally intermediate in character. For example, pure metals are good conductors of electricity, nonmetals are nonconductors. Metalloids, a class that includes boron (B), silicon (Si), germanium (Ge), arsenic (As), antimony (Sb), tellurium (Te), polonium (Po), and astatine (At), are semi-conductors.

- The vertical groups labeled IA, IIA, *etc.* represent *groups* of elements with many similar properties.

- *Group IA* elements, known as the *alkali metals*, have a valence of +1 and include lithium (Li), sodium (Na), potassium (K), rubidium (Rb), cesium (Cs) and francium (Fr). These are silver-gray metals that are very hazardous in the elemental form. They are soft such that they can be cut with a knife. Group IA metals are quick to react with water, oxygen, and other chemicals. They are never found free (uncombined) in nature and thus are rarely encountered. Alkali metals, being extremely reactive with oxygen, are usually stored under mineral oil or kerosene to minimize explosion hazards and to maintain the purity of the metals. Alkali metal *compounds* are highly water soluble and are found in salt water and salt deposits.

- Although hydrogen is shown at the top of Group IA in the Periodic Table, hydrogen is not considered to be part of that group. In fact, hydrogen is a nonmetal with many other unique properties to be discussed later in this chapter under such topics as corrosives, acids/bases, and organic chemistry. Often, the top member of a group differs in chemical properties from the lower members of that group.

- *Group IIA,* elements known as *alkaline earth metals*, have a valence of +2 and include beryllium (Be), magnesium (Mg), calcium (Ca), strontium (Sr), barium (Ba), and radium (Ra). Their melting points are higher than Group IA metals. They have low densities even though their densities are a bit higher than Group IA metals. As metals, the alkaline earth metals are also reactive. However, they are less reactive than the alkali metals.

- The first element in *Group IIIA* is boron (B), a metalloid with predominantly nonmetal properties. The remainder of the elements in this group—aluminum (Al), gallium (Ga), *etc.*—form ions with a +3 charge. The density and metallic character increase as the atomic number increases within this group. Aluminum is adjacent to two metalloids in the Periodic Table and is predominantly metallic in character.

Oxides of aluminum, along with several other metals, exhibit a property important to hazardous materials managers, namely that of being *amphoteric*. In their oxide forms aluminum (Al), chromium (Cr), and zinc (Zn) will react with *either* strong acids *or* strong bases, thus exhibiting both metal and nonmetal properties.

- The *Group IVA carbon family* embraces carbon (C), silicon (Si), germanium (Ge), tin (Sn), and lead (Pb). Carbon is totally nonmetallic in character. But as the atomic number increases in this family, the elements become more metallic. The last two elements, tin and lead, are typical metals. The outer orbitals of this family have four electrons.

Carbon is the fundamental element in the huge field of *organic chemistry,* which is discussed later in this chapter. However, carbon forms three inorganic compounds important from an environmental and hazard standpoint: carbon monoxide (CO, a colorless, odorless poisonous gas), carbon dioxide (CO_2, a colorless, odorless gas that can act as an asphyxiant in moderate or high concentrations); and cyanides, which include hydrogen cyanide (HCN), a very poisonous gas with a bitter-almond odor and sodium and potassium cyanides ($NaCN$ and KCN), the most common cyanide forms used in industry. These solid and very poisonous cyanides form hydrogen cyanide gas if they come into contact with acid. Carbon is also part of a very important class of inorganic chemicals when combined with oxygen to form carbonates. Potassium carbonate (K_2CO_3), for example, consists of a carbon joined to three oxygen atoms. Carbonates are found widely in nature combined with metals.

- In *Group VA*, as with Group IVA, definite nonmetals are found at the top of the table—nitrogen (N) and phosphorus (P)—followed by metalloids as atomic numbers increase—arsenic (As) and antimony (Sb)—and the heavy metal bismuth (Bi). The outer orbitals of this family have five electrons.

- *Group VIA* is the *oxygen family*. As one would by now expect from the group name of *VIA*, the outer shells of this family contain six electrons. The group comprises an unusual cast of characters including oxygen (O), sulfur (S), selenium (Se), tellurium (Te), and polonium (Po). The properties of these elements vary as atomic number increases, from the definitely nonmetallic for oxygen to the somewhat metallic for polonium.

- *Group VIIA* elements, known as the *halogens*, have properties that are somewhat more predictable than the elements in the preceding two groups. Fluorine (F), chlorine (Cl), bromine (Br), iodine (I), and astatine (At) are all *salt formers* (which is what halogen means in Greek). For example, chlorine (Cl) reacts with lithium (Li) to form lithium chloride, a water-soluble salt.

In the elemental form, all halogens are **diatomic,** meaning they have two atoms per molecule. Three other common elements are also diatomic: oxygen, hydrogen, and nitrogen. Like the alkali metals, halogens are too reactive to be found free in nature. *Fluorine is the most nonmetallic of all the elements* and is thus highly reactive in the elemental form. Both wood and rubber ignite spontaneously in fluorine gas.

Fluorine and chlorine exist as gases at room temperature. Chlorine is a greenish-yellow gas that reacts with nearly all elements. Bromine is the only halogen to exist in the liquid form at room temperature. Iodine and astatine are solids at room temperature.

- *Group VIIIA* elements, know as the *noble gases* or *inert gases* contain eight outer shell electrons in their natural state. As a result, they tend to be nonreactive. These elements include helium (He), neon (Ne), argon (Ar), krypton (Kr), xenon (Xe) and radon (Ra). Unlike the halogens, these gases are all *monatomic*—one atom per molecule, as opposed to the *diatomic*, or two atoms per molecule discussed above.

Although Group VIIIA metals are termed *noble* due to their nonreactivity, they present a physical hazard when stored under pressure in cylinders or in the cryogenic state. Additionally, gases, noble or otherwise, can present an asphyxiation hazard due to displacement of oxygen in a confined-space environment. Fatalities from asphyxiation have occurred when performing Metal-Inert-Gas (MIG) welding inside of open-topped containers less than 4-feet in height (which are not confined-space by OSHA's definition) due to the displacement of air by argon gas from a leaking joint in the welding head.

- The *transition metals*, known as *B Series elements,* are located in the central region of elements in the Periodic Table. In general, the properties of these elements are quite similar. The *B* elements (IB–VIIB) are all metals and exhibit metallic physical and chemical properties such as, malleability, ductility, *etc.* The transition metals are more brittle, harder, and have higher melting and boiling points than do other metals. A number of metals familiar to the hazardous materials manager reside in this region—chromium (Cr), nickel (Ni), cobalt (Co), silver (Ag), and mercury (Hg). Note that mercury is the only liquid metal at room temperature, and as such has a high vapor pressure. Chemically, the transition metals differ from those discussed in earlier groups in that they can more readily lose a variable number of electrons to form positive ions with different charges. The hazardous materials manager must recognize that these different valence states may create differing hazard and chemical properties for a given element. Some common examples of multiple valence states include iron +2 and iron +3—the ferrous and ferric forms of iron—and copper +1 and copper +2—the cuprous and cupric forms.

Final Comments and Recap on Atomic Theory. The reason that elements in a given group have similar chemical properties is that the number of electrons in their outer orbitals are identical. It should be noted that the number at the top of each column is equal to the number of electrons in the outer orbital. Thus, calcium (Ca, Group IIA) has 2 electrons in the outer orbital while phosphorus (P, Group VA) has 5 electrons in the outer orbital. There are family effects within the transition metals, but such effects are weaker.

The *Octet Rule* explains the group effect on properties. The Octet Rule states that atoms strive to reach an ultimate state of stability. In order to reach this state, all atoms must have eight electrons in the outer orbital. Once this state occurs, the atom will not react with anything else. The common feature in a group is the number of electrons needed to be added or removed to reach a filled outer shell. Please note that hydrogen and helium are exceptions and require only two electrons to be stable. Also, atoms in the 3rd period need eighteen electrons.

The Noble Gases (Group VIIIA), which include neon (Ne), radon (Rn), *etc.*, have eight electrons in their outer shell. Helium, while shown in Group VIIIA, is similar to hydrogen, in that it is stable with the outer orbital containing only two electrons. Thus chemists have identified the *Duet*

Rule, which states that hydrogen and helium reach their ultimate state of stability when two electrons fill the outer orbital.

Ionic and Covalent Bonding of Compounds. An ionic compound is one that is made up of positive and negative ions. Ionic compounds exist by virtue of an ionic bond which is the attraction between ions having opposite charges. In hazardous materials chemistry, this usually translates to some degree of water solubility.

Organic vs. Inorganic Compounds. Any compound that is covalent and contains carbon is said to be an **organic compound**. An **inorganic compound** is any compound that is *not* classified as organic. These two fundamental classes of compounds are discussed in more detail in sections that follow.

Covalent bonds exist when two atoms in a molecule share a pair of electrons. Thus methane (CH_4), an organic compound, contains covalent

bonds, while sodium chloride, NaCl, an inorganic compound, is bonded ionically.

Physical, Chemical, and Biochemical Properties

All chemicals, including hazardous ones, are described in terms of their physical, chemical, and biological properties. In order to use this information fully, it is necessary to understand the meaning and importance of the various individual properties, and also to have some grasp of the significance of the various numerical values within the context of chemicals at large. These properties can then be used along with other information to predict the likely behavior of hazardous chemicals, and to recognize and avoid potentially dangerous situations. The first step is to define and comment on several of the more critical properties that are useful in the handling of hazardous materials (Table 1).

Table 1. List of Commonly Measured Physical and Chemical Properties

Property	Abbreviation
Physical State @ 20°C	—
Boiling Point	bp
Melting Point	mp
Vapor Pressure	vp
Vapor Density	vd
Density	ρ
Specific Gravity	SG
Solubility (in water and other solvents)	K_{sp}
Flashpoint	fp
Auto-ignition Temperature (point)	—
Flammable or Explosive Limits	EL
Heat Content	Btu
Octanol/Water Partition Coefficient	K_{ow}
Biochemical Oxygen Demand after 5 days	BOD_5
Theoretical Oxygen Demand	ThOD
Threshold Limit Value	TLV
pH	—
pK_a	—
Molecular Weight	MW
Chemical Formula	—
Fire point	—
Color	—
Odor	—

[handwritten annotation: heat of comb]

Physical State at 20°C. The *physical state* is the nature of the chemical (solid, liquid, or gas) at a defined temperature. (*i.e.*, 20°C or room temperature). Changing the temperature may alter the physical state, depending on the magnitude and direction of the change relative to the melting and boiling points of the chemical. For example, water changes from water to ice when the temperature goes below 32°F (0°C).

Boiling Point. The temperature at which a liquid changes to gas under standard atmospheric pressure (760 mm mercury) is the *boiling point* (bp). The boiling point of water is 100°C at sea level, while the boiling points of ethyl alcohol and *n*-hexane are 78.4°C and 68.7°C, respectively. Lowering the atmospheric pressure (*e.g.*, by applying a vacuum) will lower the boiling point; conversely, higher pressures result in elevated boiling points. Generally, the lower the boiling point of a flammable liquid, the lower the ignition or flashpoint of the liquid. (See the following section on the chemistry of flammables.)

Melting and Freezing Points. The temperature at which a crystalline solid changes to a liquid is the *melting point* (mp). Ionic compounds usually have very high melting points while organic compounds have much lower melting points. The melting point is not particularly sensitive to atmospheric pressure, but it is responsive to dissolved particles (atoms, molecules, or ions) that depress the melting point. Thus, it is common in winter to use one of several available salt compounds in order to keep water from freezing on sidewalks. The salt compounds work by depressing the melting point of water. The temperature at which a liquid changes to a crystalline solid is called the *freezing point*.

Vapor Pressure. *Vapor pressure* (vp) is a measure of the relative volatility of chemicals. It is the pressure exerted by the vapor in equilibrium with its liquid at a given temperature. Flammable liquids with high vapor pressures generally represent a greater fire hazard than those with lower vapor pressures. For a given liquid, the vapor pressure increases with increasing temperature. Consequently, drummed materials with high vapor pressures should not be stored in direct sunlight, as some overheating of the materials and resultant increases in vapor pressures could result in bulging drums with failed or weakened seams.

Vapor pressure values can be used to predict the relative rate of evaporation of pure chemicals and dissolved solvents from water. Vapor pressure is frequently expressed in millimeters of mercury (mmHg) as measure by a mercury (Hg) manometer. At 20°C, water, ethanol, and benzene have vapor pressures of 17.5 mmHg, 43.9 mmHg, and 74 mmHg, respectively. Benzene can be expected to evaporate about 4 times faster than water, with ethanol evaporating at an intermediate rate. Adding water to ethanol will slow the rate of ethanol evaporation by reducing the vapor pressure of the ethanol escaping from the ethanol/water solution.

It must be noted that some solvents, such as benzene, are relatively insoluble in water and form two-phase liquid systems. The evaporation rate of a floating or sunken solvent in water is an important concept but beyond the scope of this chapter.

Vapor Density. The *vapor density* (vd) is the mass per unit volume of a given vapor/gas relative to that of air. Thus, acetaldehyde with a vapor density of 1.5 is heavier than air and will accumulate in low spots, while acetylene with a vapor density of 0.9 is lighter than air and will rise and disperse. Heavy vapors present a particular hazard because of the way they accumulate; if toxic, they may poison workers; if nontoxic, they may displace air and cause suffocation by oxygen deficiency; if flammable, once presented with an ignition source, they represent a fire or explosion hazard. Gases heavier than air include carbon dioxide, chlorine, gasoline, hydrogen sulfide, and sulfur dioxide. *Beware; most common gases encountered by hazardous materials managers are heavier than air and thus dangerous!* Key exceptions to this are hydrogen (H_2), helium (He), acetylene (C_2H_2), methane (CH_4), and ammonia (NH_3); these are *hazardous* gases that are *lighter* than air.

Density. The *density* is the mass per unit volume of any substance, including liquids. Densities of elements increase with increasing atomic numbers. The density of a liquid determines whether a spilled material that is insoluble in or immiscible with water will sink or float on water. Knowledge of this behavior is essential in checking whether to use water to suppress a fire involving the material. Density is also a critical parameter when assessing potential remediation methods for water insoluble chemicals reaching groundwater. The density of water is 1.0 g/milliliter (ml) at 4°C or 8.33 lb/gal.

Specific Gravity. The ratio of the density of a liquid as compared with that of water is the *specific gravity* (SG). Insoluble materials will sink or float in water depending on the SG. Materials heavier than water have SGs > 1, and materials lighter than water have SGs < 1. Thus lead, mercury, and carbon tetrachloride, with SGs of 11.3, 13.6, and 1.6, respectively, will sink in water, whereas gasoline with a SG of 0.66 to 0.69 will float on water.

Solubility. The amount of any substance, whether solid, gas, or liquid (the solute) that dissolves in a unit volume of a liquid (the solvent) is the *solubility*. This property is of importance in the handling and recovery of spilled hazardous materials. Water-insoluble chemicals are much easier to recover from water than spills of water-soluble chemicals. Acetone, which is soluble (miscible) in water in all proportions, is not readily recoverable from water. In contrast, benzene, which is lighter than water and insoluble as well, can be readily trapped by using a physcial removal method such as a skimmer. For organic compounds, solubility tends to decrease with increasing molecular weight and chlorine content. Many inorganic compounds are quite soluble in water, *e.g.*, acids, bases, many salts, *etc.*

Flashpoint. The *flashpoint* (fp) is the lowest temperature at which a liquid gives off enough vapor to form an ignitable mixture with air near its surface. Two tests are used to determine flashpoint: Open Cup and Closed Cup. Generally, the Open Cup method results in flashpoints 5° to 10° higher than the Closed Cup method. A flashpoint <140°F (Closed Cup) is the criterion used by EPA to decide whether a waste is hazardous by virtue of its *ignitability*. With the exception of some special cases, DOT regulates materials with flashpoints of <141°F as *flammable* and between 141°F and 200°F as *combustible*.

Fire Point. The *fire point* is the temperature at which a liquid gives off enough vapor to continue to burn when ignited.

Auto-Ignition Temperature. The temperature at which ignition occurs without an ignition source

and the material continues to burn without further heat input is called the *auto-ignition temperature*.

Flammable or Explosive Limits. The *flammable or explosive limits* are the upper and lower vapor concentrations at which a mixture will burn or explode. The lower explosive limit of *p*-xylene is 1.1 percent by volume in air, whereas the upper explosive limit is 7.0 percent in air. A mixture of *p*-xylene vapor and air having a concentration of < 1.1 percent in air is too lean in *p*-xylene vapor to burn. By subtraction (7.0 – 1.1 = 5.9), *p*-xylene is said to have a flammable range of 5.9.

Heat Content. The *heat content* is the heat released by complete combustion of a unit-weight of material. Methane has a heat content of about 21,500 Btu/lb., while benzene contains about 17,250 Btu/lb.

Octanol/Water Partition Coefficient. The equilibrium ratio of the concentrations of material partitioned between octanol and water is called the *octanol/water partition coefficient* or (K_{ow}). This coefficient is considered to be an index of the potential of a chemical to be bioaccumulated. Higher values of K_{ow} are associated with greater bioaccumulation potential.

Biochemical Oxygen Demand at Five Days (BOD$_5$). The quantity of oxygen required by microbes for the oxidative breakdown of a given waste material during a 5-day test period is called the *biochemical oxygen demand at five days* (BOD$_5$). The BOD$_5$ is usually taken as an index of the ultimate oxygen demand (*i.e.*, oxygen required when sufficient time is allowed to achieve maximum microbial decomposition). BOD$_5$ is used to predict the impact of a spill or release of material on the oxygen content of a body of water.

Theoretical Oxygen Demand. The *theoretical oxygen demand* (Th$_{OD}$) is the cumulative amount of oxygen needed to completely oxidize a given material. The Th$_{OD}$ is the upper limit for BOD$_5$ values, although it seldom is achieved. A comparison of the BOD$_5$ and Th$_{OD}$ values for a given chemical provides an indication of the biodegradability of that chemical.

Threshold Limit Value. The *threshold limit value* (TLV) is the exposure level under which most people can work for eight hours a day, day after day, with no harmful effects. The American Conference of Governmental Industrial Hygienists annually publishes a table of the values and accompanying precautions for most common industrial materials.

Additional Key Chemical Concepts of Environmental Significance

The processes of dissolution/precipitation (for inorganic chemicals), dissolution/phase separation (for organics), adsorption, and volatilization control the distribution of a spilled material in the environment. Conversely, knowledgeable manipulation of these same processes can be advantageous in either cleaning up or mitigating the effects of spilled material. For example, ground water contaminated with volatile organics of limited aqueous solubility can be decontaminated by air-stripping. The air-stripped compounds can then be concentrated by adsorption on activated carbon for subsequent disposal.

With this in mind, the hazardous materials manager needs some additional chemical tools in his or her arsenal. A few of these tools are discussed below.

Concentrations. Chemists, especially environmental chemists, seldom encounter pure solutions of materials in environmental media. Therefore, their task is to quantify the levels of contaminants and other materials in a mixture. Units of concentration in common usage include

- *Parts per million* (ppm). Identical with milligrams per liter (mg/l) for aqueous solutions or mg/kg (milligrams per kilogram) for solids.

- *Parts per billion* (ppb). Identical with micrograms per liter (µg/l) for liquids or micrograms per kilogram (µg/kg) for solids.

- *Moles per liter* or *molar solutions*. The weight of substance equivalent to the gram-molecular or gram-atomic weight in a liter of solution.

- *Equivalents per liter.* Commonly used for acids and bases, a liter of a one-equivalent-per-liter

solution of acid is stated to be a *one Normal solution* and will neutralize 40 grams (1 mole) of sodium hydroxide.

- *Percent by weight* (%W/W) or *volume* (%V/V). Units that are often used for vapors, gases, mists, and particulates in air. As discussed later, these units can be related to concentrations that are expressed as parts per million (ppm) and micrograms per m³.

Adsorption. Adsorption is an important physical-chemical phenomenon used in the treatment of hazardous wastes or in predicting the behavior of hazardous materials in natural systems. *Adsorption* is the concentration or accumulation of substances at a surface or interface between media. Adsorption of organic hazardous materials onto soils or sediments is an important factor affecting their mobility in the environment. Adsorption may be predicted by use of a number of equations most commonly relating the concentration of a chemical at the surface or interface to the concentration in air or in solution, at equilibrium. These equations may be solved graphically using laboratory data to plot *isotherms*. The most common application of the adsorption property is the removal of organic compounds from water by activated carbon.

Volatilization. *Volatilization* is the tendency of a material to transfer from a liquid phase (either pure or dissolved, as in aqueous systems) to a gaseous phase (commonly mixed with air). Volatilization, or *evaporation* as it is more commonly called, is controlled by a number of factors, the most important of which are

- The vapor pressure of the material and temperature (vapor pressure increases with temperature)

- The air/material interfacial surface area

- The action of active mass transfer agents such as wind

Hazardous Waste Categories. The reader is referred to the earlier discussion of regulatory definitions of *characteristic hazardous wastes*. When wastes do not appear on an EPA hazardous waste list (and the generator does not have process information to use in determining a waste's hazard category), EPA requires the generator to analyze the waste using official laboratory protocols. These protocols determine if a waste is *RCRA hazardous* according to limits set in 40 CFR 261.20–261.24, which defines the categories of characteristic hazardous wastes. In the discussion to follow, various chemical groups will be examined primarily in the context of three of these categories, namely corrosivity, reactivity, and ignitability.

(Note: Determinations of TCLP toxicity, the fourth hazardous characteristic, rely on a laboratory protocol specified by EPA that measures the extractability of certain identified *toxic* chemicals in a weakly acid medium. See also the chapter on industrial toxicology for background on how a chemical is determined to be *toxic* to humans and other live organisms.)

Acids, Bases, and Corrosivity

Acids, bases, and corrosive chemicals are frequently encountered in the field of hazardous materials management. As a hazard class, corrosives are among the most common materials. Acids and bases are primary contributors to corrosion and play a number of other roles in hazardous materials management and pollution control.

While the RCRA definition of corrosivity, used in hazardous waste characterization, is limited to pH ranges of <2.0 and >12.5, the *chemical* property of corrosivity can occur at intermediate pH levels. For example, liquids with pHs in the ranges of 2–5 and 8–12 can be chemically corrosive. Salts of strong acids and weak bases such as ammonium sulfate and ammonium chloride hydrolyze in water to form acids which have corrosive activity. More generally, materials in water that exhibit intermediate pH ranges should be evaluated carefully from the standpoint of handling, treatment, personal safety, and environmental impact.

Acids and pH

pH is a measure of the hydrogen ion concentration in an aqueous solution. pH ranges from 1 (strongly acidic) to 7 (neutral), and to 14 (strongly basic). pH is the negative log of the hydrogen ion (H^+) concentration:

$$pH = -\log [H^+] \tag{1}$$

Given the logarithmic pH scale, with each increase of 1 pH unit, the hydrogen ion (H^+) concentration decreases by a factor of 10 and the hydroxyl ion (OH^-) concentration increases by a factor of 10. The pH of lemon juice is approximately 2, while the pH of sodium hydroxide (NaOH, lye) is approximately 14. Pure water has a pH of 7 (neutral) and is neither acidic or basic. Table 2 shows the relative strengths of acids commonly encountered.

Neutralization of Bases by Acids, Three Examples.

Example (1)

$$H^{+1} + OH^{-1} \rightarrow H_2O \tag{2}$$

A hydrogen ion (H^{+1} or proton) from any source neutralizes a hydroxyl ion from any source (a base) to form water. This is the fundamental neutralization reaction.

Example (2)

$$HCl + NaOH \rightarrow H_2O + NaCl \tag{3}$$

Table 2. Relative Strengths of Acids in Water

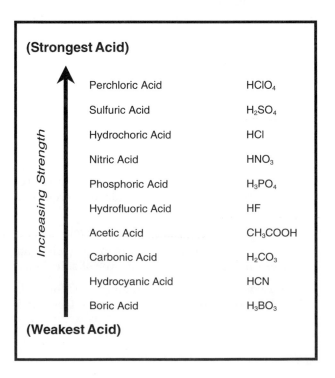

(Strongest Acid)	
Perchloric Acid	$HClO_4$
Sulfuric Acid	H_2SO_4
Hydrochoric Acid	HCl
Nitric Acid	HNO_3
Phosphoric Acid	H_3PO_4
Hydrofluoric Acid	HF
Acetic Acid	CH_3COOH
Carbonic Acid	H_2CO_3
Hydrocyanic Acid	HCN
Boric Acid	H_3BO_3
(Weakest Acid)	

Increasing Strength →

Hydrochloric acid (containing the proton) neutralizes sodium hydroxide (containing the basic OH⁻ group).

Example (3)

$$CaCO_3 + 2HCl \rightarrow$$
$$CaCl_2 + H_2O + CO_2 \uparrow \qquad (4)$$

This equation shows that calcium carbonate in water acts as a base by neutralizing hydrochloric acid (HCl). Following neutralization (in water), neutral calcium chloride salt and water are formed with the evolution of carbon dioxide as a gas.

Bases. A *base* is any material that produces hydroxide ions (OH^-) when it is dissolved in water. The words **alkaline, basic**, and **caustic** are often used interchangeably. Common bases include sodium hydroxide (lye, NaOH), potassium hydroxide (potash lye, KOH), and calcium hydroxide (slaked lime, $CaOH_2$), and ammonia (NH_3).

The concepts of strong versus weak bases and concentrated versus dilute bases are exactly analogous to those for acids. Strong bases such as sodium hydroxide dissociate completely, while weak bases such as the organic amines ($R–NH_2$, where R is a carbon compound and $–NH_2$ is an amine) dissociate only partially. As with acids, bases can be either inorganic or organic. Typical reactions of bases include neutralization of acids, reaction with metals, and reaction with salts. The reactions of bases with acids were illustrated in the previous section.

Reaction of a Base with Metals. In the reaction below, metallic aluminum reacts with the hydroxyl ion supplied by sodium hydroxide to create heat with the potential for an explosion due to formation of hydrogen gas:

$$2Al° + 6NaOH \rightarrow 2Na_3AlO_3 + 3H_2 \uparrow \qquad (5)$$

Reaction of a Base with Salts. In the reaction of lead nitrate with sodium hydroxide shown below, the resulting lead hydroxide is insoluble in water. It precipitates out, thus lowering the hydroxyl ion concentration in the solution.

$$Pb(NO_3)_2 + 2NaOH \rightarrow$$
$$Pb(OH)_2 \downarrow + 2NaNO_3 \qquad (6)$$

Some important hazard properties and good practices for common acids and bases are presented in Table 3.

Concentrated / Dilute vs. *Strong / Weak*. The terms *concentrated* and *dilute* refer to the concentrations of a chemical in solution. Adding a concentrated acid into water will produce a *dilute* acid. For example, a water (aqueous) solution saturated with HCl (a gas) is approximately 12 molar (M), while a solution of aqueous HCl used in a titration may be only 0.5 M. The latter is a more *dilute* acid solution. *Caution: when mixing an acid with water, always add the acid into the water, never add water into acids!*

Strong and *weak* **acids** or **bases** are classified by how completely they ionize in solution. For example, perchloric, nitric, hydrochloric, hydrobromic, hydriodic, and sulfuric acids are classified as strong acids. Examples of weak acids include boric, hydrocyanic, carbonic, and acetic acids. Aqueous hydrofluoric ($HF_{(aq)}$) is not classified as a strong acid because it does not dissociate completely in water. However, it is a very dangerous acid if it contacts human tissues. HF burns are slow to heal, and the fluoride ion causes severe pain in any joint it reaches (*e.g.*, the elbow from a hand burn).

Common strong bases include lithium hydroxide (LiOH), sodium hydroxide (NaOH), potassium hydroxide (KOH), and quaternary amine hydroxides (R_4NOH). Common weak bases include ammonium hydroxide (NH_4OH), sodium carbonate (Na_2CO_3), certain organic amines, and more.

Be aware that some salts may form acidic or basic solutions and thus exhibit corrosive properties in water. As a benchmark, a salt such as NaCl that is derived from a strong acid and strong base, yields a neutral solution because the ions do not react with water. But the salt of a strong acid and weak base yields an acidic solution because the cation acts as a weak acid. For example, ammonium chloride in water is acidic because the ammonium ion (NH_4^+) is a weak acid while the chloride ion is neither acidic or basic. Ammonia is a base because it forms the ammonium ion in water, leaving a strongly basic hydroxide ion. This is an extended definition of a base with the reaction:

$$NH_3 + H_2O \leftrightarrow NH_4^{+1} + OH^{-1} \qquad (7)$$

Table 3. Properties and Good Practices for Some Common Acids and Bases

---

Acids–Sulfuric, Nitric, Hydrochloric, Acetic

- These acids are highly soluble in water. Concentrated solutions are highly corrosive and will attack materials and tissue.

- If spilled on skin, flushing with lots of water will dilute the acids and reduce tissue damage.

- Sulfuric and nitric acids are strong oxidizers and should not be stored or mixed with any organic material.

- Sulfuric, nitric, and hydrochloric acids will attack metals upon contact and generate hydrogen gas, which is explosive.

- Acetic acid (glacial), an organic acid, is extremely flammable. Its vapors form explosive mixtures in the air. It is dangerous when stored with any oxidizing material, such as nitric and sulfuric acids, peroxides, sodium hypochlorite, *etc.*

- Breathing the concentrated vapors of any of these acids can be extremely harmful. Wear appropriate personal protective equipment.

- When mixing with water, always add acids to water, never water to acids.

Bases (Caustic)–Sodium Hydroxide, Ammonium Hydroxide, Calcium Hydroxide (Slaked Lime), Calcium Oxide (Quick Lime)

- These bases are highly soluble in water.

- Concentrated solutions are highly corrosive. They are worse than most acids because they penetrate the skin and essentially make "soap" out of body fat. That is, caustics turn tissue fatty acids into salts. (In emulsion chemistry, the reaction is termed *saponification*.)

- If spilled on skin, flush immediately with lots of water.

- When mixed with water, they generate a significant amount of heat—especially sodium hydroxide and calcium oxide.

- Do not store or mix concentrated acids and bases, as this gives off much heat—dilute, then mix.

- Do not store or mix ammonium hydroxide with other strong bases. It can release ammonia gas, which is extremely toxic.

- Do not store or mix ammonium hydroxide with chlorine or other oxidizing compounds (*i.e.*, sodium hypochlorite). It can release chlorine gas, which is extremely toxic.

Conversely, the salt of a weak acid and strong base yields a basic solution in water because the anion acts as a weak base. As an example, sodium acetate in water is basic because the acetate anion (OAc^{-1}) forms acetic acid (HOAc) from water by the reaction:

$$OAc^{-1} + H_2O \leftrightarrow HOAc + OH^{-1} \qquad (8)$$

Thus, the terminology *strong acid* versus *weak acid* may bear little relationship to the nature or extent of potential hazard of a corrosive in water, while the terms *concentrated* versus *dilute* most often do. (Note: Chemists commonly use the terms *dilute acid* and *dilute base* to refer to 6 Normal solutions.)

Corrosion and Corrosivity. *Rust* is the most common product of corrosion. Rust is formed when metallic iron oxidizes in the presence air and moisture. However, corrosive agents other than air and water exist. Corrosive agents can be placed in four main groups: oxygen and oxidants, acidic materials, salts, and alkalis (bases).

EPA, under the RCRA hazardous waste regulations, defines corrosivity in terms of pH (*i.e.*, liquid wastes with pH < 2.0 and > 12.5 are RCRA hazardous). DOT, in 49 CFR 173.36 and 173.137 (c)(2) defines corrosivity in terms of a material's ability to corrode steel or aluminum at a rate of > 6.25 mm (0.250 inches) per year at a temperature of 55°C (130°F), (For the purpose of testing steel P3 (ISO 9328–1) or a similar type, and for testing aluminum, non-clad types 7075–T6 or AZ5GU–T6 should be used. An acceptable test is described in ASTM G 31–72). OSHA defines a corrosive as any material that causes visible destruction or irreversible alterations in living tissue at the site of contact. Under both OSHA and DOT, acids and bases are grouped under the *corrosive* definition. For more information on other corrosive materials, see the section on substances that produce acidic solutions. More examples of corrosive chemicals are given in the discussion that follows.

Chemistry of Water-Reactive Materials

The characteristics of a solid waste that would categorize it as a reactive hazardous waste as defined under RCRA include

- It reacts violently with water
- It forms potentially explosive mixtures with water
- When mixed with water, it generates toxic gases, vapors, or fumes in a quantity sufficient to present a danger to human health or the environment

Because water is the most common fire suppressant, the RCRA hazardous waste characteristic of reactivity is especially relevant since the application of water to eliminate or prevent the spread of fires involving RCRA reactive materials may be counterproductive rather than helpful. Several categories of chemicals will be discussed from this standpoint.

Substances that Produce Hydrogen Gas: Metals.
Several metals in a pure state react with water and air. The extent of reactivity depends upon the physical state of the metal. The highly reactive pure or *elemental* metals such as lithium, sodium, and potassium are pyrophoric (*i.e.*, they ignite spontaneously in air without an ignition source). In contrast, the less reactive metals such as magnesium, zirconium, titanium, aluminum, uranium, and zinc, are highly pyrophoric only as dusts.

Lithium, sodium, and potassium (alkali metals in Group IA on the Periodic Table) react rapidly with water to release hydrogen (H_2) gas. For example:

$$2Na + 2H_2O \rightarrow 2Na^+ + 2OH^- + H_2\uparrow \qquad (9)$$

Sufficient heat is generated during the reaction to ignite the hydrogen gas so that it can react explosively with the oxygen in air.

Metals like magnesium, aluminum, titanium, and zirconium in pure form also react with water to release H_2 gas, but heat must be supplied, as in a fire, to initiate the reaction. The generalized representation is:

$$\text{metal} + \text{water} + \text{heat} \rightarrow$$
$$\text{metal oxide or hydroxide} + H_2\uparrow \qquad (10)$$

Substances that Produce Hydrogen Gas: Hydrides.
True hydrides (*i.e.*, those in which the hydrogen is in its anionic or most reduced form) are salt-like compounds in which the hydrogen is combined with alkali metals, either alone as simple hydrides or in association with other elements as complex hydrides. Hydrides react with water to release hydrogen:

Simple hydrides (e.g., lithium hydride).

$$LiH + H_2O \rightarrow H_2\uparrow + 2LiOH \qquad (11)$$

Complex hydrides.

$$AlH_4Li + 4H_2O \rightarrow$$
$$Al(OH)_3 + LiOH + 4H_2\uparrow \qquad (12)$$

Peroxides.
Compounds containing the O^{2-} ion are hazardous primarily as oxidizing agents (sometimes causing explosions) and exhibit reactivity in water. An example is the liberation of oxygen from the mixture of sodium peroxide and water:

$$2Na_2O_2 + 2H_2O \rightarrow 4NaOH + O_2\uparrow \qquad (13)$$

Substances that Produce Alkaline Aqueous Solutions and Explosive Gases. Nitrides, carbides, and phosphides exemplify this group of nonmetals (see Periodic Table Groups IIIA, IVA and VA). Nitrides will react with water to generate ammonia (NH_3), that can be released to the atmosphere depending on how alkaline the solution becomes.

$$Mg_3N_2 + 6H_2O \rightarrow 3Mg(OH)_2 + 2NH_3\uparrow \qquad (14)$$

Carbides, which are binary compounds containing anionic carbon, occur as covalent and as salt-like compounds. The salt-like carbides are water-reactive and, upon hydrolysis, yield flammable hydrocarbons. Typical hydrolysis reactions include

$$CaC_2 + 2H_2O \rightarrow Ca(OH)_2 + C_2H_2\uparrow \qquad (15)$$

$$Al_4C_3 + 12H_2O \rightarrow 4Al(OH)_3 + 3CH_4\uparrow \qquad (16)$$
$$\text{(methane)}$$

Other similar carbide-like compounds include Be_2C and Mg_2C_3. Notably, each reaction is sufficiently exothermic to ignite the specific gas formed upon hydrolysis.

Phosphides are binary compounds containing anionic phosphorous (P^{-3}). Heavy metal, alkali, and alkaline earth metal phosphides exist, but few of them are commercially important. Phosphides may be encountered, however, in laboratory or chemical research situations. Phosphides hydrolyze to the flammable and toxic gas phosphine (PH_3). The hydrolysis reaction of aluminum phosphide is

$$AlP + 3H_2O \rightarrow PH_3\uparrow + Al(OH) \qquad (17)$$

Substances that Produce Acidic Aqueous Solutions

Inorganic Chlorides/Halides. Metals near the center of the Periodic Table such as aluminum (Al), nonmetals, and some of their oxides form compounds with chlorine and other halogens. Such compounds exhibit corrosive properties because they form markedly acidic solutions. Aluminum chloride is a good example of a chemical that is corrosive owing to its acidity. Acidity, in this instance, results from hydrolysis that produces aluminum oxide and chloride ions. Anhydrous aluminum chloride ($AlCl_3$) hydrolyzes violently when contacted by water.

Several nonmetallic chlorides also react with water with varying degrees of violence to produce hydrochloric acid. Although these compounds are themselves nonflammable, the heat generated by hydrolysis is sufficient to ignite adjacent flammable materials. These nonmetallic chlorides include antimony pentachloride ($SbCl_5$), boron trichloride (BCl_3), phosphorus oxychloride ($POCl_3$), phosphorus pentachloride (PCl_5), phosphorus trichloride (PCl_3), silicon tetrachloride ($SiCl_4$), thionyl chloride ($SOCl_2$), sulfuryl chloride (SO_2Cl_2) and titanium tetrachloride ($TiCl_4$). Because of their acid-producing tendencies, many of these chlorides are considered to be corrosive.

Organic Chlorides/Halides. Several organic compounds also are hydrolyzed (or react with water) to produce corrosive materials. Notable inclusions among these compounds are acetic anhydride ($[CH_3CO_2]_2O$) and acetyl chloride (CH_3COCl), both of which produce acetic acid upon reaction with water. Both acetic anhydride and acetyl chloride are corrosive. In addition, mixtures of the vapors of acetic anhydride and acetic acid are flammable in air, and acetyl chloride itself is flammable.

Oxidation/Reduction Phenomena

Oxidation/reduction (*redox*) reactions, the bane of high school chemistry students, can be similarly unkind to hazardous materials managers. The explosive potential of oxidation/reduction reactions has resulted time and time again in chemical disasters. The explosion of the *S.S. Grandcamp* at Texas City, Texas in 1947, is an example of a disastrous detonation of ammonium nitrate. It led to the deaths of over 600 people and over $33 million (1947 dollars) damage. The addition or loss of electrons in redox reactions involves an accompanying transfer of energy, often a violently *exothermic* (heat-releasing) transfer. The substance that gives up electrons (and is therefore oxidized) is the reducing agent. The substance that gains electrons (and is therefore reduced) is the oxidizing agent.

Oxidizing agents generally are recognizable by their structures or names. They tend to have a high oxygen ratio in their structures and sometimes release oxygen as a result of thermal decomposition. Oxidizing agents often have *per-* prefixes (perchlorate, peroxides, and permanganate) and end in *-ate* (chromate, nitrate, chlorate).

Strong oxidizers have more potential incompatibilities than perhaps any other chemical group (with the possible exception of water-reactive substances). Oxidizers should not be stored or mixed with any other material except under carefully controlled conditions. Certainly, storing oxidizing and reducing agents where they could mix can be a recipe for disaster. More generally, materials compatibilities should always be determined as a first step in establishing a chemical storage system. Common oxidizing agents listed in decreasing order of oxidizing strength include

- Fluorine
- Chlorine
- Ozone
- Sulfuric acid (concentrated)
- Hydrogen peroxide
- Oxygen
- Perchloric acid (concentrated)
- Hypochlorous acid
- Metallic iodates
- Metal chlorates
- Bromine
- Lead dioxide
- Ferric (iron $^{+3}$) salts
- Metallic permanganates
- Iodine
- Metallic dichromates
- Sulfur
- Nitric acid (concentrated)
- Stannic (tin^{+4}) salts

Reducing agents present hazard situations that are similar to oxidizing agents. They react with a broad spectrum of chemical classes, and the reactions can be exothermic and violent. Reducing agents are, by definition, highly oxidizable, and may react with air or moisture in the air. Common reducing agents include

- Hydrogen
- Sulfides
- Metals (Li, Na, K, Ca, Sr, Ba)
- Sulfites
- Hydrazine
- Iodides
- Metal acetylides
- Nitrides
- Complex hydrides
- Nitrites
- Metal hydrides
- Phosphites
- Metal hypoborates
- Metallic azides
- Metal hypophosphites

Nomenclature and General Properties of Organic Chemicals

Most compounds in which carbon is the key element are classified as *organic*. Organic chemicals encountered in daily life include fingernail polish remover (acetone), vodka (50% ethanol in water), engine coolant (ethylene glycol) and many more. Common industrial examples of organic compounds include degreasing solvents, lubricants, and heating and motor fuels.

This section will highlight some of the more common characteristics of organic chemicals. Various relevant classes of organics will be presented in terms of chemical behavior and physical properties. In order to facilitate the discussion to follow, a few basic definitions will be presented first.

Key Organic Chemical Classes and Definitions

Hydrocarbons—Chemical compounds consisting primarily of carbon and hydrogen.

Aliphatic—A class of organic compounds with the carbon backbone arranged in branched or straight chains (*e.g.*, propane or octane).

Aromatic—Organic molecular structures having the benzene ring (C_6H_6) as the basic unit (*e.g.*, toluene, xylene, polynuclear aromatics [PNAs]).

Note: When burning, aromatic compounds often give off large quantities of black smoke, owing to incomplete combustion.

Saturated—The condition of an organic compound in which each constituent carbon is covalently linked to four different atoms. This is generally a stable configuration (*e.g.*, propane [$CH_3CH_2CH_3$]). CH_3—CH_3 is a chemical depiction of a *saturated alkane*, namely ethane. However, if a hydrogen is removed from each carbon through a chemical *oxidation* process, ethene (also known as ethylene) is formed with a double bond between the two carbons. Ethene (CH_2=CH_2) is termed *unsaturated* because each carbon has the capacity to bond with one additional atom.

Unsaturated—An organic compound containing double or triple bonds between carbons (*e.g.*, ethene [CH_2=CH_2]). Multiple bonds tend to be sites of reactivity.

Isomers—Different structural arrangements with the same chemical formulas (*e.g.*, *n*-butane and *t*-butane):

n-butane CH_3—CH_2—CH_2—CH_3
(normal butane)

$$CH_3$$
$$|$$
$$CH_3—C—CH_3$$
$$|$$
$$CH_3$$

t-butane
(tertiary-butane)

Functional group—An atom or group of atoms, other than hydrogen, bonded to the chain or ring of carbon atoms (*e.g.*, the –OH group of alcohols, the –COOH group of carboxylic acids, the –O– group of ethers). Functional groups determine the behavior of molecules. Consequently, the unique hazards of an organic compound are often determined by its functional group(s).

General Properties of Organic Compounds. Most organic compounds tend to melt and boil at lower temperatures than most inorganic substances. Because many organic compounds volatilize easily at room temperature and possess relatively low specific heats and ignition temperatures, they tend to burn easily. Many organic compounds are flammable. Moreover, organic vapors often have high heats of combustion. Therefore upon ignition, vapors facilitate the ignition of surrounding chemicals, thus compounding the severity of the hazard.

Most organic compounds are less stable than inorganic compounds. However, the presence of one or more halogen atom (F, Cl, Br, I) in the molecular structure of an organic compound increases its stability and inertness to combustion. Thus, partially halogenated hydrocarbons burn with less ease than their nonhalogenated analogues. Fully halogenated derivatives, such as carbon tetrachloride (CCl_4), chlorofluorcarbon refrigerants, and certain polychlorinated biphenyls (PCBs), are almost noncombustible. Polybrominated compounds are used as fire retardants in plastic materials.

Most organic compounds are water-insoluble. This characteristic is of importance in fire fighting, because the compound may sink or float on water, depending on its specific gravity, thus becoming a major determinant of the suitability of water for use in suppressing fires involving the chemical.

Notable exceptions are certain lower-molecular-weight alcohols, aldehydes, ketones, and carboxylic acids, all known to be *polar* molecules that dissolve in water. Water is a polar molecule: other polar molecules tend to dissolve in water. Conversely, except for flammability and oxidation, organic compounds tend to to react slowly with other chemicals.

Organic Nomenclature. This section will familiarize the reader with the naming system for some of the more common and simple organic groups, and present the salient characteristics of these groups. The basic system of aliphatic organic nomenclature is shown in Table 4.

The prefix for the name of an organic compound is based on the number of carbons involved and

Table 4. Nomenclature and Physical Properties of Straight-Chain Alkanes

Name	Number of Carbons	Formula	Melting Point (°C)	Boiling Point (°C)
Methane	1	CH_4	−183	−162
Ethane	2	CH_3CH_3	−172	−89
Propane	3	$CH_3CH_2CH_3$	−187	−42
Butane	4	$CH_3(CH_2)_2CH_3$	−138	0
Pentane	5	$CH_3(CH_2)_3CH_3$	−130	36
Octane	8	$CH_3(CH_2)_6CH_3$	−57	126
Decane	10	$CH_3(CH_2)_8CH_3$	−30	174

(Adapted from Ebbing)

remains the same for each type of compound described. The suffix is determined by the type of compound and is independent of the number of carbons in the molecule. Thus methane, methanol, methanal (formaldehyde), and methanoic (formic) acid represent an alkane, an alcohol, an aldehyde, and a carboxylic acid, respectively; each with one carbon per molecule. The differences are nothing more than increasing oxidation states of the basic alkane hydrocarbon. In contrast, methanol, ethanol, and propanol are all alcohols, but with one, two, and three carbons per molecule, respectively.

Homologous Series and Properties. The boiling points provided in Table 4 illustrate systematic trends in physical properties of this *homologous series* of alkanes. As the number of carbons (and the molecular weight) per alkane molecule increases, boiling and melting points increase.

The same trends hold in general, within a homologous group substituted to form alcohols, aldehydes, ketones, or carboxylic acids. For example octanol is less volatile and has a higher melting point than a lower-molecular-weight alcohol such as butanol. Systematic trends can also be observed for other properties, such as water solubility. It should be noted that the boiling points provided in Table 4 are for the straight-chain isomers of the molecules. When the values for branched chain molecules are included, the comparisons become complicated.

Alkenes and alkynes are similar in structure to the alkanes except that the alkenes contain a carbon-to-carbon double bond (C=C) and the alkynes contain a carbon-to-carbon triple bond

(C≡C). These two types of bonds represent intermediate oxidation states of the basic alkane hydrocarbon (similar to aldehydes, ketones, alcohols, and organic acids). The name prefixes are exactly the same as for the alkanes with the same number of carbons, but the endings are -*ene* for compounds with double bonds and their derivatives and -*yne* for compounds with triple bonds and their derivatives. Ethene (ethylene) and propene (propylene) are alkenes. Ethyne (acetylene) is an alkyne.

Aromatics are molecules based on single or multiple benzene rings. Some of the more common aromatics include benzene, toluene, xylene, and phenol. Aromatic rings are quite stable. The substitution of a methyl group (–CH_3) for one of the hydrogens gives methylbenzene, known more commonly as toluene. The substitution of another methyl group gives dimethylbenzene or xylene. Substitution of a hydroxyl (–OH) for a hydrogen on the benzene ring yields hydroxybenzene, more commonly known as phenol.

Aromatics can also be named more specifically based on a system of assigning names or numbers to various positions on the benzene ring. By using the numbering system for the carbons on single or multiple benzene rings in combination with the names of the relevant substituents, any aromatic compound can be assigned a unique name. Because of the bewildering multiplicity of nomenclature systems developed by chemists over the years, wary hazardous materials managers should consult handbooks or tables that list several of the most common names for a suspect hazardous chemical to make sure they understand which compound they are encountering.

Properties of Individual Functional Groups

Alkanes (C_nH_{2n+2}) are saturated hydrocarbons. The lower-molecular-weight alkanes (ethane through butane) are gases at standard temperature and pressure. The remaining alkanes (as well as alkenes discussed below) are water-insoluble liquids that are lighter than water and thus form films or oil slicks on the surface of water. Hence, water is not used to suppress fires involving materials, such as gasoline, that include substantial proportions of liquid alkanes. Alkanes are relatively unreactive with most acids, bases, and mild oxidizing agents. However, with addition of sufficient heat, alkanes will react and burn in air or oxygen when ignited. In fact, low-molecular-weight alkanes (liquid petroleum gas [LPG], butane, and gasoline) are commonly used as fuels. Consequently, the biggest hazard from alkanes is flammability.

Alkenes (C_nH_{2n}) are also known as *olefins*. Alkene compounds are unsaturated hydrocarbons with a single carbon-to-carbon double bond per molecule. Alkenes frequently have more than one double bond. *e.g.*, butadiene, isoprene, *etc*. Alkenes are very similar to the alkanes in boiling point, specific gravity, and other physical characteristics. Like alkanes, alkenes are essentially nonpolar. Alkenes have very low solubilities in water and other polar solvents but are quite soluble in nonpolar solvents like benzene. Because of the double bond(s) alkenes are more reactive than alkanes.

Organic acids (R$\overset{\overset{\text{O}}{\|}}{\text{C}}$OR) are usually weak acids compared to mineral acids such as hydrochloric or sulfuric acids. Mineral acids completely dissociate in water (give up their protons) and thus are *stronger* than organic acids, which do not ionize completely in water. Organic acids can be very corrosive to skin. Carboxylic acids are the most common type of organic acid and are depicted as RCOOH. (Note: *R* is used to depict a generic organic chain to which the substituent group is bonded.) The substitution of Cl atoms on the carbon next to the carboxylic carbon produces a stronger acid. Thus, trichloroacetic acid is a stronger acid than acetic acid.)

Picric acid (trinitrophenol, $C_6H_2[NO_3]_3OH$) represents a different type of organic acid that does not contain a carboxyl group (–COOH). This acid, often found in old laboratories, is sold containing 28% water and is safe to handle when fresh. Over time the water may be lost and dry picric acid can accumulate on the lid of the container forming an extremely hazardous material that can easily be detonated. Just turning the cap may be enough to cause a significant explosion. A trained explosives disposal squad should handle picric acid when found.

Organic sulfonic acids (RSO_3H) generally are stronger acids than organic carboxylic acids.

Organic bases (such as amines, RNH_2, R_2NH, and R_3N) are weak bases but can be corrosive to skin or other tissue.

Alcohols (ROH) are not very reactive. Alcohols with lower molecular-weights (methanol, ethanol, and propanol) are completely miscible with water, but the heavier alcohols tend to be less soluble. Most common alcohols are flammable. Their flashpoints are: methanol (methyl alcohol) 52°F, ethanol (ethyl alcohol) 55°F, and n-propanol (propyl alcohol) 72°F. Aromatic alcohols like phenol (with a flashpoint of 175°F) are not as flammable and, with a solubility of 9 g/l, are fairly water-soluble.

Esters generally are not very reactive. Esters are formed when a carboxylic acid reacts with an alcohol. Only esters that have low molecular-weights have appreciable solubility in water (for example, ethyl acetate with a solubility of 8%). Methyl and ethyl esters are more volatile than the corresponding uncombined acids. Most common esters are flammable. Esters are often easily recognizable due to their sweet to pungent odors, *e.g.*, ethyl acetate has the characteristic aroma of banana oil.

Ethers (R–O–R) are low on the scale of chemical reactivity but they can be very hazardous. Aliphatic ethers generally are volatile, flammable liquids with low boiling points and low flashpoints. Diethyl ether, dimethyl ether, and tetrahydrofuran are well-known ethers. Beyond flammability, ethers present an additional hazard because they react with atmospheric oxygen in the presence of light to form explosive organic peroxides (see next paragraph). This is why old vessels/bottles of ethers should not be handled unless precautions for explosions are taken. Call the local explosives disposal unit for removal/relocation actions when old ether vessels are encountered.

Organic peroxides (R–O–O–R) are very hazardous. Most organic peroxides are so sensitive to friction, heat, and shock that they cannot be handled without dilution in water. As a result, organic peroxides present a serious fire and explosion hazard. Be aware that crystals forming in the threads of a container lid can detonate when it is unscrewed. As with old ethers, call the explosives disposal squad when planning to handle or dispose of organic peroxides. Commonly encountered organic peroxides include benzyl peroxide, peracetic acid, and methyl ethyl ketone peroxide.

Aldehydes and ketones ($R-\overset{\overset{O}{\|}}{C}H$ and $R-\overset{\overset{O}{\|}}{C}-R$, respectively) share many chemical properties because they possess the carbonyl (C=O) group as a common structural feature. Aldehydes and ketones have lower boiling points and higher vapor pressures than their alcohol counterparts. Aldehydes and ketones through C_4 are soluble in water and have pronounced odors. Ketones are relatively inert, while aldehydes are easily oxidized to their counterpart organic acids.

The Chemistry of Flammables

The elements required for combustion are represented by the *Fire Triangle*, which is composed of a substrate or fuel, oxygen, and a source of ignition. The substrate/fuel, or flammable material, occurs in many classes of compounds but most often is organic. Generally, compounds within a given class exhibit increasing heat contents per gram molecular weights with increasing molecular weights.

Other properties specific to the substrate that are important in determining flammable hazards are the autoignition temperature, boiling point, vapor pressure, and vapor density.

The *autoignition temperature* (the temperature at which a material will spontaneously ignite) is important in fire prevention (*e.g.*, knowing what fire protection is needed to keep temperatures below the ignition point). This information can also be important in spill or material handling situations. For example, gasoline has been known to spontaneously ignite when spilled onto an overheated engine or manifold.

The *boiling point* and *vapor pressure* of a material are important not only because vapors are more easily ignited than liquids, but also because vapors are more readily transportable than liquids (they may disperse, or when heavier than air, flow to a source of ignition). Vapors with densities greater than one do not tend to disperse but rather settle into sumps, basements, depressions in the ground, or other low areas, thus representing active explosion hazards.

Oxygen, the second requirement for combustion, generally is not limiting. Oxygen in the air is sufficient to support combustion of most materials within certain limits. These limitations are compound-specific and are called *the explosive limits in air* The upper and lower explosive limits (UEL and LEL) of several common materials are given in Table 5. Materials such as nitrates or perchlorates have oxygen as part of their structure, and some reactions, even including detonations, do not require additional oxygen.

The *source of ignition* may be physical (such as a spark for an electrical arc, small flame, cigarette, welding operation, or hot piece of equipment), or it may be chemical, such as an exothermic reaction.

Table 5. Explosive Limits of Hazardous Materials

Compound	Lower Explosive Limit (%)	Upper Explosive Limit (%)	Flashpoint (° F)	Vapor Density
Acetone	2.15	13	−4	2.0
Acetylene	2.50	100	Gas	0.9
Ammonia (anhydrous)	16	25	Gas	0.6
Benzene	1.30	7.1	12	7.8
Carbon monoxide	12.4	74	Gas	1.0
Gasoline	1.4	7.6	−45	3.4
Hexane	1.1	7.5	−7	3.0
Toluene	1.2	7.1	40	3.1
Vinyl chloride	3.6	33	Gas	2.2
p–xylene	1.0	6.0	90	3.7

In any case, when working with or storing flammables, controlling the source of ignition is often the easiest and safest way to avoid fires or explosions.

Flammability, the tendency of a material to burn, can only be defined subjectively. Many materials that we normally do not consider flammable will burn, given high enough temperatures. Nor can flammability be gauged by the heat content of materials. Fuel oil has a higher heat content than many materials that are considered to be more flammable because of their lower flashpoints. In fact, flashpoint has become the standard for gauging flammability.

The most common systems for designating flammability are found in definitions of the

- National Fire Protection Association's (NFPA) system

- Department of Transportation (DOT)

- Environmental Protection Agency's (EPA) Resource Conservation and Recovery Act (RCRA) definition of ignitable wastes

The NFPA diamond, which comprises the backbone of the NFPA Hazard Signal System, uses a four-quadrant diamond to display the hazards of a material. The top quadrant (red quadrant) contains flammability information in the form of numbers ranging from zero to four. Materials designated as zero will not burn. Materials designated as four rapidly or completely vaporize at atmospheric pressure and ambient temperature, and will burn readily (flashpoint < 73°F, boiling point < 100°F).

The NFPA defines a flammable liquid as one having a flashpoint of 200°F or lower, and divides these liquids into five categories:

1) Class IA: liquids with flashpoints below 73°F and boiling points below 100°F. An example of a Class IA flammable liquid is *n*-pentane (NFPA Diamond: 4).

2) Class IB: liquids with flashpoints below 73°F and boiling points at or above 100°F. Benzene, gasoline and acetone (NFPA Diamond: 3) are examples of Class IB flammable liquids.

3) Class IC: liquids with flashpoints at or above 73°F and below 100°F. Turpentine and *n*-butyl acetate (NFPA Diamond: 2) are examples of Class IC flammable liquids.

4) Class II: liquids with flashpoints at or above 100°F but below 140°F. Kerosene and camphor oil (NFPA Diamond: 2) are examples of Class II flammable liquids.

5) Class III: liquids with flashpoints at or above 140°F but below 200°F. Creosote oils, phenol, and naphthalene are examples of Class III liquids. Liquids in this category generally are termed combustible rather than flammable (NFPA Diamond: 2).

The DOT system generally designates those materials at ambient temperature with a flashpoint of 140°F or less as flammable, those between 140°F and 200°F as combustible, and those with a flashpoint of greater than 200°F as nonflammable. There are some exceptions to these designations. Refer to 49 CFR 173.120 for more information. EPA, under RCRA designates those wastes with a flashpoint of less than 140°F as ignitable hazardous wastes.

It is quite apparent that the various terms describing *flammability* can be confusing. Please refer to Figure 2, which shows in graphic format how the various terms discussed above interrelate based on flashpoints.

These designations serve as useful guides in storage, transportation, and spill response. However, they do have limitations. Since these designations are somewhat arbitrary, it is useful to understand the basic concepts of flammability.

Petroleum Chemistry

Crude oil is the frame of reference of petroleum chemistry. Crude oil is a complex mixture of organic chemicals containing mostly paraffins (high-molecular-weight waxy compounds), napthalenes (polynuclear benzene-based compounds), as well as other aromatics and alkanes (with straight and branched chains) that have molecular weights ranging from the lightest molecular weights (benzene with a MW of 150) to molecular weights of over five hundred. Crude oil contains thousands of identified compounds, with carbon, hydrogen, oxygen, and sulfur being the main elements.

Originally, crude oil was separated into products according to boiling points through simple fractional distillation. Now, crude oil is refined to

Figure 2. Definitions of Flammable and Combustible Liquids[1]

Ignitable			◄ EPA	
Flammable				◄ DOT
BP<100° F: Class IA	Class IC	Class II	Class III	◄ NFPA
BP>100° F: Class IB				
Flashpoint 73° F	100° F	140° F	200° F	

Adapted from Cox and Browman 1990.

[1] DOT definitions for liquids at ambient temperature. Refer to 49 CFR 173.120 for more information.

more useful products through the process of catalytic cracking and reblending. The most common petroleum products in commercial use are gasoline, kerosene, and diesel fuel.

Gasoline is a complex mixture of branched chain aliphatics (C_5–C_{12}), and low-molecular-weight aromatics. Until the mid-1980s tetraethyl lead (TEL) was added to gasoline to improve its performance. Aromatic additives replaced TEL because of its toxicity. Additives designed to clean the injectors such as methytertiarybutylether (MTBE) have further enhanced gasoline's performance in fuel-injected engines. MTBE has received a lot of attention due to its aroma, taste, and potential health risks when released into ground water from leaking underground storage tanks. See EPA and other Internet web sites for more information.

Kerosene is similar in composition to gasoline except that the primary aliphatics have higher molecular weights (C_{12}–C_{16}). Its primary uses are for jet fuel and as a heating fuel.

Diesel fuel is very similar to kerosene except that it contains even higher-molecular-weight aliphatics (C_{15}–C_{18}). Its primary use is as a fuel for motor vehicles. Bunker C, a common marine fuel oil, is frequently encountered by hazardous materials managers working in waterways, rivers, *etc.*

A number of other categories of products are derived from petroleum:

- The fuel gases: methane, ethane, propane, and butane (C_1–C_4)

- The petroleum ethers (C_5–C_7)

- The lubricating oils and greases (C_{16}–C_{18})

- From the residuum (the solid residue left after processing): paraffin wax (C_{20} – C_{30}), asphalts, petrolatum (petroleum jelly), petroleum coke; and, when blended with distillate, #4, #5, and #6 fuel oils

The regulation of underground storage tanks (USTs) has made petroleum chemistry more important to a wide spectrum of environmental professionals. It is essential in UST remediation work to analyze petroleum in soils and in groundwater by gas chromatography in order to determine the diesel-range organics (C_{15}–C_{18}) and gasoline-range organics (C_5–C_{12}).

Once a petroleum fire has started, control of the fire can be accomplished in several ways: through water systems (by reducing the temperature), carbon dioxide or foam systems (by limiting oxygen), or through the removal of the substrate (by shutting off valves or other controls). However, water systems are not effective nor used on gasoline or lower molecular weight petroleum fires since their flash points are often lower than the water temperature and they float and burn on the water. Aqueous film forming foams (AFFFs or *A Triple Fs*) are used in place of water for such fires.

Toxic Chemicals

Toxicity is broadly defined and encompasses a large spectrum of chemical classes, therefore it is beyond the scope of this chapter to do more than discuss the general characteristics of a few important classes of toxic chemicals. For more comprehensive information on toxic effects of specific chemicals, see the Agency for Toxic Substances and Disease Registry's (ATSDR) Internet site at:

<http://www.atsdr.cdc.gov/toxfaq.html>

Toxic Metals

The most common toxic metals in industrial use are beryllium, cadmium, chromium, lead, silver, and mercury. Arsenic, selenium, (both metalloids), and barium are less commonly used.

Cadmium, a metal commonly found in alloys and a myriad of other industrial uses, is fairly mobile in the environment and is responsible for many maladies including renal failure and a degenerative bone disease called *itai itai*.

Chromium, most often found in plating wastes, is also environmentally mobile. Chromium compounds are toxic in the Cr^{+3} oxidation state, especially when highly water-soluble. Compounds containing hexavalent chromium (Cr^{+6}) are carcinogenic.

Historically, lead has been used in tetraethyl lead, an antiknock compound in gasoline and, along with chromium (as lead chromate), in paint and pigments. Because of these and other historical uses, lead is ubiquitous. It is fairly mobile and is particularly soluble in acid environments.

Silver is used widely in the electronics industry. Intake of silver compounds can result in permanent discoloration of the skin and may result in damage to kidneys, lungs, mucous membranes, and other organs. In the environment silver is a potent biocide and is found in prescription burn ointments.

Mercury has gained its seeming environmental ubiquity due to its use as a fungicide, as an electrode in the chlorine production process, and as a pollutant resulting from the combustion of fossil fuels. Elemental mercury is relatively immobile in soils, but is readily transformed to more mobile organometallic compounds through microbial action. Mercury is the responsible agent for the infamous Minimata as well as the Mad Hatter's syndrome that is characterized by degeneration of the central nervous system. Mercury is used in thermometers and fluorescent lamps. Mercury has been used extensively to recover gold from gold-containing ore. Methyl mercury, an organomercury compound, is deadly in very small doses; it is capable of being absorbed through the skin. It may be found in research laboratories and has been responsible for the deaths of several researchers. The US Food and Drug Administration web site has an extensive listing of studies on the presence and toxicity of methyl mercury in fish.

Arsenic and selenium are both commonly used to decolorize glass or to impart a desirable color. Arsenic occurs in a number of important forms, many of which have been used as contact herbicides. Important forms of arsenic include arsenic trioxide and pentoxide. Arsenic also reacts to form arsenic acids, arsenites, and arsenates, and various organic arsenic compounds. Selenium often occurs as selenous acid. Both arsenic and selenium are fairly mobile in soils.

In general, toxic metals can be readily removed from aqueous solution through precipitation reactions, either as the sulfide or (more commonly) as the hydroxide, or by ion-exchange systems. Various processes are available to stabilize metals in contaminated soil, but all the processes are expensive. It should be pointed out that metals cannot be destroyed, only concentrated chemically, fixed within a matrix, or reduced in toxicity.

Cyanides

Cyanides (CN^-) are dangerously toxic materials that can cause death within minutes. They are encountered in a number of industrial situations such as in sludges and baths from plating operations, or heap leach systems used in mining operations. Cyanide salts are extremely soluble, and many cyanide compounds, when mixed with acid, release deadly hydrogen cyanide gas. Cyanide is sometimes formed during the combustion of various nitrile, cyanohydrin, and methacrylate compounds. Cyanides commonly are treated by chlorine oxidation to the less toxic cyanate (CNO^-) form, then acid-hydrolyzed to CO_2 and N_2. Clearly, care should be taken that the cyanide oxidation is complete prior to acid hydrolysis of the cyanate.

Hydrogen Sulfide

Hydrogen sulfide is a commonly occurring decomposition product of organic matter that has the distinctive smell of rotten eggs. But its odor can't be counted on for protection since it swiftly anesthetizes the sense of smell. Hydrogen sulfide is actually more toxic than cyanide gas. It is relatively water-soluble at higher pHs where it dissociates into H^+ and S^{-2} ions. As the pH is decreased below 7, gaseous H_2S begins to predominate and is released. Since its vapor density is greater than 1.0, H_2S gas tends to settle in low places and creates a toxic hazard. H_2S is readily oxidized by a number of means to less toxic $(SO_3)^{-2}$ or $(SO_4)^{-2}$ forms.

Pesticides

Pesticides include the broad categories of insecticides, fungicides, rodenticides, and herbicides. These hazardous materials are regulated under the Federal Insecticide, Fungicide and Rodenticide Act (FIFRA) discussed in a separate chapter in this *Desk Reference*. The detailed chemistry, hazards, and FIFA requirements should be determined prior to handling pesticides by consulting the product label or the Material Safety Data Sheet.

Insecticides. Insecticides, in common use, fall into three categories. The *chloroinsecticides* have chlorine in their structure. They are less soluble than the other insecticide forms and much less biodegradable (*i.e.*, more persistent). While they are less acutely toxic, several have been identified as potential carcinogens. *Carbamates* are less persistent and less toxic than chloroinsecticides, but some are also suspected carcinogens. *Organophosphate insecticides* generally are more acutely toxic than the other categories but they are not persistent.

Arsenic-based preservatives such as chromate copper arsenate used in wood preservation are the subject of EPA scrutiny and rule making. See

<http://www.epa.gov/oppad001/reregistration/cca/>

Herbicides. Many formerly common herbicides now have been banned or restricted in their use; *e.g.*, 2,4-D and 2,4,5-T. However, the number and diversity of herbicides far exceeds that of insecticides. There are both organic and inorganic herbicides. Examples of inorganic herbicides are $CuSO_4$ and $NaClO_3$. There are at least 22 chemical families of organic herbicides. Even a cursory treatment of the chemistry of these materials would be extensive. Herbicides of limited toxicity (Treflan, Atrazine) as well as extremely toxic ones (Paraquat, Dinoseb) are in use. They range from water-soluble to water-insoluble. The detailed chemistry of each should be determined prior to handling.

Chemical Incompatibilities

Chemical incompatibility can manifest itself in many ways; however, our discussions will be limited to those combinations resulting in fires, explosions, extreme heat, evolution of gas (both toxic and nontoxic), and polymerization.

Because of the number of chemicals and subsequent multiple number of potential reactions, it is impractical and (perhaps impossible) to list all potential reactions. Several systems exist for determining the reactions between classes of chemicals. The incompatibilities of the most broadly distributed chemicals are provided by by Bretherick and Hatayaya in the two publications listed in the Bibliography.

The volume by Bretherick is divided into two sections. The first lists general classes of compounds and gives reactivity information regarding interactions of these classes with other classes and with specific chemicals. The second and much larger section lists specific compounds and references specific adverse reactions as they have been observed or reported in the chemical literature. The work by Hatayaya provides a matrix format compatibility chart listing 40 classes of chemicals. While both of these volumes are extremely helpful, they are not and do not claim to be definitive works on material compatibility. They are, however, useful guides for identifying potential reactions.

Because all of the potential reactions for individual chemicals are not catalogued and because there are few pure solutions of waste materials, laboratory compatibility testing is recommended for most materials. An appropriate protocol for compatibility testing would involve the following steps:

- Obtain all available information about the material. If it is a surplus or off-specification product, obtain an analysis or a Material Safety Data Sheet. If it is a waste, check for previous analyses, and if none exists, arrange for one to be done. Even if a previous analysis exists for this stream, consider running a few screening-type field analyses for confirmation of important properties such as pH, redox potential or other oxidizer test, cyanide, sulfide, and flashpoint.

- Once the identity of the material is known, one of the cited references can be consulted to determine potential reactions. At this point, incompatibility may be obvious. If not, then laboratory testing for compatibility is required.

Compatibility testing is almost by nature an experiment with the unknown. Therefore, compatability testing should not be attempted without advanced procedural and safety training. Procedures for compatibility testing should take into account the most severe adverse reaction possible, not just that expected. Such testing should always be performed under an adequate fume hood while wearing, as a minimum, face shield, rubber apron, and gloves. Generally, compatibility testing entails mixing a small volume of one substance with another and observing for heat, gas generation, or polymerization.

Polymerization need not be violent to cause problems. Anyone who has ever had to chisel out or replace a tank of solidified material can attest to this. Often it is advisable to heat the mixture to expected storage or process temperature and then observe for further heat, gas, or polymerization.

Observation of a reaction does not necessarily preclude mixing. Moderate heat or gas generation may not present a problem. However, a number of safety precautions should be taken before mixing the material if any heat or gas generation occurs. If heat is generated, the amount should be determined and a heat balance calculated so that effects of heating on the storage tank and tank base can be calculated. Expansion of the material with heating should also be considered, so as to avoid overfilling the receiving tank.

Generation of gas requires a gas analysis before mixing. If the gas is toxic or if discharge of the resultant gas violates an air-quality constraint, the materials should not be mixed. If the gas is nontoxic, care should still be taken to ensure that the gas generation rate does not exceed the design venting capacity of the tank. Remember that most tanks are designed to withstand a water gauge internal pressure of only about 8 inches (a typical person can provide pressure of 24 inches water gauge by blowing). Also, even if the gas is nontoxic, it may still displace air and, for inside tanks especially, create an asphyxiation hazard.

Gases

Space occupied by gases is mostly *empty* owing to the very nature of gases. Thirty-two grams of liquid oxygen occupy a space of 0.026 liters. At Standard Temperature and Pressure (STP) of 0°C, 1 atmosphere, this same weight of oxygen occupies 22.4 liters; over 861 times as much volume. If the oxygen is pure, the molecules represent less than 0.1% or 1/1000 of the volume of the gas.

The *Ideal Gas Law* is widely used for calculating the quantity (moles) of an enclosed gas when the pressure, volume, and temperature of the container are known. The Ideal Gas Law equation is:

$$PV = nRT \tag{18}$$

Where:

P = pressure (atm)
V = volume (liters)
n = the number of moles of gas
T = temperature (Kelvin)
R = 0.0820 (the gas constant which is dependent upon the units used)

(Note that zero degrees Celsius (0°) is equivalent to 273.15 Kelvin.)

Inspection of the above equation leads one quickly to realize that the quantity of gas (moles), its temperature, pressure, and its volume are all interrelated. Examples using the Ideal Gas Law equation for practical purposes can be found in most basic chemistry texts.

When referring to pollutant concentrations in parts per million or parts per billion, the EPA National Ambient Air Quality Standards use *volume-to-volume* ratios (as opposed to weight-to-weight ratios) for all gases including CO, O_3, NO_2 and SO_2. Additionally, it is also acceptable to refer to the concentrations in terms of *weight-to-volume*, commonly expressed as micrograms per cubic meter (ug/m^3). This applies to gaseous pollutants as well as particulates. The only exception is CO; the concentration of CO is high enough that it is expressed in milligrams per cubic meter (mg/m^3).

The hazardous materials manager may encounter pollutant concentrations in parts per million by volume (ppm_V) or parts per billion by volume (ppb_V) and need to convert them to either mg/m^3 or $\mu g/m^3$. One g-mole of any ideal gas has a volume of 24.5 liters at the standard conditions of 25°C and 760 mmHg, used in making air pollution measurements. Therefore, the conversions are as follows:

Micrograms/cubic meter ($\mu g/m^3$) =   (20)
  (ppm_V) x molecular weight of gas x 10^3

Milligrams/cubic meter ($\mu g/m^3$) =   (21)
  (ppm_V) x molecular weight of gas

It should also be noted that the above conversions apply to vapors or fumes as well as gases when molecular weights are known or can be estimated.

Conversions Between Volume-to-Volume and Weight-to-Weight Expressions of Pollutant Concentrations. The hazardous materials manager might encounter air pollutant concentrations in parts per million expressed as weight ratios (ppm by weight, or ppm_w) rather than by the more common volume-to-volume expressions. The distinction between ppm_V and ppm_W should be taken into consideration when there is a need to convert these to mg/m^3 or $\mu g/m^3$ since the conversion calculations differ. Although the calculations appear almost identical, the difference between the two is the molecular weight

that is used in the equations. In the conversion from ppm_v, the molecular weight of the subject (gaseous pollutant) is used, in ppm_w the molecular weight of the matrix (air) is used.

Although air is not a molecule per se, but rather a mixture of nitrogen, oxygen, and argon (ignoring other minor components), it is useful to consider it as such for calculation purposes. If the issue at hand is to calculate the concentration of 1 gram ozone (O_3) contained within 1 cubic meter of air, we must first find the *molecular weight* of air. This can be done using the following equation that sums the contributions of 78% nitrogen, 21% oxygen, and 0.9% argon:

$$MW_{air} = (.78N_2)(MW_{N2}) + (.21O_2)(MW_{O2}) \quad (22)$$
$$+ (.009\ Ar)(MW_{Ar}) =$$

(.78 mole)(28 g/mole) + (.21 mole)(32 g/mole) + (.009 mole)(40 g /mole) = 28.9 g/mole air

Where:

MW_x = molecular weight of the component

By knowing the molecular weight of air, and with the molecular weight of ozone being 48, we are now able to calculate the concentrations of 1 gram of ozone within the 1 cubic meter of air as parts per million by weight and parts per million by volume.

Example (1). Concentration of Ozone in Air as Parts per Million by Weight

1 g O_3/m^3 air = (1 g O_3/m^3) x ($m^3/10^3$ liters)   (23)
  x (24.5 liters/mol air) x (mol air /28.9g air) x
  (10^6 micrograms $O_3/$ g O_3) =

848 micrograms O_3/g air or 848 ppm_w

Example (2). Concentration of Ozone in Air as Parts per Million by Volume

1 g O_3/m^3 − (1 O_3/m^3) x (1 mole $O_3/48$ g O_3) x   (24)
  (24.5 liters $O_3/$ mole O_3) x ($m^3/10^3$ liters air) x
  (10^6 microliters $O_3/$ liter O_3) =

510 microliters $O_3/$ liter air) or 510 ppm_v

To convert from micrograms per cubic meter to milligrams per cubic meter, divide by 1000.

For a more detailed discussion of gases and gas laws, refer to Myer 2004.

Final Comments

The concepts presented in this overview of chemistry come into play in one form or another in the practice of hazardous materials management. Those who wish to excel in this field are encouraged to *understand and memorize* as many of the terms, concepts, and principles as time and interest permit. They constitute a significant portion of the everyday vocabulary and considerations of this profession. Based on the writer's personal experience, the time invested will be well spent.

Bibliography

Bretherick, L., and P. G. Urben, Eds., *Bretherick's Handbook of Reactive Chemical Hazards.* 6th ed. Philadelphia, PA: Butterworth-Heinemann, 1999.

Burke, R. *Hazardous Materials Chemistry for Emergency Responders.* 2nd ed. Boca Raton, FL: Lewis Publishers, Inc., 2003.

Cooper, A. R., Sr., Ed. *Cooper's Toxic Exposures Desk Reference.* Boca Raton, FL: Lewis Publishers, Inc., 1996.

Cox, Doye B. and M. G. Browman. "Chemistry of Hazardous Materials." in *Handbook on Hazardous Materials Management.* H. T. Carson and D. B. Cox, Eds. Rockville, MD: Institute of Hazardous Materials Management, 1990.

Ebbing, Darrell D and S. D. Gammon. *General Chemistry,* 7th ed. Boston, MA: Houghton Mifflin Company, 2001.

Hatayaya, H. K., *et al. A Method for Determining the Compatibility of Hazardous Wastes.* EPA–600/2–80–076. Washington, DC: EPA, 1980.

International Code Council. *2003 International Fire Code,* Falls Church, VA: ICC, 2003.

Kent, J. A., Ed. *Riegel's Handbook of Industrial Chemistry,* 10th ed. Norwell, MA: Springer, 2003.

Lewis, R. J., Ed. *Hawley's Condensed Chemical Dictionary,* 14th ed. Hoboken, NJ: Wiley-Interscience, 2001.

Lewis, R. J. *Hazardous Chemicals Desk Reference,* 5th ed. Hoboken, NJ: John Wiley & Sons, 2002.

Lide, D. R., Ed. *CRC Handbook of Chemistry and Physics.* 86th ed. Boca Raton, FL: CRC, 2005.

Manahan, S. E. *Environmental Chemistry,* 8th ed. Boca Raton, FL: CRC Press, 2004.

Meyer, E. *Chemistry of Hazardous Materials,* 4th ed. Upper Saddle River, NJ: Prentice-Hall, 2004.

National Institute for Occupational Safety and Health. *NIOSH Pocket Guide To Chemical Hazards.* NIOSH Publication No. 94–140. Washington, DC: NIOSH.

O'Neil, M. J., A. Smith, P. E. Heckelman, and S. Budavari, Eds. *The Merck Index.* 13th ed. Hoboken, NJ: John Wiley & Sons, 2001.

Patnaik, P. *A Comprehensive Guide to the Hazardous Properties of Chemical Substances.* 2nd ed. Hoboken, NJ: John Wiley & Sons, 1998.

Perry, R. H., Ed., *et al. Perry's Chemical Engineers' Handbook,* Platinum ed. New York, NY: McGraw Hill, 1999.

United States Department of Transportation *2004 Emergency Response Guidebook.* Washington, DC: USDOT, 2004.

Richard E. Hagen served as Director of Environmental Management, Bristol-Myers Squibb (B-MS) Nutritionals Group, and as Chairman of the B-MS Corporate Environmental Committee. His areas of expertise and interest include industrial hazardous materials management and management systems to achieve environmental quality. The author especially wishes to thank the following reviewers for their extremely penetrating and helpful comments:

- *James E. Gano, PhD, Professor Emeritus of Chemistry, University of Toledo*

- *Michael A. Kay, ScD, CHMM., President, AMBRY, Inc., Milwaukie, Oregon.*

- *Lynne Murray Koby, BS, PG, CHMM. Tennessee Department of Environment and Conservation, Division of Solid Waste Management.*

- *Daniel L. Todd, MS, CHMM, QEP, President, Air Quality Services, LLC, Evansville, Indiana*

The author also acknowledges Doye B. Cox, PE, CHMM, and Michael G. Browman PhD, who prepared portions of this chapter first used in the Handbook on Hazardous Materials, Fifth Edition. 1995.

CHAPTER 47

Multimedia Sampling

W. Scott Butterfield, MS, CHMM

Introduction

Site investigations frequently require the collection and analysis of multimedia samples (*e.g.*, soil, sediment, air, aqueous, waste, *etc.*) to

- Identify contaminants

- Identify the source(s) of contaminants

- Determine the extent of contamination

- Prepare and implement Health and Safety plans

- Establish threat to public health and environment

- Evaluate remedial options

- Confirm site cleanup

One or more of the above reasons for sampling is the Data Use Objective(s) (DUO) of the sampling program. DUOs are important drivers in the planning process, since they provide a basis for determining the sampling procedures required, analytical methodologies to be used by the laboratory, and quality assurance (QA) procedures necessary to provide analytical data needed to meet the DUO(s). DUOs will be discussed in more detail later in this chapter.

Sampling and subsequent analysis can result in a significant expenditure of time and money during the assessment of a particular site. Decisions based on the interpretation of sampling results can have significant financial impacts on the parties involved in the planning and implementation of site remediation programs. Thus it is extremely important to prepare for and conduct a cost-effective sampling program that provides a valid representation of site conditions. This is true whether there is concern about the contents of a few drums or the extent of contamination on a multi-acre property. The United States Environmental Protection Agency (EPA) has developed the Data Quality Objectives (DQO) process to help their staff in determining the type and quantity of data needed to support EPA decisions. The reader is encouraged to review the references listed at the end of this chapter to gain a better understanding of this planning process. The blueprint for accomplishing the established goal of the DQO process is the *sampling plan*. A properly prepared and executed sampling plan will result in the generation of data of known quality. This means all components associated with the generation of the data are thoroughly documented and the documentation is verifiable and defensible.

This chapter provides an introduction to the process of planning and executing multimedia sampling programs. Basic terminology is defined and a suggested format for sampling plans is described. Emphasis is placed on the importance of quality assurance/quality control (QA/QC) throughout the process. Significant references, which contain detailed information on QA/QC, sampling plan preparation, and sample collection techniques, and analytical methodologies, are also provided. Upon completion of this chapter the reader should be able to understand the planning process, identify appropriate sampling procedures, select appropriate analytical methodologies, and prepare a basic sampling plan. In order to gain proficiency in multimedia sampling, the reader must develop his/her skills under the supervision of experienced multimedia samplers.

Multimedia Samples

The assessment of sites to determine the presence of hazardous materials may involve the collection and analysis of samples from various media on and adjacent to the site. The media can vary greatly: from liquid and solid materials contained in on-site containers (*e.g.*, drums, tanks, *etc.*) to contaminated site soils and sludges, from ground and surface waters (on and off-site) to air gases and particulates. The various media can be broken down into the following general categories:

- Surface water

- Ground water

- Soil/sediment

- Air/soil gas

- Wastes

These media may or may not be contaminated with hazardous materials to various degrees. In general, when planning to collect samples from and around hazardous waste sites, *samples* are categorized as one of two types: *hazardous* or *environmental*. Hazardous samples contain materials classified as hazardous by the United States Department of Transportation (USDOT) and are thus subject to USDOT shipping regulations. Hazardous samples are sometimes further categorized based on the level of contamination, such as high and moderate hazard samples. The determination of sample type is based on existing analytical data, background information (*e.g.*, past activities conducted at the site, container labels, *etc.*) and/or policy. Policy determinations reflect an organization's desire to ensure the health and safety of those involved with sampling programs and to avoid the liability of improper shipment of samples. Some organizations have a simple policy of "if the sample is collected from on-site, then the sample is hazardous" and "if the sample is collected from off-site, then the sample is environmental". In any event the relative concentrations and/or hazards must be determined prior to sample collection in order to determine

- Proper health and safety precautions

- Required sampling procedures

- Required sample shipping procedures

- Appropriate analytical methodologies

The collection of high-hazard samples will normally take longer and cost more than environmental samples because of the higher level of personal protection required (*i.e.*, Level C or B versus Level D) and the more stringent sample shipping requirements. Analytical procedures also differ for high-hazard samples and subsequently cost more.

Types of Samples

There are basically two types of multimedia sample collection techniques used during hazardous waste site investigations: grab and composite sampling. A *grab sample* is a discrete aliquot collected from one specific sampling location at one specific point in time. The analytical results from a grab sample should provide a good representation of the concentrations of the contaminants present at the point the sample was taken. An example is a surface soil sample collected from a specific point or *station* on a site. A *composite sample* is a nondiscrete sample composed of two or more equal aliquots collected at various points and/or times. The analytical results from a composite sample provide average concentrations of the contaminants present. The collection and mixing (homogenizing) of two aliquots of surface material from a pile of *waste* material would result in the generation of a composite sample of the pile.

Grab sampling is preferred in many situations because it minimizes the time and expense that would be required to collect the multiple aliquots required for composite samples. It also reduces the potential health risks of combining unknown and potentially reactive materials. Grab samples are appropriate when the objective is to document the condition of a particular location such as an area of stained soil or the contents of individual containers. Since the sample is collected from a particular point or container, that point or container can be further investigated later, if required. Grab sampling may be appropriate to characterize stratified materials occurring in drums, tanks, lagoons, or wells. Under these circumstances, a grab sample from each layer or phase may be collected.

Composite sampling is often appropriate when sampling areas or containers of similar material (*e.g.*, pile of homogeneous waste material, drums of similar material, *etc,*) or when a large area is being surveyed to determine the extent or presence

of contamination. An example would be the evaluation of a multi-acre site where contaminants are suspected of being disposed but no obvious signs of disposal areas (*e.g.*, stained soil, distressed vegetation, *etc.*) dictate the need for grab sample collection. For such a situation a grid could be superimposed over the site and composite samples could be collected from each grid or a portion of the grids. If contaminants are detected in any of the grids, a more rigorous but localized sampling program can be conducted within the *contaminated* grids using grab-sampling techniques to better define the extent and magnitude of contamination. Because the act of combining materials during composite sampling causes a dilution effect on the components of the aliquots combined, the resultant concentration of contaminants generally is lower than the maximum of any of the aliquots. This dilution effect must be considered when determining the required detection limits of the analytical procedures selected for sampling programs, to avoid false negative analytical results.

Four types of composite samples are generally considered: areal, vertical, flow-proportional, and time. Areal and vertical composite samples are routinely collected during the investigation of hazardous waste sites. *Areal composites* are composed of equal aliquots (grab samples) collected from a defined area such as the surface of a waste pile or an established grid. *Vertical composites* are composed of equal aliquots collected along a defined vertical interval such as a borehole or test pit (for example, the combination of five aliquots taken every foot during the installation of a 5-foot soil boring). *Flow-proportional composite sampling* is generally associated with stream or wastewater discharge samples and is thus not normally used in the investigation of hazardous waste sites. *Time composite sampling* is also normally not associated with hazardous waste site investigations, because the intent of such investigations is to determine as quickly as possible what is present on site at the *present* time. For health and safety reasons, however, a form of time compositing is used in determining air quality on and around hazardous waste sites. Here ambient air is drawn over a filter or adsorbent material at a set flow rate for a period of time. The result is the generation of an average concentration of contaminant(s) per volume of ambient air.

Composite sampling generates average concentrations within the composited interval. Thus, one cannot draw conclusions concerning the maximum and minimum concentrations of the contaminant in question.

Sampling Strategies

In addition to the types of samples and sample collection techniques, the sampling strategies must also be considered. Three basic strategies to consider during the development of sampling programs are: judgmental, random, and systematic.

Judgmental sampling is subjective. Sampling points are located where contaminants are thought to exist, such as in areas of stained soil or in containers. Judgmental sampling locations may also be identified through historical site information (including photographs), which identifies areas of concern based on past site operations/conditions (*e.g.*, waste discharge points, storage areas, lagoons). Judgmental sampling generally provides information on worst-case conditions, which is useful for identifying contaminants of concern at a site but not the extent of contamination that will require additional sampling using other approaches.

Random sampling is the opposite of judgmental sampling, where locations are arbitrarily assigned using a random selection procedure such as random number tables. Random sampling is used when statistical evaluations of the data are required (*e.g.*, probability statements). When used alone, random sampling is generally not appropriate for evaluating hazardous waste sites, because a key assumption of homogeneity cannot be made due to the inherent heterogeneity of hazardous waste sites. Random sampling, in combination with other strategies such as grid sampling is frequently used on large, relatively homogeneous areas of extensive sites to help determine the extent of contamination (see below).

Systematic sampling involves the establishment of a reproducible scheme such as a grid or transect to which sampling points can be referenced. Samples are then collected at the points grid lines intersect (nodes) or defined distances along the transect line. The number of samples collected will depend on the area covered by the grid and the cell size established (the smaller the cells, the larger the number of nodes generated) or by the spacing of the points along the transects. As discussed above, random sampling can be combined with a systematic approach when the areas within the grids are relatively homogeneous. This approach allows probability statements to be developed about the extent of contamination within the individual grids.

Detailed information on the above topics can be found in the publications listed at the end of this chapter. The majority of these publications can be accessed via the Internet at the sites listed at the end of this chapter.

Analytical Methods

The selection of appropriate analytical methods depends on many factors, including media to be analyzed, expected analyte/contaminant concentrations, State-specific regulatory requirements and required detection limits. The EPA has either developed or adopted methods for its various regulatory programs, which are readily available to the general public via the Internet. The EPA Office of Water (OW) publishes methods for the analysis of the chemical and biological components of waste-water, drinking water and sediment that are required by regulations under the Clean Water Act (CWA) and the Safe Drinking Water Act (SDWA). These methods are compiled in *Methods for Chemical Analysis of Water and Wastes* (MCAWW), EPA/600/4–79–020.

The EPA Office of Solid Waste and Emergency Response (OSWER) provides *Test Methods for Evaluating Solid Waste, Physical/Chemical Methods*, that is generally referred to as SW–846. This is a compilation of methods and guidance approved by EPA for conducting evaluations needed to satisfy the Resource Conservation and Recovery Act (RCRA). SW–846 contains procedures for determining the hazardous constituents in wastes and the hazardous characteristics of wastes (toxicity, ignitability, reactivity and corrosivity). It also provides guidance on how to select appropriate methods.

The EPA Office of Research and Development (ORD) National Risk Management Research Laboratory (NRMRL) has assembled a compendium of analytical methods for determining toxic organic compounds in ambient air. This is also available via EPA's web page.

Analytical methods are also available from non-government sources such as the American Society for Testing and Materials (ASTM) and the American Public Health Association (APHA). Analytical chemists should routinely be consulted during the selection process in order to ensure that appropriate methods are selected and implemented.

Multimedia Sampling Plan

Sampling and subsequent analysis can result in a significant expenditure of time and money during the assessment of a particular site. Decisions based on the interpretation of sampling results can have significant financial impacts on the parties involved in the planning and implementation of site remediation programs. Thus, it is extremely important to prepare for and conduct a cost-effective sampling program that provides a valid representation of site conditions. This is true whether there is a concern about the contents of a few drums or the extent of contamination on a multi-acre property. The blueprint for attaining this goal is the *sampling plan*. A properly prepared and executed sampling plan should provide data of known quality, which means all components associated with the generation of the data are thoroughly documented and the documentation is verifiable and defensible.

The EPA and various state environmental departments have prepared many good guidance documents on the preparation of sampling plans. An excellent series on representative sampling is available from the EPA Environmental Response Team, which is available from their Web page (listed in the Internet Resources section) at no charge. Other references are provided at the end of this chapter. In general sampling plans should cover the following topics:

- Introduction/background
- Objectives
- Data use
- Quality assurance
- Sampling approach and methods

- Organization and responsibilities
- Quality assurance requirements
- Deliverables

A discussion of each of the eight topics is presented below.

Introduction/Background

The development of an effective sampling plan requires a thorough evaluation of current as well as past site conditions. A thorough file search should be conducted with appropriate/potential regulatory agencies (Federal, State, and local) to determine if information exists on past environmental issues (*e.g.*, spills, fires, citations, permits, *etc.*). An important part of this review is a determination of land use histories of sites to gain a better understanding of potential hazards (*e.g.*, contaminants of concern, buried lagoons, underground pipe runs and tanks, existing and past building uses and locations, *etc.*). Historical insurance maps and aerial photographs can be very useful in this regard. In addition to identifying types of contaminants, the volumes, locations, and concentrations of these materials should be quantified. This information will assist planners in identifying appropriate sampling and analytical methodologies and detection limits.

Not only is it important to determine the location of potential sources of contaminants, the potential migration pathways should also be identified. United States Geological Survey (USGS) topographic maps and aerial photographs provide good information for identifying these pathways. A site reconnaissance should also be conducted prior to the finalization of the sampling plan in order to confirm site conditions and to refine the evaluation of potential migration pathways. An off-site reconnaissance is appropriate when the site is relatively small, potential sources of contaminants are visible, access has not yet been attained, and/or current site information is required to prepare for an on-site reconnaissance. An on-site reconnaissance can provide a great deal more information about site conditions, but it also requires proper planning, since the investigators will be working in areas potentially contaminated with hazardous materials. This is where the gathered background information becomes extremely valuable.

In order to conduct an on-site reconnaissance, a health and safety plan (HASP), which identifies potential on-site hazards and specifies levels of personal protection, must be prepared and implemented. During the on-site reconnaissance, portable monitoring and analytical equipment can be used to better define the areas of contamination and help identify contaminants of concern. A site map should be developed during the reconnaissance that denotes the locations of on-site structures, areas of potential contamination, containers and tanks, *etc*. On-site drainage patterns and potential off-site receptors near the site should also be identified and indicated on the site map.

Objectives

The objectives of the sampling plan set the stage for the sampling strategy, the selection of sampling procedures and analytical methods, and QA/QC requirements. Two subjects that must be addressed in this section are Data Use Objectives and the Quality Assurance Objectives.

Data Use Objectives (DUOs) address specific goals of the sampling program. The goal may be as simple as determining the contents of a single drum in order to arrange for proper disposal, or as complex as determining the impact of a site with multiple sources of unknown contaminants on human and ecological receptors. The DUOs should be stated as clearly as possible, including purpose the data will serve, the questions that must be answered by the data, and what decisions will be based on the data that is generated. Examples of these follow.

The Data Use Objective(s) of this sampling program is (are)

- To determine the RCRA characteristics of materials contained in each on-site drum in order to classify these materials as RCRA hazardous or nonhazardous materials

- To determine the concentration of volatile organic compounds (VOCs) in residential tap water samples in order to compare these concentrations to State (specify the State agency) drinking water

standards and EPA Maximum Contaminant Levels (MCLs)

- To verify the attainment of the site-specific soil cleanup goal for lead (specify the level), prior to backfilling the excavation with clean fill material

If appropriate, the statement should include what the analytical results will be compared to, such as State or Federal regulatory requirements, permits, guidelines, standards, *etc*. These benchmarks will provide a basis for determining QA requirements such as analytical methods and detection limits.

Quality Assurance Objectives (QAOs) are statements about the desired reliability of the data to be generated. They are defined by determining how precise, accurate, representative, complete, and comparable the data must be to satisfy the DUO. Detailed discussions on the above quality assurance terms can be found in the references listed at the end of this chapter. Various agencies, including EPA, have established QA *Levels* that address predefined QAOs. For example, OSWER uses a three-level QAO system (QA1, QA2, and QA3) in the development of their sampling plans. In brief, the objectives of these levels are as follows:

QA1—Screening objective used to afford a quick, preliminary assessment of site contamination. Data collected for this objective provide neither definitive identification of pollutants nor definitive quantification of concentration levels.

QA2—Verification objective used to verify analytical results. Here a small percentage of the sample results are verified to provide a certain level of confidence for a portion of the results. An inference is then made on the quality of the remainder of the data.

QA3—Definitive objective used to assess the accuracy of the concentration level as well as the identity of the analytes of interest. This objective is appropriate when a high level of qualitative and quantitative accuracy is required for all sampling results.

In turn, each QA Level specifies the types and numbers of QA samples (*e.g.*, blanks, duplicates, *etc*.) required to satisfy the selected QA Level.

Sampling Approach and Methods

This section of the sampling plan should address the sampling strategy, the sampling procedures (including decontamination procedures), sample management, sample containers, sample shipment and sample documentation. Sufficient detail should be included to permit an experienced sampling team to carry out the sampling program. The sampling strategy should discuss the types and numbers of samples to be collected, their locations and reasons for their collection (*e.g.*, background or contaminant source sample, *etc.*). A sample numbering/identification system should also be developed to ensure sample identity. When numerous samples are required, a tabular presentation of this information should be provided. A site map should also be developed to show the locations of the sampling points or stations. Included in the approach should be the sequence of sample collection. For example, stream sampling for water and sediments should be initiated at the farthest downstream collection point and then conducted in a sequential, upstream direction to the farthest upstream sampling point. This methodology serves to prevent the influence of disturbed sediments on the downstream sampling points. Consideration should also be given to collecting background and low concentration samples prior to the collection of high concentration samples, thereby minimizing the potential for cross-contamination.

The sampling procedures for the required samples should be specified. This can be accomplished by either detailing the procedures in this section or by referencing standard operating procedures (SOPs) and attaching the detailed SOP to the Sampling Plan. Procedures should be specified for each aspect of the sampling program including procedures for equipment decontamination, sample collection, sample preparation (*e.g.*, homogenization, compositing, *etc.*), and the collection of QA samples. The handling procedures for waste materials generated during the sampling program (*e.g.*, decontamination fluids, used disposable sampling equipment, personal protective equipment (PPE), *etc.*) should also be described.

An important consideration is the composition of the sampling equipment needed for the sampling program. Because the levels of concern for contaminants can be very low, the physical composition of sampling equipment must not impact the final results through the release of minute amounts of the contaminants of concern. For example, the use of a chrome-plated scoop could impact the concentration of chromium in a sample. As a rule of thumb, sampling equipment should be constructed of stainless steel, Teflon, or glass. The sampling SOPs generally will specify the materials that are acceptable and appropriate decontamination procedures.

Once the samples are collected, the effort turns to maintaining the integrity of the samples; that is, ensuring that the material collected continues to be representative of the point or area sampled. This is the role of the sample management program. Beginning with the selection of the appropriate sample containers, specifications for sample containers should include size/volume, material (glass, plastic, *etc.*), lid/cap construction/material, *etc.* The sample containers must be cleaned according to procedures that have been established by either the agency (EPA, state, *etc.*,) that requires the results or the analytical laboratory utilized for the analyses. Pre-cleaned sample containers are readily available from commercial suppliers. Often, the analytical laboratory that ultimately will analyze the samples will provide the pre-cleaned sample containers, as specified by the sampling plan. After sample collection the outside of the sample containers should be cleaned with the appropriate decontamination fluid (*e.g.*, deionized water).

To prevent the reduction in analyte concentration within the sample due to decomposition, vaporization, *etc.*, samples should be preserved shortly after collection. Preservation techniques include temperature reduction (down to 4°C) and pH adjustment. Once preserved, sample containers should be placed in plastic zipper-lock bags to contain any spillage should the container break in transport. To prevent possible cross contamination *high* concentration samples should not be placed in the same shipping container as *low* concentration samples.

Maintaining samples at 4°C during transport or shipping can be difficult at times, particularly during the summer or when working in warmer climates (*e.g.*, Hawaii, Puerto Rico). To help ensure that the proper temperature is maintained, the samples should be chilled on ice prior to packing them into transport/shipping containers. When ready for transport or shipping, the samples should be packed with fresh ice. The fresh ice should be double-bagged in plastic zipper-lock bags and placed on top and around the sample containers. Packaging material, usually vermiculite, should then be placed in the shipping container (usually a cooler) to insulate the samples and the ice.

Once a sample has been preserved, the specified holding time for the requested analysis must not be exceeded. Holding times vary according to analytes of concern and the regulatory agency desiring the analytical results. Attention must also be paid to the acceptable method of holding time calculation, which can be either from the time of sample collection or the time of sample receipt by the laboratory.

A good way to track this information is to develop a table which lists sample number, analytical parameter, matrix, container types and numbers, preservation requirements, and holding times. QC samples (blanks, duplicates, *etc*.) can also be included in the table.

Sample transport or shipping procedures should be included as part of the sample management plan. Once the samples are collected and preserved (if required) the sampling team must ensure the samples reach the analytical laboratory in good condition and in a timely manner. Sample bottles must be intact, samples held at the proper temperature (if required), and analyzed within a sufficient time frame to ensure compliance with prescribed holding times. When analytical laboratories are relatively close to the site of sample collection, the samples may be transported to the laboratory by the sampling team or by a courier from the laboratory. The sampling team must be aware that the transport or shipment of samples containing hazardous or potentially hazardous materials over roadways subject to United States Department of Transportation (DOT) regulations, requires compliance with current Federal regulations, as specified in the *Code of Federal Regulations* (CFR) (specifically, Title 49, Parts 171 through 178 [49 CFR 171–178]). To be in compliance the proper shipping name, identification number, packaging, labeling, packing, and paperwork requirements must be determined. In addition, personnel responsible for shipping hazardous materials must meet DOT training requirements. If the shipment of potentially

hazardous materials involves overnight shipment by air, International Air Transport Association (IATA) regulations must be applied. Following current IATA regulations ensures compliance with DOT requirements. It is also a good practice to include with the sample shipping papers a notice to laboratory personnel as to the relative hazard of the samples, so they can take proper precautionary measures. In order to avoid possible violation of shipping regulations, do not ship hazardous samples in the same shipping container as environmental samples.

Finally, the documentation procedures for the sampling program should be specified. These procedures can be as simple as the maintenance of a handwritten log book in which sampling activities are described (who, what, when, and why). Photography and videotaping can also be useful in addition to written records. Additionally, variations to the SOPs specified in the sampling plan should be documented.

Organization and Responsibilities

This section is fairly straightforward and can be satisfied with a table that shows who is responsible for appropriate sampling program activities, such as Project Manager, Sample Management, Health and Safety, *etc*. Depending on the magnitude of the sampling program, sampling personnel may assume a multitude of roles. It is very important that the sampling personnel know their roles prior to implementation of the program, so they can prepare properly.

Quality Assurance/Quality Control

This section should address procedures necessary to ensure the desired quality of the data generated by field sampling activities. Included should be a discussion on field monitoring equipment calibration and preventative maintenance procedures. These procedures normally are based on the manufacturer's instructions. Also included are discussions on the number, types, and method of collection of QA/QC samples required for the sampling program. QA/QC sample requirements are determined by a number of factors, including the data use and quality assurance objectives, total number of samples and sampling procedures (dedicated versus nondedicated sampling equipment). These samples may include blanks (trip, equipment rinsate), duplicates, splits, *etc*. It is a good practice to list each QA/QC sample in a table, to ensure that the sampling team is aware of the requirements.

The analytical procedures that the laboratory will follow must be specified, along with a discussion of the appropriate analytical data validation procedures. These procedures are also directly related to the data use and quality objectives of the sampling program. For example, analytical method detection limits must be less than decision criteria concentrations.

Deliverables

Finally, reports or other deliverables required from the sampling program should be identified. This could be a basic data summary or an in-depth report that discusses each aspect of the sampling program. It is a good practice to prepare an interim or trip report which details the field activity conducted and describes any problems encountered and any variations/modifications to SOPs specified in the sampling plan.

Internet Resources

Two significant, no-cost, sources of information on sample planning, sampling methods, and QA are found on the Internet. The first is the EPA Office of Environmental Information (OEI) located at

<http://www.epa.gov/quality/qa_docs.html>

Many of the QA documents listed below can be accessed through this site. Also available are several computer-based training courses on QA planning and field sampling that can be downloaded. The second site is maintained by the EPA Environmental Response Team (ERT) and is located at

<http://www.ert.org/>

EPA representative sampling guidance documents, along with compendiums of sampling

procedures, are available from this site. Also available from the ERT are individual SOPs on sampling methods, and a computer program for generating sampling plans.

Information on analytical methods can be found on the following web sites:

<http://www.epa.gov/waterscience/methods>

<http://www.epa.gov/epaoswer/hazwaste/test/main.htm>

<http://www.epa.gov/epahome/indexsources.htm>

<http://www.epa.gov/ttn/amtic/airtox.html>

<http://www.astm.org>

<http://www.apha.org>

Bibliography

American Society for Testing and Materials, *ASTM Standards on Environmental Sampling*, 2nd ed. W. Conshohocken, PA: ASTM, 1997.

Clesceri, Lenore. S., Arnold E. Greenberg, and Andrew D. Eaton. *Standard Methods for the Examination of Water and Wastewater*, 20th ed. Washington, DC:American Public Health Association, American Water Works Association, and Water Environment Federation, 1998.

Environmental Protection Agency. *Compendium of ERT Surface Water and Sediment Sampling Procedures*. EPA/540/P–91/005. Washington, DC: EPA Office of Solid Waste and Emergency Response, 1991.

Environmental Protection Agency. *Compendium of ERT Waste Sampling Procedures*. EPA/540/P–91/008. Washington, DC: EPA Office of Solid Waste and Emergency Response, 1991.

Environmental Protection Agency. *A Compendium of Superfund Field Operations Methods*. EPA/540/P–87/001 (OSWER Directive 9355.0–14). Washington, DC: EPA, Office of Emergency and Remedial Response, 1987.

Environmental Protection Agency. *EPA Guidance for Quality Assurance Project Plans, EPA QA/G–5.* EPA/240/R–02/009. Washington, DC: EPA, Office Environmental Information, 2002.

Environmental Protection Agency. *EPA Requirements for Quality Assurance Project Plans. EPA QA/R–5.* Washington, DC: EPA, Office of Environmental Information, 2001.

Environmental Protection Agency. *Guidance for the Data Quality Objectives Process, EPA QA/G–4.* EPA/600/R–96/055. Washington, DC: Office of Environmental Information, 2000.

Environmental Protection Agency. *Handbook for Sampling and Sample Preservation of Water and Wastewater.* EPA–600/4–82–029. Cincinnati, OH: EPA, Environmental Monitoring and Support Laboratory, 1982.

Environmental Protection Agency. *Management of Investigation-Derived Wastes During Site Inspections.* OERR Directive 9345.3–02. Washington, DC: EPA Office of Emergency and Remedial Response, 1991.

Environmental Protection Agency. *Quality Assurance/Quality Control Guidance for Removal Activities, Sampling QA/QC Plan and Data Validation Procedures.* EPA/540/G–90/004. Washington, DC: EPA, Office of Emergency and Remedial Response, 1990.

Environmental Protection Agency. *Removal Program Representative Sampling Guidance, Volume 1: Soil.* OSWER Directive 9360.4–10. Washington, DC: EPA, Office of Solid Waste and Emergency Response, 1991.

Environmental Protection Agency. *Superfund Program Representative Sampling Guidance, Volume 4: Waste.* OSWER Directive 9360.4-14. Washington, D.C.: EPA Office of Solid Waste and Emergency Response, 1995.

Environmental Protection Agency. *Superfund Program Representative Sampling Guidance, Volume 5: Water and Sediment, Part I–Surface Water and Sediment.* OSWER Directive 9360.4–16. Washington, DC: EPA Office of Solid Waste and Emergency Response, 1995.

Environmental Protection Agency. *Sampler's Guide to the Contract Laboratory Program.* EPA/540/R–96/032. Washington, DC: EPA Office of Solid Waste and Emergency Response, 1996.

Environmental Protection Agency. *Superfund Program Representative Sampling Guidance, Volume 5: Water and Sediment, Part II–Ground Water.* OSWER Directive 9360.4–16. Washington, DC: EPA Office of Solid Waste and Emergency Response, 1995.

Environmental Protection Agency. *Test Methods for Evaluating Solid Waste, Physical/Chemical Methods,* SW–846, Washington, DC: EPA Office of Solid Waste and Emergency Response, 1998.

"Hazardous Materials Regulations." *Code of Federal Regulations.* Title 49. Pt. 172–178, 1996.

International Air Transport Association. *Dangerous Goods Regulations,* 37th ed. Montreal–Geneva: IATA, 1996.

New Jersey Department of Environmental Protection. *Field Sampling Procedures Manual.* Trenton, NJ: NJDEP, 1992.

W. Scott Butterfield, CHMM, is a Senior Program Manager with Weston Solutions, Inc. Mr. Butterfield has over 24 years experience in the hazardous waste field conducting and managing emergency response activities, removal operations, and remedial projects, as well as R & D programs. Mr. Butterfield currently is the Program Manager of the EPA Region II Site Assessment Team (SAT) contract. Mr. Butterfield has authored papers on biological sampling at abandoned hazardous waste sites (Proceedings of the 3rd National Conference on Management of Uncontrolled Hazardous Waste Sites, 1982) *and on the effects of exposure to municipal and chemical landfill leachate on aquatic organisms* (Proceedings of the International Symposium on Industrial and Hazardous Solid Wastes, 1983).

Acronyms

Symbols

%V/V	Percent by volume
%W/W	Percent by weight
ρ	Density

A

AAI	All Appropriate Inquiries
AAQCDs	Ambient Air Quality Criteria Documents
AAS	Atomic Absorption Spectrometry
ABIH	American Board of Industrial Hygiene
ΛCBM	Asbestos-Containing Building Material
ACGIH	American Conference of Governmental Industrial Hygienists
ACGIH TLVs	American Conference of Governmental Industrial Hygienists Threshold Limit Values
ACHMM	Academy of Certified Hazardous Materials Managers
ACL	Alternate Concentration Level
ACM	Asbestos-Containing Material
ACS	American Chemical Society
ADA	Americans with Disabilities Act
ADI	Lifetime Acceptable Daily Intake
AEA	Atomic Energy Act
AFFFs	Aqueous film forming foams

AHERA	Asbestos Hazard Emergency Response Act
AHM	Acutely Hazardous Material
AIA	American Institute of Architects
AIChE	American Institute of Chemical Engineers
AIDS	Acquired Immune Deficiency Syndrome
AIHA	American Industrial Hygiene Association
aka	also known as
AL	Action Level
ALARA	As Low As Reasonably Achievable
ANPR	Advance Notice of Proposed Rulemaking
ANPRM	Advance Notice of Proposed Rulemaking
ANSI	American National Standards Institute
APHA	American Public Health Association
API	American Petroleum Institute
APR	Air-Purifying Respirator
ARARs	Applicable or Relevant and Appropriate Requirements
ARS	Alternative Release Scenario
ASHARA	Asbestos School Hazard Abatement Reauthorization Act
ASHRAE	American Society of Heating, Refrigerating, and Air-Conditioning Engineers
ASME	American Society of Mechanical Engineers
AST	Aboveground Storage Tank
ASTM	American Society for Testing and Materials
ATF	Bureau of Alcohol, Tobacco and Firearms
atm	Atmosphere
ATSDR	Agency for Toxic Substances and Disease Registry
AWWA	American Water Works Association

B

BACM	Best Available Control Measures
BACT	Best Available Control Technology
BART	Best Available Retrofit Technology
BAT	Best Available Technology
BATEA	Best Available Technology Economically Achievable
BBP	Bloodborne Pathogen
BCPC	Biological and Chemical Protective Clothing
BCT	Best Control Technology
BCT	Best Conventional Technology

BDAT	Best Demonstrated Available Technology
BEI	Biological Exposure Indices
BEMR	Baseline Environmental Management Report
BFPP	Bona Fide Prospective Purchasers
BIF	Boilers and Industrial Furnaces
BIODG	Biodegradation
BLEVE	Boiling Liquid Expanding Vapor Explosion
BMPs	Best Management Practices
BMR	Baseline Monitoring Report
BOD	Biochemical or Biological Oxygen Demand
BOD5	Biochemical Oxygen Demand at Five Days
BOMA	Building Owners Management Association
bp	Boiling Point
BRI	Building Related Illness
Btu	British Thermal Unit
Btu/lb	British Thermal Units per Pound
BUN	Blood-urea nitrogen

C

C	Centigrade
C	Corrosive (RCRA)
CAA	Clean Air Act
CAAA	Clean Air Act Amendments
CAER	Chemical Accident Emergency Response
CAFO	Combined Animal Feeding Operations
CAIR	Clear Air Interstate Rule
CAM	Continuous Air Monitor
CAMEO	Computer-Aided Management of Emergency Operations
CAMU	Corrective Action Management Unit
CAR	Corrective Action Report
CAS	Chemical Abstracts Service
CASAC	Clean Air Scientific Advisory Committee
CASTNET	Clean Air Status Trends Network
CBI	Confidential Business Information
CBRN	Chemical, Biological, Radiological, and Nuclear
CBW	Chemical and Biological Weapons
cc	Cubic centimeters

CCA	Chromated copper arsenates
CCL	Contaminant Candidate List
CDC	Centers for Disease Control and Prevention
CDI	Chronic Daily Intake
CEMS	Continuous Emissions Monitoring System
CEPPO	Chemical Emergency Preparedness and Prevention Office
CEQ	Council on Environmental Quality
CERCLA	Comprehensive Environmental Response, Compensation, and Liability Act
CERCLIS	Comprehensive Environmental Response, Compensation, and Liability Information System
CESQG	Conditionally Exempt Small Quantity Generator
CFC	Chlorofluorocarbon
CFR	Code of Federal Regulations
CFS	Chemical fixation/solidification
CGA	Compressed Gas Association
CHEMTREC	Chemical Transportation Emergency Center
CHFS	Cabinet for Health and Family Services (Kentucky)
CHMM	Certified Hazardous Materials Manager
CHO	Chemical Hygiene Officer
CHOXD	Chemical Oxidation
CHP	Chemical Hygiene Plan
CIH	Certified Industrial Hygienist
CIP	Compliance Incentive Program
CISD	Critical Incident Stress Debriefing
CKD	Cement kiln dust
CLO	Clandestine Lab Officer
CLP	Contract Laboratory Program
CMA	Chemical Manufacturers Association
CMBST	Combustion
CMI	Corrective Measures Implementation
CMS	Corrective Measures Study
C_nH_{2n}	Alkenes
C_nH_{2n+2}	Alkanes
CNS	Central nervous system
CO	Carbon Monoxide
CoC	Certificates of Completion
COHMED	Cooperative Hazardous Materials Enforcement Development

COI	Chemicals of Interest
COMAR	Code of Maryland Regulations
COPC	Chemicals of Potential Concern
CORRACT	Corrective Action Report System
CPC	Chemical Protective Clothing
cpm	counts per minute
CPO	Contiguous Property Owner
CPR	Cardiopulmonary Resuscitation
CPSC	Consumer Product Safety Commission
CPU	Central Processing Unit
CQA	Construction Quality Assurance
CRC	Chemical Rubber Company
CSA	Controlled Substances Act
CSF	Confidential Statement of Formula
CSHO	Compliance Safety and Health Officer
CSM	Conceptual Site Model
CSP	Certified Safety Professional
CWA	Clean Water Act
CWS	Community Water Systems

D

DATCP	Department of Agriculture, Trade and Consumer Protection
dB	Decibel
DCI	Data Call-In
DCO	Direct Chemical Oxidation
DDESB	Department of Defense Explosives Safety Board
DDT	Dichlorodiphenyltrichloroethane
DEACT	Deactivation
DfE	Design for Environment
DFO	Disaster Field Office
DHHS	Department of Health and Human Services
DHS	Department of Homeland Security
DLA	Defense Logistics Agency
DNA	Deoxyribonucleic acid
DNAPL	Dense Non-Aqueous Phase Liquid
DNFA	Determination of No Further Action
DNT	Dinitrotoluene

DoD	Department of Defense
DOE	Department of Energy
DOI	Department of the Interior
DOJ	Department of Justice
DOT	Department of Transportation
dpm	disintegrations per minute
DQO	Data Quality Objective
DRE	Destruction/Removal Efficiency
dscm	Dry standard cubic meter
DUO	Data Use Objective

E

E	Toxicity (RCRA)
EA	Environmental Assessment
EC	European Community
ECOS	Environmental Council of the States
ED50	Median effective dose
EDTA	Ethylene Diamine Tetraacetic Acid
EEGL	Emergency Exposure Guidance Limits
EEI	Edison Electric Institute
EHS	Environmental Health and Safety
EHS	Extremely Hazardous Substance(s)
EI	Environmental Indicator
EIA	Environmental Information Association
EIHR	Earthquake Induced Hazardous Materials Releases
EIS	Environmental Impact Statement
EISOPQAM	Environmental Investigation Standard Operating Procedures and Quality Assurance Manual
EJ	Environmental Justice
EL	Excursion Limit
EL	Explosion Limit
EL	Exposure Level
EMAS	Eco-Management and Audit Scheme
EMP	Environmental Management Program
EMS	Emergency Medical Services
EMS	Environmental Management System
EMT	Emergency Medical Technician

ENRD	Environment and Natural Resources Division
EOC	Emergency Operation Center
EPA	Environmental Protection Agency
EPCRA	Emergency Planning and Community Right-to-Know Act
EPRI	Electric Power Research Institute
ERAP	Emergency Response Action Plan
ERG	Emergency Response Guidebook
ERPG	Emergency Response Planning Guidelines
ERT	Environmental Response Team
ESF	Emergency Support Function
ESLI	End-Of-Service-Life Indicator

F

F	Fahrenheit
F/M	Foot to mass ratio
FAQ	Frequently Asked Questions
FAR	Federal Acquisition Regulations by the General Services Administration
FCO	Federal Coordinating Officer
FDA	Food and Drug Administration
FEMA	Federal Emergency Management Agency
FESOP	Federally Enforceable State Operating Permit
FFCA	Federal Facility Compliance Agreement
FFCAct	Federal Facility Compliance Act of 1992
FFDCA	Federal Food, Drug, and Cosmetic Act
FIFRA	Federal Insecticide, Fungicide, and Rodenticide Act
FIRESCOPE	Fire Resources of Southern California Organized for Potential Emergencies
FIRM	Field Inspection Reference Manual
FMEA	Failure Mode and Effects Analysis
FOIA	Freedom of Information Act
FONSI	Finding of No Significant Impact
FOTW	Federally Owned Treatment Works
fp	Flashpoint
FQPA	Food Quality Protection Act
FR	Federal Register
FRP	Facility Response Plan
FRP	Federal Response Plan
FSLA	Fair Labor Standards Act

FTA	Fault Tree Analysis
FWPCA	Federal Water Pollution Control Act
FY	Fiscal Year

G

g/L	Grams per liter
GAAP	Generally Accepted Accounting Principles
GACT	Generally Achievable Control Technology
GAO	General Accounting Office
GI	Gastrointestinal
G-M	Geiger-Mueller
GPO	Government Printing Office
GPRA	Government Performance and Results Act
GSA	General Services Administration
GWPS	Groundwater Protection Standard

H

H	Acutely Hazardous (RCRA)
H_2S	Hydrogen Sulfide
HA	Hazard Assessment
HAD	Health Assessment Document
HAP	Hazardous Air Pollutant
HASP	Health and Safety Plan
HAZMAT	Hazardous Material
HAZOP	Hazard and Operability Study
HAZWOPER	Hazardous Waste Operations and Emergency Response
HBV	Hepatitis B Virus
HCl	Hydrogen Chloride
HCLO	Hazard Clandestine Lab Officer
HCN	Hydrogen Cyanide
HCS	Hazard Communication System
HCS	Hazard Communications Standard
HCV	Hepatitis C Virus
HDD	Halogenated Dibenzodioxin
HDF	Halogenated Dibenzofuran
HEAs	Health Effects Assessments
HEAST	Health Effects Assessment Summary Tables

HEEDs	Health and Environmental Effects Documents
HEEPs	Health and Environmental Effects Profiles
HEPA	High Efficiency Particulate Air
HHEM	Human Health Evaluation Manual
HHRA	Human Health Risk Assessment
HHW	Household Hazardous Waste
HI	Hazard Index
HIV	Human Immunodeficiency Virus
HLW	High-Level Waste (radioactive)
HMIS	Hazardous Materials Information System
HMR	Hazardous Materials Regulations
HMTA	Hazardous Materials Transportation Act
HMTUSA	Hazardous Materials Transportation Uniform Safety Act
HP Tech	Health Physics Technician
HQ	Hazard Quotient
HSWA	Hazardous and Solid Waste Amendments
HTMR	High Temperature Metal Recovery
HUD	Department of Housing and Urban Development
HVAC	Heating Ventilation and Air Conditioning
HWIR	Hazardous Waste Identification Rule
HWIR-Media	Hazardous Waste Identification Rule for Contaminated Media
HWMU	Hazardous Waste Management Unit
HWSA	Hazardous and Solid Waste Amendments

I

I	Ignitability (RCRA)
I/M	Inspection and Maintenance
IARC	International Agency for Research on Cancer
IATA	International Air Transport Association
IBC	Intermediate Bulk Containers
IC	Incident Commander
ICC	International Code Council
ICC	Interstate Commerce Commission
ICP	Integrated Contingency Plan
ICP-AES	Inductively Coupled Plasma-Atomic Emission Spectroscopy
ICR	Ignitable, Corrosive, Reactive (RCRA)
ICS	Incident Command System

IDLH	Immediately Dangerous to Life or Health
IFMA	International Facility Managers Association
IHMM	Institute of Hazardous Materials Management
IHR	Induced Hazardous Materials Release
INEEL	Idaho National Engineering and Environmental Laboratory (Formerly INEL)
INEL	Idaho National Engineering Laboratory (See INL)
INL	Idaho National Laboratory (Formerly INEEL)
IR	Infrared (radiation)
IRIS	Integrated Risk Information System
ISEA	International Standards Equipment Association
ISO	International Organization for Standardization
IUPAC	International Union of Pure and Applied Chemistry
IUR	Inventory Update Rule

J

JFO	Joint Federal Office
JOC	Joint Operations Center

K

kg	Kilograms
K_{ow}	Octanol/Water Partition Coefficient
kPa	kiloPascal
KSP	Kentucky State Police
K_{sp}	Solubility constant

L

LADI	Lifetime Average Daily Intake
LAER	Lowest Achievable Emission Rate
LBPPPA	Lead-Based Paint Poisoning Prevention Act
LC50	Median lethal concentration 50 percent
LD50	Median lethal dose 50 percent
LDR	Land Disposal Restriction
LEL	Lower Explosive Limit
LEPC	Local Emergency Planning Committee
LGAC	Local Government Advisory Committee
LLMW	Low-Level Mixed Waste
LLRW	Low-Level Radioactive Waste

LLRWDF	Low-Level Radioactive Waste Disposal Facility
LLW	Low-Level Waste (LLRW)
LNAPL	Light Non-Aqueous Phase Liquids
LOAEL	Lowest Observed Adverse Effect Level
LOC	Level of Concern
LP	Liquid Petroleum
LPG	Liquid Petroleum Gas
LQG	Large Quantity Generator
LSD	D-Lysergic Acid Diethylamide
LUST	Leaking Underground Storage Tanks
LWAKs	Lightweight Aggregate Kilns

M

m^3	Cubic meter
MACT	Maximum Achievable Control Technology
MAI	Maximum Allowable Increase
MAK	Federal Republic of Germany Maximum Acceptable Concentration Values in the Workplace
MAP	methamphetamine
MAP	Model Accreditation Plan
MCAWW	Methods for Chemical Analysis of Water and Wastes
MCL	Maximum Contaminant Level
MCLGs	Maximum Contaminant Level Goal
MCS	Media Cleanup Standards
MCS	Multiple Chemical Sensitivity
MDMA	3,4-methylenedioxymethamphetamine (Ecstasy)
MF	Modifying Factor
µg/kg	Micrograms per kilogram
mg/kg	Milligrams per kilogram
µg/l	Micrograms per liter
mg/L	Milligrams per liter
MHLW	Mixed High-Level Waste
MIG	Metal-Inert-Gas
mm	Millimeter
ml	Milliliter
MLSS	Mixed liquor suspended solids
mmHg	Millimeters of mercury

MMR	Military Munitions Rule
MMS	Minerals Management Service
MOA	Memorandum of Agreement
MOU	Memorandum of Understanding
MOVP	Maximum Organic Vapor Pressure
mp	Melting Point
mppcf	Million particles per cubic foot of air
MPRSA	Marine Protection, Research, and Sanctuaries Act
MS4s	Municipal Separate Storm Sewer Systems
MSDS	Material Safety Data Sheet
MSGP	Multi-Sector General Permit
MSHA	Mine Safety and Health Administration
MSW	Municipal Solid Waste
MTBE	Methytertiarybutylether
MTD	Maximum Tolerated Dose
MTRU	Mixed Transuranic Waste
MW	Mixed Waste (radioactive and RCRA-Hazardous)
MW	Molecular Weight

N

N	Normal
N.O.S.	Not Otherwise Specified
NA	North America
NAAQS	National Ambient Air Quality Standards
NACE	National Association of Corrosion Engineers
NAICS	North American Industry Classification Code
NAIN	National Antimicrobial Information Network
NAMS	National Air Monitoring Stations
NAPL	Non-Aqueous Phase Liquid
NARM	Naturally Occurring and/or Accelerator-Produced Radioactive Material
NAS	National Academy of Sciences
NCEPI	National Center for Environmental Publications and Information
NCERQA	National Center for Environmental Research and Quality Assurance
NCP	National Contingency Plan
NCP	National Oil and Hazardous Substances Pollution Contingency Plan
NCWS	Non-Community Water System
NEC	National Electrical Code

NEPA	National Environmental Policy Act
NEPPS	National Environmental Performance Partnership System
NEPT	National Environmental Performance Track
NESHAPs	National Emissions Standards for Hazardous Air Pollutants
NFA	No Further Action
NFPA	National Fire Protection Association
NIOSH	National Institute for Occupational Safety and Health
NIST	National Institute of Standards and Technology
NMOG	Non-Methane Organic Gas
NOA	Notice of Availability
NOAA	National Oceanic and Atmospheric Administration
NOAEL	No Observed Adverse Effect Level
NOEL	No Observed Effect Level
NOI	Notice of Intent
NORA	National Organization Research Agenda
NO_x	Nitrogen oxides
NPDES	National Pollutant Discharge Elimination System
NPDWR	National Primary Drinking Water Regulation
NPFC	National Pollution Funds Center
NPL	National Priorities List
NR	Net Revenue
NRC	National Response Center
NRC	Nuclear Regulatory Commission
NRC	National Response Center
NRMRL	National Risk Management Research Laboratory
NRP	National Response Plan
NRR	Noise Reduction Rating
NRT	National Response Team
NSOH	Non-salaried Overheads
NSPS	New Source Performance Standards
NSR	New Source Review
NTIS	National Technical Information Service
NTNCWS	Non-Transient, Non-Community Water System
NTP	National Toxicology Program
NUMARC	Nuclear Management and Resources Council, Inc.
NUREG	Nuclear Regulatory Commission Regulation
NWP	Nationwide Permit

NYSDEC   New York State Department of Environmental Conservation

O

OCA   Off-site Consequence Analysis

OCIR   Office of Congressional and Intergovernmental Relations

OCP   One Cleanup Program

OCSLA   Outer Continental Shelf Lands Act Amendments of 1978

OEI   Office of Environmental Information

OEL   Occupational Exposure Limit

OERR   Office of Emergency and Remedial Response

ONRWs   Outstanding National Resource Waters

OPA   Oil Pollution Act

OPAREAS   Operating Areas

OPIM   Other Potentially Infectious Materials

OPPTS   Office of Prevention, Pesticides, and Toxic Substances

ORD   Office of Research and Development

ORM   Other Regulated Material

ORNL   Oak Ridge National Laboratory

OSC   On-Scene Coordinator

OSH   Occupational Safety and Health

OSH Act   Occupational Safety and Health Act

OSHA   Occupational Safety And Health Administration

OSLR   Office of State and Local Relations

OSWER   Office of Solid Waste and Emergency Response

OTAG   Ozone Transport Assessment Group

OTC   Over the counter

OTI   OSHA Training Institute

OW   Office of Water

P

P&ID   Piping and Instrumentation Diagram

P2   Pollution Prevention

P2P   phenyl-2-propanone (precursor to meth)

P-450   Cytochrome P-450 mono-oxygenase

PA   Preliminary Assessment

PACM   Presumed Asbestos-Containing Material

PACT   Powdered activated carbon

PADRE	Protective Action Dose Reduction Estimator
PAMS	Photochemical Assessment Monitoring Stations
PAPR	Powered Air-Purifying Respirator
PBTs	Persistent, bioaccumulative, and toxic chemicals
PCB	Polychlorinated Biphenyl
PCM	Phase Contrast Microscopy
PCP	phencyclidine (street names include angel dust, ozone, wack, and rocket fuel)
PDCA	Plan, Do, Check, Act
PE	Professional Engineer
PEIS	Programmatic Environmental Impact Statement
PEL	Permissible Exposure Limit
PESP	Pesticide Environmental Stewardship Program
PFD	Process Flow Diagram
PFO	Principal Federal Official
PG	Packing Group
pH	the negative log of the hydrogen ion concentration
PHA	Process Hazard Analysis
pKa	the pH at which a chemical is 50% ionized
PL	Public Law
PLM	Polarized Light Microscopy
PM	Particulate Matter
PM_{10}	Particulate Matter less than 10 Microns in diameter
$PM_{2.5}$	Particulate Matter less than 2.5 Microns in diameter
PMN	Premanufacture Notification
PNA	Polynuclear Aromatics
PNS	Peripheral nervous system
POC	Point of Compliance
POHC	Principal Organic Hazardous Constituent
POTW	Publicly Owned Treatment Works
PPA	Performance Partnership Agreement
PPA	Pollution Prevention Act
PPA	Prospective-Purchaser Agreement
ppb	parts per billion
PPE	Personal Protective Equipment
ppm	parts per million
ppmv	Parts per million by volume
PRGs	Preliminary Remediation Goals

PR-Notice	Pesticide Registration Notice
PRP	Potentially Responsible Party
PSD	Prevention of Significant Deterioration
psi	Pounds per Square Inch
psia	Pounds per Square Inch Absolute
PSM	Process Safety Management
PSN	Proper Shipping Name
PTC	Permit to Construct
PVC	Polyvinyl Chloride
PWS	Public Water System

Q

QA	Quality Assurance
QA/QC	Quality Assurance/Quality Control
QAOs	Quality Assurance Objectives
QMS	Quality Management System

R

R	Reactivity (RCRA)
RACM	Reasonably Available Control Measures
RACM	Regulated Asbestos-Containing Material
RACT	Reasonably Achievable Emissions Control Technology
RAGS	Risk Assessment Guidance for Superfund
RAP	Remedial Action Plan
RASH	Rapid Screening of Hazard
RBCA	Risk-Based Corrective Action
RCA	Radiological Controlled Area
R–CHO	Aldehydes
RCOOH	Organic Carboxylic Acids
RCOOR	Esters
R–CRO	Ketones
RCRA	Resource Conservation and Recovery Act
RCT	Radiation Control Technician
RED	Re-registration Eligibility Document
redox	Oxidation/reduction
REI	Restricted Entry Interval
REL	Recommended Exposure Limit

RF	Radiofrequency
RFA	RCRA Facility Assessment
RfD	Reference Dose
RfDI	Inhalation Reference Dose
RFI	RCRA Facility Investigation
RFP	Reasonable Further Progress
RI/FS	Remedial Investigation/Feasibility Study
RIDS	Response Information Data Sheets
RM Plan	Risk Management Plan
RME	Reasonable Maximum Exposure
RMP	Risk Management Program
RMP Rule	Risk Management Program Rule
RMW	Radioactive mixed waste
RNH_2	Amines
ROD	Record of Decision
ROH	Alcohols
R–O–O–R	Organic Peroxides
R–O–R	Ethers
RPM	Revolutions per minute
RPMs	Remedial Program Managers
RQ	Reportable Quantity
RRPI	Readiness and Range Preservation Initiative
RRT	Regional Response Team
RSO_2H	Organic Sulfonic Acids
RSPA	Research and Special Programs Administration
RTECS	Registry of Toxic Effects of Chemical Substances (NIOSH)
RU	Regulated Units
RWP	Radiation Work Permit

S

SACM	Superfund Accelerated Cleanup Model
SAE	Society of Automotive Engineers
SAP	Sampling and Analysis Plan
SAR	Supplied-Air Respirator
SARA	Superfund Amendments and Reauthorization Act
SAT	Site Assessment Team
SBREFA	Small Business Regulatory Enforcement Fairness Act

SBS	Sick Building Syndrome
SCAC	Small Community Advisory Committee
SCBA	Self-Contained Breathing Apparatus
SDI	Subchronic Daily Intake
SDWA	Safe Drinking Water Act
SEI	Safety Equipment Institute
SEM	Strategic Environmental Management
SEP	Supplemental Environmental Project
SERC	State Emergency Response Commission
SF	Slope Factor
SG	Specific Gravity
SI	International System of Units
SI	Site Investigation
SIC	Standard Industrial Classification
SIGMA	Sustainability–Integrated Guidelines for Management
SIP	State Implementation Plan
SLAMS	State and Local Air Monitoring Stations
SNAP	Significant New Alternatives Policy Program
SNUR	Significant New Use Rule
SOP	Standard Operating Procedure
SO_x	Sulfur Oxides
SPCC	Spill Prevention, Containment, and Countermeasure (CWA)
SPCC	Spill Prevention, Control, and Countermeasure
SPEGL	Short-Term Public Emergency Guidance Levels
SPMS	Special Purpose Monitoring Stations
SQG	Small Quantity Generator
SRD	Self-Reading Dosimeter
SRRP	Source Reduction Review Project
SSA	Sole Source Aquifer
SSU	Saybolt Second Unit
STABL	Stabilization
StATS	State Authorization Tracking System
STEL	Short Term Exposure Limit
STP	Site Treatment Plan
STP	Standard Temperature and Pressure
STTF	Small Town (Environmental Planning) Task Force
SWDA	Solid Waste Disposal Act

SWMU	Solid Waste Management Unit
SWOT	Strengths, Weaknesses, Opportunities, and Threats
SWPPP	Storm Water Pollution Prevention Plans

T

T	Toxic (RCRA)
T/yr	Tons per year
TACO	Tiered Approach to Corrective Action
TAPAA	Trans-Alaska Pipeline Authorization Act of 1973
TB	Tuberculosis
TC	Technical Committee
TCDD	Tetrachlorodibenzo-p-Dioxin
TCLO	Toxic Concentration Low
TCLP	Toxicity Characteristic Leaching Procedure
TDI	Toluene-2,4-Diisocyanate
TDLO	Toxic Dose Low
TEL	Tetraethyl Lead
TEM	Transmission Electron Microscopy
TEQ	Toxicity Equivalent
ThOD	Theoretical Oxygen Demand
TI	Technical Impracticability
TIP	Tribal Implementation Plan
TLD	Thermoluminescent Dosimeter
TLV	Threshold Limit Value
TLV-C	Threshold Limit Value—Ceiling
TLV-STEL	Threshold Limit Value—Short Term Exposure Limit
TLV-TWA	Threshold Limit Value—Time-Weighted Average
TMDL	Total Maximum Daily Load
TNCWS	Transient Non-Community Water System
TOC	Total Organic Carbon
TPQ	Threshold Planning Quantity
TQ	Threshold Quantity
TRI	Toxic Release Inventory
TRU	Transuranic Waste
TSCA	Toxic Substances Control Act
TSD	Treatment, Storage, and Disposal
TSDF	Treatment, Storage, and Disposal Facility

TSI	Thermal System Insulation
TU	Temporary Unit
TWA	Time-Weighted Average

U

UCMR	Unregulated Contaminant Monitoring Rule
UEL	Upper Explosive Limit
UF	Uncertainty Factors
UHC	Underlying Hazardous Constituent
UIC	Underground Injection Control
UMTRCA	Uranium Mill Tailings Radiation Control Act
UN	United Nations
URL	Universal Resource Locator
US	United States
USC	United States Code
USCG	United States Coast Guard
USDA	United States Department of Agriculture
USDOT	United States Department of Transportation
USDW	Underground Source of Drinking Water
USGS	United States Geological Survey
USPHS	United States Public Health Service
USPS	United States Postal Service
USSG	United States Sentencing Guidelines
UST	Underground Storage Tank
UTS	Universal Treatment Standard
UV	Ultraviolet (radiation)
UXO	Unexploded Ordnance

V

vd	Vapor Density
VDT	Video display terminals
VO	Volatile Organic
VOC	Volatile Organic Compound
vp	Vapor Pressure
VPP	Voluntary Protection Program
VSD	Virtually Safe Dose

W

WAP	Waste Analysis Plan
WBS	Work breakdown structure
WCS	Worst-Case Release Scenario
WEEL	Workplace Environmental Exposure Limit
WH	Wellhead Protection Program
WIPP	Waste Isolation Pilot Plant
WMD	Weapons of Mass Destruction
WPS	Worker Protection Standard
WSR	Waste Shipment Record
WWTF	Wastewater Treatment Facility

X

XRF	X-Ray Fluorescence Analysis

Y

Yds^3	Cubic yards

Glossary

A

Abandoned—Under the Resource Conservation and Recovery Act, discarded by being disposed of, burned or incinerated; or accumulated, stored, or treated before, or in lieu of, being disposed of, burned, or incinerated.

Absorbed dose—The amount of energy deposited in any material by ionizing radiation. The unit of absorbed dose, the rad, is a measure of energy absorbed per gram of material. The unit used in countries other than the United States is the gray. One gray equals 100 rad.

Absorption—The process by which chemicals cross cell membranes and enter the bloodstream. Major sites of absorption are the skin, lungs, gastrointestinal (GI) tract, and parenteral (*e.g.*, intravenous, subcutaneous).

AC—Military designation for hydrogen cyanide as a chemical weapon, a *blood agent*.

Acceptable ceiling concentration—As defined by the Occupational Safety and Health Administration at 29 CFR 1900.1000(b)(2), the acceptable ceiling concentration is a limit for an employee's exposure to substances listed Table Z–2. The limit applies to an 8-hour shift and cannot exceed the maximum concentration and duration that is also listed in the table.

Accidental release—Under the Risk Management Program rules, an unanticipated emission of a regulated substance or other extremely hazardous substances (EHS) into the atmosphere from a *stationary source*.

Accrual basis—In business, an accounting standard that assigns *revenues* to the periods in which they are earned and matches *expenses* with the revenues. The objective is to recognize the effects of revenues and expenses when they are earned or incurred, not when the cash is received or paid.

Accumulated speculatively—Under the Resource Conservation and Recovery Act, having accumulated or stored (except for commercial chemical products) for alleged or actual future recycling, and not meeting RCRA recycling criteria, as established at 40 CFR 261.1(e)(8), that are intended to discourage sham recycling.

Acid—In chemistry, any substance that dissociates in solution to produce a proton (H^+).

Acid deposition or *acid rain*—The acidic fallout of rain, gases, or dust caused by the emissions of SO_2 and NO_x originating from the combustion of fossil fuels.

Acquired immune deficiency syndrome (AIDS)—An ultimately fatal illness caused by the Human Immunodeficiency Virus (HIV). When the HIV attacks the immune system, the symptoms of AIDS emerge.

Action level—As defined by the Occupational Safety and Health Administration and the National Institute for Occupational Safety and Health the action level is typically one-half of the occupational exposure limit. Exposures above the action level will trigger implementation of control measures such as medical surveillance, increased exposure monitoring, worker training, or use of personal protective devices.

Acts—Actions taken by Congress, such as the Clean Air Act Amendments of 1990, the Superfund Amendments and Reauthorization Act of 1986, or the Toxic Substances Control Act of 1976, and considered to be law.

Acute exposure—A brief exposure to high concentrations of a hazardous chemical that results in rapid onset of symptoms and may result in severe biological harm or death. Acute exposures are usually characterized as lasting no longer than a day. An example of an acute exposure is the inhalation of high concentrations of solvent vapors.

Acutely toxic—In toxicology, the characteristic of a substance that produces an immediate reaction in the body, characterized by rapid onset and short duration of symptoms. Damage to the body from acute reactions may be reversible or irreversible.

Addition—As interpreted under the Clean Water Act by EPA and the courts, any introduction of a pollutant into a body of water with the exception of pollutants that are present in the discharge only because they were present in the intake water, if the discharge is released back into the same body of water; and the discharge of water from dams.

Additive effect—In toxicology, the combined effect of exposure to two chemicals that have both the same mechanism of action and target organ. The effect is equal to the sum of the effects of exposure to each chemical when given alone (*e.g.*, 3 + 5 = 8).

Administrative enforcement—In law, all enforcement actions taken by the Environmental Protection Agency.

Administrator—In the environmental laws and regulations, a term that generally refers to the Administrator of the United States Environmental Protection Agency.

Aerobic—The use of air or oxygen in a process, such as the treatment of certain types of hazardous wastes.

Aerosols—As understood by industrial hygienists, microscopic solid or liquid particles dispersed in the air. Typical industrial aerosols occur as dusts, fumes, mists and fogs, and smoke.

Affected employees—Under the Occupational Safety and Health Administration's lockout/tagout rules, employees who operate or use the machinery, processes, or systems that are being maintained or serviced and contain energy.

Agreement state—A state that has been granted the authority by the Nuclear Regulatory Commission to regulate the management and disposal of radioactive waste.

Air-purifying respirator (APR)—A respirator that removes contaminants from the ambient air.

ALARA—The guiding principle behind radiation protection is that radiation exposures should be kept *As Low As Reasonably Achievable* (ALARA), economic and social factors being taken into account. This commonsense approach means that radiation doses for both workers and the public typically are kept lower than their regulatory limits.

Alcohols—In chemistry, alkanes with a substituted hydroxyl group.

Aldehydes and ketones—In chemistry, organic compounds that possess the carbonyl (C=O) group as a common structural feature.

Aliphatic—In chemistry, a class of organic compounds with the carbon backbone arranged in branched or straight chains (*e.g.*, propane or octane).

Alkaline—In chemistry, the property of material that produces hydroxide ions (OH^-) when it is dissolved in water. The terms *alkaline, basic,* and *caustic* are used interchangeably.

Alkanes—In chemistry, saturated hydrocarbons such as butane, octane, *etc.*

Alkenes—In chemistry, organic compounds also known as *olefins* that are unsaturated hydrocarbons with a single carbon-to-carbon double bond per molecule.

Allergic (hypersensitive, sensitization) reactions—In toxicology, the production of antibodies in response to the allergen. This includes the production of antigens, (reaction Types I, II, and III) or mediation via specialized immune cells (Type IV) in response to a substance.

Allowable emissions—Under the Clean Air Act, the levels of pollutants that a source may emit as specifically identified in the source's air permit.

Allowance—Under the Clean Air Act, the authorization for a unit regulated under Title IV, Acid Deposition Control, to emit one ton of SO_2 during a calendar year

Alpha (α) particle—One form of ionizing radiation. Alpha (α) particles are composed of two protons and two neutrons. Alpha particles do not travel very far from their radioactive source. They cannot pass through a piece of paper, clothes or even the layer of dead cells that normally protects the skin. Because alpha particles cannot penetrate human skin, they are not considered an *external exposure hazard*. This means that if the alpha particles stay outside the human body they cannot harm it. However, alpha particle sources located within the body may pose an *internal* health hazard if they are present in great enough quantities. The risk from indoor radon is due to inhaled alpha particle sources that irradiate lung tissue.

Alternative release scenario (ARS) analysis—Under the Risk Management Program rules, an analysis of potential releases that are more likely to occur than the *worst-case release scenario* (WCS) and that will reach an end point off-site. The ARS is required of an operator of a stationary source for all flammable and toxic substances in covered processes.

Anaerobic—The absence of air or oxygen in a process, such as the treatment of certain types of hazardous wastes.

Anions—In chemistry, negative *ions.*

Antagonistic effect—In toxicology, when an exposure to two chemicals together interferes each with the other's toxic actions (*e.g.*, 4 + 6 = 8), or one chemical interferes with the toxic action of the other chemical, such as in antidotal therapy (*e.g.*, 0 + 4 = 2).

Antidegradation policy—Under the Clean Water Act, a set of rules that should be followed when addressing activities that could lower the quality of high quality waters.

Applicable or relevant and appropriate requirement (ARARs)—Under the Comprehensive Environmental Response, Compensation, and Liability Act, a requirement that has to be met in the identification of cleanup standards and selection of a remedial alternative.

Appropriate safer medical device—Under the Occupational Safety and Health Administration's Bloodborne Pathogen standard, a device that, when used (based on reasonable judgment in individual cases) will not jeopardize patient or employee safety or be medically contraindicated.

Aquifer—Any geologic formation capable of holding water in sufficient quantities to produce *free water*. Aquifers can be unconsolidated soil or rock formations.

Area sources—Under the Clean Air Act, **stationary** or nonroad sources that are too small and/or too numerous to be included in a stationary source inventory. Examples of area sources include: water heaters, gas furnaces, fireplaces, and wood stoves.

Areal composite samples—Environmental samples that are composed of equal aliquots (grab samples) collected from a defined area such as the surface of a waste pile or an established grid.

Areas of concern—For human health risk assessments, the general locations at or near the site of concern.

Aromatic—In chemistry, a class of chemicals with organic molecular structures having single of multiple benzene rings (C_6H_6) as the basic unit (*e.g.*, toluene, xylene, polynuclear aromatics or PNAs).

Articles—Under the Occupational Safety and Health Administration rules, manufactured items that are formed to specific shapes during manufacture. They have end-use functions dependent upon their shapes during end use. They do not release or otherwise result in exposure to a hazardous chemical under normal conditions of use.

As generated wastes—Under the Resource Conservation and Recovery Act, wastes from on-going hazardous waste operations.

Asbestos—A noncombustible chemical-resistant mineral that includes chrysotile, amosite, crocidolite, tremolite asbestos, anthophyllite asbestos, actinolite asbestos, and any of these minerals that have been chemically treated and/or altered.

Asbestos-containing building material (ACBM)—Asbestos-containing material found in or on interior structural members or other parts of a building.

Asbestos-containing material (ACM)—Any material or product containing greater than 1 percent asbestos.

Asbestosis—Also known as *white lung*, a scarring of lung tissue, which forms from an accumulation of asbestos fibers in the lung. Asbestosis is the most common asbestos-related disease. The symptoms of asbestosis are similar to those of emphysema.

Assets—In business, economic resources owned by a company such as cash, accounts receivable, inventory, supplies, equipment, buildings and land.

Atmosphere-supplying respirator—A respirator that provides air from a source other than the surrounding atmosphere.

Atom—In chemistry, the smallest and generally indivisible unit of matter. Atoms of a particular element such as sodium have the same average mass, and other properties are the same. Atoms of different elements generally have different average masses (or *atomic weights*) and different properties.

Atomic number—In chemistry, the number of protons in the nucleus.

Attainment areas—Under the Clean Air Act, geographic areas in which the air quality is cleaner than the NAAQS (*i.e.,* the concentrations of the *criteria pollutants* are below the standard).

Audit—In *environmental management,* a comparison of actual conditions to expected conditions, and a determination as to whether the actual conditions are in conformance or not in conformance with the expected conditions. Under the *Clean Air Act* and in 40 CFR 68, audits of an RMP will generally include an evaluation of the RMP for its adequacy. Audits are used to identify whether the underlying risk management program is being implemented properly. Facilities may be selected for audits based on any of several criteria set out 40 CFR 68.220: (1) accident history of the facility and of other facilities in same industry, (2) quantity of regulated substances handled at the facility, (3) location and proximity to public and environmental receptors, (4) the presence of specific regulated substances, and (5) hazards identified at the facility. See also *Inspections* and *Reviews.*

Audit objective(s)—In an audit process, the reason an audit is being conducted. Usually the reason is to demonstrate conformance to stated criteria.

Audit scope —In an audit process, the nature of the audit—a company, a site, or unit within a site or company.

Auditee—In an audit process, the entity being audited.

Auditor—In an audit process, the person or team actually collecting evidence and determining findings.

Authorized employees—Under the Occupational Safety and Health Administration's lockout/tagout rules, employees who actually perform service or maintenance on systems that contain energy.

Authorized state—Under the Resource Conservation and Recovery Act, a state that has been granted the authority by the Environmental Protection Agency to regulate the management and disposal of hazardous waste.

Auto-ignition temperature—The temperature at which ignition occurs without an ignition source and the material continues to burn without further heat input.

Automobile insurance—In business, a type of insurance coverage that is mandatory if the company owns any vehicles. Most states have minimum coverage requirements.

Available treatment technology and disposal capacity—As defined by the Environmental Protection Agency, any facility that is "commercially available to treat or dispose of a particular waste and has either (1) a RCRA permit or interim status; (2) a research, development, and demonstration permit under 40 CFR 270.65; or (3) a land treatment permit under 40 CFR 270.63."

Average atomic weight—In chemistry, the atomic weight (as generally found in nature) shown in the Periodic Table. The average atomic weight represents the weighted average of the isotopic forms.

B

Backsliding—As defined by the Clean Water Act, a term that refers to the lowering of a discharge effluent limit or a pollution control requirement.

Balance sheet—In accounting, a report that provides information on a company's financial status by listing the types and dollar amounts of assets, liabilities, and equity of the business on a given date.

Base—In chemistry, any material that produces hydroxide ions (OH⁻) when it is dissolved in water. A base can also be thought of as any substance that accepts a proton.

Baseline conditions—In an Environmental Management System (EMS), the state of the existing EMS relative to the requirements of a system standard like ISO 14000.

Basic—In chemistry, the property of material that produces hydroxide ions (OH⁻) when it is dissolved in water. The terms *alkaline, basic,* and *caustic* are used interchangeably.

Best available control measures (BACM)—Under the Clean Air Act, emissions control technologies (typically used for fugitive dust, residential wood burning, and prescribed burning) that may be used for the management of particulate matter emissions.

Best available control technology (BACT)—Under the Clean Air Act, an emission limitation based on the maximum achievable degree of reduction for a pollutant, taking into account energy, environmental, and economic impacts, and other costs.

Best available retrofit technology (BART)—Under the Clean Air Act, an emissions control technology that may be implemented to control regional haze. BART takes into account the availability of the control technology, cost of compliance, current pollution control equipment used by the source, and the expected improvement in visibility.

Best management practices—Under the Clean Water Act, common-sense actions that are industry-specific and are used to protect water quality.

Best practices—Under the Occupational Safety and Health Act, the best possible engineering and administrative means (over and above the specific requirements of law) that is provided by the employer to control hazards in the workplace.

Beta (β) particle—One form of ionizing radiation. Beta (β) particles are similar to electrons except that they come from the atomic nucleus and are not bound to any atom. Beta particles cannot travel very far from their radioactive source. For example, they can travel only about one half an inch in human tissue, and they may travel a few yards in air. They are not capable of penetrating something as thin as a pad of paper.

Bioactivation—In toxicology, the biotransformation of a relatively nontoxic chemical into one or more toxic metabolites.

Biochemical oxygen demand at five days (BOD₅)—The quantity of oxygen required by microbes for the oxidative breakdown of a given waste material during a 5-day test period. The BOD_5 usually is taken as an index of the ultimate oxygen demand (*i.e.*, oxygen required when sufficient time is allowed to achieve maximum microbial decomposition).

Biological effects of complex chemical or other mixtures—In toxicology, one approach to *in vitro* toxicological studies that examines the synergistic, additive, and antagonistic effects of exposure to a number of chemicals, as well as the correlation between chemical and physical agents, (*i.e.*, noise, temperature, humidity, vibration, and stress), and between chemical and environmental interactions, (circadian rhythms, seasonal changes), *etc.*

***Biological hazards* (*biohazards*)**—In industrial hygiene, hazards posed by living organisms and their toxins.

Biological indicators—Under the Occupational Safety and Health Administration's HAZWOPER rules, dead animals or vegetation that may indicate the presence of hazards that could be Immediately Dangerous to Life and Health.

Biological plausibility—One of the factors used in epidemiological studies to determine the confidence level of the data. Biological plausibility means that the investigated agent is known to cause the health effect.

Biological weapons—Living organisms or the by-products of living organisms used as instruments for waging conflict. In essence, biological warfare is the deliberate spread of disease. Biological weapons generally are categorized as ***infectious agents*** or ***toxins***.

Biota of concern—In human health risk assessment, organisms that are likely to be consumed by humans.

Biotransformation—In toxicology, the process by which living organisms can chemically change a substance (also known as metabolism).

Blister agents—Also known as *vesicants* blister agents are a class of chemical weapons used to produce casualties and to force opposing troops to wear full protective equipment. Blister agents are used to degrade fighting efficiency rather than to kill, although exposure to such agents can be fatal. Vesicants burn and blister the skin or any other part of the body they contact. They may act on the eyes, mucous membranes, lungs, and skin; mustards may act on blood-forming organs. They damage the respiratory tract when inhaled and cause vomiting and diarrhea when ingested.

Blood agents—A class of chemical weapons that produce their effects by interfering with oxygen utilization at the cellular level. Inhalation is the usual route of entry. Hydrogen cyanide (AC) and cyanogen chloride (CK) are the important agents in this group. All blood agents are nonpersistent.

Bloodborne pathogens—Pathogenic microorganisms that are present in human blood and can cause disease in humans.

Body of standing law—Laws that are amended, revised and republished to reflect all permanent amendments. Also called ***statutes***.

Boiling point (bp)—In *chemistry,* the temperature at which a liquid changes to gas under standard atmospheric pressure (760 mm mercury). Under the *Process Safety Management rules*, this refers specifically to the boiling point of a liquid at a pressure of 14.7 pounds per square inch absolute (psia).

Bona fide *prospective purchaser (BFPP) protection*—Under the Comprehensive Environmental Response, Compensation, and Liability Act, a protection offered to a prospective from potential liability for a release or threatened release if all of the statutory requirements in CERCLA §101(40), which sets forth BFPP eligibility, are met. The BFPP protection is based solely on the purchaser's status as an owner or operator of a facility.

Bottom-up approach—In project management, the process that defines all of the tasks that need to be completed in a project, grouping similar tasks together.

Brownfields—Abandoned, idled, or underutilized industrial and commercial facilities where expansion or redevelopment is complicated by real or perceived environmental contamination (GAO, *Superfund: Barriers to Brownfield Redevelopment*, 1996).

Building related illness—A defined illness where a causative agent resulting from exposure to the indoor air has been identified for the associated health complaint.

Burned for energy recovery or used to produce a fuel product—Under the Resource Conservation and Recovery Act, to be ***discarded*** by the indicated recycling methods (applicable to materials except commercial chemical products that are already fuels).

Business plan—In business, a document that consolidates the various aspects of the business unit. It assesses the current status of the business and competitive environment, and offers projections into the future.

By-product—Under the Resource Conservation and Recovery Act, a material that is not one of the primary products of a production process and is not solely or separately produced by the production process.

C

CAMU-eligible waste—Under the Resource Conservation and Recovery Act, waste that meets minimum treatment standards for its principal hazardous constituents.

Cancer—The unrestrained proliferation of immature or abnormal cells that leads to tumor formation and, eventually, to the inhibition of the normal function of the organ or tissue.

Capital spending plan—In business, a plan that includes all of the equipment, inventory, and fixtures that must be purchased before any revenue is received. For a start-up company, this also includes licenses, insurance, initial deposits, advertising, office supplies, *etc.*

Carcinogen—A chemical that causes abnormal malignant growth of body tissues.

Cash basis—In business, an accounting standard that recognizes ***revenues*** when cash is received and ***expenses*** when cash is paid.

Cash flow forecast—In business, a report that calculates the monthly profit (or loss) figures in the *pro forma*. Adjustments are made for time differences in ***accounts receivable*** and ***accounts payable***. Impacts of credit sales and collections, credit purchases and payments, tax withholding, depreciation, debt payments, and asset purchases (from the ***Capital Spending Plan***) are also considered.

Catastrophic injuries—Under the Occupational Safety and Health Administration rules, any single incident resulting in the hospitalization of three or more employees.

Catastrophic release—Under the Occupational Safety and Health Administration Process Safety Management rules, a major uncontrolled emission, fire, or explosion involving one or more highly hazardous chemicals that presents a serious danger to employees in the workplace.

Categorical exclusion—Under the National Environmental Policy Act, the first level of action a Federal agency may take on a detailed environmental analysis if it meets certain criteria, which have been previously determined as having no significant environmental impact.

Cations—In chemistry, positive ***ions***.

Caustic—In chemistry, the property material that produces hydroxide ions (OH⁻) when it is dissolved in water. The terms *alkaline, basic,* and *caustic* are used interchangeably.

Ceiling—The highest concentration of air contaminants to which any employee may be intentionally exposed.

Central nervous system (CNS) depression (narcosis)—A reversible effect that may be caused by exposure to a substance which is characterized by drowsiness, headache, nausea, slurred speech, difficulty in concentrating, dizziness, loss of coordination, and possibly coma and death in extreme situations.

Central nervous system (CNS) toxicity—The damage a substance may cause to the brain and spinal cord.

CG—Military designation for the chemical weapon phosgene, a *choking agent.*

Characteristic hazardous wastes—Under the Resource Conservation and Recovery Act, wastes not found on an EPA hazardous waste list that are hazardous because they exhibit ignitable, corrosive, reactive, or toxic characteristics, as defined in RCRA regulations at 40 CFR 261, Subpart C.

Characteristic of corrosivity (D002)—Under the Resource Conservation and Recovery Act, one of the characteristics of hazardous waste in which the waste exhibits either of the following properties: (1) it is aqueous and has a pH of less than or equal to 2 or greater than or equal to 12.5, as determined by a pH meter, using the Environmental Protection Agency (EPA) publication SW–846; (2) it is a liquid and corrodes steel at a rate greater than 6.35 mm (0.25 inch) per year at a temperature of 55°C.

Characteristic of ignitability (D001)—Under the Resource Conservation and Recovery Act, one of the characteristics of hazardous waste in which the waste exhibits any of the following properties: (1) it is a liquid other than aqueous solution containing less than 24% alcohol by volume and has a flash point less than 140°F (60°C), as determined by a Pensky Marten closed cup tester (American Society for Testing and Materials [ASTM] method D–93–79 or D–93–80) or Setaflash closed cup tester using method ASTM–D–3278–78; (2) it is a liquid and is capable under standard temperature and pressure of causing a fire through friction, absorption of moisture, or spontaneous chemical changes; and when ignited burns so vigorously and persistently that it creates a hazard; (3) it is an ignitable compressed gas as defined in 49 CFR 173.300 and as determined by the test methods described in the above regulations or equivalent test methods approved under 40 CFR 260.20 and 260.21; (4) it is an oxidizer as defined in 49 CFR 173.151.

Characteristic of reactivity (D003)—Under the Resource Conservation and Recovery Act, one of the characteristics of hazardous waste in which the waste has any of the following properties: (1) it normally is unstable and readily undergoes violent changes without detonating; (2) it reacts violently with water; (3) it forms a potentially explosive mixture with water; (4) it generates toxic gases, vapors, or fumes when mixed with water; (5) it is a cyanide- or a sulfide- bearing waste which, when exposed to pH conditions between 2–12.5, can generate toxic gases, vapors, or fumes; (6) it is capable of detonation or causing an explosive reaction if subjected to heat or initiators; (7) it is readily capable of explosive decomposition or reaction at standard temperature and pressure; (8) it is a forbidden explosive defined in 49 CFR 173.51, 49 CFR 173.53, and 49 CFR 173.88.

Characteristically hazardous waste—Under the Resource Conservation and Recovery Act, wastes that are hazardous because they are ignitable, corrosive, reactive, and toxic or otherwise or acutely toxic or hazardous.

Chart of accounts—In accounting, a complete listing of a business' financial information and includes the firm's budget line items such as *assets* (cash, accounts receivable); property, plant, and equipment (land, buildings, furniture); *liabilities* (accounts payable, long term liabilities); owner's equity accounts (capital investments and withdrawals by owner); *revenue* (fees, income); and *expenses* (salaries, advertising, utilities, travel, *etc.*)

Chemical hygiene plan (CHP)—A comprehensive plan that is a major component of the OSHA Laboratory Standard and includes the development and implementation of a chemical hygiene plan capable of (1) protecting employees from health hazards associated with hazardous chemicals in that laboratory, and (2) keeping exposures below specified OSHA permissible exposure limits.

Chemical substance—Under the Toxic Substances Control Act, any organic or inorganic substance of a particular molecular identity including any combination of substances occurring in whole or in part as a result of a chemical reaction or occurring in nature, or any element or uncombined radical. It does not include mixtures; pesticides as defined by FIFRA; tobacco; *source, special nuclear* or *by-product materials* as defined in the 1954 Atomic Energy Act; any article the sale of which is subject to the tax imposed by the 1986 Internal Revenue Code; and any food, food additive, drug, cosmetic or device as defined by the Federal Food, Drug, and Cosmetic Act.

Chemical treatment—A method of treating hazardous waste that includes all forms of chemical reactions such as reduction, oxidation, thermal oxidation, precipitation, neutralization, electrochemical, photolytic, biological degradation, *etc.*

Chemical weapons—Poisons that incapacitate, injure, or kill through their toxic effect on the human body. They are generally classified as blister, blood, choking, incapacitating, or nerve agents, depending on which part of the body they are designed to affect. Some chemical agents can be lethal when vaporized and inhaled in amounts as small as a few milligrams. The Chemical Weapons Convention defines chemical weapons as: (a) Toxic chemicals and their precursors, except where intended for purposes not prohibited under this Convention, as long as the types and quantities are consistent with such purposes; (b) Munitions and devices, specifically designed to cause death or other harm through the toxic properties of those toxic chemicals specified in subparagraph (a), which would be released as a result of the employment of such munitions and devices; (c) Any equipment specifically designed for use directly in connection with the employment of munitions and devices specified in subparagraph (b).

Chemistry—The science of matter, energy, and their reactions.

Choking agents—A class of chemical weapons that attack lung tissue, primarily causing pulmonary edema. They include phosgene (CG), diphosgene (DP), chlorine, and chloropicrin (PS). Agents in this class are called lung-damaging agents because irritation of the bronchi, trachea, larynx, pharynx, and nose may occur and, with pulmonary edema, contribute to the sensation of choking.

Chronic exposure—In industrial hygiene, repeated exposure to low concentrations of hazardous agents over a long period of time, perhaps years, which results in slowly developing symptoms of illness. An example of chronic exposure is the gradual development of silicosis after frequent, long-term inhalation of very low concentrations of airborne silicon dioxide (silica) dust.

Chronic reference dose—In human health risk assessment, an estimate of a daily exposure level for the human population, including sensitive subpopulations, that is likely to not result in appreciable risk of deleterious effects during a lifetime. See also, *reference dose.*

Chronic toxin—In toxicology, substance that exhibits no symptoms or mild symptoms to the body at the time of exposure, but may build after a series of exposures. Chronic reactions may be triggered by a build-up of the material (*e.g.,* lead) in body tissues, or by the immune system becoming sensitized to specific toxins, such as organic solvents.

CK—Military designation for cyanogen chloride a chemical weapon, a *blood agent.*

Claims-made policy—In business, a type of insurance policy that protects the insured against claims that are reported while the policy is in force, or during the extended reporting period. A claims-made policy may reach back in time to provide coverage for services provided years before the policy period.

Class I—Under the Occupational Safety and Health Administration asbestos rules, activities involving the removal of Thermal System Insulation (TSI) and surfacing asbestos-containing material and presumed asbestos-containing material.

Class I areas—Under the Clean Air Act, geographic areas that allow for very little deterioration of air quality and include all international parks; national wilderness areas and memorial parks larger than 5000 acres; and national parks exceeding 6000 acres.

Class I wells—Under the Safe Drinking Water Act, industrial, municipal, and other injection wells intended for disposal of fluids into subsurface or ground water; including industrial, municipal, and privately owned disposal wells for disposal of industrial waste, domestic sewage, or other waste that is not hazardous or radioactive. These wells are prohibited in many states.

Class II—Under the Occupational Safety and Health Administration asbestos rules, activities involving the removal of asbestos-containing material that is not thermal system insulation or surfacing material (miscellaneous materials). Examples are removal of floor or ceiling tiles, siding, roofing, and transite panels.

Class II areas—Under the Clean Air Act, all geographic areas other than Class I areas or areas that have been redesignated from ***Class II*** to ***Class III***. Class II areas allow for moderate deterioration of air quality.

Class II wells—Under the Safe Drinking Water Act, oil or gas production and storage wells.

Class III—Under the Occupational Safety and Health Administration asbestos rules, repair and maintenance operations where asbestos-containing material (ACM) including thermal system insulation and surfacing materials is likely to be disturbed. It includes repair and maintenance activities involving intentional disturbance of ACM or presumed asbestos-containing material (PACM). It is limited to ACM/PACM.

Class III areas—Under the Clean Air Act, the least restrictive class of geographic areas that result from redesignation of ***Class II areas***. To date, no areas in the United States have been redesignated to Class III.

Class III wells—Under the Safe Drinking Water Act, wells containing injected fluids for extraction of minerals.

Class IV—Under the Occupational Safety and Health Administration asbestos rules, maintenance and custodial work, including cleanup, during which employees contact asbestos-containing material or presumed asbestos-containing material.

Class IV wells—Under the Safe Drinking Water Act, wells containing injected hazardous wastes or radioactive contaminants into or above the formation containing an underground source of drinking water. These wells are widely prohibited.

Class V wells—Under the Safe Drinking Water Act, all corrective action wells associated with aquifer restoration not defined in other classes.

Clean alternative fuel—Fuel that meets certain low emissions standards and is useable by a certified clean-fuel vehicle. Examples include ethanol, gasohol mixtures >85% by alcohol by volume, reformulated gasoline, diesel, natural gas, liquified petroleum gas, hydrogen, and electricity.

Client—In an audit process, the party commissioning the audit.

Closure—Under the Resource Conservation and Recovery Act, the prescribed activities at treatment, storage, and disposal facilities (TSDFs) intended to leave the facilities in an environmentally safe condition with minimum maintenance requirements after operations have ceased. The types of closure include **risked-based clean closure** and **dirty closure**.

Code of Federal Regulations (CFR)—The body of standing regulation (48 Titles), accurate as of the annual publication date of each title.

Cold substances—Substances that are considered hazardous to the touch because they are 32°F (0°C) or colder.

Combustible liquid—Liquid substances that burn readily once ignited. Various Federal agencies and industry organizations have different technical definitions. Which standard (and which definition) applies to a specific situation will depend on which agency has jurisdiction (*i.e.,* Occupational Safety and Health Administration (OSHA), National Fire Protection Association (NFPA), Environmental Protection Agency (EPA), Department of Transportation (DOT), *etc.*).

Commerce clause of the Constitution—A clause in the Constitution that authorizes Congress to regulate interstate and foreign commerce.

Common law—The various rules of law that have evolved over centuries from judicial decisions that relied on usages and customs of the people. Also call *case law*.

Community—In human health risk assessment, a complex association in which populations of different species live together.

Community water system—Under the Safe Drinking Water Act, any **public water system** that serves more than twenty-five people or greater than fifteen connections year-round. For example, a community water system can be either a municipal water system or a water system that serves a mobile home park or a rural apartment house.

Competent person—Under the Occupational Safety and Health Administration asbestos standards, a person who directs the establishment and supervision of regulated work areas established where airborne concentrations of asbestos fibers may be expected to equal or exceed the PEL. The competent person (1) establishes negative pressure enclosures where necessary, (2) supervises exposure monitoring, (3) designates appropriate personal protective equipment, (4) ensures training of workers with respect to proper use of said equipment, (5) ensures the establishment and use of hygiene facilities, and (6) ensures that proper engineering controls are used throughout the project.

Composite sample—In environmental sampling, a nondiscrete sample composed of two or more equal aliquots collected at various points or times. The analytical results from a composite sample provide average concentrations of the contaminants present. The collection and mixing (homogenizing) of two aliquots of surface material from a pile of "waste" material would result in the generation of a composite sample of the pile.

Compound—In chemistry, a substance that is chemically combined in a fixed ratio and contains more than one element.

Concordance—One of the factors used in epidemiological studies to determine the confidence level of the data. Concordance occurs when the same end point or type of pathological change (*e.g.,* type of tumor) arises in more than one species, strain, or sex, and/or in both animals and humans.

Cone of depression—In hydrogeology, the cone-shaped depression of the water table that results from removal of ground water from a pumping well.

Confined spaces—As defined by the Occupational Safety and Health Administration, spaces that are: (1) large enough for an employee to enter, (2) have a limited or restricted means of entry or exit, and (3) have not been designed for continuous occupancy. OSHA further separates confined spaces into two categories: *non-permit required confined spaces* and *permit-required confined spaces*.

Connected piping—As defined by the Underground Storage Tank rules, all buried piping, including valves, elbows, joints, and flexible connectors, attached to tank systems through which regulated substances flow.

Consistency—One of the factors used in epidemiological studies to determine the confidence level of the data. Consistency occurs when two or more studies yield comparable findings of excess risk, preferably using different test models.

Construction activity discharges—Under the Clean Water Act, discharges that can affect any industry sector and are covered under EPA's General Construction Permit.

Contained-in policy—Under the Resource Conservation and Recovery Act, the policy that a mixture of hazardous waste and material other than solid waste, such as soil, ground water, and debris, must be managed as if the entire mixture were hazardous waste unless, or until the hazardous waste is determined to no longer be present.

Container— Under the *Occupational Safety and Health Act*, any bag, barrel, bottle, box, can, cylinder, drum, reaction vessel, storage tank or the like. Under the *Resource Conservation and Recovery Act* rules, any portable device ranging up to and including transport vehicles.

Containment buildings—Under the Resource Conservation and Recovery Act, units that meet certain design, operation, and closure standards and are constructed for a variety of operations that cannot be readily performed with containerized waste or bulk waste in tanks (such as storage and manipulation of otherwise unconfined waste piles and/or performance of complex treatment processes without the need to otherwise confine the waste to RCRA-compliant tanks or containers).

Contaminant candidate list—Under the Safe Drinking Water Act, a list published by EPA that identifies contaminants known to occur in public water systems and which may require regulation.

Contiguous property owner protection—Under the Comprehensive Environmental Response, Compensation, and Liability Act, a property owner who is "contiguous to or otherwise similarly situated with respect to, and that is or may be contaminated by a release or threat of release of *hazardous substances* from" property owned by someone else is protected from potential liability. Congress intended this provision to protect landowners who "are essentially victims of pollution incidents caused by their neighbor's actions."

Contract—In business, a formal, detailed, elaborate, legal and binding document in which relevant conditions of an agreement are spelled out.

Contract-based remedies—In law, actions that are based on an agreement between two parties.

Contractual relationship—As defined in the Comprehensive Environmental Response, Compensation, and Liability Act, §9601(35)(A) includes, but is not limited to, land contracts, deeds, easements, leases or other instruments transferring title or possession.

Corporation—In business, a group of persons authorized to act as a separate legal entity, thus limiting the liability exposure of individual investors.

Corrective action management unit—Under the Resource Conservation and Recovery Act, an area within a facility that is designated to manage remediation waste generated from corrective action activities.

Corrosive chemicals—In toxicology, substances that disintegrate body tissues. Corrosive chemicals affect in particular the water and fatty tissues of the body, and are capable of causing rapid and deep destruction of tissue.

Covalent—In chemistry, bonds that exist when two atoms in a molecule share a pair of electrons.

Coverage trigger—In insurance, the event that causes insurance coverage to be invoked.

Covered process—Under the *Process Safety Management* and *Risk Management Program* rules, any activity involving the use, storage, manufacturing, handling, or on-site movement of a regulated substance, or combination of these activities with a highly hazardous chemical in excess of a TQ amount.

Cradle-to-grave—Under the Resource Conservation and Recovery Act, a term used to describe the generator's responsibility for tracking hazardous waste from generation through final disposition.

Criteria pollutants—Under the Clean Air Act, six pollutants (ozone, carbon monoxide, particulate matter—PM_{10} and $PM_{2.5}$—lead, nitrogen dioxide, and sulfur oxides—SO_2) that generally are associated with urban areas and have associated National Ambient Air Quality Standards.

Critical path—In project management, the longest possible path between the start and completion of the project.

Cryogenics—Extremely cold substances that are considered hazardous to the touch because they are −148°F (−100°C) or colder.

Cumulative effects—Under the Council on Environmental Quality regulations, "the impact on the environment which results from the incremental impact of the action when added to other past, present, and reasonably foreseeable future actions regardless of what agency (Federal or non-Federal) or person undertakes such other actions." Also, cumulative impacts can result from individually minor but collectively significant actions taking place over a period of time. (40 CFR 1508.7)

CX—Military designation for the chemical weapon phosgene oxime, a *blister agent.*

D

Data quality objectives—In human health risk assessment, qualitative and quantitative statements established prior to data collection that specify the quality of the data required to support agency decisions during remedial response activities.

Data use objectives (DUO)—In environmental sampling, objectives that address specific goals of the sampling program including what the data is needed for, the questions that must be answered, and what decisions have to be made based on the data generated. The goal may be as simple as determining the contents of a single drum in order to arrange for proper disposal, or as complex as determining the impact of a site with multiple sources of unknown contaminants on numerous human and ecological resource targets.

De minimis *losses*—Under the Resource Conservation and Recovery Act, generally denotes minor leaks and spills, sample purgings, relief device discharges, rinsate from empty containers or containers that are rendered empty by that rinsing, and minor laboratory waste contributions normal to a well-designed and -operated facility.

Debris—Under the Resource Conservation and Recovery Act, LDR regulations, solid material that is greater than 60 mm (2.5 in) particle size that is intended for disposal and is a manufactured object, plant or animal matter, or geologic material, except for: (1) materials for which a specified technology treatment standard is already established, (2) process residuals, and (3) intact containers of hazardous waste that retain at least 75% of their original volume.

DECIDE process—A decision-making process authored by L. Brenner for hazardous materials incident response: Detect, Estimate, Choose, Identify, Do, Evaluate

Deed restrictions—One method of managing risk on brownfields properties. Deed restrictions provide public notification of use constraints and grant a variety of options for enforcing compliance with them.

Deferred UST—According to the Underground Storage Tank rules, an UST for which EPA has deferred the Subpart B (design, construction, installation, and notification), Subpart C (general operations requirements), Subpart D (release detection), Subpart E (release reporting, investigation, and confirmation), and Subpart G (closure) regulations. Until EPA decides how to regulate these USTs fully, the only regulations that apply are Subpart A (interim prohibition) and Subpart F (release response and corrective action). Examples of deferred tanks include underground, field-constructed, bulk storage tanks, and UST systems that contain radioactive wastes.

Delaney clause—Part of the Federal Food Drug and Cosmetic Act, added to the law in 1958. The clause basically stated that carcinogens could not purposely be added to food. The Delaney clause prohibited the setting of tolerances for carcinogens on processed foods, even though a tolerance may already have existed for the raw commodity from which the processed food was derived.

Delayed or chronic toxicity—In toxicology, a reaction by the body that manifests itself after a period of latency (may be many years) following exposure.

Delegation—The authorization of a state by an agency (EPA) to establish permitting and enforcement programs which would be operated by the state in lieu of the Federal program.

Delisting petition—Under the Resource Conservation and Recovery Act, a request submitted to EPA to delete a waste at a particular facility from the hazardous wastes listed by EPA in 40 CFR 261, Subpart D and to exclude certain wastes that are recycled.

Density—In chemistry, the mass per unit volume of any substance.

Derived-from rule—Under the Resource Conservation and Recovery Act, a rule that states that any solid waste generated from the treatment, storage, or disposal of a listed hazardous waste (such as sludge from a wastewater treatment plant and incinerator ash) is also a listed waste and bears the same listed waste codes regardless of whether or not the hazardous waste was listed on the basis of characteristic(s) only. Any solid waste generated from the treatment, storage, or disposal of a waste that is hazardous by characteristic only, is hazardous only if it exhibits one or more hazardous characteristic.

Dermal and eye corrosion—In toxicology, an irreversible destruction of tissue with pain, ulcerations, and scarring.

Dermal irritation—In toxicology, a localized, nonimmune, inflammatory response of the skin that is characterized by reversible redness, swelling, and pain at the site of contact.

Dermal sensitization—In toxicology, a skin reaction triggered by an immune response to allergens. This reaction is characterized by redness, swelling, crusting/scaling and vesicle formation.

Designated use—Under the Clean Water Act, a use such as recreation, aquatic habitat, industrial water supply, and drinking water supply. It does not include waste transport.

Developmental toxicity—In toxicology, the damage a substance may cause to the developing organism (due to the exposure of either parent).

Dew point temperature—The temperature at which air is saturated and water droplets condense from the air.

Diatomic—In chemistry, having two atoms per molecule.

Dip tank—Under Occupational Safety and Health Administration rules, any tank or other container which contains a flammable or combustible liquid and in which articles or materials are immersed for any process.

Direct marketing—In business, a marketing technique that includes written materials; such as magazine ads, business cards, brochures, newsletters, and statement of qualifications. Other approaches include maintaining a dynamic website, exhibiting at a trade show, making cold calls, and utilizing a direct mail campaign.

Directions for use—Under the Federal Insecticide, Fungicide, and Rodenticide Act, statements on a pesticide label that describe how much of the product to use, for what applications the pesticide can be used (*e.g.*, which crops, pests, locations, *etc.*), and how to apply it.

Dirty closure—Under the Resource Conservation and Recovery Act, all closures that are not clean closures and may involve partial removal or decontamination, waste stabilization measures and, usually, installation of low permeability cover or *cap* with run-on/run-off controls to minimize infiltration by precipitation. This type of closure is typical for land disposal units (*e.g.*, landfills) and nonland-based units from which all waste or contamination above allowable risk levels cannot be removed. Also known as *closure with waste in place*.

Discarded—Under the Resource Conservation and Recovery Act, a material that has been ***abandoned***, ***recycled*** (accumulated, stored, or treated before recycling by being: ***used in a "manner constituting disposal", burned for energy recovery or used to produce a fuel product, reclaimed***, or ***accumulated speculatively, inherently waste-like,*** or a ***military munition specifically identified as a solid waste***.

Discharge—Under the Clean Water Act, any addition of any pollutant to navigable waters from any point source.

Disposal—Under the Resource Conservation and Recovery Act, virtually any action that introduces waste or waste constituents into the environment (*i.e.*, on/into air, water or land) including placement in waste piles outside of a RCRA-compliant containment building.

Distribution—In toxicology, the movement of chemicals throughout the body after they have been absorbed.

Diversity jurisdiction—In law, the ability of a defendant to remove a case from a State court to the Federal court due to the party's diverse citizenship.

Docket—The official administrative record that is established for a particular regulation in order to document that all administrative procedures, as well as any procedures specified in the enabling legislation, are followed. All comments that are submitted in response to a proposed regulation are kept with this docket.

***Doctrine of* Respondeat Superior**—In law, gives employers responsibility for the acts of their employees in the course of their employment.

Dosage—In toxicology, the most critical factor in determining whether a toxic response will take place. Dosage is defined as the unit of chemical per unit of biological system (*e.g.*, mg/kg body weight, mg/ body surface area, ml/kg body weight, *etc.*).

Dose—In radiation protection, the effect that radiation has on any material. Radiation dose is simply the quantity of radiation energy deposited in a material. There are several additional descriptive terms used in radiation protection which provide precise information on how the dose was deposited, the method used to calculate the dose, and how the radiation energy deposited in tissue will affect humans. See ***absorbed dose*** and ***equivalent dose***.

Dose-response—In toxicology, the quantitative (measurable) relationship between the dose of a chemical or agent (*e.g.*, mg chemical/kg body weight) and an effect (response) caused by the chemical or agent. The dose-response relationship is the most fundamental concept in toxicology.

Dose-response evaluation—In human health risk assessment, the process of quantitatively evaluating the toxicity information and characterizing the relationship between the dose of the contaminant administered or received and the incidence of adverse health effects in the exposed population.

DP—Military designation for the chemical weapon diphosgene a ***choking agent***.

Due diligence—In property assessments, all appropriate inquiry that is made into the previous ownership and use of property that is consistent with good commercial or customary practice at the time of land acquisition.

Duration of exposure—In toxicology, the length of time a person or animal is exposed. The duration can be acute (*e.g.*, usually a single dose), subchronic (*e.g.*, days to years), and chronic (*e.g.*, years to a lifetime).

Dusts—In industrial hygiene, solid aerosols that are typically generated from a bulk solid by mechanical action, such as crushing, drilling, or grinding.

E

Ecological assessment—In human health risk assessment, a qualitative and/or quantitative appraisal of the actual or potential effects of a hazardous waste site on plants, animals, and domesticated species.

Ecosystems—Geographic areas that are characterized by a complex set of relationships between living resources. Ecosystems vary by climactic, topographical, geological, chemical, and biotic factors.

Effective porosity—In hydrogeology, the volume of available pore space in an aquifer, taking into account the void space of the aquifer that are too small to pass water or are unavailable for fluid flow; always less than the total ***porosity***.

Effective safer medical device—Under the Occupational Safety and Health Administration's Bloodborne Pathogen standard, a device that, based on reasonable judgment, will make an exposure incident involving a contaminated sharp less likely to occur in the application in which it is used.

EJ Community—Any aggregated or dispersed population that 1) is a low-income population based on the Bureau of the Census Current Population Reports (Series P–60 on Income and Poverty), 2) is over 50 percent minority, or 3) contains a minority population percentage meaningfully greater than the minority population percentage in the general population or other appropriate unit of geographic analysis. For example, Federally Recognized Indian Tribes or groups within tribes, which are made up of minority individuals, may be identified as EJ Communities.

Electrons—In chemistry, the particles that surround the nucleus, are negatively charged, and contribute an insignificant amount to atomic weight.

Elements—In chemistry, extremely small, normally indivisible particles called **atoms**.

Eligible Response Site—Brownfield sites as defined in the Comprehensive Environmental Response, Compensation, and Liability Act, Section 101(39)(A) and (B). Also, sites contaminated by chemicals identified as Controlled Substances, petroleum and petroleum products otherwise excluded from CERCLA, and mine-scarred land, are included in the definition.

Emergency—As defined by the Federal Emergency Management Agency, any event that threatens to, or actually does, inflict damage to property or people.

Emergency response action plan (ERAP)—Under the Oil Pollution Act of 1990, the part of the Facility Response Plan that contains all information that is needed to combat a spill; organized for easy reference such as: (1) information on the individual who certified the plan, (2) emergency notification phone list, (3) spill response notification form, (4) list of response equipment and its location, (5) schedule of response equipment testing and deployment drills, (6) list of response team members, (7) evacuation plan, (8) description of the response resources for small, medium, and worst-case discharges, and (9) the facility diagram.

Emission standard or limitation—Under the Clean Air Act, State or Federal requirements relating to the quantity or rate of emissions and including: (1) a schedule or timetable of compliance, and emission limitation, standard of performance, or emissions standard; (2) a control or prohibition of a motor vehicle fuel or fuel additive; (3) a permit condition or requirement relating to attainment and nonattainment areas; any state implementation plan requirement relating to transportation control measures, air quality maintenance plans, vehicle inspection and maintenance programs, vapor recovery, visibility, and ozone protection; and (5) a standard, limitation, or schedule issued under the Title V program.

Emissions offsets—Under the Clean Air Act, surplus emissions reductions that are required in order for a **new source** to obtain a permit in a **nonattainment area.** The emissions offset are intended to compensate for the sources' impact on air quality and further the progress toward achieving clean air.

Employment relationship—In business, a term that distinguishes between an independent contractor and an employee subject to the Fair Labor Standards Act. An employee, as distinguished from an independent contractor, is one who, "as a matter of economic reality, follows the usual path of an employee and is dependent on the business which he or she serves."

Encroachment—Under the Federal Facilities Compliance Act of 1992, the term used to describe the ongoing and growing conflicts of military range operation and the with other uses on range lands— *(e.g.,* environmental management), use of surrounding lands, airspace, and radio frequency allocations.

End use product—Under the Federal Insecticide, Fungicide, and Rodenticide Act, a pesticide product whose labeling includes directions for use of the product (as distributed or sold, or after combination by the user with other substances) for controlling pests or defoliating, desiccating, or regulating the growth of plants, and does not state that the product may be used to manufacture or formulate other pesticide products.

Engineering controls—Under the Occupational Safety and Health Administration regulations, all control measures that isolate or remove a hazard from the workplace.

Environment—Under the *National Environmental Policy Act*, the natural and physical environment (air, water, geography, and geology) as well as the relationship of people with that environment including health and safety, socioeconomics (jobs, housing, schools, transportation), cultural resources, noise, and aesthetics. Under the *Comprehensive Environmental Response, Compensation, and Liability Act*, (1) the navigable water, the waters of the contiguous zone, and the ocean waters of which the natural resources are under the exclusive management authority of the United States under the Magnuson Fishery Conservation and Management Act, and (2) any other surface water, ground water, drinking water supply, land surface or subsurface strata or ambient air within the United States or under the jurisdiction of the United States.

Environmental aspects—In ISO 14000, any element of the organization's activities, products, and services that can interact with the environment, that it can control and over which it can be expected to have a significant impact. The impact is the change that occurs in the environment, positive or negative, current as well as in the future.

Environmental assessment (EA)—Under the National Environmental Policy Act, a concise public document that is prepared in order to determine whether an ***environmental impact statement*** (EIS) is necessary or whether a ***finding of no significant impact*** (FONSI) can be made.

Environmental contractors—Business entities that specialize in providing environmentally related services. Environmental contractors include remediation firms, emergency response contractors, well drillers, environmental system construction contractors and specialty contractors such as soil treatment contractors, artificial wetland or stream restoration contractors.

Environmental impact statement (EIS)—Under the National Environmental Policy Act, a detailed statement required as part of Federal agency decision-making. The statement describes (1) the environmental impact of the proposed project, (2) any adverse environmental effects which cannot be avoided, (3) alternatives to the proposed action, (4) the relationship between local short-term uses of man's environment and the maintenance and enhancement of long-term productivity and (5) any irreversible and irretrievable commitments of resources that would be involved in the proposed action should it be implemented.

Environmental justice—The basic precept that certain populations may experience disproportionate environmental impacts and exposures to pollutants. Environmental justice (EJ) is the pursuit of equal justice and equal protection for all people under the environmental statutes and regulations. Under the National Environmental Policy Act, EJ means ensuring that low-income and minority populations (*i.e.*, the ***EJ Community***) are not exposed to unjustly high and adverse environmental impacts from any proposed action.

Environmental management system (EMS)—The part of an organization's overall management system that includes organizational structure, strategic planning activities, responsibilities, practices, procedures, processes and resources for developing, implementing, achieving, reviewing and maintaining an organization's environmental policy. An environmental management system is directed towards an overall quality improvement in the organization's environmental matters.

Environmental professional—As set forth in proposed 40 CFR 312.10 (see 69 FR 52541), a person who possesses sufficient specific education training and experience necessary to exercise professional judgment to develop opinions and conclusions as to the environmental condition of a property. Specifically: a Professional Engineer or Professional Geologist with three-years full-time relevant experience; an individual licensed by the government to perform environmental inquiries who has three-years full-time relevant experience; a person who has a baccalaureate or higher degree in a relevant discipline of engineering, environmental science or earth science plus the equivalent of five-years full-time relevant experience; or a person having a baccalaureate or higher degree in any field with ten-years full-time relevant experience.

Environmental receptor—Under the Risk Management Program rules, natural areas such as national or state parks, forests, or monuments; officially designated wildlife sanctuaries, preserves, refuges, or areas; and Federal wilderness areas which could be exposed to an accidental release.

Environmental sample—In environmental sampling, samples that present a relatively low risk to health or the environment because of the potential level and type of contamination. Policy determinations reflect an organization's desire to ensure the health and safety of all involved with sampling programs and to avoid the liability of improper shipment of samples. Some organizations have a simple policy of "if it is on-site, the sample is hazardous" and "if it is off-site, the sample is environmental".

Environmentally sound recycling—In the context of the Resource Conservation and Recovery Act, activities defined under the hazardous waste regulations as *recycling* in 40 CFR 261.1(c)(4), (5), and (7). This includes materials that are used, reused, or reclaimed. A material is reclaimed if it is processed to recover a usable product, or if it is regenerated.

Equipment suppliers—Businesses that specialize in supplying relatively small and inexpensive handheld instruments to large pieces of process equipment.

Equivalent dose (dose equivalent)—In radiation safety, the concept of equivalent dose involves the impact that different types of radiation have on humans. Not all types of radiation produce the same effect in humans. The equivalent dose takes into account the type of radiation and the absorbed dose. For example when considering beta, x-ray, and gamma ray radiation, the equivalent dose (expressed in rems) is equal to the absorbed dose (expressed in rads). For alpha radiation, the equivalent dose is assumed to be twenty times the absorbed dose.

Ergonomics—In industrial hygiene, the discipline that examines the capabilities and limitations of people. The word *ergonomics* comes from a combination of the Greek words for *work* and *management*.

Errors and omissions insurance—In business, a type of insurance that is sometimes referred to as E&O or *professional liability insurance*, is the equivalent of malpractice insurance. This type of insurance protects the firm and its owners, operators, directors, employees (present, past and temporary) from injury, either physical or financial, as a result of an error or omission by the professional. This coverage is only for the services provided by the insured firm.

Esters—In chemistry, compounds that are formed when a carboxylic acid is reacted (*neutralized*) by an alcohol. Esters often are easily recognizable due to their sweet to pungent odors.

Ethers—In chemistry, compounds that generally are volatile, flammable liquids with low boiling points and low flashpoints.

Evaporation—In chemistry, the tendency of a material to transfer from a liquid phase (either pure or dissolved, as in aqueous systems) to a gaseous phase (commonly mixed with air). Also known as *volatilization.*

Excretion—In toxicology, the elimination of chemicals from the body.

Executive branch—The part of the United States government where the regulatory agencies are located. The Executive Branch is headed by the President, who names the administrators of the regulatory agencies.

Executive order—An order issued by the President that can be used to delegate to agencies authority that the President may have as a direct result of the office or as a result of a Congressional delegation of authority.

Existing source—Under the Clean Air Act, any source other than a new source.

Existing USTs—As defined by the Underground Storage Tank rules, tanks for which installation commenced on or before December 22, 1988.

Exothermic—In chemistry, the characteristic of a chemical reaction in which heat is released.

Expenses—In accounting, outflows, or the using up of assets, as a result of the operations of a business.

Experimental animal-human comparisons—One approach to *in vitro* toxicological studies that examines existing human data and compares exposure levels and effects to studies performed on animals. This experimental methodology attempts to establish correlations between the effects observed in animals and those observed in humans.

Exposure—In *toxicology*, the amount of an agent available for absorption into the body. In *radiation safety*, the measure of the amount of ionization produced by x-rays or gamma rays as they travel through air. The unit of radiation exposure is the roentgen.

Exposure assessment—In human health risk assessment, the determination or estimation (qualitative or quantitative) of the magnitude, frequency, duration, and route of exposure.

Exposure control—In indoor air quality, an administrative approach for the removal or reduction of indoor air contaminants.

Exposure pathway—In human health risk assessment, the course that a chemical or physical agent takes from the source to the exposed individual.

Exposure points—In human health risk assessment, points of potential contact with the chemical of concern.

Extremely hazardous substance (EHS)—Substances identified in a published list by EPA, pursuant to Section 302 of *Superfund Amendments and Reauthorization Act,* Title III. In the United States, when a facility inventories an EHS in quantities equal to or greater than a trigger quantity, the facility is subject to emergency planning and notification requirements. Under the *Risk Management Program* rules, any substance that, if released to the atmosphere, could cause death or serious injury because of its acute toxic effect, or as a result of an explosion or fire, or which causes substantial property damage by blast, fire, toxicity, reactivity, flammability, volatility, or corrosivity.

Eye irritation—In toxicology, a localized, nonimmune, inflammatory response of the eye that is characterized by reversible redness, swelling, pain, and tearing of the eyes.

F

Facility—Under the *Comprehensive Environmental Response, Compensation, and Liability Act,* (1) any building, structure, installation, equipment, pipe or pipeline (including any pipe into a sewer or publicly owned treatment works), well, pit, pond, lagoon, impoundment, ditch, landfill, storage container, motor vehicle, rolling stock, or aircraft (2) any site or area where a ***hazardous substance*** has been deposited, stored, disposed of, or placed, or otherwise come to be located; but does not include any consumer product in consumer use or any vessel. Under the *Oil Pollution Act* of 1990, any structure, group of structures, equipment, or device (other than a vessel) that is used for exploring, drilling, producing, storing, handling, transferring, processing, or transporting oil. The term also includes any motor vehicle, rolling stock, or pipeline used for these purposes. Facilities are further subdivided into onshore and offshore facilities. The boundaries of a facility may depend on several site-specific factors, such as the ownership or operation of buildings, structures, and equipment on the same site and the types of activity at the site. Under the *Process Safety Management* rules, the buildings, containers or equipment which contain a process.

Facility response plan (FRP)—Under the Oil Pollution Act of 1990, a plan that addresses how a facility will respond to a worst-case oil discharge and a substantial threat of such a discharge.

Facility siting—Under the Process Safety Management rules, the physical location of the covered processes on the plant's property.

Federally enforceable state operating permit—Under the Clean Air Act, a permit that is given to a **synthetic minor source**, that has the theoretical capacity to operate as a major source but the owner/operator has voluntarily accepted an enforceable limitation in order to keep its emissions below the levels for a major source.

Federally owned treatment works (FOTW)—Water treatment facilities owned by the Federal government that operate under a permit issued under Section 402 of the Federal Water Pollution Control Act (Clean Water Act).

Female reproductive toxicity—In toxicology, the damage a substance may cause to the female reproductive system.

Financial plan—In business, an element of the **Business Plan** and includes **Capital Spending Plan**, the **Cash Flow Forecast**, a Risk Analysis and day-to-day tactics.

Finding—In environmental auditing, the determination, when evidence is compared to the applicable criteria, of whether the audited entity does or does not conform to a standard.

Finding of no significant impact (FONSI)—Under he National Environmental Policy Act, one of the outcomes of the **Environmental Assessment** that indicates no significant environmental impacts for a proposed project.

Fire point—The temperature at which a liquid gives off enough vapor to continue to burn when ignited.

Fire tube boilers—A method of treatment for hazardous waste using industrial boilers. Heat is transferred from hot combustion products flowing inside tubes to the water surrounding them. Combustion takes place in a cylindrical furnace within the shell. Fire tubes run the length of the shell above and around the furnace.

Fixation—A method of treatment for hazardous waste which reduces or eliminates the toxicity or the hazard potential of a certain waste stream by lowering the solubility and leachability of the toxic or hazardous components. Also called **stabilization.**

Flammable gas—Under the Department of Transportation hazardous material regulations, any compressed gas meeting the requirements for lower flammability limit, flammability limit range, flame projection, or flame propagation criteria.

Flammable liquid substances—Liquid substances that are easily ignitable. Various Federal agencies and industry organizations have different technical definitions. Which standard (and which definition) applies to a specific situation will depend on which agency has jurisdiction (*i.e.,* Occupational Safety and Health Administration–OSHA, National Fire Protection Association–NFPA, Environmental Protection Agency –EPA, Department of Transportation–DOT, *etc.*).

Flammable or explosive limits—The upper and lower vapor concentrations at which a mixture will burn or explode.

Flammable solids—Any solid material, other than explosives, that is liable to cause fires through friction, absorption of moisture, spontaneous chemical changes, retained heat from manufacturing or processing, or which can be ignited readily and when ignited burns so vigorously and persistently as to create a serious transportation hazard.

Flashpoint—The lowest temperature of a liquid at which it gives off enough vapor to form, with air, an ignitable mixture near the surface of the liquid. Two tests are used to determine flashpoint: Open Cup and Closed Cup.

Flow-proportional composite sampling—In environmental sampling, a type of sample that generally is associated with stream or wastewater discharge samples and thus is not normally utilized in the investigation of hazardous waste sites.

Fluid—Under the Safe Drinking Water Act, a material or substance that flows or moves whether in a semi-solid, liquid, sludge, gas, or any other form or state.

Fogs—In industrial hygiene, suspended droplets of liquid formed by condensation from the vapor state.

Force majeure—In business, circumstances and events that occur that are beyond the control of the contractor.

Foreseeable emergency—Under the Occupational Safety and Health regulations, any potential occurrence (*e.g.*, equipment failure, rupture of containers, *etc.*) that could result in an uncontrolled release of a hazardous chemical into the workplace.

Free water—In hydrogeology, ground water not incorporated into the soil as moisture.

Freezing point—In chemistry, the temperature at which a liquid changes to a crystalline solid.

Frequency of exposure—In toxicology, the number of exposures per time period. The frequency influences the amount of substance available for absorption into the body.

Friable asbestos-containing material—Material that, when dry, may be crumbled, pulverized, or reduced to powder by hand pressure and includes any damaged nonfriable material.

Full emergency (major event alert)—An emergency that impacts the public and necessitates full mobilization of facility and community resources, such as a major plant explosion.

Fumes—In industrial hygiene, solid, microscopic, airborne particles formed by condensation of vapors generated from evaporating (*e.g.,* molten) substances. For example, in welding, metal fumes are generated from the molten electrodes and base metals.

Functional group—In chemistry, an atom or group of atoms, other than hydrogen, bonded to the chain or ring of carbon atoms (*e.g.*, the –OH group of alcohols, the –COOH group of carboxylic acids, the –O– group of ethers). Functional groups determine the behavior of molecules. Consequently, the unique hazards of an organic compound often are determined by its functional group(s).

G

GA—Military designation for the chemical weapon, Tabun a *nerve agent*.

G-agent—A type of chemical weapon that is classified as a nerve agent and is less persistent in the environment. G-agents tend to be volatile liquids (see also *V-agent*).

Gaining streams—In hydrogeology, streams that act as discharge points for ground water.

Gamma (γ) rays—An example of electromagnetic radiation, as is visible light. Gamma rays originate from the nucleus of an atom. They are capable of traveling long distances through air and most other materials. Gamma rays require more *shielding* material, such as lead or steel, to reduce their numbers than is required for alpha and beta particles.

Gantt chart—In project management, a tool used to demonstrate chronologically the description of tasks within a project. The chart may also show resources, duration, and costs.

Gap analysis—In ISO 14000, a process used to develop a clear understanding of the gap between current environmental management activities and documentation and ISO 14001 requirements. This is accomplished through a section-by-section review of current environmental management activities against the ISO 14001 criteria.

Gases—In industrial hygiene, substances that are in the gaseous state at room temperature (25° C) and one atmosphere pressure (760 mm Hg).

GB—Military designation for the chemical weapon, Sarin a **nerve agent**.

GD—Military designation for the chemical weapon Soman, a **nerve agent**.

General duty clause—In *safety*, Section 5 (a) 1 of the Occupational Safety and Health Act, which declares that each employer has a duty to furnish to his employees a workplace free from recognized hazards that are likely to cause serious physical harm or death. The implication of the clause is that employers must use common sense in providing a safe and healthful workplace. Employers operating facilities at which regulated or any other highly hazardous chemicals are present, regardless of the quantity, are subject to the EPA and OSHA general duty clauses. In the *Risk Management Program,* the general duty clause applies to owners and operators of stationary sources at which regulated or any other EHSs are present in a process, regardless of the amount of the substance. Under OSHA's *Process Safety Management* rules, the general duty clause requires employers to design and maintain a safe plant, identify hazards, and prevent or minimize the consequences of accidental releases of chemicals.

General liability insurance—In business, a type of insurance that provides coverage in the event that someone is injured or has property damaged while on the insured's premises, the customer's premises, or while using the company's products or services.

General partnership—Under the Federal Uniform Partnership Act, a business that is owned by two or more persons who share in the risk and the rewards.

Generally achievable control technology (GACT)—Under the Clean Air Act, an alternative emissions control standard that may be applied to **area sources** of Hazardous Air Pollutants in order to control the most significant HAPs emissions.

Genotoxicity—In toxicology, the ability of a substance to cause damage to the genetic material (*e.g.*, DNA).

GF—Military designation for the chemical weapon Cycloarin, a **nerve agent**.

Grab sample—In environmental sampling, a discrete aliquot taken from one specific sampling location at a specific point in time. The analytical results from a grab sample should provide a good representation of the concentrations of the contaminants present at the point the sample was taken.

Gravity-based penalties—That portion of the penalty over and above the economic benefit. They reflect the egregiousness of the violator's behavior and constitute the punitive portion of the penalty.

Greenfields—Uncontaminated properties outside of urban areas that have not previously been sites of industrial or commercial uses (as contrasted to ***brownfields***).

Gross profit—In business, revenue or income minus the cost of goods sold.

H

Half-life—The time required for a population of atoms of a given radionuclide to decrease, by radioactive decay, to exactly one-half of its original number is called the radionuclide's half-life. No operation, either chemical or physical, can change the decay rate of a radioactive substance. Half-lives range from much less than a microsecond to more than a billion years. The longer the half-life, the more stable the nuclide. After one half-life, half the original atoms will remain; after two half-lives, one fourth (or ½ of ½) will remain; after three half-lives, one eighth of the original number (½ of ½ of ½) will remain; and so on.

Hazard—In *toxicology,* an inherent property of the chemical that would exist no matter what quantity was present. Under the *Process Safety Management rules*, an inherent characteristic of a material, system, process, or plant that must be controlled in order to avoid undesirable consequences. Typical hazards associated with processes involving highly hazardous chemicals include: combustible/flammable, explosive, toxic, simple and chemical asphyxiant, corrosive, chemical reactant, thermal, potential energy, kinetic energy, electrical energy, and pressure source hazards.

Hazard assessment (HA)—Under *OSHA safety standards,* a survey of the job area to identify sources of hazards, and consideration of the following categories of hazards: impact, penetration, compression, chemical, heat, harmful dust, light radiation, falling, *etc.*; the sources or potential problem areas for these hazards; the potential for injuries. Under the *Risk Management Program* rules, the evaluation of the off-site consequences of accidental releases to public health and the environment. See also ***Hazard or toxicity assessment (dose-response assessment).***

Hazard identification—The first step in risk assessment. Hazard Identification is used to determine the hazardous chemical's relative toxicity, concentration, extent of contamination, and toxicological end point(s) of concern.

Hazard or toxicity assessment (dose-response assessment)—In risk assessment, a methodology used to determine whether dose-response information is available for the chemical of interest. A hazard assessment relies on toxicological and epidemiological data to ascertain specific threshold exposure levels. It examines and attempts to quantify the severity of a potential hazard. This assessment requires information to establish risks for both carcinogens and noncarcinogenic agents. See also ***hazard assessment.***

Hazard quotient—For noncarcinogens, a quantitative appraisal of the levels of exposure that may pose risks because they exceed the ambient levels found in an unexposed population. The hazard quotient is calculated using the Maximum Allowable Daily Intake, the Chronic Daily Intake, and the Reference Dose.

Hazardous chemicals—As defined by the Occupational Safety and Health Administration, all chemicals listed by OSHA with a permissible exposure limit (PEL) or by the American Conference of Governmental Industrial Hygienists (ACGIH) with a Threshold Limit Value (TLV) or those listed in the National Toxicology Program (NTP) Annual Report on Carcinogens (latest edition) or have been found to be a potential carcinogen in the International Agency for Research on Cancer (IARC) Monographs (latest editions), or by OSHA. Hazardous waste; tobacco or tobacco products; wood or wood products; food, drugs, or cosmetics that are intended for personal use; or ***articles*** are not considered to be hazardous chemicals.

Hazardous material—Under the Department of Transportation rules, a substance or material that has been determined by the Secretary of Transportation to be capable of posing an unreasonable risk to health, safety, and property when transported in commerce, and which has been so designated. The term includes hazardous substances, hazardous wastes, marine pollutants, and elevated-temperature materials, materials designated as hazardous under the provisions of 49 CFR 172.101, and materials that meet the defining criteria for hazard classes and divisions in 49 CFR 173. The hazard categories include: (1) explosives, (2) gases, (3) flammable liquids, (4) flammable solids, (5) spontaneous combustibles, and dangerous when wet, (6) oxidizers and organic peroxides, (7) poisons and infectious substances, (8) corrosives and (9) all other hazardous materials.

Hazardous samples—In environmental sampling, samples that present a relatively high risk to health or the environment because of the potential level and type of contamination. Hazardous samples can be classified as high and moderate hazard samples. The determination of sample type is based on existing analytical data, background information (*e.g.*, past activities conducted at the site, container labels, *etc.*) and/or policy. Some organizations have a simple policy of "if it is on-site, the sample is hazardous" and "if it is off-site, the sample is environmental".

Hazardous substance USTs—One of the two broad categories of underground storage tanks that contain either: (1) hazardous substances as defined in Section 101(14) of the Comprehensive Environmental Response, Compensation, and Liability Act (CERCLA), 40 CFR 302.4, but not including any of the substances regulated as a hazardous waste under RCRA Subtitle C, or (2) any mixture of such CERCLA-listed substances and petroleum that is not a petroleum UST system.

Hazardous substances—Under the Comprehensive Environmental Response, Compensation, and Liability Act, elements, compounds, mixtures, solutions, and substances which, when released into the environment, may present substantial danger to public health and welfare or the environment. CERCLA hazardous substances are specifically listed in EPA's regulation 40 CFR 302.4, which specifies reportable quantities (RQs) for each substance. When the RQ is exceeded in a chemical release incident, a facility owner is required to report the release to the National Response Center. Substances designated under Sections 307(a) and 311(b)(4) of the CWA, hazardous air pollutants listed under Section 112 of the CAA, RCRA hazardous wastes and chemicals or mixtures for which EPA has taken action under Section 7 of the Toxic Substances Control Act (TSCA) are also CERCLA hazardous substances and EPA has the authority to designate additional hazardous substances as well.

Hazardous waste—Under the Resource Conservation and Recovery Act, a waste defined pursuant to RCRA in 40 CFR 261 that is a solid waste which, because of quantity, concentration, or physical, chemical, or infectious characteristics: (1) causes or significantly increases mortality or serious irreversible or incapacitating reversible illness, or (2) poses a substantial present or potential hazard to human health or the environment when improperly managed.

Hazardous waste manifest—Under the Resource Conservation and Recovery Act, a chain of custody for a hazardous waste that tracks the waste in transport.

Hazmat employee—Under the Department of Transportation hazardous materials regulations, an employee who handles hazardous materials and directly affects hazardous material transportation safety.

HD—Military designation for Mustard Gas (also H, Sulfur Mustard; HD, distilled mustard) often in combination with Lewisite (L), a ***blister agent***.

Health hazard—As defined by the *Occupational Safety and Health Administration*, a hazard associated with a chemical for which there is statistically significant evidence, based on at least one study conducted in accordance with established scientific principles, that acute or chronic health effects may occur in exposed workers. Health hazards are categorized as: toxic or highly toxic, reproductive toxins, carcinogens, irritants, corrosives, sensitizers, hepatotoxins (liver), nephrotoxins (kidney), neurotoxins (nerve), hematopoietic (blood) or other agents that damage the lungs, eyes, skin, and mucous membranes. In *industrial hygiene*, an agent or mixture of agents for which there is statistically significant evidence based on at least one study conducted in accordance with established scientific principles that acute or chronic health effects may occur in exposed employees.

Heat content—In chemistry, the heat released by complete combustion of a unit-weight of material.

Hematotoxicity—In toxicology, the damage a substance may cause to the formed elements of the blood (*e.g.*, red blood cells, white blood cells, platelets, *etc.*) and/or the bone marrow (area of blood cell formation).

Hepatitis B carriers—An individual who has had the hepatitis B virus in his/her blood for more than six months.

Hepatitis B virus (HBV)—A disease caused by a highly infectious virus that attacks the liver. HBV infection can lead to severe illness, liver damage, and in some cases death, and is the most common cause of liver cancer worldwide.

Hepatitis C virus (HCV)—A viral illness that affects the liver that is spread by blood-to-blood contact, and is therefore a bloodborne pathogen. Some of the most common ways of spreading the virus are: (1) transfusion of blood products, (2) intravenous drug use, (3) tattooing and body piercing, (4) sharing needles. Menstrual blood can contain the virus.

Hepatotoxicity—In toxicology, the damage a substance may cause to the liver. Hepatotoxicity can be caused by cell death (necrosis), accumulation of lipids, damage to the bile ducts, inflammation (hepatitis), and the presence of fibrotic tissue in the liver.

Highly hazardous chemical—Under the Process Safety Management rules, a substance possessing toxic, reactive, flammable, or explosive properties. Appendix A to the PSM Rule lists 137 highly hazardous chemicals, toxics, and reactives. Also covered by the Rule are flammable liquids and gases in quantities of 10,000 pounds or more.

HN—Military designation for nitrogen mustards a class of chemical weapons, *blister agents.*

Hot substances—Substances that are considered thermally hazardous because they are 120°F (49°C) or hotter to the touch.

Hot work—Under the Process Safety Management rules, work involving electric or gas welding, cutting, brazing, or similar flame, or spark-producing operations.

Human environment—Under the National Environmental Policy Act, encompasses the natural and physical environment (air, water, geography, and geology) as well as the relationship of people with that environment including health and safety, socioeconomics (jobs, housing, schools, transportation), cultural resources, noise, and aesthetics.

Hydraulic conductivity—In an aquifer, the length (distance traveled)/ time (potential velocity) value.

Hydrocarbons—In chemistry, chemical compounds consisting primarily of carbon and hydrogen.

Hydrofracing—The practice of injecting fluids at high pressure to enhance the production of oil, gas, or water wells by increasing the size and extent of fractures in the bedrock.

Hydrologic cycle—In hydrogeology, the constant movement of water by precipitation, overland runoff, and evaporation.

I

Identification number—Under the Department of Transportation hazardous materials regulations, a four-digit number assigned to the commodity, or group of similar commodities, by the United Nations or the United States.

IDLH concentration—In industrial hygiene, an atmospheric concentration of any toxic, corrosive, or asphyxiant substance that poses an immediate threat to life or would interfere with an individual's ability to escape from a dangerous atmosphere (29 CFR 1910.120).

Ignitable, corrosive, reactive (ICR) wastes—Under the Resource Conservation and Recovery Act, wastes that exhibit any one or more of the characteristics of ignitability, corrosivity, and reactivity. These chemical properties can be immediately dangerous if improperly managed and thus merit special protective measures in the regulations.

Immediate or acute toxicity—In toxicology, a reaction by the body that occurs rapidly after a single exposure to a toxic substance.

Imminent danger—Under the Occupational Safety and Health Act, any condition where there is the reasonable certainty that an immediate danger exists that may cause death or serious physical harm before the danger can be eliminated through normal enforcement procedures.

In vitro *methods*—In toxicology, laboratory scale toxicological studies performed in test tubes. These tests are performed on tissue or cells in order to observe changes in the structure or growth of cells.

Incident command system (ICS)—A system used for the management of an emergency response and is based upon basic business management practices. The main functional areas of planning, directing, organizing, coordinating, communicating, delegating, and evaluating are under the overall direction of the Incident Commander.

Incineration—A process used for the treatment of hazardous waste that utilizes thermal decomposition via oxidation to reduce carbonaceous matter.

Income—An accounting term defining the money received by a business in a given period of time as a result of operating the business; the goods and services sold. Also called revenue, or sales. Sometimes used to mean profit or earnings as a shortened form of net income.

Income statement—In accounting, a report that shows whether the business earned a profit (net income is positive) or a loss. By describing the change in owner's equity, the income statement links the company's balance sheets from the beginning to the end of the reporting period.

Independent effect—In toxicology, toxicity of substances that are asserted independently of each other.

Indirect marketing—In business, a type of marketing that does not involve direct advertising, yet it increases visibility and credibility. Examples include: developing and nurturing a professional network, lecturing to professional or community groups, organizing and leading seminars, joining and participating in trade associations, authoring and presenting papers. High quality work products are, in and of themselves, oftentimes the most valuable marketing tools.

Indirect sources—Under the Clean Air Act, sources that do not produce pollution but have the ability to attract vehicles, or other mobile sources of pollution. Examples include: buildings, parking lots, garages, roads, and highways.

Indoor air quality—The quality of the air inside a building including the concentrations of pollutants and thermal conditions that affect health, comfort, and performance of occupants.

Industrial activity stormwater discharges—Under the Clean Water Act, discharges of stormwater that are permitted through a general permit system called the Multi-Sector General Permit, or through an individual permit.

Infectious agents—Biological weapons agents that can produce numerous bacteria, viruses, or fungi. The infectious agents can mutate similar to other living organisms and will reproduce in a host organism. The infectious agents, unchecked in a population, will spread to cause high casualty counts. Examples include anthrax and the plague.

Inherently waste-like—Under the Resource Conservation and Recovery Act, materials that ordinarily are managed as waste or that pose a substantial hazard when recycled, including specific dioxin- and furan-containing wastes.

Initial training—Under the Occupational Safety and Health Administration's Process Safety Management rules, training that is required before an employee begins participating in operations that use highly hazardous chemicals.

Injunction—A court order directing the defendant to take some action or to refrain from an action.

Inland marine coverage—In business, a type of insurance coverage that provides for property that is actually in transit, is at a fixed location awaiting transport, or is a movable type of goods that is often at different locations.

Innocent landowner defense—Under the Comprehensive Environmental Response, Compensation, and Liability Act, a defense established by a preponderance of the evidence that the defendant: (a) exercised due care with respect to the hazardous substance concerned, and (b) took precautions against foreseeable acts or omissions of any such third party and the consequences that could foreseeably result from such actions or omissions.

Inorganic compound—In chemistry a compound that is not classified as an ***organic compound***.

In-process wastes—Under the Resource Conservation and Recovery Act, hazardous wastes generated in product or raw material tanks, transport vehicles or vessels, pipelines, manufacturing process units (except surface impoundments), until removed or until 90 days after the process ceases.

Inspections—Under the Clean Air Act and in the Risk Management rules in 40 CFR 68, inspections are site visits to check on the accuracy of the RMP data and on implementation of all 40 CFR 68 elements. Inspections will focus on the underlying risk management program. See also ***Audits*** and ***Reviews.***

Intakes—In human health risk assessment, exposure estimates that represent the normalized exposure rate.

Interim measures—Under the Resource Conservation and Recovery Act, actions used to mitigate any immediate threats to the environment from a waste management unit while a comprehensive corrective action strategy is developed and implemented. Interim measures range from simple actions, such as fencing an area to prevent access, to complex groundwater pump-and-treat operations to prevent further contaminant migration.

Into the environment—Under the Comprehensive Environmental Response, Compensation, and Liability Act, the status of a release of a hazardous substance when it is not completely contained within a building or structure, even if it remains on the plant or facility grounds.

Ion—In chemistry, a charged particle that is produced when an atom or group of atoms gains or loses one or more electrons.

Ionized compounds—Chemical materials (acids, bases, and salts) that are present in a charged state.

Ionizing radiation—Radiation that has enough energy to cause atoms to lose electrons and become ions. **Alpha** and **beta particles**, as well as **gamma** and **x-rays**, are all examples of ionizing radiation. Ultraviolet, infrared, and visible light are examples of non-ionizing radiation. Radiation can cause the body's molecules to break apart and form electrically charged particles called **ions** that bond readily with other body chemicals and form toxicants such as hydrogen peroxide.

Irreversible effects—In toxicology, adverse effects to the body that do not reverse after the exposure ceases.

Isomers—In chemistry, different structural arrangements with the same chemical formulas (*e.g.*, *n*-butane and *t*-butane).

Isopleths—In hydrogeology, contour lines drawn between points of equal ground water elevations.

Isotopes—In chemistry, atoms of a given element that have the same number of protons but different numbers of neutrons.

J

Joint venture—A business relationship that is much like a **general partnership** except the relationship is for a limited time period or for a specific project.

Judgmental sampling—A method of environmental sampling that provides information on worst-case conditions and is useful for identifying contaminants of concern at a site but not the extent of contamination that will require additional sampling utilizing other approaches.

Judicial branch—The part of the United States government where the court system is located and where environmental laws are interpreted and enforced.

Judicial enforcement—Enforcement that occurs once the agency takes a case to the courthouse for lawsuit or criminal prosecution.

K

K_{ow}—See Octanol/Water Partition Coefficient.

L

Lab packs—Under the Resource Conservation and Recovery Act and Department of Transportation hazardous materials standards, a means of preparing numerous small containers of hazardous waste (*e.g.*, discarded chemicals) for transportation and disposal.

Label—Under Federal Insecticide, Fungicide and Rodenticide Act, all labels and other written, printed, or graphic matter that is attached to the pesticide device or any of its containers or wrappers and that accompanies the pesticide or device at any time. A reference may be made on the label or in literature accompanying the pesticide or device.

Labor yield—In business, the product of the firm's utilization and net multiplier.

Laboratory—As defined in the Occupational Safety and Health Administration Laboratory Standard, a facility where the laboratory use of hazardous chemicals occurs and where relatively small quantities of hazardous chemicals are used on a nonproduction basis.

Laboratory scale—As defined in the Occupational Safety and Health Administration Laboratory Standard, work with substances in which the containers used for reactions, transfers, and other handling of substances are designed to be easily and safely manipulated by one person and excludes commercial quantities of materials.

Laboratory use of hazardous chemicals—As defined in the Occupational Safety and Health Administration Laboratory Standard, the handling or use of chemicals in which: (1) chemical manipulations are carried out on a *laboratory scale*, (2) multiple chemical procedures or chemicals are used, (3) the procedures involved are not part of a production process, nor in any way simulate a production process, and (4) protective laboratory practices and equipment are available and in common use to minimize the potential for employee exposure to hazardous chemicals.

Land-based units—Under the Resource Conservation and Recovery Act, units such as surface impoundments, waste piles, land treatment units, and landfills, that are used for land treatment, storage, or disposal of hazardous waste and pose relatively high risk of contaminating ground water.

Land disposal—Broadly defined under the Resource Conservation and Recovery Act to include virtually any temporary or permanent placement of hazardous waste in or on the land (such as in surface impoundments, waste piles, landfills, or land treatment facilities).

Land disposal units—Under the Resource Conservation and Recovery Act, surface impoundments, landfills, and land treatment units.

LDR-prohibited waste—Under the Resource Conservation and Recovery Act, an ***LDR-restricted waste*** that is actually prohibited from land disposal. Generally, a restricted waste is a prohibited waste upon the effective date of the treatment standard if the waste does not meet the applicable treatment standard and no other variances are applicable.

LDR-restricted waste—Under the Resource Conservation and Recovery Act, a waste that has a promulgated land disposal restriction treatment standard.

Lead-based paint—As defined by the Department of Housing and Urban Development, any paint, varnish or shellac that contains a minimum of 1 mg/cm^2 lead (XRF) or more than 0.5% lead in the dried solid (paint chip).

Legislative branch—The part of the United States Government that enacts laws and creates regulatory agencies with the authority to carry out their responsibilities.

Letter of Intent—In business, the simplest and least formal kind of ***contract***. The terms of the agreement are clearly defined within the body of the letter, but in a less formal language than a general contract.

Level A—Under the Occupational Safety and Health Administration regulations, the level of protection that is required when there is the greatest potential for exposure to skin, respiratory and eye hazards. Level A includes respiratory protection with positive pressure, full face-piece self-contained breathing apparatus (SCBA), or positive pressure supplied-air respirator with escape SCBA; totally encapsulated chemical- and vapor-protective suits; inner and outer chemical-resistant gloves; and disposable protective suits, gloves, and boots.

Level B—Under the Occupational Safety and Health Administration regulations, the level of protection that is required when the highest level of respiratory protection but a lesser level of skin protection is needed. Level B includes respiratory protection with positive pressure, full face-piece self-contained breathing apparatus (SCBA) or positive pressure supplied air respirator with escape SCBA; inner and outer chemical-resistant gloves; faceshield; hooded chemical-resistant clothing, coveralls, and outer chemical-resistant boots.

Level C—Under the Occupational Safety and Health Administration regulations, the level of protection that is required when the concentration and type of airborne substances are known and the criteria for using air-purifying respirators are met. Typical Level C equipment includes full-face air-purifying respirators, inner and outer chemical-resistant gloves, hard hat, escape mask and disposable chemical-resistant outer boots.

Level D—Under the Occupational Safety and Health Administration regulations the minimum level of protection. Level D may be sufficient when no contaminants are present or work operations preclude splashes, immersion, or the other potential for unexpected inhalation or contact with hazardous chemicals. Appropriate Level D protective equipment may include gloves, coveralls, safety glasses, faceshield, and chemical-resistant, steel-toe boots or shoes.

Level of training—In incident response, levels outlined in OSHA standard 29 CFR 1920.120: First Responder Operations, Hazardous Materials Technician, Awareness, and Incident Commander levels.

Liabilities—In accounting, the debts to others including accounts payable, salaries and wages, taxes payable, notes payable, and interest payable.

Lifetime acceptable daily intake (ADI)—A "safe" lifetime dose of a substance that has been interpolated from dose-response curves, taking into account safety and other modifying factors.

Limited emergencies (standby notification alert)—Emergencies that have no public danger and require a limited staff for the Command Post, which may be a temporary setup in an office or near the scene, such as a break in a water pipe in an office area requiring immediate maintenance attention.

Limited liability company—A form of business structure where the stockholders are not personally liable for the debt that the company incurs. A Limited Liability Company (LLC) provides the tax efficiencies and operational flexibility of a partnership and the limited liability features of a corporation. LLCs are distinguished from regular corporations in that they can not have more than two of the four characteristics that define corporations: limited liability to the extent of assets; continuity of life; centralization of management; and free transferability of ownership interests.

Limited partnership—A form of business structure where the liability of the partners is limited to the amount of their investment. The general partner bears the risk and has day-to-day control; other investors have limited exposure.

Listed hazardous wastes—Under the Resource Conservation and Recovery Act, wastes that are specifically listed in 40 CFR 261, Subpart D as hazardous on the basis that they may exhibit hazardous characteristic(s) such as ignitability, corrosivity, reactivity, or toxicity; or otherwise may be toxic or acutely hazardous.

Local toxicity—In toxicology, the reaction of a body to a substance that occurs at the site of chemical contact. The chemical need not be absorbed to cause this reaction.

Long-term recovery—In disaster response, the activities that continue until the entire disaster area is completely redeveloped, either as it was in the past or for entirely new purposes that are less disaster-prone.

Losing streams—In hydrogeology, streams that can actually help recharge the ground water, frequently found in carbonate areas.

Loudness—In industrial hygiene, the sound level measured in decibels. The sound level of a quiet room is about 40 decibels, a person speaking about 65 decibels, a vacuum cleaner about 75 decibels, a power lawn mower about 95 decibels, and a gunshot above 120 decibels. The OSHA limit for continuous noise exposure for a normal 8-hour work shift is 90 decibels.

Lowest achievable emissions rate (LAER)—Under the Clean Air Act, the most stringent achievable emissions limitation for a particular source. Unlike ***BACT***, LAER does not take into account economic impacts and other costs.

Lowest observed adverse effect level—In human health risk assessment, the lowest level at which no adverse effect is observed.

[handwritten: ?: should this be "an"]

M

Macro-encapsulation—A method of treatment for hazardous waste in which the solid waste is encapsulated within an impervious layer in order to eliminate the exposure to leaching.

Magnitude of exposure—In human health risk assessment, the estimated amount of an agent available at the exchange boundaries during a specified time period.

Major fiber release—Under the Environmental Protection Agency asbestos regulations, an event in which "greater than three square or linear feet of asbestos-containing building material becomes dislodged from its substrate."

Major source—Under the Clean Air Act, a ***stationary source*** that emits or has the potential to emit a significant quantity (as defined in the CAA) of one or more air pollutants.

Male reproductive toxicity—In toxicology, the damage a substance may cause to the male reproductive system.

Management representative—In ISO 14000, the person who champions the effort to implement an Environmental Management System by taking the lead in coordinating the implementation of the EMS, overseeing development of EMS documentation, and obtaining employee buy-in into the program.

Management—As defined by the Federal Emergency Management Agency, the coordination of an organized effort to attain specific goals or objectives.

Manufacture—Under the Toxic Substances Control Act, *manufacture* means to "import, produce, or manufacture" a toxic substance.

Manufacturing use product—Under the Federal Insecticide, Fungicide and Rodenticide Act, any pesticide product that is not an ***end use product***.

Margin of profit (margin)—In business, gross profit or revenue divided by net sales. Margin is used to measure a firm's operating efficiency and pricing policies in order to determine how competitive the firm is within the industry.

Market—In business, the products or services offered by a company and also the geographical area and clients or customers that the business serves.

Marketing plan—In business, a plan that describes the company's market and how the company plans to acquire new customers and keep existing ones.

Material safety data sheet (MSDS)—Under the Occupational Safety and Health Administration regulations, a document that provides the user with important safety, health, and environmental information about a chemical product.

Materials and supplies—In business, the items needed to run a business. For and environmental business, this may include such diverse items as personal protective equipment, spill control materials, sediment and erosion control products, wastewater treatment chemicals, and specialty microbe mixtures for soil or wastewater treatment.

Maximum achievable control technology (MACT)—Under the Clean Air Act, a control technology based on the average emissions limitation achieved by the best 12% of existing sources in a particular category. If there are fewer than 30 sources in the category, then the emissions limitation is based on the best performing 5 sources.

Maximum allowable increase (MAI)—Under the Clean Air Act, the upper limit for the level of increase for permitted emissions from a ***stationary source***. In the regulations, MAI is referred to as an *ambient air increment,* and the permitted emissions levels result in *consumption* of the increment.

Maximum contaminant level—Under the Safe Drinking Water Act, the highest allowable level and enforceable limit for a certain contaminants in drinking water.

Maximum contaminant level goals—Under the Safe Drinking Water Act, concentration levels for contaminants that are less than the ***Maximum Contaminant Levels*** and are set at a value where there are no known or anticipated adverse health effects. They are public health goals and are not enforceable limits.

Mechanical treatment—In the treatment of hazardous waste, those procedures that modify the physical properties of waste materials; for example: filtration, phase separation, filter pressing of suspended materials, centrifugation, agitation, adsorption, *etc.* Also known as ***physical treatment.***

Media cleanup standards (MCS)—Under the Resource Conservation and Recovery Act, the concentrations of hazardous waste or hazardous waste constituents that must be achieved in groundwater, surface water, soils, and air in order to comply with the standards for corrective measures. MCSs are the established concentrations set for each medium that ensures the protection of human health and the environment.

Media of concern—In human health risk assessment, any currently contaminated media to which individuals may be exposed or through which chemicals may be transported to potential receptors; and any currently uncontaminated media that may become contaminated in the future due to contaminant transport.

Median effective dose (ED_{50})—The single dose of a substance that can be expected to cause a particular effect (other than lethality) to occur in 50% of the exposed population.

Median lethal concentration (LC_{50})—The single dose of a chemical, quantified as an exposure concentration (*e.g.*, concentration in air such as ppm or mg/m^3) that can be expected to cause death in 50% of the exposed population. The LC_{50} is similar to the LD_{50} except that the chemical is quantified as an exposure concentration rather than a dose (*e.g.*, mg/kg-body weight).

Median lethal dose (LD_{50})—The single dose of a chemical that can be expected to cause death in 50% of the exposed population.

Melting point (mp)—The temperature at which a solid changes to a liquid.

Mesothelioma—A malignancy of the lining of the chest or abdominal cavity. Pleural mesothelioma is a malignant growth of the pleura, the exterior lining of the lungs. Peritoneal mesothelioma is a malignancy of the peritoneum of the abdominal cavity. Either form of the disease spreads quickly and is always fatal.

Meth psychosis—The mental state brought on by methamphetamine abuse; characterized by frustration, restlessness, anxiety and unprovoked violence.

Micro-encapsulation—A method of treatment for hazardous waste in which a semi-homogeneous product results from the treatment of finely divided powders, sludges, or viscous liquids.

Milestone—In project management, individual project segment or grouping of similar project tasks. Objectives may be used to measure the progress of the project. See *objective.*

Military munition specifically identified as a solid waste—Under the Resource Conservation and Recovery Act, a specific category of hazardous waste specified in 40 CFR 266, Subpart M.

Minor emergencies (minor event alert)—Emergencies that are handled on a regular day-to-day basis by routine procedure, such as an employee with a laceration requiring first aid.

Miscellaneous materials—Under the Environmental Protection Agency asbestos regulations, mostly nonfriable asbestos products and materials such as floor tile, ceiling tile, roofing felt, concrete pipe, outdoor siding, and fabrics.

Mists—In industrial hygiene, suspended droplets of liquid formed from a bulk liquid by mechanical action, such as spraying.

Mitigation—According to the *Federal Emergency Management Agency*, those actions and activities taken to reduce or eliminate the chance of occurrence or the effects of a disaster. Under the *National Environmental Policy Act*, actions taken to reduce otherwise significant environmental effects, which includes (1) avoiding the impact altogether by not taking a certain action or parts of an action, (2) minimizing impact by limiting the degree or magnitude of the action and its implementation, (3) rectifying the impact by repairing, rehabilitating, or restoring the affected environment, (4) reducing or eliminating the impact over time by preservation and maintenance operations during the life of the action, (5) compensating for the impact by replacing or providing substitute resources or environments.

Mitigation system—Under the Risk Management Program rules, specific activities, technologies, or equipment designed or deployed to capture or control substances upon loss of containment to minimize exposure to the public or the environment. Passive mitigation means equipment, devices, or technologies that function without human, mechanical, or energy input; common examples include dikes, berms, and flame arresters. Active mitigation systems are equipment, devices, or technologies that require human, mechanical, or energy input to function. Examples include relief and isolation valves, sprinkler systems, and fire brigades.

Mixed transuranic waste (MTU)—Waste that has a hazardous component and radioactive elements heavier than uranium.

Mixed waste (MW)—Under the *Resource Conservation and Recovery Act*, a hazardous waste that also contains certain radioactive constituents subject to the Atomic Energy Act or constituents (PCBs) subject to TSCA. Under the *Federal Facilities Compliance Act of 1992*, waste that is a mixture of hazardous wastes (as defined under RCRA), and source, special nuclear, or by-product (*i.e.*, radioactive) material subject to the Atomic Energy Act (AEA) of 1954.

Mixing zone assessment—Under the Clean Water Act, an assessment that assumes that there is an allocated zone within the receiving water where exceedances of the chronic water quality criteria is allowed, provided the designated use of the water is not impaired.

Mixture—Under the Toxic Substances Control Act, any combination of two or more chemical substances if the combination does not occur in nature and is not, in whole or in part, the result of a chemical reaction. There are two exceptions to this definition: (1) The combination is *not* a mixture if it occurs as the result of a chemical reaction in which there are no new chemical substances; and (2) the combination is *not* a mixture if it could have been manufactured for commercial purposes without a chemical reaction at the time the combination's chemical substances were combined.

Mixture rule—Under the Resource Conservation and Recovery Act, a rule that applies to listed hazardous waste mixed with solid waste, and specifies that the waste codes of the hazardous waste apply to the mixture unless the hazardous waste was listed on the basis of hazardous characteristic(s) only and the mixture exhibits none of the characteristics.

Mobile sources—Under the Clean Air Act, sources that are not ***stationary sources***, such as vehicles, airplanes, and other forms of transportation.

Mode of response—In incident response, the choice of a defensive or offensive approach to the incident; to avoid (defensive) or make contact with (offensive) hazardous materials to prevent or control further harm due to the incident. Defensive mode responses should be considered before offensive responses are made.

Model accreditation plan (MAP)—Under the Environmental Protection Agency asbestos regulations, a plan that established five areas of accreditation as the appropriate training requirements for individuals who would: (1) perform inspections, (2) prepare management plans for buildings, (3) supervise abatement projects, (4) serve as workers on abatement projects, or (5) design abatement projects.

Modified source—Under the Clean Air Act, a ***stationary source*** that has been physically changed or is operated in a manner that increases the emissions of existing or new pollutants.

Molecule—In chemistry, a group of atoms that are chemically bonded together; *e.g.,* O_2, BF_3, CH_4, *etc.*

Molecular and experimental embryology—In toxicology, one approach to *in vitro* studies which is used to detect abnormal changes at the molecular and embryonic levels.

Monte Carlo analysis—In risk analysis, a method used to evaluate the risk analyses for site conditions that have many complex variables. In Monte Carlo analysis, the probability curves for various uncertainty parameters are inserted into the calculations of risk.

Multiple chemical sensitivity—A condition in which a building occupant may be sensitive to a broad range of chemicals in the indoor air, each of which may occur at a very low concentration.

Multistate ozone nonattainment areas—Under the Clean Air Act, single ozone nonattainment areas that cover more than one state and are required to coordinate their implementation plans with other states.

Mutagens—In toxicology, substances that alter the genetic code in the gametes (sperm and/or eggs) of the body so that the appearance or function of the affected part of the body is changed and the change is passed along to following generations as a permanent alteration of the genetic structure.

N

National air monitoring stations (NAMS)—Under the Clean Air Act, more than a thousand key ambient air monitoring sites, located in areas of high population within the State and Local Air Monitoring Stations network, that are used to measure maximum pollutant concentrations.

National ambient air quality standards (NAAQS)—Under the Clean Air Act, health-based concentrations that are established for the six criteria air pollutants that threaten public health and welfare.

Navigable waters—Under the *Clean Water Act*, all "waters of the United States," including waters used in interstate commerce, waters subject to tides, interstate waters, and intrastate lakes, rivers, streams, wetlands, sloughs, prairie potholes, wet meadows, playa lakes, or natural ponds. Waters used by interstate travelers and migratory birds are also included. Ground water is not included unless there is a hydrological connection between the ground water and surface water or unless ground water is specifically included under a state program. Under the *Oil Pollution Act of 1990*, all waters that are used in interstate or foreign commerce, all interstate waters including wetlands, and all intrastate waters, such as lakes, rivers, streams, wetlands, sloughs, prairie potholes, wet meadows, playa lakes, or natural ponds.

Needleless system—Under the Occupational Safety and Health Administration's Bloodborne Pathogen standard, a device that does not use needles for A) the collection of bodily fluids or withdrawal of bodily fluids after initial venous or arterial access is established, B) the administration of medication or fluids, or C) any other procedure involving the potential for occupational exposure to bloodborne pathogens due to percutaneous injuries from contaminated sharps.

Negligence—Under tort law, a breach of duty or duty owed by the defendant to the plaintiff that causes damage to the plaintiff.

Nephrotoxicity—In toxicology, the damage a substance may cause to various portions of nephrons (the functional units of the kidney that produce urine including the glomerulus and the proximal tubule).

Nerve agents—A group of highly toxic organic esters of phosphoric acid derivatives. They are similar to certain kinds of pesticides (insect killers) called organophosphates in terms of how they work and what kind of harmful effects they cause. However, nerve agents are much more potent being among the deadliest of chemical agents. All the nerve agents cause their toxic effects by preventing the proper operation of the chemical that acts as the body's "off switch" for glands and muscles. Without an "off switch," the glands and muscles are constantly being stimulated. They may tire and no longer be able to sustain breathing function. They include such agents as Tabun (GA), Sarin (GB), Soman (GD), and VX.

Net income—In accounting, the profit earned when revenues exceed expenses over a certain period of time.

Net loss—In accounting, loss incurred when expenses exceed revenues over a certain period of time.

Net revenue—In business, gross sales less returns and allowances, freight out, and cash discounts allowed. Same as net sales.

Net sales—In business, gross sales less returns and allowances, freight out, and cash discounts allowed. Same as net revenue.

Neutron—The part of the nucleus of an atom that contributes mass or weight to the atom that is neutral in charge (neither a positive nor a negative charge). Neutrons are about the same size as protons.

New chemical substance—Under the Toxic Substances Control Act, any chemical substance that is not included in the chemical substance list compiled and published under Title 15, Section 2607 (b) of the United States Code.

New source—Under the Clean Air Act, a **stationary source** that intends to but has not yet started construction.

New source performance standards (NSPS)—Under the Clean Air Act, source-specific emission control limitations and requirements intended to promote the best technological system of continuous emissions reduction.

New source review (NSR)—Under the Clean Air Act, a scoping process for a proposed project that includes a review of emissions limitations, and public involvement similar to the ***prevention of significant deterioration*** process.

New tank system—As defined in the Underground Storage Tank rules, tanks for which installation commenced after December 22, 1988. All new tank systems must meet the requirements of Subparts B, C, and D before they can commence operation.

No action alternative—Under the National Environmental Policy Act, the action that would happen to the environment if the Federal agency's proposed action was not implemented.

No migration—The concept that waste constituents will not migrate from the facility; *i.e.*, there is no migration pathway.

No observed adverse effect level (NOAEL)—In toxicology, the highest dose at which no adverse effects have been detected.

Noise—In industrial hygiene and safety, unwanted sound that can be a safety hazard when present at high levels. Exposure to high levels of noise may cause hearing loss and other harmful health effects.

Nonattainment areas—Under the Clean Air Act, geographic areas in which the air quality is poorer than the National Ambient Air Quality Standards (*i.e.*, the concentrations of the ***criteria pollutants*** are above the standard).

Non-community water systems—Under the Safe Drinking Water Act, ***public water systems*** that do not serve a permanent resident population.

Non-ionized compound—In chemistry, a material that is not electrically charged.

Non-permit required confined spaces—As defined by the Occupational Safety and Health Administration, spaces that are: (1) large enough for an employee to enter, (2) have a limited or restricted means of entry or exit, and (3) have not been designed for continuous occupancy.

Nonpersistent agents—Chemical weapons agents that dissipate (lose their strength) within a few hours and pose mainly a threat to the lungs.

Non-point sources—In the Clean Water Act, sources of pollution that are diffuse, not emanating from a specific location or pipe. Examples include forestry, construction, urban area, and mining. Pollution from non-point sources generally enters the water as a result of stormwater runoff.

Non-transient, non-community water systems—Under the Safe Drinking Water Act, ***public water systems*** that serve at least twenty-five people, the same people all of the time, at least six months of the year.

Nontransportation-related facilities—Under the Oil Pollution Act of 1990, all fixed facilities, including support equipment (but excluding certain pipelines) railroad tank cars en route, transport trucks en route, and equipment associated with the transfer of bulk oil to or from water transportation vessels. The term also includes mobile or portable facilities such as drilling or workover rigs, production facilities, and portable fueling facilities while in a fixed, operating mode.

Nonwastewaters—Under the Resource Conservation and Recovery Act LDR regulations, wastes which have >1 wt% total organic carbon (TOC) and >1 wt% total suspended solids.

Normally unoccupied remote facility—Under the Process Safety Management rules, a facility that is operated, maintained, or serviced by employees who visit the facility only periodically to check its operation and to perform necessary operating or maintenance tasks. No employees are permanently stationed at the facility.

Not otherwise specified (NOS)—Under the Department of Transportation hazardous materials regulations, a material that meets the definition of a DOT hazard class but is not listed by a specific name in the hazardous materials table 172.101.

Notice of intent (NOI)—Under the National Environmental Policy Act, a notice published in the *Federal Register* that describes the proposed action, possible alternatives the agency is considering, background information on issues and potential impacts, and the proposed scoping process including whether, when, and where any scoping meeting will be held. The NOI also provides a contact point within the agency for further information.

Nuclear radiation—Energy in the form of waves or particles (also known as *radiation*). Radiation is a part of our natural world. People have always been exposed to radiation that originates from within the Earth (*terrestrial* sources) and from outer space (*cosmogenic* or *galactic* sources). Radiation also comes from sources such as radioactive material or from equipment such as x-ray machines, or accelerators.

Nucleus—The center of an atom that contains all the positive charges (protons) and neutrons of the atom, as well as all of the atom's weight.

O

O&M services—A type of environmental business that offers operations and maintenance services such as waste collection, treatment and disposal; hazardous materials/waste transportation; and industrial cleaning services.

Objectives—In an *environmental management system* (like ISO 14000) the goals the organization sets for itself based on its environmental policy and significant aspects. In *project management*, individual project segment or grouping of similar project tasks. Objectives may be used to measure the progress of the project. See *milestone.*

Occurrence policy—In business, a type of insurance policy that requires the insurance company to pay claims arising out of an occurrence causing bodily injury or property damage during the policy period regardless of when the claim is reported. The occurrence policy's *coverage trigger* is tied to the date of the event or accident that generates the claim.

Octanol/water partition coefficient (K_{ow})—The equilibrium ratio of the concentrations of material partitioned between octanol and water. This coefficient is considered to be an index of the potential of a chemical to be bioaccumulated. Higher values of K_{ow} are associated with greater bioaccumulation potential.

Off-site consequence analysis (OCA)—Under the Risk Management Program rules, an analysis of at least one worst-case release scenario and one alternative release scenario that addresses the impacts to off-site populations and the environment in areas beyond the property boundary of the stationary source or areas within the property boundary to which the public has routine and unrestricted access, both during or outside business hours.

Off-specification used oil—Under the Resource Conservation and Recovery Act, fuel (used oil that is not classified under the regulations as a hazardous waste fuel) that does not meet the criteria for ***specification used oil***.

Oil—Under the Clean Water Act, oil of any kind or in any form, including, but not limited to, petroleum, sludge, oil refuse, and oil mixed with wastes other than dredged spoil.

Operator—As defined in the Underground Storage Tank rules, any person in control of or having responsibility for the daily operation of the UST system.

Orbitals—In chemistry, the way the electrons organize themselves in the regions of space around an atom.

Organic bases—In chemistry, weak bases, such as amines, that can be corrosive to skin or other tissue.

Organic carboxylic acids—In chemistry, generally weak acids that can be very corrosive to skin.

Organic compound—In chemistry, a compound that contains carbon that is covalently bonded to hydrogen and may contain other compounds.

Organic peroxides—In chemistry, very hazardous and shock-sensitive compounds that present a serious fire and explosion hazard. Commonly encountered organic peroxides include benzyl peroxide, peracetic acid, and methyl ethyl ketone peroxide.

Organic sulfonic acids—In chemistry, generally stronger acids than organic carboxylic acids.

Other potentially infectious materials (OPIM)—Under OSHA's Bloodborne Pathogen standard, bodily fluids which may contain pathogenic organisms; includes (1) human body fluids such as semen, vaginal secretions, cerebrospinal fluid, synovial fluid, pleural fluid, pericardial fluid, peritoneal fluid, amniotic fluid, (2) saliva in dental procedures, (3) any body fluid visibly contaminated with blood, (4) all body fluids in situations where differentiation between body fluids is difficult. This would include waste mixtures such as vomit, toilet overflow, sewage, and leachate associated with refuse containers.

Outstanding national resource waters—Under the Clean Water Act, waters that warrant protection as an outstanding national resource, such as waters of National and State parks and wildlife refuges and waters of exceptional recreational or ecological significance.

Overpacks—Under the Department of Transportation hazardous materials regulations, a type of packaging used for materials that are consolidated in accordance with the provisions of 49 CFR 172.404.

Owner/operator—Under the *Comprehensive Environmental Response, Compensation, and Liability Act*, any person owning or operating a facility or the person who owned, operated or otherwise controlled activities at a facility immediately prior to such facility's transfer to a unit of state or local government due to bankruptcy, foreclosure, tax delinquency, abandonment or similar means. The term owner or operator does not include a person who, without participating in the management of a facility, holds indicia of ownership primarily to protect his security interest in the facility. Under the *Risk Management Program* rules, any person who owns, operates, leases, controls, or supervises a stationary source and its processes. For RM Plan registration purposes, the owner or operator normally is the highest-ranking company executive on-site.

Oxidation—In a chemical reaction, the process of losing electrons

P

P2—Under the Pollution Prevention Act and subsequent EPA publications, ***source reduction*** as well as other practices that reduce or eliminate the creation of pollutants through 1) increased efficiency in the use of raw materials, energy, water or any other resources and 2) protection of natural resources by conservation. P2 applies to releases of contaminants to all media (air emissions, wastewater and storm water discharges and spills, releases to soil or groundwater, as well as solid and hazardous waste generation) and means Also known as ***pollution prevention***.

Partnership—A type of business where two or more partners share ownership of a single business. The law does not distinguish between the business and its owners.

Performance standard—A standard, usually promulgated by a regulatory agency that requires the employers to *effectively* implement a program (as opposed to following specific rules).

Peripheral nervous system (PNS) toxicity—In toxicology, the damage a substance may cause to the sensory and motor nerves of the extremities; is often reversible.

Permeability—In hydrogeology, a measure of how easily water will flow through an aquifer. Unlike ***hydraulic conductivity***, permeability is a function only of the aquifer materials.

Permissible exposure limit—As defined by the Occupational Safety and Health Administration, an enforceable regulatory and limit on the amount and concentration of a substance in workplace air. It may also contain a skin designation.

Permit—Permission issued by a Federal or State agency that has been delegated authority under Federal law that allows a permittee to conduct an activity that has an impact on the environment.

Permit by rule—Under the Resource Conservation and Recovery Act, qualifying hazardous waste management facilities that are permitted under other laws (injection wells permitted under SDWA, POTWs with NPDES permits, ocean disposal authorized under the Marine Protection, Research, and Sanctuaries Act) where requirements are set forth in those other permits and thus are also deemed to have a RCRA permit.

Permit-required confined space—As defined by the Occupational Safety and Health Administration, a ***confined space*** that: (1) contains or has the potential to contain a hazardous atmosphere, (2) contains a material that has the potential to engulf an entrant, (3) has inwardly converging walls or a floor which slopes downward and tapers to a smaller cross-section so that an entrant could be trapped or asphyxiated inside, (4) contains any other recognized serious safety or health hazard.

Permit shield—Under Title V, Operating Permits, of the Clean Air Act, a determination made by the regulating agency that a source is in compliance with all aspects of the Clean Air Act. The permit shield does not extend to noncompliance with permit conditions, applicable requirements that were not covered in the permit application, or new requirements promulgated after issuance of the Title V permit.

Persistent agents—Chemical weapons agents that remain hazardous for as long as a month when deposited on soil, vegetation, or objects, and pose mainly a skin contamination threat.

Personal protective equipment (PPE)—Items of clothing and equipment which are used by themselves or in combination with other protective clothing and equipment to isolate the individual wearer from a particular hazard or a number of hazards or to protect the environment from the individual.

Pest—Under the Federal Insecticide, Fungicide, and Rodenticide Act, an organism deleterious to man or the environment. This includes any vertebrate animal other than man; any invertebrate animal, including but not limited to any insect, other arthropod, nematode, or mollusk such as a slug and snail, but excluding any internal parasite on living man or other animals; any plant growing where not wanted, including any mosses, alga, liverwort, or other plant of any higher order, and any plant part such as a root; or any fungus, bacterium, virus, or other microorganisms, except those on or in living man or other living animals and those on or in processed food or processed animal feed, beverages, drugs and cosmetics (as defined under FFDCA Sections 201[g][1] and 201[i]).

Pesticide—Under the Federal Insecticide, Fungicide, and Rodenticide Act, any substance or mixture of substances intended for preventing, destroying, repelling, or mitigating any pest, or intended for use as a plant regulator, defoliant, or desiccant, other than any article that: is a new animal drug under the FFDCA Section 201(w); is an animal drug that has been determined by regulation of the Secretary of Health and Human Services not to be a new animal drug; or an animal feed under the FFDCA Section 201(x) that bears or contains any substances described above.

Pesticide product—Under the Federal Insecticide, Fungicide, and Rodenticide Act, a pesticide in a particular form (including composition, packaging, and labeling) in which the pesticide is, or is intended to be, distributed or sold. The term includes any physical apparatus used to deliver or apply the pesticide if distributed or sold with the pesticide.

Petroleum USTs—One of the two broad categories of underground storage tanks that contain petroleum or a mixture of petroleum with *de minimis* quantities of other regulated substances. These systems include tanks containing motor fuel, jet fuel, distillate fuel oil, residual fuel oil, lubricants, petroleum solvents, or used oil.

pH—In chemistry, the negative logarithm of the hydrogen ion (H^+) concentration and a measure of a chemical's acidity or basicity.

Photochemical assessment monitoring stations (PAMS)—Under the Clean Air Act, ambient air monitoring stations that are required in any ozone **nonattainment area** that has been designated as serious, severe, or extreme.

Physical hazard—As defined by the Occupational Safety and Health Administration, a hazard associated with a chemical for which there is scientifically valid evidence that it is a combustible liquid, a compressed gas, an organic peroxide, an oxidizer, or is otherwise explosive, flammable, pyrophoric (may spontaneously ignite in air at 130°F or less), unstable (reactive), or water-reactive.

Physical state—The nature of the substance (solid, liquid, gas, fume, mist dust, vapor, *etc.*) at a defined temperature (*i.e.*, 20°C or room temperature).

Physical treatment—In the treatment of hazardous waste, those procedures that modify the physical properties of waste materials—for example: filtration, phase separation, filter pressing of suspended materials, centrifugation, agitation, adsorption, *etc.* Also known as **mechanical treatment.**

pKₐ—In chemistry, the negative logarithm of the equilibrium constant for acids or bases. Strong acids; such as sulfuric and hydrochloric acids have low pK_as (*i.e.*, < 1.1). Bases such as potassium hydroxide and sodium hydroxide have pK_as closer to 14.0 Weak acids and weak bases have pK_as that fall between these two extremes.

Plan, Do, Check, Improve—The fundamental philosophy of Total Quality Management.

Pleural effusion—A collection of fluid around the lung and the most common effect of inhalation of asbestos dust.

Pleural plaque—A thickening of tissue under the parietal pleura, which can become calcified.

Pleural thickening—A thickening of the visceral (lung) and/or parietal (chest wall) pleura. The thickening can vary from 0.5 to 2 cm in thickness and results in increased difficulty in breathing.

Pneumatic and hydraulic high-pressure hazards—Hazards resulting from pressurized gases and liquids.

Point of compliance (POC)—Under the *Resource Conservation and Recovery Act*, the point at which the permitted concentrations of hazardous waste are enforced at a RCRA-permitted hazardous waste treatment, storage, and disposal facility (TSDF). The point of compliance is the vertical surface located at the hydraulically downgradient edge of the area where waste will be placed, and extending down to the uppermost aquifer. Under *RCRA corrective action*, the location or locations at which media cleanup standards are achieved, which is generally set on a site- and media-specific basis.

Point source—Under the Clean Water Act, any discernible, confined, and discrete conveyance, including but not limited to, any pipe, ditch, channel, tunnel, conduit, well, discrete fissure, container, rolling stock, concentrated animal feeding operation, or vessel or other floating craft from which pollutants are or may be discharged. Point sources can include vehicles, natural conveyances, and intermittent sources such as stormwater outfalls.

Pollutant—Under the Clean Water Act, any material which can contaminate water including: dredge spoil, solid waste, incinerator residue, sewage, garbage, sewage sludge, munitions, chemical wastes, biological materials, radioactive materials, heat, wrecked or discarded equipment, rock, sand, cellar dirt, and industrial, municipal, and agricultural waste discharged into water.

Pollution contractors' liability insurance—In business, a type of insurance policy that provides coverage for a pollution event, or related testing, monitoring, consulting, *etc.*

Pollution prevention—Under the Pollution Prevention Act and subsequent EPA publications, ***source reduction*** as well as other practices that reduce or eliminate the creation of pollutants through 1) increased efficiency in the use of raw materials, energy, water or any other resources and 2) protection of natural resources by conservation. Pollution prevention applies to releases of contaminants to all media (air emissions, wastewater and storm water discharges and spills, releases to soil or groundwater, as well as solid and hazardous waste generation) and means Also known as ***P2***.

Population—In human health risk assessment, a group of organisms of the same species, generally occupying a contiguous area, and capable of interbreeding.

Porosity—In hydrogeology, a measure of the maximum amount of water a rock or soil can hold if it is saturated; see ***total porosity*** and ***effective porosity***.

Potential disaster (response alert)—An emergency that is one step beyond a ***limited emergency*** and has a potential public impact. Under these conditions, additional staff is required at the Command Post and the Incident Command System in its more formal structure is implemented. A hazardous materials release being handled by First Responder Operations trained employees would be a possible example.

Potentially responsible parties (PRPs)—As identified in §9607(a) of the Comprehensive Environmental Response, Compensation, and Liability Act, four classes of parties liable for cleanup which include: (1) the (current) owner and operator of a facility (2) any person who at the time of disposal of any ***hazardous substance*** owned or operated any facility at which such hazardous substances were disposed of (3) any person who by contract, agreement, or otherwise arranged for disposal or treatment or transport of hazardous substances; and (4) any person who accepts or accepted any hazardous substances for transport to a disposal or treatment facility selected by such person.

Potentiating effect—In toxicology, when exposure to one substance, having very low or no significant toxicity, enhances the toxicity of another (*e.g.*, 0 + 5 = 15); the result is a more severe injury than that which the toxic substance would have produced by itself.

Potentiometric maps—In hydrogeology, visual images of the top of water tables that are generated by mapping the elevation of the water at numerous locations.

Potentiometric surface—In an aquifer, the boundary between the unsaturated and saturated zones where the pressure exerted by the surface of the water table is equal to the atmospheric pressure at that depth.

Preamble—The part of a proposed regulation that describes the rationale for the regulation and how it complies with and/or fulfills the requirements of the underlying statutes. This section also summarizes the input received from interested parties to date and how this feedback has impacted development of the regulation.

Predecessor—In project management, an item that must be completed before the task can be started.

Preparedness—In disaster response, the planning how to respond in case an emergency or disaster occurs, and working to increase the resources that are available to respond effectively.

Presumed asbestos-containing material (PACM)—Thermal insulation and surfacing material found in buildings constructed no later than 1980.

Prevention—In safety, a nonoccurrence of a harmful event that ultimately provides additional long-term benefits of employee dedication, productivity, efficiency, and safety.

Prevention of significant deterioration—Under the Clean Air Act, a requirement that major sources stationary sources of criteria pollutants in attainment areas evaluate their impact on the ambient air quality prior to starting construction.

Primacy—Under the Safe Drinking Water Act, the primary enforcement authority that is granted to a state by the Environmental Protection Agency.

Priority toxic pollutant—Under the Clean Water Act, any one of the 126 identified pollutants that must be considered in setting water quality criteria.

Private nuisance—Under tort law, an intentional act by the defendant that substantially and unreasonably interferes with the plaintiff's use and enjoyment of his land.

Pro forma—In business, a refinement of the break-even analysis. In developing the *pro forma*, each number should be closely examined to ensure it reflects the best knowledge available, and is presented on a month-by-month basis, projecting for two to five years. To assure an effective process, budget line items should be used in this step.

Probability bounds analysis—In risk assessment and statistics, an addition to variability analysis that provides bounds or an envelope for a distribution analysis.

Process—Under the *Process Safety Management* rules, any activity involving a highly hazardous chemical in excess of a Threshold Quantity amount including any use, storage, manufacturing, handling, or on-site movement of such chemicals, or combination of these activities. Any group of vessels that are interconnected, and separate vessels that are located such that a highly hazardous chemical could be involved in a potential release, are considered as single processes. Under the *Risk Management Program* rules, any activity involving a regulated substance, including any use, storage, manufacturing, handling, or onsite movement of such substances, or combination of these activities.

Process hazard analysis (PHA)—Under the Risk Management Program and OSHA Process Safety Management rules, an analysis that identifies, evaluates, and controls the hazards involved with the design, operation, and maintenance of processes containing regulated substances.

Professional industrial hygienist—A person having a baccalaureate or graduate degree from an accredited college or university in industrial hygiene, biology, chemistry, engineering, physics, or a closely related physical or biological science who, by virtue of special studies and training, has acquired competence in industrial hygiene.

Professional liability insurance—In business, insurance that is sometimes referred to as *errors and omissions* or E&O, is the equivalent of malpractice insurance. This type of insurance protects the firm and its owners, operators, directors, employees (present, past and temporary) from injury, either physical or financial, as a result of an error or omission by the professional. This coverage is only for the services provided by the insured firm.

Professional service providers—In the environmental business, businesses that provide services such as traditional architectural and engineering, environmental consulting, geotechnical, as well as specialty, or niche environmental services.

Profit margin—In business, gross profit or revenue divided by net sales. Profit margin is used to measure a firm's operating efficiency and pricing policies in order to determine how competitive the firm is within the industry.

Program 1, 2, 3 eligibility—Three program levels established under the Risk Management Program rules. All stationary sources must assign each covered process a program level, based on the size and complexity of a source's processes.

Project goal—In project management, the desired outcome of the project and when that outcome should be achieved.

Project plan—In project management, the tactical approach to the endeavor, which aids a manager to both define and meet goals.

Proper shipping name (PSN)—Under the Department of Transportation hazardous materials regulations, an assigned name to a hazardous material that determines whether the material is legal to move, how to package, label, mark, and placard the shipment, whether special provisions apply, *etc.*

Property insurance—A type of insurance that generally covers the loss of real and personal property, as well as loss of income, due to earthquakes, flood, tornadoes, fire, hail, lightning, smoke, wind, *etc.*

Proton—The part of the nucleus of an atom that has a single positive charge. While protons and neutrons are about 2,000 times heavier than electrons, they are still very small particles. A grain of sand weighs about a hundred million trillion (100,000,000,000,000,000,000) times more than a proton or a neutron.

PS—Military designation for the chemical weapon chloropicrin, a *choking agent*.

Public nuisance—Under tort law, a use of one's property to intentionally cause or permit a condition to exist that injures or endangers the public health, welfare, or safety.

Public receptor—Under the Risk Management Program rules, receptors that include off-site residences, institutions (schools, hospitals), industrial, commercial, and office buildings, parks, or recreational areas occupied by the public at any time without restriction where members of the public could be exposed to toxic concentrations, radiant heat, or overpressure, as a result of an accidental release of a regulated substance. Roads are not included as public receptors but should be considered when coordinating with emergency planning organizations.

Public scoping—Under the National Environmental Policy Act, a process in which the agency involves the public and other State and Federal agencies in determining the range of alternatives and actions to be discussed in an *environmental assessment* or *environmental impact statement,* in order to identify alternatives or other significant environmental issues that may have been overlooked by the agency in their development of the proposed action.

Public vessel—A vessel that (1) is owned, or demise-chartered, and operated by the United States government or a government of a foreign country; and (2) is not engaged in commercial service (33 CFR 151.1006).

Public water system—Under the Safe Drinking Water Act, a system of pipes or other constructed conveyances that provides water for human consumption to the public. The system must have at least fifteen service connections, or regularly serve at least twenty-five individuals to qualify as a public water system.

Pulmonary toxicity—In toxicology, the damage a substance may cause to the lungs. Pulmonary toxicity can be caused by obstruction of the airways (*e.g.*, by swelling or constriction), damage to the area of gas exchange (alveolar area) in the lungs, and various types of immune reactions.

Punitive damages—Damages imposed in addition to actual damages that compensate the plaintiff for his injury.

Purchase order—In business, a document authorizing the supplier to provide goods or services. The purchase order is generated by the customer and is typically in a pre-printed format. In addition to the items listed in a *Letter of Intent*, it includes the purchaser's terms and conditions. It is a legal and binding document.

Pyrolysis—A process used for the treatment of hazardous waste that is theoretically a zero-air indirect-heat process (air-starved incineration).

Pyrophoric liquid—Any liquid that may ignite spontaneously when exposed to air that is 55°C (130°F) or below.

Q

QA1—In environmental sampling, a screening objective used to obtain a quick, preliminary assessment of site contamination. Data collected for this objective provide neither definitive identification of pollutants nor definitive quantification of concentration levels.

QA2—In environmental sampling, a verification objective used to verify analytical results. Here a small percentage of the sample results are verified to provide a certain level of confidence for a portion of the results. An inference is then made on the quality of the remainder of the data.

QA3—In environmental sampling, a definitive objective used to assess the accuracy of the concentration level as well as the identity of the analytes of interest. This objective is appropriate when a high level of qualitative and quantitative accuracy is required for all sampling results.

Quality assurance (QA) objectives—In environmental sampling, statements about the desired reliability of the data to be generated. The statements are defined by determining how precise, accurate, representative, complete and comparable the data must be to satisfy the data use objective.

Quality—In project management, providing clients with a superior product in an efficient manner.

R

Radiation—The emission and propagation of energy through space. Radiation can be classified as either ionizing radiation (alpha particles, beta particles, gamma rays, x-rays, neutrons, high-speed electrons, high-speed protons, and other particles capable of producing ions) or non-ionizing radiation (sound, radio, microwaves, or visible, infrared, and ultraviolet light).

Radioactive decay—The process where an energetically unstable atom transforms itself to a more energetically favorable, or stable, state. The unstable atom can emit ionizing radiation in order to become more stable. This atom is said to be *radioactive*, and the process of change is called **radioactive decay**.

Radioactive mixed waste (RMW)—Waste that contains both a hazardous component regulated under the Resource Conservation Recovery Act and radioactive material regulated under the Atomic Energy Act. The applicability of Subtitle I to RMW depends on whether those USTs are regulated under RCRA Subtitle C.

Radioactivity—The spontaneous emission of certain types of radiation (alpha, beta, and gamma) by unstable atomic nuclei.

Random sampling—Environmental sampling in which locations are arbitrarily assigned using a random selection procedure such as random number tables. Random sampling would be used when statistical evaluations of the data are required (*e.g.*, probability statements). Random sampling is the opposite of judgmental sampling.

Raw labor—In accounting, the hourly wage for an employee less benefit costs.

Raw labor multiplier—In business, the number applied to an employee's base salary in order to determine a billable rate. For professional service providers the raw labor multiplier is usually benchmarked at 3.0.

RCRA corrective action—Under the Resource Conservation and Recovery Act, a program that directs RCRA permit holders and permit applicants to investigate, and in some cases, remediate releases of hazardous wastes from solid waste management units at the operating hazardous waste management facilities.

Reactive chemicals—Substances that produce a violent reaction when exposed to or mixed with another substance, sometimes even water or air.

Reasonable compensation—In business, wages that are within the range of salary expected within the industry for the person's qualifications.

Reasonable maximum exposure—In human health risk assessment, the highest exposure that is reasonably expected to occur at a site.

Reasonably achievable emissions control technology (RACT)—Under the Clean Air Act, a control technology that is reasonably available and which may be incorporated into a SIP for devices, systems process modifications, or other apparatus or techniques. RACT takes into account the necessity of imposing the controls as well as their social, environmental, and economic impacts.

Reasonably available control measures (RACM)—Under the Clean Air Act, emissions control technologies (typically used for fugitive dust, residential wood burning, and prescribed burning) that may be used for the management of particulate matter emissions.

Receptors—In human health risk assessment, those humans who are potential recipients of chemical contaminants by way of one of several pathways.

Recharge area—Under the Safe Drinking Water Act, the area above the aquifer where surface water or precipitation replenishes the aquifer by infiltration. Also known as the *recharge zone.*

Recharge zone—Under the Safe Drinking Water Act, the area above the aquifer where surface water or precipitation replenishes the aquifer by infiltration. Also known as the *recharge area.*

Reclaimed—Under the Resource Conservation and Recovery Act, *discarded* by recycling by being regenerated or processed to recover a usable product (except slugs and by-products that exhibit a characteristic of hazardous waste but which are not listed as a hazardous waste, and commercial chemical products).

Recognized environmental conditions—As defined by the Comprehensive Environmental Response, Compensation, and Liability Act, the presence or likely presence of any hazardous substances or petroleum products on a property under conditions that indicate a release, a past release, or a material threat of any hazardous substances or petroleum products into structures on the property or into the ground, groundwater, or surface water of the property.

Record of decision (ROD)—Under the National Environmental Policy Act, the notification of the public of the agency's decision on a proposed action and the reasons for that decision.

Recovery activities—In disaster response, the activities that occur until all community systems return to normal or nearly normal conditions. This includes both *short-term* and *long-term* recovery actions.

Recyclable materials—Under the Resource Conservation and Recovery Act, hazardous wastes that are legitimately recycled and generally are subject to less than full Subtitle C regulation in order to encourage recycling.

Recycled—Under the Resource Conservation and Recovery Act, a material that has been *used in a "manner constituting disposal*, burned for energy recovery, or used to produce a fuel product, reclaimed, accumulated speculatively or accumulated, stored, or treated before recycling."

Reduction—In a chemical reaction, the process of gaining electrons.

Reference dose (RfD)—In toxicology, a dosage value calculated from the NOAEL using uncertainty and modifying factors, given the differences in animal and human responses and the varying sensitivities of humans. See also *chronic reference dose.*

Refresher training—Under the Occupational Safety and Health Administration's Process Safety Management rules, training that is required a minimum of every three years by employees and contractors who work on or around the process equipment containing highly hazardous chemicals.

Regulated Substance—The list of regulated substances under the *EPA List Rule* (40 CFR 68.130) that includes 77 volatile toxic substances and 63 flammable substances. Under the *Resource Conservation and Recovery Act*, the regulated substances for which notification is necessary include petroleum, (including crude oil, crude oil fractions, and petroleum-based substances, as well as CERCLA hazardous substances but excluding RCRA hazardous wastes).

Regulation—A specific procedure promulgated by an agency for the administration and enforcement of environmental laws. The terms *rule* and *regulation* are synonymous, and both terms are used interchangeably in the law.

Regulatory compliance review—A type of audit that evaluates an organization's compliance with environmental regulations.

Relative humidity—The ratio of the amount of water vapor actually in the air compared to the maximum amount of water vapor that the air could hold at a specific temperature and pressure.

Release—As defined in §9602(22) of the Comprehensive Environmental Response, Compensation, and Liability Act, any spilling, leaking, pumping, pouring, emitting, emptying, discharging, injecting, escaping, leaching, dumping, or disposing of hazardous substances to the environment.

Remedial action—Under the Comprehensive Environmental Response, Compensation, and Liability Act, remedies that are protective of human health and the environment, that maintain protection over time, and minimize untreated wastes.

Removal action—Under the Comprehensive Environmental Response, Compensation, and Liability Act, an immediate action taken over the short term to address a release or threatened release of a hazardous substance.

Reopeners—Legal requirements setting forth the bases on which additional cleanup of the brownfield property can be required in addition to what was originally agreed upon with the State agency. These reopeners vary from state to state, but can include: (1) fraudulent or misrepresented information has been provided to the agency, (2) an imminent threat to human health or the environment occurs on the property, (3) a previously unknown condition or new information comes to the agency's attention, and (4) the risk on which the agreed-upon cleanup was based significantly changes so that additional cleanup to prevent endangerment to human health and the environment is required.

Replacement in kind—Under the Process Safety Management rules, a replacement that satisfies the design specification.

Reportable quantity (RQ)—The amount of a hazardous substance which, when released to the environment, must be reported to governmental authorities under the CWA, CERCLA, SARA Title III, or RCRA.

Reregistration—A process started after the Federal Insecticide, Fungicide, and Rodenticide Act went through a major revision in 1988. Active ingredients of pesticides that had been initially registered before 1984 are put through a process of complete reevaluation. This evaluation covers labels, formulae, and especially supporting data. A determination is made whether or not an active ingredient should be eligible for reregistration, and what additional supporting data, if any, is needed to complete the cost-benefit picture.

Resource leveling—In project management, making certain that each task can be adequately performed in the time required by assigning personnel to the task.

Resource loading—In project management, the comparison and subsequent assignment of project team members to tasks.

Resources—In project management, the items needed to complete a project.

Respiratory sensitization—In toxicology, a pulmonary (lung) reaction triggered by an immune response to allergens. Pulmonary reactions are characterized by coughing, labored breathing, tightness in the chest, and shortness of breath.

Response—As defined by the Federal Emergency Management Agency, the effective and efficient application of assets and activities to resolve the immediate impacts of an event.

Response costs—Under the Comprehensive Environmental Response, Compensation, and Liability Act, indirectly defined at §9601(25) to mean costs related to both *removal actions*, see §9601(23) and *remedial actions*, see §9601(24).

Responsible corporate officer doctrine—In law, a doctrine that allows the criminal conviction of a corporate officer based purely on the fact that he was in a position of responsibility and authority within the corporation which would have allowed him to prevent the violation.

Responsible party—Under the Oil Pollution Act of 1990, the owner or operator of a facility from which oil is discharged who is liable for the costs associated with the cleanup of the spill and any damages resulting from an oil spill.

Restricted-use pesticide—Under the Federal Insecticide, Fungicide, and Rodenticide Act, a pesticide whose toxicity (typically, acute toxicity) is high enough that the EPA restricts its use.

Reuse—Under the Resource Conservation and Recovery Act, the recycling of a material in a particular function or application as an effective substitute for a commercial product. Reuse is also a form of *use*.

Revenue—In accounting, inflows of assets received in exchange for goods and services provided, income.

Reversible effects—In toxicology, adverse effects to the body that wear off (or reverse), given sufficient time after the exposure ceases.

Reviews—Under the Clean Air Act and in 40 CFR 68, an implementing agency is required to review Risk Management Plans. Reviews are relatively quick checks of the plans in order to determine whether they are complete and/or contain any information that is clearly problematic. See also *Audits* and *Inspections*.

Right-to-Know—Under the Occupational Safety and Health Administration's Hazard Communication standard, the fundamental philosophy that employees have a right to know about the chemical hazards present in their workplace.

Risk—In toxicology, the likelihood (probability) that an adverse effect (injury or harm) will occur in a given situation. OSHA defines risk as a function of both hazard and the amount of exposure (see 59 FR 6126). Risk can be expressed as a value that ranges from zero (no injury or harm will occur) to one (harm or injury will definitely occur).

Risk analysis—As defined by the *Society for Risk Analysis*, the detailed examination including risk assessment, risk evaluation, and risk management alternatives, performed to understand the nature of unwanted, negative consequences to human life, health, property, or the environment; an analytical process of quantification of the probabilities and expected consequences for identified risks. In *toxicology,* a quantitative appraisal of the levels of exposure that may pose risks because they exceed the ambient levels found in an unexposed population. In *incident response decision-making*, a tool that is used to evaluate the hazard, the exposure vulnerability, and the risk in the proposed action or inaction.

Risk-based clean closure—Under the Resource Conservation and Recovery Act, closure in which some contaminants remain in place but are at protective levels. The regulator. in the context of closure plan approval, determines allowable residual contamination.

Risk-based corrective action (RBCA)—A technically defensible risk assessment strategy used for decision making in a variety of remediation scenarios.

Rotary kiln—A cylindrical, horizontal, refractory-lined shell used in the treatment of hazardous waste.

Routes of exposure—The manner in which a substance enters a body. Routes of exposure include the gastrointestinal tract (ingestion), lungs (inhalation), and skin (dermal, topical, or percutaneous).

Rule—A specific procedure promulgated by an agency for the administration and enforcement of environmental laws. The terms *rule* and *regulation* are synonymous, and both terms are used interchangeably in the law.

Rulemaking—The process by which regulations are developed.

Rural transport areas—Under the Clean Air Act, rural (ozone) nonattainment areas associated with a larger metropolitan area.

S

Safe condition—Under the Occupational Safety and Health Administration rules, the requirement that compressed gas containers be maintained in accordance with the requirements of the DOT Hazardous Materials Regulations and the Compressed Gas Association standards.

Safety—the probability that adverse effects (harm) will *not occur* under specified conditions (the inverse of risk).

Sampling plan—In environmental sampling, the blueprint for accomplishing the established goal of the Data Quality Objectives that results in the generation of data of known quality. The sampling plan ensures that all components associated with the generation of the data are thoroughly documented and the documentation is verifiable and defensible.

Satellite accumulation—The provision under the Resource Conservation and Recovery Act that allows generators to accumulate small quantities of hazardous waste at the worksite.

Saturated—In chemistry, the condition of an organic compound in which each constituent carbon is covalently linked to four different atoms.

Saturated zone—In soil, an area beneath the unsaturated zone where soil particles are completely surrounded by water and no air is present and which makes up an aquifer.

Sensitive subpopulations—In human health risk assessment, those receptors that have pre-existing medical or physical conditions that may make them more sensitive to the health effects of chemical exposure.

Sensitizers—In toxicology, substances that change the body's proteins so that the body fails to recognize them as its own and reacts by stimulating the immune system to produce antibodies. Sensitizers can cause an allergic reaction to occur as the body's antibodies try to destroy the altered proteins.

Sharps with engineered sharps injury protections—Under the Occupational Safety and Health Administration's Bloodborne Pathogen standard, a nonneedle sharp or a needle device used for withdrawing body fluids, accessing a vein or artery, or administering medications or other fluids, with a built-in safety feature or mechanism that effectively reduces the risk of an exposure incident.

Short titles—Those portions of the law that are enacted by Congress at a point in time. These laws may be original acts that create an entirely new regulatory area, or (more often) acts that amend existing laws.

Short-term exposure limit (STEL)—Under Occupational Safety and Health Administration regulations, a 15-minute *Time-Weighted Average* exposure that may not be exceeded at any time during the day.

Short-term recovery—In disaster response, the activities aimed at returning vital life-support systems to minimum operating standards.

Sick Building Syndrome—A catch-all term used to describe a series of nonspecific, acute symptoms experienced by building occupants for which no specific illness or cause can be identified.

Slope factor—In human health risk assessment, a plausible upper-bound estimate of the probability of a response per unit intake of a chemical over a lifetime.

Smokes—In industrial hygiene, the products of combustion of a bulk material. Smoke can be pure, as when magnesium is burned in air to form magnesium oxide, or it can be a complex mixture of gases, vapors, fumes, and ash, as in the combustion of coal.

Sole proprietorship—A type of business structure where one person has 100% ownership, 100% control, and 100% risk associated with the operation of a business.

Solid waste—As defined by the Resource Conservation and Recovery Act, any garbage, refuse, sludge, and other discarded material, including solids, semisolids, liquids, and contained gases. Note that solid waste is not restricted to solid phase material. The statutory definition includes specific exceptions for several wastes, chiefly on the basis that they are regulated under other statutes.

Solid waste management unit (SWMU)—Under the Resource Conservation and Recovery Act, any discernible unit in which solid wastes have been placed at any time, regardless of whether or not the unit was intended for the management of solid or hazardous wastes. Such units include any area at a facility where solid wastes have been routinely and systematically released.

Solidification—A method of treatment for hazardous waste in which monoliths with considerable structural strength are formed.

Solubility—In *chemistry,* the amount of a given substance (the solute) that dissolves in a unit volume of a liquid (the solvent). In *biological fluid / material* such as blood and lipids (fat), the solubility may affect the absorption of a substance into the body, its movement (distribution) within the body and its potential for storage in the body (*e.g.* in fat or bone).

Source control—In indoor air quality, the removal or reduction of the indoor air contaminant (source).

Source reduction—As defined in Section 6605(5)(A) of the Pollution Prevention Act, any practice which 1) reduces the amount of any hazardous substance, pollutant, or contaminant entering any waste stream or otherwise released into the environment (including fugitive emissions) prior to recycling, treatment, or disposal and 2) reduces the hazards to public health and the environment associated with their release.

Special purpose monitoring stations (SPMS)—Under the Clean Air Act, monitoring stations installed by State and local air pollution control agencies in order to support their air programs.

Specific gravity (SG)—The ratio of the density of a liquid as compared with that of water.

Specific retention—In hydrogeology, the volume of water that is retained as a coating on soil or rock particles after gravity draining.

Specific yield—The volume of water that will drain by gravity from a specific volume of rock or soil.

Specification used oil—Under the Resource Conservation and Recovery Act, fuel (used oil that is not classified under the regulations as a hazardous waste fuel) that meets the following criteria: arsenic (<5 ppm), cadmium (<2 ppm), chromium (<10 ppm), lead (<100 ppm), flash point (>100°F), and total halogens (<4000 ppm).

Stabilization—A method of treatment for hazardous waste that reduces or eliminates the toxicity or the hazard potential of a certain waste stream by lowering the solubility and leachability of the toxic or hazardous components. Also call ***fixation.***

Stabilization initiative—Under the Resource Conservation and Recovery Act, corrective action management philosophy in which the overall goal is to control or abate threats, or to prevent or minimize the further migration of contaminants while long-term remedies are pursued.

State and local air monitoring stations (SLAMS)—Under the Clean Air Act, a network of 4000 ambient air monitoring stations generally set up in urban areas to meet the needs of State and local air pollution control agencies.

State implementation plan (SIP)—Under the Clean Air Act, a plan, prepared by a state, that contains a detailed description regarding how the state will fulfill its responsibilities toward achieving and maintaining clean air. The plan is essentially a collection of rules that the state uses to control air pollution.

Statement of cash flows—In accounting, a report that highlights the major activities that directly and indirectly impact cash flows and the overall cash balance.

Stationary sources—Under the *Clean Air Act,* sources of air pollution that don't move, such as a building, structure, facility, or other installation. Under the *Risk Management Program* rules, all buildings, structures, equipment, or substance-emitting stationary activities that belong to the same industrial group, located on one or more contiguous properties, under the control of the same person(s), from which accidental release may occur.

Statutes—Laws that are amended, revised and republished to reflect all permanent amendments. Also called the ***body of standing law***.

Statutory law—Federal statutes enacted by the legislative bodies.

Storage—Under the Resource Conservation and Recovery Act, holding waste temporarily, pending future management.

Strategic environmental management (SEM)—The adaptation and integration of traditional business and engineering theory and practice toward the maximization of profit, to the responsible management of environmental issues with the goal of minimizing costs and potential liability.

Strict liability—In law, abnormally dangerous activities that may cause a defendant to be liable for harm to the person, land, or personal property of another resulting from that activity, although the defendant has exercised the utmost care to prevent the harm.

Structure/activity relationships—In toxicology, one approach to *in vitro* toxicological studies that involves the assessment of the toxicity of a chemical based upon its molecular structure. A ***hazard or toxicity assessment*** is also referred to as a ***dose-response assessment*** because it seeks to determine whether dose response information is available for the chemical of interest.

Subchapter S corporation—A type of business structure that allows the owners (shareholders) to treat the earnings and profits as distributions, which appear as such on their personal tax return. The shareholder, if working for the company, and if there is a profit, must receive wages, which must meet standards of reasonable compensation.

Substantial authority personnel—In law, high-level personnel or individuals within a corporation who exercise substantial supervisory authority (such as a plant manager) and any other individuals, who, although not part of an organization's management, nevertheless exercise substantial discretion when acting within the scope of their authority (such as an individual with authority to set, negotiate, or approve price levels or contracts).

Substantial harm facility—Under the Oil Pollution Act of 1990, a facility that meets the following: (1) the facility transfers oil over water to or from vessels and has a total oil storage capacity of at least 42,000 gallons, or (2) the total oil storage capacity at the facility is at least 1 million gallons and at least one of the following criteria is met: (a) the facility's secondary containment for each AST area will not hold the volume of the largest single AST plus sufficient freeboard for precipitation, (b) a discharge could injure fish, wildlife, or sensitive environments, (c) a discharge would shut down operations at a public drinking water intake, (d) the facility has had a reportable spill of at least 10,000 gallons within the last five years.

Successor—In project management, a task that follows a **predecessor** task.

Surfacing material—Asbestos-containing material that has been sprayed or troweled on surfaces (walls, ceilings, and structural members) for acoustical decorative or fireproofing purposes. This includes plaster and fireproofing insulation.

Sustainable development—As defined by the United Nations World Commission on Environment and Development (the Bruntland Commission, 1987), "development that meets the needs of the present without compromising the ability of future generations to meet their own needs." In addition to consideration of residuals (air emissions, waste water, solid and hazardous waste) sustainable development focuses on energy and material inputs and outputs associated with a process and the life-cycle environmental costs of the product or service produced. This idea is possibly best summarized by the SIGMA Guidelines as "capacity for continuance into long term future."

Synergistic effect—In toxicology, when exposure to two chemicals has a combined effect much greater than the sum of the effects of each substance when given alone (*e.g.*, 3 + 5 = 30); each substance magnifies the toxicity of the other.

Synthetic minor source—Under the Clean Air Act, a source having the capacity to operate as a *major source* but voluntarily operating below an enforceable limitation in order to keep its emissions below the significant quantities for major sources, as defined in the Act.

System—A combined or organized whole from many parts.

System safety—In industrial hygiene, the application of engineering and management principles, criteria, and techniques to optimize all aspects of safety within the constraints of operational effectiveness, time, and cost throughout all phases of the system life cycle.

Systematic sampling—Environmental sampling that involves the establishment of a reproducible scheme such as a grid or transect to which sampling points can be referenced. Samples are then taken at the points where grid lines intersect (nodes) or at defined distances along the transect line.

Systemic toxicity—In toxicology, the reaction of a body to a substance that occurs at a site or sites distant from the site of chemical absorption.

T

Tagout system—Under the Occupational Safety and Health Administration's lockout/tagout rules, a system that is used to control injuries due to hazardous energy sources. A tagout system uses only a tag, without a lock, to isolate the source and notify other employees. The system can only be used when the energy source cannot be locked out and proper training is vital for effective employee protection.

Tank vessels—Vessels that are constructed, adapted to carry, or that carry oil or hazardous materials in bulk as cargo or cargo residue and that are US documented vessels, operate in United States waters, or transfer oil or hazardous material in a place subject to the jurisdiction of the United States.

Tanks—Under the Resource Conservation and Recovery Act, stationary devices made primarily of nonearthen materials.

Target organs—In toxicology, the organs that will sustain major adverse effects as a result of exposure to a certain chemical.

Targets—In an environmental management system, like ISO 14000, the detailed performance requirements arising from identified ***objectives***.

TCLP extract—The waste after filtration in the ***TCLP test procedure***. See ***toxicity characteristic leaching procedure (TCLP) extract***.

TCLP test procedure—A test detailed in SW-846 used to identify whether or not a waste exhibits the characteristic of toxicity. See ***toxicity characteristic leaching procedure (TCLP)***.

Teaming—A business strategy that companies may use to refer customers to each other, usually for one of two reasons: to provide for customer needs during times of overbooking, or in situations where one company provides a product (or service) that the other does not.

Temporary unit—Under the Resource Conservation and Recovery Act, a tank or container storage unit used to treat and store remediation waste generated at a facility that would not be subject to minimum technology or procedural hazardous waste regulations.

Teratogens—In toxicology, substances that produce genetic changes or tumors in developing fetuses so that there is some change in the appearance or function of the body but the genetic code of the gametes is not changed and so the changes are not passed on to following generations.

The bends—In industrial hygiene, a decompression illness that occurs when a person who has worked under high pressure for a period of time is returned to atmospheric pressure (decompressed) too rapidly. The resulting condition can affect several organs including the lungs, blood, muscles, and nervous system.

Theoretical oxygen demand (Th$_{OD}$)—The cumulative amount of oxygen needed to completely oxidize a given material. The Th$_{OD}$ is the upper limit for BOD$_5$ values, although it is seldom achieved. A comparison of the BOD$_5$ and Th$_{OD}$ values for a given chemical provides an indication of the biodegradability of that chemical.

Thermal hazards—Hazards associated with substances that are cold or hot. These divisions are *not* related to heat or cold stress from exposure to the environment.

Thermal system insulation—Under the OSHA asbestos regulations, insulation used to inhibit heat transfer or prevent condensation on pipes, boilers, tanks, ducts, and other components of hot and cold water systems and heating ventilation and air condition (HVAC) systems. This includes pipe lagging and pipe wrap; block, batt, and blanket insulation; cement and "mud," and other products such as gaskets and ropes.

Threshold dose—The lowest dose of a chemical at which a specified measurable effect is observed and below which it is not observed (*e.g.*, no observed effect level [NOEL]).

Threshold limit value (TLV)—In industrial hygiene, the airborne concentrations of chemical substances that represent an exposure level that nearly all workers can be exposed to, day after day, over a working lifetime, without experiencing adverse effects. TLVs are intended to protect workers who are normal, healthy adults. The American Conference of Governmental Industrial Hygienists publishes a table of the values and accompanying precautions for most common industrial materials.

Threshold planning quantities (TPQ)—Under the Community Right-to-Know regulation, trigger quantities for chemicals appearing on EPA's Extremely Hazardous Substance (EHS) list. When a facility inventories an EHS in quantities equal to or greater than a trigger quantity, the facility is subject to emergency planning and notification requirements.

Threshold quantity (TQ)—Under the Risk Management Program rules, the maximum amount of a substance used in a single process that triggers the requirement for the substance to be reported and included in the emergency response plans for chemical spills and releases. The threshold quantity applies to a ***stationary source*** that uses the regulated substances listed in 40 CFR 68.130.

Time composite sampling—Environmental sampling that is used to determine the concentrations of contaminants over time. Time composite sampling is normally not utilized during hazardous waste site investigations because the intent of such investigations is to determine as quickly as possible what is present on site at the "present" time. For health and safety reasons, a form of time compositing is utilized to determine air quality on and around sites.

Time-weighted average (TWA)—The measured concentration of the chemical multiplied by the duration of the exposure.

Threshold Limit Value-Ceiling (TLV-C)—The concentration of a hazardous substance that should not be exceeded during any part of the working exposure. (ACGIH)

Threshold Limit Value-Short Term Exposure Limit (TLV-STEL)—A 15-minute time-weighted average exposure to a hazardous substance that should not be exceeded at any time during the workday, even if the 8-hour time-weighted average is within the TLV-TWA. It is believed that workers exposed continuously for a short period of time at the TLV-STEL will not experience 1) irritation, 2) chronic or irreversible tissue damage 3) dose-rate dependent toxic effects, or 4) narcosis of sufficient degree to increase the possibility of accidental injury, impair self-rescue, or materially reduce work efficiency. Exposure times above the TLV-TWA up to the TLV-STEL should be less than 15 minutes, should occur less than four times per day, and there should be at least 60 minutes between success exposures in this range. (ACGIH)

Threshold Limit Value, Time Weighted Average (TLV-TWA)—The time-weighted average concentration for a conventional 8-hour workday and a 40-hour workweek. It is believed that nearly all workers may be repeatedly exposed at the TLV-TWA, day after day, without adverse effect. Although calculating the average concentration during a workweek rather than a workday, may be appropriate in some instances, the ACGIH does not offer guidance regarding such exposures. (ACGIH)

Top-down approach—In project management, a method of achieving the project goal by breaking the project into logical segments, similar to climbing steps, moving down from one project level to another.

Tort—A legal wrong committed upon the person or property of another, independent of contract.

Total maximum daily load—Under the Clean Water Act, the maximum amount of a particular pollutant that a water body can hold and still meet the established water quality standard.

Total porosity—In hydrogeology, the ratio of empty spaces (voids) in between the particles of soil, sand, gravel or fractured rock to the total volume that tells us the maximum amount of water a rock or soil can hold if it is saturated.

Toxicity characteristic leaching procedure (TCLP)—Under the Resource Conservation and Recovery Act, a test specified in EPA Publication SW–846 designed to quantify the leachability of hazardous constituents in a waste.

Toxicity characteristic leaching procedure (TCLP) extract—Under the Resource Conservation and Recovery Act, the waste that is analyzed after filtration step of the TCLP.

Toxic concentration low (TC$_{LO}$)—The lowest concentration of a substance in air to which humans or animal have been exposed for any given period of time that has produced any toxic effect in humans or has produced teratogenic or reproductive effects in animals.

Toxic dose low (TD$_{LO}$)—The lowest concentration of a substance introduced by any route, other than inhalation, over any given period of time and reported to produce any toxic effect in humans or to produce teratogenic or reproductive effects in animals

Toxicity—In *toxicology*, the ability of a chemical, physical, or biological agent to cause acute or chronic damage to biological material. In *industrial hygiene,* the capacity or ability of a chemical to harm or injure a living organism by other than mechanical means. Under the *Resource Conservation and Recovery Act*, a hazardous waste characteristic based on the toxic properties of 8 metals and 32 organic compounds.

Toxicokinetics—In toxicology, the movement of toxic substances (chemicals) within the body. This movement is usually divided into four inter-related processes termed absorption, distribution, biotransformation (metabolism), and excretion.

Toxicology—The study of the adverse effects of chemical, physical, and biological agents on living organisms.

Toxins—Are biological weapons agents that unlike ***infectious agents***, cannot reproduce. They are the toxic products of certain living organisms. These poisonous substances require no incubation period (unlike infectious agents), and some can cause incapacitation or death within minutes or hours. Examples of deadly toxins used in biological weapons include botulinum toxin from the bacterium *Clostridium botulinum* and ricin a by-product of the castor bean.

Trade secret—As defined by Occupational Safety and Health Administration and included in the *Hazard Communication* and *Process Safety Management* rules, any confidential formula, pattern, process, device, information, or compilation of information that is used in a particular company, that gives the company an opportunity to gain an advantage over competitors who do not know or use it.

Transient non-community water systems—Under the Safe Drinking Water Act, facilities such as roadside stops, commercial campgrounds, *etc.*, that have their own water supplies and serve a transient population for at least sixty days per year.

Transmissivity—In an aquifer, the measure of an aquifer's capacity to deliver water. Transmissivity is the product of the hydraulic conductivity and the aquifer thickness.

Treatment train—A series of treatments used to treat hazardous waste effluents.

Treatment—Under the Resource Conservation and Recovery Act, virtually any action that changes a hazardous waste to neutralize it, recover material or energy from it, or make it less hazardous, safer, or easier to manage.

Trespass—Under tort law, a physical invasion of another's rights, whether in his person, personal property, or land.

TRIAD Approach—Under the Resource Conservation and Recovery Act, a corrective action approach that relies on a three-pronged strategy to identify and manage the uncertainty associated with the information used to make decisions.

Tribal implementation plan (TIP)—Under the Clean Air Act, a plan, prepared by a tribe that contains a detailed description regarding how the tribe will fulfill its responsibilities toward achieving and maintaining clean air. The plan is essentially a collection of rules that the tribe uses to control air pollution.

Trigger task—Under the Occupational Safety and Health Act regulations lead standard, any task, such as sanding, scraping, manual demolition, heat gun removal of paint, spray painting, abrasive blasting, torch burning, welding, cutting, and tool cleaning that results in an occupational exposure to lead above the permissible exposure limit of 50 $\mu g/m^3$.

Tumorogens—In toxicology, substances that cause benign (noncancerous) or malignant (cancerous) growths, usually seen as a swelling or enlargement, in the body by altering the genetic code in body tissues.

U

Umbrella coverage—In business, a type of insurance policy that provides coverage for excess liability over and above the basic liability coverage for ***Professional liability insurance*** or ***Errors and Omissions Insurance, General liability insurance*** and ***Automobile insurance.***

Unclassified area—Under the Clean Air Act, a geographic area (primarily rural) that has insufficient available air monitoring data for making an ***attainment*** or ***nonattainment*** determination.

Underground source of drinking water—Under the Safe Drinking Water Act, an aquifer or its portion that supplies any ***public water system*** or that contains a sufficient quantity of ground water to supply a public water system, and currently supplies drinking water for human consumption or contains fewer than 10,000 mg/L of total dissolved solids.

Underground storage tank (UST)—As defined in the Resource Conservation and Recovery Act, Subtitle I, any tank or combination of tanks (including connected underground pipes) that is used to contain an accumulation of regulated substances, the volume of which (including the volume of connected underground pipes) is 10% or more beneath the surface of the ground.

United States Code (USC)—The official cumulative set of all Federal statutes with all amendments up to the date of publication. The USC is organized into *Titles* that place statutes of similar subject matter in the same volume.

United States sentencing guidelines (USSG)—Guidelines developed by the United States Sentencing Commission intended to increase the uniformity of sentencing, remove the uncertainty of sentences caused by the parole system, and ensure proportionality in sentencing criminal conduct of different severity.

Universal precautions—Under the Occupational Safety and Health Administration's Bloodborne Pathogens standard, a means of infection control that requires employees to assume that all human blood and body fluids contain potentially infectious bloodborne pathogens, and to handle those articles and substances as if they were pathogenic.

Universal wastes—Under the Resource Conservation and Recovery Act, certain hazardous wastes (in particular batteries, pesticide stocks that have been recalled or which are being collected and managed under a waste pesticide collection program, and certain mercury-containing thermostats) that are generated in large quantity by a variety of generators, that may, if adopted by the authorized state, be managed in accordance with EPA's Standards for Management of Universal Waste.

Unsaturated—In chemistry, the property in which an organic compound contains double or triple bonds between carbons (*e.g.*, ethylene [$CH_2=CH_2$]). Multiple bonds tend to be sites of reactivity.

Unsaturated zone—In hydrogeology, an area directly beneath the soil surface in which the soil particles are surrounded in varying degrees by air and water. This area is also called the *vadose zone.*

Upper respiratory tract irritation—In toxicology, a reversible inflammatory reaction that occurs in the nose and throat. This reaction is characterized by sneezing, nasal discharge, coughing, hoarseness, the production of phlegm, and nasal inflammation (rhinitis).

Use—Under the Resource Conservation and Recovery Act, the recycling of a material in a particular function or application as an effective substitute for a commercial product. *Reuse* is also a form of use.

Used in a "manner constituting disposal"—Under the Resource Conservation and Recovery Act, a material that has been placed on the land directly or as an ingredient in a product (except commercial chemical products ordinarily applied to the land).

Utilization—In business, the percentage of hours billed to a client or profit-generating project in relation to total hours available.

V

Vadose zone—In hydrogeology, an area directly beneath the soil surface in which the soil particles are surrounded in varying degrees by air and water. This area is also called the *unsaturated zone.*

V-agent—A type of chemical weapon that is classified as a nerve agent and has the property of being persistent in the environment (see also *G-agent*).

Valence orbitals—In chemistry, an element's outermost orbitals. Electrons in the valence orbitals are available for atomic bonding.

Vapor density (VD)—The mass per unit volume of a given vapor/gas relative to that of air.

Vapor pressure (VP)—A measure of the relative volatility of a chemical. It is the pressure exerted by the vapor in equilibrium with its liquid at a given temperature.

Vapors—In industrial hygiene, the gaseous phase of a substance that is normally a liquid or solid at room temperature and pressure. Thus, a liquid solvent will generate airborne vapor from its surface in concentrations proportional to its vapor pressure.

Vertical composite samples—Environmental samples that are composed of equal aliquots collected along a defined vertical interval such as a borehole or test pit (for example, the combination of five aliquots taken every foot during the installation of a 5-foot bore hole).

Vessel—Every description of watercraft or other artificial contrivance used, or capable of being used, as a means of transportation on water.

Virtually safe dose (VSD)—That dose in which the risk is very low (10^{-6} or one excess tumor, *etc.* per one million persons). This is the value accepted as the "safe dose" for humans by regulatory policy.

Volatilization—In chemistry, the tendency of a material to transfer from a liquid phase (either pure or dissolved, as in aqueous systems) to a gaseous phase (commonly mixed with air). Also known as *evaporation.*

Voluntary disclosure—One of the actions which can be taken by a defendant and used by the Department of Justice as a mitigating factor in deciding whether to bring a criminal prosecution for a violation of an environmental statute.

Vulnerability—In human health risk assessment, the susceptibility of life, property, and the environment to injury or damage.

VX—A *nerve agent* chemical weapon.

W

Waste codes D004 through D043—Under the Resource Conservation and Recovery Act, the characteristic codes for hazardous waste and their relevant characteristic levels (concentrations) as determined by TCLP (Toxicity Characteristic Leaching Procedure) for concentration-based constituents.

Waste load allocation—Under the Clean Water Act, the fraction of the Total Maximum Daily Load for the water body that is assigned to the source.

Waste minimization—As currently defined by the Environmental Protection Agency, includes *source reduction* and *environmentally sound recycling* of wastes regulated under the Resource Conservation and Recovery Act, particularly hazardous wastes.

Wastewaters—Under the Resource Conservation and Recovery Act Land Disposal Restriction regulations, wastes with <1 wt% total organic carbon (TOC) and <1 wt% total suspended solids. All other wastes are considered to be *nonwastewaters*.

Water quality criteria—Under the Clean Water Act, levels of quality that protect the designated use, including conditions such as pollutant concentrations, temperature, pH, turbidity, and toxicity.

Water quality standard—Under the Clean Water Act, the desired condition of a water body. It is used for determining if the water quality is impaired, setting NPDES permit limits, and determining the Total Maximum Daily Load for a pollutant.

Water table aquifers—Unconfined aquifers in which the water table forms the upper boundary. Water table aquifers are usually in unconsolidated material and where the water table rises and falls seasonally. Water tables tend to rise in winter when more rainfall infiltrates, and tend to fall in summer due to less rainfall infiltration.

Water tube boilers—A method of treatment for hazardous waste using industrial boilers. Water is circulated throughout the combustion chamber in thousands of feet of steel tubing. Heat is transferred from the path of the flue gas into the adjacent water tubes.

Waters of the United States—Under the Clean Water Act, navigable waters, ground waters, surface waters, and underground waters.

Watershed Approach—Under the Clean Water Act, an approach that integrates the suite of tools provided by the Act on a watershed basis and engages the community of stakeholders to find solutions to water quality problems.

Weapons of mass destruction (WMD)—As defined in the United States Code, Title 50, any weapon or device that is intended, or has the capability, to cause death or serious bodily injury to a significant number of people through the release, dissemination, or impact of (A) toxic or poisonous chemicals or their precursors; (B) a disease organism; or (C) radiation or radioactivity.

Well—Under the Safe Drinking Water Act, a bored, drilled, or driven shaft whose depth is greater than the largest surface dimension, or a dug hole whose depth is greater than the largest surface dimension or an improved sinkhole, or a subsurface fluid distribution system. Wells are further defined as *Class I wells*, *Class II wells*, *Class III wells*, *Class IV wells* and *Class V wells*, depending on their function.

Well field—Under the Safe Drinking Water Act, an area containing one or more drinking water wells that produce a usable amount of water.

Well injection—Under the Safe Drinking Water Act, the subsurface emplacement of fluids through a well.

Wellhead protection area—Under the Safe Drinking Water Act, the area surrounding a drinking water well or well field that is protected to prevent contamination of the wells.

Wetlands—Under the Clean Water Act, areas that are inundated or saturated by surface or groundwater at a frequency and duration sufficient to support a prevalence of vegetation typically adapted for life in saturated soil conditions. In order for a site to be classified as a wetland, the appropriate vegetation, soils, and hydrology must be present.

Windfall lien—In Brownfields, a lien by EPA for unrecovered response costs on the property of a *Bona Fide* Prospective Purchaser if the response action increased the fair market value of the property.

Work breakdown structure—In project management, the outline of project milestone divisions (WBS). The top level is the project goal or "Level 1". The milestones or objectives are "Level 2". Tasks and subtasks are "Level 3" and "Level 4", respectively.

Workers' compensation insurance—In business, a type of insurance policy that is required by almost all states and provides coverage for employees that may be injured on the job. It is necessary to procure this type insurance in each state where the work is performed (as opposed to the state of the company's office or the workers' location).

Workplace environmental exposure limits (WEELs)—In industrial hygiene, values intended as estimates of concentration ranges where one might reasonably anticipate observing adverse effects as a consequence of exposure to a specific substance.

Worst-case release scenario (WRS) analysis—Under the Risk Management Program rules, an analysis of the potential releases that reach the greatest distance beyond the stationary source's boundary.

X

X-rays—An example of electromagnetic radiation that arises as electrons are deflected from their original paths (inner orbital electrons change their orbital levels around the atomic nucleus). X-rays, like gamma rays, are capable of traveling long distances through air and most other materials. Like gamma rays, x-rays require more shielding to reduce their intensity than do beta or alpha particles. x- and gamma rays differ primarily in their origin: x-rays originate in the electronic shell, gamma rays originate in the nucleus.

Conversion Table

To Convert	into	Multiply by	To Convert	into	Multiply by
A					
Acres	Sq ft	43,560.0	Btu	Hp-hrs	3.931×10^{-4}
	Sq meters	4,047		Joules	1,054.8
	Sq miles	1.562×10^{-3}		Kilogram-calories	0.2520
	Sq yards	4,840		Kilogram-meters	107.5
Acre-feet	Cu feet	43,560.0		Kilowatt-hrs	2.928×10^{-4}
	Gallons	3.259×10^{5}			
Ares	Acres	0.02471	Btu/hr	Foot-pounds/sec	0.2162
	Sq meters	100.0		Gram-calories/sec	0.0700
Atmospheres	Cm of Hg (@ 0°C)	76.0		Horsepower	3.929×10^{-4}
	Ft of water (@ 4°C)	33.90		Kilowatts	0.01757
	In of Hg(@ 0°C)	29.92		Watts	17.57
	Kg/sq cm	1.0333	Bushels	Cu feet	1.2445
	Kg/sq meter	10,332		Cu inches	2, 150.4
	Pounds/sq inch	14.70		Cu meters	0.03524
	Tons (short)/sq ft	1.058		Liters	35.24
				Pecks	4.0
B				Pints (US dry)	64.0
Barrels (oil)	Gallons (oil)	42.0		Quarts (US dry)	32.0
Bars	Atmospheres	0.9869			
	Dynes/sq cm	10^{6}	**C**		
	Kg/sq meter	1.020×10^{4}			
	Pounds/sq ft	2,089.0	Centares	Sq meters	1.0
	Pounds/sq inch	14.50	Centigrade	Fahrenheit	(C° x 9/5) + 32
	Ergs	1.0550×10^{10}	Centigrams	Grams	0.01
	Foot-pounds	778.3			
	Gram-calories	252.0			

To Convert	into	Multiply by	To Convert	into	Multiply by
Centiliters	Liters	0.01	Cubic inches	Gallons (US liq)	4.329×10^{-5}
Centimeters	Feet	3.281×10^{-2}		Liters	0.01639
	Inches	0.3937		Pints (US liq)	0.03463
	Kilometers	10^{-5}		Quarts (US liq)	0.01732
	Meters	0.01	Cubic meters	Bushels (dry)	28.38
	Miles	6.214×10^{-6}		Cu centimeters	10^{6}
	Millimeters	10.0		Cu feet	35.31
	Mils	393.7		Cu inches	61,023.0
	Yards	1.094×10^{-2}		Cu yards	1.308
Centimeter-dynes	Cm-grams	1.020×10^{-3}		Gallons (US liq)	264.2
	Meter-kg	1.020×10^{-8}		Liters	1000.0
	Pound-ft	7.376×10^{-8}		Pints (US liq)	2,113.0
Centimeter-grams	Cm-dynes	980.7		Quarts (US liq)	1,057
	Meter-kg	10^{-5}	Cu yards	Cu cm	7.646×10^{5}
	Pound-ft	7.233×10^{-5}		Cu feet	27
Cm of Hg (@ 0°C)	Atmospheres	0.01316		Cu inches	46,656.0
	Ft of water (@ 4°C)	0.4461		Cu meters	0.7646
	Kg/sq meter	136.0		Gallons (US liq)	202.0
	Pounds/sq ft	27.85		Liters	764.6
	Pounds/sq in	0.1934		Pints (US liq)	1,615.9
Centimeters/sec	Feet/min	1.1969		Quarts (US liq)	807.9
	Feet/sec	0.03281			
	Kilometers/hr	0.036	**D**		
	Knots (international)	0.1943			
	Meters/min	0.6	Days	Hours	24.0
	Miles/hr	0.02237		Minute	1,440.0
	Miles/min	3.728×10^{-4}		Second	86,400.0
Cubic centimeters	Cu feet	3.531×10^{-5}	Decigrams	Grams	0.1
	Cu inches	0.06102	Deciliters	Liters	0.1
	Cu meters	10^{-6}	Decimeters	Centimeters	0.1
	Cu yards	1.308×10^{-6}	Degrees (Angles)	Minutes	60.0
	Gallons (US liq)	2.642×10^{-4}		Quadrants	0.01111
	Liters	0.001		Radians	0.01745
	Pints (US liq)	2.113×10^{-3}		Seconds	3,600.0
	Quarts (US liq)	1.057×10^{-3}	Dekagrams	Grams	10.0
Cubic feet	Bushels (dry)	0.8036	Dekaliters	Liters	10.0
	Cu centimeters	28,320.0	Dekameters	Meters	10.0
	Cu inches	1,728.0	Drams	Grams	1.7718
	Cu meters	0.02832		Grains	27.3437
	Cu yards	0.03704		Ounces (avdp)	0.0625
	Gallon (US liq)	7.48052			
	Liters	28.32	**E**		
	Pints (US liq)	59.84			
	Quarts (US liq)	29.92	Ergs	Btu	9.480×10^{-11}
Cubic inches	Cu centimeters	16.39		Foot-pounds	7.367×10^{-8}
	Cu feet	5.787×10^{-4}		Gram-calories	0.2389×10^{-7}
	Cu meters	1.639×10^{-5}		Gram-cm	1.020×10^{-3}
				Hp-hrs	3.7250×10^{-14}

To Convert	into	Multiply by	To Convert	into	Multiply by
Ergs	Joules	10^{-7}	**G**		
	Kg-calories	2.389×10^{-11}			
	Kg-meters	1.020×10^{-8}	Gallons (US liq)	Cu centimeters	3,785.0
	Kw-hours	0.2778×10^{-10}		Cu feet	0.1337
				Cu inches	231.0
F				Cu meters	3.785×10^{-3}
				Cu yards	4.951×10^{-3}
Fahrenheit	Centigrade	(F°-32) x 5/9		Liters	3.785
Fathoms	Feet	6.0		Pints (US liq)	8.0
Feet	Centimeters	30.48		Quarts (US liq)	4.0
	Kilometers	3.048×10^{-4}	Gallons (Imperial)	Gallons (US liq)	1.20095
	Meters	0.3048	Gallons (US liq)	Gallons (Imperial)	0.83267
	Miles (nautical)	1.645×10^{-4}	Gallons of water	Pounds of water	8.3453
	Miles (statute)	1.894×10^{-4}	Gallons (US liq)/min	Cu feet/sec	2.228×10^{-3}
	Millimeters	304.8		Liters/sec	0.06308
	Mils	1.2×10^4		Cu feet/hr	8.0280
Ft of water (@ 4°C)	Atmospheres	0.02950	Gills (US)	Liters	0.1183
	In of Hg(@ 0°C)	0.8826		Pints (US liq)	0.25
	Kg/sq cm	0.03048		Grams	0.06480
	Kg/sq meter	304.8		Ounces (avdp)	2.0833×10^{-3}
	Pounds/sq foot	62.43		Pennyweight (troy)	0.04167
	Pounds/sq inch	0.4335	Grains/gal (US)	Parts/million	17.118
Feet/minute	Cm/sec	0.5080		Pounds/million gal	142.86
	Feet/sec	0.01667	Grains/gal (Imperial)	Parts/million	14.286
	Kilometers/sec	0.01829	Grams	Grains	15.43
	Meters/min	0.3048		Kilograms	0.001
	Miles/hr	0.01136		Milligrams	1,000.0
	Miles/min	0.01136		Ounces (avdp)	0.03527
Feet per 100 feet	Per cent grade	1.0		Ounces (troy)	0.03215
Foot-pounds	Btu	1.286×10^{-3}		Poundals	0.07093
	Ergs	1.356×10^7	Grams	Pounds (avdp)	2.205×10^{-3}
	Gram-calories	0.3238	Grams/cm	Pounds/inch	5.600×10^{-3}
	Hp-hours	5.050×10^{-7}	Grams/cu cm	Pounds/cu ft	62.43
	Kg-calories	3.24×10^{-4}		Pounds/cu inch	0.03613
	Kg-meters	0.1383		Pounds/circ mil-ft	3.405×10^{-7}
	Kw-hours	3.766×10^{-7}	Grams/liter	Grains/gal	58.417
Foot-pounds/min	Btu/min	1.286×10^{-3}		Lb/1,000 gal	8.345
	Foot-pounds/sec	0.01667		Parts/million	1,000.0
	Horsepower	3.030×10^{-5}	Grams/sq cm	Pounds/sq ft	2.0481
	Kg-calories/min	3.24×10^{-4}	Gram-calories	Btu	3.9683×10^{-3}
	Kilowatts	2.260×10^{-5}		Ergs	4.1868×10^7
Foot-pounds/sec	Btu/hr	4.6263		Foot-pounds	3.0880
	Btu/min	0.07717		Hp-hours	1.5596×10^{-6}
	Horsepower	1.818×10^{-3}		Kw-hours	1.1630×10^{-6}
	Kg-calories/min	0.01945		Watt-hours	1.1630×10^{-3}
	Kilowatts	1.356×10^{-3}	Gram-calories/sec	Btu/hour	14.286
Furlongs	Rods	40.0	Gram-centimeters	Btu (IST)	9.297×10^{-8}
	Feet	660.0		Ergs	980.7

To Convert	into	Multiply by	To Convert	into	Multiply by
Gram-centimeters	Kg-calorie	2.343×10^{-8}	In of Water (@ 4°C)	In of Hg(@ 0°C)	0.07355
	Kg-meters	10^{-5}		Kg/sq cm	2.540×10^{-3}
				Ounces/sq inch	0.5781
H				Pounds/sq ft	5.204
				Pounds/sq inch	0.03613
Hectares	Acres	2.471			
	Sq feet	1.076×10^{5}	**J**		
Hectograms	Grams	100.0			
Hectoliters	Liters	100.0	Joules	Btu	9.480×10^{-4}
Hectometers	Meters	100.0		Ergs	10^{7}
Hectowatts	Watts	100.0		Foot-pounds	0.7376
Horsepower	Btu/min	42.44		Kg-calories	2.389×10^{-4}
	Foot-pounds/min	33,000		Kg-meters	0.1020
	Foot-pounds/sec	550.0		Watt-hours	2.778×10^{-4}
Horsepower (metric) (542.5 ft-lb/sec)	Horsepower (550 ft-lb/sec)	0.9863	**K**		
Horsepower (550 ft-lb/sec)	Horsepower(metric) (542.5 ft-lb/sec)	1.014	Kilograms	Dynes	980,665
Horsepower	Kg-calories/min	10.68		Grams	1,000.0
	Kilowatts	0.7457		Poundals	70.93
	Watts	745.7		Pounds	2.205
Horsepower (Boiler)	Kilowatts	9.803		Tons (long)	9.842×10^{-4}
Horsepower-hours	Btu	2,547		Tons (short)	1.102×10^{-3}
	Ergs	2.6845×10^{13}	Kilograms/cu meter	Grams/cu cm	0.001
	Foot-pounds	1.98×10^{6}		Lb/cu ft	0.06243
	Gram-calories	641,190		Lb/cu inch	3.613×10^{-5}
	Kg-calories	641.19	Kilograms/meter	Pounds/ft	0.6720
	Kg-meters	2.737×10^{5}	Kilograms/sq cm	Atmospheres	0.9678
	Kw-hours	0.7457		Ft of water (@39.2°F)	32.81
Hours	Days	4.167×10^{-2}		In of Hg (@ 0°C)	28.96
	Minutes	60		Pounds/sq ft	2,048
	Seconds	3,600		Pounds/sq inch	14.22
	Weeks	5.952×10^{-3}	Kilograms/sq meter	Atmospheres	9.678×10^{-5}
				Bars	98.07×10^{-6}
I				Ft of water (@39.2°F)	3.281×10^{-3}
				In of Hg (@ 0°C)	2.869×10^{-3}
Inches	Centimeters	2.540		Pounds/sq ft	0.2048
	Feet	8.333×10^{-2}		Pounds/sq inch	1.422×10^{-3}
	Meters	2.540×10^{-2}	Kilogram./sq mm	Kg/cu meter	10^{6}
	Miles	1.578×10^{-5}	Kilogram-calories	Btu	3.968
	Millimeters	25.40		Foot-pounds	3,088
	Mils	1,000.0		Hp-hours	1.560×10^{-3}
	Yards	2.788×10^{-2}		Joules	4,186
In of Hg(@ 0°C)	Atmospheres	0.03453		Kg-meters	426.9
	Ft of water	1.133 (at 39.2°F)		Kilojoules	4.186
	Kg/sq cm	0.03453		Kw-hours	1.163×10^{-3}
	Kg/sq meter	345.3	Kilogram-meters	Btu	9.294×10^{-3}
	Pounds/sq ft	70.73		Ergs	9.804×10^{7}
	Pounds/sq inch	0.4912		Foot-pounds	7.233
In of water (@ 4°C)	Atmospheres	2.458×10^{-3}			

To Convert	into	Multiply by	To Convert	into	Multiply by
Kilogram-meters	Joules	9.804	Links (surveyor's)	Inches	7.92
	Kg-calories	2.342×10^{-3}	Liters	Bushels (dry)	0.03531
	Kw-hours	2.723×10^{-6}		Cu centimeters	1,000.0
Kiloliters	Liters	1000.0		Cu feet	0.03531
Kilometers	Centimeters	10^5		Cu inches	61.02
	Feet	3,281		Cu meters	0.001
	Inches	3.937×10^4		Cu yards	$1.308\ 10^{-3}$
	Meters	1000.0		Gallon (US liq)	0.2642
	Miles	0.6214		Pints (US liq)	2.113
	Millimeters	10^6		Quarts (US liq)	1.057
	Yards	1,094.0	Liters/min	Cu ft/sec	5.886×10^{-4}
Kilometers/hr	Cm/sec	27.78		Gallons/sec	4.403×10^{-3}
	Feet/min	54.68			
	Feet/sec	0.9113	**M**		
	Knots	0.5396			
	Meters/min	16.67	Meters	Centimeters	100.0
	Miles(statute)/hr	0.6214		Feet	3.281
Kilowatts	Btu/min	56.92		Inches	39.37
	Foot-pounds/min	4.426×10^4		Kilometers	0.001
	Foot-pounds/sec	737.6		Miles (nautical)	5.396×10^{-4}
	Horsepower	1.341		Miles (statute)	6.214×10^{-4}
	Kg-calories/min	14.34		Millimeters	1000.0
	Watts	1000.0		Varas	1.179
Kilowatt-hour	Btu	3,413		Yards	1.094
	Ergs	3.600×10^{13}	Meters/min	Cm/sec	1.667
	Foot-pounds	2.655×10^6		Feet/min	3.281
	Gram-calories	859,850		Feet/sec	0.05468
	Hp-hours	1.341		Kilometers/hr	0.06
	Joules	3.6×10^6		Knots	0.03238
	Kg-calories	859.85		Miles (statute)/hour	0.03728
	Kg-meters	3.671×10^5	Meters/sec	Feet/min	196.8
	Lb H$_2$O evaporated from and at 212°F	3.53		Feet/sec	3.281
				Kilometers/hr	3.6
	Lb H$_2$O raised from 62° to 212°F	22.75		Kilometers/min	0.06
				Miles (statute)/hour	2.237
Knots	Feet/hr	6,080		Miles/min	0.03728
	Kilometers/hr	1.8532	Micrograms	Grams	10^{-6}
	Miles (nautical)/hr	1.0	Microliters	Liters	10^{-6}
	Miles (statute)/hr	1.151	Miles (nautical)	Feet	6,076.103
	Yards/hr	2,027		Kilometers	1.852
	Feet/sec	1.689		Meters	1,852
				Miles (statute)	1.1508
				Yards	2,025.4
L			Miles (statute)	Centimeters	1.609×10^5
				Feet	5, 280
League (statute)	Mile (statute)	3.0		Inches	6.336×10^4
Links (engineer's)	Inches	12.0		Kilometers	1.609
				Meters	1,609

To Convert	into	Multiply by	To Convert	into	Multiply by
Miles (statute)	Miles (nautical)	0.8684		Grams	28.349527
	Yards	1,760		Pounds	0.0625
Miles/hr	Cm/sec	44.70		Ounces (troy)	0.9115
	Feet/min	88.0		Tons (long)	2.790×10^{-5}
	Feet/sec	1.467		Tons (metric)	2.8355×10^{-5}
	Kilometers/hr	1.609	Ounces (US liq)	Cu inches	1.805
	Kilometers/min	0.02682		Liters	0.02957
	Knots	0.8684	Ounces (troy)	Grains	480.0
	Meters/min	26.82		Grams	31.103481
	Miles/min	0.01667		Ounces (avdp)	1.09714
Miles/min	Cm/sec	2,682		Pennyweights (troy)	20.0
	Feet/sec	88.0		Pounds (troy)	0.08333
	Kilometers/min	1.609	Ounces/sq inch	Pounds/sq inch	0.0625
	Miles (nautical)/min	0.8684			
	Miles/hr	60.0	**P**		
Milliers	Kilograms	1000.0			
Milligrams	Grams	0.001	Parts/million	Grains/gal (US liq)	0.0584
Milligrams/Liter	Parts/million	1.0		Grains/gal (Imperial)	0.07016
Milliliters	Liters	0.001		Lbs/million gallons	8.345
Millimeters	Centimeters	0.1	Pennyweights (troy)	Grains	24.0
	Feet	3.281×10^{-3}		Grams	1.55517
	Inches	0.03937		Ounces (troy)	0.05
	Kilometers	10^{-6}		Pounds (troy)	4.1667×10^{-3}
	Meters	0.001	Pints (dry)	Cu inches	33.60
	Miles	6.214×10^{-7}	Pints (US liq)	Cu cm	473.2
	Mils	39.37		Cu feet	0.01671
	Yards	1.094×10^{-3}		Cu inches	28.87
Million gallons/day	Cu feet/sec	1.54723		Cu meters	4.732×10^{-4}
Mils	Centimeters	2.540×10^{-3}		Cu yards	6.189×10^{-4}
	Feet	8.333×10^{-5}		Gallons (US liq)	0.125
	Inches	0.001		Liters	0.4732
	Kilometers	2.540×10^{-8}		Quarts (US liq)	0.5
	Yards	2.788×10^{-5}	Poundals	Grams	14.10
Miner's inches	Cu feet/min	1.5		Kilograms	0.01410
Minutes (angles)	Degrees	0.01667		Pounds	0.03108
	Quadrants	1.852×10^{-4}	Pounds (avdp)	Drams (avdp)	256.0
	Radians	2.909×10^{-4}		Grains	7,000
	Seconds	60.0		Grams	453.5924
Myriagrams	Kilograms	10.0		Kilograms	0.4536
Myriameters	Kilometers	10.0		Ounces (avdp)	16.0
				Ounces (troy)	14.5833
N				Poundals	32.17
				Pounds (troy)	1.21528
Nepers	Decibels	8.686		Tons (short)	0.0005
			Pounds (troy)	Grains	5,760
O				Grams	373.24177
				Ounces(avdp)	13.1657
Ounces (avdp)	Drams (avdp)	16.0		Ounces (troy)	12.0
	Grains	437.5			

To Convert	into	Multiply by	To Convert	into	Multiply by
Pounds (troy)	Pennyweights (troy)	240.0		Minutes	3,438
	Pounds (avdp)	0.822857		Quadrants	0.6366
	Tons (long)	3.6735×10^{-4}		Seconds	2.063×10^{5}
	Tons (metric)	3.7324×10^{-4}	Rods	Feet	16.5
	Tons (short)	4.1143×10^{-4}			
Pounds of water	Cu feet	0.01602	**S**		
	Cu inches	27.68			
	Gallons	0.1198	Seconds (angles)	Degrees	2.788×10^{-4}
Pounds of water/min	Cu feet/sec	2.670×10^{-4}		Minutes	0.01667
Pound-feet	Cm-dynes	1.356×10^{7}		Quadrants	3.087×10^{-6}
	Cm-grams	13,825		Radians	4.848×10^{-6}
	Meter-kg	0.1383	Square centimeters	Sq feet	1.076×10^{-3}
Pounds/cu feet	Grams/cu cm	0.01602		Sq inches	0.1550
	Kg/cu cm	16.02		Sq meters	0.0001
	Pounds/cu inch	5.787×10^{-4}		Sq miles	3.861×10^{-11}
Pounds/cu inch	Grams/cu cm	27.68		Sq millimeters	100.0
	Kg/cu meter	2.768×10^{4}		Sq yards	1.196×10^{-4}
	Pound/cu ft	1,728.0	Square feet	Acres	2.296×10^{-5}
Pounds/foot	Kg/meter	1.488		Sq centimeters	929.0
Pounds/inch	Grams/cm	178.6		Sq inches	144.0
Pounds/sq foot	Atmospheres	4.725×10^{-4}		Sq meters	0.09290
	Feet of water	0.01602		Sq miles	3.587×10^{-8}
	In of Hg (@ 0°C)	0.01414		Sq millimeters	9.290×10^{4}
	Kgs/sq meter	4.882		Sq yards	0.1111
	Pounds/sq inch	6.944×10^{-3}	Square inches	Sq centimeters	6.452
Pounds/sq inch	Atmospheres	0.06804		Sq feet	6.944×10^{-3}
	Feet of water	2.307		Sq millimeters	645.2
	In of Hg (@ 0°C)	2.036		Sq mils	10^{4}
	Kgs/sq meter	703.1		Sq yards	7.716×10^{-4}
	Pounds/sq ft	144.0	Square kilometers	Acres	247.1
				Sq centimeters	10^{10}
Q				Sq feet	10.76×10^{6}
				Sq inches	1.550×10^{9}
Quadrants (angles)	Degrees	90.0		Sq meters	10^{6}
	Minutes	5,400.0		Sq miles	0.3861
	Radians	1.571		Sq yards	1.196×10^{6}
	Seconds	3.24×10^{5}	Square meters	Acres	2.471×10^{-4}
Quarts (dry)	Cu inches	67.20		Sq centimeters	10^{4}
Quarts (US liq)	Cu cm	946.4		Sq feet	10.76
	Cu feet	0.03342		Sq inches	1,550
	Cu inches	57.75		Sq miles	3.861×10^{-7}
	Cu meters	9.464×10^{-4}		Sq millimeters	10^{6}
	Cu yards	1.238×10^{-3}		Sq yards	1.196
	Gallons (US liq)	0.25	Square miles	Acres	640.0
	Liters	0.9463		Sq feet	27.88×10^{6}
				Sq km	2.590
R				Sq meters	2.590×10^{6}
Radians	Degrees	57.30		Sq yards	3.098×10^{6}

To Convert	into	Multiply by
Square Millimeters	Sq cms	0.01
	Sq feet	1.076×10^{-5}
	Sq inches	1.550×10^{-3}
Square Yards	Acres	2.066×10^{-4}
	Sq cms	8,361
	Sq feet	9.0
	Sq inches	1,296
	Sq meters	0.8361
	Sq miles	3.228×10^{-7}
	Sq millimeters	8.361×10^{5}

T

To Convert	into	Multiply by
Temp (°C) + 273	Absolute Temp (°C)	1.0
Temp (°C) + 17.78	Temp (°F)	1.8
Temp (°F) + 460	Absolute Temp (°F)	1.0
Temp (°F) – 32	Temp (°C)	5/9
Tons (long)	Kilograms	1,016
	Pounds	2,240
	Tons (short)	1.120
Tons (metric)	Kilograms	1,000.0
	Pounds	2,205
Tons (short)	Kilograms	907.1848
	Ounces	32,000.0
	Ounces (troy)	29,166.66
	Pounds	2,000.0
	Pounds (troy)	2,430.56
	Tons (long)	0.89287
	Tons (metric)	0.9078
Tons (short)/sq ft	Kg/sq meter	9,765.0
	Pounds/sq in	2,000.0
Tons of H_2O/ 24 hrs	Pounds of H_2O/hr	83.333
	Gallons/min	0.16643
	Cu feet/hr	1.3349

Y

To Convert	into	Multiply by
Yards	Centimeters	91.44
	Feet	3.0
	Inches	36.0
	Kilometers	9.144×10^{-4}
	Meters	0.9144
	Miles (nautical)	4.934×10^{-4}
	Miles (statute)	5.682×10^{-4}
	Millimeters	914.4

Index

Notes

Notes

Notes

Notes

Notes

Notes

Notes

Notes

Notes

Notes

Notes

Notes

Notes

Notes

Notes

Notes

Notes

Notes

Notes

Notes

Notes

Notes